SOLUTIONS M... STUD...

Kevin Bodden • Randy Gallaher
Lewis & Clark Community College

INTERMEDIATE ALGEBRA
A Graphing Approach
THIRD EDITION

K. Elayn Martin-Gay
Margaret Greene

PEARSON
Prentice Hall

Upper Saddle River, NJ 07458

Senior Acquisitions Editor: Paul Murphy
Project Manager: Mary Beckwith
Assistant Editor: Christina Simoneau
Executive Managing Editor: Vince O'Brien
Production Editor: Jeffrey Rydell
Supplement Cover Manager: Paul Gourhan
Supplement Cover Designer: Joanne Alexandris
Manufacturing Buyer: Ilene Kahn

© 2005 Pearson Education, Inc.
Pearson Prentice Hall
Pearson Education, Inc.
Upper Saddle River, NJ 07458

Pearson Prentice Hall® is a trademark of Pearson Education, Inc.

Printed in the United States of America

10   9   8   7   6

ISBN   0-13-149361-2

Pearson Education Ltd., *London*
Pearson Education Australia Pty. Ltd., *Sydney*
Pearson Education Singapore, Pte. Ltd.
Pearson Education North Asia Ltd., *Hong Kong*
Pearson Education Canada, Inc., *Toronto*
Pearson Educación de Mexico, S.A. de C.V.
Pearson Education—Japan, *Tokyo*
Pearson Education Malaysia, Pte. Ltd.

Table of Contents

Chapter 1

Exercise Set 1.2

1. $5x = 5(7) = 35$

3. $9.8z = 9.8(3.1) = 30.38$

5. $ab = \left(\dfrac{1}{2}\right)\left(\dfrac{3}{4}\right) = \dfrac{3}{8}$

7. $3x + y = 3(6) + (4) = 22$

9. $400t = 400(5) = 2000$ miles

11. $lw = (5.1)(4) = 20.4$
The display needs 20.4 sq. ft. of floor space.

13. $2948t = 2948(3.6) = \$10{,}612.80$

15. $\{1, 2, 3, 4, 5\}$

17. $\{11, 12, 13, 14, 15, 16\}$

19. $\{0\}$

21. $\{0, 2, 4, 6, 8\}$

23.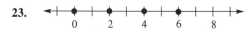

25.

27.

29. Answers may vary. If the empty set were not a subset of a given set A, then there would be at least one element in the empty set that is not in the set A. Since the empty set contains no elements, there are no elements in the empty set that are not in the set A. Thus, the empty set must be a subset of a given set A.

31. $\left\{3, 0, \sqrt{36}\right\}$

33. $\left\{3, \sqrt{36}\right\}$

35. $\left\{\sqrt{7}\right\}$

37. $-11 \in \{x \mid x \text{ is an integer}\}$

39. $0 \notin \{x \mid x \text{ is a positive integer}\}$

41. $12 \notin \{1, 3, 5, \ldots\}$

43. $0 \notin \{1, 2, 3, \ldots\}$

45. True

47. True

49. False

51. False

53. True

55. False; the number $\sqrt{7}$, for example, is a real number, but it is not a rational number.

57. Answers may vary. We can always write a natural number as a fraction with a denominator of 1. Therefore, every natural number can be expressed as a ratio of two integers, making them rational numbers as well. In order for a rational number to be a natural number, the number must be positive and the denominator must evenly divide into the numerator. Not every rational number meets these conditions (e.g. $-\dfrac{2}{1}$ or $\dfrac{3}{5}$) so not every rational number is a natural number.

59. $-|2| = -2$ (the opposite of $|2|$)

61. $|-4| = 4$ since -4 is located 4 units from 0 on the number line.

63. $|0| = 0$ since 0 is located 0 units from 0 on the number line.

65. $-|-3| = -(3) = -3$ (the opposite of $|-3|$).

67. Answers may vary. $-(-2)$ means the opposite of -2 which is 2. Since $|-2| = 2$, $-|-2|$ really means the opposite of 2 which is -2. That is, $-|-2| = -(2) = -2$.

69. The opposite of -6.2 is $-(-6.2) = 6.2$.

71. The opposite of $\frac{4}{7}$ is $-\frac{4}{7}$.

73. The opposite of $-\frac{2}{3}$ is $-\left(-\frac{2}{3}\right) = \frac{2}{3}$.

75. The opposite of 0 is 0.

77. $2x$

79. $2x + 5$

81. $x - 10$

83. $x + 2$

85. $\frac{x}{11}$

87. $3x + 12$

89. $x - 17$

91. $2(x + 3)$

93. $\frac{5}{4 - x}$

95. China = 137
USA = 100
France = 91
Spain = 69
Hong Kong = 56

97. Answers may vary. The ▶Frac command attempts to write the result in fractional form as the ratio of two integers. Since $\sqrt{\frac{4}{9}}$ can be expressed as $\frac{2}{3}$, it is a rational number. The ▶Frac command is unable to express $\sqrt{7}$ as such a ratio so the calculator suggests that this is an irrational number.

Mental Math 1.3

1. B, C

2. A, B

3. B, D

4. A, D

5. B

6. A

Exercise Set 1.3

1. $-3 + 8 = 5$

3. $-14 + (-10) = -24$

5. $-4.3 - 6.7 = -4.3 + (-6.7) = -11$

7. $13 - 17 = 13 + (-17) = -4$

9. $\frac{11}{15} - \left(-\frac{3}{5}\right) = \frac{11}{15} + \frac{9}{15} = \frac{20}{15} = \frac{4}{3}$

11. $19 - 10 - 11 = 9 - 11 = 9 + (-11) = -2$

13. $(-5)(12) = -60$

15. $(-8)(-10) = 80$

17. $\frac{-12}{-4} = 3$

19. $\frac{0}{-2} = 0$

21. $(-4)(-2)(-1) = 8(-1) = -8$

23. $\frac{-6}{7} \div 2 = \frac{-6}{7} \cdot \frac{1}{2} = \frac{-3}{7} = -\frac{3}{7}$

25. $\left(-\frac{2}{7}\right)\left(-\frac{1}{6}\right) = \frac{2}{42} = \frac{1}{21}$

27. $-7^2 = -(7 \cdot 7) = -49$

29. $(-6)^2 = (-6)(-6) = 36$

31. $(-2)^3 = (-2)(-2)(-2) = 4(-2) = -8$

33. $\sqrt{49} = 7$ since 7 is positive and $7^2 = 49$.

35. $-\sqrt{\frac{1}{9}} = -\frac{1}{3}$ since $\frac{1}{3}$ is positive and $\left(\frac{1}{3}\right)^2 = \frac{1}{9}$.

37. $\sqrt[3]{64} = 4$ since $4^3 = 64$.

39. $\sqrt[4]{81} = 3$ since 3 is positive and $3^4 = 81$.

41. $\sqrt{-100}$ is not a real number.

43. $3(5-7)^4 = 3(-2)^4 = 3(16) = 48$

45. $-3^2 + 2^3 = -9 + 8 = -1$

47. $\dfrac{3-(-12)}{-5} = \dfrac{3+12}{-5} = \dfrac{15}{-5} = -3$

49. $|3.6 - 7.2| + |3.6 + 7.2| = |-3.6| + |10.8|$
$$= 3.6 + 10.8$$
$$= 14.4$$

51. $\dfrac{(3-\sqrt{9})-(-5-1.3)}{-3} = \dfrac{(3-3)-(-6.3)}{-3}$
$$= \dfrac{0+6.3}{-3}$$
$$= \dfrac{6.3}{-3}$$
$$= -2.1$$

53. $\dfrac{|3-9| - |-5|}{-3} = \dfrac{6-5}{-3} = \dfrac{1}{-3} = -\dfrac{1}{3}$

55. $(-3)^2 + 2^3 = 9 + 8 = 17$

57. $4[8 - (2-4)] = 4[8 - (-2)] = 4(10) = 40$

59. $2 - [(7-6) + (9-19)] = 2 - [1 + (-10)]$
$$= 2 - (-9)$$
$$= 11$$

61. $\dfrac{(-9+6)(-1^2)}{-2-2} = \dfrac{(-3)(-1)}{-4} = \dfrac{3}{-4} = -\dfrac{3}{4}$

63. $(\sqrt[3]{8})(-4) - (\sqrt{9})(-5) = (2)(-4) - (3)(-5)$
$$= -8 - (-15)$$
$$= -8 + 15$$
$$= 7$$

65. $25 - [(3-5) + (14-18)]^2 = 25 - [(-2) + (-4)]^2$
$$= 25 - (-6)^2$$
$$= 25 - 36$$
$$= -11$$

67. $\dfrac{\frac{1}{3} \cdot 9 - 7}{3 + \frac{1}{2} \cdot 4} = \dfrac{3-7}{3+2} = \dfrac{-4}{5} = -\dfrac{4}{5}$

69. $\dfrac{3(-2+1)}{5} - \dfrac{-7(2-4)}{1-(-2)} = \dfrac{3(-1)}{5} - \dfrac{-7(-2)}{3}$
$$= \dfrac{-3}{5} - \dfrac{14}{3}$$
$$= \dfrac{-9}{15} - \dfrac{70}{15}$$
$$= -\dfrac{79}{15}$$

71. $\dfrac{\frac{-3}{10}}{\frac{42}{50}} = \dfrac{-3}{10} \cdot \dfrac{50}{42} = -\dfrac{5}{14}$

73. $x^2 + z^2 = (-2)^2 + (3)^2 = 4 + 9 = 13$

75. $-5(-x + 3y) = -5(-(-2) + 3(-5))$
$$= -5(2 - 15)$$
$$= -5(-13)$$
$$= 65$$

77. $\dfrac{3z - y}{2x - z} = \dfrac{3(3) - (-5)}{2(-2) - (3)}$
$$= \dfrac{9+5}{-4-3}$$
$$= \dfrac{14}{-7}$$
$$= -2$$

79. $3x - 2y = 3(1.4) - 2(-6.2)$
$$= 4.2 - (-12.4)$$
$$= 4.2 + 12.4$$
$$= 16.6$$

81. $\dfrac{|x-y|}{2y} = \dfrac{|1.4 - (-6.2)|}{2(-6.2)}$
$$= \dfrac{|1.4 + 6.2|}{-12.4}$$
$$= \dfrac{|7.6|}{-12.4}$$
$$= \dfrac{7.6}{-12.4}$$
$$\approx -0.61$$

83. $-3\left(x^2 + y^2\right) = -3\left(\left(1.4\right)^2 + \left(-6.2\right)^2\right)$

$$= -3\left(1.96 + 38.44\right)$$

$$= -3\left(40.4\right)$$

$$= -121.2$$

85.

Expression	Variable values	Value
$x^2 + 2y$	$x = -2.7, y = 0.9$	$x^2 + 2y = 9.09$

87.

Expression	Variable values	Value
$a^2 + b^2$	$a = 4, b = -2.5$	$a^2 + b^2 = 22.25$

89. a.

```
2→X
              2
(1/2)X
              1
1/2X
              1
█
```

$\left(1/2\right)x = 1$ and $1/2x = 1$

b. The results are the same. Explanations may vary.

91. a. When $y = 5$, $8 + 2y = 8 + 2\left(5\right)$

$$= 8 + 10$$

$$= 18$$

When $y = 7$, $8 + 2y = 8 + 2\left(7\right)$

$$= 8 + 14$$

$$= 22$$

When $y = 10$, $8 + 2y = 8 + 2\left(10\right)$

$$= 8 + 20$$

$$= 28$$

When $y = 100$, $8 + 2y = 8 + 2\left(100\right)$

$$= 8 + 200$$

$$= 208$$

Length y	5	7	10	100
Perimeter $8 + 2y$	18	22	28	208

b. The perimeter increases as the length increases.

93. a. When $x = 10$, $\dfrac{100x + 5000}{x}$

$$= \dfrac{100\left(10\right) + 5000}{10}$$

$$= \dfrac{1000 + 5000}{10}$$

$$= \dfrac{6000}{10}$$

$$= 600$$

When $x = 100$, $\dfrac{100x + 5000}{x}$

$$= \dfrac{100\left(100\right) + 5000}{100}$$

$$= \dfrac{10,000 + 5000}{100}$$

$$= \dfrac{15,000}{100}$$

$$= 150$$

When $x = 1000$, $\dfrac{100x + 5000}{x}$

$$= \dfrac{100\left(1000\right) + 5000}{1000}$$

$$= \dfrac{100,000 + 5000}{1000}$$

$$= \dfrac{105,000}{1000}$$

$$= 105$$

Number of shelves	x	10	100	1000
Cost per shelf	$\dfrac{100x + 5000}{x}$	600	150	105

b. The cost per bookshelf decreases as more bookshelves are made.

95. $1 - \dfrac{1}{5} - \dfrac{3}{7} = \dfrac{35}{35} - \dfrac{7}{35} - \dfrac{15}{35} = \dfrac{13}{35}$

97. $10,203 - 5998 = 4205$
The volcano is 4205 meters above sea level.

99.

Year	Increase in Life Expectancey (years)
1950	$71.1 - 65.7 = 5.4$
1960	$73.2 - 71.1 = 2.1$
1970	$74.9 - 73.2 = 1.7$
1980	$77.5 - 74.9 = 2.6$
1990	$78.9 - 77.5 = 1.4$
2000	$79.6 - 78.9 = 0.7$

101. $6-(5\cdot2+2)=6-(10+2)$
$$=6-12$$
$$=-6$$

103. Answers may vary. A negative number raised to an odd power is still negative.

105. $\sqrt{273}\approx16.5227$

107. $\sqrt{19.6}\approx4.4272$

109. $\dfrac{(-5.161)(3.222)}{7.955-19.676}=\dfrac{-16.628742}{-11.721}$
$$\approx1.4187$$

111. 13.2%

113. $12.9\%-2.1\%=10.8\%$

115. b; The colors all have the same area.

117. d; Yellow has the smallest area.

119. Yes. Two players have 6 points each (third player has 0 points), or two players have 5 points each (third has 2 points).

Exercise Set 1.4

1. $0>-2$ since 0 is further to the right than -2 on a number line.

3. $7.4=7.40$ since 7.4 and 7.40 are at the same point on a number line.

5. $-7.9<-7.09$ since -7.9 is further to the left than -7.09 on a number line.

7. $2x+5=-14$

9. $3(x+1)=7$

11. $\dfrac{n}{5}=4n$

13. $z-2=2z$

15. $7x\le-21$

17. $-2+x\ne10$

19. $2(x-6)>\dfrac{1}{11}$

21. $5y-7=6$

23. $2(x-6)=-27$

	Number	Opposite	Reciprocal
25.	5	-5	$\dfrac{1}{5}$
27.	-8	8	$-\dfrac{1}{8}$
29.	$-\dfrac{1}{7}$	$\dfrac{1}{7}$	-7
31.	0	0	Undefined
33.	$\dfrac{7}{8}$	$-\dfrac{7}{8}$	$\dfrac{8}{7}$

35. Zero. For every real number x, $0\cdot x\ne1$, so 0 has no reciprocal. It is the only real number that has no reciprocal because if $x\ne0$, then $x\cdot\dfrac{1}{x}=1$ by definition.

37. $7x+y=y+7x$

39. $z\cdot w=w\cdot z$

41. $\dfrac{1}{3}\cdot\dfrac{x}{5}=\dfrac{x}{5}\cdot\dfrac{1}{3}$

43. No, subtraction is not commutative. Answers may vary (for example, $8-5\ne5-8$).

45. $5\cdot(7x)=(5\cdot7)x$

47. $(x+1.2)+y=x+(1.2+y)$

49. $(14z)\cdot y=14(z\cdot y)$

51. $12-(5-3)=10$; $(12-5)-3=4$; Subtraction is not associative.

53. $3(x+5)=3x+15$

55. $-(2a+b)=-2a-b$

57. $2(6x+5y+2z)=12x+10y+4z$

59. $-4(x-2y+7)=-4x+8y-28$

61. $0.5x(6y-3)=3xy-1.5x$

63. $6+3x$

65. 0

67. 7

69. $(10\cdot2)y$

71. Associative property of addition.

73. Commutative property of multiplication.

75. $a(b+c)=ab+ac$

77. In words: $\boxed{\text{Value of a dime}}\cdot\boxed{\text{Number of dimes}}$
Translate: $0.1\cdot d$ or $0.1d$

79. If two numbers have a sum of 112 and one number is x, then the other number is the "rest of 112." So, in other words, we have
$\boxed{\text{One hundred twelve}}-\boxed{x}$
Translate: $112-x$

81. In words: $\boxed{\text{Ninety}}-\boxed{5x}$
Translate: $90-5x$

83. In words: $\boxed{\text{Cost of a book}}\cdot\boxed{\text{Number of books}}$
Translate: $\$35.61y$

85. The next even integer would be 2 more than the given even integer. In words:
$\boxed{\text{Even integer}}+\boxed{\text{Two}}$
Translate: $2x+2$

87. $5y-14+7y-20y=5y+7y-20y-14$
$\qquad=(5+7-20)y-14$
$\qquad=-8y-14$

89. $-11c-(4-2c)=-11c-4+2c$
$\qquad=-11c+2c-4$
$\qquad=(-11+2)c-4$
$\qquad=-9c-4$

91. $(8-5y)-(4+3y)=8-5y-4-3y$
$\qquad=-5y-3y+8-4$
$\qquad=(-5-3)y+4$
$\qquad=-8y+4$
$\qquad$ or $4-8y$

93. $-4(yz+3)-7yz+1+y^2$
$\qquad=-4yz-12-7yz+1+y^2$
$\qquad=y^2-4yz-7yz-12+1$
$\qquad=y^2+(-4-7)yz-11$
$\qquad=y^2-11yz-11$

95. $-(8-t)+(2t-6)=-8+t+2t-6$
$\qquad=t+2t-8-6$
$\qquad=(1+2)t-14$
$\qquad=3t-14$

97. $5(2z^3-6)+10(3-z^3)=10z^3-30+30-10z^3$
$\qquad=10z^3-10z^3-30+30$
$\qquad=(10-10)z^3+0$
$\qquad=0$

99. $7n+3(2n-6)-2=7n+6n-18-2$
$\qquad=(7+6)n-20$
$\qquad=13n-20$

101. $6.3y-9.7+2.2y-11.1=6.3y+2.2y-9.7-11.1$
$\qquad=(6.3+2.2)y-20.8$
$\qquad=8.5y-20.8$

103. $\dfrac{7}{8}a-\dfrac{11}{12}-\dfrac{1}{2}a+\dfrac{5}{6}=\dfrac{7}{8}a-\dfrac{1}{2}a-\dfrac{11}{12}+\dfrac{5}{6}$
$\qquad=\left(\dfrac{7}{8}-\dfrac{1}{2}\right)a-\dfrac{11}{12}+\dfrac{10}{12}$
$\qquad=\left(\dfrac{7}{8}-\dfrac{4}{8}\right)a-\dfrac{1}{12}$
$\qquad=\dfrac{3}{8}a-\dfrac{1}{12}$

105. $\frac{1}{3}(6x-33y)-\frac{1}{8}(24x-40y+1)-\frac{1}{3}$

$= 2x-11y-3x+5y-\frac{1}{8}-\frac{1}{3}$

$= 2x-3x-11y+5y-\frac{3}{24}-\frac{8}{24}$

$= (2-3)x+(-11+5)y-\frac{11}{24}$

$= -x-6y-\frac{11}{24}$

107. $5.8(-9.6-31.2y)-18.65$

$= -55.68-180.96y-18.65$

$= -180.96y-55.98-18.65$

$= -180.96y-74.33$

109. $6.5y-4.4(1.8x-3.3)+10.95$

$= 6.5y-7.92x+14.52+10.95$

$= 6.5y-7.92x+25.47$

111. It is not the case that two rectangles with the same perimeter will necessarily have the same area. Take a rectangle that is 5 in. by 5 in. and another that is 8 in. by 2 in. Both have the same perimeter, but the areas are 25 square inches and 16 square inches, respectively.

113. 80 million

115. 35 million

117. $\boxed{2.5}\cdot\boxed{\%\text{ over 65 in 1950}}=\boxed{\%\text{ in 2050}}$

$(2.5)(8.1\%)=20.25\%$

Integrated Review

1. $z^2=(-4)^2=(-4)(-4)=16$

2. $-z^2=-(-4)^2=-(-4)(-4)=-16$

3. $\dfrac{4x-z}{2y}=\dfrac{4(-1)-(-4)}{2(3)}$

$=\dfrac{-4+4}{6}$

$=\dfrac{0}{6}$

$=0$

4. $x(y-2z)=(-1)((3)-2(-4))$

$=(-1)(3+8)$

$=(-1)(11)$

$=-11$

5. $-7-(-2)=-7+2=-5$

6. $\dfrac{9}{10}-\dfrac{11}{12}=\dfrac{54}{60}-\dfrac{55}{60}=\dfrac{54-55}{60}=-\dfrac{1}{60}$

7. $\dfrac{-13}{2-2}=\dfrac{-13}{0}$ is undefined

8. $(1.2)^2-(2.1)^2=1.44-4.41=-2.97$

9. $\sqrt{64}-\sqrt[3]{64}=8-4=4$

10. $-5^2-(-5)^2=-25-25=-50$

11. $9+2\left[(8-10)^2+(-3)^2\right]=9+2\left[(-2)^2+9\right]$

$=9+2[4+9]$

$=9+2(13)$

$=9+26$

$=35$

12. $8-6\left[\sqrt[3]{8}(-2)+\sqrt{4}(-5)\right]$

$=8-6\left[2(-2)+2(-5)\right]$

$=8-6[-4-10]$

$=8-6(-14)$

$=8+84$

$=92$

13. $-15-2x$

14. $3x+5$

15. 0

16. True. By definition, an irrational number is a real number that is not rational.

17. $-5(9x)=(-5\cdot9)x=-45x$

18. $(3x-7)-(4x+1) = 3x-7-4x-1$
$$= 3x-4x-7-1$$
$$= (3-4)x+(-7-1)$$
$$= -x-8$$

19. $8.6a+2.3b-a+4.9b$
$$= 8.6a-a+2.3b+4.9b$$
$$= (8.6-1)a+(2.3+4.9)b$$
$$= 7.6a+7.2b$$

20. $\dfrac{2}{3}y-\dfrac{2}{3}+y-\dfrac{1}{9}y+\dfrac{9}{10}$
$$= \dfrac{2}{3}y+y-\dfrac{1}{9}y-\dfrac{2}{3}+\dfrac{9}{10}$$
$$= \left(\dfrac{2}{3}+1-\dfrac{1}{9}\right)y+\left(-\dfrac{2}{3}+\dfrac{9}{10}\right)$$
$$= \left(\dfrac{6}{9}+\dfrac{9}{9}-\dfrac{1}{9}\right)y+\left(-\dfrac{20}{30}+\dfrac{27}{30}\right)$$
$$= \dfrac{14}{9}y+\dfrac{7}{30}$$

Mental Math 1.5

1. $8x+21$

2. $11y+18$

3. $6n-7$

4. $3m-4$

5. $-4x-1$

6. $-6x-3$

7. Expression

8. Equation

9. Equation

10. Expression

11. $2x+3 = 2x+3$
$$3 = 3; \text{ True}$$
All real numbers

12. $2x+1 = 2x+3$
$$1 = 3; \text{ False}$$
No solution

13. $5x-2 = 5x-7$
$$-2 = -7; \text{ False}$$
No solution

14. $5x-3 = 5x-3$
$$-3 = -3; \text{ True}$$
All real numbers

Exercise Set 1.5

1. $-3x = 36$
$$\dfrac{-3x}{-3} = \dfrac{36}{-3}$$
$$x = -12$$

Check: $\qquad -3x = 36$
$$-3(-12) = 36$$
$$36 = 36 \text{ True}$$

```
-12→X
         -12
-3X
          36
```

The solution is -12.

3. $\qquad x+2.8 = 1.9$
$$x+2.8-2.8 = 1.9-2.8$$
$$x = -0.9$$

Check: $\qquad x+2.8 = 1.9$
$$(-0.9)+2.8 = 1.9$$
$$1.9 = 1.9 \text{ True}$$

```
-0.9→X
          -.9
X+2.8
          1.9
```

The solution is -0.9.

5.
$$5x - 4 = 26$$
$$5x - 4 + 4 = 26 + 4$$
$$5x = 30$$
$$\frac{5x}{5} = \frac{30}{5}$$
$$x = 6$$

Check:
$$5x - 4 = 26$$
$$5(6) - 4 = 26$$
$$30 - 4 = 26$$
$$26 = 26 \ \text{True}$$

```
6→X
                6
5X-4
               26
```

The solution is 6.

7.
$$-4 = 3x + 11$$
$$-4 - 11 = 3x + 11 - 11$$
$$-15 = 3x$$
$$\frac{-15}{3} = \frac{3x}{3}$$
$$-5 = x$$

Check:
$$-4 = 3x + 11$$
$$-4 = 3(-5) + 11$$
$$-4 = -15 + 11$$
$$-4 = -4 \ \text{True}$$

```
-5→X
               -5
3X+11
               -4
```

The solution is −5.

9.
$$-4.1 - 7z = 3.6$$
$$-4.1 - 7z + 4.1 = 3.6 + 4.1$$
$$-7z = 7.7$$
$$\frac{-7z}{-7} = \frac{7.7}{-7}$$
$$z = -1.1$$

Check:
$$-4.1 - 7z = 3.6$$
$$-4.1 - 7(-1.1) = 3.6$$
$$-4.1 + 7.7 = 3.6$$
$$3.6 = 3.6 \ \text{True}$$

```
-1.1→Z
              -1.1
-4.1-7Z
               3.6
```

The solution is −1.1.

11.
$$5y + 12 = 2y - 3$$
$$5y + 12 - 2y = 2y - 3 - 2y$$
$$3y + 12 = -3$$
$$3y + 12 - 12 = -3 - 12$$
$$3y = -15$$
$$\frac{3y}{3} = \frac{-15}{3}$$
$$y = -5$$

Check:
$$5y + 12 = 2y - 3$$
$$5(-5) + 12 = 2(-5) - 3$$
$$-25 + 12 = -10 - 3$$
$$-13 = -13 \ \text{True}$$

```
-5→Y
               -5
5Y+12
              -13
2Y-3
              -13
```

The solution is −5.

13.
$$8x - 5x + 3 = x - 7 + 10$$
$$3x + 3 = x + 3$$
$$2x = 0$$
$$x = 0$$

Check:
$$8x - 5x + 3 = x + 7 - 10$$
$$8(0) - 5(0) + 3 = (0) + 7 - 10$$
$$0 + 3 = 3$$
$$3 = 3 \ \text{True}$$

```
0→X
                0
8X-5X+3
                3
X-7+10
                3
```

The solution is 0.

15. $5x + 12 = 2(2x + 7)$

$5x + 12 = 4x + 14$

$x + 12 = 14$

$x = 2$

Check: $5x + 12 = 2(2x + 7)$

$5(2) + 12 = 2(2(2) + 7)$

$10 + 12 = 2(4 + 7)$

$22 = 2(11)$

$22 = 22$ True

```
2→X
              2
5X+12
             22
2(2X+7)
             22
```

The solution is 2.

17. $3(x - 6) = 5x$

$3x - 18 = 5x$

$-18 = 2x$

$-9 = x$

Check: $3(x - 6) = 5x$

$3((-9) - 6) = 5(-9)$

$3(-15) = -45$

$-45 = -45$ True

```
-9→X
             -9
3(X-6)
            -45
5X
            -45
```

The solution is -9.

19. $-2(5y - 1) - y = -4(y - 3)$

$-10y + 2 = -4y + 12$

$-7y + 2 = 12$

$-7y = 10$

$y = -\dfrac{10}{7}$

Check:

$-2(5y - 1) - y = -4(y - 3)$

$-2\left(5\left(-\dfrac{10}{7}\right) - 1\right) - \left(-\dfrac{10}{7}\right) = -4\left(\left(-\dfrac{10}{7}\right) - 3\right)$

$-2\left(-\dfrac{50}{7} - 1\right) + \dfrac{10}{7} = -4\left(-\dfrac{31}{7}\right)$

$-2\left(-\dfrac{57}{7}\right) + \dfrac{10}{7} = \dfrac{124}{7}$

$\dfrac{114}{7} + \dfrac{10}{7} = \dfrac{124}{7}$

$\dfrac{124}{7} = \dfrac{124}{7}$ True

```
-10/7→Y:Ans▶Frac
                 -10/7
-2(5Y-1)-Y▶Frac
                 124/7
-4(Y-3)▶Frac
                 124/7
```

The solution is $-\dfrac{10}{7}$.

21. a. $4(x + 1) + 1 = 4x + 4 + 1 = 4x + 5$

b. $4(x + 1) + 1 = -7$

$4x + 4 + 1 = -7$

$4x + 5 = -7$

$4x = -12$

$x = -3$

Check: $4(x + 1) + 1 = -7$

$4(-3 + 1) + 1 \overset{?}{=} -7$

$4(-2) + 1 \overset{?}{=} -7$

$-8 + 1 \overset{?}{=} -7$

$-7 = -7$ True

```
-3→X
             -3
4(X+1)+1
             -7
```

The solution is -3.

c. Answers may vary. We solve an equation by using properties of equality to get the variable of interest by itself on one side. When simplifying an expression, we write a simpler equivalent expression by removing grouping symbols and collecting like terms.

23.
$$\frac{x}{2} + \frac{2}{3} = \frac{3}{4}$$
$$12\left(\frac{x}{2} + \frac{2}{3}\right) = 12\left(\frac{3}{4}\right)$$
$$6x + 8 = 9$$
$$6x = 1$$
$$x = \frac{1}{6}$$

Check:
$$\frac{x}{2} + \frac{2}{3} = \frac{3}{4}$$
$$\frac{(1/6)}{2} + \frac{2}{3} = \frac{3}{4}$$
$$\frac{1}{12} + \frac{2}{3} = \frac{3}{4}$$
$$\frac{1}{12} + \frac{8}{12} = \frac{3}{4}$$
$$\frac{9}{12} = \frac{3}{4}$$
$$\frac{3}{4} = \frac{3}{4} \text{ True}$$

```
1/6→X:Ans▶Frac
                1/6
X/2+2/3▶Frac
                3/4
```

The solution is $\frac{1}{6}$.

25.
$$\frac{3t}{4} - \frac{t}{2} = 1$$
$$4\left(\frac{3t}{4} - \frac{t}{2}\right) = 4(1)$$
$$3t - 2t = 4$$
$$t = 4$$

Check:
$$\frac{3t}{4} - \frac{t}{2} = 1$$
$$\frac{3(4)}{4} - \frac{(4)}{2} = 1$$
$$3 - 2 = 1$$
$$1 = 1 \text{ True}$$

```
4→T
                4
3T/4-T/2
                1
```

The solution is 4.

27.
$$\frac{n-3}{4} + \frac{n+5}{7} = \frac{5}{14}$$
$$28\left(\frac{n-3}{4}\right) + 28\left(\frac{n+5}{7}\right) = 28\left(\frac{5}{14}\right)$$
$$7(n-3) + 4(n+5) = 2(5)$$
$$7n - 21 + 4n + 20 = 10$$
$$11n - 1 = 10$$
$$11n = 11$$
$$n = 1$$

Check:
$$\frac{n-3}{4} + \frac{n+5}{7} = \frac{5}{14}$$
$$\frac{(1)-3}{4} + \frac{(1)+5}{7} = \frac{5}{14}$$
$$\frac{-2}{4} + \frac{6}{7} = \frac{5}{14}$$
$$\frac{-1}{2} + \frac{6}{7} = \frac{5}{14}$$
$$-\frac{7}{14} + \frac{12}{14} = \frac{5}{14}$$
$$\frac{5}{14} = \frac{5}{14} \text{ True}$$

```
1→N
                1
(N-3)/4+(N+5)/7▶
Frac
             5/14
```

The solution is 1.

29.
$$0.6x - 10 = 1.4x - 14$$
$$-0.8x - 10 = -14$$
$$-0.8x = -4$$
$$x = 5$$

Check:
$$0.6x - 10 = 1.4x - 14$$
$$0.6(5) - 10 = 1.4(5) - 14$$
$$3 - 10 = 7 - 14$$
$$-7 = -7 \text{ True}$$

```
5→X
                5
0.6X-10
               -7
1.4X-14
               -7
```

The solution is 5.

31. $4(n+3)=2(6+2n)$

$4n+12=12+4n$

$4n+12=4n+12$

This is true for all n. Therefore, all real numbers are solutions.

33. $3(x-1)+5=3x+7$

$3x-3+5=3x+7$

$3x+2=3x+7$

$2=7$

This is false for any x. Therefore, the solution set is $\varnothing$.

35. Answers may vary. The equation $x+7=x+6$ will yield the contradiction $7=6$ and therefore has no solution. The equation $x+7=x+7$ will yield the identity $7=7$ and therefore has all real numbers as solutions.

37. Equation: $6x-5=4x-21$

Solution: $x=-8$

39. Equation: $3(n-3)+2=-1+n$

Solution: $n=3$

41. $6x+9=51$

$6x=42$

$x=7$

The solution is 7.

43. $-5x+1.5=-19.5$

$-5x=-21$

$x=4.2$

The solution is 4.2.

45. $x-10=-6x+4$

$7x=14$

$x=2$

The solution is 2.

47. $3x-4-5x=x+4+x$

$-2x-4=2x+4$

$-4x=8$

$x=-2$

The solution is -2.

49. $5(y+4)=4(y+5)$

$5y+20=4y+20$

$y=0$

The solution is 0.

51. $-1.2x+20=-2.8x+28$

$1.6x=8$

$x=5$

The solution is 5.

53. $6x-2(x-3)=4(x+1)+4$

$6x-2x+6=4x+4+4$

$4x+6=4x+8$

$6=8$ False

This is a contradiction so the solution is $\varnothing$.

55. $\dfrac{3}{8}+\dfrac{b}{3}=\dfrac{5}{12}$

$24\left(\dfrac{3}{8}\right)+24\left(\dfrac{b}{3}\right)=24\left(\dfrac{5}{12}\right)$

$9+8b=10$

$8b=1$

$b=\dfrac{1}{8}$

The solution is $\dfrac{1}{8}$.

57. $z+3(2+4z)=6(z+1)+5z$

$z+6+12z=6z+6+5z$

$13z+6=11z+6$

$2z=0$

$z=0$

The solution is 0.

59. $\dfrac{3t+1}{8}=\dfrac{5+2t}{7}+2$

$56\left(\dfrac{3t+1}{8}\right)=56\left(\dfrac{5+2t}{7}\right)+56(2)$

$7(3t+1)=8(5+2t)+112$

$21t+7=40+16t+112$

$21t+7=16t+152$

$5t=145$

$t=29$

The solution is 29.

61.
$$\frac{m-4}{3} - \frac{3m-1}{5} = 1$$
$$15\left(\frac{m-4}{3}\right) - 15\left(\frac{3m-1}{5}\right) = 15(1)$$
$$5(m-4) - 3(3m-1) = 15$$
$$5m - 20 - 9m + 3 = 15$$
$$-4m - 17 = 15$$
$$-4m = 32$$
$$m = -8$$

The solution is -8.

63.
$$5(x-2) + 2x = 7(x+4) - 38$$
$$5x - 10 + 2x = 7x + 28 - 38$$
$$7x - 10 = 7x - 10$$
$$0 = 0$$

This is true for all x. Therefore, all real numbers are solutions.

65.
$$y + 0.2 = 0.6(y+3)$$
$$y + 0.2 = 0.6y + 1.8$$
$$0.4y = 1.6$$
$$y = 4$$

The solution is 4.

67.
$$-(3x-5) - (2x-6) + 1 = -5(x-1) - (3x+2) + 3$$
$$-3x + 5 - 2x + 6 + 1 = -5x + 5 - 3x - 2 + 3$$
$$-5x + 12 = -8x + 6$$
$$3x = -6$$
$$x = -2$$

The solution is -2.

69.
$$2(x-8) + x = 3(x-6) + 2$$
$$2x - 16 + x = 3x - 18 + 2$$
$$3x - 16 = 3x - 16$$
$$0 = 0$$

This is true for all x. Therefore, all real numbers are solutions.

71.
$$\frac{3x-1}{9} + x = \frac{3x+1}{3} + 4$$
$$9\left(\frac{3x-1}{9} + x\right) = 9\left(\frac{3x+1}{3} + 4\right)$$
$$(3x-1) + 9x = 3(3x+1) + 36$$
$$3x - 1 + 9x = 9x + 3 + 36$$
$$12x - 1 = 9x + 39$$
$$3x = 40$$
$$x = \frac{40}{3}$$

The solution is $\frac{40}{3}$.

73.
$$1.5(4-x) = 1.3(2-x)$$
$$10[1.5(4-x)] = 10[1.3(2-x)]$$
$$15(4-x) = 13(2-x)$$
$$60 - 15x = 26 - 13x$$
$$-2x = -34$$
$$x = 17$$

The solution is 17.

75.
$$-2(b-4) - (3b-1) = 5b + 3$$
$$-2b + 8 - 3b + 1 = 5b + 3$$
$$-5b + 9 = 5b + 3$$
$$-10b = -6$$
$$b = \frac{6}{10} = \frac{3}{5}$$

The solution is $\frac{3}{5}$.

77.
$$\frac{1}{3}(y+4) + 5 = \frac{1}{4}(3y-1) - 2$$
$$12\left[\frac{1}{3}(y+4) + 5\right] = 12\left[\frac{1}{4}(3y-1) - 2\right]$$
$$4(y+4) + 60 = 3(3y-1) - 24$$
$$4y + 16 + 60 = 9y - 3 - 24$$
$$4y + 76 = 9y - 27$$
$$-5y = -103$$
$$y = \frac{103}{5}$$

The solution is $\frac{103}{5}$.

79.
$$3.2x + 4 = 5.4x - 7$$
$$3.2x + 4 - 4 = 5.4x - 7 - 4$$
$$3.2x = 5.4x - 11$$

From this we see that $K = -11$.

81. $\frac{x}{6}+4=\frac{x}{3}$

$6\left(\frac{x}{6}+4\right)=6\left(\frac{x}{3}\right)$

$x+24=2x$

From this we see that $K=24$.

83. $x(x-6)+7=x(x+1)$

$x^2-6x+7=x^2+x$

$-6x+7=x$

$7=7x$

$1=x$

The solution is 1.

85. $3x(x+5)-12=3x^2+10x+3$

$3x^2+15x-12=3x^2+10x+3$

$15x-12=10x+3$

$5x=15$

$x=3$

The solution is 3.

87. $2.569x=-12.48534$

$\frac{2.569x}{2.569}=\frac{-12.48534}{2.569}$

$x=-4.86$

The solution is -4.86.

89. $2.86z-8.1258=-3.75$

$2.86z=4.3758$

$\frac{2.86z}{2.86}=\frac{4.3758}{2.86}$

$z=1.53$

The solution is 1.53.

91. Not a fair game.

Exercise Set 1.6

1. $y+y+y+y=4y$

3. $z+(z+1)+(z+2)=3z+3$

5. $5x+10(x+3)=5x+10x+30$

$\qquad\qquad\qquad=(15x+30)$ cents

7. $4x+3(2x+1)=4x+6x+3=10x+3$

9. Let $x=$ the number.

$4(x-2)=2+6x$

$4x-8=2+6x$

$-2x=10$

$x=-5$

The number is -5.

11. Let $x=$ 1st number; then $5x=$ 2nd number.

$x+5x=270$

$6x=270$

$x=45$

$5x=5(45)=225$

The numbers are 45 and 225.

13. $30\%\cdot260=0.30\cdot260=78$

15. $12\%\cdot16=0.12\cdot16=1.92$

17. $29\%\cdot2271=0.29\cdot2271=658.59$;

$2271-658.59=1612.41$.

Approximately 1612.41 million acres are not federally owned.

19. $85\%\cdot2342=0.85\cdot2342=1990.7$;

Approximately 1991 minor earthquakes occurred.

21. $33\frac{1}{3}\%\cdot1290\approx0.3333\cdot1290=429.957$

$1290-429.957=860.043$.

About 860 shoppers would be expected to not spend more than they intended.

23. 17%

25. $6\%\cdot112,500=0.06\cdot112,500=6750$

You would expect 6750 users to check their e-mail about once a week.

27. $3x+21.1=205.9$

$3x=184.8$

$x=61.6$

$x+15.3=61.6+15.3=76.9$

$x+5.8=61.6+5.8=67.4$

The Los Angeles airport has 61.6 million annual arrivals and departures. The Atlanta airport has 76.9 million annual arrivals and departures. The Chicago airport has 67.4 million annual arrivals and departures.

29. Let x = no. of seats in the 737-200; then
$x + 21$ = no. in the 737-300 and
$2x - 36$ = no. in the 757-200.
$$x + (x + 21) + (2x - 36) = 437$$
$$4x - 15 = 437$$
$$4x = 452$$
$$x = 113$$
$$x + 21 = 113 + 21 = 134$$
$$2x - 33 = 2(113) - 36 = 190$$
The 737-200 has 113 seats.
The 737-300 has 134 seats.
The 757-200 has 190 seats.

31. Let x = price before taxes.
$$x + 0.08x = 464.4$$
$$1.08x = 464.40$$
$$x = 430$$
The price was \$430 before taxes.

33. Let x = number seats in Heinz Field;
then $x + 11,675$ = no. seats in Mile High.
$$x + (x + 11,675) = 140,575$$
$$2x + 11,675 = 140,575$$
$$2x = 128,900$$
$$x = 64,450$$
$$x + 11,675 = 64,450 + 11,675 = 76,125$$
Mile High stadium has 76,125 seats and Heinz
Field has 64,450 seats.

35. Let x = number of subscribers to MSN; Then
$x + 700,000$ = no. sub. to Earthlink
and $5x + 3,700,000$ = no. sub. to AOL.
$$x + (x + 700,000) + (5x + 3,700,000) = 32,400,000$$
$$7x + 4,400,000 = 32,400,000$$
$$7x = 28,000,000$$
$$x = 4,000,000$$
$$x + 700,000 = (4,000,000) + 700,000$$
$$= 4,700,000$$
$$5x + 3,700,000 = 5(4,000,000) + 3,700,000$$
$$= 23,700,000$$
MSN had 4,000,000 subscribers.
Earthlink had 4,700,000 subscribers.
AOL had 23,700,000 subscribers.

37. Let x = population in 2000.
$$x + 0.091x = 31.2$$
$$1.091x = 31.2$$
$$x \approx 28.6$$
The population of Morocco in 2000 was
approximately 28.6 million.

39. a. Let x = no. of operators in 1998
$$x - 0.139x = 185,000$$
$$0.861x = 185,000$$
$$x \approx 214,866$$
There were approximately 214,866
switchboard operators in 1998.

   b. Answers may vary.

41. Let x = first integer; then $x + 1$ = next integer and
$x + 2$ = third integer.
$$x + (x + 1) + (x + 2) = 228$$
$$3x + 3 = 228$$
$$3x = 225$$
$$x = 75$$
$$x + 1 = 75 + 1 = 76$$
$$x + 2 = 75 + 2 = 77$$
The integers are 75, 76, and 77.

43. Let x = measure of second angle; then
$2x$ = measure of first angle and
$3x - 12$ = measure of third angle.
$$x + 2x + (3x - 12) = 180$$
$$6x - 12 = 180$$
$$6x = 192$$
$$x = 32$$
$$2x = 2(32) = 64$$
$$3x - 12 = 3(32) - 12 = 84$$
The angles measure 64°, 32°, and 84°.

45. Let x = height of sign; then
$2x + 12$ = width of sign.
$$2x + 2(2x + 12) = 312$$
$$2x + 4x + 24 = 312$$
$$6x + 24 = 312$$
$$6x = 288$$
$$x = 48$$
$$2x + 12 = 2(48) + 12 = 108$$
The height is 48 inches and the width is 108
inches.

47. Let x = width of room; then
$2x + 2$ = length of room.
$$2x + 2(2x + 2) = 40$$
$$2x + 4x + 4 = 40$$
$$6x + 4 = 40$$
$$6x = 36$$
$$x = 6$$
$$2x + 2 = 2(6) + 2 = 14$$
The width is 6 centimeters and the length is 14 centimeters.

49. $x + (x + 20) = 180$
$$2x + 20 = 180$$
$$2x = 160$$
$$x = 80$$
$$x + 20 = (80) + 20 = 100$$
The angles measure 80° and 100°.

51. $x + 5x = 90$
$$6x = 90$$
$$x = 15$$
$$5x = 5(15) = 75$$
The angles measure 15° and 75°.

53. Let x = measure of the smaller angle; then
$180 - x$ = measure of its supplement.
$$180 - x = 3x + 20$$
$$180 = 4x + 20$$
$$160 = 4x$$
$$40 = x$$
$$180 - x = 180 - 40 = 140$$
The angles measure 140° and 40°.

55. Let x = width of tank; then
$5(x + 1)$ = height of tank.
$$x + 5(x + 1) = 55.4$$
$$x + 5x + 5 = 55.4$$
$$6x + 5 = 55.4$$
$$6x = 50.4$$
$$x = 8.4$$
$$5(x + 1) = 5[(8.4) + 1] = 5(9.4) = 47$$
The width is 8.4 meters and the height is 47 meters.

57. Let x = hours for halogen; then
$25x$ = hours for fluorescent and
$x - 2500$ = hours for incandescent.
$$x + 25x + (x - 2500) = 105,500$$
$$27x - 2500 = 105,500$$
$$27x = 108,000$$
$$x = 4000$$
$$25x = 100,000; \quad x - 2500 = 1500$$
The halogen has 4000 bulb hours.
The fluorescent has 100,000 bulb hours.
The incandescent has 1500 bulb hours.

59. Let x = number of returns filed electronically in 1999; then $x + 1.564x$ = number in 2002
$$x + 1.564x = 54.1$$
$$2.564x = 54.1$$
$$x \approx 21.1$$
Approximately 21.1 million returns were filed electronically in 1999.

61. Let x = homeruns by Sexson; then
$x + 2$ = homeruns by Palmeiro and
$x + 4$ = homeruns by Thome.
$$x + (x + 2) + (x + 4) = 141$$
$$3x + 6 = 141$$
$$3x = 135$$
$$x = 45$$
$$x + 2 = 47; \quad x + 4 = 49$$
Sexson hit 45 homeruns, Palmeiro hit 47 homeruns, and Thome hit 49 homeruns during the 2001 season.

63. Let x = millions of trees worth of newsprint recycled; then $x + 30$ = millions of trees used.
$$x = 0.27(x + 30)$$
$$x = 0.27x + 8.1$$
$$0.73x = 8.1$$
$$x = 11$$
About 11 million trees' worth of newsprint is recycled.

65. a.
$$y = -64.45x + 2795.5$$
$$0 = -64.45x + 2795.5$$
$$64.45x = 2795.5$$
$$x \approx 43;$$
$$1990 + 43 = 2033$$
The average annual number of cigarettes smoked will be 0 during the year 2033.

b. $y = -64.45x + 2795.5$

$y = -64.45(15) + 2795.5$

$y = 1828.75$

Each American will smoke an average of about 1828.75 cigarettes annually in 2005.

c. $1828.75 \div 365 \approx 5$

Each American adult will smoke an average of 5 cigarettes a day in 2005.

No; this is the daily number of cigarettes for all American adults – smokers and non-smokers.

67. Let x = first odd integer; then

$x + 2$ = next odd integer

$7x = 5(x + 2) + 54$

$7x = 5x + 10 + 54$

$7x = 5x + 64$

$2x = 64$

$x = 32$, which is not an odd interger.

Therefore, no such odd integers exist.

69. $R = C$

$60x = 50x + 5000$

$10x = 5000$

$x = 500$

$R = 60x = 60(500) = 30,000$

$C = 50x + 5000 = 50(500) + 5000 = 30,000$

To break even, 500 boards must be sold.

You need $30,000 to produce the 500 boards.

71. The company makes a profit.

Mental Math 1.7

1. F

2. A

3. B

4. E

5. D

6. C

Exercise Set 1.7

1. Go to the Y= editor and enter $y_1 = x^3$. The x values start at 7 and increment by 1 so we use these values in the Table Setup.

side, x	7	8	9	10	11
volume, x^3	343	512	729	1000	1331

a. In the table, locate the 9 entry in the x column. Read the corresponding y_1 value to find the volume of the cube.

The volume is 729 cu. cm.

b. In the table, locate the 11 entry in the x column. Read the corresponding y_1 value to find the volume of the cube.

The volume is 1331 cu. ft.

c. In the table, locate the 343 entry in the y_1 column. Read the corresponding x value to find the length of a side.

The length of its side is 7 in.

3. Go to the Y= editor and enter $y_1 = 25 + 7x$. The x values start at 39 and increment by 0.5 so we use these values in the Table Setup.

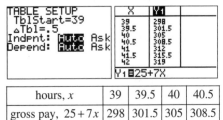

hours, x	39	39.5	40	40.5
gross pay, $25 + 7x$	298	301.5	305	308.5

a. In the table, scroll down until you reach the 333 entry in y_1. Read the corresponding x value to find the number of hours.

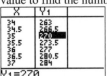

It will take 44 hours to earn $333.

b. In the table, scroll up until you reach the 270 entry in y_1. Read the corresponding x value to find the number of hours.

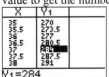

It will take 35 hours to earn $270.

c. In the table, scroll down until you reach the 284 entry in y_1. Read the corresponding x value to get the number of hours.

It will take 37 hours to earn $284.

5. a. x = number of hours for rough draft
The cost for preparing a rough draft is given by $y_1 = 5.25x$.

b. x = number of hours for final manuscript
The cost for preparing a final manuscript is given by $y_2 = 7x$.

c. Go to the Y= editor and enter $y_1 = 5.25x$ and $y_2 = 7x$. The x values start at 1 and increment by 0.25 so we use these values in the Table Setup.

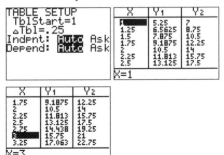

From the calculator screens, we can fill in the table as follows:

Hours	1	1.25	1.5	1.75	2
Rough Draft	5.25	6.56	7.88	9.19	10.50
Manuscript	7	8.75	10.5	12.25	14

Hours	2.25	2.5	2.75	3
Rough Draft	11.81	13.13	14.44	15.75
Manuscript	15.75	17.5	19.25	21

d. Since she can type 2 pages in 15 minutes, she averages 1 page in 7.5 minutes. Therefore, 10 pages would take $10 \cdot 7.5 = 75$ minutes, or 1.25 hours.

$$\frac{15 \text{ min}}{2 \text{ pages}} \cdot \frac{1 \text{ hr}}{60 \text{ min}} \cdot 10 \text{ pages} = 1.25 \text{ hr}$$

According to the table, Emily would charge $6.56 to type the rough draft.

e. Using the result from part **b.** we get $y_2 = 7(10.75) = 75.25$.

Emily will charge $75.25 if she spends 10.75 hours typing a bound manuscript.

7. Go to the Y= editor and enter $y_1 = 2\pi x$ and $y_2 = \pi x^2$. The x values start at 2 but have no common increment. Thus, we use the Ask option in the Table Setup.

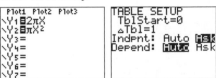

From the calculator screens, we can complete the table below. Note: it may be necessary to highlight the y value to see the decimal places.

Radius	2	5	21	94.2
Circumf.	12.57	31.42	131.95	591.88
Area	12.57	78.54	1385.44	27,877.36

a.

$Y_1 = 188.495559215$ $Y_2 = 2827.43338823$

A circle with a radius of 30 yards has a circumference of about 188.5 yards and an area of about 2827.43 square yards.

b.

$Y_1 = 493.230046614$ $Y_2 = 19359.2793296$

A circle with a radius of 78.5 mm has a circumference of about 493.23 mm and an area of about 19,359.28 sq. mm.

9. a. To model this problem, we let x represent the selling price of the home she sells and y represent her monthly gross income.
In words:

| Gross pay | is | 4% | of | sales | plus | $500 |

Translate: $y = 0.04x + 500$

Go to the Y= editor and enter $y_1 = 0.04x + 500$. The x values start at 125,000 but there is no common increment. Thus, we use the Ask option in the Table Setup.

$Y_1 = .04X + 500$

From the calculator screen, we can complete the table.

Sales (thou.)	125	200	250	350	400
Pay	5500	8500	10,500	14,500	16,500

b. If Krista sells an average of one home per month, her average monthly gross income would be between $5500 and $16,500.

11. a. There is a basic charge of $12.96 that does not depend on how much water is used, as well as a charge of $1.10 per thousand gallons of water. Thus, the total cost is:
$y_1 = 12.96 + 1.10x$

b. Go to the Y= editor and enter $y_1 = 12.96 + 1.10x$. The x values start at 0 and increment by 1 so we use these values in the Table Setup.

$Y_1 = 12.96 + 1.10X$

Gallons used (thousands)	0	1	2	3
Monthly Cost (dollars)	12.96	14.06	15.16	16.26

Gallons used (thousands)	4	5	6
Monthly Cost (dollars)	17.36	18.46	19.56

13. a. The computers are infected at a rate of 8 per minute. Therefore, after x minutes there will be $8x$ computers infected. This means that $500 - 8x$ computers will not be infected.
$y_1 = 500 - 8x$

b. Go to the Y= editor and enter

$y_1 = 500 - 8x$. The x values start at 0 and increment by 10 so we use these values in the Table Setup.

Minutes	0	10	20	30	40
Computers not infected	500	420	340	260	180

Minutes	50	60	70
Computers not infected	100	20	−60

c. From the table, after 30 minutes there will be 260 computers left that are not infected.

d. After 60 minutes, there are 20 computers remaining that are not infected. Since the computers are infected at a rate of 8 per minute, it will take an additional 2.5 minutes to infect the remaining computers. Therefore, after 62.5 minutes all of the computers will be infected.

$$500 \text{ comp.} \cdot \frac{1 \text{ min}}{8 \text{ comp.}} = \frac{500}{8} \text{ min} = 62.5 \text{ min}$$

15. a. To model this situation, we can let

$x = $ current year on the job,

$y_1 = $ salary for first job, and

$y_2 = $ salary for second job.

Since raises do not start until the second year on the job, we get:

$$y_1 = 14,500 + 1000(x-1)$$
$$= 14,500 + 1000x - 1000$$
$$= 13,500 + 1000x$$
$$y_2 = 20,000 + 575(x-1)$$
$$= 20,000 + 575x - 575$$
$$= 19,425 + 575x$$

Year	5	10	15	20
1st job	18,500	23,500	28,500	33,500
2nd job	22,300	25,175	28,050	30,925

b. Answers may vary. Some factors to consider would be how long she plans to work and how retirement benefits (if any) are computed. For instance, after 20 years, Kelsey will have a higher salary with the first job, but her total earnings for the second job would be about $30,000 more.

17. a. total cost = monthly fee + electricity cost

$$y_1 = 15 + 0.08924x$$

b.

kWh	0	500	1000	1500	2000
Monthly Cost ($)	15	59.62	104.24	148.86	193.48

19. a. The football team consumes 42 chickens every 30 minutes (half hour). So they consume chickens at a rate of $\frac{42}{30}$ per minute. Since x is the number of minutes past 5 pm and the restaurant has 150 chickens at 5pm, the number of chickens remaining after x minutes is given by

remaining = initial − eaten   .

$$y_1 = 150 - \frac{42}{30}x \quad \text{or} \quad y_1 = 150 - \frac{7}{5}x$$

b.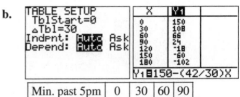

Min. past 5pm	0	30	60	90
Chickens left	150	108	66	24

c. We know the football players eat the chickens at a rate of 42 every 30 minutes. This means that it will take $\frac{30}{42}$ minutes to eat one chicken. To eat 150 chickens would take

$$\frac{30 \text{ min}}{42 \text{ chickens}} \cdot \frac{150 \text{ chickens}}{1} \approx 107.14 \text{ min}$$

Kevin will run out of chickens in about 107 minutes (6:47 pm).

21. a. If x is the number of miles, then driving in the city will use $\frac{x}{15}$ gallons of gas. The number of remaining gallons would be remaining gallons = initial − used .

$$y_1 = 24 - \frac{x}{15}$$

b. If x is the number of miles, then driving on the highway will use $\frac{x}{25}$ gallons of gas. The number of remaining gallons would be

$$y_2 = 24 - \frac{x}{25}.$$

c.

Miles	0	100	200	300	400	500	600
City	24	17.3	10.7	4	−2.7	−9.3	−16
Hwy	24	20	16	12	8	4	0

d. Locate 100 in the row marked Miles and find the corresponding value in the row marked City. After 100 miles of city driving, there will be 17.3 gallons left in the tank.

e. Locate 100 in the row marked Miles and find the corresponding value in the row marked Hwy. After 100 miles of highway driving, there will be 20 gallons left in the tank.

f. Locate 0 in the row marked Hwy. She can drive for 600 miles on the highway before running out of gas.

g. For each gallon of gas, she can travel 15 miles in the city. After 300 miles she still has 4 gallons of gas remaining so she can still travel an additional $4 \cdot 15 = 60$ miles. Thus, she can travel 360 miles in the city before running out of gas.

h. Answers may vary. Negative entries indicate that she cannot travel the given number of miles without purchasing additional gallons of gas. The absolute value of the entries indicate how many additional gallons are needed.

23. a. A discount of 35% means that the sale prices will be 65% of the original price.
sale price = original price − discount

$$y_1 = x - 0.35x$$
$$y_1 = 0.65x$$

b.

Item	Blouse	Skirt	Shorts	Shoes
Price tag	$29.95	$35.95	$19.25	$39.95
Sale price	$19.47	$23.37	$12.51	$25.97

Item	Purse	Earrings	Backpack
Price tag	$17.95	$9.95	$25.75
Sale price	$11.67	$6.47	$16.74

c.
$$\text{sale total} = 19.47 + 23.37 + 12.51 + 25.97$$
$$+ 11.67 + 6.47 + 16.74$$
$$= 116.20$$
Her total before taxes would be $116.20.

d.
$$\text{tax of total} = \text{rate} \cdot \text{total}$$
$$= 0.07(116.20)$$
$$= 8.134 \approx \$8.13$$
$$\text{total after taxes} = \text{pre-tax total} + \text{tax of total}$$
$$= 116.20 + 8.13$$
$$= 124.33$$
Judy's total after taxes would be $124.33.

e. original total $= 29.95 + 35.95 + 19.25 + 39.95$
$$+ 17.95 + 9.95 + 25.75$$
$$= 178.75$$
savings $=$ original total $-$ sale total
$$= 178.75 - 116.20$$
$$= 62.55$$
Judy would save $\$62.55$ before taxes by waiting for the sale.

25. The break-even point is the point where cost and revenue are equal. The fixed cost is $\$3500$ and the per calculator cost is $\$55$. Therefore, the total cost is given by:
$$\text{cost} = y_1 = 3500 + 55x$$
The calculators sell for $\$75$ so the revenue is given by:
$$\text{revenue} = y_2 = 75x$$

x calculators	100	125	150	175	200
Cost	9000	10,375	11,750	13,125	14,500
Revenue	7500	9375	11,250	13,125	15,000

Scrolling through the table, we see that the cost and revenue are equal when 175 calculators are sold.

27. Since revenue exceeds cost by $\$500$ when 200 calculators are produced and sold, the profit is $\$500$.

29. Recall that the radius of a circle is half of the diameter. If we let $x =$ the diameter of a circle, then the radius is given by $\dfrac{x}{2}$ and we have the following:
$$y_1 = \text{circumference} = \pi x$$
$$y_2 = \text{area} = \pi\left(\frac{x}{2}\right)^2 = \frac{\pi x^2}{4}$$

Cost – Circumference Method:
$$y_3 = (0.25)\pi x$$

Cost – Area Method:
$$y_4 = (0.05)\frac{\pi x^2}{4}$$

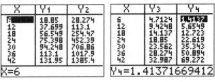

Diameter (inches)	Area	Circum-ference	Cost (Area)	Cost (Circum-ference)
6	28.274	18.85	$\$1.41$	$\$4.71$
12	113.1	37.699	$\$5.65$	$\$9.42$
18	254.47	56.549	$\$12.72$	$\$14.14$
24	452.39	75.398	$\$22.62$	$\$18.85$
30	706.86	94.248	$\$35.34$	$\$23.56$
36	1017.88	113.10	$\$50.89$	$\$28.27$

The owner should use the Circumference Method for pizzas that have a diameter of 18 inches or less. For larger pizzas, the owner should use the Area Method.

31. a.

Seconds	1	2	3	4	5
Height (ft)	1569	1606	1611	1584	1525

b. From the initial table, it appears that the maximum height occurs between 2 and 4 seconds. To get a better approximation, we can start at 2 in the table and adjust our increment.

X	Y1			X	Y1	
2	1606			2.4	1611.8	
2.1	1607.9			2.5	1612.5	
2.2	1609.6			2.6	1612.8	
2.3	1610.9			2.7	1612.9	
2.4	1611.8			2.8	1612.6	
2.5	1612.5			2.9	1611.9	
2.6	1612.8			3	1611	
X=2				X=2.7		

From the table, it appears that the maximum height of the rocket is about 1613 feet.

33. a. Let x = number of miles driven and y = cost of daily rental. In general we have

total daily cost = daily rate + mileage

$$y = \text{daily rate} + \text{mileage}$$

Anne: $y_1 = 25 + 0.08x$

$$= 25 + 0.08(300)$$
$$= 25 + 24$$
$$= 49$$

Michelle: $y_2 = 35 + 0.05x$

$$= 35 + 0.05(300)$$
$$= 35 + 15$$
$$= 50$$

A one day rental with 300 miles will cost Anne $49 and cost Michelle $50.

b. $25 + 0.08x = 35 + 0.05x$

$$0.08x = 10 + 0.05x$$
$$0.03x = 10$$
$$x = \frac{10}{0.03} = 333\frac{1}{3}$$

Anne will pay less for a one day rental if the distance traveled is less than $333\frac{1}{3}$ miles.

35. a. total charges = inital fee + hourly charge

$$C = 90 + 75x$$

b.

TABLE SETUP
TblStart=2
ΔTbl=2
Indpnt: **Auto** Ask
Depend: **Auto** Ask

X	Y1	
2	240	
4	390	
6	540	
8	690	
10	840	
12	990	
14	1140	
Y1=90+75X		

Hours	2	4	6	8
Total fee ($)	240	390	540	690

37. a. We can begin with a table of values to get an idea of where the maximum might be.

TABLE SETUP
TblStart=0
ΔTbl=2
Indpnt: **Auto** Ask
Depend: **Auto** Ask

X	Y1	
0	0	
2	2.24	
4	3.36	
6	3.36	
8	2.24	
10	0	
12	-3.36	
X=0		

From the table, it appears that the maximum height occurs when the frog is between 4 and 6 feet from the starting point. We can start our table at 4 and adjust our increment.

TABLE SETUP
TblStart=4
ΔTbl=.1
Indpnt: **Auto** Ask
Depend: **Auto** Ask

X	Y1	
4.6	3.4776	
4.7	3.4874	
4.8	3.4944	
4.9	3.4986	
5	3.5	
5.1	3.4986	
5.2	3.4944	
X=5		

Scrolling down the table we see that the maximum height is about 3.5 feet.

b. From the last set of tables, we scroll down until we find the maximum height. The corresponding x value is the horizontal distance. According to the table, the frog is 5 feet from the starting point when it reaches its maximum height.

c. When the frog lands, his height will be 0. From the original table above, we can see that the frog's height will be 0 when it is 10 feet from the starting point. Thus, the frog will travel a horizontal distance of 10 feet before landing on the ground.

39. a.

TABLE SETUP
TblStart=0
ΔTbl=1
Indpnt: **Auto** Ask
Depend: **Auto** Ask

X	Y1	
0	5.11	
1	6.06	
2	6.73	
3	7.12	
4	7.23	
5	7.06	
6	6.61	
Y1=-.14X²+1.09X...		

For May 1 we have $x = 2$.

From the table we see that on May 1, sunrise will be at 6.73 hours past midnight.

Since $0.73 \text{ hrs} \cdot \frac{60 \text{ min}}{1 \text{ hr}} = 43.8 \text{ min}$

we can say that the sunrise will be at about 6:44 am.

b.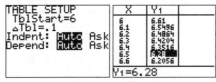

Scrolling down the table we see that sunrise is latest when $x = 4$. This corresponds to July 1.

c. The latest sunrise occurs 7.23 hours after midnight. Since

$$0.23 \text{ hrs} \cdot \frac{60 \text{ min}}{1 \text{ hr}} = 13.8 \text{ min}$$

we can say that the latest sunrise occurs at about 7:14 am.

d. September 15 would correspond to an x value of about 6.5. We could use this value for x in our model, or simply change our table settings.

The sunrise on September 15 would occur 6.28 hours after midnight. Since

$$0.28 \text{ hrs} \cdot \frac{60 \text{ min}}{1 \text{ hr}} = 16.8 \text{ min}$$

we can say that the sunrise would occur at about 6:17 am.

e. Answers may vary. The model does not appear to work for all months of the year. For example, sunrise on January 1 would occur at about 2:01 am (2.01 hours) or at about 2:23 am (2.38 hours) depending on which way we scroll in the table. These times do not seem realistic.

Mental Math 1.8

1. $2x + y = 5$

$$y = 5 - 2x$$

2. $7x - y = 3$

$$-y = 3 - 7x$$
$$y = 7x - 3$$

3. $a - 5b = 8$

$$a = 5b + 8$$

4. $7r + s = 10$

$$s = 10 - 7r$$

5. $5j + k - h = 6$

$$k = h - 5j + 6$$

6. $w - 4y + z = 0$

$$z = 4y - w$$

Exercise Set 1.8

1. $D = rt$

$$\frac{D}{r} = \frac{rt}{r}$$
$$\frac{D}{r} = t$$
$$t = \frac{D}{r}$$

3. $I = PRT$

$$\frac{I}{PT} = \frac{PRT}{PT}$$
$$\frac{I}{PT} = R$$
$$R = \frac{I}{PT}$$

5. $9x - 4y = 16$

$$9x - 4y - 9x = 16 - 9x$$
$$-4y = 16 - 9x$$
$$\frac{-4y}{-4} = \frac{16 - 9x}{-4}$$
$$y = \frac{9x - 16}{4}$$

7. $P = 2L + 2W$

$$P - 2L = 2W$$
$$\frac{P - 2L}{2} = \frac{2W}{2}$$
$$\frac{P - 2L}{2} = W$$
$$W = \frac{P - 2L}{2}$$

9. $J = AC - 3$

$J + 3 = AC$

$\dfrac{J+3}{C} = \dfrac{AC}{C}$

$\dfrac{J+3}{C} = A$

$A = \dfrac{J+3}{C}$

11. $W = gh - 3gt^2$

$W = g(h - 3t^2)$

$\dfrac{W}{h - 3t^2} = \dfrac{g(h - 3t^2)}{h - 3t^2}$

$\dfrac{W}{h - 3t^2} = g$

$g = \dfrac{W}{h - 3t^2}$

13. $T = C(2 + AB)$

$T = 2C + ABC$

$T - 2C = 2C + ABC - 2C$

$T - 2C = ABC$

$\dfrac{T - 2C}{AC} = \dfrac{ABC}{AC}$

$\dfrac{T - 2C}{AC} = B$

$B = \dfrac{T - 2C}{AC}$

15. $C = 2\pi r$

$\dfrac{C}{2\pi} = \dfrac{2\pi r}{2\pi}$

$\dfrac{C}{2\pi} = r$

$r = \dfrac{C}{2\pi}$

17. $E = I(r + R)$

$E = Ir + IR$

$E - IR = Ir + IR - IR$

$E - IR = Ir$

$\dfrac{E - IR}{I} = \dfrac{Ir}{I}$

$\dfrac{E - IR}{I} = r$

$r = \dfrac{E - IR}{I}$

19. $s = \dfrac{n}{2}(a + L)$

$2s = 2 \cdot \dfrac{n}{2}(a + L)$

$2s = n(a + L)$

$2s = na + nL$

$2s - na = na + nL - an$

$2s - na = nL$

$\dfrac{2s - na}{n} = \dfrac{nL}{n}$

$\dfrac{2s - na}{n} = L$

$L = \dfrac{2s - na}{n}$

21. $N = 3st^4 - 5sv$

$N - 3st^4 = 3st^4 - 5sv - 3st^4$

$N - 3st^4 = -5sv$

$\dfrac{N - 3st^4}{-5s} = \dfrac{-5sv}{-5s}$

$\dfrac{3st^4 - N}{5s} = v$

$v = \dfrac{3st^4 - N}{5s}$

23. $S = 2LW + 2LH + 2WH$

$S - 2LW = 2LW + 2LH + 2WH - 2LW$

$S - 2LW = 2LH + 2WH$

$S - 2LW = H(2L + 2W)$

$\dfrac{S - 2LW}{2L + 2W} = \dfrac{H(2L + 2W)}{2L + 2W}$

$\dfrac{S - 2LW}{2L + 2W} = H$

$H = \dfrac{S - 2LW}{2L + 2W}$

25. $A = P\left(1 + \dfrac{r}{n}\right)^{nt} = 3500\left(1 + \dfrac{0.03}{n}\right)^{10n}$

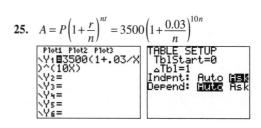

Y₁◻3500(1+.03/X...   Y₁=4713.99252292

Note: you have to highlight the y_1 value to see the decimal places (see last figure above).

n	1	2	4
A	\$4703.71	\$4713.99	\$4719.22

n	12	365
A	\$4722.74	\$4724.45

27. $A = P\left(1+\dfrac{r}{n}\right)^{nt} = 6000\left(1+\dfrac{0.04}{n}\right)^{5n}$

  a. $n = 2$

$$A = 6000\left(1+\frac{0.04}{2}\right)^{5 \cdot 2} \approx 7313.97$$

$7313.97

  b. $n = 4$

$$A = 6000\left(1+\frac{0.04}{4}\right)^{5 \cdot 4} \approx 7321.14$$

$7321.14

  c. $n = 12$

$$A = 6000\left(1+\frac{0.04}{12}\right)^{5 \cdot 12} \approx 7325.98$$

$7325.98

29. $C = \dfrac{5}{9}(F-32)$

$$C = \frac{5}{9}(104-32)$$

$$C = \frac{5}{9}(72)$$

$$C = 40°$$

The day's high temperature was 40°C.

31.
$$d = rt$$
$$2(90 \text{ mi}) = 50t$$
$$180 = 50t$$
$$\frac{180}{50} = t$$
$$t = 3.6$$

She takes 3.6 hours or 3 hours, 36 minutes to make the round trip.

33. $A = s^2 = (64)^2 = 4096 \text{ ft}^2$; $\dfrac{4096}{24} \approx 171$

There should be 171 packages of tiles bought.

35. $A = \dfrac{1}{2}bh$

$$18 = \frac{1}{2}(4)h$$

$$18 = 2h$$

$$9 = h$$

The height is 9 feet.

37. The area of one pair of opposite walls is $2(14 \cdot 8) = 224 \text{ ft}^2$ and the area of the other walls is $2(16 \cdot 8) = 256 \text{ ft}^2$ for a total of 480 ft². Multiplying by 2, the number of coats, yields 960 ft². Dividing this by 500 yields 1.92. Thus, 2 gallons should be purchased.

39. **a.** $V = \pi r^2 h$

$$V = \pi(4.2)^2(21.2)$$

$$V = 1174.86$$

The volume of the cylinder is 1174.86 cubic meters.

  b. $V = \dfrac{4}{3}\pi r^3$

$$V = \frac{4}{3}\pi(4.2)^3$$

$$V = 310.34$$

The volume of the sphere is 310.34 cubic meters.

  c. $V = 1174.86 + 310.34 = 1485.20$

The volume of the tank is 1485.20 cubic meters.

41. Note that the radius of the circle is equal to $22{,}248 + 4000 = 26{,}248$.

$$C = 2\pi r$$

$$C = 2\pi(26{,}248)$$

$$C = 52{,}496\pi$$

$$C \approx 164{,}921.0479$$

The "length" of the Clarke belt is approximately 164,921 miles.

43. $V = \pi r^2 h$

1 mile = 5280 feet

1.3 miles = 6864 feet

$3800 = \pi(r)^2(6864)$

$0.176 \approx r^2$

$0.42 = r$

The radius of the hole is 0.42 feet.

45. $C = \pi d$

$= \pi(41.125)$

$= 41.125\pi$ ft

≈ 129.1325 ft

The circumference of Eartha is $41.125\pi \approx 129.1325$ feet.

47. $A = P\left(1+\dfrac{r}{n}\right)^{nt}$

$= 10,000\left(1+\dfrac{0.085}{4}\right)^{4\cdot2}$

$= 10,000(1+0.02125)^{4\cdot2}$

$= \$11,831.96$

$\$11,831.96 - \$10,000 = \$1831.96$

$\$10,000$ will earn about $\$1831.96$ in interest if compounded quarterly at 8.5%.

49. $C = 4h+9f+4p$

$C-4h-4p = 9f$

$\dfrac{C-4h-4p}{9} = f$

$f = \dfrac{C-4h-4p}{9}$

51. $C = 4h+9f+4p$

$C = 4(7)+9(14)+4(6)$

$C = 178$

There are 178 calories in this serving.

53. $C = 4h+9f+4p$

$130 = 4(31)+9(0)+4p$

$130 = 124+4p$

$6 = 4p$

$\dfrac{6}{4} = p$

$p = 1.5$

There are 1.5 g of protein provided by this serving of raisins.

55. $AU = \dfrac{\text{miles in millions}}{92.9}$

Planet	AU from the Sun
Mercury	0.388
Venus	0.723
Earth	1.00
Mars	1.523
Jupiter	5.202
Saturn	9.538
Uranus	19.193
Neptune	30.065
Pluto	39.505

57. Answers may vary.

$\dfrac{1,700,000,000}{250,000,000} = 6.8$

It cost $\$6.80$ per person to build the *Endeavour*.

59. Answers may vary. Ideally, when borrowing money, it is better to have interest compounded less frequently, assuming you make the same monthly payments. This allows you to pay off more of the principal before being charged interest.

61. $\dfrac{168\text{ mi}}{1\text{ hr}} \cdot \dfrac{5280\text{ ft}}{1\text{ mi}} \cdot \dfrac{1\text{ hr}}{60\text{ min}} \cdot \dfrac{1\text{ min}}{60\text{ sec}}$

$= 246.4$ ft/sec

$d = rt$

60.5 ft $= 246.6$ ft/sec$\cdot t$

0.25 sec $= t$

The ball would reach the plate in approximately 0.25 second.

63. $\dfrac{2}{8} = \dfrac{1}{4}$

65. $\dfrac{3}{8}$

67. $\dfrac{3}{8}$

69. $\dfrac{6}{8} = \dfrac{3}{4}$

71. $\dfrac{8}{8} = 1$

73. 1

Exercise Set 1.9

1. $\bar{x} = \dfrac{19+19+17+20+18}{5} = \dfrac{93}{5} = 18.6$

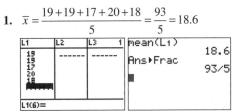

The mean number of reissued films for the years 1998 through 2002 is 18.6.

3. $\bar{x} = \dfrac{4.69+5.08+5.39+5.66+5.81}{5}$

$= \dfrac{26.63}{5}$

$= 5.326$

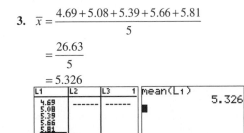

The mean annual admission price of a movie for the years 1998 through 2002 is about $5.33.

5. $\bar{x} = \dfrac{97.0+118.4+134.6}{3} = \dfrac{350}{3} \approx 116.7$

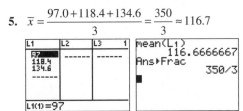

The mean number of cell phone subscribers for the years 200 through 2002 was about 116.7 million.

7. **a.**

Year	Increase in Cell Sites (in thousands)
1993	
1994	3
1995	5
1996	$25-20=5$
1997	$39-25=14$
1998	$58-39=19$
1999	$74-58=16$
2000	$96-74=22$
2001	$114-96=18$
2002	$131-114=17$

b. $\bar{x} = \dfrac{3+5+5+14+19+16+22+18+17}{9}$

$= \dfrac{119}{9}$

≈ 13.2

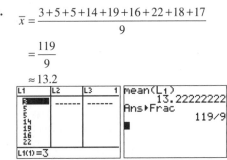

The average yearly increase in cell sites is 13.2 thousand.

9. Start by putting the data in increasing order:
    75, 76, 81, 83, 85, 85, 85, 87, 90, 91, 92, 92, 93
    The most frequently occurring value is 85 so the mode is 85.

11. With $15,000 to invest, the empty nester should invest the following in each category:
    Small Company/Aggressive Growth:
    $(0.25)(15,000) = \$3750$
    Growth/Income Stock:
    $(0.35)(15,000) = \$5250$
    International Stock:
    $(0.20)(15,000) = \$3000$
    Bonds:
    $(0.20)(15,000) = \$3000$

13. Answers may vary.

15. $509+452+452+442+421+415+391$
    $+384+381+374 = 4221$

    $\bar{x} = \dfrac{4221}{10} = 422.1$

    The mean height for the ten tallest buildings in the world is 422.1 meters.

17. To find the median height, first put the heights in increasing order.
374, 381, 384, 391, 415, 421, 442, 452, 452, 509
Since there are an even number of values, we need to average the two middle terms.

$$\frac{415+421}{2} = \frac{836}{2} = 418$$

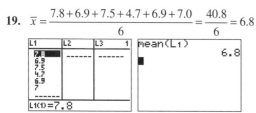

The median height is 418 meters.

19. $\overline{x} = \dfrac{7.8+6.9+7.5+4.7+6.9+7.0}{6} = \dfrac{40.8}{6} = 6.8$

The mean time is 6.8 seconds.

21. Start by arranging the data in increasing order:
4.7, 6.9, 6.9, 7.0, 7.5, 7.8

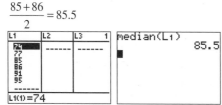

The most frequently occurring value is 6.9 so the mode is 6.9 seconds.

23. Start by arranging the data in increasing order:
74, 77, 85, 86, 91, 95

Since there is an even number of values, we need to average the two middle values.

$$\frac{85+86}{2} = 85.5$$

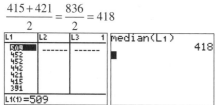

The median score for the student is 85.5.

25. $78+80+66+68+71+64+82+71+70$
$+65+70+75+77+86+72 = 1095$

$$\overline{x} = \frac{1095}{15} = 73$$

The mean pluse rate for the group is 73.

27. Start by arranging the data in increasing order:
64, 65, 66, 68, 70, 70, 71, 71, 72,
75, 77, 78, 80, 82, 86

The most frequently occurring values are 70 and 71 which both occur twice. Thus, there are two modes: 70 and 71

29. The mean is 73. Looking at the ordered list we see that 9 of the pluse rates are below 73.

31. There are an odd number of values so the median is the middle value. Thus, 20 needs to be one of the values. The mode is the most frequent value so the two remaining values should be 21.
16, 18, 20, 21, 21

33. According to the graph, police officers walk the farthest.

35. According to the graph, a nurse walks an average of 940 miles each year.

37. Answers may vary.

39. The Democrat political party shows the greatest percent of the adult population for most of the years shown.

41. According to the graph, the greatest difference in percent of Democrats and percent of Republicans occurred in 1964.

43. In 1992, about 50% of the adult population was identified as Democrat, about 38% was identified as Republican, and about 10% was identified as Independent/Other.

45. Answers may vary. For the most part, the percentages were relatively stable until after 1998. The year 2000 was the first year on the graph when Democrats did not hold the largest percentage.

47. 58% of back-to-school spending is on clothes.
$$(0.58)(363) = \$210.54$$
An average of $210.54 is spent on back-to-school clothes.

49. 16% of the amount spent on clothes was paid using a credit card. Using the result from **47.** we get: $(0.16)(210.54) \approx \$33.69$

About $33.69 for clothes was paid using a credit card.

51. $\overline{x} = \dfrac{28.7 + 27.4 + 23.4 + 21.2 + 20.8}{5} = \dfrac{121.5}{5} = 24.3$

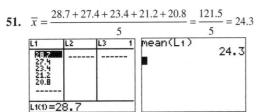

The mean population for the five most populous cities is about 24.3 million.

53. Start by arranging the data in increasing order.
10.6, 11.6, 12.4, 13.1, 14.3, 17.0, 17.6, 17.6, 18.8, 19.4, 20.8, 21.2, 23.4, 27.4, 28.7
Since there are an odd number of values, the median is the middle value.

The median for the 15 most populous cities is 17.6 million

55.

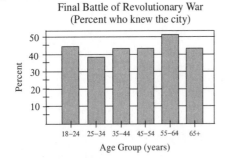

Final Battle of Revolutionary War
(Percent who knew the city)

57. Answers may vary.

59. No. The mean of a set of data must always lie between the smallest and largest values.

61. If the smallest value in a set of data (not the mode) is replaced with a smaller value, the mean will be lowered, but the median and mode will remain unchanged.

Chapter 1 Review

1. $7x = 7(3) = 21$

2. $st = (1.6)(5) = 8$

3. One hour is $60(60) = 3600$ seconds.
$90t = 90(3600) = 324,000$
324,000 wing beats per hour

4. $\{-1, 1, 3\}$

5. $\{-2, 0, 2, 4, 6\}$

6. $\varnothing$

7. $\varnothing$

8. $\{6, 7, 8, \ldots\}$

9. $\{\ldots, -1, 0, 1, 2\}$

10. True

11. False

12. True, since $\sqrt{169} = 13$.

13. True, since zero is not an element of the empty set.

14. False, since π is irrational.

15. True, since π is a real number.

16. False, since $\sqrt{4} = 2$.

17. True, since –9 is a rational number.

18. True

19. True, since C is not a subset of B.

20. False, since all integers are rational numbers.

21. True, since the empty set is a subset of all sets.

22. True, since every set is a subset of itself.

23. True, since every element of D is also an element of C.

24. True, since every integer is a real number.

25. True, since every irrational number is also a real number.

26. False, since B does not contain the *set* {5}.

27. True, since {5} is a subset of B.

28. $\left\{5, \dfrac{8}{2}, \sqrt{9}\right\}$

29. $\left\{5, \dfrac{8}{2}, \sqrt{9}\right\}$

30. $\left\{5, -\dfrac{2}{3}, \dfrac{8}{2}, \sqrt{9}, 0.3, 1\dfrac{5}{8}, -1\right\}$

31. $\left\{\sqrt{7}, \pi\right\}$

32. $\left\{5, -\dfrac{2}{3}, \dfrac{8}{2}, \sqrt{9}, 0.3, \sqrt{7}, 1\dfrac{5}{8}, -1, \pi\right\}$

33. $\left\{5, \dfrac{8}{2}, \sqrt{9}, -1\right\}$

34. The opposite of $-\dfrac{3}{4}$ is $-\left(-\dfrac{3}{4}\right) = \dfrac{3}{4}$.

35. The opposite of 0.6 is –0.6.

36. The opposite of 0 is $-0 = 0$.

37. The opposite of 1 is –1.

38. The reciprocal of $-\dfrac{3}{4}$ is $\dfrac{1}{\left(-\dfrac{3}{4}\right)} = -\dfrac{4}{3}$.

39. The reciprocal of 0.6 is $\dfrac{1}{0.6}$.

40. The reciprocal of 0 is $\dfrac{1}{0}$ which is undefined.

41. The reciprocal of 1 is $\dfrac{1}{1} = 1$.

42. $-7 + 3 = -4$

43. $-10 + (-25) = -35$

44. $5(-0.4) = -2$

45. $(-3.1)(-0.1) = 0.31$

46. $-7 - (-15) = -7 + 15 = 8$

47. $9 - (-4.3) = 9 + 4.3 = 13.3$

48. $(-6)(-4)(0)(-3) = 0$

49. $(-12)(0)(-1)(-5) = 0$

50. $(-24) \div 0$ is undefined.

51. $0 \div (-45) = 0$

52. $(-36) \div (-9) = 4$

53. $60 \div (-12) = -5$

54. $\left(-\dfrac{4}{5}\right) - \left(-\dfrac{2}{3}\right) = -\dfrac{4}{5} + \dfrac{2}{3} = -\dfrac{12}{15} + \dfrac{10}{15} = -\dfrac{2}{15}$

55. $\left(\dfrac{5}{4}\right) - \left(-2\dfrac{3}{4}\right) = \dfrac{5}{4} + \dfrac{11}{4} = \dfrac{16}{4} = 4$

56. $1 - \dfrac{1}{4} - \dfrac{1}{3} = \dfrac{12}{12} - \dfrac{3}{12} - \dfrac{4}{12} = \dfrac{5}{12}$

57. $-5 + 7 - 3 - (-10) = 2 - 3 + 10$
$= -1 + 10$
$= 9$

58. $8 - (-3) + (-4) + 6 = 8 + 3 - 4 + 6$
$= 11 - 4 + 6$
$= 7 + 6$
$= 13$

59. $3(4 - 5)^4 = 3(-1)^4 = 3(1) = 3$

60. $6(7 - 10)^2 = 6(-3)^2 = 6(9) = 54$

61. $\left(-\dfrac{8}{15}\right)\cdot\left(-\dfrac{2}{3}\right)^2 = -\dfrac{8}{15}\cdot\dfrac{4}{9} = -\dfrac{32}{135}$

62. $\left(-\dfrac{3}{4}\right)^2\cdot\left(-\dfrac{10}{21}\right) = \left(\dfrac{9}{16}\right)\left(-\dfrac{10}{21}\right) = -\dfrac{15}{56}$

63. $-\dfrac{6}{15}\div\dfrac{8}{25} = -\dfrac{6}{15}\cdot\dfrac{25}{8} = -\dfrac{150}{120} = -\dfrac{5}{4}$

64. $\dfrac{4}{9}\div\left(-\dfrac{8}{45}\right) = \dfrac{4}{9}\cdot\left(-\dfrac{45}{8}\right) = -\dfrac{180}{72} = -\dfrac{5}{2}$

65. $-\dfrac{3}{8}+3(2)\div 6 = -\dfrac{3}{8}+6\div 6$

$\qquad\qquad = -\dfrac{3}{8}+1$

$\qquad\qquad = -\dfrac{3}{8}+\dfrac{8}{8}$

$\qquad\qquad = \dfrac{5}{8}$

66. $5(-2)-(-3)-\dfrac{1}{6}+\dfrac{2}{3} = -10+3-\dfrac{1}{6}+\dfrac{2}{3}$

$\qquad\qquad = -7-\dfrac{1}{6}+\dfrac{2}{3}$

$\qquad\qquad = -\dfrac{42}{6}-\dfrac{1}{6}+\dfrac{4}{6}$

$\qquad\qquad = -\dfrac{39}{6}$

$\qquad\qquad = -6\dfrac{1}{2}$

67. $\left|2^3-3^2\right|-\left|5-7\right| = \left|8-9\right|-\left|-2\right|$

$\qquad\qquad = \left|-1\right|-2$

$\qquad\qquad = 1-2$

$\qquad\qquad = -1$

68. $\left|5^2-2^2\right|+\left|9\div(-3)\right| = \left|25-4\right|+\left|-3\right|$

$\qquad\qquad = \left|21\right|+3$

$\qquad\qquad = 21+3$

$\qquad\qquad = 24$

69. $(2^3-3^2)-(5-7) = (8-9)-(-2)$

$\qquad\qquad = -1+2$

$\qquad\qquad = 1$

70. $(5^2-2^4)+[9\div(-3)] = (25-16)+(-3)$

$\qquad\qquad\qquad\qquad = 9+(-3)$

$\qquad\qquad\qquad\qquad = 6$

71. $\dfrac{(8-10)^3-(-4)^2}{2+8(2)\div 4} = \dfrac{(-2)^3-16}{2+16\div 4}$

$\qquad\qquad\qquad = \dfrac{-8-16}{2+4}$

$\qquad\qquad\qquad = \dfrac{-24}{6}$

$\qquad\qquad\qquad = -4$

72. $\dfrac{(2+4)^2+(-1)^5}{12\div 2\cdot 3-3} = \dfrac{(6)^2+(-1)}{6\cdot 3-3}$

$\qquad\qquad\qquad = \dfrac{36-1}{18-3}$

$\qquad\qquad\qquad = \dfrac{35}{15}$

$\qquad\qquad\qquad = \dfrac{7}{3}$

73. $\dfrac{(4-9)+4-9}{10-12\div 4\cdot 8} = \dfrac{(-5)+4-9}{10-3\cdot 8}$

$\qquad\qquad\qquad = \dfrac{-1-9}{10-24}$

$\qquad\qquad\qquad = \dfrac{-10}{-14}$

$\qquad\qquad\qquad = \dfrac{5}{7}$

74. $\dfrac{3-7-(7-3)}{15+30\div 6\cdot 2} = \dfrac{-4-(4)}{15+5\cdot 2}$

$\qquad\qquad\qquad = \dfrac{-8}{15+10}$

$\qquad\qquad\qquad = \dfrac{-8}{25}$

$\qquad\qquad\qquad = -\dfrac{8}{25}$

75. $\dfrac{\sqrt{25}}{4+3\cdot 7} = \dfrac{5}{4+21} = \dfrac{5}{25} = \dfrac{1}{5}$

76. $\dfrac{\sqrt{64}}{24-8\cdot 2} = \dfrac{8}{24-16} = \dfrac{8}{8} = 1$

77. $x^2 - y^2 + z^2 = (0)^2 - (3)^2 + (-2)^2$
$= 0 - 9 + 4$
$= -5$

78. $\dfrac{5x+z}{2y} = \dfrac{5(0)+(-2)}{2(3)} = \dfrac{0-2}{6} = \dfrac{-2}{6} = -\dfrac{1}{3}$

79. $\dfrac{-7y-3z}{-3} = \dfrac{-7(3)-3(-2)}{-3}$
$= \dfrac{-21+6}{-3}$
$= \dfrac{-15}{-3}$
$= 5$

80. $(x-y+z)^2 = (0-3+(-2))^2$
$= (-3-2)^2$
$= (-5)^2$
$= 25$

81. a. When $r = 1$,
$2\pi r = 2\pi(1) = 2(3.14) = 6.28$.
When $r = 10$,
$2\pi r = 2\pi(10) = 20(3.14) = 62.8$.
When $r = 100$,
$2\pi r = 2\pi(100) = 200(3.14) = 628$.

r	1	10	100
$2\pi r$	6.28	62.8	628

b. As the radius increases, the circumference increases.

82. $5xy - 7xy + 3 - 2 + xy$
$= 5xy - 7xy + xy + 3 - 2$
$= (5 - 7 + 1)xy + (3 - 2)$
$= (-1)xy + 1$
$= -xy + 1$

83. $4x + 10x - 19x + 10 - 19$
$= (4 + 10 - 19)x + (10 - 19)$
$= -5x + (-9)$
$= -5x - 9$

84. $6x^2 + 2 - 4(x^2 + 1) = 6x^2 + 2 - 4x^2 - 4$
$= 6x^2 - 4x^2 + 2 - 4$
$= (6-4)x^2 + (2-4)$
$= 2x^2 + (-2)$
$= 2x^2 - 2$

85. $-7(2x^2 - 1) - x^2 - 1$
$= -14x^2 + 7 - x^2 - 1$
$= -14x^2 - x^2 + 7 - 1$
$= (-14-1)x^2 + (7-1)$
$= -15x^2 + 6$

86. $(3.2x - 1.5) - (4.3x - 1.2)$
$= 3.2x - 1.5 - 4.3x + 1.2$
$= 3.2x - 4.3x - 1.5 + 1.2$
$= (3.2 - 4.3)x - 0.3$
$= -1.1x - 0.3$

87. $(7.6x + 4.7) - (1.9x + 3.6)$
$= 7.6x + 4.7 - 1.9x - 3.6$
$= 7.6x - 1.9x + 4.7 - 3.6$
$= (7.6 - 1.9)x + 4.7 - 3.6$
$= 5.7x + 1.1$

88. $12 = -4x$

89. $n + 2n = -15$

90. $4(y + 3) = -1$

91. $6(t - 5) = 4$

92. $z - 7 = 6$

93. $9x - 10 = 5$

94. $x - 5 \geq 12$

95. $-4 < 7y$

96. $\dfrac{2}{3} \neq 2\left(n + \dfrac{1}{4}\right)$

97. $t + 6 \leq -12$

98. Associative Property of Addition

99. Distributive Property

100. Additive Inverse Property

101. Commutative Property of Addition

102. Associative and Commutative Properties of Multiplication
To see this: $(XY)Z = X(YZ) = (YZ)X$

103. Multiplicative Inverse Property

104. Multiplication Property of Zero

105. Associative Property of Multiplication

106. Additive Identity Property

107. Multiplicative Identity Property

108. $5x - 15z = 5(x - 3z)$

109. $(7 + y) + (3 + x) = (3 + x) + (7 + y)$

110. $0 = 2 + (-2)$, for example

111. $1 = 2 \cdot \dfrac{1}{2}$, for example

112. $[(3.4)(0.7)]5 = (3.4)[(0.7)(5)]$

113. $7 = 7 + 0$

114. $-9 > -12$ since -9 is further to the right than -12 on a number line.

115. $0 > -6$ since 0 is further to the right than -6 on a number line.

116. $-3 < -1$ since -3 is further to the left than -1 on a number line.

117. $7 = |-7|$ since 7 and -7 are both 7 units away from 0 on a number line.

118. $-5 < -(-5)$, since $-(-5) = 5$ and -5 is further to the left than 5 on a number line.

119. $4(x - 5) = 2x - 14$
$4x - 20 = 2x - 14$
$2x = 6$
$x = 3$

120. $x + 7 = -2(x + 8)$
$x + 7 = -2x - 16$
$3x = -23$
$x = -\dfrac{23}{3}$

121. $3(2y - 1) = -8(6 + y)$
$6y - 3 = -48 - 8y$
$14y = -45$
$y = -\dfrac{45}{14}$

122. $-(z + 12) = 5(2z - 1)$
$-z - 12 = 10z - 5$
$-11z = 7$
$z = -\dfrac{7}{11}$

123. $0.3(x - 2) = 1.2$
$10[0.3(x - 2) = 10(1.2)$
$3(x - 2) = 12$
$3x - 6 = 12$
$3x = 18$
$x = 6$

124. $1.5 = 0.2(c - 0.3)$
$1.5 = 0.2c - 0.06$
$100(1.5) = 100(0.2c - 0.06)$
$150 = 20c - 6$
$156 = 20c$
$7.8 = c$

125. $-4(2 - 3h) = 2(3h - 4) + 6h$
$-8 + 12h = 6h - 8 + 6h$
$-8 + 12h = 12h - 8$
$-8 = -8$ True
All real numbers

126. $6(m - 1) + 3(2 - m) = 0$
$6m - 6 + 6 - 3m = 0$
$3m = 0$
$m = 0$

127. $6 - 3(2g + 4) - 4g = 5(1 - 2g)$

$6 - 6g - 12 - 4g = 5 - 10g$

$-6 - 10g = 5 - 10g$

$-6 = 5$ False

No solution, $\varnothing$.

128. $20 - 5(p + 1) + 3p = -(2p - 15)$

$20 - 5p - 5 + 3p = -2p + 15$

$15 - 2p = -2p + 15$

$15 = 15$ True

All real numbers

129. $\dfrac{x}{3} - 4 = x - 2$

$3\left(\dfrac{x}{3} - 4\right) = 3(x - 2)$

$x - 12 = 3x - 6$

$-2x = 6$

$x = -3$

130. $\dfrac{9}{4}y = \dfrac{2}{3}y$

$12\left(\dfrac{9}{4}y\right) = 12\left(\dfrac{2}{3}y\right)$

$27y = 8y$

$19y = 0$

$y = 0$

131. $\dfrac{3n}{8} - 1 = 3 + \dfrac{n}{6}$

$24\left(\dfrac{3n}{8} - 1\right) = 24\left(3 + \dfrac{n}{6}\right)$

$9n - 24 = 72 + 4n$

$5n = 96$

$n = \dfrac{96}{5}$

132. $\dfrac{z}{6} + 1 = \dfrac{z}{2} + 2$

$6\left(\dfrac{z}{6} + 1\right) = 6\left(\dfrac{z}{2} + 2\right)$

$z + 6 = 3z + 12$

$-2z = 6$

$z = -3$

133. $\dfrac{b - 2}{3} = \dfrac{b + 2}{5}$

$15 \cdot \left(\dfrac{b - 2}{3}\right) = 15 \cdot \left(\dfrac{b + 2}{5}\right)$

$5(b - 2) = 3(b + 2)$

$5b - 10 = 3b + 6$

$2b = 16$

$b = 8$

134. $\dfrac{2t - 1}{3} = \dfrac{3t + 2}{15}$

$15\left(\dfrac{2t - 1}{3}\right) = 15\left(\dfrac{3t + 2}{15}\right)$

$5(2t - 1) = 3t + 2$

$10t - 5 = 3t + 2$

$7t = 7$

$t = 1$

135. $\dfrac{x - 2}{5} + \dfrac{x + 2}{2} = \dfrac{x + 4}{3}$

$30\left(\dfrac{x - 2}{5} + \dfrac{x + 2}{2}\right) = 30\left(\dfrac{x + 4}{3}\right)$

$6(x - 2) + 15(x + 2) = 10(x + 4)$

$6x - 12 + 15x + 30 = 10x + 40$

$21x + 18 = 10x + 40$

$11x = 22$

$x = 2$

136. $\dfrac{2z - 3}{4} - \dfrac{4 - z}{2} = \dfrac{z + 1}{3}$

$12\left(\dfrac{2z - 3}{4} - \dfrac{4 - z}{2}\right) = 12\left(\dfrac{z + 1}{3}\right)$

$3(2z - 3) - 6(4 - z) = 4(z + 1)$

$6z - 9 - 24 + 6z = 4z + 4$

$12z - 33 = 4z + 4$

$8z = 37$

$z = \dfrac{37}{8}$

137. Let x = the number.

$2(x - 3) = 3x + 1$

$2x - 6 = 3x + 1$

$-7 = x$

The number is -7.

138. Let x = smaller number, then
$x + 5$ = larger number.
$$x + x + 5 = 285$$
$$2x = 280$$
$$x = 140$$
$x + 5 = 145$
The numbers are 140 and 145.

139. $40\% \cdot 130 = 0.40 \cdot 130 = 52$

140. $1.5\% \cdot 8 = 0.015 \cdot 8 = 0.12$

141. Let x = viewers in 1995.
$x - 40\%$ of $x = 33$ million
$$x - 0.40x = 33$$
$$0.60x = 33$$
$$x = 55$$
There were 55 million Oscar viewers in 1995.

142. Let n = the first integer, then
$n + 1$ = the second integer,
$n + 2$ = the third integer, and
$n + 3$ = the fourth integer.
$$(n+1) + (n+2) + (n+3) - 2n = 16$$
$$n + 6 = 16$$
$$n = 10$$
Therefore, the integers are 10, 11, 12, and 13.

143. Let x = smaller odd integer, then
$x + 2$ = larger odd integer.
$$5x = 3(x+2) + 54$$
$$5x = 3x + 6 + 54$$
$$2x = 60$$
$$x = 30$$
Since this is not odd, no such consecutive odd integers exist.

144. Let w = width of the playing field, then
$2w - 5$ = length of the playing field.
$$2w + 2(2w - 5) = 230$$
$$2w + 4w - 10 = 230$$
$$6w = 240$$
$$w = 40$$
Then $2w - 5 = 2(40) - 5 = 75$
The field is 75 meters long and 40 meters wide.

145. Let m = number of miles driven.
$$2(29.95) + 0.15\left(m - 2(100)\right) = 83.6$$
$$59.9 + 0.15(m - 200) = 83.6$$
$$59.9 + 0.15m - 30 = 83.6$$
$$29.9 + 0.15m = 83.6$$
$$0.15m = 53.7$$
$$m = 358$$
The customer drove 358 miles.

146. Solve $R = C$.
$$16.50x = 4.50x + 3000$$
$$12x = 3000$$
$$x = 250$$
Thus, 250 calculators must be produced and sold in order to break even.

147. Solve $R = C$.
$$40x = 20x + 100$$
$$20x = 100$$
$$x = 5$$
$$R = 40x = 40 \cdot 5 = 200$$
She will break even if she sells 5 plants. The revenue will be $200.

148. Go to the Y= editor and enter $y_1 = \frac{10}{3}\pi x^2$. The x values start at 1 and increment by 0.5 so we will use these values in the Table Setup.

The table can be completed from the screen above.

x	1	1.5	2	2.5	3
$\frac{10}{3}\pi x^3$	10.47	23.56	41.89	65.45	94.25

149. Go to the Y= editor and enter $y_1 = 30 + 2x$.

The *x* values start at 2, but there is no common increment. Thus, we will use the Ask option in Table Setup.

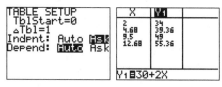

The table can be completed from the screen above.

x	2	4.68	9.5	12.68
$30 + 2x$	34	39.36	49	55.36

150. Let *x* = number of hours worked and *y* = gross pay. Since Gina makes \$5.75 per hour, her gross pay will be $5.75x$.

Go to the Y= editor and enter $y_1 = 5.75x$.

The *x* values start at 5 and increment by 5 so we will use these values in Table Setup.

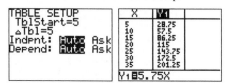

The table can be completed from the screen above.

Hours	5	10	15	20	25	30
Gross Pay (Dollars)	28.75	57.5	86.25	115	143.75	172.5

151. Let *x* = thousands of gallons of water and let *y* = total charge.

Coast Waterworks charges \$8 for the first 4 thousand gallons and \$1.10 for each additional thousand gallons used. The total charge for using *x* thousand gallons would be:

$y_1 = 8 + 1.10(x - 4)$

Cross Gates Water Company charges \$12 for the first 5 thousand gallons and \$1.50 for each additional thousand gallons used. The total charge for using *x* thousand gallons would be:

$y_2 = 12 + 1.50(x - 5)$

The *x* values start at 5 and increment by 1 so we will use these values in Table Setup.

The table can be completed from the screen above.

Gallons (Thousands)	5	6	7	8
Coast Charge (Dollars)	9.10	10.20	11.30	12.40
Cross Gates Charge (Dollars)	12.00	13.50	15.00	16.50

152. a. Go to the Y= editor and enter

$y_1 = -16x^2 + 40x + 500$.

The *x* values start at 0 and increment by 1 so we will use these values in Table Setup.

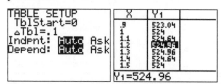

The table can be completed from the screen above.

Seconds	0	1	2	3	4	5
Height (ft)	500	524	516	476	404	300

b. From the table, it appears that the maximum height occurs between 0 and 2 seconds. We can change the table increment to get more precision.

The maximum height is about 525 feet.

c. The rock will strike the ground when the height is 0. Using the original increment of 1 unit, we can scroll down the table looking for 0 in the y_1 column.

The value in y_1 changes sign when x goes from 6 to 7. This means that the rock will hit the ground somewhere between 6 and 7 seconds after it is thrown. We can again change the table increment to get more precision.

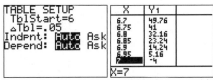

It appears that the rock will hit the ground in about 7 seconds.

153. $V = lwh$

$$w = \frac{V}{lh}$$

154. $C = 2\pi r$

$$\frac{C}{2\pi} = r$$

155. $5x - 4y = -12$

$$5x + 12 = 4y$$

$$y = \frac{5x + 12}{4}$$

156. $5x - 4y = -12$

$$5x = 4y - 12$$

$$x = \frac{4y - 12}{5}$$

157. $y - y_1 = m(x - x_1)$

$$m = \frac{y - y_1}{x - x_1}$$

158. $$y - y_1 = m(x - x_1)$$
$$y - y_1 = mx - mx_1$$
$$y - y_1 + mx_1 = mx$$
$$\frac{y - y_1 + mx_1}{m} = x$$

159. $$E = I(R + r)$$
$$E = IR + Ir$$
$$E - IR = Ir$$
$$\frac{E - IR}{I} = r$$

160. $$S = vt + gt^2$$
$$S - vt = gt^2$$
$$\frac{S - vt}{t^2} = g$$

161. $T = gr + gvt$
$$T = g(r + vt)$$
$$g = \frac{T}{r + vt}$$

162. $$I = Prt + P$$
$$I = P(rt + 1)$$
$$\frac{I}{rt + 1} = P$$

163. $$A = \frac{h}{2}(B + b)$$
$$2A = hB + hb$$
$$2A - hb = hB$$
$$\frac{2A - hb}{h} = B$$

164. $$V = \frac{1}{3}\pi r^2 h$$
$$3V = \pi r^2 h$$
$$\frac{3V}{\pi r^2} = h$$

165. $$R = \frac{r_1 + r_2}{2}$$
$$2R = r_1 + r_2$$
$$2R - r_2 = r_1$$

166.

$$\frac{V_1}{T_1} = \frac{V_2}{T_2}$$
$$T_2 V_1 = T_1 V_2$$
$$T_2 = \frac{T_1 V_2}{V_1}$$

167. $A = P\left(1 + \frac{r}{n}\right)^{nt} = 3000\left(1 + \frac{0.03}{n}\right)^{7n}$

a. $A = 3000\left(1 + \frac{0.03}{2}\right)^{14} \approx \$3695.27$

b. $A = 3000\left(1 + \frac{0.03}{52}\right)^{364} \approx \$3700.81$

168. Let x = original width,
then $x + 2$ = original length.
$$(x+4)(x+2+4) = x(x+2) + 88$$
$$(x+4)(x+6) = x^2 + 2x + 88$$
$$x^2 + 10x + 24 = x^2 + 2x + 88$$
$$8x = 64$$
$$x = 8$$
$$x + 2 = 10$$
The original width is 8 in. and the original length is 10 in.

169. a. Let x = degrees Celsius. Go to the Y= editor and enter $y_1 = \frac{9x + 160}{5}$ to find the corresponding degrees Fahrenheit. Since the increment is not constant we use the Ask option in the Table Setup.

```
TABLE SETUP            X    Y1
TblStart=0           -40   -40
ΔTbl=1               -15    5
Indpnt: Auto Ask      10    50
Depend: Auto Ask      60   140

Y1 ◘ (9X+160)/5
```

The table can be completed using the screen above.

Celsius	−40	−15	10	60
Fahrenheit	−40	5	50	140

b. Let $C = 100$.
$$F = \frac{9(100) + 160}{5} = \frac{900 + 160}{5} = \frac{1060}{5} = 212$$
The boiling point of water is $212°F$.

c. Let $C = 0$.
$$F = \frac{9(0) + 160}{5} = \frac{160}{5} = 32$$
The freezing point of water is $32°F$.

171. Area $= 18 \times 21 = 378 \text{ ft}^2$
$$\text{Packages} = \frac{378}{24} = 15.75$$
There are 16 packages needed.

170. a. Let $y_1 = 55x$
Note that 15 minutes = 0.25 hours.

```
TABLE SETUP            X     Y1
TblStart=0            0      0
ΔTbl=.25             .25    13.75
Indpnt: Auto Ask     .5     27.5
Depend: Auto Ask     .75    41.25
                     1      55
                     1.25   68.75
                     1.5    82.5

Y1 ◘ 55X
```

Hours	0	0.25	0.5	0.75	1.0	1.25	1.5
Distance (miles)	0	13.75	27.5	41.25	55	68.75	82.5

b. We can scroll down the table until we find the value 192.5 in the y_1 column. The corresponding value in the x column is the time of travel.

```
X      Y1
2.75   151.25
3      165
3.25   178.75
3.5    192.5
3.75   206.25
4      220
4.25   233.75

Y1=192.5
```

It would take 3.5 hours to travel 192.5 miles at a speed of 55 miles per hour.

172. $V_{box} = lwh = 8 \cdot 5 \cdot 3 = 120 \text{ in}^3$, while
$$V_{cyl} = \pi r^2 h = \pi \cdot 3^2 \cdot 6 = 54\pi \approx 170 \text{ in}^3$$
Therefore, the cylinder holds more ice cream.

173. $d = rt$ or $r = \frac{d}{t}$
11:00 A.M. to 1:15 P.M. is 2.25 hours.
$$r = \frac{130}{2.25} \approx 58$$
His average speed was 58 mph.

174. If we let $h = 6$, the volume of the cone is given by:

$$V = \frac{1}{3}\pi r^2 (6) = 2\pi r^2$$

Let x = length of the radius. Then enter $y_1 = 2\pi x^2$ in the Y= editor to find the corresponding volumes.

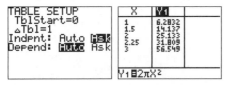

The table can be completed using the screen above.

Height, h	6	6	6	6	6
Radius, x	1	1.5	2	2.25	3
Volume, y_1	6.28	14.14	25.13	31.81	56.55

175. If we let $h = 10$, the volume of the cone is given by:

$$V = \frac{1}{3}\pi r^2 (10) = \frac{10}{3}\pi r^2$$

Let x = length of the radius. Then enter $y_1 = \frac{10}{3}\pi x^2$ in the Y= editor to find the corresponding volumes.

The table can be completed using the screen above.

Height, h	10	10	10	10	10
Radius, x	1.5	2.1	2.75	3	3.5
Volume, y_1	23.56	46.18	79.19	94.25	128.28

176. Mean:

$$\bar{x} = \frac{21 + 28 + 16 + 42 + 38}{5} = \frac{145}{5} = 29$$

Median:
Start by placing the values in increasing order.
16, 21, 28, 38, 42
Since there is an odd number of values, the median is the middle value. The median is 28.

Mode:
Since no value occurs more frequently than any other, there is no mode.

177. Mean:

$$\bar{x} = \frac{42 + 35 + 36 + 40 + 50}{5} = \frac{203}{5} = 40.6$$

Median:
Start by placing the values in increasing order.
35, 36, 40, 42, 50
Since there is an odd number of values, the median is the middle value. The median is 40.

Mode:
Since no value occurs more frequently than any other, there is no mode.

178. Mean:

$$\bar{x} = \frac{7.6 + 8.2 + 8.2 + 9.6 + 5.7 + 9.1}{6} = \frac{48.4}{6} \approx 8.07$$

Median:
Start by placing the values in increasing order.
5.7, 7.6, 8.2, 8.2, 9.1, 9.6
Since there is an even number of values, the median is the average of the two middle values.

$$\frac{8.2 + 8.2}{2} = \frac{16.4}{2} = 8.2$$

The median is 8.2.

Mode:
The value 8.2 occurs twice, which is more than any other value. Therefore, the mode is 8.2.

179. Mean:
$$\bar{x} = \frac{4.9 + 7.1 + 6.8 + 6.8 + 5.3 + 4.9}{6} = \frac{35.8}{6} \approx 5.97$$

Median:
Start by placing the values in increasing order.
4.9, 4.9, 5.3, 6.8, 6.8, 7.1
Since there is an even number of values, the median is the average of the two middle values.
$$\frac{5.3 + 6.8}{2} = \frac{12.1}{2} = 6.05$$
The median is 6.05.

Mode:
Both 4.9 and 6.8 occur twice which is more than any other value. Therefore, there are two modes: 4.9 and 6.8.

180. Mean:
$$\bar{x} = \frac{0.2 + 0.3 + 0.5 + 0.6 + 0.6 + 0.9 + 0.2 + 0.7 + 1.1}{9}$$
$$= \frac{5.1}{9}$$
$$\approx 0.57$$

Median:
Start by placing the values in increasing order.
0.2, 0.2, 0.3, 0.5, 0.6, 0.6, 0.7, 0.9, 1.1
Since there is an odd number of values, the median is the middle value. The median is 0.6.

Mode:
Both 0.2 and 0.6 occur twice, which is more than any other value. Therefore, there are two modes: 0.2 and 0.6.

181. Mean:
$$\bar{x} = \frac{0.6 + 0.6 + 0.8 + 0.4 + 0.5 + 0.3 + 0.7 + 0.8 + 0.1}{9}$$
$$= \frac{4.8}{9}$$
$$\approx 0.53$$

Median:
Start by placing the values in increasing order.
0.1, 0.3, 0.4, 0.5, 0.6, 0.6, 0.7, 0.8, 0.8
Since there is an odd number of values, the median is the middle value. The median is 0.6.

Mode:
Both 0.6 and 0.8 occur twice, which is more than any other value. Therefore, there are two modes: 0.6 and 0.8.

182. The largest pie sector is for Federal loans, so most students receive Federal loans.

183. Federal Loans: $(0.57)(50.3) \approx 28.67$

Fed. grants/ work study: $(0.17)(50.3) \approx 8.55$

State grants: $(0.06)(50.3) \approx 3.02$

Institutional/other grants: $(0.20)(50.3) = 10.06$

About \$28.67 billion is spent on Federal loans, \$8.55 billion on Federal grants/work study, \$3.02 billion on State grants, and \$10.06 billion on Institutional/other grants.

184. Go to the top of the bar labeled 11-24. Then move across to the vertical axis to estimate the percent. According to the graph, about 44% of employees receive health benefits at companies with 11-24 employees.

185. The shortest bar belongs to the category 'less than 10'. Therefore, companies with less than 10 employees have the smallest percent of employees receiving health benefits. The percent is roughly 29%.

186. The highest bar belongs to the category '1000 and over'. Therefore, companies with at least 1000 employees have the highest percent of employees receiving health benefits. The percent is roughly 75%.

187. Answers may vary. The graph indicates that larger companies are more likely to provide health benefits to employees.

Chapter 1 Test

1. True; -2.3 lies to the right of -2.33 on the number line.

2. False; $-6^2 = -36$, while $(-6)^2 = 36$.

3. False; $-5-8 = -13$, while
$-(5-8) = -(-3) = 3$.

4. False; $(-2)(-3)(0) = 0$, while $\dfrac{(-4)}{0}$ is undefined.

5. True

6. False; for example, $\dfrac{1}{2}$ is a rational number that is not an integer.

7. $5-12\div 3(2) = 5-4(2) = 5-8 = -3$

8. $5^2 - 3^4 = 25-81 = -56$

9. $(4-9)^3 - |-4-6|^2 = (-5)^3 - |-10|^2$
$$= -125 - 10^2$$
$$= -125 - 100$$
$$= -225$$

10. $12 + \{6 - [5 - 2(-5)]\} = 12 + \{6 - [5 + 10]\}$
$$= 12 + (6-15)$$
$$= 12 + (-9)$$
$$= 12 - 9$$
$$= 3$$

11. $\dfrac{6(7-9)^3 + (-2)}{(-2)(-5)(-5)} = \dfrac{6(-2)^3 - 2}{10(-5)}$
$$= \dfrac{6(-8)-2}{-50}$$
$$= \dfrac{-48-2}{-50}$$
$$= \dfrac{-50}{-50}$$
$$= 1$$

12. $\dfrac{(4-\sqrt{16})-(-7-20)}{-2(1-4)^2} = \dfrac{(4-4)-(-27)}{-2(-3)^2}$
$$= \dfrac{0+27}{-2(9)}$$
$$= \dfrac{27}{-18}$$
$$= -\dfrac{3}{2}$$

13. $q^2 - r^2 = (4)^2 - (-2)^2 = 16 - 4 = 12$

14. $\dfrac{5t-3q}{3r-1} = \dfrac{5(1)-3(4)}{3(-2)-1} = \dfrac{5-12}{-6-1} = \dfrac{-7}{-7} = 1$

15. a. When $x = 1$, $5.75x = 5.75(1) = 5.75$.
When $x = 3$, $5.75x = 5.75(3) = 17.25$.
When $x = 10$, $5.75x = 5.75(10) = 57.50$.
When $x = 20$, $5.75x = 5.75(20) = 115.00$.

x	1	3	10	20
$5.75x$	5.75	17.25	57.50	115.00

b. As the number of adults increases the total cost increases.

16. $2(x+5) = 30$

17. $\dfrac{(6-y)^2}{7} < -2$

18. $\dfrac{9z}{|-12|} \neq 10$

19. $3\left(\dfrac{n}{5}\right) = -n$

20. $20 = 2x - 6$

21. $-2 = \dfrac{x}{x+5}$

22. Distributive Property

23. Associative Property of Addition

24. Additive Inverse Property

25. Multiplication Property of Zero

26. $0.05n + 0.1d$

27. $-2(3x + 7) = -6x - 14$

28. $\dfrac{1}{3}a - \dfrac{3}{8} + \dfrac{1}{6}a - \dfrac{3}{4} = \dfrac{1}{3}a + \dfrac{1}{6}a - \dfrac{3}{8} - \dfrac{3}{4}$

$$= \left(\dfrac{1}{3} + \dfrac{1}{6}\right)a - \dfrac{3}{8} - \dfrac{3}{4}$$

$$= \left(\dfrac{2}{6} + \dfrac{1}{6}\right)a - \dfrac{3}{8} - \dfrac{6}{8}$$

$$= \left(\dfrac{3}{6}\right)a - \dfrac{9}{8}$$

$$= \dfrac{1}{2}a - \dfrac{9}{8}$$

29. $4y + 10 - 2(y + 10) = 4y + 10 - 2y - 20$

$$= 4y - 2y + 10 - 20$$

$$= (4 - 2)y - 10$$

$$= 2y - 10$$

30. $(8.3x - 2.9) - (9.6x - 4.8)$

$$= 8.3x - 2.9 - 9.6x + 4.8$$

$$= 8.3x - 9.6x - 2.9 + 4.8$$

$$= (8.3 - 9.6)x + 1.9$$

$$= -1.3x + 1.9$$

31. $0.2x^3 + 5x^2 - 6.2x + 3$

$$= 0.2(-3.1)^3 + 5(-3.1)^2 - 6.2(-3.1) + 3$$

$$= 0.2(-29.791) + 5(9.61) - 6.2(-3.1) + 3$$

$$= -5.9582 + 48.05 + 19.22 + 3$$

$$= 64.3118$$

32. $C = \pi d$, $\quad A = \pi r^2$, $\quad r = \dfrac{d}{2}$

Let x = length of diameter. Then define $y_1 = \dfrac{x}{2}$ to find the corresponding radii. Also define $y_2 = \pi x$ to find the corresponding circumferences and $y_3 = \pi \left(\dfrac{x}{2}\right)^2$ to find the corresponding areas.

The table can be completed by using the screens above.

Diameter, d	2	3.8	10	14.9
Radius, r	1	1.9	5	7.45
Circumference, πd	6.28	11.94	31.42	46.81
Area, πr^2	3.14	11.34	78.54	174.37

33. $8x + 14 = 5x + 44$

$$3x = 30$$

$$x = 10$$

34. $3(x + 2) = 11 - 2(2 - x)$

$$3x + 6 = 11 - 4 + 2x$$

$$3x + 6 = 2x + 7$$

$$x = 1$$

35. $3(y - 4) + y = 2(6 + 2y)$

$$3y - 12 + y = 12 + 4y$$

$$4y - 12 = 12 + 4y$$

$$-12 = 12 \quad \text{False}$$

This is a contradiction so the solution is $\varnothing$.

36. $7n - 6 + n = 2(4n - 3)$

$$8n - 6 = 8n - 6$$

$$-6 = -6$$

All real numbers

37. $\dfrac{7w}{4} + 5 = \dfrac{3w}{10} + 1$

$$20\left(\dfrac{7w}{4} + 5\right) = 20\left(\dfrac{3w}{10} + 1\right)$$

$$35w + 100 = 6w + 20$$

$$29w = -80$$

$$w = -\dfrac{80}{29}$$

38. $3x - 4y = 8$

$$3x - 8 = 4y$$

$$y = \dfrac{3x - 8}{4}$$

39. $S = gt^2 + gvt$

$S = g(t^2 + vt)$

$g = \dfrac{S}{t^2 + vt}$

40. $F = \dfrac{9}{5}C + 32$

$F - 32 = \dfrac{9}{5}C$

$C = \dfrac{5}{9}(F - 32)$

41. $12\% \cdot 80 = 0.12 \cdot 80 = 9.6$

42. Let x = employees in 1996

$x + 1.8x = 461,000$

$2.18x = 461,000$

$x = 211,468$

The number of people employed in these occupations in 1996 was 211,468.

43. Recall that $C = 2\pi r$. Here $C = 78.5$.

$78.5 = 2\pi r$

$r = \dfrac{78.5}{2\pi} = \dfrac{39.25}{\pi}$

Also, recall that $A = \pi r^2$.

$A = \pi\left(\dfrac{39.25}{\pi}\right)^2 = \dfrac{39.25^2}{3.14} \approx 490.63$

Dividing this by 60 yields approximately 8.18. Therefore, about 8 hunting dogs could safely be kept in the pen.

44. Solve $R > C$

$7.4x > 3910 + 2.8x$

$4.6x > 3910$

$x > 850$

Therefore, more than 850 sunglasses must be produced and sold in order for them to yield a profit.

45. Here we need the compound interest equation.

$A = P\left(1 + \dfrac{r}{n}\right)^{n \cdot t}$

$t = 10$, $P = 2500$, $r = 0.035$, $n = 4$

$A = 2500\left(1 + \dfrac{0.035}{4}\right)^{4 \cdot 10}$

$= 2500(1.00875)^{40}$

$\approx 2500(1.416909)$

≈ 3542.27

After 10 years, there would be about $3542.27 in the account.

46. a. Let x = monthly sales. Then define $y_1 = 1500 + 0.05x$ as Ann-Margaret's gross monthly pay.

```
TABLE SETUP         X     Y1
 TblStart=8000     8000   1900
 ΔTbl=1000         9000   1950
Indpnt: Auto Ask  10000   2000
Depend: Auto Ask  11000   2050
                  12000   2100
                  13000   2150
                  14000   2200
                  Y1◻1500+0.05X
```

The table can be completed by using the screen above.

Sales (Dollars)	8000	9000	10,000	11,000	12,000
Gross Monthly Pay (Dollars)	1900	1950	2000	2050	2100

b. Scan the row for Sales until you find 11,000. Then read the corresponding entry for her Gross Monthly Pay. If Ann-Margaret has sales of $11,000, her gross monthly pay will be $2050. Multiply this by 12 to get her gross annual pay.

$2050 \cdot 12 = 24,600$

Her gross annual pay would be $24,600.

c. Scan the y_1 column to find 2200. Then read the corresponding value in the x column.

```
 X      Y1
8000   1900
9000   1950
10000  2000
11000  2050
12000  2100
13000  2150
14000  2200
X=14000
```

To have a gross monthly pay of $2200, she needs to have monthly sales of $14,000.

47. a. A table of values can help us what is happening. We will start at time 0, when the rocket is launched, and increment by 0.5 seconds.

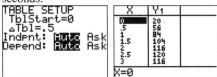

From the table, it appears that the rocket will be 116 feet high after 2 seconds and after 3 seconds.

b. From the previous table, the rocket's maximum height appears to be 120 feet. To check, we can change the increment on our table.

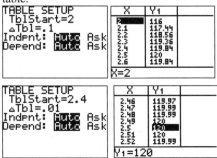

It does appear that the maximum height of the rocket is 120 feet.

c. According to the table, the rocket reaches its maximum height after 2.5 seconds.

d. Since the rocket reaches its maximum height after 2.5 seconds, and it explodes 0.5 seconds after it reaches its maximum height, the rocket will explode after 3 seconds.

48. $\overline{x} = \dfrac{12+0+6+5+2+10+3+1+5+7+1+5}{12}$

$= \dfrac{57}{12}$

$= 4.75$

The mean number of books checked out per week is 4.75.

49. Start by placing the values in increasing order.
0, 1, 1, 2, 3, 5, 5, 5, 6, 7, 10, 12
Since there is an even number of values, the median is the average of the two middle values.

$$\frac{5+5}{2} = \frac{10}{2} = 5$$

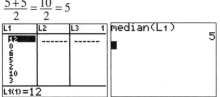

The median number of books checked out is 5.

50. The value 5 occurs three times, which is more than any other value. Therefore, the mode is 5.

51. Go along the horizontal axis to the year 1970. Move up to locate the corresponding point on the Fresh Fruit graph. Then move horizontally to the vertical axis to determine the summer plans. From the graph, it appears that in 1970 about 80 pounds of fresh fruit was consumed by each person in the US.

52. Go along the horizontal axis to the year 1995. Move up to locate the corresponding point on the Fresh Vegetables graph. Then move horizontally to the vertical axis to determine the summer plans. From the graph, it appears that in 1995 about 119 pounds of fresh fruit was consumed by each person in the US.

53. From the graph, the two line graphs are furthest apart in the year 2000. Therefore, the greatest difference in consumption of vegetables and fruit appears to have occurred in 2000.

54. Answers may vary. While both line graphs illustrate an increasing trend, it appears that the Fresh Vegetables graph is increasing at a faster rate than the Fresh Fruit graph.

Chapter 2

Mental Math 2.1

1. Point A is (5, 2).

2. Point B is (2, 5).

3. Point C is (3, 0).

4. Point D is (–1, 3).

5. Point E is (–5, –2).

6. Point F is (–3, 5).

7. Point G is (–1, 0).

8. Point H is (0, –3).

9. (2, 3) is in quadrant I.

10. (0, 5) is on the y-axis.

11. (–2, 7) is in quadrant II.

12. (–3, 0) is on the x-axis.

13. (–1, –4) is in quadrant III.

14. (4, –2) is in quadrant IV.

15. (0, –100) is on the y-axis.

16. (10, 30) is in quadrant I.

17. (–10, –30) is in quadrant III.

18. (0, 0) is on both the x- and y-axis.

19. (–87, 0) is on the x-axis.

20. (–42, 17) is in quadrant II.

Exercise Set 2.1

1. (3, 2) is in quadrant I

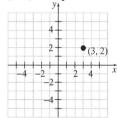

3. (–5, 3) is in quadrant II.

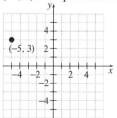

5. $\left(5\frac{1}{2}, -4\right)$ is in quadrant IV.

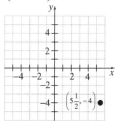

7. (0, 3.5) is on the y-axis.

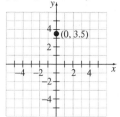

9. (–2, –4) is in quadrant III.

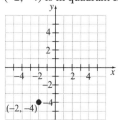

11. quadrant IV

13. x-axis

15. quadrant III

17. (2, 8) ; quadrant I

19. (1, –4) ; quadrant IV

46

21. Answers may vary. One possibility is $[-10, 10, 1]$ by $[-20, 20, 1]$. The result is shown below.

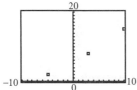

23. Answers may vary. One possibility is $[-100, 100, 10]$ by $[-100, 100, 10]$. The result is shown below.

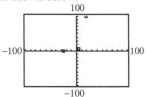

25. C

27. B

29. Defining $y_1 = 3x - 5$ and using a table on the graphing utility, we obtain the following:

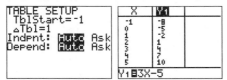

From the table, we see that the x-coordinate -1 is paired with the y-coordinate -8 and that the x-coordinate 0 is paired with the y-coordinate -5.

Likewise, if we graph $y_1 = 3x - 5$ in an integer window centered at $(0,0)$ and if we trace to the point with x-coordinate -1, we find the y-coordinate -8. If we trace to point with x-coordinate 0, we find the y-coordinate -5.

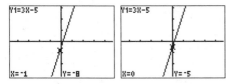

Thus, $(-1, -8)$ is a solution of $y = 3x - 5$, but $(0, 5)$ is not a solution.

We can manually verify the above results as follows:

Let $x = 0$ and $y = 5$.

$$y = 3x - 5$$
$$5 \overset{?}{=} 3(0) - 5$$
$$5 \overset{?}{=} 0 - 5$$
$$5 = -5 \quad \text{False}$$

Let $x = -1$ and $y = -8$.

$$y = 3x - 5$$
$$-8 \overset{?}{=} 3(-1) - 5$$
$$-8 \overset{?}{=} -3 - 5$$
$$-8 = -8 \quad \text{True}$$

31. To enter the equation in the Y= editor, we first solve for y:

$$-6x + 5y = -6$$
$$6x - 6x + 5y = 6x - 6 \quad \text{Add } 6x \text{ to both sides.}$$
$$5y = 6x - 6$$
$$y = \frac{6x - 6}{5} \quad \text{Divide both sides by 5.}$$

Defining $y_1 = \frac{6x - 6}{5}$ and using a table on the graphing utility, we obtain the following:

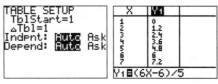

From the table, we see that the x-coordinate 1 is paired with the y-coordinate 0 and that the x-coordinate 1 is paired with the y-coordinate $1.2 = 6/5$.

Likewise, if we graph $y_1 = \frac{6x - 6}{5}$ in an integer window centered at $(0,0)$ and if we trace to the point with x-coordinate 0, we find the y-coordinate 0. If we trace to point with x-coordinate 1, we find the y-coordinate $1.2 = 6/5$.

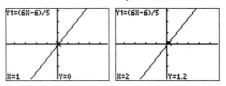

Thus, both $(1, 0)$ and $\left(2, \dfrac{6}{5}\right)$ are solutions of

$-6x + 5y = -6$.

We can manually verify the above results as follows:

Let $x = 1$ and $y = 0$.

$$-6x + 5y = -6$$

$$-6(1) + 5(0) \overset{?}{=} -6$$

$$-6 + 0 \overset{?}{=} -6$$

$$-6 = -6 \quad \text{True}$$

Let $x = 2$ and $y = \dfrac{6}{5}$.

$$-6x + 5y = -6$$

$$-6(2) + 5\left(\dfrac{6}{5}\right) \overset{?}{=} -6$$

$$-12 + 6 \overset{?}{=} -6$$

$$-6 = -6 \quad \text{True}$$

33. Defining $y_1 = 2x^2$ and using a table on the graphing utility, we obtain the following:

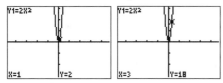

From the table, we see that the x-coordinate 1 is paired with the y-coordinate 2 and that the x-coordinate 3 is paired with the y-coordinate 18.

Likewise, if we graph $y_1 = 2x^2$ in an integer window centered at $(0,0)$ and if we trace to the point with x-coordinate 1, we find the y-coordinate 2. If we trace to point with x-coordinate 3, we find the y-coordinate 18.

Thus, both $(1, 2)$ and $(3, 18)$ are solutions of $y = 2x^2$.

We can manually verify the above results as follows:

Let $x = 1$ and $y = 2$.

$$y = 2x^2$$

$$2 \overset{?}{=} 2(1)^2$$

$$2 \overset{?}{=} 2(1)$$

$$2 = 2 \quad \text{True}$$

Let $x = 3$ and $y = 18$.

$$y = 2x^2$$

$$18 \overset{?}{=} 2(3)^2$$

$$18 \overset{?}{=} 2(9)$$

$$18 = 18 \quad \text{True}$$

35.

Equation	Linear or Nonlinear	Shape
$y - x = 8$	linear	line
$y = 6x$	linear	line
$y = x^2 + 3$	nonlinear	parabola
$y = 6x - 5$	linear	line
$y = -|x| + 2$	nonlinear	V-shaped
$y = 3x^2$	nonlinear	parabola
$y = -4x + 2$	linear	line
$y = -|x|$	nonlinear	V-shaped
$y = x^3$	nonlinear	cubic

37.
$$2x + y = 10$$
$$-2x + 2x + y = -2x + 10 \quad \text{Add } -2x \text{ to both sides.}$$
$$y = -2x + 10$$

39.
$$-7x - 3y = 4$$
$$7x - 7x - 3y = 7x + 4 \quad \text{Add } 7x \text{ to both sides.}$$
$$-3y = 7x + 4$$
$$y = \dfrac{7x + 4}{-3} \quad \text{Divide both sides by } -3.$$

41. Define $y_1 = 2x^2 + 1.2x - 5.6$.

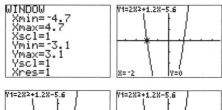

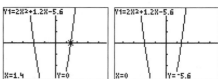

48

The coordinates of the x-intercepts are $(-2,0)$ and $(1.4,\ 0)$. The coordinates of the y-intercept is $(0,-5.6)$.

43. D $(1.2,-4.2)$. The x-coordinate of this ordered pair is not an integer. Therefore, this ordered pair would not be displayed when an integer window is used.

45. C

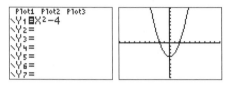

47. A

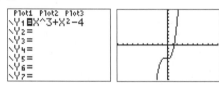

49. D

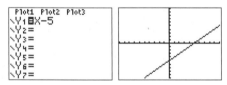

51. C

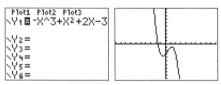

53. A

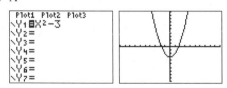

55. C

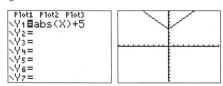

57. Graph $y = x$.

Let $x = 0$, then $y = 0$.
Let $x = 1$, then $y = 1$.
Let $x = 2$, then $y = 2$.

The points $(0,0)$, $(1,1)$, and $(2,2)$ are on the graph of $y = x$.

Graph $y = x + 2$.

Let $x = 0$, then $y = 0 + 2$, or 2.
Let $x = 1$, then $y = 1 + 2$, or 3.
Let $x = 2$, then $y = 2 + 2$, or 4.

The points $(0,2)$, $(1,3)$, and $(2,4)$ are on the graph of $y = x + 2$.

Graph $y = x - 3$.

Let $x = 0$, then $y = 0 - 3$, or -3.
Let $x = 1$, then $y = 1 - 3$, or -2.
Let $x = 2$, then $y = 2 - 3$, or -1.

The points $(0,-3)$, $(1,-2)$, and $(2,-1)$ are on the graph of $y = x - 3$.

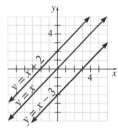

Define $y_1 = x$, $y_2 = x + 2$, and $y_3 = x - 3$. Use the viewing window shown below to obtain the graph.

Pattern: The graphs of $y = x$, $y = x + 2$, and $y = x - 3$ are all parallel. That is, the graphs of $y = x + 2$ and $y = x - 3$ look the same as the graph of $y = x$ except shifted up 2 units and down 3 units, respectively.

59. Graph $y = -x^2$.

Let $x = -2$, then $y = -(-2)^2$, or -4.
Let $x = -1$, then $y = -(-1)^2$, or -1.
Let $x = 0$, then $y = -(0)^2$, or 0.
Let $x = 1$, then $y = -(1)^2$, or -1.
Let $x = 2$, then $y = -(2)^2$, or -4.

The points $(-2,-4)$, $(-1,-1)$, $(0,0)$, $(1,-1)$, and $(2,-4)$ are on the graph of $y = -x^2$.

Graph $y = -x^2 + 1$.

Let $x = -2$, then $y = -(-2)^2 + 1$, or -3.
Let $x = -1$, then $y = -(-1)^2 + 1$, or 0.
Let $x = 0$, then $y = -(0)^2 + 1$, or 1.
Let $x = 1$, then $y = -(1)^2 + 1$, or 0.
Let $x = 2$, then $y = -(2)^2 + 1$, or -3.

The points $(-2,-3)$, $(-1,0)$, $(0,1)$, $(1,0)$, and $(2,-3)$ are on the graph of $y = -x^2 + 1$.

Graph $y = -x^2 - 2$.

Let $x = -2$, then $y = -(-2)^2 - 2$, or -6.
Let $x = -1$, then $y = -(-1)^2 - 2$, or -3.
Let $x = 0$, then $y = -(0)^2 - 2$, or -2.
Let $x = 1$, then $y = -(1)^2 - 2$, or -3.
Let $x = 2$, then $y = -(2)^2 - 2$, or -6.

The points $(-2,-6)$, $(-1,-3)$, $(0,-4)$, $(1,-3)$, and $(2,-6)$ are on the graph of $y = -x^2$.

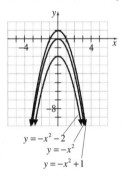

$y = -x^2 - 2$
$y = -x^2$
$y = -x^2 + 1$

Define $y_1 = -x^2$, $y_2 = -x^2 + 1$, and $y_3 = -x^2 - 2$. Use the viewing window that is shown below to obtain the graph.

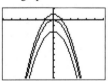

Pattern: The graphs of $y = -x^2 + 1$ and $y = -x^2 - 2$ look the same as the graph of $y = -x^2$ except shifted up 1 unit and down 2 units, respectively.

61. Let $x = -2$, then $-2 + y = 3$
$$-2 + y + 2 = 3 + 2$$
$$y = 5$$
Let $x = 0$, then $0 + y = 3$
$$y = 3$$
Let $x = 2$, then $2 + y = 3$
$$2 + y - 2 = 3 - 2$$
$$y = 1$$

The points $(-2,5)$, $(0,3)$, and $(2,1)$ are on the graph of $x + y = 3$.

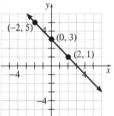

Checking with a graphing utility:
Solve $x + y = 3$ for y.
$$y = -x + 3$$
Define $y_1 = -x + 3$. Use the window shown to obtain the graph.

 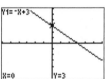

63. Let $x = -1$, then $y = 4(-1)$, or -4.
Let $x = 0$, then $y = 4(0)$, or 0.
Let $x = 1$, then $y = 4(1)$, or 4.

The points $(-1,-4)$, $(0,4)$, and $(1,4)$ are on the graph of $y = 4x$.

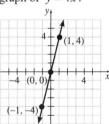

Checking with a graphing utility: Define $y_1 = 4x$. Use the window shown to obtain the graph.

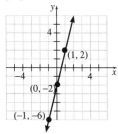

65. Let $x = -1$, then $y = 4(-1) - 2$, or -6.

Let $x = 0$, then $y = 4(0) - 2$, or -2.

Let $x = 1$, then $y = 4(1) - 2$, or 2.

The points $(-1, -6)$, $(0, -2)$, and $(1, 2)$ are on the graph of $y = 4x - 2$.

Checking with a graphing utility: Define $y_1 = 4x - 2$. Use the window shown to obtain the graph.

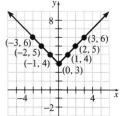

67. Let $x = -3$, then $y = |-3| + 3$, or 6.

Let $x = -2$, then $y = |-2| + 3$, or 5.

Let $x = -1$, then $y = |-1| + 3$, or 4.

Let $x = 0$, then $y = |0| + 3$, or 3.

Let $x = 1$, then $y = |1| + 3$, or 4.

Let $x = 2$, then $y = |2| + 3$, or 5.

Let $x = 3$, then $y = |3| + 3$, or 6.

The points $(-3, 6)$, $(-2, 5)$, $(-1, 4)$, $(0, 3)$, $(1, 4)$, $(2, 5)$, and $(3, 6)$ are on the graph of $y = |x| + 3$.

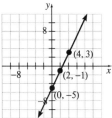

Checking with a graphing utility: Define $y_1 = |x| + 3$. Use the window shown to obtain the graph.

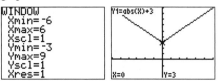

69. Let $x = 0$, then $2(0) - y = 5$
$$0 - y = 5$$
$$-y = 5$$
$$y = -5$$

Let $x = 2$, then $2(2) - y = 5$
$$4 - y = 5$$
$$-y = 1$$
$$y = -1$$

Let $x = 4$, then $2(4) - y = 5$
$$8 - y = 5$$
$$-y = -3$$
$$y = 3$$

The points $(0, -5)$, $(2, -1)$, and $(4, 3)$ are on the graph of $2x - y = 5$.

Checking with a graphing utility:
Solve $2x - y = 5$ for y.
$$-y = -2x + 5$$
$$y = 2x - 5$$

Define $y_1 = 2x - 5$. Use the window shown to obtain the graph.

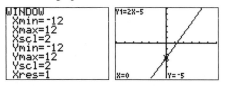

71. Let $x = -3$, then $y = 2(-3)^2$, or 18.

Let $x = -2$, then $y = 2(-2)^2$, or 8.

Let $x = -1$, then $y = 2(-1)^2$, or 2.

Let $x = 0$, then $y = 2(0)^2$, or 0.

Let $x = 1$, then $y = 2(1)^2$, or 2.

Let $x = 2$, then $y = 2(2)^2$, or 8.

Let $x = 3$, then $y = 2(3)^2$, or 18.

The points $(-3, 18)$, $(-2, 8)$, $(-1, 2)$, $(0, 0)$, $(1, 2)$, $(2, 8)$, and $(3, 18)$ are on the graph of $y = 2x^2$.

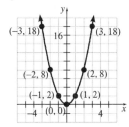

Checking with a graphing utility: Define $y_1 = 2x^2$. Use the window shown to obtain the graph.

 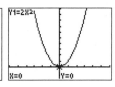

73. Let $x = -3$, then $y = (-3)^2 - 3$, or 6.

Let $x = -2$, then $y = (-2)^2 - 3$, or 1.

Let $x = -1$, then $y = (-1)^2 - 3$, or -2.

Let $x = 0$, then $y = (0)^2 - 3$, or -3.

Let $x = 1$, then $y = (1)^2 - 3$, or -2.

Let $x = 2$, then $y = (2)^2 - 3$, or 1.

Let $x = 3$, then $y = (3)^2 - 3$, or 6.

The points $(-3, 6)$, $(-2, 1)$, $(-1, -2)$, $(0, -3)$, $(1, -2)$, $(2, 1)$, and $(3, 6)$ are on the graph of $y = x^2 - 3$.

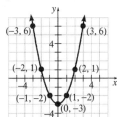

Checking with a graphing utility: Define $y_1 = x^2 - 3$. Use the window shown to obtain the graph.

 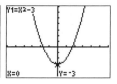

75. Let $x = -2$, then $y = -2(-2)$, or 4.

Let $x = 0$, then $y = -2(0)$, or 0.

Let $x = 2$, then $y = -2(2)$, or -4.

The points $(-2, 4)$, $(0, 0)$, and $(2, -4)$ are on the graph of $y = -2x$.

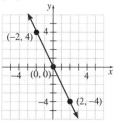

Checking with a graphing utility: Define $y_1 = -2x$. Use the window shown to obtain the graph.

 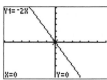

77. Let $x = -1$, then $y = -2(-1) + 3$, or 5.

Let $x = 0$, then $y = -2(0) + 3$, or 3.

Let $x = 2$, then $y = -2(1) + 3$, or 1.

The points $(-2, 5)$, $(0, 3)$, and $(2, 1)$ are on the graph of $y = -2x + 3$.

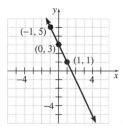

Checking with a graphing utility: Define $y_1 = -2x + 3$. Use the window shown to obtain the graph.

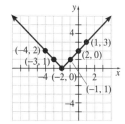

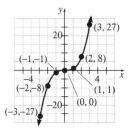

79. Let $x = -4$, then $y = \left|-4+2\right|$, or 2.

Let $x = -3$, then $y = \left|-3+2\right|$, or 1.

Let $x = -2$, then $y = \left|-2+2\right|$, or 0.

Let $x = -1$, then $y = \left|-1+2\right|$, or 1.

Let $x = 0$, then $y = \left|0+2\right|$, or 2.

Let $x = 1$, then $y = \left|1+2\right|$, or 3.

The points $(-4,2)$, $(-3,1)$, $(-2,0)$, $(-1,1)$, $(0,2)$, $(1,3)$, and $(2,4)$ are on the graph of $y = \left|x+2\right|$.

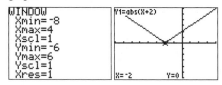

Checking with a graphing utility: Define $y_1 = \left|x+2\right|$. Use the window shown to obtain the graph.

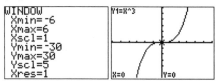

Checking with a graphing utility: Define $y_1 = x^3$. Use the window shown to obtain the graph.

83. Let $x = -3$, then $y = -\left|-3\right|$, or -3.

Let $x = -2$, then $y = -\left|-2\right|$, or -2.

Let $x = -1$, then $y = -\left|-1\right|$, or -1.

Let $x = 0$, then $y = -\left|0\right|$, or 0.

Let $x = 1$, then $y = -\left|1\right|$, or -1.

Let $x = 2$, then $y = -\left|2\right|$, or -2.

Let $x = 3$, then $y = -\left|3\right|$, or -3.

The points $(-3,-3)$, $(-2,-2)$, $(-1,-1)$, $(0,0)$, $(1,-1)$, $(2,-2)$, and $(3,-3)$ are on the graph of $y = -\left|x\right|$.

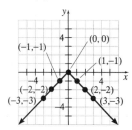

81. Let $x = -3$, then $y = (-3)^3$, or -27.

Let $x = -2$, then $y = (-2)^3$, or -8.

Let $x = -1$, then $y = (-1)^3$, or -1.

Let $x = 0$, then $y = (0)^3$, or 0.

Let $x = 1$, then $y = (1)^3$, or 1.

Let $x = 2$, then $y = (2)^3$, or 8.

Let $x = 3$, then $y = (3)^3$, or 27.

The points $(-3,-27)$, $(-2,-8)$, $(-1,-1)$, $(0,0)$, $(1,1)$, $(2,8)$, and $(3,27)$ are on the graph of $y = x^3$.

Checking with a graphing utility: Define $y_1 = -\left|x\right|$. Use the window shown to obtain the graph.

85. Plot the points $(-3,-3)$, $(-2,-2)$, $(-1,-1)$, $(0,0)$, $(1,-1)$, $(2,-2)$, and $(3,-3)$. Connect these points.

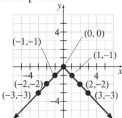

This graph is similar to that of the absolute value function $y = |x|$, except it is upside down. That is, the y-coordinates of the points are the opposites of the absolute values of the x-coordinates. Thus, it is the graph of $y = -|x|$.

87. a. parabola

   b. line

89. a. line

   b. parabola

91. a. Let $x = 0$, then $y = 2(0)+6$, or 6.
Let $x = 3$, then $y = 2(3)+6$, or 12.
Let $x = 6$, then $y = 2(6)+6$, or 18.
The points $(0,6)$, $(3,12)$, and $(6,18)$ are on the graph of $y = 2x+6$.

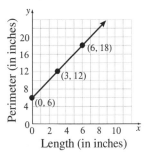

   b. We find 4 along the x-axis and move vertically upward until we reach a point on the line. We then read the corresponding y-value of 14. The rectangle with a width of 4 inches has a perimeter of 14 inches.

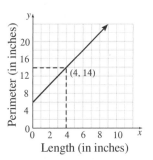

93. $3(x-2)+5x = 6x-16$
$3x-6+5x = 6x-16$
$8x-6 = 6x-16$
$2x = -10$
$x = -5$
The solution is -5.

95. $3x + \dfrac{2}{5} = \dfrac{1}{10}$

$10\left(3x + \dfrac{2}{5}\right) = 10\left(\dfrac{1}{10}\right)$

$30x + 4 = 1$

$30x = -3$

$\dfrac{30x}{30} = \dfrac{-3}{30}$

$x = -\dfrac{1}{10}$

The solution is $-\dfrac{1}{10}$.

97. B

99. C

101. a. 1991: In April it rose to $4.25.

   b. 1997: In September it rose to $5.15.

   c. Answers will vary. One possibility follows: The minimum wage rate stays constant over long intervals of time. When an increase in the rate occurs, it abruptly jumps from the old rate to the new. It then stays constant at that rate until the next increase. This causes to graph to appear stair stepped.

   d. $5.15 - $0.25 = $4.90. By 2003, the minimum wage had increased by $4.90 since it began in 1938.

103. $y = 3x+5$

Let $x = -1$, then $y = 3(-1)+5$, or 2.
Let $x = 0$, then $y = 3(0)+5$, or 5.
Let $x = 1$, then $y = 3(1)+5$, or 8.
The points $(-1,2)$, $(0,5)$, and $(1,8)$ are on the graph of $y = 3x+5$.

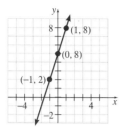

105. $y = x^2 + 2$

Let $x = -2$, then $y = (-2)^2 + 2$, or 6.

Let $x = -1$, then $y = (-1)^2 + 2$, or 3.

Let $x = 0$, then $y = (0)^2 + 2$, or 2.

Let $x = 1$, then $y = (-1)^2 + 2$, or 3.

Let $x = 2$, then $y = (2)^2 + 2$, or 6.

The points $(-2, 6)$, $(-1, 3)$, $(0, 2)$, $(1, 3)$, and $(2, 6)$ are on the graph of $y = x^2 + 2$.

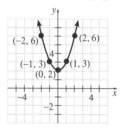

Exercise Set 2.2

1. Domain = {−1, 0, −2, 5}
Range = {7, 6, 2}
Function

3. Domain = {−2, 6, −7}
Range = {4, −3, −8}
The relation is not a function since −2 is paired with both 4 and −3.

5. Domain = {1}
Range = {1, 2, 3, 4}
The relation is not a function since 1 is paired with both 1 and 2 for example.

7. Domain = $\left\{\dfrac{3}{2}, 0\right\}$

Range = $\left\{\dfrac{1}{2}, -7, \dfrac{4}{5}\right\}$

Because $\dfrac{3}{2}$ is paired with both $\dfrac{1}{2}$ and −7, the relation is not a function.

9. Domain = {−3, 0, 3}
Range = {−3, 0, 3}
Function

11. Domain = {−1, 1, 2, 3}
Range = {2, 1}
Function

13. Domain = {Colorado, Alaska, Delaware, Illinois, Connecticut, Texas}
Range = {6, 1, 20, 30}
Function

15. Domain = {32°, 104°, 212°, 50°}
Range = {0°, 40°, 10°, 100°}
Function

17. Domain = {0}
Range = {2, −1, 5, 100}
Not a function

19. Function

21. Not a function

23. Function

25. Not a function

27. Function

29. Function

31. Not a function

33. Domain = $[0, \infty)$

Range = $(-\infty, \infty)$

The relation is not a function since it fails the vertical line test (try $x = 1$).

35. Domain = $[-1, 1]$

Range = $(-\infty, \infty)$

The relation is not a function since it fails the vertical line test (try $x = 0$).

37. Domain = $(-\infty, \infty)$

Range = $(-\infty, -3] \cup [3, \infty)$

The relation is not a function since it fails the vertical line test (try $x = 2$).

39. Domain = $[2, 7]$

Range = $[1, 6]$

The relation is not a function since it fails the vertical line test.

41. Domain = $\{-2\}$

Range = $(-\infty, \infty)$

The relation is not a function since it fails the vertical line test.

43. Domain = $(-\infty, \infty)$

Range = $(-\infty, 3]$

Function

45. Domain = $(-\infty, \infty)$

Range = $(-\infty, \infty)$

Function

47. Answers may vary. Possibilities follow:

  a. A function is a relation in which each member of the domain corresponds to exactly one member of the range.

  b. The domain is the set of all inputs of a relation or function.

  c. The range is the set of all outputs of a relation or function.

49. Yes, $y = x + 1$ is a function. Only one y-value is associated with each x-value that is substituted into the equation.

51. No, $x = 2y^2$ is not a function. If $y = 2$, then $x = 8$. Also, if $y = -2$, then $x = 8$. So, the x-value 8 corresponds with two y-values.

53. Yes, $y - x = 7$ is a function. Only one y-value is associated with each x-value that is substituted into the equation.

55. Yes, $y = \dfrac{1}{x}$ is a function. Only one y-value is associated with each x-value that is substituted into the equation.

57. Yes, $y = 5x - 12$ is a function. Only one y-value is associated with each x-value that is substituted into the equation.

59. No, $x = y^2$ is not a function. If $y = 4$, then $x = 16$. Also, if $y = -4$, then $x = 16$. So, the x-value 16 corresponds with two y-values.

61. $f(x) = 3x + 3$

$f(4) = 3(4) + 3$

$\quad\quad = 12 + 3$

$\quad\quad = 15$

63. $h(x) = 5x^2 - 7$

$h(-3) = 5(-3)^2 - 7$

$\quad\quad\;\; = 5(9) - 7$

$\quad\quad\;\; = 45 - 7$

$\quad\quad\;\; = 38$

65. $g(x) = 4x^2 - 6x + 3$

$g(2) = 4(2)^2 - 6(2) + 3$

$\quad\quad = 4(4) - 6(2) + 3$

$\quad\quad = 16 - 12 + 3$

$\quad\quad = 7$

67. $g(x) = 4x^2 - 6x + 3$

$g(0) = 4(0)^2 - 6(0) + 3$

$\quad\quad = 4(0) - 0 + 3$

$\quad\quad = 0 - 0 + 3$

$\quad\quad = 3$

69. $f(x) = \dfrac{1}{2}x$

  a. $f(0) = \dfrac{1}{2}(0)$

$\quad\quad\quad = 0$

  b. $f(2) = \dfrac{1}{2}(2)$

$\quad\quad\quad = 1$

  c. $f(-2) = \dfrac{1}{2}(-2)$

$\quad\quad\quad\; = -1$

71. $g(x) = 2x^2 + 4$

  a. $g(-11) = 2(-11)^2 + 4$

$\quad\quad\quad\;\; = 2(121) + 4$

$\quad\quad\quad\;\; = 242 + 4$

$\quad\quad\quad\;\; = 246$

  b. $g(-1) = 2(-1)^2 + 4$

$\quad\quad\quad = 2(1) + 4$

$\quad\quad\quad = 2 + 4$

$\quad\quad\quad = 6$

  c. $g\left(\dfrac{1}{2}\right) = 2\left(\dfrac{1}{2}\right)^2 + 4$

$\quad\quad\quad\; = 2\left(\dfrac{1}{4}\right) + 4$

$\quad\quad\quad\; = \dfrac{1}{2} + \dfrac{8}{2}$

$\quad\quad\quad\; = \dfrac{9}{2}$

73. $f(x) = -5$

  a. $f(2) = -5$

  b. $f(0) = -5$

  c. $f(606) = -5$

75. $f(x) = 1.3x^2 - 2.6x + 5.1$

  a. $f(2) = 1.3(2)^2 - 2.6(2) + 5.1$
$$= 1.3(4) - 5.2 + 5.1$$
$$= 5.2 - 5.2 + 5.1$$
$$= 5.1$$

  b. $f(-2) = 1.3(-2)^2 - 2.6(-2) + 5.1$
$$= 1.3(4) + 5.2 + 5.1$$
$$= 5.2 + 5.2 + 5.1$$
$$= 15.5$$

  c. $f(3.1) = 1.3(3.1)^2 - 2.6(3.1) + 5.1$
$$= 1.3(9.61) - 8.06 + 5.1$$
$$= 12.493 - 8.06 + 5.1$$
$$= 9.533$$

77. a. To find $f(-5)$, we find -5 in the X column of the table and then determine the matching value in the Y_1 column. Thus, $f(-5) = 23$.

  b. To find $f(10)$, we find 10 in the X column of the table and then determine the matching value in the Y_1 column. Thus, $f(10) = 23$.

  c. To find $f(15)$, we find 15 in the X column of the table and then determine the matching value in the Y_1 column. Thus, $f(15) = 33$.

79. Looking at the graph, $y = 7$ when $x = 2$. Thus, $f(2) = 7$.

81. $(1, -10)$

83. $(4, 56)$

85. The point $(-1, -2)$ is on the graph of $y = f(x)$. Thus, $f(-1) = -2$.

87. The point $(2, 0)$ is on the graph of $y = g(x)$. Thus, $g(2) = 0$.

89. The points $(-4, -5)$ and $(0, -5)$ are on the graph of $y = f(x)$. Thus, $x = -4$ or $x = 0$.

91. The point $(-4, -5)$ is on the graph of $y = g(x)$. Thus, $x = -4$.

93. Infinite number. A function can pass the vertical line test no matter how many x-intercept it has. For example, $y = 0$ passes the vertical line test (so it is a function) and has an infinite number of x-intercepts.

95. Evaluate $C(t) = 20 + 35t$ for the given values of t.

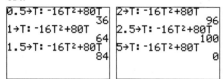

Completing the table, we have

t	1	2	3	4	5
$C(t)$	55	90	125	160	195

97. Evaluate $h(t) = -16t^2 + 80t$ for the given values of t.

  a. $h(0.5) = 36$

  b. $h(1) = 64$

  c. $h(1.5) = 84$

  d. $h(2) = 96$

  e. $h(2.5) = 100$

  f. $h(5) = 0$

99. a. $17.1 billion

  b. $16.21 billion

101. $36.464 billion

103. $f(x) = x + 7$

105. $A(r) = \pi r^2$
$A(5) = \pi(5)^2 = 25\pi$ square centimeters

107. $V(x) = x^3$
$V(14) = (14)^3 = 2744$ cubic inches

109. $H(f) = 2.59f + 47.24$
$H(46) = 2.59(46) + 47.24$
$$= 166.38 \text{ centimeters}$$

111. $D(x) = \dfrac{136}{25}x$

$D(30) = \dfrac{136}{25}(30) = 163.2$ milligrams

113. $C(x) = 1.69x + 87.54$

a. $C(5) = 1.69(5) + 87.54 = 95.99$

The per capita consumption of poultry was about 95.99 lb in 2000.

b. 2002 gives $x = 7$

$C(x) = 1.69(7) + 87.54$
$= 99.37$ pounds

115. $x - y = 5$

Let $x = 0$	Let $y = 0$	Let $x = 1$
$0 - y = 5$	$x - 0 = 5$	$1 - y = 5$
$-y = 5$	$x = 5$	$-y = 4$
$y = -5$		$y = -4$

x	0	-5	1
y	5	0	6

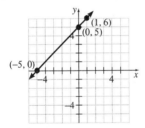

117. $7x + 4y = 8$

Let $x = 0$	Let $y = 0$	Let $x = -1$
$7(0) + 4y = 8$	$7x + 4(0) = 8$	$7x + 4(-1) = 8$
$4y = 8$	$7x = 5$	$7x - 4 = 8$
$y = 2$	$x = \dfrac{5}{7}$	$7x = 12$
		$x = \dfrac{12}{7}$

x	0	$\dfrac{8}{7}$	$\dfrac{12}{7}$
y	2	0	-1

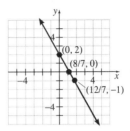

119. $y = 6x$

Let $x = 0$	Let $y = 0$	Let $x = -1$
$y = 6(0)$	$0 = 6x$	$y = 6(-1)$
$y = 0$	$0 = x$	$y = -6$

x	0	0	-1
y	0	0	-6

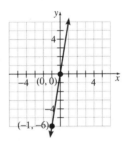

121. Yes. The two sides that are parallel to the side with length 45 meters must have a sum of 45 meters. Likewise, the two sides that are parallel to the side with length 40 meters must have a sum of 49 meters. Thus, the perimeter is $P = 2 \cdot 45 + 2 \cdot 40 = 90 + 80 = 170$ meters.

123. $g(x) = -3x + 12$

a. $g(s) = -3s + 12$

b. $g(r) = -3r + 12$

125. $f(x) = x^2 - 12$

a. $f(12) = (12)^2 - 12 = 144 - 12 = 132$

b. $f(a) = a^2 - 12$

127. Answers will vary. One possibility follows:

Input	Correspondence	Output
People in my algebra class	Final letter grade	{A,B,C,D,F}

Exercise Set 2.3

1. $f(x) = -2x$
$f(0) = -2(0) = 0$
$f(-1) = -2(-1) = 2$
$f(1) = -2(1) = -2$

x	0	−1	1
$f(x)$	0	2	−2

Plot and connect the points to obtain the graph.

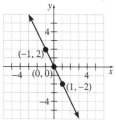

3. $f(x) = -2x + 3$
$f(0) = -2(0) + 3 = 3$
$f(-1) = -2(-1) + 3 = 5$
$f(1) = -2(1) + 3 = 1$

x	0	1	−1
y	3	1	5

Plot and connect the points to obtain the graph.

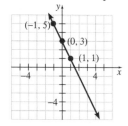

5. $f(x) = \dfrac{1}{2}x$
$f(0) = \dfrac{1}{2}(0) = 0$
$f(2) = \dfrac{1}{2}(2) = 1$
$f(4) = \dfrac{1}{2}(4) = 2$

x	0	2	4
y	0	1	2

Plot and connect the points to obtain the graph.

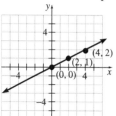

7. $f(x) = \dfrac{1}{2}x - 4$
$f(0) = \dfrac{1}{2}(0) - 4 = -4$
$f(2) = \dfrac{1}{2}(2) - 4 = -3$
$f(4) = \dfrac{1}{2}(4) - 4 = -2$

x	0	2	4
y	−4	−3	−2

Plot and connect the points to obtain the graph.

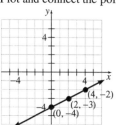

9. C

11. D

13. $x - y = 3$

Let $x = 0$ Let $y = 0$ Let $x = 2$
$0 - y = 3$ $x - 0 = 3$ $2 - y = 3$
$-y = 3$ $x = 3$ $-y = 1$
$y = -3$ $y = -1$

x	0	3	2
y	−3	0	−1

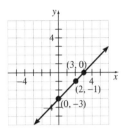

$$x - y = 3$$
$$-y = -x + 3$$
$$y = \frac{-x + 3}{-1}$$
$$y = x - 3$$
$$f(x) = x - 3$$

15. $x = 5y$

Let $x = 0$	Let $x = 5$	Let $x = -5$
$0 = 5y$	$5 = 5y$	$-5 = 5y$
$0 = y$	$1 = y$	$-1 = y$

x	0	5	-5
y	0	1	-1

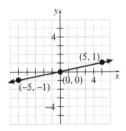

$$x = 5y$$
$$\frac{x}{5} = y$$
$$f(x) = \frac{x}{5}$$

17. $-x + 2y = 6$

Let $x = 0$	Let $y = 0$	Let $x = 2$
$-0 + 2y = 6$	$-x + 2(0) = 6$	$-2 + 2y = 6$
$2y = 6$	$-x = 6$	$2y = 8$
$y = 3$	$x = -6$	$y = 4$

x	0	-6	2
y	3	0	4

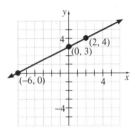

$$-x + 2y = 6$$
$$2y = x + 6$$
$$y = \frac{x + 6}{2}$$
$$y = \frac{1}{2}x + 3$$
$$f(x) = \frac{1}{2}x + 3$$

19. $2x - 4y = 8$

Let $x = 0$	Let $y = 0$	Let $x = 2$
$2(0) - 4y = 8$	$2x - 4(0) = 8$	$2(2) - 4y = 8$
$-4y = 8$	$2x = 8$	$4 - 4y = 8$
$y = -2$	$x = 4$	$-4y = 4$
		$y = -1$

x	0	4	2
y	-2	0	-1

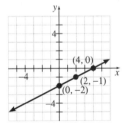

$$2x - 4y = 8$$
$$-4y = -2x + 8$$
$$y = \frac{-2x + 8}{-4}$$
$$y = \frac{1}{2}x - 2$$
$$f(x) = \frac{1}{2}x - 2$$

21. Answers may vary. One possibility follows:
To find the *x*-intercept, substitute 0 for *y* and solve for *x*. To find the *y*-intercept, substitute 0 for *x* and solve for *y*.

23. $x = -1$

This is a vertical line with x-intercept $(-1, 0)$.

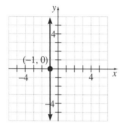

25. $y = 0$

This is a horizontal line with y-intercept $(0, 0)$ (the same as the x-axis).

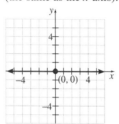

27. $y + 7 = 0$

$y = -7$

This is a horizontal line with y-intercept $(0, -7)$.

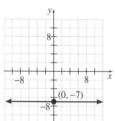

29. C

31. A

33. The only vertical line that will have a y-intercept is $x = 0$. In fact, $x = 0$ has infinitely many y-intercepts. All other vertical lines are parallel to the y-axis and, thus, do not cross it.

35. $x + 2y = 8$

x	0	8	-4
y	4	0	6

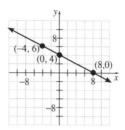

37. $3x + 5y = 7$

x	-6	-1	4
y	5	2	-1

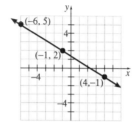

39. $x + 8y = 8$

x	0	8	-8
y	1	0	2

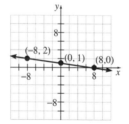

41. $5 = 6x - y$

x	0	1	2
y	-5	1	7

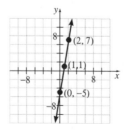

43. $-x+10y=11$

x	-11	-1	9
y	0	1	2

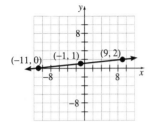

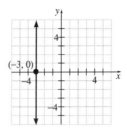

45. $y=\dfrac{3}{2}$

This is a horizontal line with y-intercept $\left(0,\dfrac{3}{2}\right)$.

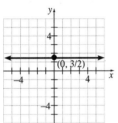

47. $2x+3y=6$

x	0	3	-3
y	2	0	4

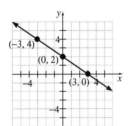

49. $x+3=0$

$x=-3$

This is a vertical line with x-intercept at $(-3,0)$.

51. $f(x)=\dfrac{3}{4}x+2$

x	-4	0	4
$f(x)$	-1	2	5

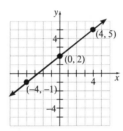

53. $f(x)=x$

x	-3	0	3
$f(x)$	-3	0	3

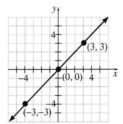

55. $f(x)=\dfrac{1}{2}x$

x	-2	0	2
$f(x)$	-1	0	1

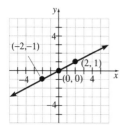

57. $f(x) = 4x - \dfrac{1}{3}$

x	-1	0	1
$f(x)$	$-\dfrac{13}{3}$	$-\dfrac{1}{3}$	$\dfrac{11}{3}$

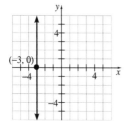

59. $x = -3$

This is a vertical line with x-intercept $(-3, 0)$.

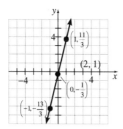

61. B and D

63. Define $y_1 = 15.75(40) + 1.5(15.75)x$ and graph in a $[0, 15, 1]$ by $[0, 1000, 100]$ window. Use the graph to complete the table.

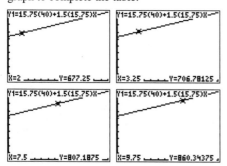

x	2	3.25	7.5	9.75
$S(x)$	677.25	706.78	807.19	860.34

65. $\dfrac{-6-3}{2-8} = \dfrac{-9}{-6} = \dfrac{3}{2}$

67. $\dfrac{-8-(-2)}{-3-(-2)} = \dfrac{-8+2}{-3+2} = \dfrac{-6}{-1} = 6$

69. $\dfrac{0-6}{5-0} = \dfrac{-6}{5} = -\dfrac{6}{5}$

71. $2x + 3y = 1500$

    a. $2(0) + 3y = 1500$
$$3y = 1500$$
$$y = 500$$

    $(0, 500)$; If no tables are produced, 500 chairs can be produced.

    b. $2x + 3(0) = 1500$
$$2x = 1500$$
$$x = 750$$

    $(750, 0)$; If no chairs are produced, 750 tables can be produced.

    c. $2(50) + 3y = 1500$
$$100 + 3y = 1500$$
$$3y = 1400$$
$$y = 466.7$$

    If 50 chairs are produced, 466 chairs can be produced.

73. $C(x) = 0.2x + 24$

    a. $C(200) = 0.2(200) + 24$
$$= 40 + 24$$
$$= 64$$

    It will cost \$64 to drive the car 200 miles.

    b. Define $y_1 = 0.2x + 24$ and graph in a $[0, 500, 100]$ by $[0, 150, 25]$ window.

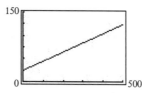

    c. We can tell that, as the number of hour increases, the total cost increases also because the graph moves upward from left to right.

75. $f(x) = 53.6x + 849.88$

    a. 2010 is 20 years after 1990, so we find

$$f(20) = 53.6(20) + 849.88$$
$$= 1072 + 849.88$$
$$= 1921.88$$

    According to the function, the yearly cost of attending a two-year college in 2010 will be $1921.88.

    b. $2000 = 53.6x + 849.88$
$$1150.12 = 53.6x$$
$$21.46 = x$$

    According to the function, the cost will exceed $2000 approximately 22 years (more than 21.46 years) after 1990. Thus, the year will be $1990 + 22 = 2012$.

    c. Answers will vary.

77. a. The graph of $y = -4x + 2$ will be parallel to $y = -4x$ but is shifted upward 2 units so that it has a y-intercept $(0, 2)$.

    b. $y = -4x - 5$ will be parallel to $y = -4x$ but is shifted downward 5 units so that it has a y-intercept $(0, -5)$.

79. B

81. A

Mental Math 2.4

1. If $m = \dfrac{7}{6}$, then the line slants upward.

2. If $m = -3$, then the line slants downward.

3. If $m = 0$, then the line is horizontal.

4. If m is undefined, then the line is vertical.

Exercise Set 2.4

1. $m = \dfrac{11-2}{8-3} = \dfrac{9}{5}$

3. $m = \dfrac{3-8}{4-(-2)} = \dfrac{3-8}{4+2} = \dfrac{-5}{6} = -\dfrac{5}{6}$

5. $m = \dfrac{-4-(-6)}{4-(-2)} = \dfrac{-4+6}{4+2} = \dfrac{2}{6} = \dfrac{1}{3}$

7. $m = \dfrac{5-5}{3-(-2)} = \dfrac{5-5}{3+2} = \dfrac{0}{5} = 0$

9. $m = \dfrac{-5-1}{-1-(-1)} = \dfrac{-5-1}{-1+1} = \dfrac{-6}{0}$; undefined slope

11. $m = \dfrac{4-2}{-3-(-1)} = \dfrac{4-2}{-3+1} = \dfrac{2}{-2} = -1$

13. From the graph, we can see that the line contains the points $(3, -5)$ and $(15, -13)$. Thus,
$$m = \dfrac{-13-(-5)}{15-3} = \dfrac{-13+5}{15-3} = \dfrac{-8}{12} = -\dfrac{2}{3}.$$

15. Choose two ordered pairs from the table. We will use $(0, 5)$ and $(1, 6.5)$. Thus,
$$m = \dfrac{6.5-5}{1-0} = \dfrac{1.5}{1} = 1.5 \text{ or } \dfrac{3}{2}.$$

17. Choose two ordered pairs from the table. We will use $(0, -8)$ and $(10, -6)$. Thus,
$$m = \dfrac{-6-(-8)}{10-0} = \dfrac{-6+8}{10-0} = \dfrac{2}{10} = \dfrac{1}{5} \text{ or } 0.2.$$

19. l_1 slants downward, so it has a negative slope. l_2 slants upward, so it has a positive slope. Thus, l_2 has the greater slope.

21. l_1 slants downward, so it has a negative slope. l_2 is horizontal, so it has a slope of zero. Thus, l_2 has the greater slope.

23. l_1 and l_2 both slant upward, so they both have positive slopes. Now, l_2 is the steeper of the two lines, so it has the greater slope.

25. $f(x) = 5x - 2$
$m = 5, b = -2$

27. $2x + y = 7$
$$y = -2x + 7$$
$m = -2, b = 7$

29. $2x - 3y = 10$
$$-3y = -2x + 10$$
$$\dfrac{-3y}{-3} = \dfrac{-2x}{-3} + \dfrac{10}{-3}$$
$$y = \dfrac{2}{3}x - \dfrac{10}{3}$$
$m = \dfrac{2}{3}, b = -\dfrac{10}{3}$

31. $f(x) = \frac{1}{2}x$

$f(x) = \frac{1}{2}x + 0$

$m = \frac{1}{2}, b = 0$

33. A

35. B

37. Because $x = 1$ is a vertical line, m is undefined.

39. Because $y = -3$ is a horizontal line, $m = 0$.

41. $x + 2 = 0$

$x = -2$

Since this is a vertical line, m is undefined

43. Answers may vary. A possible answer follows: If the line slants upward from left to right, the slope is positive. If the line slants downward from left to right, the slope is negative. If the line is horizontal, its slope is zero. If the line is vertical, its slope is undefined.

45. $f(x) = -x + 5 = -1x + 5$

$m = -1, b = 5$

47. $-6x + 5y = 30$

$5y = 6x + 30$

$\frac{5y}{5} = \frac{6x}{5} + \frac{30}{5}$

$y = \frac{6}{5}x + 6$

$m = \frac{6}{5}, b = 6$

49. $3x + 9 = y$

$y = 3x + 9$

$m = 3, b = 9$

51. $y = 4$

$y = 0x + 4$

$m = 0, b = 4$

53. $f(x) = 7x = 7x + 0$

$m = 7, b = 0$

55. $6 + y = 0$

$y = -6$

$y = 0x - 6$

$m = 0, b = -6$

57. $2 - x = 3$

$-x = 1$

$x = -1$

This is a vertical line, so m is undefined and there is no y-intercept.

59. $f(x) = -3x + 6 \qquad g(x) = 3x + 5$

$m = -3 \qquad\qquad m = 3$

Neither, since their slopes are not equal and since the product of their slope does not equal -1.

61. $-4x + 2y = 5 \qquad\qquad 2x - y = 7$

$\quad 2y = 4x + 5 \qquad\qquad -y = -2x + 7$

$\quad y = \frac{4x}{2} + \frac{5}{2} \qquad\qquad y = \frac{-2x}{-1} + \frac{7}{-1}$

$\quad y = 2x + \frac{5}{2} \qquad\qquad y = 2x + 7$

$m = 2 \qquad\qquad\qquad\qquad m = 2$

Parallel, since they have the same slope.

63. $-2x + 3y = 1 \qquad\qquad 3x + 2y = 12$

$\quad 3y = 2x + 1 \qquad\qquad 2y = -3x + 12$

$\quad \frac{3y}{3} = \frac{2x}{3} + \frac{1}{3} \qquad\qquad \frac{2y}{2} = -\frac{3x}{2} + \frac{12}{2}$

$\quad y = \frac{2}{3}x + \frac{1}{3} \qquad\qquad y = -\frac{3}{2}x + 6$

$m = \frac{2}{3} \qquad\qquad\qquad m = -\frac{3}{2}$

Perpendicular, since the product of their slopes is -1.

65. Two lines, both with positive slopes, cannot be perpendicular. Explanation may vary. One possibility follows:
If two lines are perpendicular, then the product of their slopes is -1. This cannot happen if both line have positive slopes because the product of two positive number is positive, not negative.

67. From the graph, we can see that the line contains the points (0, 0) and (2, 3). Thus,

$m = \frac{3 - 0}{2 - 0} = \frac{3}{2}$

69. From the graph, we can see that the line contains the points (4, 0) and (0, 2). Thus,

$m = \frac{2 - 0}{0 - 4} = \frac{2}{-4} = -\frac{1}{2}$

71. The side of the roof for which we are finding the slope is slanting downward, so the slope is negative: $m = -\dfrac{8 \text{ feet}}{12 \text{ feet}} = -\dfrac{2}{3}$.

73. $m = \dfrac{-1600 \text{ ft.}}{2.5 \text{ mi}}$

$= \dfrac{-1600 \text{ ft.}}{2.5(5280 \text{ ft.})}$

$= \dfrac{-1600 \text{ ft.}}{13,200 \text{ ft.}}$

≈ -0.12

75. $y = 1545.4x + 33,858.4$

a. 2005 is 8 year after 1997 $(2005 - 1997 = 8)$, so $y = 1545.4(8) + 33,858.4 = 46,221.6$
The man's average income will be about $46,221.60.

b. $m = 1545.4$; The annual income increases $1545.40 every year.

c. $b = 33,858.4$; At year $x = 0$, or in 1997, the annual average income of an American man with an associate degree was about $33,858.40.

77. a. $-245x + 10y = 59$

$10y = 245x + 59$

$\dfrac{10y}{10} = \dfrac{245x}{10} + \dfrac{59}{10}$

$y = 24.5x + 5.9$

$m = 24.5$; $b = 5.9$

b. The number of public wireless internet access points is projected to increase 24.5 thousand every year.

c. There were about 5.9 thousand wireless internet access points in 2002.

79. $f(x) = 174.4x + 2074.38$

a. $m = 174.4$; The total cost of tuition and fees increase $174.4 every year.

b. $b = 2074.38$; The total cost of tuition and fees was $2074.38 in 1990.

81. $f(x) = -\dfrac{7}{2}x - 6$; $m = -\dfrac{7}{2}$

A line parallel to $f(x) = -\dfrac{7}{2}x - 6$ will have the same slope $-\dfrac{7}{2}$.

83. $f(x) = -\dfrac{7}{2}x - 6$; $m = -\dfrac{7}{2}$

A line perpendicular to $f(x) = -\dfrac{7}{2}x - 6$ will have the slope $\dfrac{2}{7}$ (so that the product of the slopes is -1).

85. $5x - 2y = 6$

$-2y = -5x + 6$

$\dfrac{-2y}{-2} = \dfrac{-5x}{-2} + \dfrac{6}{-1}$

$y = \dfrac{5}{2}x - 3$; $m = \dfrac{5}{2}$

A line parallel to $5x - 2y = 6$ will have the same slope $\dfrac{5}{2}$.

87. $5x - 2y = 6$

$-2y = -5x + 6$

$\dfrac{-2y}{-2} = \dfrac{-5x}{-2} + \dfrac{6}{-1}$

$y = \dfrac{5}{2}x - 3$; $m = \dfrac{5}{2}$

A line perpendicular to $5x - 2y = 6$ will have the slope $-\dfrac{2}{5}$ (so that the product of the slope is -1).

89. There are 2 B's out of the 11 cards, so $P(B) = \dfrac{2}{11}$.

91. There are 2 I's and 1 T out of the 11 cards, so $P(I \text{ or } T) = \dfrac{3}{11}$.

93. There are 4 vowels out of the 11 cards, so $P(\text{vowel}) = \dfrac{4}{11}$.

95. $y - 0 = -3[x - (-10)]$

$y = -3(x + 10)$

$y = -3x - 30$

97. $y - 9 = -8[x - (-4)]$

$y - 9 = -8(x + 4)$

$y - 9 = -8x - 32$

$y = -8x - 23$

99. a. B (6, 20)

  b. C (10, 13)

  c. $m = \dfrac{13-20}{10-6} = \dfrac{-7}{4} = -\dfrac{7}{4} = -1.75$

  The rate of change between points B and C is -1.75 yards per second.

  d. $F(22, 2)$, $G(26, 8)$

  $m = \dfrac{8-2}{26-22} = \dfrac{6}{4} = \dfrac{3}{2} = 1.5$

  The rate of change between points F and G is 1.5 yards per second.

101.
$$-4x + 2y = 5 \qquad\qquad 2x - y = 7$$
$$2y = 4x + 5 \qquad\qquad -y = -2x + 7$$
$$y = \dfrac{4x}{2} + \dfrac{5}{2} \qquad\qquad y = \dfrac{-2x}{-1} + \dfrac{7}{-1}$$
$$y = 2x + \dfrac{5}{2} \qquad\qquad y = 2x - 7$$

Define $y_1 = 2x + \dfrac{5}{2}$ and $y_2 = 2x - 7$, and graph the equations in a standard viewing window.

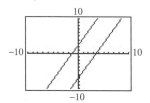

The graphs support the finding in Exercise 61 that the two lines are parallel.

103. a. Define $y_1 = \dfrac{1}{2}x + 1$, $y_2 = x + 1$, and $y_3 = 2x + 1$, and graph the equations in a standard viewing window.

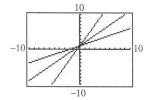

  b. Define $y_1 = -\dfrac{1}{2}x + 1$, $y_2 = -x + 1$, and $y_3 = -2x + 1$, and graph the equations in a standard viewing window.

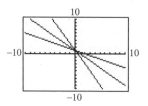

  c. True

Mental Math 2.5

1. $m = -4$, $b = 12$

2. $m = \dfrac{2}{3}$, $b = -\dfrac{7}{2}$

3. $m = 5$, $b = 0$

4. $m = -1$, $b = 0$

5. $m = \dfrac{1}{2}$, $b = 6$

6. $m = -\dfrac{2}{3}$, $b = 5$

7. Parallel, since the slopes are both 12.

8. Parallel, since the slopes are both -5

9. Neither, since the slopes -9 and $\dfrac{3}{2}$ are not equal and do not have a product of -1.

10. Neither, since the slopes 2 and $\dfrac{1}{2}$ are not equal and do not have a product of -1.

Exercise Set 2.5

1. $m = -1$, $b = 1$
$y = mx + b$
$y = -1x + 1$ or $y = -x + 1$

3. $m = 2$, $b = \dfrac{3}{4}$
$y = mx + b$
$y = 2x + \dfrac{3}{4}$

5. $m = \dfrac{2}{7}$, $b = 0$

$y = mx + b$

$y = \dfrac{2}{7}x + 0$ or $y = \dfrac{2}{7}x$

7. For $y = 5x$, the slope is 5 and the y-intercept is at 0. Begin at $(0, 0)$ and move up 5 units and to the right 1 unit to find the point $(1, 5)$.

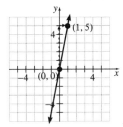

9. $x + y = 7$

$\quad y = -x + 7$

The slope is -1 and the y-intercept is at 7. Begin at $(0, 7)$ and move down 1 unit and to the right 1 unit to find the point $(1, 6)$.

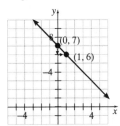

11. $-3x + 2y = 3$

$\quad 2y = 3x + 3$

$\quad \dfrac{2y}{2} = \dfrac{3x}{2} + \dfrac{3}{2}$

$\quad y = \dfrac{3}{2}x + \dfrac{3}{2}$

The slope is $\dfrac{3}{2}$ and the y-intercept is at $\dfrac{3}{2}$.

Begin at $\left(0, \dfrac{3}{2}\right)$ and move up 3 units and to the

right 2 units to find the point $\left(2, \dfrac{9}{2}\right)$.

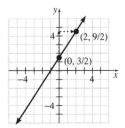

13. $y - y_1 = m(x - x_1)$

$\quad y - 2 = 3(x - 1)$

$\quad y - 2 = 3x - 3$

$\quad\quad y = 3x - 1$

15. $y - y_1 = m(x - x_1)$

$\quad y - (-3) = -2(x - 1)$

$\quad\quad y + 3 = -2x + 2$

$\quad\quad\quad y = -2x - 1$

17. $y - y_1 = m(x - x_1)$

$\quad y - 2 = \dfrac{1}{2}[x - (-6)]$

$\quad y - 2 = \dfrac{1}{2}(x + 6)$

$\quad y - 2 = \dfrac{1}{2}x + 3$

$\quad\quad y = \dfrac{1}{2}x + 5$

19. $y - y_1 = m(x - x_1)$

$\quad y - 0 = -\dfrac{9}{10}[x - (-3)]$

$\quad\quad y = -\dfrac{9}{10}(x + 3)$

$\quad\quad y = -\dfrac{9}{10}x - \dfrac{27}{10}$

21. The line contains the points $(0, 3)$ and $(1, 1)$.

$m = \dfrac{1-3}{1-0} = \dfrac{-2}{1} = -2$; $b = 3$

$y = mx + b$

$y = -2x + 3$

$2x + y = 3$

23. The line contains the points $(-2, 1)$ and $(4, 5)$.

$m = \dfrac{5-1}{4-(-2)} = \dfrac{4}{6} = \dfrac{2}{3}$

$$y - 1 = \frac{2}{3}(x + 2)$$

$$3(y - 1) = 3 \cdot \frac{2}{3}(x + 2)$$

$$3(y - 1) = 2(x + 2)$$

$$3y - 3 = 2x + 4$$

$$2x - 3y = -7$$

25. $m = \dfrac{6 - 0}{4 - 2} = \dfrac{6}{2} = 3$

$$y - 0 = 3(x - 2)$$

$$y = 3x - 6$$

$$f(x) = 3x - 6$$

27. $m = \dfrac{13 - 5}{-6 - (-2)} = \dfrac{8}{-4} = -2$

$$y - 5 = -2[x - (-2)]$$

$$y - 5 = -2(x + 2)$$

$$y - 5 = -2x - 4$$

$$y = -2x + 1$$

$$f(x) = -2x + 1$$

29. $m = \dfrac{-3 - (-4)}{-4 - (-2)} = \dfrac{1}{-2} = -\dfrac{1}{2}$

$$y - (-4) = -\frac{1}{2}[x - (-2)]$$

$$y + 4 = -\frac{1}{2}(x + 2)$$

$$y + 4 = -\frac{1}{2}x - 1$$

$$y = -\frac{1}{2}x - 5$$

$$f(x) = -\frac{1}{2}x - 5$$

31. $m = \dfrac{-9 - (-8)}{-6 - (-3)} = \dfrac{-1}{-3} = \dfrac{1}{3}$

$$y - (-8) = \frac{1}{3}[x - (-3)]$$

$$y + 8 = \frac{1}{3}(x + 3)$$

$$y + 8 = \frac{1}{3}x + 1$$

$$y = \frac{1}{3}x - 7$$

$$f(x) = \frac{1}{3}x - 7$$

33. Answers may vary. One possibility follows: Substitute the coordinates into the equation and see if the result is true. If it is true, then the point is on the line. Otherwise the point is not on the line.

$$2(1.4) - 4(-1.05) \overset{?}{=} 7 \qquad 2(0) - 4(-1.75) \overset{?}{=} 7$$

$$2.8 + 4.2 \overset{?}{=} 7 \qquad\qquad 0 + 7 \overset{?}{=} 7$$

$$7 = 7 \text{ True} \qquad\qquad 7 = 7 \text{ True}$$

Thus, the line $2x - 4y = 7$ passes through both $(1.4, -1.05)$ and $(0, -1.75)$.

35. The point $(0, -2)$ is on the graph, so $f(0) = -2$.

37. The point $(2,\ 2)$ is on the graph, so $f(2) = 2$

39. The point $(-2, -6)$ is on the graph of the line, so if $f(x) = -6$, then $x = -2$.

41. A horizontal line must have an equation of the form $y = b$. Since the line passes through the point $(-2, -4)$, it must have the y-intercept $(0, -4)$. Thus, its equation is $y = -4$.

43. A vertical line must have an equation of the form $x = c$. Since the line passes through the point $(4,\ 7)$, its must have the x-intercept $(4,\ 0)$. Thus, its equation is $x = 4$.

45. A horizontal line must have an equation of the form $y = b$. Since the line passes through the point $(0,\ 5)$, the y-intercept, its equation is $y = 5$.

47. The slope of the line we seek is $m = 4$, the same as the slope of $y = 4x - 2$. The equation of the line is

$$y - 8 = 4(x - 3)$$

$$y - 8 = 4x - 12$$

$$y = 4x - 4$$

$$f(x) = 4x - 4$$

Check:

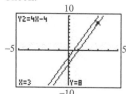

49. The slope of the line we seek is $m = -3$, the negative reciprocal of the slope of the line
$$3y = x - 6$$
$$\frac{3y}{3} = \frac{x}{3} - \frac{6}{3}$$
$$y = \frac{1}{3}x - 2$$

Thus, the equation of the line we seek is
$$y - (-5) = -3(x - 2)$$
$$y + 5 = -3x + 6$$
$$y = -3x + 1$$
$$f(x) = -3x + 1$$

Check:

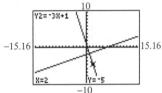

51. The slope of the line we seek is $m = -\frac{3}{2}$, the same as the slope of the line
$$3x + 2y = 5$$
$$2y = -3x + 5$$
$$y = -\frac{3}{2}x + \frac{5}{2}$$

Thus, the equation of the line we seek is
$$y - (-3) = -\frac{3}{2}[x - (-2)]$$
$$2(y + 3) = -3(x + 2)$$
$$2y + 6 = -3(x + 2)$$
$$2y + 6 = -3x - 6$$
$$y = -\frac{3}{2}x - 6$$
$$f(x) = -\frac{3}{2}x - 6$$

Check:

53.
$$y - 3 = 2[x - (-2)]$$
$$y - 3 = 2(x + 2)$$
$$y - 3 = 2x + 4$$
$$y = 2x + 7$$
$$-2x + y = 7 \ \text{ or } \ 2x - y = -7$$

55. $m = \dfrac{2 - 6}{5 - 1} = \dfrac{-4}{4} = -1$
$$y - 6 = -1(x - 1)$$
$$y - 6 = -x + 1$$
$$y = -x + 7$$
$$f(x) = -x + 7$$

57.
$$y = -\frac{1}{2}x + 11$$
$$2y = 2\left(-\frac{1}{2}x + 11\right)$$
$$2y = -x + 22$$
$$x + 2y = 22$$

59. $m = \dfrac{-6 - (-4)}{0 - (-7)} = \dfrac{-2}{7} = -\dfrac{2}{7}$
$$y = -\frac{2}{7}x - 6$$
$$7y = 7\left(-\frac{2}{7}x - 6\right)$$
$$7y = -2x - 42$$
$$2x + 7y = -42$$

61.
$$y - 0 = -\frac{4}{3}[x - (-5)]$$
$$y = -\frac{4}{3}(x + 5)$$
$$3y = 3\left(-\frac{4}{3}\right)(x + 5)$$
$$3y = -4(x + 5)$$
$$3y = -4x - 20$$
$$4x + 3y = -20$$

63. A vertical line must have an equation of the form $x = c$. Since the line passes through the point $(-2, -10)$, its must have the x-intercept $(-2, 0)$. Thus, its equation is $x = -2$.

65. The slope of the line we seek is $m = -\frac{1}{2}$, the same as the slope of the line
$$2x + 4y = 8$$
$$4y = -2x + 8$$
$$\frac{4y}{4} = \frac{-2x}{4} + \frac{8}{4}$$
$$y = -\frac{1}{2}x + 2$$

Thus, the equation of the line we seek is

$$y-(-2) = -\frac{1}{2}(x-6)$$
$$y+2 = -\frac{1}{2}x+3$$
$$y = -\frac{1}{2}x+1$$
$$2y = 2\left(-\frac{1}{2}x+1\right)$$
$$2y = -x+2$$
$$x+2y = 2$$

67. $y-12 = 0[x-(-9)]$
$\qquad y-12 = 0$
$\qquad\qquad y = 12$

69. The slope of the line we see we seek is $m = 8$, the same as the slope of the line
$$8x-y = 9$$
$$y = 8x-9$$
Thus, the equation of the line we seek is
$$y-1 = 8(x-6)$$
$$y-1 = 8x-48$$
$$8x-y = 47$$

71. The line $y = 9$ is horizontal, so the line perpendicular to it must be vertical and have the form $x = c$. Now, a vertical line through the point $(5,-6)$ must have the *x*-intercept $(5, 0)$. Thus, the equation of the line we seek is $x = 5$

73. $m = \dfrac{-5-(-8)}{-6-2} = \dfrac{3}{-8} = -\dfrac{3}{8}$
$$y-(-8) = -\frac{3}{8}(x-2)$$
$$8(y+8) = -3(x-2)$$
$$8y+64 = -3x+6$$
$$y = -\frac{3}{8}x-\frac{29}{4}$$
$$f(x) = -\frac{3}{8}x-\frac{29}{4}$$

75. a. The information provided gives the ordered pairs (1, 30000) and (4, 66000).
$$m = \frac{66,000-30,000}{4-1} = 12,000$$
$$y-30,000 = 12,000(x-1)$$
$$y = 12,000x+18,000$$
$$P(x) = 12,000x+18,000$$

b. $P(7) = 12,000(7)+18,000 = 102,000$
At the end of the seventh year, the company's profit will be $102,000.

c. $12,000x+18,000 = 126,000$
$\qquad\qquad 12,000x = 108,000$
$\qquad\qquad\qquad x = 9$
Profit should reach $126,000 at the end the ninth year.

77. a. The information provided gives the ordered pairs (3, 10000) and (5, 8000).
$$m = \frac{8000-10,000}{5-3} = -1000$$
$$y-10,000 = -1000(x-3)$$
$$y-10,000 = -1000x+3,000$$
$$y = -1000x+13,000$$

b. $y = -1000(3.5)+13,000 = 9500$
If the price is $3.50, the daily sales will be 9500 Fun Noodles.

79. a. The information provided gives the ordered pairs (0, 133300) and (3, 147802).
$$m = \frac{147,802-133,300}{3-0}$$
$$= \frac{14502}{3}$$
$$= 4834$$
$$y-133,300 = 4834(x-0)$$
$$y-133,300 = 4834x$$
$$y = 4834x+133,300$$

b. $x = 2008-1999 = 9$
$\quad y = 4834(9)+133,300 = 176,806$
We predict that the median price of an existing home will be $176,806 in 2008.

c. The median price of a home is rising $4834 every year.

81. a. The information provided gives the ordered pairs (0, 757) and (10, 1052).
$$m = \frac{1052-757}{10-0} = \frac{295}{10} = 29.5$$
$$y-757 = 29.5(x-0)$$
$$y-757 = 29.5x$$
$$y = 29.5x+757$$

b. $x = 2004-2000 = 4$
$\quad y = 29.5(4)+757 = 875$
We estimate that 875 thousand people will be employed as medical assistants in 2004.

83. The function found in Exercise 55 was
$f(x) = -x + 7$. Define $y_1 = -x + 7$ and graph in
the standard viewing window. Press the
[TRACE] button, type 1 and press [ENTER] to
see that $(1, 6)$ is on the line. Next, type 5 and
press [ENTER] to see that $(5, 2)$ is on the line.

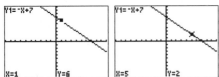

85. The equation found in Exercise 61 was
$$4x + 3y = -20$$
$$3y = -4x - 20$$
$$\frac{3y}{3} = \frac{-4x}{3} - \frac{20}{3}$$
$$y = -\frac{4}{3}x - \frac{20}{3}$$

Define $y_1 = -\frac{4}{3}x + \frac{20}{3}$ and graph in the standard

viewing window. We can tell that the line has a
negative slope because it slants downward from
left to right. Press the [TRACE] button, type in
-5, and press [ENTER] to see that $(-5, 0)$ is
on the line.

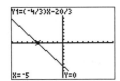

87. $2x - 7 = 21$
$2x = 28$
$x = 14$

89. $5(x - 2) = 3(x - 1)$
$5x - 10 = 3x - 3$
$2x = 7$
$x = \frac{7}{2}$

91. $\frac{x}{2} + \frac{1}{4} = \frac{1}{8}$
$8\left(\frac{x}{2} + \frac{1}{4}\right) = 8\left(\frac{1}{8}\right)$
$4x + 2 = 1$
$4x = -1$
$x = -\frac{1}{4}$

93. Step 1: The midpoint of the line segment with
endpoints $(3, -1)$ and $(-5, 1)$ is
$$\left(\frac{3 + (-5)}{2}, \frac{-1 + 1}{2}\right) = (-1, 0).$$
Step 2: The slope of this line segment is
$$m = \frac{1 - (-1)}{-5 - 3} = \frac{2}{-8} = -\frac{1}{4}.$$
Step 3: A line perpendicular to this segment
will have a slope of $m = 4$.
Step 4: The equation of the perpendicular
bisector of this line segment is
$$y - 0 = 4[x - (-1)]$$
$$y = 4(x + 1)$$
$$y = 4x + 4$$
$$-4x + y = 4$$

95. Step 1: The midpoint of the line segment with
endpoints $(-2, 6)$ and $(-22, -4)$ is
$$\left(\frac{-2 + (-22)}{2}, \frac{6 + (-4)}{2}\right) = (-12, 1).$$
Step 2: The slope of this line segment is
$$m = \frac{-4 - 6}{-22 - (-2)} = \frac{-10}{-20} = \frac{1}{2}.$$
Step 3: A line perpendicular to this segment
will have a slope of $m = -2$.
Step 4: The equation of the perpendicular
bisector of this line segment is
$$y - 1 = -2[x - (-12)]$$
$$y - 1 = -2(x + 12)$$
$$y - 1 = -2x - 24$$
$$2x + y = -23$$

97. Step 1: The midpoint of the line segment with
endpoints $(2, 3)$ and $(-4, 7)$ is
$$\left(\frac{2 + (-4)}{2}, \frac{3 + 7}{2}\right) = (-1, 5).$$
Step 2: The slope of this line segment is
$$m = \frac{7 - 3}{-4 - 2} = \frac{4}{-6} = -\frac{2}{3}.$$
Step 3: A line perpendicular to this segment
will have a slope of $m = \frac{3}{2}$.
Step 4: The equation of the perpendicular
bisector of this line segment is
$$y - 5 = \frac{3}{2}[x - (-1)]$$
$$2(y - 5) = 3(x + 1)$$
$$2y - 10 = 3x + 3$$
$$3x - 2y = -13$$

99. True

Integrated Review

1. For $y = -2x$, the slope is -2 and the y-intercept is at 0. Begin at $(0, 0)$ and move down 2 units and to the right 1 unit to find the point $(1, -2)$.

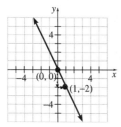

2. $3x - 2y = 6$

Let $x = 0$ Let $y = 0$ Let $x = 4$

$3(0) - 2y = 6$ $3x - 2(0) = 6$ $3(4) - 2y = 6$

$\quad -2y = 6$ $3x = 6$ $12 - 2y = 6$

$\qquad y = -3$ $x = 2$ $-2y = -6$

$\qquad\qquad\qquad\qquad\qquad\qquad\qquad y = 3$

x	0	2	4
y	-3	0	3

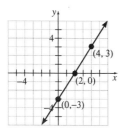

3. $x = -3$

This is a vertical line with x-intercept $(-3, 0)$.

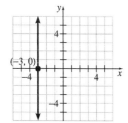

4. $y = 1.5$

This is a horizontal line with y-intercept $(0, 1.5)$.

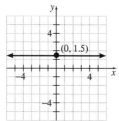

5. $m = \dfrac{-5 - (-5)}{3 - (-2)} = \dfrac{0}{5} = 0$

6. $m = \dfrac{5 - 2}{0 - 5} = \dfrac{3}{-5} = -\dfrac{3}{5}$

7. $y = 3x - 5$
$m = 3; \ (0, -5)$

8. $5x - 2y = 7$

$\quad -2y = -5x + 7$

$\qquad y = \dfrac{5}{2}x - \dfrac{7}{2}$

$m = \dfrac{5}{2}; \ \left(0, -\dfrac{7}{2}\right)$

9. $y = 8x - 6$ $y = 8x + 6$
$m = 8$ $m = 8$
Parallel, since the two slopes are equal.

10. $y = \dfrac{2}{3}x + 1$ $2y + 3x = 1$

$m = \dfrac{2}{3}$ $2y = -3x + 1$

$\qquad\qquad\qquad\qquad y = -\dfrac{3}{2}x + \dfrac{1}{2}$

$\qquad\qquad\qquad\qquad m = -\dfrac{3}{2}$

Perpendicular, since the product of their slopes is -1.

11. $m = \dfrac{2 - 6}{5 - 1} = \dfrac{-4}{4} = -1$

$y - 1 = -1(x - 6)$

$y - 1 = -x + 6$

$\quad\ y = -x + 7$

12. A vertical line must have an equation of the form $x = c$. Since the line passes through the point $(-2, -10)$, its must have the x-intercept $(-2, 0)$. Thus, its equation is $x = -2$.

13. A vertical line must have an equation of the form
$y = b$. Since the line passes through the point
$(1,\ 0)$, its must have the y-intercept $(0,\ 0)$.
Thus, its equation is $y = 0$.

14. $m = \dfrac{-5-(-8)}{-6-2} = \dfrac{3}{-8} = -\dfrac{3}{8}$

$y-(-8) = -\dfrac{3}{8}(x-2)$
$8(y+8) = -3(x-2)$
$8y+64 = -3x+6$
$8y = -3x-58$
$\dfrac{8y}{8} = \dfrac{-3x}{8} - \dfrac{58}{8}$
$y = -\dfrac{3}{8}x - \dfrac{29}{4}$
$f(x) = -\dfrac{3}{8}x - \dfrac{29}{4}$

15. $y-4 = -5[x-(-2)]$
$y-4 = -5(x+2)$
$y-4 = -5x-10$
$y = -5x-6$
$f(x) = -5x-6$

16. $f(x) = -4x + \dfrac{1}{3}$

17. $f(x) = \dfrac{1}{2}x - 1$

18. $y-0 = 3\left(x-\dfrac{1}{2}\right)$

$y = 3x - \dfrac{3}{2}$

19. The slope of the line we seek is $m = 3$, the same
as the slope of the line
$3x - y = 5$
$-y = -3x+5$
$y = 3x-5$
The equation of the line we seek is
$y-(-5) = 3[x-(-1)]$
$y+5 = 3(x+1)$
$y+5 = 3x+3$
$y = 3x-2$

20. The slope of the line we seek is $m = -\dfrac{5}{4}$, the
negative reciprocal of the slope of the line

$4x - 5y = 10$
$-5y = -4x+10$
$y = \dfrac{4}{5}x - 2$
The equation of the line we seek is
$y-4 = -\dfrac{5}{4}(x-0)$
$y-4 = -\dfrac{5}{4}x$
$y = -\dfrac{5}{4}x + 4$

21. The slope of the line we seek is $m = \dfrac{1}{4}$, the
negative reciprocal of the line
$4x + y = \dfrac{2}{3}$
$y = -4x + \dfrac{2}{3}$
The equation of the line we seek is
$y-(-3) = \dfrac{1}{4}(x-2)$
$y+3 = \dfrac{1}{4}x - \dfrac{1}{2}$
$y = \dfrac{1}{4}x - \dfrac{7}{2}$

22. The slope of the line we seek is $m = -\dfrac{5}{2}$, the
same as the slope of the line
$5x + 2y = 2$
$2y = -5x + 2$
$y = -\dfrac{5}{2}x + 1$
The equation of the line we seek is
$y-0 = -\dfrac{5}{2}[x-(-1)]$
$y = -\dfrac{5}{2}(x+1)$
$2y = -5(x+1)$
$2y = -5x-5$
$y = -\dfrac{5}{2}x - \dfrac{5}{2}$

23. A line having undefined slope is vertical. If this
vertical line must pass through the point $(-1,\ 3)$,
it must have an x-intercept of $(-1,\ 0)$. Thus, the
equation is $x = -1$.

24. $y - 3 = 0[x - (-1)]$
   $y - 3 = 0$
     $y = 3$

Exercise Set 2.6

1. $f(2009) = 1.558(2009) - 3092 = 38.022$

The Pharmaceutical Manufactures Association will spend $38.022 billion in 2009 on research and development.

3. $1.618x + 32.17 = 41$
    $1.618x = 8.83$
       $x \approx 5.457$
Now, $1990 + 5.457 = 1995.457$. The price was approximately $41 in the year 1995.

5. a. Enter the data into L1 and L2. Find an appropriate window and graph the data. We use [0, 50, 10] by [0, 600000, 100000].

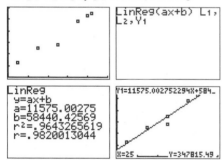

If a and b are rounded to three decimal places, the linear regression equation is $y = 11,575.003x + 58,440.426$.

b. Note that 2010 will be 50 years after 1960. Since the equation is stored in Y1, we evaluate the equation for the year 2010 by finding Y1(50).

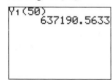

Note that 637,191 thousand = 637,191,000. If the trend continues to increase at the same rate, then there will be 637,191,000 outpatient visits in 2010.

c. Note that 11,575 thousand = 11,575,000. The number of visits is increasing by 11,575,000 visits per year.

7. a. Enter the data into L1 and L2. Find an appropriate window and graph the data. We use [0, 50, 10] by [0, 40, 10].

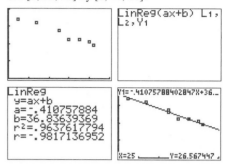

If a and b are rounded to three decimal places, the linear regression equation is $y = -0.411x + 36.836$.

b. Note that 2011 will be 51 years after 1960. Since the equation is stored in Y1, we evaluate the equation for the year 2011 by finding Y1(51).

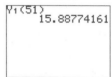

If the trend continues to decrease at the same rate, then the percent of female smokers in 2011 will be 15.9%.

c. Female smokers are decreasing at a rate of 0.411% per year.

9. a. Enter the data into L1 and L2. Find an appropriate window and graph the data. We use [-5, 25, 5] by [0, 100, 10].

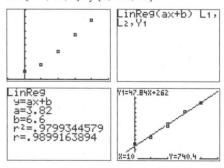

The regression equation is $y = 3.82x + 6.6$.

b. Note that 2009 will be 29 years after 1980. Since the equation is stored in Y1, we evaluate the equation for the year 2009 by finding Y1(29).

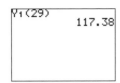

In 2009 there will be 117 thousand (or 117,000) female prisoners if the trend continues to increase at the same rate.

c. Female prisoners are increasing at a rate of 4 thousand per year (or 4000 per year).

11. Enter the data into L1 and L2. Find an appropriate window and graph the data. We use [1400, 3100, 100] by [75000, 325000, 25000].

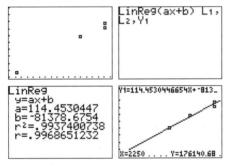

If *a* and *b* are rounded to three decimal places, the linear regression equation is
$y = 114.453x - 81,378.675$.

13. Evaluate the equation at $x = 2200$:
$y = 114.453(2200) - 81,378.675$
$= 170,417.925$

A house with 2200 square feet of space will have a selling price of approximately $170,418.

15. Enter the data into L1 and L2. Find an appropriate window and graph the data. We use [0, 9000, 1000] by [500, 1500, 100].

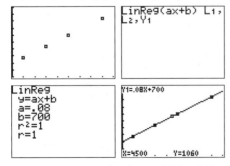

The regression equation is $y = 0.08x + 700$.

17. a. Enter the data into L1 and L2. Find an appropriate window and graph the data. We use [0, 4, 1] by [0, 2, 0.2].

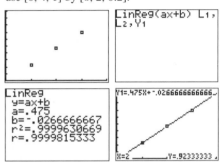

Rounding *b* to three decimal places, the regression equation is $y = 0.475x - 0.027$.

b. Note that 2010 will be 10 years after 2000. Since the equation is stored in Y1, we evaluate the equation for the year 2010 by finding Y1(10).

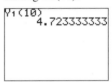

If the trend continues to increase at the same rate, the DVD rental revenue will be $4.723 billion in 2010.

c. DVD rental revenue is increasing at a rate of $0.475 billion per year (or $475,000,000 per year).

19. a. Enter the years into L1 with $x = 0$ represented by $x = 0$ and the corresponding life expectancy in L2.

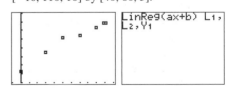

Find a window and graph the data. We use [−10, 110, 10] by [40, 80, 5].

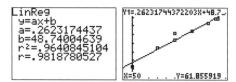

If *a* and *b* are rounded to three decimal places, the linear regression equation is
$y = 0.262x + 48.740$.

b. The life expectancy of males at birth is increasing at a rate of 0.262 years annually.

c. Note that 2010 will be 110 years after 1900. Since the equation is stored in Y1, we evaluate the equation for the year 2010 by finding Y1(110).

The life expectancy of males at birth will be 77.6 years in 2010 if the trend continues to increase at the same rate.

21. a. Enter the years into L1 with 1990 represented by $x = 0$ and the corresponding number of PPO members L2.

Find a window and graph the data. We use [0, 15, 1] by [40, 140, 10].

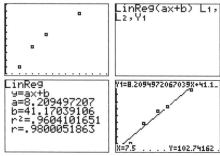

If *a* and *b* are rounded to three decimal places, the linear regression equation is
$y = 8.209x + 41.170$.

b. Note that 2010 will be 20 years after 1990. Since the equation is stored in Y1, we evaluate the equation for the year 2010 by finding Y1(20).

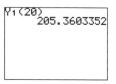

The number of people receiving care in PPOs will be 205.36 million in 2010 if the trend continues to increase at the same rate.

c.
$$8.209x + 41.170 = 240$$
$$8.209x = 198.830$$
$$x \approx 24.22$$

$$1990 + 24.22 = 2014.22$$

Thus, in 2015, there will be *over* 240 million members in PPOs.

d. The slope tells us that the number of PPO member is increasing at a rate of 8.209 million per year.

23. a. Enter the years into L1 with 1970 represented by $x = 0$ and the corresponding average top ticket price in L2.

Find a window and graph the data. We use [0, 40, 5] by [0, 150, 10].

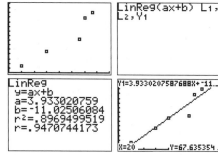

If *a* and *b* are rounded to three decimal places, the linear regression equation is
$y = 3.933x - 11.025$.

b. Note that 2013 will be 43 years after 1970. Since the equation is stored in Y1, we evaluate the equation for the year 2013 by finding Y1(43).

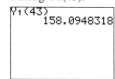

If the trend continues to increase at the same rate, the average top-ticket price for Broadway musicals will be $158.09 in 2013.

c. The cost is rising at a rate of $3.93 per year.

25. a. Enter the data into L1 and L2. Find an appropriate window and graph the data. We use [5, 15, 1] by [0, 2, 0.2].

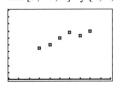

b. Find and graph the linear regression equation.

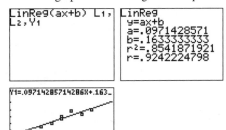

If *a* and *b* are rounded to three decimal places, the linear regression equation is $y = 0.097x + 0.163$.

c. The cost of a 30-second commercial during the Academy Awards is increasing at a rate of $0.097 million (or $97,000) per year.

d. Note that 2010 will be 20 years after 1990. Since the equation is stored in Y1, we evaluate the equation for the year 2010 by finding Y1(20).

```
Y1(20)
        2.106190476
```

If the trend continues to increase at the same rate, the cost of a 30-second commercial during the 2010 Academy Award presentation will be $2.106 million.

27. $7x + 2 = 9x - 14$
$-2x = -16$
$x = 8$

29. $\dfrac{y}{7} + \dfrac{y}{3} = \dfrac{1}{21}$

$21\left(\dfrac{y}{7} + \dfrac{y}{3}\right) = 21\left(\dfrac{1}{21}\right)$

$3y + 7y = 1$

$10y = 1$

$y = \dfrac{1}{10}$

31. Enter the years into L1 with 1980 represented by $x = 0$, the corresponding number of "dine in" meals in L2, and the corresponding number of "take out" meals in L3.

L1	L2	■ 3
4	69	43
8	68	53
10	64	55
12	63	57
17	64	66
20	69	73
23	70	76

L3 = {43, 53, 55, 57...

Find a linear regression equation for the "dine in" data and store it in Y1.

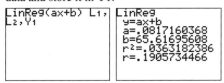

If *a* and *b* are rounded to three decimal places, the linear regression equation is $y_1 = 0.082x + 65.617$.

Find a linear regression equation for the "take out" data and store it in Y2.

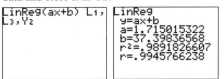

If *a* and *b* are rounded to three decimal places, the linear regression equation is $y_2 = 1.715x + 37.398$.

To estimate the year that the two types of dining occurred the same number of times, we find where $y_1 = y_2$.

$y_1 = y_2$
$0.082x + 65.617 = 1.715x + 37.398$
$-1.633x = -28.219$
$x \approx 17.28$

Now $1980 + 17.28 = 1997.28$, so the "dine in" and "take out" occurred the same number of times in the year 1997.

We can verify this result by graphing the two regression lines and finding where they intersect. Now the equations were stored in Y1 and Y2 when we found them above. We choose an appropriate window so that both lines can be seen and graph the lines. We use the window [0, 25, 5] by [40, 80, 10]. Using the intersect feature of the calculator, we verify our previous results.

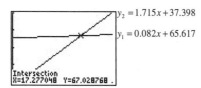

33. Answers will vary.

Chapter 2 Review

1. Point $A(2, -1)$ is in quadrant IV.
Point $B(-2, 1)$ is in quadrant II.
Point $C(0, 3)$ is on the y-axis.
Point $D(-3, -5)$ is in quadrant III.

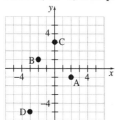

2. Point $A(-3, 4)$ is in quadrant II.
Point $B(4, -3)$ is in quadrant IV.
Point $C(-2, 0)$ is on the x-axis.
Point $D(-4, 1)$ is in quadrant II.

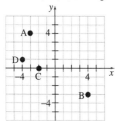

3. Let $x = 0$ and $y = 56$.
$$7x - 8y = 56$$
$$7(0) - 8(56) \overset{?}{=} 56$$
$$0 - 448 \overset{?}{=} 56$$
$$-448 = 56 \quad \text{False}$$

Let $x = 8$ and $y = 0$.
$$7x - 8y = 56$$
$$7(8) - 8(0) \overset{?}{=} 56$$
$$56 - 0 \overset{?}{=} 56$$
$$56 = 56 \quad \text{True}$$

Thus, $(0, 56)$ is not a solution of $7x - 8y = 56$, but $(8, 0)$ is a solution.

4. Let $x = -5$ and $y = 0$.
$$-2x + 5y = 10$$
$$-2(-5) + 5(0) \overset{?}{=} 10$$
$$10 + 0 \overset{?}{=} 10$$
$$10 = 10 \quad \text{True}$$

Let $x = 1$ and $y = 1$.
$$-2x + 5y = 10$$
$$-2(1) + 5(1) \overset{?}{=} 10$$
$$-2 + 5 \overset{?}{=} 10$$
$$3 = 10 \quad \text{False}$$

Thus, $(5, 0)$ is a solution of $-2x + 5y = 10$, but $(1, 1)$ is not a solution.

5. Let $x = 13$ and $y = 5$.
$$x = 13$$
$$13 = 13 \quad \text{True}$$

Let $x = 13$ and $y = 13$.
$$x = 13$$
$$13 = 13 \quad \text{True}$$

Thus, both $(13, 5)$ and $(13, 13)$ are solutions of $x = 13$.

6. Let $x = 7$ and $y = 2$.
$$y = 2$$
$$2 = 2 \quad \text{True}$$

Let $x = 2$ and $y = 7$.
$$y = 2$$
$$7 = 2 \quad \text{False}$$

Thus, $(7, 2)$ is a solution of $y = 2$, but $(7, 2)$ is not a solution.

7. The equation $y = 3x$ is linear.
Let $x = -1$, then $y = 3(-1)$, or -3.
Let $x = 0$, then $y = 3(0)$, or 0.
Let $x = 1$, then $y = 3(1)$, or 3.

The points $(-1,-3)$, $(0,0)$, and $(1,3)$ are on the graph of $y=3x$.

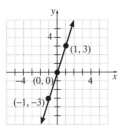

8. The equation $y=5x$ is linear.

Let $x=-1$, then $y=5(-1)$, or -5.

Let $x=0$, then $y=5(0)$, or 0.

Let $x=1$, then $y=5(1)$, or 5.

The points $(-1,-5)$, $(0,0)$, and $(1,5)$ are on the graph of $y=5x$.

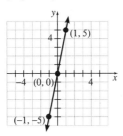

9. The equation $3x-y=4$ is linear.

Let $x=0$, then $3(0)-y=4$
$$0-y=4$$
$$-y=4$$
$$y=-4$$

Let $x=1$, then $3(1)-y=4$
$$3-y=4$$
$$-y=1$$
$$y=-1$$

Let $x=2$, then $3(2)-y=4$
$$6-y=4$$
$$-y=-2$$
$$y=2$$

The points $(0,-4)$, $(1,-1)$, and $(2,2)$ are on the graph of $3x-y=4$.

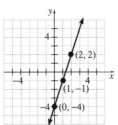

10. The equation $x-3y=2$ is linear.

Let $x=-1$, then $-1-3y=2$
$$-3y=3$$
$$y=-1$$

Let $x=-4$, then $-4-3y=2$
$$-3y=6$$
$$y=-2$$

Let $x=2$, then $2-3y=2$
$$-3y=0$$
$$y=0$$

The points $(-1,-1)$, $(-4,-2)$, and $(2,0)$ are on the graph of $x-3y=2$.

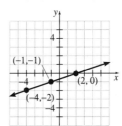

11. The equation $y=|x|+4$ is nonlinear.

Let $x=-3$, then $y=|-3|+4$, or 7.

Let $x=-2$, then $y=|-2|+4$, or 6.

Let $x=-1$, then $y=|-1|+4$, or 5.

Let $x=0$, then $y=|0|+4$, or 4.

Let $x=1$, then $y=|1|+4$, or 5.

Let $x=2$, then $y=|2|+4$, or 6.

Let $x=3$, then $y=|3|+4$, or 7.

The points $(-3,7)$, $(-2,6)$, $(-1,5)$, $(0,4)$, $(1,5)$, $(2,6)$, and $(3,7)$ are on the graph of $y=|x|+4$.

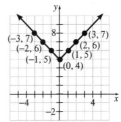

12. The equation $y=x^2+4$ is nonlinear.

Let $x=-3$, then $y=(-3)^2+4$, or 13.

Let $x=-2$, then $y=(-2)^2+4$, or 8.

Let $x=-1$, then $y=(-1)^2+4$, or 5.

Let $x=0$, then $y=(0)^2+4$, or 4.

Let $x = 1$, then $y = (1)^2 + 4$, or 4.

Let $x = 2$, then $y = (2)^2 + 4$, or 8.

Let $x = 3$, then $y = (3)^2 + 4$, or 13.

The points $(-3, 13)$, $(-2, 8)$, $(-1, 5)$, $(0, 4)$, $(1, 5)$, $(2, 8)$, and $(3, 13)$ are on the graph of $y = x^2 + 4$.

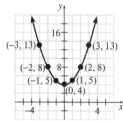

13. The equation $y = -\dfrac{1}{2}x + 2$ is linear.

The slope is $m = -\dfrac{1}{2}$ and the *y*-intercept is at 2.

Begin at $(0, 2)$ and move down 1 unit and to the right 2 units to find the point $(1, 2)$.

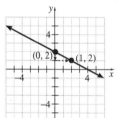

14. The equation $y = -x + 5$ is linear.

The slope is $m = -1$ and the *y*-intercept is at 5. Begin at $(0, 5)$ and move down 1 unit and to the right 1 unit to find the point $(1, 4)$.

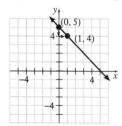

15. D

16. A

17. C

18. B

19. Domain = $\left\{-\dfrac{1}{2}, 6, 0, 25\right\}$

Range = $\left\{\dfrac{3}{4}, -12, 25\right\}$

Function

20. Domain = $\left\{\dfrac{3}{4}, -12, 25\right\}$

Range = $\left\{-\dfrac{1}{2}, 6, 0, 25\right\}$

The relation is not a function since $\dfrac{3}{4} = 0.75$ is paired with both $-\dfrac{1}{2}$ and 6.

21. Domain = {2, 4, 6, 8}
Range = {2, 4, 5, 6}
The relation is not a function since 2 is paired with both 2 and 4.

22. Domain = {Triangle, Square, Rectangle, Parallelogram}
Range = {3, 4}
Function

23. Domain = $(-\infty, \infty)$
Range: $(-\infty, -1] \cup [1, \infty)$
The relation is not a function since it fails the vertical line test (try $x = 0$).

24. Domain = {−3}
Range = $(-\infty, \infty)$
The relation is not a function since it fails the vertical line test.

25. Domain = $(-\infty, \infty)$
Range = {4}
Function

26. Domain = [−1, 1]
Range = [−1, 1]
The relation is not a function since it fails the vertical line test (try $x = 0$).

27. $f(x) = x - 5$
$f(2) = (2) - 5 = -3$

28. $g(x) = -3x$
$g(0) = -3(0) = 0$

29. $g(x) = -3x$
$g(-6) = -3(-6) = 18$

30. $h(x) = 2x^2 - 6x + 1$

$\quad h(-1) = 2(-1)^2 - 6(-1) + 1$

$\qquad\quad = 2(1) - 6(-1) + 1$

$\qquad\quad = 2 + 6 + 1$

$\qquad\quad = 9$

31. $h(x) = 2x^2 - 6x + 1$

$\quad h(1) = 2(1)^2 - 6(1) + 1$

$\qquad\quad = 2(1) - 6(1) + 1$

$\qquad\quad = 2 - 6 + 1$

$\qquad\quad = -3$

32. $f(x) = x - 5$

$\quad f(5) = (5) - 5 = 0$

33. $J(x) = 2.54x$

$\quad J(150) = 2.54(150) = 381$

The equivalent weight on Jupiter of a person who weighs 150 pounds on Earth is 381 pounds.

34. $J(x) = 2.54x$

$\quad J(2000) = 2.54(2000) = 5080$

The equivalent weight on Jupiter of a 2000-pound probe on Earth is 5080 pounds.

35. The point $(-1, 0)$ is on the graph of $y = f(x)$. Thus, $f(-1) = 0$.

36. The point $(1, -2)$ is on the graph of $y = f(x)$. Thus, $f(1) = -2$.

37. The points $(-2, 1)$ and $(4, 1)$ are on the graph of $y = f(x)$. Thus, the solutions of $f(x) = 1$ are $x = -2$ or $x = 4$.

38. The points $(0, -1)$ and $(2, -1)$ are on the graph of $y = f(x)$. Thus, the solutions of $f(x) = -1$ are $x = 0$ or $x = 2$.

39. The slope of $f(x) = x$ is $m = 1$, and the y-intercept is at 0. Begin at $(0, 0)$ and move up 1 unit and to the right 1 unit to find the point $(1, 1)$.

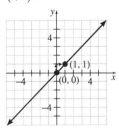

40. The slope of $f(x) = -\dfrac{1}{3}x$ is $m = -\dfrac{1}{3}$, and the y-intercept is at 0. Begin at $(0, 0)$ and move down 1 unit and to the right 3 units to find the point $(3, -1)$.

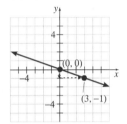

41. The slope of $g(x) = 4x - 1$ is $m = 4$, and the y-intercept is at -1. Begin at $(0, -1)$ and move up 4 units and to the right 1 unit to find the point $(1, 3)$.

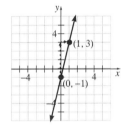

42. C

43. A

44. B

45. D

46. $4x + 5y = 20$

Let $x = 0$ $\qquad\qquad$ Let $y = 0$

$4(0) + 5y = 20$ $\qquad$ $4x + 5(0) = 20$

$\qquad 5y = 20$ $\qquad\qquad\quad 4x = 20$

$\qquad\quad y = 4$ $\qquad\qquad\quad\ x = 5$

The y-intercept is $(0, 4)$, and the x-intercept is $(5, 0)$.

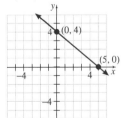

47. $3x - 2y = -9$

Let $x = 0$	Let $y = 0$
$3(0) - 2y = -9$	$3x - 2(0) = -9$
$-2y = -9$	$3x = -9$
$y = \dfrac{9}{2}$	$x = -3$

The y-intercept is $\left(0, \dfrac{9}{2}\right)$, and the x-intercept is

$(-3, 0)$.

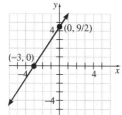

48. $4x - y = 3$

Let $x = 0$	Let $y = 0$
$4(0) - y = 3$	$4x - (0) = 3$
$-y = 3$	$4x = 3$
$y = -3$	$x = \dfrac{3}{4}$

The y-intercept is $(0, -3)$, and the x-intercept is

$\left(\dfrac{3}{4}, 0\right)$.

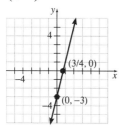

49. $2x + 6y = 9$

Let $x = 0$	Let $y = 0$
$2(0) + 6y = 9$	$2x + 6(0) = 9$
$6y = 9$	$2x = 9$
$y = \dfrac{9}{6}$ or $\dfrac{3}{2}$	$x = \dfrac{9}{2}$

The y-intercept is $\left(0, \dfrac{3}{2}\right)$, and the x-intercept is

$\left(\dfrac{9}{2}, 0\right)$.

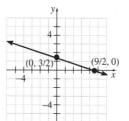

50. $y = 5$

This is a horizontal line with y-intercept $(0, 5)$. It has no x-intercept.

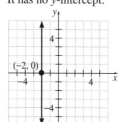

51. $x = -2$

This is a vertical line with x-intercept $(-2, 0)$. It has no y-intercept.

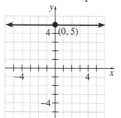

52. $x - 2 = 0$

$x = 2$

This is a vertical line with x-intercept 2.

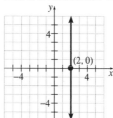

53. $y + 3 = 0$

$y = -3$

This is a horizontal line with y-intercept $(0, -3)$.

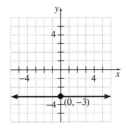

54. a. $C(150) = 0.3(150) + 42$
$= 45 + 42$
$= 87$
The cost $87 to drive the minivan150 miles.

b. Define $y_1 = 0.3x + 42$ and graph in a [0, 600, 100] by [[0, 250, 50] window.

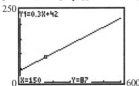

55. $m = \dfrac{-4 - 8}{6 - 2} = \dfrac{-12}{4} = -3$

56. $m = \dfrac{13 - 9}{5 - (-3)} = \dfrac{4}{8} = \dfrac{1}{2}$

57. $m = \dfrac{6 - (-4)}{-3 - (-7)} = \dfrac{10}{4} = \dfrac{5}{2}$

58. $m = \dfrac{7 - (-2)}{-5 - 7} = \dfrac{9}{-12} = -\dfrac{3}{4}$

59. $6x - 15y = 20$
$-15y = -6x + 20$
$y = \dfrac{2}{5}x - \dfrac{4}{3}$
$m = \dfrac{2}{5}, \ b = -\dfrac{4}{3}$

60. $4x + 14y = 21$
$14y = -4x + 21$
$y = -\dfrac{2}{7}x + \dfrac{3}{2}$
$m = -\dfrac{2}{7}, \ b = \dfrac{3}{2}$

61. $y - 3 = 0$
$y = 3$
This is the equation of a horizontal line, so the slope is 0.

62. $x = -5$
This is the equation of a vertical line, so the slope is undefined.

63. l_1 slants downward, so its slope is negative. l_2 slants upward, so its slope is positive. Therefore l_2 has the greater slope.

64. l_1 is horizontal, so its slope is zero. l_2 slants upward, so its slope is positive. Therefore l_2 has the greater slope.

65. l_1 and l_2 both slant upward, so they both have positive slopes. Now l_2 is the steeper of the two lines, so it has the greater slope.

66. l_1 is horizontal, so its slope is zero. l_2 slants downward, so its slope is negative. Therefore, l_1 has the greater slope.

67. a. $m = 0.3$. The cost increases by $0.30 for each mile driven.

b. $b = 42$. The cost for 0 miles driven is $42.

68. $f(x) = -2x + 6 \qquad g(x) = 2x - 1$
$m = -2 \qquad\qquad m = 2$
Neither; The slopes are not the same and their product is not -1.

69. $-x + 3y = 2 \qquad 6x - 18y = 3$
$y = \dfrac{1}{3}x + \dfrac{2}{3} \qquad y = \dfrac{1}{3}x - \dfrac{1}{6}$
$m = \dfrac{1}{3} \qquad\qquad m = \dfrac{1}{3}$
Parallel, since their slopes are equal.

70. For $y = -x + 1$, the slope is -1 and the y-intercept is at 1. Begin at (0, 1) and move down 1 unit and to the right 1 unit to find the point (1, 0).

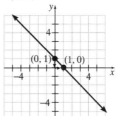

71. For $y = 4x - 3$, the slope is 4 and the y-intercept is at -3. Begin at $(0, -3)$ and move up 4 units and to the right 1 unit to find the point $(1, 1)$.

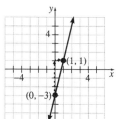

72. $3x - y = 6$
$-y = -3x + 6$
$y = 3x - 6$

The slope is 3, and the y-intercept is at -6. Begin at $(0, -6)$ and move up 3 units and to the right 1 unit to find the point $(1, -3)$.

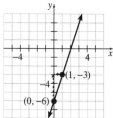

73. For $y = -5x$, the slope is -5 and the y-intercept is at 0. Begin at $(0, 0)$ and move down 5 units and to the right 1 unit to find the point $(1, -5)$.

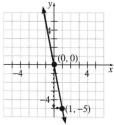

74. A horizontal line must have an equation of the form $y = b$. Since the line passes through $(3, -1)$, it must have the y-intercept $(0, -1)$. Thus, the equation is $y = -1$.

75. A vertical line must have an equation of the form $x = c$. Since the line passes through the point $(-2, 1)$, it must have the x-intercept $(-2, 0)$. Thus, the equation is $x = -2$.

76. Since the line we seek is parallel to the vertical line $x = 6$, it must also be vertical and of the form $x = c$. Since the line passes through the point $(-4, -3)$, it must have the x-intercept $(-4, 0)$. Thus, the equation is $x = -4$.

77. $y - 5 = 0(x - 2)$
$y - 5 = 0$
$y = 5$

78. $y - 5 = 3[x - (-3)]$
$y - 5 = 3(x + 3)$
$y - 5 = 3x + 9$
$-3x + y = 14$ or $3x - y = -14$

79. $y - (-2) = 2(x - 5)$
$y + 2 = 2x - 10$
$-2x + y = -12$ or $2x - y = 12$

80. $m = \dfrac{-2 - (-1)}{-4 - (-6)} = \dfrac{-1}{2} = -\dfrac{1}{2}$

$y - (-1) = -\dfrac{1}{2}[x - (-6)]$
$2(y + 1) = -(x + 6)$
$2y + 2 = -x - 6$
$x + 2y = -8$

81. $m = \dfrac{-8 - 3}{-4 - (-5)} = \dfrac{-11}{1} = -11$

$y - 3 = -11[x - (-5)]$
$y - 3 = -11(x + 5)$
$y - 3 = -11x - 55$
$11x + y = -52$

82. Since the line we seek is perpendicular to the vertical line $x = 4$, it must be horizontal and its must have an equation of the form $y = b$. Since this horizontal line passes through the point $(-2, 3)$, it must have the y-intercept $(0, 3)$. Thus, its equation is $y = 3$.

83. Since the line we seek is parallel to the horizontal line $y = 8$, it must also be horizontal. Since this horizontal line passes through the point $(-2, -5)$, it must have the y-intercept $(0, -5)$. Thus, its equation is $y = -5$.

84. $y = -\dfrac{2}{3}x + 4$ or $f(x) = -\dfrac{2}{3}x + 4$

85. $y = -x - 2$ or $f(x) = -x - 2$

86. The slope of the line we seek is $m = -2$, the same as the slope of
$$6x + 3y = 5$$
$$3y = -6x + 5$$
$$y = -2x + \frac{5}{3}$$
The equation of the line we seek is
$$y - (-6) = -2(x - 2)$$
$$y + 6 = -2x + 4$$
$$y = -2x - 2 \text{ or } f(x) = -2x - 2$$

87. The slope of the line we seek is $m = -\frac{3}{2}$, the same as the slope of
$$3x + 2y = 8$$
$$2y = -3x + 8$$
$$y = -\frac{3}{2}x + 4$$
The equation of the line we seek is
$$y - (-2) = -\frac{3}{2}[x - (-4)]$$
$$y + 2 = -\frac{3}{2}(x + 4)$$
$$y + 2 = -\frac{3}{2}x - 6$$
$$y = -\frac{3}{2}x - 8 \text{ or } f(x) = -\frac{3}{2}x - 8$$

88. The slope of the line we seek is $m = \frac{3}{4}$, the negative reciprocal of the slope of
$$4x + 3y = 5$$
$$3y = -4x + 5$$
$$y = -\frac{4}{3}x + \frac{5}{3}$$
The equation of the line we seek is
$$y - (-1) = \frac{3}{4}[x - (-6)]$$
$$y + 1 = \frac{3}{4}(x + 6)$$
$$y + 1 = \frac{3}{4}x + \frac{9}{2}$$
$$y = \frac{3}{4}x + \frac{7}{2} \text{ or } f(x) = \frac{3}{4}x + \frac{7}{2}$$

89. The slope of the line we seek is $m = -\frac{3}{2}$, the negative reciprocal of the slope of
$$2x - 3y = 6$$
$$-3y = -2x + 6$$
$$y = \frac{2}{3}x - 2$$
The equation of the line we seek is
$$y - 5 = -\frac{3}{2}[x - (-4)]$$
$$y - 5 = -\frac{3}{2}(x + 4)$$
$$y - 5 = -\frac{3}{2}x - 6$$
$$y = -\frac{3}{2}x - 1 \text{ or } f(x) = -\frac{3}{2}x - 1$$

90. a. The information provided gives the ordered pairs (0, 65) and (12, 81).
$$m = \frac{81 - 65}{12 - 0} = \frac{16}{12} = \frac{4}{3}$$
$$y - 65 = \frac{4}{3}(x - 0)$$
$$y - 65 = \frac{4}{3}x$$
$$y = \frac{4}{3}x + 65$$

b. $x = 2009 - 1990 = 19$
$$y = \frac{4}{3}(19) + 65 \approx 90.3$$
We predict that 90% of US drivers will be wearing seat belts in 2009.

91. a. The information provided gives the ordered pairs (0, 43) and (22, 60)
$$m = \frac{60 - 43}{22 - 0} = \frac{17}{22}$$
$$y - 43 = \frac{17}{22}(x - 0)$$
$$y - 43 = \frac{17}{22}x$$
$$y = \frac{17}{22}x + 43$$

b. $x = 2010 - 1998 = 12$
$$y = \frac{17}{22}(12) + 43 \approx 52.3$$
We predict that there will be 52 million people reporting arthritis in 2010.

92. a. Enter the years into L1 with 1970 represented by $x = 0$ and the corresponding populations in L2. Find a window and graph the data. We use $[-10, 40, 10]$ by $[190000, 280000, 10000]$.

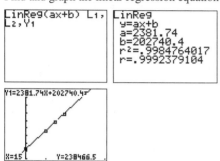

b. Find and graph the linear regression equation

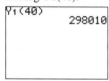

The linear regression equation is
$y = 2381.74x + 202740.4$.

c. Note that 2010 will be 40 years after 1970. Since the equation is stored in Y1, we evaluate the equation for the year 2010 by finding Y1(40).

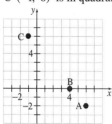

Note that 298,010 thousand = 298,010,000. The population of the United States will be 298,010,000 in 2010 if the trend continues to increase at the same rate.

Chapter 2 Test

1. A $(6, -2)$ is in quadrant IV.

B $(4, 0)$ is on the x-axis (not in a quadrant).

C $(-1, 6)$ is in quadrant II.

2. Let $x = -6$: $2y - 3(-6) = 12$
$$2y + 18 = 12$$
$$2y = -6$$
$$y = -3$$

The ordered pair is $(-6, -3)$.

3. $2x - 3y = -6$
$$-3y = -2x - 6$$
$$y = \frac{2}{3}x + 2$$

The slope is $\frac{2}{3}$ and the y-intercept is at 2. Begin at $(0, 2)$ and move up 2 units and to the right 3 units to find the point $(3, 4)$.

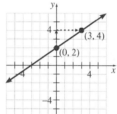

4. $4x + 6y = 7$

Let $x = 0$ Let $y = 0$

$4(0) + 6y = 7$ $4x + 6(0) = 7$

$6y = 7$ $4x = 7$

$y = \frac{7}{6}$ $x = \frac{7}{4}$

The y-intercept is $\left(0, \frac{7}{6}\right)$, and the x-intercept is $\left(\frac{7}{4}, 0\right)$.

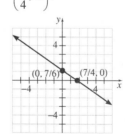

5. For $f(x) = \frac{2}{3}x$, the slope is $\frac{2}{3}$ and the y-intercept is at 0. Begin at $(0, 0)$ and move up 2 units and to the right 3 units to find the point $(3, 2)$.

87

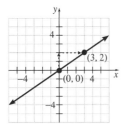

6. $y = -3$

This is a horizontal line with y-intercept at -3.

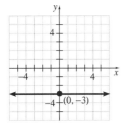

7. $m = \dfrac{10-(-8)}{-7-5} = \dfrac{18}{-12} = -\dfrac{3}{2}$

8. $3x + 12y = 8$

$$12y = -3x + 8$$

$$\frac{12y}{12} = \frac{-3x}{12} + \frac{8}{12}$$

$$y = -\frac{1}{4}x + \frac{2}{3}$$

$$m = -\frac{1}{4}, \ b = \frac{2}{3}$$

9. A horizontal line must have an equation of the form $y = b$. Since the line passes through the point $(2, -8)$, it must have the y-intercept $(0, -8)$. Thus, its equation is $y = -8$.

10. A vertical line must have an equation of the form $x = c$. Since the line passes through the point $(-4, -3)$, it must have the x-intercept $(-4, 0)$. Thus, its equation is $x = -4$.

11. Since the line we seek is perpendicular to the vertical line $x = 5$, it must be horizontal and its must have an equation of the form $y = b$. Since this horizontal line passes through the point $(3, -2)$, it must have the y-intercept $(0, -2)$. Thus, its equation is $y = -2$.

12. $y - (-1) = -3(x-4)$

$$y + 1 = -3x + 12$$

$$3x + y = 11$$

13. $y - (-2) = 5(x-0)$

$$y + 2 = 5x$$

$$-5x + y = -2 \ \text{ or } \ 5x - y = 2$$

14. $m = \dfrac{-3-(-2)}{6-4} = \dfrac{-1}{2} = -\dfrac{1}{2}$

$$y - (-2) = -\frac{1}{2}(x-4)$$

$$y + 2 = -\frac{1}{2}x + 2$$

$$y = -\frac{1}{2}x \ \text{ or } \ f(x) = -\frac{1}{2}x$$

15. The slope of the line we seek is $-\dfrac{1}{3}$, the negative reciprocal of the slope of the line
$3x - y = 4$
$$-y = -3x + 4$$
$$y = 3x - 4$$
The equation of the line we seek is

$$y - 2 = -\frac{1}{3}[x - (-1)]$$

$$y - 2 = -\frac{1}{3}(x+1)$$

$$y - 2 = -\frac{1}{3}x - \frac{1}{3}$$

$$y = -\frac{1}{3}x + \frac{5}{3} \ \text{ or } \ f(x) = -\frac{1}{3}x + \frac{5}{3}$$

16. The slope of the line we seek is $-\dfrac{1}{2}$, the same as the slope of the line
$2y + x = 3$
$$2y = -x + 3$$
$$y = -\frac{1}{2}x + \frac{3}{2}$$
The equation of the line we seek is

$$y - (-2) = -\frac{1}{2}(x-3)$$

$$y + 2 = -\frac{1}{2}x + \frac{3}{2}$$

$$y = -\frac{1}{2}x - \frac{1}{2} \ \text{ or } \ f(x) = -\frac{1}{2}x - \frac{1}{2}$$

17. $L_1: \ 2x - 5y = 8$

$$-5y = -2x + 8$$

$$\frac{-5y}{-5} = \frac{-2x}{-5} + \frac{8}{-5}$$

$$y = \frac{2}{5}x - \frac{8}{5}$$

Thus, the slope of L_1 is $m_1 = \frac{2}{5}$.

The slope of L_2 is $m_2 = \frac{-1-4}{-1-1} = \frac{-5}{-2} = \frac{5}{2}$.

Since these slopes are not equal and since the product of these slopes is not –1, the lines L_1 and L_2 are neither parallel nor perpendicular.

18. B

19. A

20. D

21. C

22. Domain = $(-\infty, \infty)$

Range = $\{5\}$

Function

23. Domain = $\{-2\}$

Range = $(-\infty, \infty)$

The relation is not a function since it fails the vertical line test.

24. Domain = $(-\infty, \infty)$

Range = $[0, \infty)$

Function

25. Domain = $(-\infty, \infty)$

Range = $(-\infty, \infty)$

Function

26. a. $x = 1998 - 1996 = 2$

$f(2) = 732(2) + 21,428 = 22,892$

The average earnings in 1998 were $22,892.

b. $x = 2005 - 1996 = 9$

$f(9) = 732(9) + 21,428 = 28,016$

The average earnings in 2005 will be $28,016.

c. $732x + 21,428 = 30,000$

$$732x = 8572$$

$$x = \frac{8572}{732} \approx 11.71$$

Note that $1996 + 11.71 = 2007.71$. The average earnings will be greater than $30,000 in 2008.

d. The slope of the equation is $m = 732$. It means that the yearly earnings for high school graduates is increasing at a rate of $732 per year.

e. The y-intercept is $b = 21,428$. It means that the yearly earnings for a high school graduate in 1996 was $21,428.

27. a. Enter the years into L1 with 1970 represented by $x = 0$ and the corresponding populations in L2. Find a window and graph the data. We use $[-10, 40, 10]$ by $[0, 20000, 1000]$.

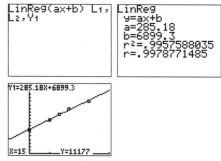

b. Find and graph the linear regression equation

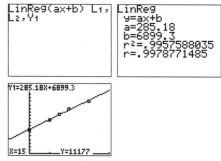

The linear regression equation is $y = 285.18x + 6899.3$.

c. Note that 2010 will be 40 years after 1970. Since the equation is stored in Y1, we evaluate the equation for the year 2010 by finding Y1(40).

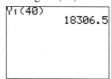

Note that 18,306.5 thousand = 18,306,500. The population of Florida will be 18,306,500 in 2010 if the trend continues to increase at the same rate.

Chapter 2 Cumulative Review

1. $3(15) - (4) = 45 - 4 = 41$

2. a. $-4 + (-3) = -7$

   b. $\frac{1}{2} - \left(-\frac{1}{3}\right) = \frac{1}{2} + \frac{1}{3} = \frac{3}{6} + \frac{2}{6} = \frac{5}{6}$

   c. $7 - 20 = -13$

3. a. True. 3 is a real number

   b. False. $\frac{1}{5}$ is rational, not irrational.

   c. False. Every rational number is not an integer. For example, $\frac{3}{4}$ is a rational number, but it is not an integer.

   d. False. 1 is not in the second set.

4. a. The opposite of -7 is 7.

   b. The opposite of 0 is 0.

   c. The opposite of $\frac{1}{4}$ is $-\frac{1}{4}$.

5. a. $2 - 8 = 2 + (-8) = -6$

   b. $-8 - (-1) = -8 + 1 = -7$

   c. $-11 - 5 = -11 + (-5) = -16$

   d. $10.7 - (-9.8) = 10.7 + 9.8 = 20.5$

   e. $\frac{2}{3} - \frac{1}{2} = \frac{4}{6} - \frac{3}{6} = \frac{1}{6}$

   f. $1 - 0.06 = 0.94$

   g. $4 - 7 = 4 + (-7) = -3$

6. a. $\frac{-42}{-6} = 7$

   b. $\frac{0}{14} = 0$

   c. $-1(-5)(-2) = 5(-2) = -10$

7. a. $3^2 = 3 \cdot 3 = 9$

   b. $\left(\frac{1}{2}\right)^4 = \frac{1}{2} \cdot \frac{1}{2} \cdot \frac{1}{2} \cdot \frac{1}{2} = \frac{1}{16}$

   c. $-5^2 = -(5 \cdot 5) = -25$

   d. $(-5)^2 = (-5)(-5) = 25$

   e. $-5^3 = -(5 \cdot 5 \cdot 5) = -125$

   f. $(-5)^3 = (-5)(-5)(-5) = -125$

8. a. Distributive Property

   b. Commutative Property of Addition

9. a. $-1 > -2$

   b. $\frac{12}{4} = 3$

   c. $-5 < 0$

   d. $-3.5 < -3.05$

10. a. $2(7)^2 = 2(49) = 98$

   b. $2(-7)^2 = 2(49) = 98$

11. a. The reciprocal of 11 is $\frac{1}{11}$.

   b. The reciprocal of -9 is $-\frac{1}{9}$.

   c. The reciprocal of $\frac{7}{4}$ is $\frac{4}{7}$.

12. $-2 + 3[5 - (7 - 10)] = -2 + 3[5 - (-3)]$
$$= -2 + 3(8)$$
$$= -2 + 24$$
$$= 22$$

13. $0.6 = 2 - 3.5c$
$-1.4 = -3.5c$
$\frac{-1.4}{-3.5} = \frac{-3.5c}{-3.5}$
$0.4 = c$
The solution is 0.4.

14. $2(x - 3) = -40$
$2x - 6 = -40$
$2x = -34$
$x = -17$
The solution is -17.

15. $3x + 5 = 3(x + 2)$
$3x + 5 = 3x + 6$
$5 = 6$ False
The equation has no solution. That is, $\varnothing$ or { }.

16. $5(x - 7) = 4x - 35 + x$
$5x - 35 = 5x - 35$
$-35 = -35$ True for any number
The solution is the set of all real numbers.

17. 16% of $25 = 0.16(25) = 4$

18. 25% of $16 = 0.25(16) = 4$

19. Let x = the first quiz score
$x+2$ = second quiz score
$x+4$ = the third quiz score

$$x+(x+2)+(x+4) = 264$$
$$3x+6 = 264$$
$$3x = 258$$
$$x = 86$$

$x+2 = 86+2 = 88$
$x+4 = 86+4 = 90$

Kelsey's quiz scores were 86, 88, and 90.

20. Let x = first odd integer
$x+2$ = next odd integer
$x+4$ = third odd integer

$$x+(x+2)+(x+4) = 213$$
$$3x+6 = 213$$
$$3x = 207$$
$$x = 69$$

$x+2 = 69+2 = 71$
$x+4 = 69+4 = 73$

The integers are 69, 71, and 73.

21. $V = lwh$

$$\frac{V}{lw} = \frac{lwh}{lw}$$
$$\frac{V}{lw} = h$$

22. $7x+3y = 21$
$$3y = -7x+21$$
$$y = -\frac{7}{3}x+7$$

23. To find the median, first put the data into ascending order:
76, 76, 77, 79, 80, 82, <u>82, 85</u>, 86, 87, **89, 89, 89**, 92
Since we have an even number of data values (namely 14), the median will be the average of the middle two data values (82 and 85). Thus, the median is $\dfrac{82+85}{2} = \dfrac{167}{2} = 83.5$.

The mode is the most frequently occurring data value. In this case, we have three 89s, so the mode is 89.

24. The mean is
$$\frac{106+118+98+56+112+58+73+118}{8}$$
$$= \frac{739}{8}$$
$$= 92.375$$

To find the median, first put the data values in ascending order:
56, 58, 73, <u>98, 106</u>, 112, **118, 118**
Since we have an even number of data values (namely 8), the median will be the average of the middle two data values (98 and 106). Thus, the median is $\dfrac{98+106}{2} = \dfrac{204}{2} = 102$.

The mode is the most frequently occurring data value. In this case, we have two 118s, so the mode is 118.

25. a. $(2,-1)$ is in quadrant IV.

  b. $(0, 5)$ is on the y-axis, not in a quadrant.

  c. $(-3, 5)$ is in quadrant II.

  d. $(-2, 0)$ is on the x-axis, not in a quadrant.

  e. $\left(-\dfrac{1}{2}, -4\right)$ is in quadrant III.

  f. $(1.5, 1.5)$ is in quadrant I.

26. a. $(0,-2)$ is on the y-axis.

  b. $(-3,-2.5)$ is in quadrant III.

  c. $\left(\dfrac{1}{2}, 0\right)$ is on the x-axis.

  d. $(4,-0.5)$ is in quadrant IV.

27. Let $x = 0$ and $y = -12$.
$$3x - y = 12$$
$$3(0) - (-12) \overset{?}{=} 12$$
$$0+12 \overset{?}{=} 12$$
$$12 = 12 \quad \text{True}$$

Let $x = 1$ and $y = 9$.
$$3x - y = 12$$
$$3(1) - (9) \overset{?}{=} 12$$
$$3-9 \overset{?}{=} 12$$
$$-6 = 12 \quad \text{False}$$

Let $x = 2$ and $y = -6$.
$$3x - y = 12$$
$$3(2) - (-6) \overset{?}{=} 12$$
$$6+6 \overset{?}{=} 12$$
$$12 = 12 \quad \text{True}$$

The ordered pairs $(0,-12)$ and $(2,-6)$ are solutions, but $(1, 9)$ is not a solution,.

28. $7x + 2y = 10$
$$2y = -7x + 10$$
$$y = -\frac{7}{2}x + 5$$
$$m = -\frac{7}{2}, \ b = 5$$

29. Yes, $y = 2x + 1$ is a function. If we graph this line, it passes the vertical line test.

30. No, it is not a function. If fails the vertical line test. (Try $x = 0$.)

line test).

31. a. y-intercept $= \left(0, \dfrac{3}{7}\right)$

    b. y-intercept $= (0, -3.2)$

32. $m = \dfrac{9 - 6}{0 - (-1)} = \dfrac{3}{1} = 3$

33. Slope of $\dfrac{3}{4}$ means $m = \dfrac{3}{4}$; y-intercept $(0, -3)$ means $b = -3$. Using the equation $y = mx + b$, we have $y = \dfrac{1}{4}x - 3$.

34. A vertical line must have an equation of the form $x = c$. Since the line passes through the point $\left(-2, -\dfrac{3}{4}\right)$, it must have the x-intercept $(-2, \ 0)$. Thus, its equation is $x = -2$.

35. A horizontal line must have an equation of the form $y = b$. Since the line passes through the point $\left(-2, -\dfrac{3}{4}\right)$, it must have the y-intercept $\left(0, -\dfrac{3}{4}\right)$. Thus, its equation is $y = -\dfrac{3}{4}$.

36. $m = \dfrac{7 - 5}{-4 - (-2)} = \dfrac{7 - 5}{-4 + 2} = \dfrac{2}{-2} = -1$
$$y - 5 = -1[x - (-2)]$$
$$y - 5 = -1(x + 2)$$
$$y - 5 = -x - 2$$
$$x + y = 3$$

Chapter 3

Mental Math 3.1

1. $4x = 24$.
$$\frac{4x}{4} = \frac{24}{4}$$
$$x = 6$$

2. $6x = -12$
$$\frac{6x}{6} = \frac{-12}{6}$$
$$x = -2$$

3. $2x + 10 = 20$
$$2x + 10 - 10 = 20 - 10$$
$$2x = 10$$
$$\frac{2x}{2} = \frac{10}{2}$$
$$x = 5$$

4. $5x + 25 = 30$
$$5x + 25 - 25 = 30 - 25$$
$$5x = 5$$
$$\frac{5x}{5} = \frac{5}{5}$$
$$x = 1$$

5. $-3x = 0$
$$\frac{-3x}{-3} = \frac{0}{-3}$$
$$x = 0$$

6. $-2x = -14$
$$\frac{-2x}{-2} = \frac{-14}{-2}$$
$$x = 7$$

Exercise Set 3.1

1. $5x + 2 = 3x + 6$

Algebraic Solution:
$$5x + 2 = 3x + 6$$
$$2x + 2 = 6$$
$$2x = 4$$
$$x = 2$$
The solution is 2.

Graphical Solution:
Graph $y_1 = 5x + 2$ and $y_2 = 3x + 6$ in a
$[-20, 20, 5]$ by $[-20, 20, 5]$ viewing window
and find the intersection point.

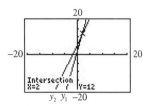

The point of intersection $(2, 12)$ indicates that
the solution is 2.

3. $9 - x = 2x + 12$

Algebraic Solution:
$$9 - x = 2x + 12$$
$$9 = 3x + 12$$
$$-3 = 3x$$
$$-1 = x$$
The solution is -1 .

Graphical Solution:
Graph $y_1 = 9 - x$ and $y_2 = 2x + 12$ in a
$[-20, 20, 5]$ by $[-20, 20, 5]$ viewing window
and find the intersection point.

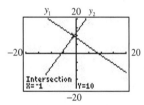

The point of intersection $(-1, 10)$ indicates that
the solution is -1 .

5. $8 - (2x - 1) = 13$

Algebraic Solution:
$$8 - (2x - 1) = 13$$
$$8 - 2x + 1 = 13$$
$$-2x + 9 = 13$$
$$-2x = 4$$
$$x = -2$$
The solution is -2 .

Graphical Solution:
Graph $y_1 = 8 - (2x - 1)$ and $y_2 = 13$ in a
$[-20, 20, 5]$ by $[-20, 20, 5]$ viewing window
and find the intersection point.

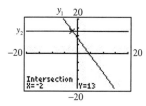

The point of intersection $(-2, 13)$ indicates that the solution is -2.

7.
$$y_1 = y_2$$
$$2(x-5)+3 = 3x-13$$

The point of intersection $(6, 5)$ indicates that the solution is 6.

9.
$$y_1 = y_2$$
$$-(2x+3)+2 = 5x-1-7x$$

The two equations have the same graph, so the solution is the set of all real numbers.

11. $7(x-6) = 5(x+2)+2x$

Algebraic Solution:
$$7(x-6) = 5(x+2)+2x$$
$$7x-42 = 5x+10+2x$$
$$7x-42 = 7x+10$$
$$-42 = 10 \quad \text{False}$$

This equation is a false statement no matter what value the variable x might have. The equation is a contradiction and has no solution. The solution set is $\varnothing$ or { }.

Graphical Solution:
Graph $y_1 = 7(x-6)$ and $y_2 = 5(x+2)+2x$ in a $[-20, 20, 5]$ by $[-20, 20, 5]$ viewing window.

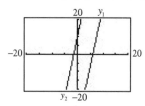

The parallel lines indicate that the equation is a contradiction and has no solution. The solution set is $\varnothing$ or { }.

13. $3x-(6x+2) = -(3x+2)$

Algebraic Solution:
$$3x-(6x+2) = -(3x+2)$$
$$3x-6x-2 = -3x-2$$
$$-3x-2 = -3x-2$$

Since both sides are the same, this equation is a true statement no matter what value the variable x might have. The equation is an identity and the solution set is all real numbers.

Graphical Solution:
Graph $y_1 = 3x-(6x+2)$ and $y_2 = -(3x+2)$ in a $[-20, 20, 5]$ by $[-20, 20, 5]$ viewing window.

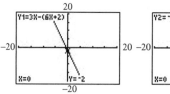 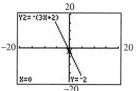

The graphs of y_1 and y_2 are the same. When we trace along y_1, we have the same ordered pairs as when we trace along points of y_2. We know that the lines are identical because two points uniquely determine a line. The equation is an identity and the solution is the set of all real numbers.

15. $5(x+1)-3(x-7) = 2(x+4)-3$

Algebraic Solution:
$$5(x+1)-3(x-7) = 2(x+4)-3$$
$$5x+5-3x+21 = 2x+8-3$$
$$2x+26 = 2x+5$$
$$26 = 6 \quad \text{False}$$

This equation is a false statement no matter what value the variable x might have. The equation is a contradiction and has no solution. The solution set is $\varnothing$ or { }.

Graphical Solution:
Graph $y_1 = 5(x+1)-3(x-7)$ and $y_2 = 2(x+4)-3$ in a $[-20, 20, 5]$ by $[-20, 20, 5]$ viewing window.

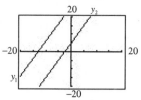

The parallel lines indicate that the equation is a contradiction and has no solution. The solution set is $\varnothing$ or { }.

17. $3(x+2)-6(x-5) = 36-3x$

Algebraic Solution:
$$3(x+2)-6(x-5) = 36-3x$$
$$3x+6-6x+30 = 36-3x$$
$$-3x+36 = -3x+36$$

Since both sides are the same, this equation is a true statement no matter what value the variable x might have. The equation is an identity and the solution set is all real numbers.

Graphical Solution:
Graph $y_1 = 3(x+2)-6(x-5)$ and $y_2 = 36-3x$ in an integer viewing window centered at the origin.

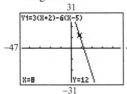 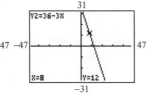

The graphs of y_1 and y_2 are the same. When we trace along y_1, we have the same ordered pairs as when we trace along points of y_2. We know that the lines are identical because two points uniquely determine a line. The equation is an identity and the solution is the set of all real numbers.

19. $(x+2.1)-(0.5x+3) = 12$

Algebraic Solution:
$$(x+2.1)-(0.5x+3) = 12$$
$$x+2.1-0.5x-3 = 12$$
$$0.5x-0.9 = 12$$
$$0.5x = 12.9$$
$$x = 25.8$$
The solution is 22.4.

Graphical Solution:
Graph $y_1 = (x+2.1)-(0.5x+3)$ and $y_2 = 12$ in an integer viewing window centered at the origin and find the intersection point.

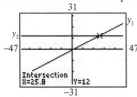

The point of intersection $(25.8, 12)$ indicates that the solution is 25.8.

21. $5(a-12)+2(a+15) = a-9$

Algebraic Solution:
$$5(a-12)+2(a+15) = a-9$$
$$5a-60+2a+30 = a-9$$
$$7a-30 = a-9$$
$$6a-30 = -9$$
$$6a = 21$$
$$a = \frac{21}{6} = \frac{7}{2} = 3.5$$

The solution is $\frac{7}{2} = 3.5$.

Graphical Solution:
Graph $y_1 = 5(x-12)+2(x+15)$ and $y_2 = x-9$ in an integer viewing window centered at the origin and find the intersection point.

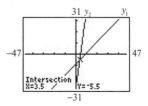

The point of intersection $(3.5, -5.5)$ indicates that the solution is 3.5.

23. $8(p-4)-5(2p+3) = 3.5(2p-5)$

Algebraic Solution:
$$8(p-4)-5(2p+3) = 3.5(2p-5)$$
$$8p-32-10p-15 = 7p-17.5$$
$$-2p-47 = 7p-17.5$$
$$-9p-47 = -17.5$$
$$-9p = 29.5$$
$$p = \frac{29.5}{-9} \approx -3.28$$

The solution is approximately -3.28.

Graphical Solution:
Graph $y_1 = 8(x-4)-5(2x+3)$ and $y_2 = 3.5(2x-5)$ in a $[-10, 10, 1]$ by $[-100, 100, 10]$ viewing window and find the intersection point.

The point of intersection $(-3.27778, -40.44444)$

95

Rounded to the nearest hundredth, the point of intersection $(-3.28, -40.44)$ indicates that the solution is approximately -3.28.

25. $5(x-2)+2x=7(x+4)$

Algebraic Solution:
$$5(x-2)+2x=7(x+4)$$
$$5x-10+2x=7x+28$$
$$7x-10=7x+28$$
$$-10=28 \quad \text{False}$$

This equation is a false statement no matter what value the variable x might have. The equation is a contradiction and has no solution. The solution set is $\varnothing$ or { }.

Graphical Solution:
Graph $y_1=5(x-2)+2x$ and $y_2=7(x+4)$ in a $[-20, 20, 5]$ by $[-20, 20, 5]$ viewing window.

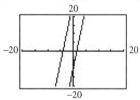

The parallel lines indicate that the equation is a contradiction and has no solution. The solution set is $\varnothing$ or { }.

27. $y+0.2=0.6(y+3)$

Algebraic Solution:
$$y+0.2=0.6(y+3)$$
$$y+0.2=0.6y+1.8$$
$$0.4y=1.6$$
$$y=4$$

The solution is 4.

Graphical Solution:
Graph $y_1=x+0.2$ and $y_2=0.6(x+3)$ in a standard viewing window and find the intersection point.

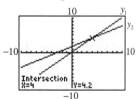

The point of intersection $(4, 4.2)$ indicates that the solution is 4.

29. $2y+5(y-4)=4y-2(y-10)$

Algebraic Solution:
$$2y+5(y-4)=4y-2(y-10)$$
$$2y+5y-20=4y-2y+20$$
$$7y-20=2y+20$$
$$5y-20=20$$
$$5y=40$$
$$y=8$$

The solution is 8.

Graphical Solution:
Graph $y_1=2x+5(x-4)$ and $y_2=4x-2(x-10)$ in a $[-20, 20, 5]$ by $[-100, 100, 10]$ viewing window and find the intersection point.

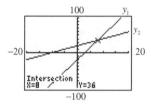

The point of intersection $(8, 36)$ indicates that the solution is 8.

31. $2(x-8)+x=3(x-6)+2$

Algebraic Solution:
$$2(x-8)+x=3(x-6)+2$$
$$2x-16+x=3x-18+2$$
$$3x-16=3x-16$$

Since both sides are the same, this equation is a true statement no matter what value the variable x might have. The equation is an identity and the solution set is all real numbers.

Graphical Solution:
Graph $y_1=2(x-8)+x$ and $y_2=3(x-6)+2$ in a $[-20, 20, 5]$ by $[-20, 20, 5]$ viewing window.

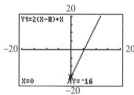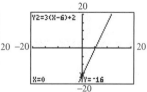

The graphs of y_1 and y_2 are the same. When we trace along y_1, we have the same ordered pairs as when we trace along points of y_2. We know that the lines are identical because two points uniquely determine a line. The equation is an identity and the solution is the set of all real numbers.

33. $\dfrac{5x-1}{6} - 3x = \dfrac{1}{3} + \dfrac{4x+3}{9}$

Algebraic Solution:

$$\dfrac{5x-1}{6} - 3x = \dfrac{1}{3} + \dfrac{4x+3}{9}$$

$$18\left(\dfrac{5x-1}{6} - 3x\right) = 18\left(\dfrac{1}{3} + \dfrac{4x+3}{9}\right)$$

$$3(5x-1) - 18(3x) = 6 + 2(4x+3)$$

$$15x - 3 - 54x = 6 + 8x + 6$$

$$-39x - 3 = 8x + 12$$

$$-47x - 3 = 12$$

$$-47x = 15$$

$$x = \dfrac{15}{-47} = -\dfrac{15}{47} \approx -0.32$$

The solution is $-\dfrac{15}{47} \approx -0.32$.

Graphical Solution:

Graph $y_1 = \dfrac{5x-1}{6} - 3x$ and $y_2 = \dfrac{1}{3} + \dfrac{4x+3}{9}$ in a

standard viewing window and find the intersection point.

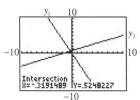

Rounded to the nearest hundredth, the point of intersection $(-0.32,\ 0.52)$ indicates that the solution is approximately -0.32.

35. $-2(b-4) - (3b-1) = 5b+3$

Algebraic Solution:

$$-2(b-4) - (3b-1) = 5b+3$$

$$-2b + 8 - 3b + 1 = 5b + 3$$

$$-5b + 9 = 5b + 3$$

$$-10b + 9 = 3$$

$$-10b = -6$$

$$b = \dfrac{-6}{-10} = \dfrac{3}{5} = 0.6$$

The solution is $\dfrac{3}{5} = 0.6$.

Graphical Solution:

Graph $y_1 = -2(x-4) - (3x-1)$ and $y_2 = 5x+3$

in a standard viewing window and find the intersection point.

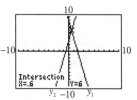

The point of intersection $(0.6, 6)$ indicates that the solution is 0.6.

37. $1.5(4-x) = 1.3(2-x)$

Algebraic Solution:

$$1.5(4-x) = 1.3(2-x)$$

$$6 - 1.5x = 2.6 - 1.3x$$

$$-0.2x + 6 = 2.6$$

$$-0.2x = -3.4$$

$$x = 17$$

The solution is 17.

Graphical Solution:

Graph $y_1 = 1.5(4-x)$ and $y_2 = 1.3(2-x)$ in a

$[-50, 50, 5]$ by $[-50, 50, 5]$ viewing window and find the intersection point.

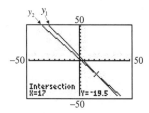

The point of intersection $(17, -19.5)$ indicates that the solution is 17.

39. $\dfrac{1}{4}(a+2) = \dfrac{1}{6}(5-a)$

Algebraic Solution:

$$\dfrac{1}{4}(a+2) = \dfrac{1}{6}(5-a)$$

$$24 \cdot \dfrac{1}{4}(a+2) = 24 \cdot \dfrac{1}{6}(5-a)$$

$$6(a+2) = 4(5-a)$$

$$6a + 12 = 20 - 4a$$

$$10a + 12 = 20$$

$$10a = 8$$

$$a = \dfrac{8}{10} = \dfrac{4}{5} = 0.8$$

The solution is $\dfrac{4}{5} = 0.8$.

Graphical Solution:

Graph $y_1 = \dfrac{1}{4}(x+2)$ and $y_2 = \dfrac{1}{6}(5-x)$ in a

standard viewing window and find the intersection point.

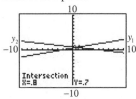

The point of intersection $(0.8, 0.7)$ indicates that the solution is 0.8.

41. a. $C_1(2) = 30 + 20(2) = \$70$

$C_2(2) = 25(2) = \$50$

If the job takes 2 hours, then the second consultant will have a lower cost.

b. $C_1(8) = 30 + 20(8) = \$190$

$C_2(8) = 25(8) = \$200$

If the job takes 8 hours, then the first consultant will have a lower cost.

c. *Algebraic Solution:*

$$C_1(x) = C_2(x)$$
$$30 + 20x = 25x$$
$$30 = 5x$$
$$6 = x$$

The cost of hiring each consultant will be the same if the job takes 6 hours.

Graphical Solution:

Graph $y_1 = 30 + 20x$ and $y_2 = 25x$ and find the point of intersection.

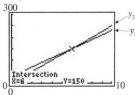

The intersection point $(6, 150)$ indicates that the cost of hiring each consultant will be the same if the job takes 6 hours.

43. a. $R_1(50) = 25 + 0.30(50) = \$40$

$R_2(50) = 28 + 0.25(50) = \$40.50$

If 50 miles are driven, then the first agency will have a lower cost.

b. $R_1(100) = 25 + 0.30(100) = \$55$

$R_2(100) = 28 + 0.25(100) = \$53$

If 100 miles are driven, then the second agency will have a lower cost.

c. *Algebraic Solution:*

$$R_1(x) = R_2(x)$$
$$25 + 0.30x = 28 + 0.25x$$
$$25 + 0.05x = 28$$
$$0.05x = 3$$
$$x = 60$$

The cost of using each agency will be the same if 60 mile are driven.

Graphical Solution:

Graph $y_1 = 25 + 0.30x$ and $y_2 = 28 + 0.25x$ and find the point of intersection.

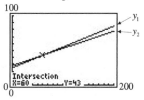

The intersection point $(60, 43)$ indicates that the cost of using each agency will be the same if 60 miles are driven.

45. $x < 0$

$\{-3, -2, -1\}$

47. $x + 5 \le 6$

$x \le 1$

$\{-3, -2, -1, \ 0, \ 1\}$

49. Answers may vary. One possible answer follows: All negative real numbers are solutions of $x < 0$.

51. From the intersection point shown on the screen, the ordered pair is $(12, \ 22)$.

53. When $x > 12$, the graph of y_1 is above the graph of y_2. Thus, if x is greater than 12, y_1 is greater than y_2.

55. Graph $y_1 = 1.75x - 2.5$ and $y_2 = 0$ in a standard viewing window and find the intersection point.

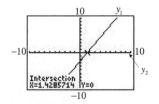

Rounding to the nearest hundredth, the point of intersection (1.43, 0) indicates that the solution is approximately 1.43.

Check.

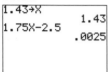

Since $0.0025 \approx 0$, the approximate solution 1.43 checks.

57. Graph $y_1 = 2.5x + 3$ and $y_2 = 7.8x - 5$ in a standard viewing window and find the intersection point.

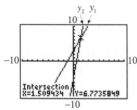

Rounding to the nearest hundredth, the point of intersection (1.51, 6.77) indicates that the solution is approximately 1.51.

Check.

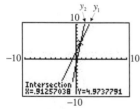

Since $6.775 \approx 6.778$, the approximate solution 1.51 checks.

59. Graph $y_1 = 3x + \sqrt{5}$ and $y_2 = 7x + \sqrt{2}$ in a standard viewing window and find the intersection point.

Rounding to the nearest hundredth, the point of intersection (0.91, 4.97) indicates that the solution is approximately 0.91.

Check.

Since $4.966067977 \approx 4.955786438$, the approximate solution 0.91 checks.

61. Graph $y_1 = 2\pi x - 5.6$ and $y_2 = 7(x - \pi)$ in a $[-50, 50, 10]$ by $[-300, 300, 50]$ viewing window and find the intersection point.

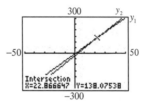

Rounding to the nearest hundredth, the point of intersection (22.87, 138.08) indicates that the solution is approximately 22.87.

Check.

Since $138.096448 \approx 138.0988514$, the approximate solution 22.87 checks.

63. If the intersection-of-graphs method leads to parallel lines, then the equation has no solution.

Mental Math 3.2

1. $x - 2 < 4$
$x < 6$
$\{x \mid x < 6\}$

2. $x - 1 > 6$
$x > 7$
$\{x \mid x > 7\}$

3. $x + 5 \geq 15$
$x \geq 10$
$\{x \mid x \geq 10\}$

4. $x + 1 \leq 8$

$x \leq 7$

$\{x \mid x \leq 7\}$

5. $3x > 12$

$x > 4$

$\{x \mid x > 4\}$

6. $5x < 20$

$x < 4$

$\{x \mid x > 4\}$

7. $\dfrac{x}{2} \leq 1$

$x \leq 2$

$\{x \mid x \leq 2\}$

8. $\dfrac{x}{4} \geq 2$

$x \geq 8$

$\{x \mid x \geq 8\}$

Exercise Set 3.2

1. $(-\infty, -3)$

3. $[0.3, \infty)$

5. $\left(\dfrac{5}{9}, \infty\right)$

7. $(-2, 5)$

9. $(-1, 5)$

11. Answers may vary. One possibility follows: If the endpoint is included in the solution (i.e., if the inequality is either $\leq$ or $\geq$), then we use a bracket on the graph. If the endpoint is not included in the solution (i.e., if the inequality symbol is < or >), then we use a parenthesis.

13. D

15. B

17. The graph of y_1 is below the graph of y_2 when $x < 4$. Thus, the solution of the inequality $y_1 < y_2$ is $(-\infty, 4)$.

19. The graph of y_1 is above the graph of y_2 when $x \geq -3$. Thus, the solution of the inequality $y_1 \geq y_2$ is $[-3, \infty)$.

21. The graph of y_1 is always below the graph of y_2, never above it. Thus, the solution of the inequality $y_1 > y_2$ is $\varnothing$.

23. $7x < 6x + 1$

$x < 1$

The solution set is $(-\infty, 1)$.

25. $8x - 7 \leq 7x - 5$

$x - 7 \leq -5$

$x \leq 2$

The solution set is $(-\infty, 2]$.

27. $\dfrac{3}{4}x \geq 2$

$\dfrac{4}{3}\left(\dfrac{3}{4}\right)x \geq \dfrac{4}{3}(2)$

$x \geq \dfrac{8}{3}$

The solution set is $\left[\dfrac{8}{3}, \infty\right)$.

29. $5x < -23.5$

$x < -4.7$

The solution set is $(-\infty, -4.7)$.

31. $-3x \geq 9$

$x \leq -3$

The solution set is $(-\infty, -3]$.

33. $-x < -4$
$x > 4$
The solution set is $(4, \infty)$.

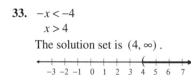

35. $-2x + 7 \geq 9$
$-2x \geq 2$
$x \leq -1$
The solution set is $(-\infty, -1]$.

37. $15 + 2x \geq 4x - 7$
$15 \geq 2x - 7$
$22 \geq 2x$
$11 \geq x$
$x \leq 11$
The solution set is $(-\infty, 11]$.

39. $3(x - 5) < 2(2x - 1)$
$3x - 15 < 4x - 2$
$-15 < x - 2$
$-13 < x$
$x > -13$
The solution set is $(-13, \infty)$.

41. $\dfrac{1}{2} + \dfrac{2}{3} \geq \dfrac{x}{6}$
$6\left(\dfrac{1}{2} + \dfrac{2}{3}\right) \geq 6\left(\dfrac{x}{6}\right)$
$3 + 4 \geq x$
$7 \geq x$
$x \leq 7$
The solution set is $(-\infty, 7]$.

43. $4(x - 1) \geq 4x - 8$
$4x - 4 \geq 4x - 8$
$-4 \geq -8$ (True for all x)
The solution is the set of all real numbers;
$(-\infty, \infty)$.

45. $7x < 7(x - 2)$
$7x < 7x - 14$
$0 < -14$ (False)
The inequality has no solution; $\varnothing$.

47. $4(2x + 1) > 4$
$8x + 4 > 4$
$8x > 0$
$x > 0$
The solution set is $(0, \infty)$.

49. $\dfrac{-5x + 11}{2} \leq 7$
$2\left(\dfrac{-5x + 11}{2}\right) \leq 2(7)$
$-5x + 11 \leq 14$
$-5x \leq 3$
$x \geq -\dfrac{3}{5}$
The solution set is $\left[-\dfrac{3}{5}, \infty\right)$.

51. $8x - 16.4 \leq 10x + 2.8$
$-2x - 16.4 \leq 2.8$
$-2x \leq 19.2$
$x \geq -9.6$
The solution set is $[-9.6, \infty)$.

53. Answers may vary. One possibility follows. The algebraic process of solving a linear inequality is very similar to the algebraic process of solving a linear equation except for the one additional rule: When we multiply or divide both sides of an inequality by a negative number, we must reverse the direction of the inequality symbol.

55. $-5x + 4 \leq -4(x - 1)$
$-5x + 4 \leq -4x + 4$
$-x \leq 0$
$x \geq 0$
The solution set is $[0, \infty)$.

57. $\dfrac{1}{4}(x - 7) \geq x + 2$
$4 \cdot \dfrac{1}{4}(x - 7) \geq 4(x + 2)$
$x - 7 \geq 4x + 8$
$-7 \geq 3x + 8$
$-15 \geq 3x$
$-5 \geq x$
$x \leq -5$
The solution set is $(-\infty, -5]$.

59. $\dfrac{2}{3}(x + 2) < \dfrac{1}{5}(2x + 7)$
$15\left[\dfrac{2}{3}(x + 2)\right] < 15\left[\dfrac{1}{5}(2x + 7)\right]$
$10(x + 2) < 3(2x + 7)$
$10x + 20 < 6x + 21$
$4x < 1$
$x < \dfrac{1}{4}$
The solution set is $\left(-\infty, \dfrac{1}{4}\right)$.

61. $4(x-6)+2x-4 \geq 3(x-7)+10x$
$4x-24+2x-4 \geq 3x-21+10x$
$6x-28 \geq 13x-21$
$-28 \geq 7x-21$
$-7 \geq 7x$
$-1 \geq x$
$x \leq -1$
The solution set is $(-\infty, -1]$.

63. $\dfrac{5x+1}{7} - \dfrac{2x-6}{4} \geq -4$
$28\left(\dfrac{5x+1}{7} - \dfrac{2x-6}{4}\right) \geq 28(-4)$
$4(5x+1) - 7(2x-6) \geq -112$
$20x+4-14x+42 \geq -112$
$6x+46 \geq -112$
$6x \geq -158$
$x \geq -\dfrac{79}{3}$
The solution set is $\left[-\dfrac{79}{3}, \infty\right)$.

65. $\dfrac{-x+2}{2} - \dfrac{1-5x}{8} < -1$
$8\left(\dfrac{-x+2}{2} - \dfrac{1-5x}{8}\right) < 8(-1)$
$4(-x+2) - (1-5x) < -8$
$-4x+8-1+5x < -8$
$x+7 < -8$
$x < -15$
The solution set is $(-\infty, -15)$.

67. $0.8x+0.6x \geq 4.2$
$1.4x \geq 4.2$
$x \geq 3$
The solution set is $[3, \infty)$.

69. $\dfrac{x+5}{5} - \dfrac{3+x}{8} \geq -\dfrac{3}{10}$
$40\left(\dfrac{x+5}{5} - \dfrac{3+x}{8}\right) \geq 40\left(-\dfrac{3}{10}\right)$
$8(x+5) - 5(3+x) \geq -12$
$8x+40-15-5x \geq -12$
$3x+25 \geq -12$
$3x \geq -37$
$x \geq -\dfrac{37}{3}$
The solution set is $\left[-\dfrac{37}{3}, \infty\right)$.

71. $\dfrac{x+3}{12} + \dfrac{x-5}{15} < \dfrac{2}{3}$
$60\left(\dfrac{x+3}{12} + \dfrac{x-5}{15}\right) < 60\left(\dfrac{2}{3}\right)$
$5(x+3) + 4(x-5) < 20(2)$
$5x+15+4x-20 < 40$
$9x-5 < 40$
$9x < 45$
$x < 5$
The solution set is $(-\infty, 5)$.

73. Let x = her score on the final. Then
$\dfrac{72+67+82+79+2x}{6} \geq 60$
$300+2x \geq 360$
$2x \geq 360$
$x \geq 30$
She must score at least 30 on the final exam.

75. Let x = weight of the luggage and cargo. Then
$6(160) + x \leq 2000$
$960 + x \leq 2000$
$x \leq 1040$
The plane can carry a maximum of 1040 pound of luggage and cargo.

77. Let x = the number of ounces. Then
$0.37 + 0.23(x-1) \leq 4.00$
$100[0.37 + 0.23(x-1)] \leq 100(4.00)$
$37 + 23(x-1) \leq 400$
$37 + 23x - 23 \leq 400$
$23x + 14 \leq 400$
$23x \leq 386$
$x \leq 16.78$
At most 16 ounces can be mailed for $4.00.

79. Let n = number of calls made in a given month. Then
$25 < 13 + 0.06n$
$12 < 0.06n$
$200 < n$ or $n > 200$
Plan 1 is more economical than Plan 2 when more than 200 calls are made.

81. $F \geq \dfrac{9}{5}C + 32$
$F \geq \dfrac{9}{5}(500) + 32$
$F \geq 932°$
Glass is a liquid at temperatures of 932°F or higher.

83. a. $60,000 < 2806.6t + 32,558$
$27,442 < 2806.6t$
$9.78 < t$
Beginning salaries will be greater than
$60,000 in $1995 + 9 = 2004$.

b. Answers will vary.

85. The consumption of whole milk is decreasing.
The graph of the line is going down over time
(i.e., the slope of the line is negative).

87. $t = 2008 - 1997 = 11$
$w = -0.13t + 8$
$w = -0.13(11) + 8$
$w = 6.57$
The consumption of whole milk will be about
6.57 gallons per person per year.

89. $-0.13t + 8 < 7$
$-0.13t < -1$
$t > 7.69$
$1997 + 7 = 2004$
Consumption of whole mike will be less than 7
gallons per person per year beginning in 2004.

91. Answers may vary. One possibility follows:
The graph for whole milk is above the graph for
skim milk over the time interval that corresponds
to the years 1997 to 2001.

93. $x < 5$ and $x > 1$
The integers are $\{2, 3, 4\}$.

95. $x \geq -2$ and $x \geq 2$
The integers are $\{2, 3, 4, \ldots\}$.

97. $\{x \mid 0 \leq x \leq 5\} = [0, 5]$

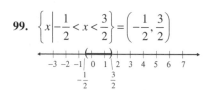

99. $\left\{ x \left| -\dfrac{1}{2} < x < \dfrac{3}{2} \right. \right\} = \left(-\dfrac{1}{2}, \dfrac{3}{2} \right)$

101. $4(x-1) \geq 4x - 8$
$4x - 4 \geq 4x - 8$
$-4 \geq -8$ (True for all x)
The solution is the set of all real numbers;
$(-\infty, \infty)$.

103. $7x < 7(x-2)$
$7x < 7x - 14$
$0 < -14$ (False)
The inequality has no solution; $\varnothing$.

105. a. Enter the years into L1 with 2000 represented
by $x = 0$ and the corresponding percentages in
L2. Find a window and graph the data. We
use $[-10, 70, 10]$ by $[0, 10, 1]$.

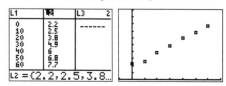

Find and graph the linear regression equation

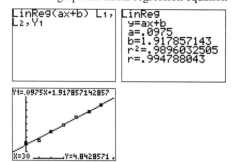

The linear regression equation is
$y = 0.098x + 1.918$.

b. From the slope of the regression equation,
we find that Medicare spending is increasing
at a rate of 0.098% per year.

c. $0.098x + 1.918 \geq 4$
$0.098x \geq 2.082$
$x \geq 21.24$ (rounded)
$2000 + 21 = 2021$
The percentage of Medicare spending will
be 4% or higher for the years 2021 and later.

Integrated Review

1. $-4x = 20$
$\dfrac{-4x}{-4} = \dfrac{20}{-4}$
$x = -5$
The solution is -5 .

2. $-4x < 20$

$\dfrac{-4x}{-4} > \dfrac{20}{-4}$

$x > -5$

The solution set is $(-5, \infty)$.

3. $\dfrac{3x}{4} \geq 2$

$4\left(\dfrac{3x}{4}\right) \geq 4(2)$

$3x \geq 8$

$x \geq \dfrac{8}{3}$

The solution set is $\left[\dfrac{8}{3}, \infty\right)$.

4. $5x + 3 \geq 2 + 4x$

$x + 3 \geq 2$

$x \geq -1$

The solution set is $[-1, \infty)$.

5. $6(y - 4) = 3(y - 8)$

$6y - 24 = 3y - 24$

$3y = 0$

$y = 0$

The solution is 0.

6. $-4x \leq \dfrac{2}{5}$

$-20x \leq 2$

$x \geq -\dfrac{1}{10}$

The solution set is $\left[-\dfrac{1}{10}, \infty\right)$.

7. $-3x \geq \dfrac{1}{2}$

$2(-3x) \geq 2\left(\dfrac{1}{2}\right)$

$-6x \geq 1$

$x \leq -\dfrac{1}{6}$

The solution set is $\left(-\infty, -\dfrac{1}{6}\right]$.

8. $5(y + 4) = 4(y + 5)$

$5y + 20 = 4y + 20$

$y = 0$

The solution is 0.

9. $7x < 7(x - 2)$

$7x < 7x - 2$

$0 < -2$ (False)

The inequality has no solution; $\varnothing$.

10. $\dfrac{-5x + 11}{2} \leq 7$

$2\left(\dfrac{-5x + 11}{2}\right) \leq 2(7)$

$-5x + 11 \leq 14$

$-5x \leq 3$

$x \geq -\dfrac{3}{5}$

The solution set is $\left[-\dfrac{3}{5}, \infty\right)$.

11. $-5x + 1.5 = -19.5$

$10(-5x + 1.5) = 10(-19.5)$

$-50x + 15 = -195$

$-50x = -210$

$x = 4.2$

The solution is 4.2.

12. $-5x + 4 = -26$

$-5x = -30$

$x = 6$

The solution is 6.

13. $5 + 2x - x = -x + 3 - 14$

$5 + x = -x - 11$

$5 + 2x = -11$

$2x = -16$

$x = -8$

The solution is -8.

14. $12x + 14 < 11x - 2$

$x + 14 < -2$

$x < -16$

The solution set is $(-\infty, -16)$.

15. $\dfrac{x}{5} - \dfrac{x}{4} = \dfrac{x - 2}{2}$

$20\left(\dfrac{x}{5} - \dfrac{x}{4}\right) = 20\left(\dfrac{x - 2}{2}\right)$

$4x - 5x = 10(x - 2)$

$-x = 10x - 20$

$-11x = -20$

$x = \dfrac{20}{11}$

The solution is $\dfrac{20}{11}$.

16. $12x - 12 = 8(x-1)$
$12x - 12 = 8x - 8$
$4x - 12 = -8$
$4x = 4$
$x = 1$
The solution is 1.

17. $2(x-3) > 70$
$2x - 6 > 70$
$2x > 76$
$x > 38$
The solution set is $(38, \infty)$.

18. $\qquad -3x - 4.7 = 11.8$
$10(-3x - 4.7) = 10(11.8)$
$-30x - 47 = 118$
$-30x = 165$
$x = -\dfrac{11}{2} = -5.5$
The solution set is $-\dfrac{11}{2} = -5.5$.

19. $-2(b-4) - (3b-1) = 5b + 3$
$-2b + 8 - 3b + 1 = 5b + 3$
$-5b + 9 = 5b + 3$
$-10b = -6$
$x = \dfrac{3}{5}$
The solution is $\dfrac{3}{5}$.

20. $8(x+3) < 7(x+5) + x$
$8x + 24 < 7x + 35 + x$
$8x + 24 < 8x + 35$
$24 < 35$ (True for all x)
The solution is the set of all real numbers; $(-\infty, \infty)$.

21. $\qquad \dfrac{3t+1}{8} = \dfrac{5+2t}{7} + 2$
$56\left(\dfrac{3t+1}{8}\right) = 56\left(\dfrac{5+2t}{7}\right) + 56(2)$
$7(3t+1) = 8(5+2t) + 112$
$21t + 7 = 40 + 16t + 112$
$21t + 7 = 16t + 152$
$5t = 145$
$t = 29$
The solution is 29.

22. $4(x-6) - x = 8(x-3) - 5x$
$4x - 24 - x = 8x - 24 - 5x$
$3x - 24 = 3x - 24$
$-24 = -24$ (True for all x)
The solution is the set of all real numbers.

23. $\qquad \dfrac{x+3}{12} + \dfrac{x-5}{15} < \dfrac{2}{3}$
$60\left(\dfrac{x+3}{12} + \dfrac{x-5}{15}\right) < 60\left(\dfrac{2}{3}\right)$
$5(x+3) + 4(x-5) < 20(2)$
$5x + 15 + 4x - 20 < 40$
$9x - 5 < 40$
$9x < 45$
$x < 5$
The solution set is $(-\infty, 5)$.

24. $\qquad \dfrac{y}{3} + \dfrac{y}{5} = \dfrac{y+3}{10}$
$30\left(\dfrac{y}{3}\right) + 30\left(\dfrac{y}{5}\right) = 30\left(\dfrac{y+3}{10}\right)$
$10y + 6y = 3(y+3)$
$16y = 3y + 9$
$13y = 9$
$y = \dfrac{9}{13}$
The solution is $\dfrac{9}{13}$.

25. $5(x-6) + 2x > 3(2x-1) - 4$
$5x - 30 + 2x > 6x - 3 - 4$
$7x - 30 > 6x - 7$
$x > 23$
The solution set is $(23, \infty)$.

26. $14(x-1) - 7x \le 2(3x-6) + 4$
$14x - 14 - 7x \le 6x - 12 + 4$
$7x - 14 \le 6x - 8$
$x \le 6$
The solution set is $(-\infty, 6]$.

27. $\dfrac{1}{4}(3x+2)-x \ge \dfrac{3}{8}(x-5)+2$

$8\left[\dfrac{1}{4}(3x+2)-x\right] \ge 8\left[\dfrac{3}{8}(x-5)+2\right]$

$2(3x+2)-8x \ge 3(x-5)+16$

$6x+4-8x \ge 3x-15+16$

$-2x+4 \ge 3x+1$

$3 \ge 5x$

$\dfrac{3}{5} \ge x$

$x \le \dfrac{3}{5}$

The solution set is $\left(-\infty, \dfrac{3}{5}\right]$.

28. $\dfrac{1}{3}(x-10)-4x > \dfrac{5}{6}(2x+1)-1$

$6\left[\dfrac{1}{3}(x-10)-4x\right] > 6\left[\dfrac{5}{6}(2x+1)-1\right]$

$2(x-10)-24x > 5(2x+1)-6$

$2x-20-24x > 10x+5-6$

$-22x-20 > 10x-1$

$-19 > 32x$

$-\dfrac{19}{32} > x \text{ or } x < -\dfrac{19}{32}$

The solution set is $\left(-\infty, -\dfrac{19}{32}\right)$.

Exercise Set 3.3

1. $C \cup D = \{2, 3, 4, 5, 6, 7\}$

3. $A \cap D = \{4, 6\}$

5. $A \cup B = \{\ldots, -2, -1, 0, 1, \ldots\}$

7. $B \cap D = \{5, 7\}$

9. $B \cup C = \{x \mid x \text{ is an odd interger or } x = 2 \text{ or } x = 4\}$

11. $A \cap C = \{2, 4\}$

13. $x < 5$ and $x > -2$

$-2 < x < 5$

The solution set is $(-2, 5)$.

15. $x+1 \ge 7$ and $3x-1 \ge 5$

$x \ge 6$ and $\quad 3x \ge 6$

$x \ge 6$ and $\quad x \ge 2$

$\qquad x \ge 6$

The solution set is $[6, \infty)$.

17. $4x+2 \le -10$ and $2x \le 0$

$4x \le -12$ and $\quad x \le 0$

$x \le -3$ and $\quad x \le 0$

$\qquad x \le -3$

The solution set is $(-\infty, -3]$.

19. $5 < x-6 < 11$

$11 < x < 17$

The solution set is $(11, 17)$.

21. $-2 \le 3x-5 \le 7$

$3 \le 3x \le 12$

$1 \le x \le 4$

The solution set is $[1, 4]$.

23. $1 \le \dfrac{2}{3}x+3 \le 4$

$-2 \le \dfrac{2}{3}x \le 1$

$-3 \le x \le \dfrac{3}{2}$

The solution set is $\left[-3, \dfrac{3}{2}\right]$.

25. $-5 \le \dfrac{x+1}{4} \le -2$

$-20 \le x+1 \le -8$

$-21 \le x \le -9$

The solution set is $[-21, -9]$.

27. $x < -1$ or $x > 0$

The solution set is $(-\infty, -1) \cup (0, \infty)$.

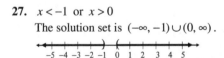

29. $-2x \le -4$ or $5x - 20 \ge 5$
$\quad\quad x \ge 2$ or $\quad\quad 5x \ge 25$
$\quad\quad x \ge 2$ or $\quad\quad x \ge 5$
$\quad\quad\quad\quad x \ge 2$
The solution set is $[2, \infty)$.

The solution set is $\left[\dfrac{3}{2}, 6\right]$.

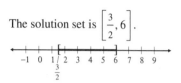

31. $3(x-1) < 12$ or $x + 7 > 10$
$\quad 3x - 3 < 12$ or $\quad\quad x > 3$
$\quad\quad 3x < 15$ or $\quad\quad x > 3$
$\quad\quad x < 5$ or $\quad\quad x > 3$
$\quad\quad$ All real numbers
The solution set is $(-\infty, \infty)$.

45. $\quad\dfrac{1}{2} < x - \dfrac{3}{4} < 2$
$\quad 4\left(\dfrac{1}{2}\right) < 4\left(x - \dfrac{3}{4}\right) < 4(2)$
$\quad\quad 2 < 4x - 3 < 8$
$\quad\quad 5 < 4x < 11$
$\quad\quad \dfrac{5}{4} < x < \dfrac{11}{4}$
The solution set is $\left(\dfrac{5}{4}, \dfrac{11}{4}\right)$.

33. Answers may very. One possibility follows:
When finding an intersection of two sets, we find the elements that the two sets have in common. Likewise, when we solve an *and*-compound inequality, we find the interval that the two inequalities phrases have in common.

47. $x + 3 \ge 3$ and $x + 3 \le 2$
$\quad\quad x \ge 0$ and $\quad x \le -1$
No solution exists.
The solution set is $\varnothing$.

35. $x < 2$ and $x > -1$
$\quad -1 < x < 2$
The solution set is $(-1, 2)$.

49. $3x \ge 5$ or $-x - 6 < 1$
$\quad\quad x \ge \dfrac{5}{3}$ or $\quad\quad -x < 7$
$\quad\quad x \ge \dfrac{5}{3}$ or $\quad\quad x > -7$
$\quad\quad\quad\quad x > -7$
The solution set is $(-7, \infty)$.

37. $x < 2$ or $x > -1$
All real numbers.
The solution set is $(-\infty, \infty)$.

39. $x \ge -5$ and $x \ge -1$
$\quad\quad x \ge -1$
The solution set is $[-1, \infty)$.

51. $0 < \dfrac{5 - 2x}{3} < 5$
$\quad 0 < 5 - 2x < 15$
$\quad \dfrac{-5}{-2} > \dfrac{-2x}{-2} > \dfrac{10}{-2}$
$\quad \dfrac{5}{2} > x > -5$
$\quad -5 < x < \dfrac{5}{2}$

41. $x \ge -5$ or $x \ge -1$
$\quad\quad x \ge -5$
The solution set is $[-5, \infty)$.

The solution set is $\left(-5, \dfrac{5}{2}\right)$.

43. $0 \le 2x - 3 \le 9$
$\quad 3 \le 2x \le 12$
$\quad \dfrac{3}{2} \le x \le 6$

53. $-6 < 3(x-2) \le 8$
$-6 < 3x - 6 \le 8$
$0 < 3x \le 14$
$0 < x \le \dfrac{14}{3}$

The solution set is $\left(0, \dfrac{14}{3}\right]$.

55. $-x + 5 > 6$ and $1 + 2x \le -5$
$-x > 1$ and $2x \le -6$
$x < -1$ and $x \le -3$
$x \le -3$
The solution set is $(-\infty, -3]$.

57. $3x + 2 \le 5$ or $7x > 29$
$3x \le 3$ or $x > \dfrac{29}{7}$
$x \le 1$ or $x > \dfrac{29}{7}$

The solution set is $(-\infty, 1] \cup \left(\dfrac{29}{7}, \infty\right)$.

59. $5 - x > 7$ and $2x + 3 \ge 13$
$-x > 2$ and $2x \ge 10$
$x < -2$ and $x \ge 5$
No solution exists.
The solution set is $\varnothing$.

61. $-\dfrac{1}{2} \le \dfrac{4x-1}{6} < \dfrac{5}{6}$
$6\left(-\dfrac{1}{2}\right) \le 6\left(\dfrac{4x-1}{6}\right) < 6\left(\dfrac{5}{6}\right)$
$-3 \le 4x - 1 < 5$
$-2 \le 4x < 6$
$-\dfrac{1}{2} \le x < \dfrac{3}{2}$

The solution set is $\left[-\dfrac{1}{2}, \dfrac{3}{2}\right)$.

63. $\dfrac{1}{15} < \dfrac{8-3x}{15} < \dfrac{4}{5}$
$15\left(\dfrac{1}{15}\right) < 15\left(\dfrac{8-3x}{15}\right) < 15\left(\dfrac{4}{5}\right)$
$1 < 8 - 3x < 12$
$-7 < -3x < 4$
$-\dfrac{4}{3} < x < \dfrac{7}{3}$

The solution set is $\left(-\dfrac{4}{3}, \dfrac{7}{3}\right)$.

65. $0.3 < 0.2x - 0.9 < 1.5$
$1.2 < 0.2x < 2.4$
$6 < x < 12$
The solution set is $(6, 12)$.

67. a. y_2 is between y_1 and y_3 for values of x between -5 and 2.5. That is,
$y_1 < y_2 < y_3$
$-5 < x < 2.5$
The solution set is $(-5, \, 2.5)$.

b. y_2 is below y_1 when x is larger than 2.5. y_2 is above y_3 when x is smaller than -5. That is,
$y_2 < y_1$ or $y_2 > y_3$
$x > 2.5$ or $x < -5$
The solution set is $(-\infty, \, -5) \cup (2.5, \, \infty)$.

69. a. y_2 is between y_1 and y_3 (inclusive) for values of x between 2 and 9 (inclusive). That is,
$y_1 \le y_2 \le y_3$
$2 \le x \le 9$
The solution set is $[2, \, 9]$.

b. y_2 is y_1 and below when x is 2 and smaller. y_2 is y_3 and above when x is 9 and larger. Therefore,
$y_2 < y_1$ or $y_2 > y_3$
$x < 2$ or $x > 9$
The solution set is $(-\infty, \, 2] \cup [9, \, \infty)$.

71. $|-7| - |19| = 7 - 19 = -12$

73. $-(-6) - |-10| = 6 - 10 = -4$

75. $|x| = 7$
$x = -7, 7$

77. $|x| = 0$
$x = 0$

79. $-29 \le C \le 35$
$-29 \le \dfrac{5}{9}(F - 32) \le 35$
$-52.5 \le F - 32 \le 63$
$-20.2 \le F \le 95$
$-20.2^\circ \le F \le 95^\circ$

81. Let x = Christian's score on the final exam.
$70 \le \dfrac{68 + 65 + 75 + 78 + 2x}{6} \le 79$
$70 \le \dfrac{286 + 2x}{6} \le 79$
$420 \le 286 + 2x \le 474$
$134 \le 2x \le 188$
$67 \le x \le 94$

If Christian scores between 67 and 94 inclusive on his final exam, he will receive a C in the course.

83. The years that the consumption of pork was greater than 48 pounds per person were 1994, 1995, 1998, and 1999.

The years that the consumption of chicken was greater than 48 pounds per person were 1994, 1995, 1996, 1997, 1998, 1999, 2000, and 2001.

The years in common are 1994, 1995, 1998, and 1999.

85. $2x - 3 < 3x + 1 < 4x - 5$
$2x - 3 < 3x + 1$ and $3x + 1 < 4x - 5$
$-x < 4$ and $-x < -6$
$x > -4$ and $x > 6$
$x > 6$
The solution set is $(6, \infty)$.

87. $-3(x - 2) \le 3 - 2x \le 10 - 3x$
$-3x + 6 \le 3 - 2x$ and $3 - 2x \le 10 - 3x$
$-x \le -3$ and $x \le 7$
$x \ge 3$
$3 \le x \le 7$
The solution set is $[3, 7]$.

89. $5x - 8 < 2(2 + x) < -2(1 + 2x)$
$5x - 8 < 4 + 2x$ and $4 + 2x < -2 - 4x$
$3x < 12$ and $6x < -6$
$x < 4$ and $x < -1$
$x < -1$
The solution set is $(-\infty, -1)$.

Mental Math 3.4

1. $|-7| = 7$

2. $|-8| = 8$

3. $-|5| = -5$

4. $-|10| = -10$

5. $-|-6| = -6$

6. $-|-3| = -3$

7. $|-3| + |-2| + |-7| = 3 + 2 + 7 = 12$

8. $|-1| + |-6| + |-8| = 1 + 6 + 8 = 15$

Exercise Set 3.4

1. $|x| = 7$
$x = 7$ or $x = -7$
The solution set is $\{-7, 7\}$.

3. $|3x| = 12.6$
$3x = 12.6$ or $3x = -12.6$
$x = 4.2$ or $x = -4.2$
The solution set is $\{-4.2, 4.2\}$.

5. $|2x - 5| = 9$
$2x - 5 = 9$ or $2x - 5 = -9$
$2x = 14$ or $2x = -4$
$x = 7$ or $x = -2$
The solution set is $\{-2, 7\}$.

7. $\left|\dfrac{x}{2}-3\right|=1$

$$\dfrac{x}{2}-3=1 \quad \text{or} \quad \dfrac{x}{2}-3=-1$$

$$2\left(\dfrac{x}{2}-3\right)=2(1) \quad \text{or} \quad 2\left(\dfrac{x}{2}-3\right)=2(-1)$$

$$x-6=2 \quad \text{or} \quad x-6=-2$$

$$x=8 \quad \text{or} \quad x=4$$

The solution set is $\{4, 8\}$.

9. $|z|+4=9$

$$|z|=5$$

$$z=-5 \text{ or } z=-5$$

The solution set is $\{-5, 5\}$.

11. $|3x|+5=14$

$$|3x|=9$$

$$3x=9 \text{ or } 3x=-9$$

$$x=3 \text{ or } x=-3$$

The solution set is $\{-3, 3\}$.

13. $|2x|=0$

$$2x=0$$

$$x=0$$

The solution set is $\{0\}$.

15. $|4n+1|+10=4$

$$|4n+1|=-6 \text{ which is impossible.}$$

The solution set is $\varnothing$.

17. $|5x-1|=0$

$$5x-1=0$$

$$5x=1$$

$$x=\dfrac{1}{5}$$

The solution set is $\left\{\dfrac{1}{5}\right\}$.

19. $|x|=5$

21. $|5x-7|=|3x+11|$

$$5x-7=3x+11 \quad \text{or} \quad 5x-7=-(3x+11)$$

$$2x=18 \quad \text{or} \quad 5x-7=-3x-11$$

$$x=9 \quad \text{or} \quad 8x=-4$$

$$x=-\dfrac{1}{2}$$

The solution set is $\left\{-\dfrac{1}{2}, 9\right\}$.

23. $|z+8|=|z-3|$

$$z+8=z-3 \quad \text{or} \quad z+8=-(z-3)$$

$$8=-3 \quad \text{or} \quad z+8=-z+3$$

$$\uparrow \qquad\qquad 2z=-5$$

$$\text{False} \qquad\qquad z=-\dfrac{5}{2}$$

The solution set is $\left\{-\dfrac{5}{2}\right\}$.

25. Answers may vary. One possibility follows:
If the equation is $|x|=a$ (positive constant), then we solve $x=a$ or $x=-a$. If the equation is $|x|=|y|$, then we solve $x=y$ or $x=-y$.

27. $y_1=|2x-3|$ and $y_2=5$ intersect at the points $(-1, 5)$ and $(4, 5)$, indicating that the solution of $|2x-3|=5$ is $x=-1$ or $x=4$. Thus, the solution set is $\{-1, 4\}$.

29. $y_1=|x-4|$ and $y_2=|1-x|$ intersect at the point $(2.5, 1.5)$, indicating that the solution of $|x-4|=|1-x|$ is $x=2.5$. Thus, the solution set is $\{2.5\}$.

31. $|x|=4$

$$x=4 \text{ or } x=-4$$

The solution set is $\{-4, 4\}$.

33. $|z|=-2$ is impossible.
The solution set is $\varnothing$.

35. $|7-3x|=7$

$$7-3x=7 \quad \text{or} \quad 7-3x=-7$$

$$-3x=0 \quad \text{or} \quad -3x=-14$$

$$x=0 \quad \text{or} \quad x=\dfrac{14}{3}$$

The solution set is $\left\{0, \dfrac{14}{3}\right\}$.

37. $|6x|-1=11$

$$|6x|=12$$

$$6x=12 \text{ or } 6x=-12$$

$$x=2 \text{ or } x=-2$$

The solution set is $\{-2, 2\}$.

39. $|x-3|+3=7$

$\qquad |x-3|=4$

$\qquad x-3=4 \ \text{ or } \ x-3=-4$

$\qquad x=7 \ \text{ or } \quad x=-1$

The solution set is $\{-1, 7\}$.

41. $\left|\dfrac{z}{4}+5\right|=-7$ is impossible.

The solution set is $\varnothing$.

43. $|9v-3|=-8$ is impossible.

The solution set is $\varnothing$.

45. $|8n+1|=0$

$\qquad 8n+1=0$

$\qquad 8n=-1 \ \text{so } n=-\dfrac{1}{8}$

The solution set is $\left\{-\dfrac{1}{8}\right\}$.

47. $|1+6c|-7=-3$

$\qquad |1+6c|=4$

$\qquad 1+6c=4 \ \text{ or } \ 1+6c=-4$

$\qquad 6c=3 \ \text{ or } \qquad 6c=-5$

$\qquad c=\dfrac{1}{2} \ \text{ or } \qquad c=-\dfrac{5}{6}$

The solution set is $\left\{-\dfrac{5}{6}, \dfrac{1}{2}\right\}$.

49. $|5x+1|=11$

$\qquad 5x+1=11 \ \text{ or } \ 5x+1=-11$

$\qquad 5x=10 \ \text{ or } \qquad 5x=-12$

$\qquad x=2 \ \text{ or } \qquad x=-\dfrac{12}{5}$

The solution set is $\left\{-\dfrac{12}{5}, 2\right\}$.

51. $|4x-2|=|-10|$

$\qquad |4x-2|=10$

$\qquad 4x-2=10 \ \text{ or } \ 4x-2=-10$

$\qquad 4x=12 \ \text{ or } \qquad 4x=-8$

$\qquad x=3 \ \text{ or } \qquad x=-2$

The solution set is $\{-2, 3\}$.

53. $|5x+1|=|4x-7|$

$\qquad 5x+1=4x-7 \ \text{ or } \ 5x+1=-(4x-7)$

$\qquad x=-8 \qquad \text{ or } \ 5x+1=-4x+7$

$\qquad\qquad\qquad\qquad\qquad 9x=6$

$\qquad\qquad\qquad\qquad\qquad x=\dfrac{2}{3}$

The solution set is $\left\{-8, \dfrac{2}{3}\right\}$.

55. $|6+2x|=-|-7|$

$\qquad |6+2x|=-7$ which is impossible.

The solution set is $\varnothing$.

57. $|2x-6|=|10-2x|$

$\qquad 2x-6=10-2x \ \text{ or } \ 2x-6=-(10-2x)$

$\qquad 4x=16 \qquad \text{ or } \ 2x-6=-10+2x$

$\qquad x=4 \qquad \text{ or } \qquad -6=-10 \ \text{ False}$

The solution set is $\{4\}$.

59. $\left|\dfrac{2x-5}{3}\right|=7$

$\qquad \dfrac{2x-5}{3}=7 \quad \text{ or } \ \dfrac{2x-5}{3}=-7$

$\qquad 2x-5=21 \ \text{ or } \ 2x-5=-21$

$\qquad 2x=26 \ \text{ or } \qquad 2x=-16$

$\qquad x=13 \ \text{ or } \qquad x=-8$

The solution set is $\{-8, 13\}$.

61. $2+|5n|=17$

$\qquad |5n|=15$

$\qquad 5n=15 \ \text{ or } \ 5n=-15$

$\qquad n=3 \ \text{ or } \quad n=-3$

The solution set is $\{-3, 3\}$.

63. $\left|\dfrac{2x-1}{3}\right|=|-5|$

$\qquad \left|\dfrac{2x-1}{3}\right|=5$

$\qquad \dfrac{2x-1}{3}=5 \quad \text{ or } \ \dfrac{2x-1}{3}=-5$

$\qquad 2x-1=15 \ \text{ or } \ 2x-1=-15$

$\qquad 2x=16 \quad \text{ or } \qquad 2x=-14$

$\qquad x=8 \quad \text{ or } \qquad x=-7$

The solution set is $\{-7, 8\}$.

65. $|2y-3|=|9-4y|$

$\qquad 2y-3=9-4y \ \text{ or } \ 2y-3=-(9-4y)$

$\qquad 6y=12 \qquad \text{ or } \ 2y-3=-9+4y$

$\qquad y=2 \qquad \text{ or } \quad -2y=-6$

$\qquad\qquad\qquad\qquad\qquad y=3$

The solution set is $\{2, 3\}$.

67. $\left|\dfrac{3n+2}{8}\right| = |-1|$

$\left|\dfrac{3n+2}{8}\right| = 1$

$\dfrac{3n+2}{8} = 1$ or $\dfrac{3n+2}{8} = -1$

$3n+2 = 8$ or $3n+2 = -8$

$3n = 6$ or $3n = -10$

$n = 2$ or $n = -\dfrac{10}{3}$

The solution set is $\left\{-\dfrac{10}{3}, 2\right\}$.

69. $|x+4| = |7-x|$

$x+4 = 7-x$ or $x+4 = -(7-x)$

$2x = 3$ or $x+4 = -7+x$

$x = \dfrac{3}{2}$ or $4 = -7$ False

The solution set is $\left\{\dfrac{3}{2}\right\}$.

71. $\left|\dfrac{8c-7}{3}\right| = -|-5|$

$\left|\dfrac{8c-7}{3}\right| = -5$ which is impossible.

The solution set is $\varnothing$.

73. Answers may vary. One possibility follows:
Many absolute value equations have two solutions because $|X| = a$ (positive) is equivalent to $X = a$ or $X = -a$, which results in two solutions.

75. 33% of cheese consumption came from cheddar cheese.

77. $32\% \cdot (120 \text{ pounds}) = 0.32(120 \text{ pounds})$
$= 38.4 \text{ pounds}$
We might expect they consumed 38.4 pounds of mozzarella.

79. Answers may vary.
All integers are solutions of $|x| \geq -2$.

81. $|y| < 0$
This equation has no solution; $\varnothing$.

83. $|x| = 2$

85. $|2x-1| = 4$

87. a. $|ax+b| = c$ will have one solution if $c = 0$.

 b. $|ax+b| = c$ will have no solution if $c < 0$.

 c. $|ax+b| = c$ will have two solutions if $c > 0$.

89. Graph $y_1 = |-7.6x+2.6|$ and $y_2 = 1.9$ in a $[-2, 2, 1]$ by $[-5, 5, 1]$ viewing window and find the intersection points.

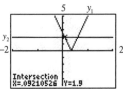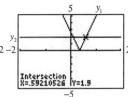

Rounding to two decimal places, y_1 and y_2 intersect at the points $(0.09, 1.9)$ and $(0.59, 1.9)$, indicating that the solution of $|-7.6x+2.6| = 1.9$ is $x \approx 0.09$ or $x \approx 0.59$. The solution set is $\{0.09, 0.59\}$.

91. Graph $y_1 = -1.2 + |5x+12.1|$ and $y_2 = -|x+7.3| + 10$ in a standard viewing window and find the intersection points.

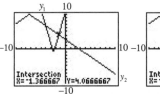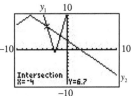

Rounding to two decimal places, y_1 and y_2 intersect at the points $(1.37, 4.07)$ and $(-4, 6.7)$, indicating that the solution of $-1.2 + |5x+12.1| = -|x+7.3| + 10$ is $x \approx -1.37$ or $x = -4$. The solution set is $\{-4, -1.37\}$.

Mental Math 3.5

1. D

2. E

3. C

4. B

5. A

Exercise Set 3.5

1. $|x| \le 4$
$-4 \le x \le 4$
The solution set is $[-4, 4]$.
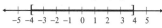

3. $|x-3| < 2$
$-2 < x-3 < 2$
$1 < x < 5$
The solution set is $(1, 5)$.

5. $|x+3| < 2$
$-2 < x+3 < 2$
$-5 < x < -1$
The solution set is $(-5, -1)$.
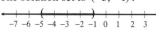

7. $|2x+7| \le 13$
$-13 \le 2x+7 \le 13$
$-20 \le 2x \le 6$
$-10 \le x \le 3$
The solution set is $[-10, 3]$.

9. $|x|+7 \le 12$
$|x| \le 5$
$-5 \le x \le 5$
The solution set is $[-5, 5]$.

11. $|3x-1| < -5$
No real solutions; $\varnothing$

13. $|x-6|-7 \le -1$
$|x-6| \le 6$
$-6 \le x-6 \le 6$
$0 \le x \le 12$
The solution set is $[0, 12]$.

15. $|x| > 3$
$x < -3$ or $x > 3$
The solution set is $(-\infty, -3) \cup (3, \infty)$.

17. $|x+10| \ge 14$
$x+10 \le -14$ or $x+10 \ge 14$
$x \le -24$ or $x \ge 4$
The solution set is $(-\infty, -24] \cup [4, \infty)$.

19. $|x|+2 > 6$
$|x| > 4$
$x < -4$ or $x > 4$
The solution set is $(-\infty, -4) \cup (4, \infty)$.
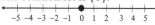

21. $|5x| > -4$ is always true.
All real numbers
The solution set is $(-\infty, \infty)$.

23. $|6x-8|+3 > 7$
$|6x-8| > 4$
$6x-8 < -4$ or $6x-8 > 4$
$6x < 4$ or $6x > 12$
$x < \dfrac{2}{3}$ or $x > 2$
The solution set is $\left(-\infty, \dfrac{2}{3}\right) \cup (2, \infty)$.
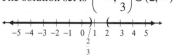

25. $|x| \le 0$
$|x| = 0$
$x = 0$
The solution set is $\{0\}$.

113

27. $|8x+3| > 0$ only excludes $|8x+3| = 0$

$8x+3 < 0$ or $8x+3 > 0$

$8x < -3$ or $8x > -3$

$x < -\dfrac{3}{8}$ or $x > -\dfrac{3}{8}$

The solution set is $\left(-\infty, -\dfrac{3}{8}\right) \cup \left(-\dfrac{3}{8}, \infty\right)$.

29. $|x| \le 2$

$-2 \le x \le 2$

The solution set is $[-2, 2]$.

31. $|y| > 1$

$y < -1$ or $y > 1$

The solution set is $(-\infty, -1) \cup (1, \infty)$.

33. $|x-3| < 8$

$-8 < x-3 < 8$

$-5 < x < 11$

The solution set is $(-5, 11)$.

35. $|0.6x - 3| > 0.6$

$0.6x - 3 < -0.6$ or $0.6x - 3 > 0.6$

$0.6x < -2.4$ or $\quad 0.6x > 3.6$

$x < 4 \quad$ or $\quad\quad x > 6$

The solution set is $(-\infty, 4) \cup (6, \infty)$.

37. $5 + |x| \le 2$

$|x| \le -3$

No real solution; $\varnothing$

39. $|x| > -4$

All real numbers; $(-\infty, \infty)$

41. $|2x-7| \le 11$

$-11 \le 2x - 7 \le 11$

$-4 \le 2x \le 18$

$-2 \le x \le 9$

The solution set is $[-2, 9]$.

43. $|x+5| + 2 \ge 8$

$|x+5| \ge 6$

$x+5 \le -6$ or $x+5 \ge 6$

$x \le -11$ or $\quad x \ge 1$

The solution set is $(-\infty, -11] \cup [1, \infty)$.

45. $|x| > 0$

$x < 0$ or $x > 0$

The solution set is $(-\infty, 0) \cup (0, \infty)$.

47. $9 + |x| > 7$

$|x| > -2$

All real numbers; $(-\infty, \infty)$

49. $6 + |4x-1| \le 9$

$|4x-1| \le 3$

$-3 \le 4x - 1 \le 3$

$-2 \le 4x \le 4$

$-\dfrac{1}{2} \le x \le 1$

The solution set is $\left[-\dfrac{1}{2}, 1\right]$.

51. $\left|\dfrac{2}{3}x + 1\right| > 1$

$\dfrac{2}{3}x + 1 < -1$ or $\dfrac{2}{3}x + 1 > 1$

$\dfrac{2}{3}x < -2$ or $\quad \dfrac{2}{3}x > 0$

$x < -3$ or $\quad\quad x > 0$

The solution set is $(-\infty, -3) \cup (0, \infty)$.

53. $|5x+3| < -6$

No real solution; $\varnothing$

55. $|8x+3| \geq 0$

All real numbers; $(-\infty, \infty)$

57. $|1+3x|+4 < 5$

$|1+3x| < 1$

$-1 < 1+3x < 1$

$-2 < 3x < 0$

$-\dfrac{2}{3} < x < 0$

The solution set is $\left(-\dfrac{2}{3}, 0\right)$.

59. $\left|\dfrac{x+6}{3}\right| > 2$

$\dfrac{x+6}{3} < -2$ or $\dfrac{x+6}{3} > 2$

$x+6 < -6$ or $x+6 > 6$

$x < -12$ or $x > 0$

The solution set is $(-\infty, -12) \cup (0, \infty)$.

61. $-15+|2x-7| \leq -6$

$|2x-7| \leq 9$

$-9 \leq 2x-7 \leq 9$

$-2 \leq 2x \leq 16$

$-1 \leq x \leq 8$

The solution set is $[-1, 8]$.

63. $\left|2x+\dfrac{3}{4}\right|-7 \leq -2$

$\left|2x+\dfrac{3}{4}\right| \leq 5$

$-5 \leq 2x+\dfrac{3}{4} \leq 5$

$-20 \leq 8x+3 \leq 20$

$-23 \leq 8x \leq 17$

$-\dfrac{23}{8} \leq x \leq \dfrac{17}{8}$

The solution set is $\left[-\dfrac{23}{8}, \dfrac{17}{8}\right]$.

65. $|2x-3| < 7$

$-7 < 2x-3 < 7$

$-4 < 2x < 10$

$-2 < x < 5$

The solution set is $(-2, 5)$.

67. $|2x-3| = 7$

$2x-3 = 7$ or $2x-3 = -7$

$2x = 10$ or $2x = -4$

$x = 5$ or $x = -2$

The solution set is $\{-2, 5\}$.

69. $|x-5| \geq 12$

$x-5 \leq -12$ or $x-5 \geq 12$

$x \leq -7$ or $x \geq 17$

The solution set is $(-\infty, -7] \cup [17, \infty)$.

71. $|9+4x| = 0$

$9+4x = 0$

$4x = -9$

$x = -\dfrac{9}{4}$

The solution set is $\left\{-\dfrac{9}{4}\right\}$.

73. $|2x+1|+4 < 7$

$|2x+1| < 3$

$-3 < 2x+1 < 3$

$-4 < 2x < 2$

$-2 < x < 1$

The solution set is $(-2, 1)$.

75. $|3x-5|+4 = 5$

$|3x-5| = 1$

$3x-5 = 1$ or $3x-5 = -1$

$3x = 6$ or $3x = 4$

$x = 2$ or $x = \dfrac{4}{3}$

The solution set is $\left\{\dfrac{4}{3}, 2\right\}$.

77. $|x+11| = -1$ is impossible.

The solution set is $\varnothing$.

79. $\left|\dfrac{2x-1}{3}\right| = 6$

$\dfrac{2x-1}{3} = 6 \quad$ or $\quad \dfrac{2x-1}{3} = -6$

$2x - 1 = 18 \quad$ or $\quad 2x - 1 = -18$

$2x = 19 \quad$ or $\qquad 2x = -17$

$x = \dfrac{19}{2} \quad$ or $\qquad x = -\dfrac{17}{2}$

The solution set is $\left\{ -\dfrac{17}{2}, \dfrac{19}{2} \right\}$.

81. $\left|\dfrac{3x-5}{6}\right| > 5$

$\dfrac{3x-5}{6} < -5 \quad$ or $\quad \dfrac{3x-5}{6} > 5$

$3x - 5 < -30 \quad$ or $\quad 3x - 5 > 30$

$3x < -25 \quad$ or $\qquad 3x > 35$

$x < -\dfrac{25}{3} \quad$ or $\qquad x > \dfrac{35}{3}$

The solution set is $\left(-\infty, -\dfrac{25}{3} \right) \cup \left(\dfrac{35}{3}, \infty \right)$.

83. a. $y_1 = |x-3| - 2$ and $y_2 = 6$ intersect at the points $(-5, 6)$ and $(11, 6)$, indicating that the solution of $|x-3| - 2 = 6$ is $x = -5$ or $x = 11$. Thus, the solution set is $\{-5, 11\}$.

b. The graph of $y_1 = |x-3| - 2$ is below the graph of $y_2 = 6$ for x values between -5 and 11. Thus, the solution of $|x-3| - 2 < 6$ is $(-5, 11)$.

c. The graph of $y_1 = |x-3| - 2$ is at or above the graph of $y_2 = 6$ for x values from -5 to 11. Thus, the solution of $|x-3| - 2 \geq 6$ is $(-\infty, -5] \cup [11, \infty)$.

85. a. $y_1 = |x+2| - 10$ and $y_2 = -4$ intersect at the points $(-8, -4)$ and $(4, -4)$, indicating that the solution of $|x+2| - 10 = -4$ is $x = -8$ or $x = 4$. Thus, the solution set is $\{-8, 4\}$.

b. The graph of $y_1 = |x+2| - 10$ is at or below the graph of $y_2 = -4$ for x values from -8 to 4. Thus, the solution of $|x+2| - 10 \leq -4$ is $[-8, 4]$.

c. The graph of $y_1 = |x+2| - 10$ is above the graph of $y_2 = -4$ for x values between -8 to 4. Thus, the solution of $|x+2| - 10 > -4$ is $(-\infty, -8) \cup (4, \infty)$.

87. $P(\text{rolling a 2}) = \dfrac{1}{6}$

89. $P(\text{rolling a 7}) = 0$

91. $P(\text{rolling a 1 or 3}) = \dfrac{2}{6} = \dfrac{1}{3}$

93.
$3x - 4y = 12$
$3(2) - 4y = 12$
$6 - 4y = 12$
$-4y = 6$
$y = -\dfrac{3}{2} = -1.5$

95.
$3x - 4y = 12$
$3x - 4(-3) = 12$
$3x + 12 = 12$
$3x = 0$
$x = 0$

97. $|x| < 7$

99. $|x| \leq 5$

101. Answers may vary. One possibility follows: When solving $|x-3| = 5$, we convert the equation to an *or*-compound equation $x - 3 = -5$ or $x - 3 = 5$. When solving $|x-3| < 5$, we convert the equation to an *and*-compound inequality $x - 3 > -5$ and $x - 3 < 5$.

103. $|3.5 - x| < 0.05$
$-0.05 < 3.5 - x < 0.05$
$-3.55 < -x < -3.45$
$3.55 > x > 3.45$
$3.45 < x < 3.55$

Exercise Set 3.6

1. $x < 2$

Graph the boundary line $x = 2$ as a dashed line because the inequality symbol is <.

Test: (0, 0)
$0 < 2$ True

Shade the half-plane that contains (0, 0).

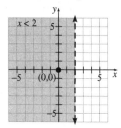

3. $x - y \geq 7$

Graph the boundary line $x - y = 7$ as a solid line because the inequality symbol is $\geq$.

Test: (0, 0)
$0 - 0 \geq 7$
$0 \geq 7$ False

Shade the half-plane that does not contain (0, 0).

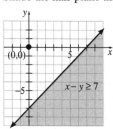

5. $3x + y > 6$

Graph the boundary line $3x + y = 6$ as a dashed line because the inequality symbol is >.

Test: (0, 0)
$3(0) + 0 > 6$
$0 > 6$ False

Shade the half-plane that does not contain (0, 0).

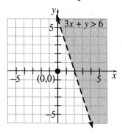

7. $y \leq -2x$

Graph the boundary line $y = -2x$ as a solid line because the inequality symbol is $\leq$.

Test: (1, 1)
$1 \leq -2(1)$
$1 \leq -2$ False

Shade the half-plane that does not contain (1, 1).

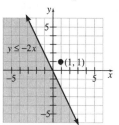

9. $2x + 4y \geq 8$

Graph the boundary line $2x + 4y = 8$ as a solid line because the inequality symbol is $\geq$.

Test: (0, 0)
$2(0) + 4(0) \geq 8$
$0 \geq 8$ False

Shade the half-plane that does not contain (0, 0).

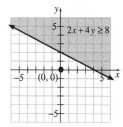

11. $5x + 3y > -15$

Graph the boundary line $5x + 3y = -15$ as a dashed line because the inequality symbol is >.

Test: (0, 0)
$5(0) + 3(0) > -15$
$0 > -15$ True

Shade the half-plane that contains (0, 0).

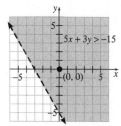

13. Answers may vary. One possibility follows: A dashed boundary line should be used when the inequality symbol is < or >. A solid boundary line should be used when the inequality symbol is ≤ or ≥.

15. $x \geq 3$ and $y \leq -2$

Graph each inequality. The intersection of the two inequalities is all points common to both regions, as shown by the shading in the graph below.

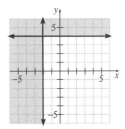

17. $x \leq -2$ or $y \geq 4$

Graph each inequality. The union of the two inequalities is both shaded regions, as shown by the shading in the graph below.

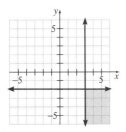

19. $x - y < 3$ and $x > 4$

Graph each inequality. The intersection of the two inequalities is all points common to both regions, as shown by the shading in the graph below.

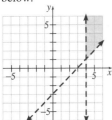

21. $x + y \leq 3$ or $x - y \geq 5$

Graph each inequality. The union of the two inequalities is both shaded regions, as shown by the shading in the graph below.

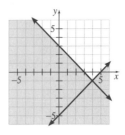

23. $y \geq -2$

Graph the boundary line $y = -2$ as a solid line because the inequality symbol is ≥.

Test: $(0, 0)$
$$0 \geq -2 \quad \text{True}$$

Shade the half-plane that contains $(0, 0)$.

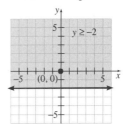

25. $x - 6y < 12$

Graph the boundary line $x - 6y = 12$ as a dashed line because the inequality symbol is <.

Test: $(0, 0)$
$$0 - 6(0) < 12$$
$$0 > 12 \quad \text{True}$$

Shade the half-plane that contains $(0, 0)$.

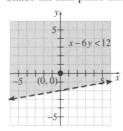

27. $x > 5$

Graph the boundary line $x = 5$ as a dashed line because the inequality symbol is >.

Test: $(0, 0)$
$$0 > 5 \quad \text{False}$$

Shade the half-plane that does not contain $(0, 0)$.

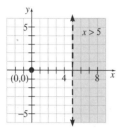

29. $-2x + y \leq 4$

Graph the boundary line $-2x + y = 4$ as a solid line because the inequality symbol is $\leq$.

Test: (0, 0)
$$-2(0) + 0 \leq 4$$
$$0 \leq 4 \quad \text{True}$$

Shade the half-plane that contains (0, 0).

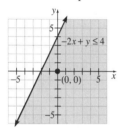

31. $x - 3y < 0$

Graph the boundary line $x - 3y = 0$ as a dashed line because the inequality symbol is <.

Test: (0, 1)
$$0 - 3(1) < 0$$
$$-3 < 0 \quad \text{True}$$

Shade the half-plane that contains (0, 1).

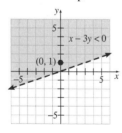

33. $3x - 2y \leq 12$

Graph the boundary line $3x - 2y = 12$ as a solid line because the inequality symbol is $\leq$.

Test: (0, 0)
$$3(0) - 2(0) \leq 12$$
$$0 \leq 12 \quad \text{True}$$

Shade the half-plane that contains (0, 0).

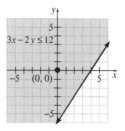

35. $x - y > 2$ or $y < 5$

Graph each inequality. The union of the two inequalities is both shaded regions, as shown by the shading in the graph below.

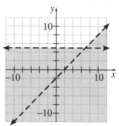

37. $x + y \leq 1$ and $y \leq -1$

Graph each inequality. The intersection of the two inequalities is all points common to both regions, as shown by the shading in the graph below.

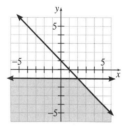

39. $2x + y > 4$ or $x \geq 1$

Graph each inequality. The union of the two inequalities is both shaded regions, as shown by the shading in the graph below.

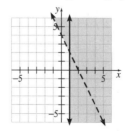

119

41. $x \geq -2$ and $x \leq 1$

Graph each inequality. The intersection of the two inequalities is all points common to both regions, as shown by the shading in the graph below.

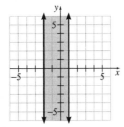

43. $x + y \leq 0$ or $3x - 6y \geq 12$

Graph each inequality. The union of the two inequalities is both shaded regions, as shown by the shading in the graph below.

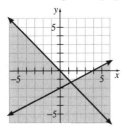

45. $2x - y > 3$ and $x > 0$

Graph each inequality. The intersection of the two inequalities is all points common to both regions, as shown by the shading in the graph below.

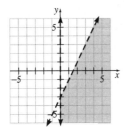

47. D

49. A

51. The boundary line is the vertical line $x = 2$. It is solid, so the inequality symbol must be either $\leq$ or $\geq$. Since the shaded region is to the right of the boundary, the inequality is $x \geq 2$.

53. The boundary line is the horizontal line $y = -3$. It is solid, so the inequality symbol must be either $\leq$ or $\geq$. Since the shaded region is below the boundary, the inequality is $y \leq -3$.

55. The boundary line is the horizontal line $y = 4$. It is dashed, so the inequality symbol must be either $<$ or $>$. Since the shaded region is above the boundary, the inequality is $y > 4$.

57. The boundary line is the vertical line $x = 1$. It is dashed, so the inequality symbol must be either $<$ or $>$. Since the shaded region is to the right of the boundary, the inequality is $x < 1$.

59. $2^3 = 2 \cdot 2 \cdot 2 = 8$

61. $-5^2 = -(5 \cdot 5) = -25$

63. $(-2)^4 = (-2)(-2)(-2)(-2) = 16$

65. $\left(\dfrac{3}{5}\right)^3 = \left(\dfrac{3}{5}\right)\left(\dfrac{3}{5}\right)\left(\dfrac{3}{5}\right) = \dfrac{27}{125}$

67. Domain: [1, 5]
Range: [1, 3]
Not a function since it fails the vertical line test.

69. The statement "study at most 20 hours" translates into $x \leq 20$. The statement "work at least 10 hours" translates into $y \geq 10$. Thus, we have the conjunction $x \leq 20$ and $y \geq 10$.

Graph each inequality. The intersection of the two inequalities is all points common to both regions, as shown by the shading in the graph below.

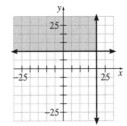

71. $\begin{cases} x \geq 0 \\ y \geq 0 \\ 2x + 4y \leq 40 \end{cases}$

Graph each inequality. The intersection of the three inequalities is all points common to all three regions, as shown by the shading in the graph below.

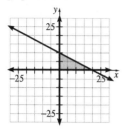

Chapter 3 Review

1. $4(x-6)+3=27$

   Algebraic Solution:
   $4(x-6)+3=27$
   $4x-24+3=27$
   $4x-21=27$
   $4x=48$
   $x=12$
   The solution is 12.

   Graphical Solution:
   Graph $y_1 = 4(x-6)+3$ and $y_2 = 27$ in a $[-50, 50, 5]$ by $[-50, 50, 5]$ viewing window and find the intersection point.

   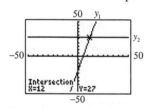

   The point of intersection $(12, 27)$ indicates that the solution is 12.

2. $15(x+2)-6=18$

   Algebraic Solution:
   $15(x+2)-6=18$
   $15x+30-6=18$
   $15x+24=18$
   $15x=-6$
   $x=\dfrac{-6}{15}=-\dfrac{2}{5}=-0.4$

   The solution is $-\dfrac{2}{5}=-0.4$.

Graphical Solution:
Graph $y_1 = 15(x+2)-6$ and $y_2 = 18$ in a $[-20, 20, 5]$ by $[-20, 20, 5]$ viewing window and find the intersection point.

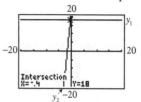

The point of intersection $(-0.4,\ 18)$ indicates that the solution is $-0.4 = -\dfrac{2}{5}$.

3. $5x+15=3(x+2)+2(x-3)$

   Algebraic Solution:
   $5x+15=3x+6+2x-6$
   $5x+15=5x$
   $15=0$ False
   This equation is a false statement no matter what value the variable x might have. The equation is a contradiction and has no solution. The solution set is $\varnothing$ or { }.

   Graphical Solution:
   Graph $y_1 = 5x+15$ and $y_2 = 3(x+2)+2(x-3)$ in a $[-20, 20, 5]$ by $[-20, 20, 5]$ viewing window.

   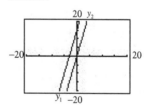

   The parallel lines indicate that the equation is a contradiction and has no solution. The solution set is $\varnothing$ or { }.

4. $2x-5+3(x-4)=5(x+2)-27$

   Algebraic Solution:
   $2x-5+3(x-4)=5(x+2)-27$
   $2x-3+3x-12=5x+10-27$
   $5x-15=5x-15$
   Since both sides are the same, this equation is a true statement no matter what value the variable x might have. The equation is an identity and the solution is the set of all real numbers.

Graphical Solution:

Graph $y_1 = 2x - 5 + 3(x - 4)$ and

$y_2 = 5(x + 2) - 27$ in a $[-20, 20, 5]$ by

$[-20, 20, 5]$ viewing window.

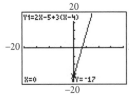 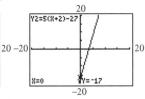

The graphs of y_1 and y_2 are the same. When we trace along y_1, we have the same ordered pairs as when we trace along points of y_2. We know that the lines are identical because two points uniquely determine a line. The equation is an identity and the solution is the set of all real numbers.

5. $14 - 2(x + 3) = 3(x - 9) + 18$

Algebraic Solution:
$$14 - 2(x + 3) = 3(x - 9) + 18$$
$$14 - 2x - 6 = 3x - 27 + 18$$
$$-2x + 8 = 3x - 9$$
$$-5x + 8 = -9$$
$$-5x = -17$$
$$x = \frac{-17}{-5} = \frac{17}{5} = 3.4$$

The solution is $\frac{17}{5} = 3.4$.

Graphical Solution:

Graph $y_1 = 14 - 2(x + 3)$ and $y_2 = 3(x - 9) + 18$ in a $[-20, 20, 5]$ by $[-20, 20, 5]$ viewing window and find the intersection point.

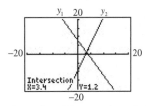

The point of intersection $(3.4, 1.2)$ indicates that the solution is $3.4 = \frac{17}{5}$.

6. $16 + 2(5 - x) = 19 - 3(x + 2)$

Algebraic Solution:
$$16 + 2(5 - x) = 19 - 3(x + 2)$$
$$16 + 10 - 2x = 19 - 3x - 6$$
$$-2x + 26 = -3x + 13$$
$$x + 26 = 13$$
$$x = -13$$

The solution is -13.

Graphical Solution:

Graph $y_1 = 16 + 2(5 - x)$ and $y_2 = 19 - 3(x + 2)$ in a $[-100, 100, 10]$ by $[-100, 100, 10]$ viewing window and find the intersection point.

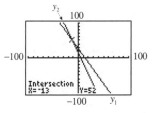

The point of intersection $(-13, 52)$ indicates that the solution is -13.

7. $0.4(x - 6) = \pi x + \sqrt{3}$

Graph $y_1 = 0.4(x - 6)$ and $y_2 = \pi x + \sqrt{3}$ in a standard viewing window and find the intersection point.

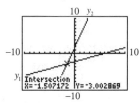

Rounding to the nearest hundredth, the point of intersection $(-1.51, -3.00)$ indicates that the solution is approximately -1.51.

8. $1.7x + \sqrt{7} = -0.4x - \sqrt{6}$

Graph $y_1 = 1.7x + \sqrt{7}$ and $y_2 = -0.4x - \sqrt{6}$ in a standard viewing window and find the intersection point.

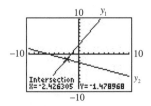

Rounding to the nearest hundredth, the point of intersection $(-2.43, -1.48)$ indicates that the solution is approximately -2.43.

9. $3(x-5) > -(x+3)$

$3x - 15 > -x - 3$

$4x - 15 > -3$

$4x > 12$

$x > 3$

The solution set is $(3, \infty)$.

10. $-2(x+7) \geq 3(x+2)$

$-2x - 14 \geq 3x + 6$

$-5x - 14 \geq 6$

$-5x \geq 20$

$x \leq -4$

The solution set is $(-\infty, -4]$.

11. $4x - (5 + 2x) < 3x - 1$

$4x - 5 - 2x < 3x - 1$

$2x - 5 < 3x - 1$

$-x - 5 < -1$

$-x < 4$

$x > -4$

The solution set is $(-4, \infty)$.

12. $3(x-8) < 7x + 2(5-x)$

$3x - 24 < 7x + 10 - 2x$

$3x - 24 < 5x + 10$

$-2x - 24 < 10$

$-2x < 34$

$x > -17$

The solution set is $(-17, \infty)$.

13. $24 \geq 6x - 2(3x-5) + 2x$

$24 \geq 6x - 6x + 10 + 2x$

$24 \geq 10 + 2x$

$14 \geq 2x$

$7 \geq x$

$x \leq 7$

The solution set is $(-\infty, 7]$.

14. $48 + x \geq 5(2x+4) - 2x$

$48 + x \geq 10x + 20 - 2x$

$48 + x \geq 8x + 20$

$-7x + 48 \geq 20$

$-7x \geq -28$

$x \leq 4$

The solution set is $(-\infty, 4]$.

15. $\dfrac{x}{3} + \dfrac{1}{2} > \dfrac{2}{3}$

$6\left(\dfrac{x}{3} + \dfrac{1}{2}\right) > 6\left(\dfrac{2}{3}\right)$

$2x + 3 > 4$

$2x > 1$

$x > \dfrac{1}{2}$

The solution set is $\left(\dfrac{1}{2}, \infty\right)$.

16. $x + \dfrac{3}{4} < -\dfrac{x}{2} + \dfrac{9}{4}$

$4\left(x + \dfrac{3}{4}\right) < 4\left(-\dfrac{x}{2} + \dfrac{9}{4}\right)$

$4x + 3 < -2x + 9$

$6x + 3 < 9$

$6x < 6$

$x < 1$

The solution set is $(-\infty, 1)$.

17. $\dfrac{x-5}{2} \leq \dfrac{3}{8}(2x+6)$

$8\left(\dfrac{x-5}{2}\right) \leq 8\left[\dfrac{3}{8}(2x+6)\right]$

$4(x-5) \leq 3(2x+6)$

$4x - 20 \leq 6x + 18$

$-2x - 20 \leq 18$

$-2x \leq 38$

$x \geq -19$

The solution set is $[-19, \infty)$.

18. $\dfrac{3(x-2)}{5} > \dfrac{-5(x-2)}{3}$

$15\left[\dfrac{3(x-2)}{5}\right] > 15\left[\dfrac{-5(x-2)}{3}\right]$

$9(x-2) > -25(x-2)$

$9x - 18 > -25x + 50$

$34x - 18 > 50$

$34x > 68$

$x > 2$

The solution set is $(2, \infty)$.

19. Let n = number of pounds of laundry.

$0.9(10) + 0.8(n-10) > 25$

$9 + 0.8n - 8 > 25$

$1 + 0.8n > 25$

$0.8n > 24$

$n > 30$

It is more economical to use the housekeeper for more than 30 pounds of laundry per week.

20. $500 \leq F \leq 1000$

$$500 \leq \frac{9}{5}C + 32 \leq 1000$$

$$468 \leq \frac{9}{5}C \leq 968$$

$$2340 \leq 9C \leq 4840$$

$$260 \leq C \leq 537.\overline{7}$$

Rounded to the nearest degree, firing temperatures range from 260°C to 538°C.

21. Let $x =$ minimum score the last judge can give.

$$\frac{9.5 + 9.7 + 9.9 + 9.7 + 9.7 + 9.6 + 9.5 + x}{8} \geq 9.65$$

$$67.6 + x \geq 77.2$$

$$x \geq 9.6$$

The last judge must give Nana at least a 9.6 for her to win a silver medal.

22. Let $x =$ the amount saved each summer.

$$4000 < 2x + 500 < 8000$$

$$3500 < 2x < 7500$$

$$1750 < x < 3750$$

She must save between \$1750 and \$3750 each summer.

23. $1 \leq 4x - 7 \leq 3$

$$8 \leq 4x \leq 10$$

$$2 \leq x \leq \frac{5}{2}$$

The solution set is $\left[2, \dfrac{5}{2}\right]$.

24. $-2 \leq 8 + 5x < -1$

$$-10 \leq 5x \leq -9$$

$$-2 \leq x \leq -\frac{9}{5}$$

The solution set is $\left[-2, -\dfrac{9}{5}\right)$.

25. $-3 < 4(2x - 1) < 12$

$$-3 < 8x - 4 < 12$$

$$1 < 8x < 16$$

$$\frac{1}{8} < x < 2$$

The solution set is $\left(\dfrac{1}{8}, 2\right)$.

26. $-6 < x - (3 - 4x) < -3$

$$-6 < x - 3 + 4x < -3$$

$$-6 < 5x - 3 < -3$$

$$-3 < 5x < 0$$

$$-\frac{3}{5} < x < 0$$

The solution set is $\left(-\dfrac{3}{5}, 0\right)$.

27. $\dfrac{1}{6} < \dfrac{4x - 3}{3} \leq \dfrac{4}{5}$

$$30\left(\frac{1}{6}\right) < 30\left(\frac{4x - 3}{3}\right) \leq 30\left(\frac{4}{5}\right)$$

$$5 < 10(4x - 3) \leq 24$$

$$5 < 40x - 30 \leq 24$$

$$35 < 40x < 54$$

$$\frac{7}{8} < x \leq \frac{27}{20}$$

The solution set is $\left(\dfrac{7}{8}, \dfrac{27}{20}\right]$.

28. $0 \leq \dfrac{2(3x + 4)}{5} \leq 3$

$$5(0) \leq 5\left[\frac{2(3x + 4)}{5}\right] \leq 5(3)$$

$$0 \leq 2(3x + 4) \leq 15$$

$$0 \leq 6x + 8 \leq 15$$

$$-8 \leq 6x \leq 7$$

$$-\frac{4}{3} \leq x \leq \frac{7}{6}$$

The solution set is $\left[-\dfrac{4}{3}, \dfrac{7}{6}\right]$.

29. $x \leq 2$ and $x > -5$

$$-5 < x \leq 2$$

The solution set is $(-5, 2]$.

30. $x \leq 2$ or $x > -5$

The solution set is $(-\infty, \infty)$.

31. $3x - 5 > 6$ or $-x < -5$

$$3x > 11 \quad \text{or} \quad x > 5$$

$$x > \frac{11}{3} \quad \text{or} \quad x > 5$$

$$x > \frac{11}{3}$$

The solution set is $\left(\dfrac{11}{3}, \infty\right)$.

32. $-2x \le 6$ and $-2x+3 < -7$
$\quad x \ge -3$ and $\quad -2x < -10$
$\quad x \ge -3$ and $\quad\quad x > 5$
$\quad\quad\quad x > 5$
The solution set is $(5, \infty)$.

33. $|x-7| = 9$
$\quad x-7 = 9$ or $x-7 = -9$
$\quad\quad x = 16$ or $\quad\quad x = -2$
The solution set is $\{-2, 16\}$.

34. $|8-x| = 3$
$\quad 8-x = 3$ or $8-x = -3$
$\quad -x = -5$ or $\quad -x = -11$
$\quad\quad x = 5$ or $\quad\quad x = 11$
The solution set is $\{5, 11\}$.

35. $|2x+9| = 9$
$\quad 2x+9 = 9$ or $2x+9 = -9$
$\quad\quad 2x = 0$ or $\quad 2x = -18$
$\quad\quad\quad x = 0$ or $\quad\quad x = -9$
The solution set is $\{-9, 0\}$.

36. $|-3x+4| = 7$
$\quad -3x+4 = 7$ or $-3x+4 = -7$
$\quad -3x = 3$ or $\quad -3x = -11$
$\quad\quad x = -1$ or $\quad\quad x = \dfrac{11}{3}$
The solution set is $\left\{-1, \dfrac{11}{3}\right\}$.

37. $|3x-2| + 6 = 10$
$\quad |3x-2| = 4$
$\quad 3x-2 = 4$ or $3x-2 = -4$
$\quad 3x = 6$ or $\quad 3x = -2$
$\quad\quad x = 2$ or $\quad\quad x = -\dfrac{2}{3}$
The solution set is $\left\{-\dfrac{2}{3}, 2\right\}$.

38. $5 + |6x+1| = 5$
$\quad |6x+1| = 0$
$\quad 6x+1 = 0$
$\quad 6x = -1$
$\quad\quad x = -\dfrac{1}{6}$
The solution set is $\left\{-\dfrac{1}{6}\right\}$.

39. $-5 = |4x-3|$ is impossible.
The solution set is $\varnothing$.

40. $|5-6x| + 8 = 3$
$\quad |5-6x| = -5$ is impossible.
The solution set is $\varnothing$.

41. $|7x| - 26 = -5$
$\quad |7x| = 21$
$\quad 7x = 21$ or $7x = -21$
$\quad\quad x = 3$ or $\quad x = -3$
The solution set is $\{-3, 3\}$.

42. $-8 = |x-3| - 10$
$\quad 2 = |x-3|$
$\quad x-3 = 2$ or $x-3 = -2$
$\quad\quad x = 5$ or $\quad x = 1$
The solution set is $\{1, 5\}$.

43. $\left|\dfrac{3x-7}{4}\right| = 2$

$\quad \dfrac{3x-7}{4} = 2$ or $\dfrac{3x-7}{4} = -2$
$\quad 3x-7 = 8$ or $3x-7 = -8$
$\quad 3x = 15$ or $\quad 3x = -1$
$\quad\quad x = 5$ or $\quad\quad x = -\dfrac{1}{3}$
The solution set is $\left\{-\dfrac{1}{3}, 5\right\}$.

44. $\left|\dfrac{9-2x}{5}\right| = -3$ is impossible.
The solution set is $\varnothing$.

45. $|6x+1| = |15+4x|$
$\quad 6x+1 = 15+4x$ or $6x+1 = -(15+4x)$
$\quad 2x+1 = 15$ or $\quad 6x+1 = -15-4x$
$\quad 2x = 14$ or $\quad 10x+1 = -15$
$\quad\quad x = 7$ or $\quad\quad 10x = -16$
$\quad\quad x = 7$ or $\quad\quad x = -\dfrac{8}{5}$
The solution set is $\left\{-\dfrac{8}{5}, 7\right\}$.

46. $|x-3| = |7+2x|$

$x-3 = 7+2x$ or $x-3 = -(7+2x)$

$-3 = 7+x$ or $x-3 = -7-2x$

$-10 = x$ or $3x-3 = -7$

$x = -10$ or $3x = -4$

$x = -10$ or $x = -\dfrac{4}{3}$

The solution set is $\left\{-10, -\dfrac{4}{3}\right\}$.

47. $|5x-1| < 9$

$-9 < 5x-1 < 9$

$-8 < 5x < 10$

$-\dfrac{8}{5} < x < 2$

The solution set is $\left(-\dfrac{8}{5}, 2\right)$.

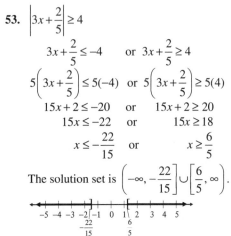

48. $|6+4x| \geq 10$

$6+4x \leq -10$ or $6+4x \geq 10$

$4x \leq -16$ or $4x \geq 4$

$x \leq -4$ or $x \geq 1$

The solution set is $(-\infty, -4] \cup [1, \infty)$

49. $|3x| - 8 > 1$

$|3x| > 9$

$3x < -9$ or $3x > 9$

$x < -3$ or $x > 3$

The solution set is $(-\infty, -3) \cup (3, \infty)$

50. $9 + |5x| < 24$

$|5x| < 15$

$-15 < 5x < 15$

$-3 < x < 3$

The solution set is $(-3, 3)$.

51. $|6x-5| \leq -1$ is impossible.

The solution set is $\varnothing$.

52. $|6x-5| \geq -1$ is true for all real values of x.

The solution set is $(-\infty, \infty)$.

53. $\left|3x+\dfrac{2}{5}\right| \geq 4$

$3x+\dfrac{2}{5} \leq -4$ or $3x+\dfrac{2}{5} \geq 4$

$5\left(3x+\dfrac{2}{5}\right) \leq 5(-4)$ or $5\left(3x+\dfrac{2}{5}\right) \geq 5(4)$

$15x+2 \leq -20$ or $15x+2 \geq 20$

$15x \leq -22$ or $15x \geq 18$

$x \leq -\dfrac{22}{15}$ or $x \geq \dfrac{6}{5}$

The solution set is $\left(-\infty, -\dfrac{22}{15}\right] \cup \left[\dfrac{6}{5}, \infty\right)$.

54. $\left|\dfrac{4x-3}{5}\right| < 1$

$-1 < \dfrac{4x-3}{5} < 1$

$-5 < 4x-3 < 5$

$-2 < 4x < 8$

$-\dfrac{1}{2} < x < 2$

The solution set is $\left(-\dfrac{1}{2}, 2\right)$.

55. $\left|\dfrac{x}{3}+6\right| - 8 > -5$

$\left|\dfrac{x}{3}+6\right| > 3$

$\dfrac{x}{3}+6 < -3$ or $\dfrac{x}{3}+6 > 3$

$\dfrac{x}{3} < -9$ or $\dfrac{x}{3} > -3$

$x < -27$ or $x > -9$

The solution set is $(-\infty, -27) \cup (-9, \infty)$.

56. $\left|\dfrac{4(x-1)}{7}\right|+10 < 2$

$\left|\dfrac{4(x-1)}{7}\right| < -8$ is impossible

The solution set is $\varnothing$.

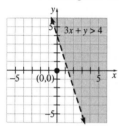

57. $3x+y > 4$

Graph the boundary line $3x+y = 4$ as a dashed line because the inequality symbol is >.

Test: (0, 0)

$3(0)+0 > 4$

$0 > 4$ False

Shade the half-plane that does not contain (0, 0).

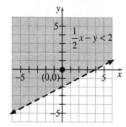

58. $\dfrac{1}{2}x-y < 2$

Graph the boundary line $\dfrac{1}{2}x-y = 2$ as a dashed line because the inequality symbol is <.

Test: (0, 0)

$\dfrac{1}{2}(0)-0 < 2$

$0 < 2$ True

Shade the half-plane that contains (0, 0).

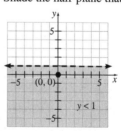

59. $5x-2y \le 9$

Graph the boundary line $5x-2y = 9$ as a solid line because the inequality symbol is $\le$.

Test: (0, 0)

$5(0)-2(0) \le 9$

$0 \le 9$ True

Shade the half-plane that contains (0, 0).

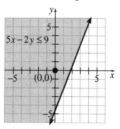

60. $3y \ge x$

Graph the boundary line $3y = x$ as a solid line because the inequality symbol is $\ge$.

Test: (0, 1)

$3(1) \ge 0$

$3 \ge 0$ True

Shade the half-plane that contains (0, 1).

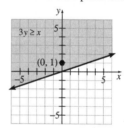

61. $y < 1$

Graph the boundary line $y = 1$ as a dashed line because the inequality symbol is <.

Test: (0, 0)

$0 < 1$ True

Shade the half-plane that contains (0, 0).

62. $x > -2$

Graph the boundary line $x = -2$ as a dashed line because the inequality symbol is >.

Test: (0, 0)

$0 > -2$ True

Shade the half-plane that contains (0, 0).

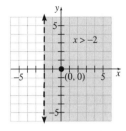

63. $y > 2x + 3$ or $x \le -3$

Graph each inequality. The union of the two inequalities is both shaded regions, as shown by the shading in the graph below.

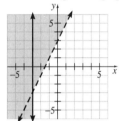

64. $2x < 3y + 8$ and $y \ge -2$

Graph each inequality. The intersection of the two inequalities is all points common to both regions, as shown by the shading in the graph below.

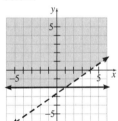

Chapter 3 Test

1. $15x + 26 = -2(x+1) - 1$

Algebraic Solution:
$15x + 26 = -2(x+1) - 1$
$15x + 26 = -2x - 2 - 1$
$15x + 26 = -2x - 3$
$17x + 26 = -3$
$17x = -29$
$x = -\dfrac{29}{17} \approx -1.71$

The solution is $-\dfrac{29}{17} \approx -1.71$.

Graphical Solution:
Graph $y_1 = 15x + 26$ and $y_2 = -2(x+1) - 1$ in a $[-10, 10, 1]$ by $[-10, 10, 1]$ viewing window and find the intersection point.

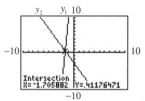

Rounding to the nearest hundredth, the point of intersection $(-1.71, 0.41)$ indicates that the solution is approximately -1.71.

2. $-3x - \sqrt{5} = \pi(x-1)$

Graph $y_1 = -3x - \sqrt{(5)}$ and $y_2 = \pi(x-1)$ in a standard viewing window and find the intersection point.

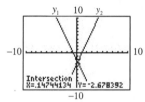

Rounding to the nearest hundredth, the point of intersection $(0.15, -6.70)$ indicates that the solution is approximately 0.15.

3. $|6x - 5| - 3 = -2$
$\quad |6x - 5| = 1$
$\quad 6x - 5 = 1$ or $6x - 5 = -1$
$\quad\quad 6x = 6$ or $\quad 6x = 4$
$\quad\quad\quad x = 1$ or $\quad\quad x = \dfrac{2}{3}$

The solution set is $\left\{ \dfrac{2}{3}, 1 \right\}$.

4. $|8 - 2t| = -6$ is impossible.
The solution set is $\varnothing$.

5. $3(2x - 7) - 4x > -(x + 6)$
$\quad 6x - 21 - 4x > -x - 6$
$\quad\quad 2x - 21 > -x - 6$
$\quad\quad\quad\quad 3x > 15$
$\quad\quad\quad\quad\quad x > 5$

The solution set is $(5, \infty)$.

128

6. $8 - \dfrac{x}{2} \geq 7$

$2\left(8 - \dfrac{x}{2}\right) \geq 2(7)$

$16 - x \geq 14$

$-x \geq -2$

$x \leq 2$

The solution set is $(-\infty, 2]$.

7. $-3 < 2(x-3) \leq 4$

$-3 < 2x - 6 \leq 4$

$3 < 2x \leq 10$

$\dfrac{3}{2} < x \leq 5$

The solution set is $\left(\dfrac{3}{2}, 5\right]$.

8. $|3x+1| > 5$

$3x+1 < -5$ or $3x+1 > 5$

$3x < -6$ or $3x > 4$

$x < -2$ or $x > \dfrac{4}{3}$

The solution set is $(-\infty, -2) \cup \left(\dfrac{4}{3}, \infty\right)$.

9. $x \leq -2$ and $x \leq -5$

$x \leq -5$

The solution set is $(-\infty, -5]$.

10. $x \leq -2$ or $x \leq -5$

$x \leq -2$

The solution set is $(-\infty, -2]$.

11. $-x > 1$ and $3x + 3 \geq x - 3$

$x < -1$ and $2x \geq -6$

$x \geq -3$

$-3 \leq x < -1$

The solution set is $[-3, -1)$.

12. $6x + 1 > 5x + 4$ or $1 - x > -4$

$x + 1 > 4$ or $5 > x$

$x > 3$ or $x < 5$

The solution set is $(-\infty, \infty)$.

13. $|x-5| - 4 < -2$

$|x-5| < 2$

$-2 < x - 5 < 2$

$3 < x < 7$

The solution set is $(3, 7)$.

14. $\left|\dfrac{5x-7}{2}\right| = 4$

$\dfrac{5x-7}{2} = 4$ or $\dfrac{5x-7}{2} = -4$

$5x - 7 = 8$ or $5x - 7 = -8$

$5x = 15$ or $5x = -1$

$x = 3$ or $x = -\dfrac{1}{5}$

The solution set is $\left\{-\dfrac{1}{5}, 3\right\}$.

15. $\left|17x - \dfrac{1}{5}\right| > -2$ is true for all real values of x.

The solution set is $(-\infty, \infty)$.

16. $|x-5| = |x+2|$

$x - 5 = x + 2$ or $x - 5 = -(x+2)$

$-5 = 2$ or $x - 5 = -x - 2$

$\uparrow$ $\qquad\qquad$ $2x - 5 = -2$

impossible $\qquad$ $2x = 3$

$x = \dfrac{3}{2}$

The solution set is $\left\{\dfrac{3}{2}\right\}$.

17. $x \leq -4$

Graph the boundary line $x = -4$ as a solid line because the inequality symbol is $\leq$.

Test: $(0, 0)$

$0 < -4$ False

Shade the half-plane that does not contain $(0, 0)$.

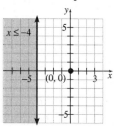

18. $2x - y > 5$

Graph the boundary line $2x - y = 5$ as a dashed line because the inequality symbol is $>$.

Test: $(0, 0)$

$2(0) - 0 > 5$

$0 > 5$ False

Shade the half-plane that does not contain $(0, 0)$.

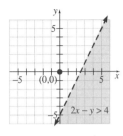

19. $2x + 4y < 6$ and $y \le 4$

Graph each inequality. The intersection of the two inequalities is all points common to both regions, as shown by the shaded region in the graph below.

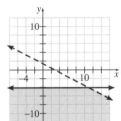

20. The graph of y_1 is below the graph of y_2 when $x < -3$. Thus, the solution of the inequality $y_1 < y_2$ is $(-\infty, -3)$.

21. The graph of y_1 is above the graph of y_2 when $x > -3$. Thus, the solution of the inequality $y_1 > y_2$ is $(-3, \infty)$.

Chapter 3 Cumulative Review

1. a. $\{2, 3, 4, 5\}$
   b. $\{101, 102, 103, \ldots\}$

2. a. $\{-2, -1, 0, 1, 2, 3, 4\}$
   b. $\{4\}$

3. a. $|3| = 3$
   b. $|-5| = 5$
   c. $-|2| = -2$
   d. $-|-8| = -8$
   e. $|0| = 0$

4. a. The opposite of $\dfrac{2}{3}$ is $-\dfrac{2}{3}$.
   b. The opposite of -9 is 9.
   c. The opposite of 1.5 is -1.5.

5. a. $-3 + (-11) = -14$
   b. $3 + (-7) = -4$
   c. $-10 + 15 = 5$
   d. $-8.3 + (-1.9) = -10.2$
   e. $-\dfrac{2}{3} + \dfrac{3}{7} = -\dfrac{14}{21} + \dfrac{9}{21} = -\dfrac{5}{21}$

6. a. $-2 - (-10) = 8$
   b. $1.7 - 8.9 = -7.2$
   c. $-\dfrac{1}{2} - \dfrac{1}{4} = -\dfrac{2}{4} - \dfrac{1}{4} = -\dfrac{3}{4}$

7. a. $\sqrt{9} = 3$
   b. $\sqrt{25} = 5$
   c. $\sqrt{\dfrac{1}{4}} = \dfrac{1}{2}$
   d. $-\sqrt{36} = -6$
   e. $\sqrt{-36}$ is not a real number

8. a. $-3(-2) = 6$
   b. $-\dfrac{3}{4}\left(-\dfrac{4}{7}\right) = \dfrac{3}{7}$
   c. $\dfrac{0}{-2} = 0$
   d. $\dfrac{-20}{-2} = 10$

9. a. $z - y = (-3) - (-1) = -2$
   b. $z^2 = (-3)^2 = 9$
   c. $\dfrac{2x + y}{z} = \dfrac{2(2) + (-1)}{-3} = \dfrac{3}{-3} = -1$

10. a. $\sqrt[4]{1} = 1$
    b. $\sqrt[3]{8} = 2$
    c. $\sqrt[4]{81} = 3$

11. a. $x + 5 = 20$

b. $2(3 + y) = 4$

c. $x - 8 = 2x$

d. $\dfrac{z}{9} = 3(z - 5)$

12. a. $-3 > -5$

b. $\dfrac{-12}{-4} = 3$

c. $0 > -2$

13. $7x + 5 = 5 + 7x$

14. $5 \cdot (7x) = (5 \cdot 7)x = 35x$

15. $2x + 5 = 9$
$2x = 4$
$x = 2$

16. $11.2 = 1.2 - 5x$
$10 = -5x$
$-2 = x$

17. $6x - 4 = 2 + 6(x - 1)$
$6x - 4 = 2 + 6x - 6$
$6x - 4 = 6x - 4$
Since both sides are the same, this equation is a true statement no matter what value the variable x might have. The equation is an identity and the solution is the set of all real numbers.

18. $2x + 1.5 = -0.2 + 1.6x$
$0.4x = -1.7$
$x = -4.25$

19. a. Let $x =$ the first integer
$x + 1 =$ the second integer
$x + 2 =$ the third integer
$x + (x + 1) + (x + 2) = 3x + 3$

b. $x + (5x) + (6x - 3) = 12x - 3$

20. a. Let $x =$ the first integer
$x + 1 =$ the second integer
$x + 2 =$ the third integer
$x + (x + 1) + (x + 2) = 3x + 3$

b. $4(3x + 1) = 12x + 4$

21. Let $x =$ the first number
$2x + 3 =$ the second number
$x + (2x + 3) = 72$
$3x + 3 = 72$
$3x = 69$
$x = 23$
Now, $2x + 3 = 2(23) + 3 = 49$.
Thus, the two numbers are 23 and 49.

22. Let $x =$ the first number
$3x + 2 =$ the second number
$(3x + 2) - x = 24$
$2x + 2 = 24$
$2x = 22$
$x = 11$
Now, $3x + 2 = 3(11) + 2 = 35$.
Thus, the two numbers are 11 and 35.

[NOTE: If we reverse the order of the difference in the first step above, two additional answers to this problem are possible:
$x - (3x + 2) = 24$
$x - 3x - 2 = 24$
$-2x - 2 = 24$
$-2x = 26$
$x = -13$
Now, $3x + 2 = 3(-13) + 2 = -37$.
The two number could also be -37 and -13.]

23. $3y - 2x = 7$
$3y = 2x + 7$
$y = \dfrac{2x + 7}{3}$, or $y = \dfrac{2x}{3} + \dfrac{7}{3}$

24. $7x - 4y = 10$
$7x = 4y + 10$
$x = \dfrac{4y + 10}{7}$, or $x = \dfrac{4y}{7} + \dfrac{10}{7}$

25. $A = \dfrac{1}{2}(B + b)h$
$2A = (B + b)h$
$2A = Bh + bh$
$2A - Bh = bh$
$\dfrac{2A - Bh}{h} = b$

26. $P = 2\ell + 2w$
$P - 2w = 2\ell$
$\dfrac{P - 2w}{2} = \ell$

27. a. $\{x \mid x \geq 2\} = [2, \infty)$

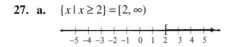

b. $\{x \mid x < -1\} = (-\infty, -1)$

```
-5 -4 -3 -2 -1  0  1  2  3  4  5
```

c. $\{x \mid 0.5 < x \leq 3\} = (0.5, 3]$

```
-5 -4 -3 -2 -1  0 / 1  2  3  4  5
                  0.5
```

28. a. $\{x \mid x \leq -3\} = (-\infty, -3]$

```
-5 -4 -3 -2 -1  0  1  2  3  4  5
```

b. $\{x \mid -2 \leq x < 0.1\} = [-2, 0.1)$

```
-5 -4 -3 -2 -1  0 \ 1  2  3  4  5
                  0.1
```

29. $-(x-3)+2 \leq 3(2x-5)+x$
$\quad -x+3+2 \leq 6x-15+x$
$\quad\quad -x+5 \leq 7x-15$
$\quad\quad\quad 20 \leq 8x$
$\quad\quad\quad \dfrac{5}{2} \leq x$
$\quad\quad\quad x \geq \dfrac{5}{2}$

The solution set is $\left[\dfrac{5}{2}, \infty\right)$.

30. $2(7x-1)-5x > -(-7x)+4$
$\quad 14x-2-5x > 7x+4$
$\quad\quad 9x-2 > 7x+4$
$\quad\quad\quad 2x > 6$
$\quad\quad\quad x > 3$

The solution set is $(3, \infty)$.

31. a. $2(x+3) > 2x+1$
$\quad 2x+6 > 2x+1$
$\quad\quad 6 > 1$ True for all real numbers x.
The solution set is $(-\infty, \infty)$.

b. $2(x+3) < 2x+1$
$\quad 2x+6 < 2x+1$
$\quad\quad 6 < 1$ Never true.
The solution set is $\varnothing$.

32. $4(x+1)-3 < 4x+1$
$\quad 4x+4-3 < 4x+1$
$\quad\quad 4x+1 < 4x+1$
$\quad\quad\quad 1 < 1$ Never true
The solution set is $\varnothing$.

33. $A \cap B = \{4, \ 6\}$

34. $\{-2, -1, 0, 1, 2, 3, 4, 5\}$

35. $x-7 < 2$ and $2x+1 < 9$
$\quad x < 9$ and $2x < 8$
$\quad x < 9$ and $x < 4$
$\quad\quad x < 4$
The solution set is $(-\infty, 4)$.

36. $x+3 \leq 1$ or $3x-1 < 8$
$\quad x \leq -2$ or $3x < 9$
$\quad x \leq -2$ or $x < 3$
$\quad\quad x < 3$
The solution set is $(-\infty, 3)$.

37. $A \cup B = \{2, \ 3, \ 4, \ 5, \ 6, \ 8\}$

38. $\varnothing$

39. $-2x-5 < -3$ or $6x < 0$
$\quad\quad -2x < 2$ or $x < 0$
$\quad\quad\quad x > -1$ or $x < 0$
The solution set is $(-\infty, \infty)$.

40. $-2x-5 < -3$ and $6x < 0$
$\quad\quad -2x < 2$ and $x < 0$
$\quad\quad\quad x > -1$ and $x < 0$
$\quad\quad\quad\quad -1 < x < 0$
The solution set is $(-1, 0)$.

41. $|p| = 2$
$\quad p = 2$ or $p = -2$
The solution set is $\{-2, 2\}$.

42. $|x| = 5$
$\quad x = 5$ or $x = -5$
The solution set is $\{-5, 5\}\}$.

43. $\left|\dfrac{x}{2}-1\right|=11$

$\dfrac{x}{2}-1=11 \ \text{ or } \ \dfrac{x}{2}-1=-11$

$\dfrac{x}{2}=12 \ \text{ or } \quad \dfrac{x}{2}=-10$

$x=24 \ \text{ or } \quad x=-20$

The solution set is $\{-20,\ 24\}$.

44. $\left|\dfrac{y}{3}+2\right|=10$

$\dfrac{y}{3}+2=10 \ \text{ or } \ \dfrac{y}{3}+2=-10$

$\dfrac{y}{3}=8 \quad \text{ or } \quad \dfrac{y}{3}=-12$

$y=24 \ \text{ or } \quad y=-36$

The solution set is $\{-36,\ 24\}$.

45. $|x-3|=|5-x|$

$x-3=5-x \ \text{ or } \ x-3=-(5-x)$

$2x=8 \qquad \text{ or } \ x-3=-5+x$

$x=4 \qquad \text{ or } \quad -3=-5$

Since $-3=-5$ is not possible, the solution set is $\{4\}$.

46. $|x+3|=|7-x|$

$x+3=7-x \ \text{ or } \ x+3=-(7-x)$

$2x=4 \qquad \text{ or } \ x-3=-7+x$

$x=2 \qquad \text{ or } \quad -3=-7$

Since $-3=-7$ is not possible, the solution set is $\{2\}$.

47. $|x|\le 3$

$-3\le x\le 3$

The solution set is $[-3,3]$.

48. $|x|>1$

$x<-1 \ \text{ or } \ x>1$

The solution set is $(-\infty,-1)\cup(1,\infty)$.

49. $|2x+9|+5>3$

$|2x+9|>-2$ is true for all real values of x.

The solution set is $(-\infty,\infty)$.

50. $|3x+1|+9<1$

$|3x+1|<-8$ Never true.

The solution set is $\varnothing$.

Chapter 4

Mental Math 4.1

1. B

2. C

3. A

4. D

Exercise Set 4.1

1. $\begin{cases} x - y = 3 \\ 2x - 4y = 8 \end{cases}$

   Let $x = 2$ and $y = -1$ in both equations.

   $$\begin{array}{ll} x - y = 3 & 2x - 4y = 8 \\ 2 - (-1) = 3 & 2(2) - 4(-1) = 8 \\ 3 = 3 \text{ True} & 4 + 4 = 8 \\ & 8 = 8 \text{ True} \end{array}$$

   The ordered pair $(2, -1)$ makes both equations true so it is a solution.

3. The graph indicates that the solution to the system is the ordered pair $\left(\dfrac{3}{2}, 1\right)$. We can verify this by letting $x = \dfrac{3}{2}$ and $y = 1$ in both equations.

   $$\begin{array}{ll} 2x + 5y = 8 & 6x + y = 10 \\ 2\left(\dfrac{3}{2}\right) + 5(1) \overset{?}{=} 8 & 6\left(\dfrac{3}{2}\right) + (1) \overset{?}{=} 10 \\ 3 + 5 \overset{?}{=} 8 & 9 + 1 \overset{?}{=} 10 \\ 8 = 8 \text{ True} & 10 = 10 \text{ True} \end{array}$$

   The ordered pair $\left(\dfrac{3}{2}, 1\right)$, or $(1.5, 1)$, makes both equations true so it is a solution.

5. The graph indicates that the solution to the system is the ordered pair $\left(-2, \dfrac{3}{4}\right)$. We can verify this by letting $x = -2$ and $y = \dfrac{3}{4}$ in both equations.

$$\begin{array}{ll} x - 4y = -5 & -3x - 8y = 0 \\ (-2) - 4\left(\dfrac{3}{4}\right) \overset{?}{=} -5 & -3(-2) - 8\left(\dfrac{3}{4}\right) \overset{?}{=} 0 \\ -2 - 3 \overset{?}{=} -5 & 6 - 6 \overset{?}{=} 0 \\ -5 = -5 \text{ True} & 0 = 0 \text{ True} \end{array}$$

The ordered pair $\left(-2, \dfrac{3}{4}\right)$, or $(-2, 0.75)$, makes both equations true so it is a solution.

7. $\begin{cases} x + y = 1 \\ x - 2y = 4 \end{cases}$

   Solve each equation for y.

   $$\begin{cases} y = -x + 1 \\ y = \dfrac{1}{2}x - 2 \end{cases}$$

   Graph $y_1 = -x + 1$ and $y_2 = \dfrac{1}{2}x - 2$ and find the point of intersection.

   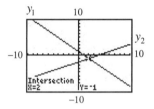

   Check:

   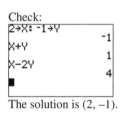

   The solution is $(2, -1)$.

134

9. $\begin{cases} 2y - 4 = 0 \\ x + 2y = 5 \end{cases}$

Solve each equation for y.

$\begin{cases} y = 2 \\ y = -\dfrac{1}{2}x + \dfrac{5}{2} \end{cases}$

Graph $y_1 = 2$ and $y_2 = -\dfrac{1}{2}x + \dfrac{5}{2}$ and find the point of intersection.

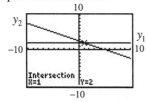

Check:

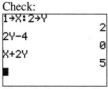

The solution is (1, 2).

11. $\begin{cases} 3x - y = 4 \\ 6x - 2y = 4 \end{cases}$

Solve each equation for y.

$\begin{cases} y = 3x - 4 \\ y = 3x - 2 \end{cases}$

Graph $y_1 = 3x - 4$ and $y_2 = 3x - 2$ and find the point of intersection.

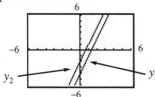

Since the two graphs do not cross (the lines are parallel), the system has no solution, $\varnothing$.

13. No. Answers may vary. For example, in the two variable case, we consider the intersection points of two lines. Since two lines cannot intersect at exactly two points, the system cannot have exactly two solutions.

15. $\begin{cases} x + y = 10 \\ y = 4x \end{cases}$

Replace y with $4x$ in the first equation.

$x + (4x) = 10$

$5x = 10$

$x = 2$

Replace x with 2 in the second equation.

$y = 4(2)$

$y = 8$

The solution is (2, 8).

Check:

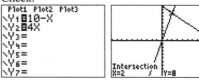

17. $\begin{cases} 4x - y = 9 \\ 2x + 3y = -27 \end{cases}$

Solve the first equation for y.

$4x - y = 9$

$y = 4x - 9$

Replace y with $4x - 9$ in the second equation.

$2x + 3(4x - 9) = -27$

$2x + 12x - 27 = -27$

$14x = 0$

$x = 0$

Replace x with 0 in the first equation.

$4(0) - y = 9$

$y = -9$

The solution is (0, –9).

Check:

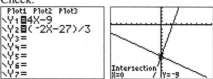

19. $\begin{cases} \dfrac{1}{2}x + \dfrac{3}{4}y = -\dfrac{1}{4} \\ \dfrac{3}{4}x - \dfrac{1}{4}y = 1 \end{cases}$

Clear the fractions by multiplying each equation by 4.

$\begin{cases} 2x + 3y = -1 \\ 3x - y = 4 \end{cases}$

Now solve the second equation for y.

$3x - y = 4$

$y = 3x - 4$

Replace y with $3x - 4$ in the first equation.

$2x + 3(3x - 4) = -1$

$2x + 9x - 12 = -1$

$11x = 11$

$x = 1$

Replace x with 1 in the equation $y = 3x - 4$.

$y = 3(1) - 4$

$y = -1$

The solution is $(1, -1)$.

Check:

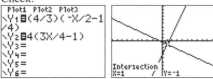

21. $\begin{cases} \dfrac{x}{3} + y = \dfrac{4}{3} \\ -x + 2y = 11 \end{cases}$

Clear fractions by multiplying the first equation by 3.

$\begin{cases} x + 3y = 4 \\ -x + 2y = 11 \end{cases}$

Solve the second equation for x.

$2y - 11 = x$

$x = 2y - 11$

Replace x with $2y - 11$ in the first equation.

$(2y - 11) + 3y = 4$

$5y = 15$

$y = 3$

Replace y with 3 in the equation $x = 2y - 11$.

$x = 2(3) - 11$

$x = -5$

The solution is $(-5, 3)$.

Check:

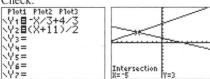

23. $\begin{cases} 2x - 4y = 0 \\ x + 2y = 5 \end{cases}$

Multiply the second equation by 2.

$\begin{cases} 2x - 4y = 0 \\ 2x + 4y = 10 \end{cases}$

Add the two equations and solve for the remaining variable.

$2x - 4y = 0$

$2x + 4y = 10$

$\overline{ 4x = 10}$

$x = \dfrac{10}{4}$

$x = \dfrac{5}{2}$

Replace x with $\dfrac{5}{2}$ in the first equation.

$\left(\dfrac{5}{2}\right) - 2y = 0$

$\dfrac{5}{2} = 2y$

$y = \dfrac{5}{4}$

The solution is $\left(\dfrac{5}{2}, \dfrac{5}{4}\right)$.

Check:

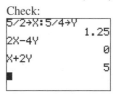

25. $\begin{cases} 5x + 2y = 1 \\ x - 3y = 7 \end{cases}$

Multiply the second equation by –5.

$\begin{cases} 5x + 2y = 1 \\ -5x + 15y = -35 \end{cases}$

Add the two equations.

$5x + 2y = 1$

$-5x + 15y = -35$

$\overline{ 17y = -34}$

$y = -\dfrac{34}{17}$

$y = -2$

Replace y with –2 in the second equation.

$x - 3(-2) = 7$

$x + 6 = 7$

$x = 1$

The solution is $(1, -2)$.

Check:

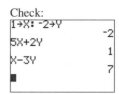

27. $\begin{cases} 5x - 2y = 27 \\ -3x + 5y = 18 \end{cases}$

Multiply the first equation by 3 and the second equation by 5.

$\begin{cases} 15x - 6y = 81 \\ -15x + 25y = 90 \end{cases}$

Add the two equations.

$\begin{array}{r} 15x - 6y = 81 \\ -15x + 25y = 90 \\ \hline 19y = 171 \\ y = 9 \end{array}$

Replace y with 9 in the first equation.

$5x - 2(9) = 27$
$5x - 18 = 27$
$5x = 45$
$x = 9$

The solution is (9, 9).

Check:

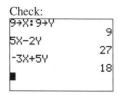

29. $\begin{cases} 3x - 5y = 11 \\ 2x - 6y = 2 \end{cases}$

Multiply the first equation by 2 and the second equation by –3.

$\begin{cases} 6x - 10y = 22 \\ -6x + 18y = -6 \end{cases}$

Add the two equations.

$\begin{array}{r} 6x - 10y = 22 \\ -6x + 18y = -6 \\ \hline 8y = 16 \\ y = 2 \end{array}$

Replace y with 2 in the second equation.

$2x - 6(2) = 2$
$2x - 12 = 2$
$2x = 14$
$x = 7$

The solution is (7, 2).

Check:

```
7→X:2→Y
           2
3X-5Y
          11
2X-6Y
           2
■
```

31. $\begin{cases} x - 2y = 4 \\ 2x - 4y = 4 \end{cases}$

Multiply the first equation by –2.

$\begin{cases} -2x + 4y = -8 \\ 2x - 4y = 4 \end{cases}$

Add the two equations.

$\begin{array}{r} -2x + 4y = -8 \\ 2x - 4y = 4 \\ \hline 0 = -4 \text{ False} \end{array}$

This is an inconsistent system. The solution is $\varnothing$.

33. $\begin{cases} 3x + y = 1 \\ 2y = 2 - 6x \end{cases}$

Put all the variables on one side.

$\begin{cases} 3x + y = 1 \\ 6x + 2y = 2 \end{cases}$

Multiply the first equation by –2.

$\begin{cases} -6x - 2y = -2 \\ 6x + 2y = 2 \end{cases}$

Add the two equations.

$\begin{array}{r} -6x - 2y = -2 \\ 6x + 2y = 2 \\ \hline 0 = 0 \text{ True} \end{array}$

This is a dependent system. The solution is $\{(x, y) \mid 3x + y = 1\}$.

35. $\begin{cases} 2x + 5y = 8 \\ 6x + y = 10 \end{cases}$

Multiply the first equation by –3.

$\begin{cases} -6x - 15y = -24 \\ 6x + y = 10 \end{cases}$

Add the two equations.

$\begin{array}{r} -6x - 15y = -24 \\ 6x + y = 10 \\ \hline -14y = -14 \\ y = 1 \end{array}$

Replace y with 1 in the second equation.

$6x + 1 = 10$
$6x = 9$
$x = \dfrac{9}{6} = \dfrac{3}{2}$

The solution is $\left(\dfrac{3}{2}, 1 \right)$.

37. $\begin{cases} x+y=1 \\ x-2y=4 \end{cases}$

Multiply the first equation by –1.

$\begin{cases} -x-y=-1 \\ x-2y=4 \end{cases}$

Add the two equations.

$$\begin{array}{r} -x-y=-1 \\ x-2y=4 \\ \hline -3y=3 \\ y=-1 \end{array}$$

Replace y with –1 in the first equation.

$$\begin{aligned} x+(-1) &= 1 \\ x-1 &= 1 \\ x &= 2 \end{aligned}$$

The solution is $(2, -1)$.

39. $\begin{cases} \dfrac{1}{3}x+y=\dfrac{4}{3} \\ -\dfrac{1}{4}x-\dfrac{1}{2}y=-\dfrac{1}{4} \end{cases}$

Clear fractions by multiplying the first equation by 3 and the second equation by 4.

$\begin{cases} x+3y=4 \\ -x-2y=-1 \end{cases}$

Add the two equations.

$$\begin{array}{r} x+3y=4 \\ -x-2y=-1 \\ \hline y=3 \end{array}$$

Replace y with 3 in the equation $x+3y=4$.

$$\begin{aligned} x+3(3) &= 4 \\ x+9 &= 4 \\ x &= -5 \end{aligned}$$

The solution is $(-5, 3)$.

41. $\begin{cases} 2x+6y=8 \\ 3x+9y=12 \end{cases}$

Multiply the first equation by –3 and the second equation by 2.

$\begin{cases} -6x-18y=-24 \\ 6x+18y=24 \end{cases}$

Add the two equations.

$$\begin{array}{r} -6x-18y=-24 \\ 6x+18y=24 \\ \hline 0=0 \quad \text{True} \end{array}$$

This is a dependent system. The solution is $\{(x, y)\,|\,3x+9y=12\}$.

43. $\begin{cases} 4x+2y=5 \\ 2x+y=-1 \end{cases}$

Multiply the second equation by –2.

$\begin{cases} 4x+2y=5 \\ -4x-2y=2 \end{cases}$

Add the two equations.

$$\begin{array}{r} 4x+2y=5 \\ -4x-2y=2 \\ \hline 0=7 \quad \text{False} \end{array}$$

This is an inconsistent system. The solution is $\varnothing$.

45. $\begin{cases} 10y-2x=1 \\ 5y=4-6x \end{cases}$

Move all the variables to one side.

$\begin{cases} 10y-2x=1 \\ 5y+6x=4 \end{cases}$

Multiply the second equation by –2.

$\begin{cases} 10y-2x=1 \\ -10y-12x=-8 \end{cases}$

Add the two equations.

$$\begin{array}{r} 10y-2x=1 \\ -10y-12x=-8 \\ \hline -14x=-7 \\ x=\dfrac{1}{2} \end{array}$$

Replace x with $\dfrac{1}{2}$ in the equation $5y=4-6x$.

$$\begin{aligned} 5y &= 4-6\left(\dfrac{1}{2}\right) \\ 5y &= 4-3 \\ 5y &= 1 \\ y &= \dfrac{1}{5} \end{aligned}$$

The solution is $\left(\dfrac{1}{2}, \dfrac{1}{5}\right)$.

47. $\begin{cases} \dfrac{3}{4}x+\dfrac{5}{2}y=11 \\ \dfrac{1}{16}x-\dfrac{3}{4}y=-1 \end{cases}$

Clear fractions by multiplying the first equation by 4 and the second equation by 16.

$\begin{cases} 3x+10y=44 \\ x-12y=-16 \end{cases}$

Multiply the second equation by –3.

$\begin{cases} 3x+10y=44 \\ -3x+36y=48 \end{cases}$

Add the two equations.

$$3x+10y=44$$
$$-3x+36y=48$$
$$\overline{\qquad 46y=92}$$
$$y=2$$

Replace y with 2 in the equation $x-12y=-16$.

$$x-12(2)=-16$$
$$x-24=-16$$
$$x=8$$

The solution is (8, 2).

49. $\begin{cases} x=3y+2 \\ 5x-15y=10 \end{cases}$

Replace x with $3y+2$ in the second equation.

$$5(3y+2)-15y=10$$
$$15y+10-15y=10$$
$$10=10 \quad \text{True}$$

The system is dependent. The solution is $\{(x,\ y)\mid x=3y+2\}$.

51. $\begin{cases} 2x-y=-1 \\ y=-2x \end{cases}$

Replace y with $-2x$ in the first equation.

$$2x-(-2x)=-1$$
$$4x=-1$$
$$x=-\frac{1}{4}$$

Replace x with $-\frac{1}{4}$ in the second equation.

$$y=-2\left(-\frac{1}{4}\right)$$
$$y=\frac{1}{2}$$

The solution is $\left(-\frac{1}{4},\frac{1}{2}\right)$.

53. $\begin{cases} 2x=6 \\ y=5-x \end{cases}$

The first equation yields $x=3$.
Replace x with 3 in the second equation.

$$y=5-3$$
$$y=2$$

The solution is (3, 2).

55. $\begin{cases} \dfrac{x+5}{2}=\dfrac{6-4y}{3} \\ \dfrac{3x}{5}=\dfrac{21-7y}{10} \end{cases}$

Multiply the first equation by 6 and the second equation by 10.

$\begin{cases} 3x+15=12-8y \\ 6x=21-7y \end{cases}$

Move all the variables to one side.

$\begin{cases} 3x+8y=-3 \\ 6x+7y=21 \end{cases}$

Multiply the first equation by –2.

$\begin{cases} -6x-16y=6 \\ 6x+7y=21 \end{cases}$

Add the two equations.

$$-6x-16y=6$$
$$6x+7y=21$$
$$\overline{\qquad -9y=27}$$
$$y=-3$$

Replace y with –3 in the equation $3x+8y=-3$.

$$3x+8(-3)=-3$$
$$3x-24=-3$$
$$3x=21$$
$$x=7$$

The solution is (7, –3).

57. $\begin{cases} 4x-7y=7 \\ 12x-21y=24 \end{cases}$

Multiply the first equation by –3.

$\begin{cases} -12x+21y=-21 \\ 12x-21y=24 \end{cases}$
$$\overline{\qquad 0=3 \quad \text{False}}$$

The system is inconsistent. The solution is $\varnothing$.

59. $\begin{cases} \dfrac{2}{3}x-\dfrac{3}{4}y=-1 \\ -\dfrac{1}{6}x+\dfrac{3}{8}y=1 \end{cases}$

Multiply the first equation by 12 and the second equation by 24.

$\begin{cases} 8x-9y=-12 \\ -4x+9y=24 \end{cases}$

Add the two equations.

$$8x-9y=-12$$
$$-4x+9y=24$$
$$\overline{\quad 4x\qquad =12}$$
$$x=3$$

Replace x with 3 in the equation $-4x+9y=24$.

$$-4(3)+9y=24$$
$$-12+9y=24$$
$$9y=36$$
$$y=4$$

The solution is (3, 4).

61. $\begin{cases} 0.7x - 0.2y = -1.6 \\ 0.2x - y = -1.4 \end{cases}$

Multiply both equations by 10.

$\begin{cases} 7x - 2y = -16 \\ 2x - 10y = -14 \end{cases}$

Multiply the first equation by –5.

$\begin{cases} -35x + 10y = 80 \\ 2x - 10y = -14 \end{cases}$

Add the two equations.

$-35x + 10y = 80$

$\underline{2x - 10y = -14}$

$-33x = 66$

$x = -2$

Replace x with –2 in the equation $7x - 2y = -16$.

$7(-2) - 2y = -16$

$-14 - 2y = -16$

$-2y = -2$

$y = 1$

The solution is (–2, 1).

63. $\begin{cases} 4x - 1.5y = 10.2 \\ 2x + 7.8y = -25.68 \end{cases}$

Multiply the second equation by –2.

$\begin{cases} 4x - 1.5y = 10.2 \\ -4x - 15.6y = 51.36 \end{cases}$

Add the two equations.

$4x - 1.5y = 10.2$

$\underline{-4x - 15.6y = 51.36}$

$-17.1y = 61.56$

$y = -3.6$

Replace y with –3.6 in the first equation.

$4x - 1.5(-3.6) = 10.2$

$4x + 5.4 = 10.2$

$4x = 4.8$

$x = 1.2$

The solution is (1.2, –3.6).

65. $\begin{cases} y = -1.65x + 3.65 \\ y = 4.56x - 9.44 \end{cases}$

Graph $y_1 = -1.65x + 3.65$ and $y_2 = 4.56x - 9.44$ and find the point of intersection.

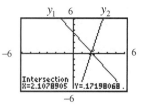

The solution is approximately $(2.11, 0.17)$.

67. $\begin{cases} 2.33x - 4.72y = 10.61 \\ 5.86x + 6.22y = -8.89 \end{cases}$

Solve each equation for y.

$\begin{cases} y = \dfrac{2.33x - 10.61}{4.72} \\ y = \dfrac{-5.86x - 8.89}{6.22} \end{cases}$

Graph $y_1 = \dfrac{2.33x - 10.61}{4.72}$ and

$y_2 = \dfrac{-5.86x - 8.89}{6.22}$, and find the point of

intersection.

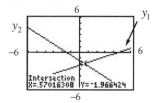

The solution is approximately $(0.57, -1.97)$.

69. $3x - 4y + 2z = 5$

$3(1) - 4(2) + 2(5) = 5$

$3 - 8 + 10 = 5$

$5 = 5$ True

71. $-x - 5y + 3z = 15$

$-(0) - 5(-1) + 3(5) = 15$

$0 + 5 + 15 = 15$

$20 = 15$ False

73. $3x + 2y - 5z = 10$

$\underline{-3x + 4y + z = 15}$

$6y - 4z = 25$

75. $10x + 5y + 6z = 14$

$\underline{-9x + 5y - 6z = -12}$

$x + 10y = 2$

77. The equilibrium point occurs when $x = 5$ and $y = 21$. Since the x-axis represents the number of DVDs in thousands and the y-axis represents the price of the DVD in dollars, supply equals demand for 5000 DVDs at $21 per DVD.

79. When $x = 7$, the graph of the supply equation is above the graph of the demand equation. Therefore, when $x = 7$, supply is greater than demand.

81. $\begin{cases} y = 2.5x \\ y = 0.9x + 3000 \end{cases}$

Substitute.
$$2.5x = 0.9x + 3000$$
$$1.6x = 3000$$
$$x = \frac{3000}{1.6}$$
$$x = 1875$$
$$y = 2.5(1875) = 4687.5$$

The point of intersection is (1875, 4687.5).

83. The company makes money because revenue is greater than cost at $x = 2000$.

85. The company makes a profit for values of $x > 1875$ because the revenue graph is higher than the cost graph after $x = 1875$.

87. Answers may vary. One possibility:
$$-2x + y = 1$$
$$x - 2y = -8$$

89. Red meat: $y = -x + 124.6$
Poultry: $y = 0.9x + 93$

   a. $m_{\text{red meat}} = -1$ and $m_{\text{poultry}} = 0.9$.

   Consumption of red meat is decreasing while consumption of poultry is increasing.

   b. $\begin{cases} y = -x + 124.6 \\ y = 0.9x + 93 \end{cases}$

   Substitute.
   $$-x + 124.6 = 0.9x + 93$$
   $$31.6 = 1.9x$$
   $$16.63 = x$$
   $$y = -(16.63) + 124.6 = 107.97$$

   The solution is (17, 108).

   c. $x = 17 \implies 1998 + 17 = 2015$

   In the year 2015, red meat and poultry consumption will each be about 108 pounds per person.

91. $\begin{cases} \dfrac{1}{x} + y = 12 \\ \dfrac{3}{x} - y = 4 \end{cases}$

Replacing $\dfrac{1}{x}$ with a, we have

$\begin{cases} a + y = 12 \\ 3a - y = 4 \end{cases}$

Adding the two new equations we get
$$4a = 16$$
$$a = 4$$

Replace a with 4 in the equation $a + y = 12$.
$$4 + y = 12$$
$$y = 8$$

Since $a = 4$, $x = \dfrac{1}{4}$.

The solution is $\left(\dfrac{1}{4}, 8 \right)$.

93. $\begin{cases} \dfrac{1}{x} + \dfrac{1}{y} = 5 \\ \dfrac{1}{x} - \dfrac{1}{y} = 1 \end{cases}$

Replace $\dfrac{1}{x}$ with a and $\dfrac{1}{y}$ with b.

$\begin{cases} a + b = 5 \\ a - b = 1 \end{cases}$

Adding the two new equations we get
$$2a = 6$$
$$a = 3$$

Replace a with 3 in the equation $a + b = 5$.
$$3 + b = 5$$
$$b = 2$$

Since $a = 3$, $x = \dfrac{1}{3}$. Similarly, $y = \dfrac{1}{2}$.

The solution is $\left(\dfrac{1}{3}, \dfrac{1}{2} \right)$.

95. $\begin{cases} \dfrac{2}{x}+\dfrac{3}{y}=-1 \\ \dfrac{3}{x}-\dfrac{2}{y}=18 \end{cases}$

Replace $\dfrac{1}{x}$ with a and $\dfrac{1}{y}$ with b.

$\begin{cases} 2a+3b=-1 \\ 3a-2b=18 \end{cases}$

Multiply the first equation by 2 and the second equation by 3 to obtain

$\begin{cases} 4a+6b=-2 \\ 9a-6b=54 \end{cases}$

Adding these last two equations we have

$13a=52$

$\quad a=4$

Replace a with 4 in the equation $2a+3b=-1$.

$2(4)+3b=-1$

$\qquad 3b=-9$

$\qquad\ b=-3$

Since $a=4$, $x=\dfrac{1}{4}$. Similarly, $y=-\dfrac{1}{3}$.

The solution is $\left(\dfrac{1}{4},-\dfrac{1}{3}\right)$.

97. $\begin{cases} \dfrac{2}{x}-\dfrac{4}{y}=5 \\ \dfrac{1}{x}-\dfrac{2}{y}=\dfrac{3}{2} \end{cases}$

Replace $\dfrac{1}{x}$ with a and $\dfrac{1}{y}$ with b.

$\begin{cases} 2a-4b=5 \\ a-2b=\dfrac{3}{2} \end{cases}$

Multiply the second equation by 2.

$\begin{cases} 2a-4b=5 \\ 2a-4b=3 \end{cases}$

This system is inconsistent. The solution is $\varnothing$.

Exercise Set 4.2

1.
$\begin{array}{ll} x+y+z=3 & -x+y+z=5 \\ (-1)+3+1=3 & -(-1)+3+1=5 \\ \qquad\quad 3=3 & \qquad\qquad 5=5 \end{array}$

A is true. \qquad\qquad B is true.

$\begin{array}{ll} -x+y+2z=0 & x+2y-3z=2 \\ -(-1)+3+2(1)=0 & (-1)+2(3)-3(1)=2 \\ \qquad\qquad 6=0? & \qquad\qquad\quad 2=2 \end{array}$

C is false. \qquad\qquad D is true.

Therefore, equations A, B, and D have $(-1,3,1)$ as a solution.

3. Yes. Answers may vary. Since $(-1,3,1)$ is a solution to each equation in the system, it is a solution to the system.

5. $\begin{cases} x-y+z=-4 \\ 3x+2y-z=5 \\ -2x+3y-z=15 \end{cases}$

Add the first equation and the second equation.

$\begin{array}{l} x-\ y+z=-4 \\ 3x+2y-z=5 \\ \hline 4x+y\qquad\ =1 \end{array}$

Add the first equation and the third equation.

$\begin{array}{l} x-\ y+z=-4 \\ -2x+3y-z=15 \\ \hline -x+2y\qquad =11 \end{array}$

Create a new system using the two new equations and solve the new system:

$\begin{cases} 4x+y=1 \\ -x+2y=11 \end{cases}$

Multiply the second equation by 4.

$\begin{cases} 4x+y=1 \\ -4x+8y=44 \end{cases}$

Add the equations.

$\begin{array}{l} 4x+y=1 \\ -4x+8y=44 \\ \hline \qquad 9y=45 \\ \qquad\ \ y=5 \end{array}$

Replace y with 5 in the equation $4x+y=1$.

$4x+5=1$

$\quad 4x=-4$

$\qquad x=-1$

Replace x with -1 and y with 5 in the first equation of the original system.

$(-1) - (5) + z = -4$
$-6 + z = -4$
$z = 2$
The solution is $(-1, 5, 2)$.

Check:
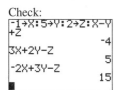

7. $\begin{cases} x + y \quad\quad = 3 \\ \quad\quad 2y \quad = 10 \\ 3x + 2y - 3z = 1 \end{cases}$

Solve the second equation for y:
$y = 5$

Replace y with 5 in the first equation.
$x + 5 = 3$
$x = -2$

Replace x with -2 and y with 5 in the third equation.
$3(-2) + 2(5) - 3z = 1$
$-6 + 10 - 3z = 1$
$4 - 3z = 1$
$-3z = -3$
$z = 1$
The solution is $(-2, 5, 1)$.

Check:
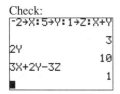

9. $\begin{cases} 2x + 2y + z = 1 \\ -x + y + 2z = 3 \\ x + 2y + 4z = 0 \end{cases}$

Add the second equation and the third equation.
$-x + y + 2z = 3$
$\underline{x + 2y + 4z = 0}$
$\quad\quad 3y + 6z = 3$ or $y + 2z = 1$

Multiply the second equation by 2 and add to the first equation.
$-2x + 2y + 4z = 6$
$\underline{2x + 2y + \ z = 1}$
$\quad\quad 4y + 5z = 7$

Create a new system using the two new equations and solve the new system:

$\begin{cases} y + 2z = 1 \\ 4y + 5z = 7 \end{cases}$

Multiply the first equation by –4.
$\begin{cases} -4y - 8z = -4 \\ 4y + 5z = 7 \end{cases}$

Add the equations.
$-4y - 8z = -4$
$\underline{4y + 5z = 7}$
$\quad -3z = 3$
$\quad\quad z = -1$

Replace z with –1 in the equation $y + 2z = 1$.
$y + 2(-1) = 1$
$y - 2 = 1$
$y = 3$

Replace y with 3 and z with –1 in the third equation of the original system.
$x + 2(3) + 4(-1) = 0$
$x + 6 - 4 = 0$
$x + 2 = 0$
$x = -2$
The solution is $(-2, 3, -1)$.

Check:
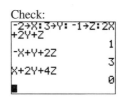

11. $\begin{cases} x - 2y + z = -5 \\ -3x + 6y - 3z = 15 \\ 2x - 4y + 2z = -10 \end{cases}$

Multiply the second equation by $-\dfrac{1}{3}$ and the third equation by $\dfrac{1}{2}$.

$\begin{cases} x - 2y + z = -5 \\ x - 2y + z = -5 \\ x - 2y + z = -5 \end{cases}$

All three equations are identical. There are infinitely many solutions.
The solution is $\{(x, y, z) \mid x - 2y + z = -5\}$.

13. $\begin{cases} 4x - y + 2z = 5 \\ 2y + z = 4 \\ 4x + y + 3z = 10 \end{cases}$

Multiply the first equation by –1 and add to the third equation.

$\begin{array}{r} -4x + y - 2z = -5 \\ 4x + y + 3z = 10 \\ \hline 2y + z = 5 \end{array}$

Multiply this equation by –1 and add to the second equation.

$\begin{array}{r} -2y - z = -5 \\ 2y + z = 4 \\ \hline 0 = -1 \quad \text{False} \end{array}$

Inconsistent system. The solution is $\varnothing$.

15. $\begin{cases} x + 5z = 0 \\ 5x + y = 0 \\ y - 3z = 0 \end{cases}$

Multiply the third equation by –1 and add to the second equation.

$\begin{array}{r} -y + 3z = 0 \\ 5x + y = 0 \\ \hline 5x + 3z = 0 \quad (4) \end{array}$

Multiply the first equation by –5 and add to equation (4).

$\begin{array}{r} -5x - 25z = 0 \\ 5x + 3z = 0 \\ \hline -22z = 0 \\ z = 0 \end{array}$

Replace z with 0 in equation (4).

$5x + 3(0) = 0$
$ 5x = 0$
$ x = 0$

Replace x with 0 in the second equation.

$5(0) + y = 0$
$ y = 0$

The solution is (0, 0, 0).

Check:
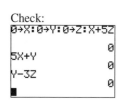

17. $\begin{cases} 6x - 5z = 17 \\ 5x - y + 3z = -1 \\ 2x + y = -41 \end{cases}$

Add the second equation and the third equation.

$\begin{array}{r} 5x - y + 3z = -1 \\ 2x + y = -41 \\ \hline 7x + 3z = -42 \quad (4) \end{array}$

Multiply equation (4) by 5, multiply the first equation by 3, and add.

$\begin{array}{r} 35x + 15z = -210 \\ 18x - 15z = 51 \\ \hline 53x = -159 \\ x = -3 \end{array}$

Replace x with –3 in the first equation.

$6(-3) - 5z = 17$
$ -18 - 5z = 17$
$ -5z = 35$
$ z = -7$

Replace x with –3 in the third equation.

$2(-3) + y = -41$
$ -6 + y = -41$
$ y = -35$

The solution is (–3, –35, –7).

Check:
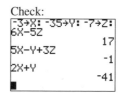

19. $\begin{cases} x + y + z = 8 \\ 2x - y - z = 10 \\ x - 2y - 3z = 22 \end{cases}$

Add the first equation and the second equation.

$\begin{array}{r} x + y + z = 8 \\ 2x - y - z = 10 \\ \hline 3x = 18 \\ x = 6 \end{array}$

Add twice the first equation to the third equation.

$\begin{array}{r} 2x + 2y + 2z = 16 \\ x - 2y - 3z = 22 \\ \hline 3x - z = 38 \end{array}$

Replace x with 6 in this equation.

$3(6) - z = 38$
$ 18 - z = 38$
$ -z = 20$
$ z = -20$

Replace x with 6 and z with –20 in the first equation.

$$6 + y + (-20) = 8$$
$$y - 14 = 8$$
$$y = 22$$

The solution is $(6, 22, -20)$.

Check:

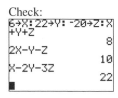

21. $\begin{cases} x + 2y - z = 5 \\ 6x + y + z = 7 \\ 2x + 4y - 2z = 5 \end{cases}$

Add the first equation and the second equation.

$$\begin{array}{r} x + 2y - z = 5 \\ 6x + y + z = 7 \\ \hline 7x + 3y \quad\;\; = 12 \;\; (4) \end{array}$$

Add twice the second equation to the third equation.

$$\begin{array}{r} 12x + 2y + 2z = 14 \\ 2x + 4y - 2z = 5 \\ \hline 14x + 6y \qquad = 19 \;\; (5) \end{array}$$

Multiply equation (4) by -2 and add to equation (5).

$$\begin{array}{r} -14x - 6y = -24 \\ 14x + 6y = 19 \\ \hline 0 = -5 \quad \text{False} \end{array}$$

Inconsistent system. The solution is $\varnothing$.

23. $\begin{cases} 2x - 3y + z = 2 \\ x - 5y + 5z = 3 \\ 3x + y - 3z = 5 \end{cases}$

Add -2 times the second equation to the first equation.

$$\begin{array}{r} 2x - 3y + z = 2 \\ -2x + 10y - 10z = -6 \\ \hline 7y - 9z = -4 \;\; (4) \end{array}$$

Add -3 times the second equation to the third equation.

$$\begin{array}{r} -3x + 15y - 15z = -9 \\ 3x + y - 3z = 5 \\ \hline 16y - 18z = -4 \;\; (5) \end{array}$$

Solve the new system:

$$\begin{cases} 7y - 9z = -4 \;\; (4) \\ 16y - 18z = -4 \;\; (5) \end{cases}$$

Multiply equation (4) by -2 and add to equation (5).

$$\begin{array}{r} -14y + 18z = 8 \\ 16y - 18z = -4 \\ \hline 2y \qquad = 4 \\ y = 2 \end{array}$$

Replace y with 2 in equation (4).

$$7(2) - 9z = -4$$
$$-9z = -18$$
$$z = 2$$

Replace y with 2 and z with 2 in the first equation.

$$2x - 3(2) + 2 = 2$$
$$x = 3$$

The solution is $(3, 2, 2)$.

Check:

25. $\begin{cases} -2x - 4y + 6z = -8 \\ x + 2y - 3z = 4 \\ 4x + 8y - 12z = 16 \end{cases}$

Add 2 times the second equation to the first equation.

$$\begin{array}{r} 2x + 4y - 6z = 8 \\ -2x - 4y + 6z = -8 \\ \hline 0 = 0 \end{array}$$

Add -4 times the second equation to the third equation.

$$\begin{array}{r} -4x - 8y + 12z = -16 \\ 4x + 8y - 12z = 16 \\ \hline 0 = 0 \end{array}$$

The system is dependent. The solution is $\{(x, y, z) \mid x + 2y - 3z = 4\}$.

27. $\begin{cases} 2x + 2y - 3z = 1 \\ \qquad y + 2z = -14 \\ 3x - 2y \quad\;\; = -1 \end{cases}$

Add the first equation to the third equation.

$$\begin{array}{r} 2x + 2y - 3z = 1 \\ 3x - 2y \quad\;\; = -1 \\ \hline 5x \quad\;\; - 3z = 0 \;\; (4) \end{array}$$

Add twice the second equation to the third equation.

$$\begin{array}{r} 2y + 4z = -28 \\ 3x - 2y \quad\;\; = -1 \\ \hline 3x + \quad 4z = -29 \;\; (5) \end{array}$$

Multiply equation (4) by 4, multiply equation (5)

by 2, and add.

$$20x - 12z = 0$$
$$\underline{9x + 12z = -87}$$
$$29x \qquad = -87$$
$$x = -3$$

Replace x with -3 in equation (4).

$$5(-3) - 3z = 0$$
$$3z = -15$$
$$z = -5$$

Replace z with -5 in the second equation.

$$y + 2(-5) = -14$$
$$y - 10 = -14$$
$$y = -4$$

The solution is $(-3, -4, -5)$.

Check:

29. $\begin{cases} x + 2y - z = 5 \\ -3x - 2y - 3z = 11 \\ 4x + 4y + 5z = -18 \end{cases}$

Add the first equation and the second equation.

$$x + 2y - z = 5$$
$$\underline{-3x - 2y - 3z = 11}$$
$$-2x \qquad - 4z = 16 \text{ or } x + 2z = -8 \quad (4)$$

Add twice the second equation to the third equation.

$$-6x - 4y - 6z = 22$$
$$\underline{4x + 4y + 5z = -18}$$
$$-2x - \qquad z = 4 \quad (5)$$

Solve the new system:

$\begin{cases} x + 2z = -8 \quad (4) \\ -2x - z = 4 \quad (5) \end{cases}$

Add twice equation (4) to equation (5).

$$2x + 4z = -16$$
$$\underline{-2x - z = 4}$$
$$3z = -12$$
$$z = -4$$

Replace z with -4 in equation (4).

$$x + 2(-4) = -8$$
$$x - 8 = -8$$
$$x = 0$$

Replace x with 0 and z with -4 in the first equation.

$$0 + 2y - (-4) = 5$$
$$2y = 1$$
$$y = \frac{1}{2}$$

The solution is $\left(0, \frac{1}{2}, -4 \right)$.

Check:

```
0→X:1/2→Y: -4→Z:X
+2Y-Z
                  5
-3X-2Y-3Z
                 11
4X+4Y+5Z
                -18
■
```

31. $\begin{cases} \dfrac{3}{4}x - \dfrac{1}{3}y + \dfrac{1}{2}z = 9 \\ \dfrac{1}{6}x + \dfrac{1}{3}y - \dfrac{1}{2}z = 2 \\ \dfrac{1}{2}x - y + \dfrac{1}{2}z = 2 \end{cases}$

Multiply the first equation by 12, multiply the second equation by 6, and multiply the third equation by 2.

$\begin{cases} 9x - 4y + 6z = 108 \quad (4) \\ x + 2y - 3z = 12 \quad (5) \\ x - 2y + z = 4 \quad (6) \end{cases}$

Add twice equation (5) to equation (4).

$$2x + 4y - 6z = 24$$
$$\underline{9x - 4y + 6z = 108}$$
$$11x \qquad = 132$$
$$x = 12$$

Add equation (5) and equation (6).

$$x + 2y - 3z = 12$$
$$\underline{x - 2y + z = 4}$$
$$2x \qquad - 2z = 16 \text{ or } x - z = 8$$

Replace x with 12 in this equation.

$$12 - z = 8$$
$$z = 4$$

Replace x with 12 and z with 4 in equation (6).

$$12 - 2y + 4 = 4$$
$$12 - 2y = 0$$
$$-2y = -12$$
$$y = 6$$

The solution is $(12, 6, 4)$.

Check:

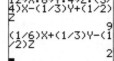

33. Let x = the first number, then
$2x$ = the second number.
$$x + 2x = 45$$
$$3x = 45$$
$$x = 15$$
$$2x = 2(15) = 30$$
The numbers are 15 and 30.

35.
$$2(x-1) - 3x = x - 12$$
$$2x - 2 - 3x = x - 12$$
$$-x - 2 = x - 12$$
$$-2x = -10$$
$$x = 5$$
The solution set is $\{5\}$.

37.
$$-y - 5(y+5) = 3y - 10$$
$$-y - 5y - 25 = 3y - 10$$
$$-6y - 25 = 3y - 10$$
$$-9y = 15$$
$$y = -\frac{15}{9} = -\frac{5}{3}$$
The solution set is $\left\{-\frac{5}{3}\right\}$.

39. Answers may vary. We can pick any coefficients we wish for the variables. Then plug in the values for the solution to determine the constant in the equation. For example, we could pick
$$2x + 3y - 4z = ?$$
To determine the constant, we substitute the values for the variables from the solution.
$$2(-1) + 3(2) - 4(-4) = -2 + 6 + 16 = 20$$
So, in order for our equation to be true for the given solution, the right hand side must be 20.
$$2x + 3y - 4z = 20$$

41. Answers may vary. Similar to problem 39, we can make up any coefficients we want for the three equations. Then we plug in the values for the variables from the solution to determine the constant for each equation. For example, we could pick
$$x + y + z = ?$$
$$2x - y + z = ?$$
$$3x + 2y - 2z = ?$$
Now plug in the values for the variables from the solution.
$$(-1) + (2) + (-4) = -3$$
$$2(-1) - (2) + (-4) = -8$$
$$3(-1) + 2(2) - 2(-4) = 9$$

So, in order to have $(-1, 2, -4)$ as a solution, we need these to be the corresponding constants in each equation.
$$x + y + z = -3$$
$$2x - y + z = -8$$
$$3x + 2y - 2z = 9$$

43. $\begin{cases} x + y + z = 1 \\ 2x - y + z = 0 \\ -x + 2y + 2z = -1 \end{cases}$

Add the first equation and the third equation.
$$x + y + z = 1$$
$$\underline{-x + 2y + 2z = -1}$$
$$3y + 3z = 0 \text{ or } y + z = 0 \quad (4)$$
Add –2 times the first equation to the second equation.
$$-2x - 2y - 2z = -2$$
$$\underline{2x - y + z = 0}$$
$$-3y - z = -2 \quad (5)$$
Add equation (4) and equation (5).
$$y + z = 0$$
$$\underline{-3y - z = -2}$$
$$-2y = -2$$
$$y = 1$$
Replace y with 1 in equation (4).
$$1 + z = 0$$
$$z = -1$$
Replace y with 1 and z with –1 in the first equation.
$$x + 1 + (-1) = 1$$
$$x = 1$$
The solution is (1, 1, –1), and
$$\frac{x}{8} + \frac{y}{4} + \frac{z}{3} = \frac{1}{8} + \frac{1}{4} - \frac{1}{3}$$
$$= \frac{3}{24} + \frac{6}{24} - \frac{8}{24}$$
$$= \frac{1}{24}.$$

45. $\begin{cases} x + y \quad - w = 0 \quad (1) \\ \quad y + 2z + w = 3 \quad (2) \\ x \quad - z \quad = 1 \quad (3) \\ 2x - y \quad - w = -1 \quad (4) \end{cases}$

Add equation (1) and equation (2).
$$x + y \quad - w = 0$$
$$\underline{y + 2z + w = 3}$$
$$x + 2y + 2z \quad = 3 \quad (5)$$
Add equation (2) and equation (4).

$$y + 2z + w = 3$$
$$\underline{2x - y \qquad - w = -1}$$
$$2x \qquad + z \qquad = 2 \ (6)$$

Add the third equation and equation (6).

$$x - z = 1$$
$$\underline{2x + z = 2}$$
$$3x \qquad = 3$$
$$x = 1$$

Replace x with 1 in the third equation.
$$1 - z = 1$$
$$z = 0$$

Replace x with 1 and z with 0 in equation (5).
$$1 + 2y + 2(0) = 3$$
$$1 + 2y = 3$$
$$2y = 2$$
$$y = 1$$

Replace y with 1, and z with 0 in the second equation.
$$1 + 2(0) + w = 3$$
$$1 + w = 3$$
$$w = 2$$

The solution is (1, 1, 0, 2).

Check:

$$1 + (-1) + 2 + w = 5$$
$$2 + w = 5$$
$$w = 3$$

The solution is (1, –1, 2, 3).

Check:

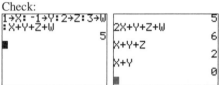

49. Answers may vary. The easiest approach may be to just write one equation as a non-zero multiple of another equation.

Exercise Set 4.3

1. Let x = the first number and y = the second number.

$$\begin{cases} x = y + 2 \\ 2x = 3y - 4 \end{cases}$$

Substitute $x = y + 2$ in the second equation.

$$2(y + 2) = 3y - 4$$
$$2y + 4 = 3y - 4$$
$$y = 8$$

Replace y with 8 in the first equation.
$$x = 8 + 2 = 10$$
The numbers are 10 and 8.

3. **a.** Let x = length of Enterprise and y = length of Nimitz.

$$\begin{cases} x + y = 2193 \\ x - y = 9 \end{cases}$$

Add the first equation and the second equation.
$$2x = 2202$$
$$x = 1101$$

Replace x with 1102 in the first equation.
$$1101 + y = 2193$$
$$y = 1092$$

The Enterprise is 1101 feet long and the Nimitz is 1092 feet long.

47.

$$\begin{cases} x + y + z + w = 5 \ (1) \\ 2x + y + z + w = 6 \ (2) \\ x + y + z \qquad = 2 \ (3) \\ x + y \qquad = 0 \ (4) \end{cases}$$

Add –1 times equation (4) to equation (3).

$$-x - y \qquad = 0$$
$$\underline{x + y + z = 2}$$
$$z = 2$$

Replace z with 2 in equations (1) and (2).

$$\begin{cases} x + y + w = 3 \ (5) \\ 2x + y + w = 4 \ (6) \end{cases}$$

Add –1 times equation (5) to equation (6).

$$-x - y - w = -3$$
$$\underline{2x + y + w = 4}$$
$$x \qquad = 1$$

Replace x with 1 in equation (4).
$$1 + y = 0$$
$$y = -1$$

Replace x with 1, y with –1, and z with 2 in equation (1).

b. $\dfrac{1 \text{ field}}{100 \text{ yds}} \cdot \dfrac{1 \text{ yd}}{3 \text{ ft}} \cdot 1101 \text{ ft} = \dfrac{1101}{300}$ fields

$$= 3.67 \text{ fields}$$

The Enterprise is 3.67 football fields in length.

5. Let p = the speed of the plane in still air and w = the speed of the wind.
$$\begin{cases} p+w = 560 \\ p-w = 480 \end{cases}$$
Add the first equation and the second equation.
$$2p = 1040$$
$$p = 520$$
Replace p with 520 in the first equation.
$$520 + w = 560$$
$$w = 40$$
The speed of the plane in still air is 520 mph and the speed of the wind is 40 mph.

7. Let x = number of quarts of 4% butterfat milk, and y = number of quarts of 1% butterfat milk.
$$\begin{cases} x + \quad y = 60 \\ 0.04x + 0.01y = 0.02(60) \end{cases}$$
Multiply the second equation by –100 and add to the first equation.
$$x + y = 60$$
$$\underline{-4x - y = -120}$$
$$-3x \quad = -60$$
$$x = 20$$
Replace x with 20 in the first equation.
$$20 + y = 60$$
$$y = 40$$
There should be 20 quarts of 4% butterfat used and 40 quarts of 1% butterfat used.

9. Let k = number of students studied abroad in the United Kingdom and s = number of students studied abroad in Spain.
$$\begin{cases} k + \quad s = 40,012 \\ \quad k = 15,428 + s \end{cases}$$
Substitute $k = 15,428 + s$ in the first equation.
$$(15,428 + s) + s = 40,012$$
$$15,428 + 2s = 40,012$$
$$2s = 24,584$$
$$s = 12,292$$
Replace s with 12,292 in the second equation.
$$k = 15,428 + 12,292 = 27,720$$
The United Kingdom had 27,720 students and Spain had 12,292 students.

11. Let l = the number of large frames and s = the number of small frames.
$$\begin{cases} l + s = 22 \\ 15l + 8s = 239 \end{cases}$$
Multiply the first equation by –8 and add to the second equation.
$$-8l - 8s = -176$$
$$\underline{15l + 8s = 239}$$
$$7l \quad = 63$$
$$l = 9$$
Replace l with 9 in the first equation.
$$9 + s = 22$$
$$s = 13$$
She bought 9 large frames and 13 small frames.

13. Let x = the first number, and y = the second number.
$$\begin{cases} x = y - 2 \\ 2x = 3y + 4 \end{cases}$$
Substitute $x = y - 2$ in the second equation.
$$2(y - 2) = 3y + 4$$
$$2y - 4 = 3y + 4$$
$$y = -8$$
Replace y with –8 in the first equation.
$$x = -8 - 2 = -10$$
The numbers are –10 and –8.

15. $$\begin{cases} y = 7x + 18.7 \\ y = 6x + 27.7 \end{cases}$$
Substitute $7x + 18.7$ for y in the second equation.
$$7x + 18.7 = 6x + 27.7$$
$$x = 9$$
$$1996 + 9 = 2005$$
The year would be 2005.

17. Let x = price of each tablet, and y = the price of each pen.
$$\begin{cases} 7x + 4y = 6.40 \\ 2x + 19y = 5.40 \end{cases}$$
Multiply the first equation by 2 and the second equation by –7 and add.
$$14x + 8y = 12.8$$
$$\underline{-14x - 133y = -37.80}$$
$$-125y = -25$$
$$y = 0.20$$
Replace y with 0.20 in the first equation.
$$7x + 4(0.20) = 6.40$$
$$7x + 0.80 = 6.40$$
$$7x = 5.60$$
$$x = 0.80$$
Tablets cost $0.80 each and pens cost $0.20 each.

19. Let p = the speed of the plane in still air, and w = the speed of the wind.

First note:

$$\frac{2160 \text{ mi}}{3 \text{ hr}} = 720 \text{ mph and}$$

$$\frac{2160 \text{ mi}}{4 \text{ hr}} = 540 \text{ mph}$$

Now,

$$\begin{cases} p + w = 720 \\ p - w = 540 \end{cases}$$

Add the first equation and the second equation.

$$2p = 1260$$
$$p = 630$$

Replace p with 630 in the first equation.

$$630 + w = 720$$
$$w = 90$$

The speed of the plane in still air is 630 mph and the speed of the wind is 90 mph.

21. a. Answers may vary. The slope of the line for men is negative which indicates a decrease over time. The slope of the line for women is positive which indicates an increase over time.

b. $$\begin{cases} y = -0.52x + 64.5 \\ y = 0.02x + 7.2 \end{cases}$$

Substitute $0.02x + 7.2$ for y in the first equation.

$$0.02x + 7.2 = -0.52x + 64.5$$
$$0.54x = 57.3$$
$$x = \frac{57.3}{0.54} \approx 106.11$$

$1990 + 106 = 2006$

They would be the same in 2006.

23. Let x = length of shortest two sides, and y = length of the longest side.

$$\begin{cases} 2x + y = 93 \\ y = x + 9 \end{cases}$$

Replace y with $x + 9$ in the first equation.

$$2x + (x + 9) = 93$$
$$3x + 9 = 93$$
$$3x = 84$$
$$x = 28$$

Replace x with 28 in the second equation.

$$y = 28 + 9 = 37$$

The lengths of the three sides are 28 cm, 28 cm, and 37 cm.

25. Let x = the daily mileage. Then we have:

Cost for Hertz: $H(x) = 25 + 0.10x$

Cost for Budget: $B(x) = 20 + 0.25x$

We want to find when $B(x) = 2 \cdot H(x)$

$$20 + 0.25x = 2(25 + 0.10x)$$
$$20 + 0.25x = 50 + 0.20x$$
$$0.05x = 30$$
$$x = 600$$

The Budget charge will be twice that of the Hertz charge at 600 miles.

27. $$\begin{cases} x + y = 180 \\ x = y - 30 \end{cases}$$

Replace x with $y - 30$ in the first equation.

Replace y with $x + 9$ in the first equation.

$$(y - 30) + y = 180$$
$$2y - 30 = 180$$
$$2y = 210$$
$$y = 105$$

Replace y with 105 in the second equation.

$$x = 105 - 30 = 75$$

The value of x is 75 and the value of y is 105.

29. $$C(x) = 30x + 10,000$$
$$R(x) = 46x$$
$$46x = 30x + 10,000$$
$$16x = 10,000$$
$$x = 625$$

625 units must be sold to break even.

31. $$C(x) = 1.2x + 1500$$
$$R(x) = 1.7x$$
$$1.7x = 1.2x + 1500$$
$$0.5x = 1500$$
$$x = 3000 \text{ units}$$

3000 units must be sold to break even.

33. $$C(x) = 75x + 160,000$$
$$R(x) = 200x$$
$$200x = 75x + 160,000$$
$$125x = 160,000$$
$$x = 1280$$

1280 units must be sold to break even.

35. a. $R(x) = 450x$

b. $C(x) = 200x + 6000$

c. $R(x) = C(x)$
$450x = 200x + 6000$
$250x = 6000$
$x = 24$ desks
24 desks must be made and sold to break even.

37. Let x = units of Mix A, y = units of Mix B, and z = units of Mix C.
$$\begin{cases} 4x + 6y + 4z = 30 & (1) \\ 6x + y + z = 16 & (2) \\ 3x + 2y + 12z = 24 & (3) \end{cases}$$
Multiply equation (2) by –6 and add to equation (1).
$-36x - 6y - 6z = -96$
$\underline{4x + 6y + 4z = 30}$
$-32x - 2z = -66$ or $16x + z = 33$ (4)
Multiply equation (2) by –2 and then add to equation (3).
$-12x - 2y - 2z = -32$
$\underline{3x + 2y + 12z = 24}$
$-9x + 10z = -8$ (5)
Multiply equation (4) by –10 and then add to equation (5).
$-160x - 10z = -330$
$\underline{-9x + 10z = -8}$
$-169x = -338$
$x = 2$
Replace x with 2 in equation (4).
$16(2) + z = 33$
$32 + z = 33$
$z = 1$
Replace x with 2 and z with 1 in equation (2).
$6(2) + y + 1 = 16$
$y = 3$
You need 2 units of Mix A, 3 units of Mix B, and 1 unit of Mix C.

39. Let x = length of shortest side, y = length of longest side, and z = length of the other two sides.
$$\begin{cases} x + y + 2z = 29 & (1) \\ y = 2x & (2) \\ z = x + 2 & (3) \end{cases}$$
Substitute $y = 2x$ and $z = x + 2$ in equation (1).
$x + (2x) + 2(x + 2) = 29$
$x + 2x + 2x + 4 = 29$
$5x = 25$
$x = 5$
Replace x with 5 in equation (2) and also in equation (3).
$-2(5) + y = 0$ $-(5) + z = 2$
$y = 10$ $z = 7$
The sides are 5 in., 7 in., 7 in., and 10 in.

41. Let x = the first number, y = the second number, and z = the third number.
$$\begin{cases} x + y + z = 40 \\ x = y + 5 \\ x = 2z \end{cases}$$
$$\begin{cases} x + y + z = 40 & (1) \\ x - y = 5 & (2) \\ x - 2z = 0 & (3) \end{cases}$$
Add equation (1) and equation (2).
$2x + z = 45$ (4)
Multiply equation (3) by –2 and then add to equation (4).
$-2x + 4z = 0$
$\underline{2x + z = 45}$
$5z = 45$
$z = 9$
Replace z with 9 in equation (3).
$x - 2(9) = 0$
$x = 18$
Replace x with 18 in equation (2).
$18 - y = 5$
$y = 13$
The numbers are 18, 13, and 9.

43. Let x = number of free throws, y = number of two-point field goals, and z = number of three-point field goals.

$$\begin{cases} x+2y+3z=698 \\ y=6z-19 \\ x=y-64 \end{cases}$$

$$\begin{cases} x+2y+3z=698 \quad (1) \\ y-6z=-19 \quad (2) \\ x-y \quad =-64 \quad (3) \end{cases}$$

Multiply equation (3) by -1 and then add to equation (1).

$$\begin{array}{r} -x+y \quad =64 \\ x+2y+3z=698 \\ \hline 3y+3z=762 \text{ or } y+z=254 \ (4) \end{array}$$

Multiply equation (4) by -1 and then add to equation (2).

$$\begin{array}{r} -y-z=-254 \\ y-6z=-19 \\ \hline -7z=-273 \\ z=39 \end{array}$$

Replace z with 39 in equation (2).
$$y-6(39)=-19$$
$$y-234=-19$$
$$y=215$$

Replace y with 215 in equation (3).
$$x-215=-64$$
$$x=151$$

She made 151 free throws, 215 two-point field goals, and 39 three-point field goals.

45.
$$\begin{cases} x+y+z=180 \\ y+2x+5=180 \\ z+2x-5=180 \end{cases}$$

$$\begin{cases} x+y+z=180 \quad (1) \\ 2x+y \quad =175 \quad (2) \\ 2x+ \quad z=185 \quad (3) \end{cases}$$

Multiply equation (1) by -1 and add to equation (2).

$$\begin{array}{r} -x-y-z=-180 \\ 2x+y \quad =175 \\ \hline x \quad -z=-5 \ (4) \end{array}$$

Add equations (3) and (4).
$$3x=180$$
$$x=60$$

Replace x with 60 in equation (4).

$$60-z=-5$$
$$z=65$$

Replace x with 60 in equation (2).
$$2(60)+y=175$$
$$120+y=175$$
$$y=55$$
$$x=60, y=55, \text{ and } z=65$$

47. $\begin{cases} 3x-y+z=2 \\ -x+2y+3z=6 \end{cases}$

Multiply the first equation by 2 and add to the second equation.

$$\begin{array}{r} 6x-2y+2z=4 \\ -x+2y+3z=6 \\ \hline 5x \quad +5z=10 \end{array}$$
$$5x+5z=10$$

49. $\begin{cases} x+2y-z=0 \\ 3x+y-z=2 \end{cases}$

Multiply the first equation by -3 and add to the second equation.

$$\begin{array}{r} -3x-6y+3z=0 \\ 3x+y-z=2 \\ \hline -5y+2z=2 \end{array}$$
$$-5y+2z=2$$

51. Let x = number filed in 1980 and y = number filed in 2001.

$$\begin{cases} y=4x+200,000 \quad (1) \\ y-x=1,100,000 \quad (2) \end{cases}$$

Substitute $y=4x+200,000$ in the second equation.
$$(4x+200,000)-x=1,100,000$$
$$3x+200,000=1,100,000$$
$$3x=900,000$$
$$x=300,000$$

Replace x with 300,000 in the first equation.
$$y=4(300,000)+200,000=1,400,000$$

There were 300,000 bankruptcy petitions filed in 1980 and 1,400,000 filed in 2001.

53. $y = ax^2 + bx + c$

$(1, 6)$: $\quad 6 = a + b + c \quad (1)$
$(-1, -2)$: $\quad -2 = a - b + c \quad (2)$
$(0, -1)$: $\quad -1 = c \quad\quad\quad (3)$

Substitute $c = -1$ in equation (1) and also in equation (2) to obtain

$$\begin{cases} a + b = 7 & \text{from equation (1)} \\ a - b = -1 & \text{from equation (2)} \end{cases}$$

Add these equations.

$2a = 6$

$\quad a = 3$

Replace a with 3 in $a + b = 7$.

$3 + b = 7$ so $b = 4$

Therefore, $a = 3$, $b = 4$, and $c = -1$.

55. $y = ax^2 + bx + c$

$(0, 1065)$: $1065 = c \quad\quad\quad\quad (1)$
$(1, 1070)$: $1070 = a + b + c \quad (2)$
$(3, 1175)$: $1175 = 9a + 3b + c \quad (3)$

Substitute $c = 1065$ in equations (2) and (3):

$$\begin{cases} a + b = 5 & (4) \\ 9a + 3b = 110 & (5) \end{cases}$$

Multiply equation (4) by –3 and then add to equation (5).

$-3a - 3b = -15$

$\underline{9a + 3b = 110}$

$6a \quad\quad = 95$

$$a = \frac{95}{6} = 15\frac{5}{6}$$

Replace a with $15\frac{5}{6}$ in $a + b = 5$.

$$\frac{95}{6} + b = 5$$

$$b = -\frac{65}{6} = -10\frac{5}{6}$$

So, $a = 15\frac{5}{6}$, $b = -10\frac{5}{6}$, and $c = 1065$.

For 2009, we have $x = 9$. Using our model we get:

$$y = \frac{95}{6}(9)^2 - \frac{65}{6}(9) + 1065 = 2250$$

Our model predicts that 2,250,000 students will take the ACT in 2009 (**note:** remember that y is in thousands).

Integrated Review

1. C

2. D

3. A

4. B

5. $\begin{cases} x + y = 4 \\ \quad y = 3x \end{cases}$

Substitute $y = 3x$ in the first equation.

$x + (3x) = 4$

$\quad 4x = 4$

$\quad\quad x = 1$

Replace x with 1 in the second equation.

$y = 3x = 3(1) = 3$

The solution is $(1, 3)$.

6. $\begin{cases} x - y = -4 \\ \quad y = 4x \end{cases}$

Substitute $y = 4x$ in the first equation.

$x - (4x) = -4$

$\quad -3x = -4$

$\quad\quad x = \frac{4}{3}$

Replace x with $\frac{4}{3}$ in the second equation.

$$y = 4x = 4\left(\frac{4}{3}\right) = \frac{16}{3}$$

The solution is $\left(\frac{4}{3}, \frac{16}{3}\right)$.

7. $\begin{cases} \quad x + y = 1 \\ x - 2y = 4 \end{cases}$

Multiply the first equation by –1 and add to the second equation.

$-x - y = -1$

$\underline{x - 2y = 4}$

$\quad -3y = 3$

$\quad\quad y = -1$

Replace y with –1 in the first equation.

$x + (-1) = 1$

$\quad x - 1 = 1$

$\quad\quad x = 2$

The solution is $(2, -1)$.

153

8. $\begin{cases} 2x - y = 8 \\ x + 3y = 11 \end{cases}$

Multiply the first equation by 3 and add to the second equation.

$6x - 3y = 24$

$\underline{x + 3y = 11}$

$7x \quad\quad = 35$

$x = 5$

Replace x with 5 in the first equation.

$2(5) - y = 8$

$10 - y = 8$

$y = 2$

The solution is (5, 2).

9. $\begin{cases} 2x + 5y = 8 \\ 6x + \;\; y = 10 \end{cases}$

Multiply the second equation by −5 and add to the first equation.

$2x + 5y = 8$

$\underline{-30x - 5y = -50}$

$-28x \quad\quad = -42$

$x = \dfrac{3}{2}$

Replace x with $\dfrac{3}{2}$ in the second equation.

$6\left(\dfrac{3}{2}\right) + y = 10$

$9 + y = 10$

$y = 1$

The solution is $\left(\dfrac{3}{2}, 1\right)$.

10. $\begin{cases} x - 4y = -5 \\ -3x - 8y = 0 \end{cases}$

Multiply the first equation by −2 and add to the second equation.

$-2x + 8y = 10$

$\underline{-3x - 8y = 0}$

$-5x \quad\quad = 10$

$x = -2$

Replace x with −2 in the first equation.

$-2 - 4y = -5$

$-4y = -3$

$y = \dfrac{3}{4}$

The solution is $\left(-2, \dfrac{3}{4}\right)$.

11. $\begin{cases} 4x - 7y = 7 \\ 12x - 21y = 24 \end{cases}$

Multiply the first equation by −3 and add to the second equation.

$-12x + 21y = -21$

$\underline{12x - 21y = 24}$

$0 = 3 \quad$ False

The system is inconsistent. The solution set is $\varnothing$.

12. $\begin{cases} 2x - 5y = 3 \\ -4x + 10y = -6 \end{cases}$

Multiply the first equation by 2 and add to the second equation.

$4x - 10y = 6$

$\underline{-4x + 10y = -6}$

$0 = 0 \quad$ True

The system is dependent. The solution set is $\{(x, y) \mid 2x - 5y = 3\}$.

13. $\begin{cases} x + y \quad\quad = 2 \quad (1) \\ -3y + z = -7 \;\; (2) \\ 2x + y - z = -1 \;\; (3) \end{cases}$

Add equations (2) and (3).

$-3y + z = -7$

$\underline{2x + y - z = -1}$

$2x - 2y \quad = -8 \;$ or $\; x - y = -4 \;$ (4)

Add equations (1) and (4).

$x + y = 2$

$\underline{x - y = -4}$

$2x \quad\quad = -2$

$x = -1$

Replace x with −1 in equation (1).

$-1 + y = 2$

$y = 3$

Replace y with 3 in equation (2).

$$-3(3) + z = -7$$
$$-9 + z = -7$$
$$z = 2$$

The solution is $(-1, 3, 2)$.

14. $\begin{cases} y + 2z = -3 & (1) \\ x - 2y = 7 & (2) \\ 2x - y + z = 5 & (3) \end{cases}$

Multiply equation (2) by –2 and then add to equation (3).

$$-2x + 4y = -14$$
$$\underline{2x - y + z = 5}$$
$$3y + z = -9 \quad (4)$$

Multiply equation (4) by –2 and then add to equation (1).

$$-6y - 2z = 18$$
$$\underline{y + 2z = -3}$$
$$-5y = 15$$
$$y = -3$$

Replace y with –3 in equation (4).

$$3(-3) + z = -9$$
$$z = 0$$

Replace y with –3 in equation (2).

$$x - 2(-3) = 7$$
$$x + 6 = 7$$
$$x = 1$$

The solution is $(1, -3, 0)$.

15. $\begin{cases} 2x + 4y - 6z = 3 & (1) \\ -x + y - z = 6 & (2) \\ x + 2y - 3z = 1 & (3) \end{cases}$

Multiply equation (3) by –2 and then add to equation (1).

$$-2x - 4y + 6z = -2$$
$$\underline{2x + 4y - 6z = 3}$$
$$0 = 1 \text{ False}$$

The system is inconsistent. The solution set is $\varnothing$.

16. $\begin{cases} x - y + 3z = 2 & (1) \\ -2x + 2y - 6z = -4 & (2) \\ 3x - 3y + 9z = 6 & (3) \end{cases}$

Divide equation (2) by –2 and divide equation (3) by 3.

$$\begin{cases} x - y + 3z = 2 \\ x - y + 3z = 2 \\ x - y + 3z = 2 \end{cases}$$

All three equations are the same so the system is dependent. The solution set is
$\{(x, y) \mid x - y + 3z = 2\}$.

17. $\begin{cases} x + y - 4z = 5 & (1) \\ x - y + 2z = -2 & (2) \\ 3x + 2y + 4z = 18 & (3) \end{cases}$

Add equation (1) and equation (2).

$$x + y - 4z = 5$$
$$\underline{x - y + 2z = -2}$$
$$2x - 2z = 3 \quad (4)$$

Multiply equation (2) by 2 and add to equation (3).

$$2x - 2y + 4z = -4$$
$$\underline{3x + 2y + 4z = 18}$$
$$5x + 8z = 14 \quad (5)$$

Multiply equation (4) by 4 and then add to equation (5).

$$8x - 8z = 12$$
$$\underline{5x + 8z = 14}$$
$$13x = 26$$
$$x = 2$$

Replace x with 2 in equation (4).

$$2(2) - 2z = 3$$
$$-2z = -1$$
$$z = \frac{1}{2}$$

Replace x with 2 and z with $\frac{1}{2}$ in equation (1).

$$2 + y - 4\left(\frac{1}{2}\right) = 5$$
$$2 + y - 2 = 5$$
$$y = 5$$

The solution is $\left(2, 5, \frac{1}{2}\right)$.

18. $\begin{cases} 2x - y + 3z = 2 & (1) \\ x + y - 6z = 0 & (2) \\ 3x + 4y - 3z = 6 & (3) \end{cases}$

Add equation (1) and equation (3).
$2x - y + 3z = 2$
$\underline{3x + 4y - 3z = 6}$
$5x + 3y \quad\quad = 8 \quad (4)$

Multiply equation (1) by 2 and then add to equation (2).
$4x - 2y + 6z = 4$
$\underline{x + y - 6z = 0}$
$5x - y \quad\quad = 4 \quad (5)$

Multiply equation (5) by 3 and then add to equation (4).
$15x - 3y = 12$
$\underline{5x + 3y = 8}$
$20x \quad\quad = 20$
$\quad\quad x = 1$

Replace x with 1 in equation (5).
$5(1) - y = 4$
$\quad -y = -1$
$\quad\quad y = 1$

Replace both x and y with 1 in equation (1).
$2(1) - (1) + 3z = 2$
$\quad\quad 1 + 3z = 2$
$\quad\quad\quad 3z = 1$
$\quad\quad\quad z = \dfrac{1}{3}$

The solution is $\left(1, 1, \dfrac{1}{3}\right)$.

19. Let x = the first number and y = the second number.
$\begin{cases} x = y - 8 \\ 2x = y + 11 \end{cases}$

Substitute $x = y - 8$ in the second equation.
$2(y - 8) = y + 11$
$2y - 16 = y + 11$
$\quad\quad y = 27$

Replace y with 27 in the first equation.
$x = 27 - 8 = 19$
The numbers are 19 and 27.

20. Let x = measure of the two smallest angles,
y = measure of the third angle, and
z = measure of the fourth angle.
$\begin{cases} 2x + y + z = 360 \\ y = x + 30 \\ z = x + 50 \end{cases}$

Substitute $y = x + 30$ and $z = x + 50$ in the first equation.
$2x + (x + 30) + (x + 50) = 360$
$\quad\quad\quad\quad 4x + 80 = 360$
$\quad\quad\quad\quad\quad\quad 4x = 280$
$\quad\quad\quad\quad\quad\quad\quad x = 70$
So $y = 70 + 30 = 100$ and $z = 70 + 50 = 120$.

The two smallest angles are 70°, the third angle is 100°, and the fourth angle is 120°.

Exercise Set 4.4

1. $\begin{cases} x + y = 1 \\ x - 2y = 4 \end{cases}$

$\begin{bmatrix} 1 & 1 & | & 1 \\ 1 & -2 & | & 4 \end{bmatrix}$

Multiply R1 by −1 and add to R2.
$\begin{bmatrix} 1 & 1 & | & 1 \\ 0 & -3 & | & 3 \end{bmatrix}$

Divide R2 by −3.
$\begin{bmatrix} 1 & 1 & | & 1 \\ 0 & 1 & | & -1 \end{bmatrix}$

This corresponds to $\begin{cases} x + y = 1 \\ \quad\quad y = -1 \end{cases}$.

Let $y = -1$ in the first equation.
$x + (-1) = 1$
$x - 1 = 1$
$x = 2$
The solution is $(2, -1)$.

3. $\begin{cases} x + 3y = 2 \\ x + 2y = 0 \end{cases}$

$\begin{bmatrix} 1 & 3 & | & 2 \\ 1 & 2 & | & 0 \end{bmatrix}$

Multiply R1 by −1 and add to R2.

$$\begin{bmatrix} 1 & 3 & | & 2 \\ 0 & -1 & | & -2 \end{bmatrix}$$

Multiply R2 by –1.

$$\begin{bmatrix} 1 & 3 & | & 2 \\ 0 & 1 & | & 2 \end{bmatrix}$$

This corresponds to

$$\begin{cases} x + 3y = 2 \\ \quad\quad y = 2 \end{cases}.$$

Let $y = 2$ in the first equation.

$x + 3(2) = 6$

$x + 6 = 2$

$x = -4$

The solution is (–4, 2).

5. $\begin{cases} x - 2y = 4 \\ 2x - 4y = 4 \end{cases}$

$$\begin{bmatrix} 1 & -2 & | & 4 \\ 2 & -4 & | & 4 \end{bmatrix}$$

Multiply R1 by –2 and add to R2.

$$\begin{bmatrix} 1 & -2 & | & 4 \\ 0 & 0 & | & -4 \end{bmatrix}$$

This corresponds to

$$\begin{cases} x - 2y = 4 \\ \quad\quad 0 = -4 \end{cases}.$$

This is an inconsistent system. The solution is $\varnothing$.

7. $\begin{cases} 3x - 3y = 9 \\ 2x - 2y = 6 \end{cases}$

$$\begin{bmatrix} 3 & -3 & | & 9 \\ 2 & -2 & | & 6 \end{bmatrix}$$

Divide R1 by 3.

$$\begin{bmatrix} 1 & -1 & | & 3 \\ 2 & -2 & | & 6 \end{bmatrix}$$

Multiply R1 by –2 and add to R2.

$$\begin{bmatrix} 1 & -1 & | & 3 \\ 0 & 0 & | & 0 \end{bmatrix}$$

This corresponds to

$$\begin{cases} x - y = 3 \\ \quad\quad 0 = 0 \end{cases}.$$

This is a dependent system. The solution is
$\{(x,\ y)\ |\ 3x - 3y = 9\}$.

9. $\begin{cases} x + y \quad\quad = 3 \\ \quad\quad 2y \quad = 10 \\ 3x + 2y - 4z = 12 \end{cases}$

$$\begin{bmatrix} 1 & 1 & 0 & | & 3 \\ 0 & 2 & 0 & | & 10 \\ 3 & 2 & -4 & | & 12 \end{bmatrix}$$

Multiply R1 by –3 and add to R3.

$$\begin{bmatrix} 1 & 1 & 0 & | & 3 \\ 0 & 2 & 0 & | & 10 \\ 0 & -1 & -4 & | & 3 \end{bmatrix}$$

Divide R2 by 2.

$$\begin{bmatrix} 1 & 1 & 0 & | & 3 \\ 0 & 1 & 0 & | & 5 \\ 0 & -1 & -4 & | & 3 \end{bmatrix}$$

Add R2 to R3.

$$\begin{bmatrix} 1 & 1 & 0 & | & 3 \\ 0 & 1 & 0 & | & 5 \\ 0 & 0 & -4 & | & 8 \end{bmatrix}$$

Divide R3 by –4.

$$\begin{bmatrix} 1 & 1 & 0 & | & 3 \\ 0 & 1 & 0 & | & 5 \\ 0 & 0 & 1 & | & -2 \end{bmatrix}$$

This corresponds to

$$\begin{cases} x + y = 3 \\ \quad\ y = 5 \\ \quad\quad z = -2 \end{cases}.$$

Let $y = 5$ in the first equation.

$x + 5 = 3$

$\quad x = -2$

The solution is (–2, 5, –2).

11. $\begin{cases} \quad\quad 2y - z = -7 \\ x + 4y + z = -4 \\ 5x - y + 2z = 13 \end{cases}$

$$\begin{bmatrix} 0 & 2 & -1 & | & -7 \\ 1 & 4 & 1 & | & -4 \\ 5 & -1 & 2 & | & 13 \end{bmatrix}$$

Interchange R1 and R2.

$$\begin{bmatrix} 1 & 4 & 1 & | & -4 \\ 0 & 2 & -1 & | & -7 \\ 5 & -1 & 2 & | & 13 \end{bmatrix}$$

Multiply R1 by –5 and add to R3.

$$\begin{bmatrix} 1 & 4 & 1 & | & -4 \\ 0 & 2 & -1 & | & -7 \\ 0 & -21 & -3 & | & 33 \end{bmatrix}$$

Divide R2 by 2.

$$\begin{bmatrix} 1 & 4 & 1 & | & -4 \\ 0 & 1 & -\frac{1}{2} & | & -\frac{7}{2} \\ 0 & -21 & -3 & | & 33 \end{bmatrix}$$

Multiply R2 by 21 and add to R3.

$$\begin{bmatrix} 1 & 4 & 1 & | & -4 \\ 0 & 1 & -\frac{1}{2} & | & -\frac{7}{2} \\ 0 & 0 & -\frac{27}{2} & | & -\frac{81}{2} \end{bmatrix}$$

Multiply R2 by $-\frac{2}{27}$.

$$\begin{bmatrix} 1 & 4 & 1 & | & -4 \\ 0 & 1 & -\frac{1}{2} & | & -\frac{7}{2} \\ 0 & 0 & 1 & | & 3 \end{bmatrix}$$

This corresponds to

$$\begin{cases} x+4y+z=4 \\ \quad y-\frac{1}{2}z=-\frac{7}{2} \\ \qquad\quad z=3 \end{cases}.$$

Let $z=3$ in the second equation.

$$y-\frac{1}{2}(3)=-\frac{7}{2}$$

$$y-\frac{3}{2}=-\frac{7}{2}$$

$$y=-2$$

Let $y=-2$ and $z=3$ in the first equation.

$$x+4(-2)+3=-4$$

$$x-8+3=-4$$

$$x=1$$

The solution is $(1, -2, 3)$.

13. $\begin{cases} x-4=0 \\ x+y=1 \end{cases}$ or $\begin{cases} x=4 \\ x+y=1 \end{cases}$

$$\begin{bmatrix} 1 & 0 & | & 4 \\ 1 & 1 & | & 1 \end{bmatrix}$$

Multiply R1 by -1 and add to R2.

$$\begin{bmatrix} 1 & 0 & | & 4 \\ 0 & 1 & | & -3 \end{bmatrix}$$

This corresponds to

$$\begin{cases} x=4 \\ y=-3 \end{cases}$$

The solution is $(4, -3)$.

15. $\begin{cases} x+y+z=2 \\ 2x\quad-z=5 \\ \quad 3y+z=2 \end{cases}$

$$\begin{bmatrix} 1 & 1 & 1 & | & 2 \\ 2 & 0 & -1 & | & 5 \\ 0 & 3 & 1 & | & 2 \end{bmatrix}$$

Multiply R1 by -2 and add to R2.

$$\begin{bmatrix} 1 & 1 & 1 & | & 2 \\ 0 & -2 & -3 & | & 1 \\ 0 & 3 & 1 & | & 2 \end{bmatrix}$$

Divide R2 by -2.

$$\begin{bmatrix} 1 & 1 & 1 & | & 2 \\ 0 & 1 & \frac{3}{2} & | & -\frac{1}{2} \\ 0 & 3 & 1 & | & 2 \end{bmatrix}$$

Multiply R2 by -3 and add to R3.

$$\begin{bmatrix} 1 & 1 & 1 & | & 2 \\ 0 & 1 & \frac{3}{2} & | & -\frac{1}{2} \\ 0 & 0 & -\frac{7}{2} & | & \frac{7}{2} \end{bmatrix}$$

Multiply R3 by $-\frac{2}{7}$.

$$\begin{bmatrix} 1 & 1 & 1 & | & 2 \\ 0 & 1 & \frac{3}{2} & | & -\frac{1}{2} \\ 0 & 0 & 1 & | & -1 \end{bmatrix}$$

This corresponds to

$$\begin{cases} x+y+z=2 \\ y+\dfrac{3}{2}z=-\dfrac{1}{2} \\ \phantom{y+\dfrac{3}{2}}z=-1 \end{cases}.$$

Let $z=-1$ in the second equation.

$$y+\dfrac{3}{2}(-1)=-\dfrac{1}{2}$$

$$y-\dfrac{3}{2}=-\dfrac{1}{2}$$

$$y=1$$

Let $y=1$ and $z=-1$ in the first equation.

$$x+1+(-1)=2$$

$$x=2$$

The solution is $(2, 1, -1)$.

17. $\begin{cases} 5x-2y=27 \\ -3x+5y=18 \end{cases}$

$$\begin{bmatrix} 5 & -2 & | & 27 \\ -3 & 5 & | & 18 \end{bmatrix}$$

Divide R1 by 5.

$$\begin{bmatrix} 1 & -\dfrac{2}{5} & \Big| & \dfrac{27}{5} \\ -3 & 5 & \Big| & 18 \end{bmatrix}$$

Multiply R1 by 3 and add to R2.

$$\begin{bmatrix} 1 & -\dfrac{2}{5} & \Big| & \dfrac{27}{5} \\ 0 & \dfrac{19}{5} & \Big| & \dfrac{171}{5} \end{bmatrix}$$

Multiply R2 by $\dfrac{5}{19}$.

$$\begin{bmatrix} 1 & -\dfrac{2}{5} & \Big| & \dfrac{27}{5} \\ 0 & 1 & | & 9 \end{bmatrix}$$

This corresponds to

$$\begin{cases} x-\dfrac{2}{5}y=\dfrac{27}{5} \\ \phantom{x-\dfrac{2}{5}}y=9 \end{cases}.$$

Let $y=9$ in the first equation.

$$x-\dfrac{2}{5}(9)=\dfrac{27}{5}$$

$$x-\dfrac{18}{5}=\dfrac{27}{5}$$

$$x=9$$

The solution is $(9, 9)$.

19. $\begin{cases} 4x-7y=7 \\ 12x-21y=24 \end{cases}$

$$\begin{bmatrix} 4 & -7 & | & 7 \\ 12 & -21 & | & 24 \end{bmatrix}$$

Divide R1 by 4.

$$\begin{bmatrix} 1 & -\dfrac{7}{4} & \Big| & \dfrac{7}{4} \\ 12 & -21 & \Big| & 24 \end{bmatrix}$$

Multiply R1 by -12 and add to R2.

$$\begin{bmatrix} 1 & -\dfrac{7}{4} & \Big| & \dfrac{7}{4} \\ 0 & 0 & | & 3 \end{bmatrix}$$

This corresponds to

$$\begin{cases} x-\dfrac{7}{4}y=\dfrac{7}{4} \\ \phantom{x-\dfrac{7}{4}y=}0=3 \end{cases}.$$

The system is inconsistent. The solution set is $\varnothing$.

21. $\begin{cases} 4x-y+2z=5 \\ 2y+z=4 \\ 4x+y+3z=10 \end{cases}$

$$\begin{bmatrix} 4 & -1 & 2 & | & 5 \\ 0 & 2 & 1 & | & 4 \\ 4 & 1 & 3 & | & 10 \end{bmatrix}$$

Divide R1 by 4.

$$\begin{bmatrix} 1 & -\dfrac{1}{4} & \dfrac{1}{2} & \Big| & \dfrac{5}{4} \\ 0 & 2 & 1 & \Big| & 4 \\ 4 & 1 & 3 & \Big| & 10 \end{bmatrix}$$

Multiply R1 by -4 and add to R3.

$$\begin{bmatrix} 1 & -\dfrac{1}{4} & \dfrac{1}{2} & \Big| & \dfrac{5}{4} \\ 0 & 2 & 1 & \Big| & 4 \\ 0 & 2 & 1 & \Big| & 5 \end{bmatrix}$$

Divide R2 by 2.

$$\begin{bmatrix} 1 & -\dfrac{1}{4} & \dfrac{1}{2} & \Big| & \dfrac{5}{4} \\ 0 & 1 & \dfrac{1}{2} & \Big| & 2 \\ 0 & 2 & 1 & \Big| & 5 \end{bmatrix}$$

Multiply R2 by -2 and add to R3.

$$\begin{bmatrix} 1 & -\frac{1}{4} & \frac{1}{2} & \Big| & \frac{5}{4} \\ 0 & 1 & \frac{1}{2} & \Big| & 2 \\ 0 & 0 & 0 & \Big| & 1 \end{bmatrix}$$

This corresponds to

$$\begin{cases} x - \frac{1}{4}y + \frac{1}{2}z = \frac{5}{4} \\ y + \frac{1}{2}z = 2 \\ 0 = 1 \end{cases}.$$

The system is inconsistent. The solution set is $\varnothing$.

23. $\begin{cases} 4x + y + z = 3 \\ -x + y - 2z = -11 \\ x + 2y + 2z = -1 \end{cases}$

$$\begin{bmatrix} 4 & 1 & 1 & | & 3 \\ -1 & 1 & -2 & | & -11 \\ 1 & 2 & 2 & | & -1 \end{bmatrix}$$

Interchange R1 and R3.

$$\begin{bmatrix} 1 & 2 & 2 & | & -1 \\ -1 & 1 & -2 & | & -11 \\ 4 & 1 & 1 & | & 3 \end{bmatrix}$$

Add R1 to R2.
Multiply R1 by –4 and add to R3.

$$\begin{bmatrix} 1 & 2 & 2 & | & -1 \\ 0 & 3 & 0 & | & -12 \\ 0 & -7 & -7 & | & 7 \end{bmatrix}$$

Divide R2 by 3.

$$\begin{bmatrix} 1 & 2 & 2 & | & -1 \\ 0 & 1 & 0 & | & -4 \\ 0 & -7 & -7 & | & 7 \end{bmatrix}$$

Multiply R2 by 7 and add to R3.

$$\begin{bmatrix} 1 & 2 & 2 & | & -1 \\ 0 & 1 & 0 & | & -4 \\ 0 & 0 & -7 & | & -21 \end{bmatrix}$$

Divide R3 by –7.

$$\begin{bmatrix} 1 & 2 & 2 & | & -1 \\ 0 & 1 & 0 & | & -4 \\ 0 & 0 & 1 & | & 3 \end{bmatrix}$$

This corresponds to

$$\begin{cases} x + 2y + 2z = -1 \\ y = -4 \\ z = 3 \end{cases}.$$

Let $y = -4$ and $z = 3$ in the first equation.

$$x + 2(-4) + 2(3) = -1$$
$$x - 8 + 6 = -1$$
$$x = 1$$

The solution is (1, –4, 3).

25. Function. For each value of the independent variable x, there is exactly one value for the dependent variable y.

27. Not a function. The graph fails the vertical line test.

29. $(-1)(-5) - (6)(3) = 5 - 18 = -13$

31. $(4)(-10) - (2)(-2) = -40 + 4 = -36$

33. $(-3)(-3) - (-1)(-9) = 9 - 9 = 0$

35. a. Solve the system

$$\begin{cases} 2.3x + y = 52 \\ -5.4x + y = 14 \end{cases}.$$

$$\begin{bmatrix} 2.3 & 1 & | & 52 \\ -5.4 & 1 & | & 14 \end{bmatrix}$$

Since getting 1 in the first column would lead to repeating decimals, we multiply R1 by –1 and add to R2.

$$\begin{bmatrix} 2.3 & 1 & | & 52 \\ -7.7 & 0 & | & -38 \end{bmatrix}$$

This corresponds to

$$\begin{cases} 2.3x + y = 52 \\ -7.7x = -38 \end{cases}.$$

From the second equation,

$$x = \frac{-3.8}{-7.7} \approx 4.935.$$

Thus, the percent of U.S. households owning black-and-white television sets was the same as the percent of U.S. households owning a microwave oven in the end of 1984 (about 4.9 years after 1980).

b. Solve the television equation for y:
$y = -2.3x + 52$.
Thus, for 1980,
$y = -2.3(0) + 52 = 52$,
and for 1993,
$y = -2.3(13) + 52 = 22.1$.

Solve the microwave equation for y:
$y = 5.4x + 14$.
Thus, for 1980
$y = 5.4(0) + 14 = 14$,
and for 1993,
$y = 5.4(13) + 14 = 84.2$.

In 1980, a greater percent of (and hence more) U.S. households owned black-and-white television sets. In 1993, more households owned a microwave oven. The percent owning black-and-white television sets is decreasing and the percent owning a microwave oven is increasing.
Answers may vary.

c. Let $y = 0$ in the television equation.
$2.3x + y = 52$
$2.3x + 0 = 52$
$x = \dfrac{52}{2.3} \approx 22.6$
According to this model, the percent of U.S. households owning a black-and-white television set will be 0% about 22.6 years after 1980, or sometime in 2002.

d. Answers may vary. The answer to part **c** is not accurate since there were still many black and white television sets in 2002.

37. Answers may vary. The matrix does not take into account the negative y coefficient in the first equation, nor the implied x coefficient of 1 in the second equation.

Exercise Set 4.5

1. $\begin{vmatrix} 3 & 5 \\ -1 & 7 \end{vmatrix} = 3(7) - 5(-1) = 21 + 5 = 26$

3. $\begin{vmatrix} 9 & -2 \\ 4 & -3 \end{vmatrix} = 9(-3) - 4(-2) = -27 + 8 = -19$

5. $\begin{vmatrix} -2 & 9 \\ 4 & -18 \end{vmatrix} = -2(-18) - 9(4) = 36 - 36 = 0$

7. $\begin{cases} 2y - 4 = 0 \\ x + 2y = 5 \end{cases}$ or $\begin{cases} 2y = 4 \\ x + 2y = 5 \end{cases}$

$D = \begin{vmatrix} 0 & 2 \\ 1 & 2 \end{vmatrix} = 0(2) - 2(1) = 0 - 2 = -2$

$D_x = \begin{vmatrix} 4 & 2 \\ 5 & 2 \end{vmatrix} = 4(2) - 2(5) = 8 - 10 = -2$

$D_y = \begin{vmatrix} 0 & 4 \\ 1 & 5 \end{vmatrix} = 0(5) - 4(1) = 0 - 4 = -4$

$x = \dfrac{D_x}{D} = \dfrac{-2}{-2} = 1$ and $y = \dfrac{D_y}{D} = \dfrac{-4}{-2} = 2$
The solution is (1, 2).

9. $\begin{cases} 3x + y = 1 \\ 2y = 2 - 6x \end{cases}$ or $\begin{cases} 3x + y = 1 \\ 6x + 2y = 2 \end{cases}$

$D = \begin{vmatrix} 3 & 1 \\ 6 & 2 \end{vmatrix} = 3(2) - 1(6) = 6 - 6 = 0$

Thus, the system cannot be solved by Cramer's rule. Since the second equation is 2 times the first equation, the system is dependent.
The solution is $\{(x, y) \mid 3x + y = 1\}$.

11. $\begin{cases} 5x - 2y = 27 \\ -3x + 5y = 18 \end{cases}$

$D = \begin{vmatrix} 5 & -2 \\ -3 & 5 \end{vmatrix} = 5(5) - (-2)(-3) = 25 - 6 = 19$

$D_x = \begin{vmatrix} 27 & -2 \\ 18 & 5 \end{vmatrix} = 27(5) - (-2)(18) = 135 + 36 = 171$

$D_y = \begin{vmatrix} 5 & 27 \\ -3 & 18 \end{vmatrix} = 5(18) - 27(-3) = 90 + 81 = 171$

$x = \dfrac{D_x}{D} = \dfrac{171}{19} = 9$ and $y = \dfrac{D_y}{D} = \dfrac{171}{19} = 9$
The solution is (9, 9).

13.
$$\begin{vmatrix} 2 & 1 & 0 \\ 0 & 5 & -3 \\ 4 & 0 & 2 \end{vmatrix}$$

$$= 2\begin{vmatrix} 5 & -3 \\ 0 & 2 \end{vmatrix} - 1\begin{vmatrix} 0 & -3 \\ 4 & 2 \end{vmatrix} + 0\begin{vmatrix} 0 & 5 \\ 4 & 0 \end{vmatrix}$$

$$= 2[5(2) - (-3)(0)] - [0(2) - 4(-3)] + 0$$

$$= 2(10) - 12$$

$$= 8$$

15.
$$\begin{vmatrix} 4 & -6 & 0 \\ -2 & 3 & 0 \\ 4 & -6 & 1 \end{vmatrix} = 0\begin{vmatrix} -2 & 3 \\ 4 & -6 \end{vmatrix} - 0\begin{vmatrix} 4 & -6 \\ 4 & -6 \end{vmatrix} + 1\begin{vmatrix} 4 & -6 \\ -2 & 3 \end{vmatrix}$$

$$= 0 - 0 + [4(3) - (-6)(-2)]$$

$$= 0$$

17.
$$\begin{vmatrix} 3 & 6 & -3 \\ -1 & -2 & 3 \\ 4 & -1 & 6 \end{vmatrix} = 3\begin{vmatrix} -2 & 3 \\ -1 & 6 \end{vmatrix} - 6\begin{vmatrix} -1 & 3 \\ 4 & 6 \end{vmatrix} + (-3)\begin{vmatrix} -1 & -2 \\ 4 & -1 \end{vmatrix}$$

$$= 3[-2(6) - 3(-1)] - 6[-1(6) - 3(4)]$$
$$\quad - 3[(-1)(-1) - (-2)(4)]$$

$$= 3(-9) - 6(-18) - 3(9)$$

$$= -27 + 108 - 27$$

$$= 54$$

19.
$$\begin{cases} 3x \quad + z = -1 \\ -x - 3y + z = 7 \\ 3y + z = 5 \end{cases}$$

$$D = \begin{vmatrix} 3 & 0 & 1 \\ -1 & -3 & 1 \\ 0 & 3 & 1 \end{vmatrix}$$

$$= 3\begin{vmatrix} -3 & 1 \\ 3 & 1 \end{vmatrix} - 0\begin{vmatrix} -1 & 1 \\ 0 & 1 \end{vmatrix} + 1\begin{vmatrix} -1 & -3 \\ 0 & 3 \end{vmatrix}$$

$$= 3[(-3)(1) - 1(3)] - 0$$
$$\quad + [(-1)(3) - (-3)(0)]$$

$$= 3(-6) - 3$$

$$= -21$$

$$D_x = \begin{vmatrix} -1 & 0 & 1 \\ 7 & -3 & 1 \\ 5 & 3 & 1 \end{vmatrix}$$

$$= -1\begin{vmatrix} -3 & 1 \\ 3 & 1 \end{vmatrix} - 0\begin{vmatrix} 7 & 1 \\ 5 & 1 \end{vmatrix} + 1\begin{vmatrix} 7 & -3 \\ 5 & 3 \end{vmatrix}$$

$$= -[(-3)(1) - 1(3)] - 0$$
$$\quad + [(7)(3) - (-3)(5)]$$

$$= 6 + 36$$

$$= 42$$

$$D_y = \begin{vmatrix} 3 & -1 & 1 \\ -1 & 7 & 1 \\ 0 & 5 & 1 \end{vmatrix}$$

$$= 3\begin{vmatrix} 7 & 1 \\ 5 & 1 \end{vmatrix} - (-1)\begin{vmatrix} -1 & 1 \\ 0 & 1 \end{vmatrix} + 1\begin{vmatrix} -1 & 7 \\ 0 & 5 \end{vmatrix}$$

$$= 3[7(1) - 1(5)] + 1[(-1)(1) - 1(0)]$$
$$\quad + [(-1)(5) - 7(0)]$$

$$= 3(2) + (-1) + (-5)$$

$$= 0$$

$$D_z = \begin{vmatrix} 3 & 0 & -1 \\ -1 & -3 & 7 \\ 0 & 3 & 5 \end{vmatrix}$$

$$= 3\begin{vmatrix} -3 & 7 \\ 3 & 5 \end{vmatrix} - 0\begin{vmatrix} -1 & 7 \\ 0 & 5 \end{vmatrix} + (-1)\begin{vmatrix} -1 & -3 \\ 0 & 3 \end{vmatrix}$$

$$= 3[(-3)(5) - 7(3)] - 0$$
$$\quad - [(-1)(3) - (-3)(0)]$$

$$= 3(-36) - (-3)$$

$$= -105$$

$$x = \frac{D_x}{D} = \frac{42}{-21} = -2, \quad y = \frac{D_y}{D} = \frac{0}{-21} = 0,$$

$$z = \frac{D_z}{D} = \frac{-105}{-21} = 5$$

The solution is (–2, 0, 5).

21. $\begin{cases} x + y + z = 8 \\ 2x - y - z = 10 \\ x - 2y + 3z = 22 \end{cases}$

$D = \begin{vmatrix} 1 & 1 & 1 \\ 2 & -1 & -1 \\ 1 & -2 & 3 \end{vmatrix}$

$= 1\begin{vmatrix} -1 & -1 \\ -2 & 3 \end{vmatrix} - 1\begin{vmatrix} 2 & -1 \\ 1 & 3 \end{vmatrix} + 1\begin{vmatrix} 2 & -1 \\ 1 & -2 \end{vmatrix}$

$= (-3 - 2) - [6 - (-1)] + [-4 - (-1)]$

$= -5 - 7 - 3$

$= -15$

$D_x = \begin{vmatrix} 8 & 1 & 1 \\ 10 & -1 & -1 \\ 22 & -2 & 3 \end{vmatrix}$

$= 8\begin{vmatrix} -1 & -1 \\ -2 & 3 \end{vmatrix} - 1\begin{vmatrix} 10 & -1 \\ 22 & 3 \end{vmatrix} + 1\begin{vmatrix} 10 & -1 \\ 22 & -2 \end{vmatrix}$

$= 8(-3 - 2) - [30 - (-22)]$

$\quad + [-20 - (-22)]$

$= 8(-5) - 52 + 2$

$\quad -40 - 52 + 2$

$= -90$

$D_y = \begin{vmatrix} 1 & 8 & 1 \\ 2 & 10 & -1 \\ 1 & 22 & 3 \end{vmatrix}$

$= 1\begin{vmatrix} 10 & -1 \\ 22 & 3 \end{vmatrix} - 8\begin{vmatrix} 2 & -1 \\ 1 & 3 \end{vmatrix} + 1\begin{vmatrix} 2 & 10 \\ 1 & 22 \end{vmatrix}$

$= [30 - (-22)] - 8[6 - (-1)] + (44 - 10)$

$= 52 - 8(7) + 34$

$= 52 - 56 + 34$

$= 30$

$D_z = \begin{vmatrix} 1 & 1 & 8 \\ 2 & -1 & 10 \\ 1 & -2 & 22 \end{vmatrix}$

$= 1\begin{vmatrix} -1 & 10 \\ -2 & 22 \end{vmatrix} - 1\begin{vmatrix} 2 & 10 \\ 1 & 22 \end{vmatrix} + 8\begin{vmatrix} 2 & -1 \\ 1 & -2 \end{vmatrix}$

$= [-22 - (-20)] - (44 - 10)$

$\quad + 8[-4 - (-1)]$

$= -2 - 34 + 8(-3)$

$= -36 - 24$

$= -60$

$x = \dfrac{D_x}{D} = \dfrac{-90}{-15} = 6, \quad y = \dfrac{D_y}{D} = \dfrac{30}{-15} = -2,$

$z = \dfrac{D_z}{D} = \dfrac{-60}{-15} = 4$

The solution is $(6, -2, 4)$.

23. $\begin{vmatrix} 10 & -1 \\ -4 & 2 \end{vmatrix} = 10(2) - (-1)(-4) = 20 - 4 = 16$

25. $\begin{vmatrix} 1 & 0 & 4 \\ 1 & -1 & 2 \\ 3 & 2 & 1 \end{vmatrix} = 1\begin{vmatrix} -1 & 2 \\ 2 & 1 \end{vmatrix} - 0\begin{vmatrix} 1 & 2 \\ 3 & 1 \end{vmatrix} + 4\begin{vmatrix} 1 & -1 \\ 3 & 2 \end{vmatrix}$

$= 1(-1 - 4) - 0 + 4[2 - (-3)]$

$= -5 + 4(5)$

$= -5 + 20$

$= 15$

27. $\begin{vmatrix} \dfrac{3}{4} & \dfrac{5}{2} \\ -\dfrac{1}{6} & \dfrac{7}{3} \end{vmatrix} = \dfrac{3}{4}\left(\dfrac{7}{3}\right) - \dfrac{5}{2}\left(-\dfrac{1}{6}\right)$

$= \dfrac{21}{12} + \dfrac{5}{12}$

$= \dfrac{26}{12}$

$= \dfrac{13}{6}$

29. $\begin{vmatrix} 4 & -2 & 2 \\ 6 & -1 & 3 \\ 2 & 1 & 1 \end{vmatrix} = 4\begin{vmatrix} -1 & 3 \\ 1 & 1 \end{vmatrix} - (-2)\begin{vmatrix} 6 & 3 \\ 2 & 1 \end{vmatrix} + 2\begin{vmatrix} 6 & -1 \\ 2 & 1 \end{vmatrix}$

$$= 4(-1-3) + 2(6-6) + 2[6-(-2)]$$
$$= 4(-4) + 2(0) + 2(8)$$
$$= -16 + 0 + 16$$
$$= 0$$

31. $\begin{vmatrix} -2 & 5 & 4 \\ 5 & -1 & 3 \\ 4 & 1 & 2 \end{vmatrix} = -2\begin{vmatrix} -1 & 3 \\ 1 & 2 \end{vmatrix} - 5\begin{vmatrix} 5 & 3 \\ 4 & 2 \end{vmatrix} + 4\begin{vmatrix} 5 & -1 \\ 4 & 1 \end{vmatrix}$

$$= -2(-2-3) - 5(10-12) + 4[5-(-4)]$$
$$= -2(-5) - 5(-2) + 4(9)$$
$$= 10 + 10 + 36$$
$$= 56$$

33. $\begin{cases} 2x - 5y = 4 \\ x + 2y = -7 \end{cases}$

$$D = \begin{vmatrix} 2 & -5 \\ 1 & 2 \end{vmatrix}$$
$$= 2(2) - (-5)(1) = 4 + 5 = 9$$

$$D_x = \begin{vmatrix} 4 & -5 \\ -7 & 2 \end{vmatrix}$$
$$= 4(2) - (-5)(-7)$$
$$= 8 - 35$$
$$= -27$$

$$D_y = \begin{vmatrix} 2 & 4 \\ 1 & -7 \end{vmatrix}$$
$$= 2(-7) - 4(1)$$
$$= -14 - 4$$
$$= -18$$

$$x = \frac{D_x}{D} = \frac{-27}{9} = -3$$
$$y = \frac{D_y}{D} = \frac{-18}{9} = -2$$

The solution is $(-3, -2)$.

35. $\begin{cases} 4x + 2y = 5 \\ 2x + y = -1 \end{cases}$

$$D = \begin{vmatrix} 4 & 2 \\ 2 & 1 \end{vmatrix}$$
$$= 4(1) - (2)(2) = 4 + 4 = 0$$

Thus, the system cannot be solved by Cramer's rule. Multiply the second equation by 2 yielding the new system:

$$\begin{cases} 4x + 2y = 5 \\ 4x + 2y = -2 \end{cases}$$

Therefore, the system is inconsistent. The solution is $\varnothing$.

37. $\begin{cases} 2x + 2y + z = 1 \\ -x + y + 2z = 3 \\ x + 2y + 4z = 0 \end{cases}$

$$D = \begin{vmatrix} 2 & 2 & 1 \\ -1 & 1 & 2 \\ 1 & 2 & 4 \end{vmatrix}$$

$$= 2\begin{vmatrix} 1 & 2 \\ 2 & 4 \end{vmatrix} - 2\begin{vmatrix} -1 & 2 \\ 1 & 4 \end{vmatrix} + 1\begin{vmatrix} -1 & 1 \\ 1 & 2 \end{vmatrix}$$
$$= 2(4-4) - 2(-4-2) + (-2-1)$$
$$= 2(0) - 2(-6) + (-3)$$
$$= 0 + 12 - 3$$
$$= 9$$

$$D_x = \begin{vmatrix} 1 & 2 & 1 \\ 3 & 1 & 2 \\ 0 & 2 & 4 \end{vmatrix}$$

$$= 1\begin{vmatrix} 1 & 2 \\ 2 & 4 \end{vmatrix} - 3\begin{vmatrix} 2 & 1 \\ 2 & 4 \end{vmatrix} + 0\begin{vmatrix} 2 & 1 \\ 1 & 2 \end{vmatrix}$$
$$= (4-4) - 3(8-2) + 0$$
$$= 0 - 3(6)$$
$$= -18$$

$$D_y = \begin{vmatrix} 2 & 1 & 1 \\ -1 & 3 & 2 \\ 1 & 0 & 4 \end{vmatrix}$$

$$= 1\begin{vmatrix} 1 & 1 \\ 3 & 2 \end{vmatrix} - 0\begin{vmatrix} 2 & 1 \\ -1 & 2 \end{vmatrix} + 4\begin{vmatrix} 2 & 1 \\ -1 & 3 \end{vmatrix}$$
$$= (2-3) - 0 + 4[6-(-1)]$$
$$= -1 + 4(7)$$
$$= -1 + 28$$
$$= 27$$

$$D_z = \begin{vmatrix} 2 & 2 & 1 \\ -1 & 1 & 3 \\ 1 & 2 & 0 \end{vmatrix}$$

$$= 1\begin{vmatrix} 2 & 1 \\ 1 & 3 \end{vmatrix} - 2\begin{vmatrix} 2 & 1 \\ -1 & 3 \end{vmatrix} + 0\begin{vmatrix} 2 & 2 \\ -1 & 1 \end{vmatrix}$$

$$= (6-1) - 2[6-(-1)] + 0$$

$$= 5 - 2(7)$$

$$= 5 - 14$$

$$= -9$$

$$x = \frac{D_x}{D} = \frac{-18}{9} = -2, \quad y = \frac{D_y}{D} = \frac{27}{9} = 3,$$

$$z = \frac{D_z}{D} = \frac{-9}{9} = -1$$

The solution is (–2, 3, –1).

39. $\begin{cases} \dfrac{2}{3}x - \dfrac{3}{4}y = -1 \\ -\dfrac{1}{6}x + \dfrac{3}{4}y = \dfrac{5}{2} \end{cases}$

$$D = \begin{vmatrix} \dfrac{2}{3} & -\dfrac{3}{4} \\ -\dfrac{1}{6} & \dfrac{3}{4} \end{vmatrix}$$

$$= \frac{2}{3}\left(\frac{3}{4}\right) - \left(-\frac{3}{4}\right)\left(-\frac{1}{6}\right)$$

$$= \frac{1}{2} - \frac{1}{8}$$

$$= \frac{3}{8}$$

$$D_x = \begin{vmatrix} -1 & -\dfrac{3}{4} \\ \dfrac{5}{2} & \dfrac{3}{4} \end{vmatrix}$$

$$= (-1)\left(\frac{3}{4}\right) - \left(-\frac{3}{4}\right)\left(\frac{5}{2}\right)$$

$$= -\frac{3}{4} + \frac{15}{8}$$

$$= \frac{9}{8}$$

$$D_y = \begin{vmatrix} \dfrac{2}{3} & -1 \\ -\dfrac{1}{6} & \dfrac{5}{2} \end{vmatrix}$$

$$= \frac{2}{3}\left(\frac{5}{2}\right) - (-1)\left(-\frac{1}{6}\right)$$

$$= \frac{5}{3} - \frac{1}{6}$$

$$= \frac{3}{2}$$

$$x = \frac{D_x}{D} = \frac{\dfrac{9}{8}}{\dfrac{3}{8}} = 3 \text{ and } y = \frac{D_y}{D} = \frac{\dfrac{3}{2}}{\dfrac{3}{8}} = 4$$

The solution is (3, 4).

41. $\begin{cases} 0.7x - 0.2y = -1.6 \\ 0.2x - y = -1.4 \end{cases}$

$$D = \begin{vmatrix} 0.7 & -0.2 \\ 0.2 & -1 \end{vmatrix}$$

$$= 0.7(-1) - (-0.2)(0.2)$$

$$= -0.7 + 0.04$$

$$= -0.66$$

$$D_x = \begin{vmatrix} -1.6 & -0.2 \\ -1.4 & -1 \end{vmatrix}$$

$$= -1.6(-1) - (-0.2)(-1.4)$$

$$= 1.6 - 0.28$$

$$= 1.32$$

$$D_y = \begin{vmatrix} 0.7 & -1.6 \\ 0.2 & -1.4 \end{vmatrix}$$

$$= 0.7(-1.4) - (-1.6)(0.2)$$

$$= -0.98 + 0.32$$

$$= -0.66$$

$$x = \frac{D_x}{D} = \frac{1.32}{-0.66} = -2 \text{ and}$$

$$y = \frac{D_y}{D} = \frac{-0.66}{-0.66} = 1$$

The solution is (–2, 1).

43. $\begin{cases} -2x+4y-2z=6 \\ x-2y+\ z=-3 \\ 3x-6y+3z=-9 \end{cases}$

$$D = \begin{vmatrix} -2 & 4 & -2 \\ 1 & -2 & 1 \\ 3 & -6 & 3 \end{vmatrix}$$

$$= -2\begin{vmatrix} -2 & 1 \\ -6 & 3 \end{vmatrix} - 4\begin{vmatrix} 1 & 1 \\ 3 & 3 \end{vmatrix} + (-2)\begin{vmatrix} 1 & -2 \\ 3 & -6 \end{vmatrix}$$

$$= -2[-6-(-6)] - 4(3-3) - 2[-6-(-6)]$$

$$= 2(0) - 4(0) - 2(0)$$

$$= 0$$

Therefore, Cramer's rule will not provide the solution. Note that the first equation is –2 times the second equation and that the third equation is 3 times the second equation. Thus, the system is dependent. The solution is

$$\{(x,\,y,\,z)\,|\,x-2y+z=-3\}.$$

45. $\begin{cases} x-2y+\ z=-5 \\ 3y+2z=4 \\ 3x-y\quad\ =-2 \end{cases}$

$$D = \begin{vmatrix} 1 & -2 & 1 \\ 0 & 3 & 2 \\ 3 & -1 & 0 \end{vmatrix}$$

$$= 1\begin{vmatrix} 3 & 2 \\ -1 & 0 \end{vmatrix} - 0\begin{vmatrix} -2 & 1 \\ -1 & 0 \end{vmatrix} + 3\begin{vmatrix} -2 & 1 \\ 3 & 2 \end{vmatrix}$$

$$= [0-(-2)] - 0 + 3(-4-3)$$

$$= 2 + 3(-7)$$

$$= -19$$

$$D_x = \begin{vmatrix} -5 & -2 & 1 \\ 4 & 3 & 2 \\ -2 & -1 & 0 \end{vmatrix}$$

$$= 1\begin{vmatrix} 4 & 3 \\ -2 & -1 \end{vmatrix} - 2\begin{vmatrix} -5 & -2 \\ -2 & -1 \end{vmatrix} + 0\begin{vmatrix} -5 & -2 \\ 4 & 3 \end{vmatrix}$$

$$= [-4-(-6)] - 2(5-4) + 0$$

$$= 2 - 2(1)$$

$$= 0$$

$$D_y = \begin{vmatrix} 1 & -5 & 1 \\ 0 & 4 & 2 \\ 3 & -2 & 0 \end{vmatrix}$$

$$= 1\begin{vmatrix} 4 & 2 \\ -2 & 0 \end{vmatrix} - 0\begin{vmatrix} -5 & 1 \\ -2 & 0 \end{vmatrix} + 3\begin{vmatrix} -5 & 1 \\ 4 & 2 \end{vmatrix}$$

$$= [0-(-4)] - 0 + 3(-10-4)$$

$$= 4 + 3(-14)$$

$$= 4 - 42$$

$$= -38$$

$$D_z = \begin{vmatrix} 1 & -2 & -5 \\ 0 & 3 & 4 \\ 3 & -1 & -2 \end{vmatrix}$$

$$= 1\begin{vmatrix} 3 & 4 \\ -1 & -2 \end{vmatrix} - 0\begin{vmatrix} -2 & -5 \\ -1 & -2 \end{vmatrix} + 3\begin{vmatrix} -2 & -5 \\ 3 & 4 \end{vmatrix}$$

$$= [-6-(-4)] - 0 + 3[-8-(-15)]$$

$$= -2 + 3(7)$$

$$= 19$$

$$x = \frac{D_x}{D} = \frac{0}{-19} = 0,\quad y = \frac{D_y}{D} = \frac{-38}{-19} = 2,$$

$$z = \frac{D_z}{D} = \frac{19}{-19} = -1$$

The solution is $(0, 2, -1)$.

47. $5x-6+x-12=6x-18$

49. $2(3x-6)+3(x-1)=6x-12+3x-3$
$$=9x-15$$

51. $f(x)=5x-6$ or $y=5x-6$

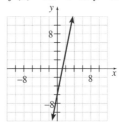

53. $h(x) = 3$ or $y = 3$

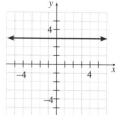

55. $\begin{vmatrix} 1 & x \\ 2 & 7 \end{vmatrix} = -3$

$1(7) - 2x = -3$

$7 - 2x = -3$

$-2x = -10$

$x = 5$

57. If the elements of a single row (or column) of a determinant are all zero, the value of the determinant will be zero. To see this, consider expanding on that row (or column) containing all zeros.

59. The array of signs for use with a 4×4 matrix is

$+ \; - \; + \; -$

$- \; + \; - \; +$

$+ \; - \; + \; -$

$- \; + \; - \; +$

61. $\begin{vmatrix} 5 & 0 & 0 & 0 \\ 0 & 4 & 2 & -1 \\ 1 & 3 & -2 & 0 \\ 0 & -3 & 1 & 2 \end{vmatrix} = 5\begin{vmatrix} 4 & 2 & -1 \\ 3 & -2 & 0 \\ -3 & 1 & 2 \end{vmatrix} - 0\begin{vmatrix} 0 & 2 & -1 \\ 1 & -2 & 0 \\ 0 & 1 & 2 \end{vmatrix}$

$+ 0\begin{vmatrix} 0 & 4 & -1 \\ 1 & 3 & 0 \\ 0 & -3 & 2 \end{vmatrix} - 0\begin{vmatrix} 0 & 4 & 2 \\ 1 & 3 & -2 \\ 0 & -3 & 1 \end{vmatrix}$

$= 5\left[(-1)\begin{vmatrix} 3 & -2 \\ -3 & 1 \end{vmatrix} - 0\begin{vmatrix} 4 & 2 \\ -3 & 1 \end{vmatrix} + 2\begin{vmatrix} 4 & 2 \\ 3 & -2 \end{vmatrix} \right]$

$= 5[-(3-6) - 0 + 2(-8-6)]$

$= 5[3 + 2(-14)]$

$= 5(3 - 28)$

$= 5(-25)$

$= -125$

63. $\begin{vmatrix} 4 & 0 & 2 & 5 \\ 0 & 3 & -1 & 1 \\ 0 & 0 & 2 & 0 \\ 0 & 0 & 0 & 1 \end{vmatrix} = 4\begin{vmatrix} 3 & -1 & 1 \\ 0 & 2 & 0 \\ 0 & 0 & 1 \end{vmatrix} - 0\begin{vmatrix} 0 & 2 & 5 \\ 0 & 2 & 0 \\ 0 & 0 & 1 \end{vmatrix}$

$+ 0\begin{vmatrix} 0 & 2 & 5 \\ 3 & -1 & 1 \\ 0 & 0 & 1 \end{vmatrix} - 0\begin{vmatrix} 0 & 2 & 5 \\ 3 & -1 & 1 \\ 0 & 2 & 0 \end{vmatrix}$

$= 4\left[3\begin{vmatrix} 2 & 0 \\ 0 & 1 \end{vmatrix} - 0\begin{vmatrix} -1 & 1 \\ 0 & 1 \end{vmatrix} + 0\begin{vmatrix} -1 & 1 \\ 2 & 0 \end{vmatrix} \right]$

$= 4[3(2-0) - 0 + 0]$

$= 4(6)$

$= 24$

Chapter 4 Review

1. $\begin{cases} 3x + 10y = 1 \\ x + 2y = -1 \end{cases}$

(1) $\begin{cases} y = \dfrac{-3x+1}{10} \\ y = \dfrac{-x-1}{2} \end{cases}$

Graph $y_1 = \dfrac{-3x+1}{10}$ and $y_2 = \dfrac{-x-1}{2}$ and find the intersection point. Using a standard viewing window, we get:

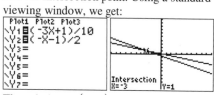

The solution is $(-3, 1)$.

(2) From the second equation:

$x = -2y - 1$

Replace x with $-2y - 1$ in the first equation.

$3(-2y - 1) + 10y = 1$

$-6y - 3 + 10y = 1$

$4y = 4$

$y = 1$

Replace y with 1 in the equation

$x = -2y - 1$.

$x = -2(1) - 1 = -3$

The solution is $(-3, 1)$.

(3) Multiply the second equation by –3 and add to the first equation.

$$3x + 10y = 1$$
$$\underline{-3x - 6y = 3}$$
$$4y = 4$$
$$y = 1$$

Replace y with 1 in the second equation.

$$x + 2(1) = -1$$
$$x + 2 = -1$$
$$x = -3$$

The solution is (–3, 1).

2. $\begin{cases} y = \dfrac{1}{2}x + \dfrac{2}{3} \\ 4x + 6y = 4 \end{cases}$

(1) $\begin{cases} y = \dfrac{1}{2}x + \dfrac{2}{3} \\ y = -\dfrac{2}{3}x + \dfrac{2}{3} \end{cases}$

Graph $y_1 = \dfrac{1}{2}x + \dfrac{2}{3}$ and $y_2 = -\dfrac{2}{3}x + \dfrac{2}{3}$ and find the point of intersection. Using a standard viewing window, we get:

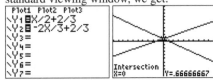

The solution is $\left(0, \dfrac{2}{3}\right)$.

(2) Replace y with $\dfrac{1}{2}x + \dfrac{2}{3}$ in the second equation.

$$4x + 6\left(\dfrac{1}{2}x + \dfrac{2}{3}\right) = 4$$
$$4x + 3x + 4 = 4$$
$$x = 0$$

Replace x with 0 in the first equation.

$$y = \dfrac{1}{2}(0) + \dfrac{2}{3} = \dfrac{2}{3}$$

The solution is $\left(0, \dfrac{2}{3}\right)$.

(3) Rewrite the system: $\begin{cases} -\dfrac{1}{2}x + y = \dfrac{2}{3} \\ 4x + 6y = 4 \end{cases}$.

Multiply the first equation by –6.

$$\begin{cases} 3x - 6y = -4 \\ 4x + 6y = 4 \end{cases}$$

Add these equations.

$$7x = 0$$
$$x = 0$$

Replace x with 0 in second equation.

$$4(0) + 6y = 4$$
$$6y = 4$$
$$y = \dfrac{4}{6} = \dfrac{2}{3}$$

The solution is $\left(0, \dfrac{2}{3}\right)$.

3. $\begin{cases} 2x - 4y = 22 \\ 5x - 10y = 16 \end{cases}$

(1) $\begin{cases} y = \dfrac{1}{2}x - \dfrac{11}{2} \\ y = \dfrac{1}{2}x - \dfrac{8}{5} \end{cases}$

Graph $y_1 = \dfrac{1}{2}x - \dfrac{11}{2}$ and $y_2 = \dfrac{1}{2}x - \dfrac{8}{5}$ and find the point of intersection. Using a standard viewing window, we get:

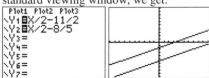

The two lines are parallel so the system is inconsistent. The solution is $\varnothing$.

(2) Solve the first equation for x.

$$2x - 4y = 22$$
$$2x = 4y + 22$$
$$x = 2y + 11$$

Replace x with $2y + 11$ in the second equation.

$$5(2y + 11) - 10y = 15$$
$$10y + 55 - 10y = 15$$
$$55 = 15 \quad \text{False}$$

This is an inconsistent system. The solution is $\varnothing$.

(3) Multiply the first equation by 5 and the second equation by –2.

$$\begin{cases} 10x - 20y = 110 \\ -10x + 20y = -32 \end{cases}$$

Add these equations.

$$10x - 20y = 110$$
$$\underline{-10x + 20y = -32}$$
$$0 = 78 \quad \text{False}$$

This is an inconsistent system. The solution is $\varnothing$.

4. $\begin{cases} 3x - 6y = 12 \\ 2y = x - 4 \end{cases}$

(1) $\begin{cases} y = \dfrac{1}{2}x - 2 \\ y = \dfrac{1}{2}x - 2 \end{cases}$

The equations are identical so the system is dependent. The solution is
$\{(x, y) \mid 3x - 6y = 12\}$.

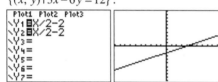

(2) Solve the second equation for x.
$$x = 2y + 4$$

Replace x with $2y + 4$ in the first equation.

$$3(2y + 4) - 6y = 12$$
$$6y + 12 - 6y = 12$$
$$12 = 12 \quad \text{True}$$

This is a dependent system. The solution is $\{(x, y) \mid 3x - 6y = 12\}$.

(3) $\begin{cases} 3x - 6y = 12 \\ -x + 2y = -4 \end{cases}$

Multiply the second equation by 3.

$$\begin{cases} 3x - 6y = 12 \\ -3x + 6y = -12 \end{cases}$$

Add these equations.

$$3x - 6y = 12$$
$$\underline{-3x + 6y = -12}$$
$$0 = 0 \quad \text{True}$$

This is a dependent system. The solution is $\{(x, y) \mid 3x - 6y = 12\}$.

5. $\begin{cases} \dfrac{1}{2}x - \dfrac{3}{4}y = -\dfrac{1}{2} \\ \dfrac{1}{8}x + \dfrac{3}{4}y = \dfrac{19}{8} \end{cases}$

(1) $\begin{cases} y = \dfrac{2}{3}x + \dfrac{2}{3} \\ y = -\dfrac{1}{6}x + \dfrac{19}{6} \end{cases}$

Graph $y_1 = \dfrac{2}{3}x + \dfrac{2}{3}$ and $y_2 = -\dfrac{1}{6}x + \dfrac{19}{6}$ and find the point of intersection. Using a standard viewing window, we get:

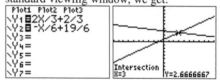

The solution is $\left(3, \dfrac{8}{3}\right)$.

(2) Clear fractions by multiplying the first equation by 4 and the second equation by 8.

$$\begin{cases} 2x - 3y = -2 \\ x + 6y = 19 \end{cases}$$

Solve the new second equation for x.
$$x = -6y + 19$$

Replace x with $-6y + 19$ in the new first equation.

$$2(-6y+19)-3y=-2$$
$$-12y+38-3y=-2$$
$$-15y=-40$$
$$y=\frac{-40}{-15}=\frac{8}{3}$$

Replace y with $\frac{8}{3}$ in the equation

$x=-6y+19$.

$$x=-6\left(\frac{8}{3}\right)+19$$
$$x=-16+19$$
$$x=3$$

The solution is $\left(3,\frac{8}{3}\right)$.

(3) Add the equations.

$$\frac{1}{2}x-\frac{3}{4}y=-\frac{1}{2}$$
$$\frac{1}{8}x+\frac{3}{4}y=\frac{19}{8}$$
$$\overline{\frac{5}{8}x\qquad=\frac{15}{8}}$$
$$5x=15$$
$$x=3$$

Replace x with 3 in the first equation.

$$\frac{1}{2}(3)-\frac{3}{4}y=-\frac{1}{2}$$
$$-\frac{3}{4}y=-2$$
$$-3y=-8$$
$$y=\frac{8}{3}$$

The solution is $\left(3,\frac{8}{3}\right)$.

6. $\begin{cases} y=32x \\ y=15x+25,500 \end{cases}$

Multiply the first equation by –1 and add to the second equation.

$$-y=-32x$$
$$y=15x+25,500$$
$$\overline{0=-17x+25,500}$$
$$17x=25,500$$
$$x=1500$$

The company must sell 1500 backpacks to break even.

7. $\begin{cases} x+\quad z=4 \ (1) \\ 2x-y\quad=4 \ (2) \\ x+y-z=0 \ (3) \end{cases}$

Adding equations (2) and (3) gives
$3x-z=4$ (4)
Adding equations (1) and (4) gives
$4x=8$ or $x=2$
Replace x with 2 in equation (1).
$2+z=4$
$z=2$
Replace x with 2 and z with 2 in equation (3).
$2+y-2=0$
$y=0$
The solution is (2, 0, 2).

8. $\begin{cases} 2x+5y\quad=4 \ (1) \\ x-5y+z=-1 \ (2) \\ 4x\quad-z=11 \ (3) \end{cases}$

Add equations (2) and (3).
$5x-5y=10$ (4)
Add equations (1) and (4).
$7x=14$
$x=2$
Replace x with 2 in equation (1).
$2(2)+5y=4$
$4+5y=4$
$5y=0$
$y=0$
Replace x with 2 in equation (3).
$4(2)-z=11$
$8-z=11$
$z=-3$
The solution is (2, 0, –3).

9. $\begin{cases} 4y+2z=5 \ (1) \\ 2x+8y\quad=5 \ (2) \\ 6x\quad+4z=1 \ (3) \end{cases}$

Multiply equation (1) by –2 and add to equation (2).

$$-8y-4z=-10$$
$$2x+8y\qquad=5$$
$$\overline{2x\qquad-4z=-5 \ (4)}$$

Add equations (3) and (4)
$8x=-4$
$$x=-\frac{1}{2}$$

Replace x with $-\frac{1}{2}$ in equation (2).

$$2\left(-\frac{1}{2}\right)+8y=5$$
$$-1+8y=5$$
$$8y=6$$
$$y=\frac{3}{4}$$

Replace x with $-\frac{1}{2}$ in equation (3).

$$6\left(-\frac{1}{2}\right)+4z=1$$
$$-3+4z=1$$
$$4z=4$$
$$z=1$$

The solution is $\left(-\frac{1}{2},\frac{3}{4},1\right)$.

10. $\begin{cases} 5x+\ 7y\ \ \ \ \ =9 & (1) \\ \ \ \ \ \ \ 14y-\ z=28 & (2) \\ 4x\ \ \ \ \ \ +2z=-4 & (3) \end{cases}$

Dividing equation (3) by 2 gives $2x+z=-2$.
Add this equation to equation (2).

$$2x\ \ \ \ \ +z=-2$$
$$\underline{\ \ \ \ 14y-z=28\ \ \ \ }$$
$$2x+14y\ \ =26 \ \text{ or } \ x+7y=13 \ (4)$$

Multiply equation (4) by -1 and add to equation (1).

$$-x-7y=-13$$
$$\underline{5x+7y=9\ \ \ \ }$$
$$4x\ \ \ \ \ \ \ =-4$$
$$x=-1$$

Replace x with -1 in equation (4).

$$1+7y=13$$
$$7y=14$$
$$y=2$$

Replace x with -1 in equation (3).

$$4(-1)+2z=-4$$
$$-4+2z=-4$$
$$2z=0$$
$$z=0$$

The solution is $(-1, 2, 0)$.

11. $\begin{cases} 3x-\ 2y+2z=5 & (1) \\ -x+\ 6y+\ \ z=4 & (2) \\ 3x+14y+7z=20 & (3) \end{cases}$

Multiply equation (2) by 3 and add to equation (1).

$$3x-\ 2y+2z=5$$
$$\underline{-3x+18y+3z=12\ \ }$$
$$16y+5z=17 \ (4)$$

Multiply equation (3) by -1 and add to equation (1).

$$3x-\ 2y+2z=5$$
$$\underline{-3x-14y-7z=-20\ \ }$$
$$-16y-5z=-15 \ (5)$$

Add equations (4) and (5).

$$16x+5z=17$$
$$\underline{-16x-5z=-15\ \ }$$
$$0=2 \ \text{ False}$$

The system is inconsistent. The solution is $\varnothing$.

12. $\begin{cases} x+\ 2y+3z=11 & (1) \\ \ \ \ \ \ \ \ \ \ y+2z=3 & (2) \\ 2x\ \ \ \ \ \ +2z=10 & (3) \end{cases}$

Multiply equation (2) by -2 and add to equation (1).

$$x+2y+3z=11$$
$$\underline{-2y-4z=-6\ \ }$$
$$x\ \ \ \ \ \ \ -z=5 \ (4)$$

Multiply equation (4) by 2 and add to equation (3).

$$2x+2z=10$$
$$\underline{2x-2z=10\ \ }$$
$$4x\ \ \ \ \ \ =20$$
$$x=5$$

Replace x with 5 in equation (3)

$$2(5)+2z=10$$
$$10+2z=10$$
$$2z=0$$
$$z=0$$

Replace z with 0 in the equation (2).

$$y+2(0)=3$$
$$y+0=3$$
$$y=3$$

The solution is $(5, 3, 0)$.

13. $\begin{cases} 7x - 3y + 2z = 0 & (1) \\ 4x - 4y - z = 2 & (2) \\ 5x + 2y + 3z = 1 & (3) \end{cases}$

Multiply equation (2) by 2 and add to equation (1).

$7x - 3y + 2z = 0$
$\underline{8x - 8y - 2z = 4}$
$15x - 11y \quad = 4 \quad (4)$

Multiply equation (2) by 3 and add to equation (3).

$12x - 12y - 3z = 6$
$\underline{5x + 2y + 3z = 4}$
$17x - 10y \quad = 10 \quad (5)$

Use equations (4) and (5) to make a new system and then solve the new system.

$\begin{cases} 15x - 11y = 4 & (4) \\ 17x - 10y = 7 & (5) \end{cases}$

Multiply equation (4) by -10, multiply equation (5) by 11, and add.

$-150x + 110y = -40$
$\underline{187x - 110y = 77}$
$37x \quad = 37$
$x = 1$

Replace x with 1 in equation (4).

$15(1) - 11y = 4$
$15 - 11y = 4$
$-11y = -11$
$y = 1$

Replace x with 1 and y with 1 in equation (1).

$7(1) - 3(1) + 2z = 0$
$4 + 2z = 0$
$2z = -4$
$z = -2$

The solution is $(1, 1, -2)$.

14. $\begin{cases} x - 3y - 5z = -5 & (1) \\ 4x - 2y + 3z = 13 & (2) \\ 5x + 3y + 4z = 22 & (3) \end{cases}$

Multiply equation (1) by -4 and add to equation (2).

$-4x + 12y + 20z = 20$
$\underline{4x - 2y + 3z = 13}$
$10y + 23z = 33 \quad (4)$

Multiply equation (1) by -5 and add to equation (3).

$-5x + 15y + 25z = 25$
$\underline{5x + 3y + 4z = 22}$
$18y + 29z = 47 \quad (5)$

Use equations (4) and (5) to make a new system and then solve the new system.

$\begin{cases} 10y + 23z = 33 & (4) \\ 18y + 29z = 47 & (5) \end{cases}$

Multiply equation (4) by 9, multiply equation (5) by -5 and add.

$90y + 207z = 297$
$\underline{-90y - 145z = -235}$
$62z = 62$
$z = 1$

Replace z with 1 in equation (4).

$10y + 23(1) = 33$
$10y = 10$
$y = 1$

Replace y with 1 and z with 1 in equation (1).

$x - 3(1) - 5(1) = -5$
$x - 8 = -5$
$x = 3$

The solution is $(3, 1, 1)$.

15. Let x = the first number, y = the second number, and z = the third number.

$\begin{cases} x + y + z = 98 & (1) \\ x + y = z + 2 & (2) \\ y = 4x & (3) \end{cases}$

Replace y with $4x$ in equation (1) and equation (2).

$x + 4x + z = 98 \qquad\qquad x + 4x = z + 2$
$5x + z = 98 \quad (4) \qquad\qquad 5x - z = 2 \quad (5)$

Add equation (4) and equation (5).

$5x + z = 98$
$\underline{5x - z = 2}$
$10x \quad = 100$
$x = 10$

Replace x with 10 in equation (3).

$y = 4(10) = 40$

Replace x with 10 and y with 40 in equation (2).

$10 + 40 = z + 2$
$50 = z + 2$
$48 = z$

The numbers are 10, 40, and 48.

16. Let x = the first number and y = the second number.

$$\begin{cases} x = 3y \\ 2(x + y) = 168 \end{cases}$$

Replace x with $3y$ in the second equation.

$2(3y + y) = 168$

$8y = 168$

$y = 21$

Replace y with 21 in the first equation.

$x = 3(21) = 63$

The numbers are 63 and 21.

17. Let x = speed of first car and y = speed of the second car.

$$\begin{cases} 4x + 4y = 492 \\ y = x + 7 \end{cases}$$

Replace y with $x + 7$ in the first equation.

$4x + 4(x + 7) = 492$

$8x + 28 = 492$

$8x = 464$

$x = 58$

Replace x with 58 in the second equation.

$y = 58 + 7 = 65$

The cars are going 58 and 65 miles per hour.

18. Let w = the width of the foundation and l = the length of the foundation.

$$\begin{cases} l = 3w \\ 2w + 2l = 296 \end{cases}$$

Replace l with $3w$ in the second equation.

$2w + 2(3w) = 296$

$2w + 6w = 296$

$8w = 296$

$w = 37$

Replace w with 37 in the first equation.

$l = 3(37) = 111$

The foundation is 37 feet wide and 111 feet long.

19. Let x = liters of 10% solution and y = liters of 60% solution.

$$\begin{cases} x + y = 50 \\ 0.10x + 0.60y = 0.40(50) \end{cases}$$

Solve the first equation for y.

$y = 50 - x$

Replace y with $50 - x$ in the second equation.

$0.10x + 0.60(50 - x) = 0.40(50)$

$10[0.10x + 0.60(50 - x)] = 10[0.40(50)]$

$x + 6(50 - x) = 4(50)$

$x + 300 - 6x = 200$

$-5x = -100$

$x = 20$

Replace x with 20 in the equation $y = 50 - x$.

$y = 50 - 20 = 30$

He should use 20 liters of 10% solution and 30 liters of 60% solution.

20. Let c = pounds of chocolate used, n = pounds of nuts used, and r = pounds of raisins used.

$$\begin{cases} r = 2n & (1) \\ c + n + r = 45 & (2) \\ 3.00c + 2.70n + 2.25r = 2.80(45) & (3) \end{cases}$$

Replace r with $2n$ in equation (2).

$c + n + 2n = 45$

$c + 3n = 45$

$c = -3n + 45$

Replace r with $2n$ and c with $-3n + 45$ in equation (3).

$3.00(-3n + 45) + 2.70n + 2.25(2n) = 126$

$-9n + 135 + 2.7n + 4.5n = 126$

$-1.8n + 135 = 126$

$-1.8n = -9$

$n = 5$

Replace n with 5 in equation (1).

$r = 2(5) = 10$

Replace n with 5 and r with 10 in equation (2)

$c + 5 + 10 = 45$

$c + 15 = 45$

$c = 30$

She should use 30 pounds of creme-filled chocolates, 5 pounds of chocolate-covered nuts, and 10 pounds of chocolate-covered raisins.

21. Let x = the number of pennies, y = the number of nickels, and z = the number dimes.

$$\begin{cases} x+y+z=53 & (1) \\ 0.01x+0.05y+0.10z=2.77 & (2) \\ y=z+4 & (3) \end{cases}$$

Clear the decimals from equation (2) by multiplying by 100.

$x+5y+10z=277$ (4)

Replace y with $z+4$ in equation (1).

$x+z+4+z=53$

$\qquad x+2z=49$ (5)

Replace y with $z+4$ in equation (4).

$x+5(z+4)+10z=277$

$\qquad x+15z=257$ (6)

Use equations (5) and (6) to make a new system and then solve the new system.

$$\begin{cases} x+2z=49 & (5) \\ x+15z=257 & (6) \end{cases}$$

Multiply equation (5) by –1 and add to equation (6).

$\quad -x-2z=-49$

$\quad \underline{x+15z=257}$

$\qquad 13z=208$

$\qquad z=16$

Replace z with 16 in equation (5).

$x+2(16)=49$

$\quad x+32=49$

$\qquad x=17$

Replace z with 16 in equation (3).

$y=16+4=20$

He has 17 pennies, 20 nickels, and 16 dimes in his jar.

22. Let l = rate of interest on the larger investment and s = the rate of interest on the smaller investment, both expressed as decimals.

$$\begin{cases} 10,000l+4000s=1250 \\ l=s+0.02 \end{cases}$$

Replace l with $s+0.02$ in the first equation.

$10,000(s+0.02)+4000s=1250$

$\quad 10,000s+200+4000s=1250$

$\qquad 14,000s=1050$

$$s=\frac{1050}{14,000}=0.075$$

Therefore, $l=0.075+0.02=0.095$.

The interest rate on the larger investment is 9.5% and the rate on the smaller investment is 7.5%.

23. Let x = length of the equal sides and y = length of the third side.

$$\begin{cases} 2x+y=73 \\ y=x+7 \end{cases}$$

Replace y with $x+7$ in the first equation.

$2x+x+7=73$

$\quad 3x=66$

$\quad x=22$

Replace x with 22 in the second equation.

$y=22+7=29$

Two sides of the triangle have length 22 cm and the third side has length 29 cm.

24. Let f = the first number, s = the second number, and t = the third number.

$$\begin{cases} f+s+t=295 & (1) \\ f=s+5 & (2) \\ f=2t & (3) \end{cases}$$

Solve equation (2) for s and equation (3) for t.

$s=f-5$

$t=\dfrac{f}{2}$

Replace s with $f-5$ and t with $\dfrac{f}{2}$ in equation (1).

$f+f-5+\dfrac{f}{2}=295$

$\qquad \dfrac{5}{2}f=300$

$\qquad f=120$

Replace f with 120 in the equation $s=f-5$.

$s=120-5=115$

Replace f with 120 the equation $\dfrac{f}{2}$.

$t=\dfrac{120}{2}=60$

The first number is 120, the second number is 115, and the third number is 60.

25. $\begin{cases} 3x+10y=1 \\ x+2y=-1 \end{cases}$

$$\begin{bmatrix} 3 & 10 & | & 1 \\ 1 & 2 & | & -1 \end{bmatrix}$$

Interchange R1 and R2.

$$\begin{bmatrix} 1 & 2 & | & -1 \\ 3 & 10 & | & 1 \end{bmatrix}$$

Multiply R1 by –3 and add to R2.

$$\begin{bmatrix} 1 & 2 & | & -1 \\ 0 & 4 & | & 4 \end{bmatrix}$$

Divide R2 by 4.

$$\begin{bmatrix} 1 & 2 & | & -1 \\ 0 & 1 & | & 1 \end{bmatrix}$$

This corresponds to

$$\begin{cases} x + 2y = -1 \\ \quad\ y = 1. \end{cases}$$

Now solve by using back-substitution:

$x + 2(1) = -1$

$\quad\ x = -3$

The solution is (–3, 1).

26. $\begin{cases} 3x - 6y = 12 \\ \quad 2y = x - 4 \end{cases}$, or $\begin{cases} 3x - 6y = 12 \\ -x + 2y = -4 \end{cases}$

$$\begin{bmatrix} 3 & -6 & | & 12 \\ -1 & 2 & | & -4 \end{bmatrix}$$

Divide R1 by 3.

$$\begin{bmatrix} 1 & -2 & | & 4 \\ -1 & 2 & | & -4 \end{bmatrix}$$

Add R1 to R2.

$$\begin{bmatrix} 1 & -2 & | & 4 \\ 0 & 0 & | & 0 \end{bmatrix}$$

This corresponds to

$$\begin{cases} x - 2y = 4 \\ \quad\ 0 = 0 \end{cases}$$

This is a dependent system. The solution is $\{x, y) \mid x - 2y = 4\}$.

27. $\begin{cases} 3x - 2y = -8 \\ 6x + 5y = 11 \end{cases}$

$$\begin{bmatrix} 3 & -2 & | & -8 \\ 6 & 5 & | & 11 \end{bmatrix}$$

Divide R1 by 3.

$$\begin{bmatrix} 1 & -\dfrac{2}{3} & | & -\dfrac{8}{3} \\ 6 & 5 & | & 11 \end{bmatrix}$$

Multiply R1 by –6 and add to R2.

$$\begin{bmatrix} 1 & -\dfrac{2}{3} & | & -\dfrac{8}{3} \\ 0 & 9 & | & 27 \end{bmatrix}$$

Divide R2 by 9.

$$\begin{bmatrix} 1 & -\dfrac{2}{3} & | & -\dfrac{8}{3} \\ 0 & 1 & | & 3 \end{bmatrix}$$

This corresponds to

$$\begin{cases} x - \dfrac{2}{3}y = -\dfrac{8}{3} \\ \quad\quad\ y = 3. \end{cases}$$

Now solve by using back-substitution:

$x - \dfrac{2}{3}(3) = -\dfrac{8}{3}$

$\quad x - 2 = -\dfrac{8}{3}$

$\quad\quad\ x = -\dfrac{2}{3}$

The solution is $\left(-\dfrac{2}{3}, 3\right)$.

28. $\begin{cases} 6x - 6y = -5 \\ 10x - 2y = 1 \end{cases}$

$$\begin{bmatrix} 6 & -6 & | & -5 \\ 10 & -2 & | & 1 \end{bmatrix}$$

Divide R1 by 6.

$$\begin{bmatrix} 1 & -1 & | & -\dfrac{5}{6} \\ 10 & -2 & | & 1 \end{bmatrix}$$

Multiply R1 by –10 and add to R2.

$$\begin{bmatrix} 1 & -1 & | & -\dfrac{5}{6} \\ 0 & 8 & | & \dfrac{28}{3} \end{bmatrix}$$

Divide R2 by 8.

$$\begin{bmatrix} 1 & -1 & | & -\dfrac{5}{6} \\ 0 & 1 & | & \dfrac{7}{6} \end{bmatrix}$$

Add R2 to R1.

$$\begin{bmatrix} 1 & 0 & | & \dfrac{1}{3} \\ 0 & 1 & | & \dfrac{7}{6} \end{bmatrix}$$

This corresponds to

$$\begin{cases} x = \dfrac{1}{3} \\ y = \dfrac{7}{6}. \end{cases}$$

The solution is $\left(\dfrac{1}{3}, \dfrac{7}{6}\right)$.

29. $\begin{cases} 3x - 6y = 0 \\ 2x + 4y = 5 \end{cases}$

$$\begin{bmatrix} 3 & -6 & | & 0 \\ 2 & 4 & | & 5 \end{bmatrix}$$

Divide R1 by 3.

$$\begin{bmatrix} 1 & -2 & | & 0 \\ 2 & 4 & | & 5 \end{bmatrix}$$

Multiply R1 by –2 and add to R2.

$$\begin{bmatrix} 1 & -2 & | & 0 \\ 0 & 8 & | & 5 \end{bmatrix}$$

Divide R2 by 8.

$$\begin{bmatrix} 1 & -2 & | & 0 \\ 0 & 1 & | & \frac{5}{8} \end{bmatrix}$$

This corresponds to

$$\begin{cases} x - 2y = 0 \\ \quad y = \frac{5}{8}. \end{cases}$$

Now solve by using back-substitution:

$$x - 2\left(\frac{5}{8}\right) = 0$$

$$x - \frac{5}{4} = 0$$

$$x = \frac{5}{4}$$

The solution is $\left(\frac{5}{4}, \frac{5}{8}\right)$.

30. $\begin{cases} 5x - 3y = 10 \\ -2x + y = -1 \end{cases}$

$$\begin{bmatrix} 5 & -3 & | & 10 \\ -2 & 1 & | & -1 \end{bmatrix}$$

Divide R1 by 5.

$$\begin{bmatrix} 1 & -\frac{3}{5} & | & 2 \\ -2 & 1 & | & -1 \end{bmatrix}$$

Multiply R1 by 2 and add to R2.

$$\begin{bmatrix} 1 & -\frac{3}{5} & | & 2 \\ 0 & -\frac{1}{5} & | & 3 \end{bmatrix}$$

Multiply R2 by –5.

$$\begin{bmatrix} 1 & -\frac{3}{5} & | & 2 \\ 0 & 1 & | & -15 \end{bmatrix}$$

This corresponds to

$$\begin{cases} x - \frac{3}{5}y = 2 \\ \quad y = -15. \end{cases}$$

Now solve by using back-substitution:

$$x - \frac{3}{5}(-15) = 2$$

$$x + 9 = 2$$

$$x = -7$$

The solution is $(-7, -15)$.

31. $\begin{cases} 0.2x - 0.3y = -0.7 \\ 0.5x + 0.3y = 1.4 \end{cases}$

$$\begin{bmatrix} 0.2 & -0.3 & | & -0.7 \\ 0.5 & 0.3 & | & 1.4 \end{bmatrix}$$

Multiply both rows by 10 to clear decimals.

$$\begin{bmatrix} 2 & -3 & | & -7 \\ 5 & 3 & | & 14 \end{bmatrix}$$

Divide R1 by 2.

$$\begin{bmatrix} 1 & -\frac{3}{2} & | & -\frac{7}{2} \\ 5 & 3 & | & 14 \end{bmatrix}$$

Multiply R1 by –5 and add to R2.

$$\begin{bmatrix} 1 & -\frac{3}{2} & | & -\frac{7}{2} \\ 0 & \frac{21}{2} & | & \frac{63}{2} \end{bmatrix}$$

Multiply R2 by $\frac{2}{21}$.

$$\begin{bmatrix} 1 & -\frac{3}{2} & | & -\frac{7}{2} \\ 0 & 1 & | & 3 \end{bmatrix}$$

This corresponds to

$$\begin{cases} x - \frac{3}{2}y = -\frac{7}{2} \\ \quad y = 3. \end{cases}$$

Now solve by using back-substitution:

$$x - \frac{3}{2}(3) = -\frac{7}{2}$$

$$x - \frac{9}{2} = -\frac{7}{2}$$

$$x = 1$$

The solution is $(1, 3)$.

32. $\begin{cases} 3x+2y=8 \\ 3x-y=5 \end{cases}$

$\begin{bmatrix} 3 & 2 & | & 8 \\ 3 & -1 & | & 5 \end{bmatrix}$

Divide R1 by 3.

$\begin{bmatrix} 1 & \frac{2}{3} & | & \frac{8}{3} \\ 3 & -1 & | & 5 \end{bmatrix}$

Multiply R1 by –3 and add to R2.

$\begin{bmatrix} 1 & \frac{2}{3} & | & \frac{8}{3} \\ 0 & -3 & | & -3 \end{bmatrix}$

Divide R2 by –3.

$\begin{bmatrix} 1 & -\frac{2}{3} & | & \frac{8}{3} \\ 0 & 1 & | & 1 \end{bmatrix}$

This corresponds to

$\begin{cases} x+\frac{2}{3}y=\frac{8}{3} \\ \phantom{x+\frac{2}{3}}y=1. \end{cases}$

Now solve by using back-substitution:

$x+\frac{2}{3}(1)=\frac{8}{3}$

$\phantom{x+\frac{2}{3}(1)}x=2$

The solution is (2, 1).

33. $\begin{cases} x+z=4 \\ 2x-y=0 \\ x+y-z=0 \end{cases}$

$\begin{bmatrix} 1 & 0 & 1 & | & 4 \\ 2 & -1 & 0 & | & 0 \\ 1 & 1 & -1 & | & 0 \end{bmatrix}$

Multiply R1 by –2 and add to R2.
Multiply R1 by –1 and add to R3.

$\begin{bmatrix} 1 & 0 & 1 & | & 4 \\ 0 & -1 & -2 & | & -8 \\ 0 & 1 & -2 & | & -4 \end{bmatrix}$

Multiply R2 by –1.

$\begin{bmatrix} 1 & 0 & 1 & | & 4 \\ 0 & 1 & 2 & | & 8 \\ 0 & 1 & -2 & | & -4 \end{bmatrix}$

Multiply R2 by –1 and add to R3.

$\begin{bmatrix} 1 & 0 & 1 & | & 4 \\ 0 & 1 & 2 & | & 8 \\ 0 & 0 & -4 & | & -12 \end{bmatrix}$

Divide R3 by –4.

$\begin{bmatrix} 1 & 0 & 1 & | & 4 \\ 0 & 1 & 2 & | & 8 \\ 0 & 0 & 1 & | & 3 \end{bmatrix}$

This corresponds to

$\begin{cases} x+z=4 \\ y+2z=8 \\ z=3. \end{cases}$

Now solve by using back-substitution:

$y+2(3)=8$

$y+6=8$

$y=2$

$x+3=4$

$x=1$

The solution is (1, 2, 3).

34. $\begin{cases} 2x+5y=4 \\ x-5y+z=-1 \\ 4x-z=11 \end{cases}$

$\begin{bmatrix} 2 & 5 & 0 & | & 4 \\ 1 & -5 & 1 & | & -1 \\ 4 & 0 & -1 & | & 11 \end{bmatrix}$

Interchange R1 and R2.

$\begin{bmatrix} 1 & -5 & 1 & | & -1 \\ 2 & 5 & 0 & | & 4 \\ 4 & 0 & -1 & | & 11 \end{bmatrix}$

Multiply R1 by –2 and add to R2.
Multiply R1 by –4 and add to R3.

$\begin{bmatrix} 1 & -5 & 1 & | & -1 \\ 0 & 15 & -2 & | & 6 \\ 0 & 20 & -5 & | & 15 \end{bmatrix}$

Divide R2 by 15.

$\begin{bmatrix} 1 & -5 & 1 & | & -1 \\ 0 & 1 & -\frac{2}{15} & | & \frac{2}{5} \\ 0 & 20 & -5 & | & 15 \end{bmatrix}$

Multiply R2 by –20 and add to R3.

$\begin{bmatrix} 1 & -5 & 1 & | & -1 \\ 0 & 1 & -\frac{2}{15} & | & \frac{2}{5} \\ 0 & 0 & -\frac{7}{3} & | & 7 \end{bmatrix}$

Multiply R3 by $-\frac{3}{7}$.

$$\begin{bmatrix} 1 & -5 & 1 & | & -1 \\ 0 & 1 & -\frac{2}{15} & | & \frac{2}{5} \\ 0 & 0 & 1 & | & -3 \end{bmatrix}$$

This corresponds to

$$\begin{cases} x - 5y + z = -1 \\ y - \frac{2}{15}z = \frac{2}{5} \\ z = -3. \end{cases}$$

Now solve by using back-substitution:

$$y - \frac{2}{15}(-3) = \frac{2}{5}$$
$$y + \frac{2}{5} = \frac{2}{5}$$
$$y = 0$$
$$x - 5(0) + (-3) = -1$$
$$x - 3 = -1$$
$$x = 2$$

The solution is $(2, 0, -3)$.

35. $\begin{cases} 3x - y = 11 \\ x + 2z = 13 \\ y - z = -7 \end{cases}$

$$\begin{bmatrix} 3 & -1 & 0 & | & 11 \\ 1 & 0 & 2 & | & 13 \\ 0 & 1 & -1 & | & -7 \end{bmatrix}$$

Interchange R1 and R2.

$$\begin{bmatrix} 1 & 0 & 2 & | & 13 \\ 3 & -1 & 0 & | & 11 \\ 0 & 1 & -1 & | & -7 \end{bmatrix}$$

Interchange R2 and R3.

$$\begin{bmatrix} 1 & 0 & 2 & | & 13 \\ 0 & 1 & -1 & | & -7 \\ 3 & -1 & 0 & | & 11 \end{bmatrix}$$

Multiply R1 by −3 and add to R3.

$$\begin{bmatrix} 1 & 0 & 2 & | & 13 \\ 0 & 1 & -1 & | & -7 \\ 0 & -1 & -6 & | & -28 \end{bmatrix}$$

Add R2 to R3.

$$\begin{bmatrix} 1 & 0 & 2 & | & 13 \\ 0 & 1 & -1 & | & -7 \\ 0 & 0 & -7 & | & -35 \end{bmatrix}$$

Divide R3 by −7.

$$\begin{bmatrix} 1 & 0 & 2 & | & 13 \\ 0 & 1 & -1 & | & -7 \\ 0 & 0 & 1 & | & 5 \end{bmatrix}$$

This corresponds to

$$\begin{cases} x + 2z = 13 \\ y - z = -7 \\ z = 5. \end{cases}$$

Now solve by using back-substitution:

$$y - 5 = -7$$
$$y = -2$$
$$x + 2(5) = 13$$
$$x = 3$$

The solution is $(3, -2, 5)$.

36. $\begin{cases} 5x + 7y + 3z = 9 \\ 14y - z = 28 \\ 4x + 2z = -4 \end{cases}$

$$\begin{bmatrix} 5 & 7 & 3 & | & 9 \\ 0 & 14 & -1 & | & 28 \\ 4 & 0 & 2 & | & -4 \end{bmatrix}$$

Divide R1 by 5.

$$\begin{bmatrix} 1 & \frac{7}{5} & \frac{3}{5} & | & \frac{9}{5} \\ 0 & 14 & -1 & | & 28 \\ 4 & 0 & 2 & | & -4 \end{bmatrix}$$

Multiply R1 by −4 and add to R3.

$$\begin{bmatrix} 1 & \frac{7}{5} & \frac{3}{5} & | & \frac{9}{5} \\ 0 & 14 & -1 & | & 28 \\ 0 & -\frac{28}{5} & -\frac{2}{5} & | & -\frac{56}{5} \end{bmatrix}$$

Divide R2 by 14.

$$\begin{bmatrix} 1 & \frac{7}{5} & \frac{3}{5} & | & \frac{9}{5} \\ 0 & 1 & -\frac{1}{14} & | & 2 \\ 0 & -\frac{28}{5} & -\frac{2}{5} & | & -\frac{56}{5} \end{bmatrix}$$

Multiply R2 by $\frac{28}{5}$ and add to R3.

$$\begin{bmatrix} 1 & \dfrac{7}{5} & \dfrac{3}{5} & \bigg| & \dfrac{9}{5} \\[2mm] 0 & 1 & -\dfrac{1}{14} & \bigg| & 2 \\[2mm] 0 & 0 & -\dfrac{4}{5} & \bigg| & 0 \end{bmatrix}$$

Multiply R3 by $-\dfrac{5}{4}$.

$$\begin{bmatrix} 1 & \dfrac{7}{5} & \dfrac{3}{5} & \bigg| & \dfrac{9}{5} \\[2mm] 0 & 1 & -\dfrac{1}{14} & \bigg| & 2 \\[2mm] 0 & 0 & 1 & \bigg| & 0 \end{bmatrix}$$

This corresponds to

$$\begin{cases} x + \dfrac{7}{5}y + \dfrac{3}{5}z = \dfrac{9}{5} \\[2mm] \quad\quad y - \dfrac{1}{14}z = 2 \\[2mm] \quad\quad\quad\quad z = 0. \end{cases}$$

Now solve by using back-substitution:

$$y - \dfrac{1}{14}(0) = 2$$
$$y = 2$$
$$x + \dfrac{7}{5}(2) + \dfrac{3}{5}(0) = \dfrac{9}{5}$$
$$x + \dfrac{14}{5} = \dfrac{9}{5}$$
$$x = -1$$

The solution is $(-1, 2, 0)$.

37. $\begin{cases} 7x - 3y + 2z = 0 \\ 4x - 4y - z = 2 \\ 5x + 2y + 3z = 1 \end{cases}$

$$\begin{bmatrix} 7 & -3 & 2 & | & 0 \\ 4 & -4 & -1 & | & 2 \\ 5 & 2 & 3 & | & 1 \end{bmatrix}$$

Interchange R1 and R2.

$$\begin{bmatrix} 4 & -4 & -1 & | & 2 \\ 7 & -3 & 2 & | & 0 \\ 5 & 2 & 3 & | & 1 \end{bmatrix}$$

Divide R1 by 4.

$$\begin{bmatrix} 1 & -1 & -\dfrac{1}{4} & \bigg| & \dfrac{1}{2} \\[2mm] 7 & -3 & 2 & \bigg| & 0 \\[2mm] 5 & 2 & 3 & \bigg| & 1 \end{bmatrix}$$

Multiply R1 by -7 and add to R2.
Multiply R1 by -5 and add to R3.

$$\begin{bmatrix} 1 & -1 & -\dfrac{1}{4} & \bigg| & \dfrac{1}{2} \\[2mm] 0 & 4 & \dfrac{15}{4} & \bigg| & -\dfrac{7}{2} \\[2mm] 0 & 7 & \dfrac{17}{4} & \bigg| & -\dfrac{3}{2} \end{bmatrix}$$

Divide R2 by 4.

$$\begin{bmatrix} 1 & -1 & -\dfrac{1}{4} & \bigg| & \dfrac{1}{2} \\[2mm] 0 & 1 & \dfrac{15}{16} & \bigg| & -\dfrac{7}{8} \\[2mm] 0 & 7 & \dfrac{17}{4} & \bigg| & -\dfrac{3}{2} \end{bmatrix}$$

Multiply R2 by -7 and add to R3.

$$\begin{bmatrix} 1 & -1 & -\dfrac{1}{4} & \bigg| & \dfrac{1}{2} \\[2mm] 0 & 1 & \dfrac{15}{16} & \bigg| & -\dfrac{7}{8} \\[2mm] 0 & 0 & -\dfrac{37}{16} & \bigg| & \dfrac{37}{8} \end{bmatrix}$$

Multiply R3 by $-\dfrac{16}{37}$.

$$\begin{bmatrix} 1 & -1 & -\dfrac{1}{4} & \bigg| & \dfrac{1}{2} \\[2mm] 0 & 1 & \dfrac{15}{16} & \bigg| & -\dfrac{7}{8} \\[2mm] 0 & 0 & 1 & \bigg| & -2 \end{bmatrix}$$

This corresponds to

$$\begin{cases} x - y - \dfrac{1}{4}z = \dfrac{1}{2} \\[2mm] \quad\quad y + \dfrac{15}{16}z = -\dfrac{7}{8} \\[2mm] \quad\quad\quad\quad z = -2. \end{cases}$$

Now solve by using back-substitution:

$$y + \dfrac{15}{16}(-2) = -\dfrac{7}{8}$$
$$y - \dfrac{15}{8} = -\dfrac{7}{8}$$
$$y = 1$$
$$x - 1 - \dfrac{1}{4}(-2) = \dfrac{1}{2}$$
$$x - 1 + \dfrac{1}{2} = \dfrac{1}{2}$$
$$x = 1$$

The solution is $(1, 1, -2)$.

38. $\begin{cases} x + 2y + 3z = 14 \\ y + 2z = 3 \\ 2x - 2z = 10 \end{cases}$

$$\begin{bmatrix} 1 & 2 & 3 & | & 14 \\ 0 & 1 & 2 & | & 3 \\ 2 & 0 & -2 & | & 10 \end{bmatrix}$$

Multiply R1 by –2 and add to R3.

$$\begin{bmatrix} 1 & 2 & 3 & | & 14 \\ 0 & 1 & 2 & | & 3 \\ 0 & -4 & -8 & | & -18 \end{bmatrix}$$

Multiply R2 by 4 and add to R3.

$$\begin{bmatrix} 1 & 2 & 3 & | & 14 \\ 0 & 1 & 2 & | & 3 \\ 0 & 0 & 0 & | & 6 \end{bmatrix}$$

This corresponds to

$$\begin{cases} x + 2y + 3z = 14 \\ y + 2z = 3 \\ 0 = 6. \end{cases}$$

This system is inconsistent. The solution is $\varnothing$.

39. $\begin{vmatrix} -1 & 3 \\ 5 & 2 \end{vmatrix} = -1(2) - 3(5) = -2 - 15 = -17$

40. $\begin{vmatrix} 3 & -1 \\ 2 & 5 \end{vmatrix} = 3(5) - (-1)(2) = 15 + 2 = 17$

41. $\begin{vmatrix} 2 & -1 & -3 \\ 1 & 2 & 0 \\ 3 & -2 & 2 \end{vmatrix}$

$= 2\begin{vmatrix} 2 & 0 \\ -2 & 2 \end{vmatrix} - (-1)\begin{vmatrix} 1 & 0 \\ 3 & 2 \end{vmatrix} + (-3)\begin{vmatrix} 1 & 2 \\ 3 & -2 \end{vmatrix}$

$= 2(4 - 0) + (2 - 0) - 3(-2 - 6)$

$= 2(4) + (2) - 3(-8)$

$= 34$

42. $\begin{vmatrix} -2 & 3 & 1 \\ 4 & 4 & 0 \\ 1 & -2 & 3 \end{vmatrix}$

$= 1\begin{vmatrix} 4 & 4 \\ 1 & -2 \end{vmatrix} - 0\begin{vmatrix} -2 & 3 \\ 1 & -2 \end{vmatrix} + 3\begin{vmatrix} -2 & 3 \\ 4 & 4 \end{vmatrix}$

$= (-8 - 4) - 0 + 3(-8 - 12)$

$= -12 + 3(-20)$

$= -12 - 60$

$= -72$

43. $\begin{cases} 3x - 2y = -8 \\ 6x + 5y = 11 \end{cases}$

$D = \begin{vmatrix} 3 & -2 \\ 6 & 5 \end{vmatrix} = 15 + 12 = 27$

$D_x = \begin{vmatrix} -8 & -2 \\ 11 & 5 \end{vmatrix} = -40 + 22 = -18$

$D_y = \begin{vmatrix} 3 & -8 \\ 6 & 11 \end{vmatrix} = 33 - (-48) = 33 + 48 = 81$

$x = \dfrac{D_x}{D} = \dfrac{-18}{27} = -\dfrac{2}{3}$

$y = \dfrac{D_y}{D} = \dfrac{81}{27} = 3$

The solution is $\left(-\dfrac{2}{3}, 3\right)$.

44. $\begin{cases} 6x - 6y = -5 \\ 10x - 2y = 1 \end{cases}$

$D = \begin{vmatrix} 6 & -6 \\ 10 & -2 \end{vmatrix} = -12 - (-60) = 48$

$D_x = \begin{vmatrix} -5 & -6 \\ 1 & -2 \end{vmatrix} = 10 - (-6) = 16$

$D_y = \begin{vmatrix} 6 & -5 \\ 10 & 1 \end{vmatrix} = 6 - (-50) = 56$

$x = \dfrac{D_x}{D} = \dfrac{16}{48} = \dfrac{1}{3}$

$y = \dfrac{D_y}{D} = \dfrac{56}{48} = \dfrac{7}{6}$

The solution is $\left(\dfrac{1}{3}, \dfrac{7}{6}\right)$.

45. $\begin{cases} 3x + 10y = 1 \\ x + 2y = -1 \end{cases}$

$D = \begin{vmatrix} 3 & 10 \\ 1 & 2 \end{vmatrix} = 6 - 10 = -4$

$D_x = \begin{vmatrix} 1 & 10 \\ -1 & 2 \end{vmatrix} = 2 - (-10) = 12$

$D_y = \begin{vmatrix} 3 & 1 \\ 1 & -1 \end{vmatrix} = -3 - 1 = -4$

$x = \dfrac{D_x}{D} = \dfrac{12}{-4} = -3$

$y = \dfrac{D_y}{D} = \dfrac{-4}{-4} = 1$

The solution is $(-3, 1)$.

46. $\begin{cases} y = \frac{1}{2}x + \frac{2}{3} \\ 4x + 6y = 4 \end{cases}$ or $\begin{cases} -\frac{1}{2}x + y = \frac{2}{3} \\ 4x + 6y = 4 \end{cases}$

$D = \begin{vmatrix} -\frac{1}{2} & 1 \\ 4 & 6 \end{vmatrix} = -3 - 4 = -7$

$D_x = \begin{vmatrix} \frac{2}{3} & 1 \\ 4 & 6 \end{vmatrix} = 4 - 4 = 0$

$D_y = \begin{vmatrix} -\frac{1}{2} & \frac{2}{3} \\ 4 & 4 \end{vmatrix} = -2 - \frac{8}{3} = -\frac{14}{3}$

$x = \dfrac{D_x}{D} = \dfrac{0}{-7} = 0$

$y = \dfrac{D_y}{D} = \dfrac{-\frac{14}{3}}{-7} = \dfrac{2}{3}$

The solution is $\left(0, \frac{2}{3}\right)$.

47. $\begin{cases} 2x - 4y = 22 \\ 5x - 10y = 16 \end{cases}$

$D = \begin{vmatrix} 2 & -4 \\ 5 & -10 \end{vmatrix} = -20 - (-20) = 0$

This cannot be solved by Cramer's rule.
Multiply the first equation by –5, multiply the second equation by 2, and add.

$-10x + 20y = -110$

$\underline{10x - 20y = 32}$

$\qquad\qquad 0 = -78$ False

This system is inconsistent. The solution is $\varnothing$.

48. $\begin{cases} 3x - 6y = 12 \\ 2y = x - 4 \end{cases}$ or $\begin{cases} 3x - 6y = 12 \\ -x + 2y = -4 \end{cases}$

$D = \begin{vmatrix} 3 & -6 \\ -1 & 2 \end{vmatrix} = 6 - 6 = 0$

This cannot be solved by Cramer's rule.
Since the first equation is –3 times the second equation, the system is dependent. The solution is $\{(x, y) \mid -x + 2y = -4\}$.

49. $\begin{cases} x \qquad + z = 4 \\ 2x - y \quad = 0 \\ x + y - z = 0 \end{cases}$

$D = \begin{vmatrix} 1 & 0 & 1 \\ 2 & -1 & 0 \\ 1 & 1 & -1 \end{vmatrix}$

$= 1\begin{vmatrix} -1 & 0 \\ 1 & -1 \end{vmatrix} - 0\begin{vmatrix} 2 & 0 \\ 1 & -1 \end{vmatrix} + 1\begin{vmatrix} 2 & -1 \\ 1 & 1 \end{vmatrix}$

$= (1 - 0) - 0 + [2 - (-1)]$

$= 1 + 3$

$= 4$

$D_x = \begin{vmatrix} 4 & 0 & 1 \\ 0 & -1 & 0 \\ 0 & 1 & -1 \end{vmatrix}$

$= 4\begin{vmatrix} -1 & 0 \\ 1 & -1 \end{vmatrix} - 0\begin{vmatrix} 0 & 1 \\ 1 & -1 \end{vmatrix} + 0\begin{vmatrix} 0 & 1 \\ -1 & 0 \end{vmatrix}$

$= 4(1 - 0) - 0 + 0$

$= 4$

$D_y = \begin{vmatrix} 1 & 4 & 1 \\ 2 & 0 & 0 \\ 1 & 0 & -1 \end{vmatrix}$

$= -4\begin{vmatrix} 2 & 0 \\ 1 & -1 \end{vmatrix} + 0\begin{vmatrix} 1 & 1 \\ 1 & -1 \end{vmatrix} - 0\begin{vmatrix} 1 & 1 \\ 2 & 0 \end{vmatrix}$

$= -4(-2 - 0) + 0 - 0$

$= 8$

$$D_z = \begin{vmatrix} 1 & 0 & 4 \\ 2 & -1 & 0 \\ 1 & 1 & 0 \end{vmatrix}$$

$$= 4\begin{vmatrix} 2 & -1 \\ 1 & 1 \end{vmatrix} - 0\begin{vmatrix} 1 & 0 \\ 1 & 1 \end{vmatrix} + 0\begin{vmatrix} 1 & 0 \\ 2 & -1 \end{vmatrix}$$

$$= 4[2 - (-1)] - 0 + 0$$

$$= 4(3)$$

$$= 12$$

$$x = \frac{D_x}{D} = \frac{4}{4} = 1, \quad y = \frac{D_y}{D} = \frac{8}{4} = 2,$$

$$z = \frac{D_z}{D} = \frac{12}{4} = 3$$

The solution is (1, 2, 3).

50. $\begin{cases} 2x + 5y = 4 \\ x - 5y + z = -1 \\ 4x - z = 11 \end{cases}$

$$D = \begin{vmatrix} 2 & 5 & 0 \\ 1 & -5 & 1 \\ 4 & 0 & -1 \end{vmatrix}$$

$$= 2\begin{vmatrix} -5 & 1 \\ 0 & -1 \end{vmatrix} - 5\begin{vmatrix} 1 & 1 \\ 4 & -1 \end{vmatrix} + 0\begin{vmatrix} 1 & -5 \\ 4 & 0 \end{vmatrix}$$

$$= 2(5 - 0) - 5(-1 - 4) + 0$$

$$= 10 + 25$$

$$= 35$$

$$D_x = \begin{vmatrix} 4 & 5 & 0 \\ -1 & -5 & 1 \\ 11 & 0 & -1 \end{vmatrix}$$

$$= 4\begin{vmatrix} -5 & 1 \\ 0 & -1 \end{vmatrix} - 5\begin{vmatrix} -1 & 1 \\ 11 & -1 \end{vmatrix} + 0\begin{vmatrix} -1 & -5 \\ 11 & 0 \end{vmatrix}$$

$$= 4(5 - 0) - 5(1 - 11) + 0$$

$$= 20 + 50$$

$$= 70$$

$$D_y = \begin{vmatrix} 2 & 4 & 0 \\ 1 & -1 & 1 \\ 4 & 11 & -1 \end{vmatrix}$$

$$= 2\begin{vmatrix} -1 & 1 \\ 11 & -1 \end{vmatrix} - 4\begin{vmatrix} 1 & 1 \\ 4 & -1 \end{vmatrix} + 0\begin{vmatrix} 1 & -1 \\ 4 & 11 \end{vmatrix}$$

$$= 2(1 - 11) - 4(-1 - 4) + 0$$

$$= -20 + 20$$

$$= 0$$

$$D_z = \begin{vmatrix} 2 & 5 & 4 \\ 1 & -5 & -1 \\ 4 & 0 & 11 \end{vmatrix}$$

$$= 4\begin{vmatrix} 5 & 4 \\ -5 & -1 \end{vmatrix} - 0\begin{vmatrix} 2 & 4 \\ 1 & -1 \end{vmatrix} + 11\begin{vmatrix} 2 & 5 \\ 1 & -5 \end{vmatrix}$$

$$= 4[-5 - (-20)] - 0 + 11(-10 - 5)$$

$$= 4(15) + 11(-15)$$

$$= 60 - 165$$

$$= -105$$

$$x = \frac{D_x}{D} = \frac{70}{35} = 2, \quad y = \frac{D_y}{D} = \frac{0}{35} = 0,$$

$$z = \frac{D_z}{D} = \frac{-105}{35} = -3$$

The solution is (2, 0, –3).

51. $\begin{cases} x + 3y - z = 5 \\ 2x - y - 2z = 3 \\ x + 2y + 3z = 4 \end{cases}$

$$D = \begin{vmatrix} 1 & 3 & -1 \\ 2 & -1 & -2 \\ 1 & 2 & 3 \end{vmatrix}$$

$$= 1\begin{vmatrix} -1 & -2 \\ 2 & 3 \end{vmatrix} - 3\begin{vmatrix} 2 & -2 \\ 1 & 3 \end{vmatrix} + (-1)\begin{vmatrix} 2 & -1 \\ 1 & 2 \end{vmatrix}$$

$$= [-3 - (-4)] - 3[6 - (-2)] - [4 - (-1)]$$

$$= 1 - 3(8) - 5$$

$$= -28$$

$$D_x = \begin{vmatrix} 5 & 3 & -1 \\ 3 & -1 & -2 \\ 4 & 2 & 3 \end{vmatrix}$$

$$= 5\begin{vmatrix} -1 & -2 \\ 2 & 3 \end{vmatrix} - 3\begin{vmatrix} 3 & -2 \\ 4 & 3 \end{vmatrix} + (-1)\begin{vmatrix} 3 & -1 \\ 4 & 2 \end{vmatrix}$$

$$= 5[-3 - (-4)] - 3[9 - (-8)] - [6 - (-4)]$$

$$= 5(1) - 3(17) - 10$$

$$= 5 - 51 - 10$$

$$= -56$$

$D_y = \begin{vmatrix} 1 & 5 & -1 \\ 2 & 3 & -2 \\ 1 & 4 & 3 \end{vmatrix}$

$= 1\begin{vmatrix} 3 & -2 \\ 4 & 3 \end{vmatrix} - 5\begin{vmatrix} 2 & -2 \\ 1 & 3 \end{vmatrix} + (-1)\begin{vmatrix} 2 & 3 \\ 1 & 4 \end{vmatrix}$

$= [9 - (-8)] - 5[6 - (-2)] - (8 - 3)$

$= 17 - 5(8) - 5$

$= 17 - 40 - 5$

$= -28$

$D_z = \begin{vmatrix} 1 & 3 & 5 \\ 2 & -1 & 3 \\ 1 & 2 & 4 \end{vmatrix}$

$= 1\begin{vmatrix} -1 & 3 \\ 2 & 4 \end{vmatrix} - 3\begin{vmatrix} 2 & 3 \\ 1 & 4 \end{vmatrix} + 5\begin{vmatrix} 2 & -1 \\ 1 & 2 \end{vmatrix}$

$= (-4 - 6) - 3(8 - 3) + 5[4 - (-1)]$

$= -10 - 3(5) + 5(5)$

$= -10 - 15 + 25$

$= 0$

$x = \dfrac{D_x}{D} = \dfrac{-56}{-28} = 2, \quad y = \dfrac{D_y}{D} = \dfrac{-28}{-28} = 1,$

$z = \dfrac{D_z}{D} = \dfrac{0}{-28} = 0$

The solution is (2, 1, 0).

52. $\begin{cases} 2x - z = 1 \\ 3x - y + 2z = 3 \\ x + y + 3z = -2 \end{cases}$

$D = \begin{vmatrix} 2 & 0 & -1 \\ 3 & -1 & 2 \\ 1 & 1 & 3 \end{vmatrix}$

$= 2\begin{vmatrix} -1 & 2 \\ 1 & 3 \end{vmatrix} - 0\begin{vmatrix} 3 & 2 \\ 1 & 3 \end{vmatrix} + (-1)\begin{vmatrix} 3 & -1 \\ 1 & 1 \end{vmatrix}$

$= 2(-3 - 2) - 0 - [3 - (-1)]$

$= 2(-5) - 4$

$= -10 - 4$

$= -14$

$D_x = \begin{vmatrix} 1 & 0 & -1 \\ 3 & -1 & 2 \\ -2 & 1 & 3 \end{vmatrix}$

$= 1\begin{vmatrix} -1 & 2 \\ 1 & 3 \end{vmatrix} - 0\begin{vmatrix} 3 & 2 \\ -2 & 3 \end{vmatrix} + (-1)\begin{vmatrix} 3 & -1 \\ -2 & 1 \end{vmatrix}$

$= (-3 - 2) - 0 - (3 - 2)$

$= -5 - 1$

$= -6$

$D_y = \begin{vmatrix} 2 & 1 & -1 \\ 3 & 3 & 2 \\ 1 & -2 & 3 \end{vmatrix}$

$= 2\begin{vmatrix} 3 & 2 \\ -2 & 3 \end{vmatrix} - 1\begin{vmatrix} 3 & 2 \\ 1 & 3 \end{vmatrix} + (-1)\begin{vmatrix} 3 & 3 \\ 1 & -2 \end{vmatrix}$

$= 2[9 - (-4)] - (9 - 2) - (-6 - 3)$

$= 2(13) - 7 + 9$

$= 26 - 7 + 9$

$= 28$

$D_z = \begin{vmatrix} 2 & 0 & 1 \\ 3 & -1 & 3 \\ 1 & 1 & -2 \end{vmatrix}$

$= 2\begin{vmatrix} -1 & 3 \\ 1 & -2 \end{vmatrix} - 0\begin{vmatrix} 3 & 3 \\ 1 & -2 \end{vmatrix} + 1\begin{vmatrix} 3 & -1 \\ 1 & 1 \end{vmatrix}$

$= 2(2 - 3) - 0 + [3 - (-1)]$

$= 2(-1) + 4$

$= -2 + 4$

$= 2$

$x = \dfrac{D_x}{D} = \dfrac{-6}{-14} = \dfrac{3}{7}, \quad y = \dfrac{D_y}{D} = \dfrac{28}{-14} = -2,$

$z = \dfrac{D_z}{D} = \dfrac{2}{-14} = -\dfrac{1}{7}$

The solution is $\left(\dfrac{3}{7}, -2, \dfrac{1}{7}\right)$.

53. $\begin{cases} x+2y+3z=14 \\ y+2z=3 \\ 2x-2z=10 \end{cases}$

$D=\begin{vmatrix} 1 & 2 & 3 \\ 0 & 1 & 2 \\ 2 & 0 & -2 \end{vmatrix}$

$= 1\begin{vmatrix} 1 & 2 \\ 0 & -2 \end{vmatrix} -0\begin{vmatrix} 2 & 3 \\ 0 & -2 \end{vmatrix} +2\begin{vmatrix} 2 & 3 \\ 1 & 2 \end{vmatrix}$

$= (-2-0)-0+2(4-3)$

$= -2+2(1)$

$= 0$

This cannot be solved by Cramer's rule. Solving the second equation for *y* gives $y=-2z+3$.

Solving the third equation for *x* gives
$2x=2z+10$

$x=z+5$.

Replace *x* with $z+5$ and *y* with $-2z+3$ in the first equation.

$(z+5)+2(-2z+3)+3z=14$

$z+5-4z+6+3z=14$

$11=14$ False

The system is inconsistent. The solution is $\varnothing$.

54. $\begin{cases} 5x+7y=9 \\ 14y-z=28 \\ 4x+2z=-4 \end{cases}$

$D=\begin{vmatrix} 5 & 7 & 0 \\ 0 & 14 & -1 \\ 4 & 0 & 2 \end{vmatrix}$

$= 5\begin{vmatrix} 14 & -1 \\ 0 & 2 \end{vmatrix} -7\begin{vmatrix} 0 & -1 \\ 4 & 2 \end{vmatrix} +0\begin{vmatrix} 0 & 14 \\ 4 & 0 \end{vmatrix}$

$= 5(28-0)-7[0-(-4)]+0$

$= 5(28)-7(4)$

$= 140-28=112$

$D_x=\begin{vmatrix} 9 & 7 & 0 \\ 28 & 14 & -1 \\ -4 & 0 & 2 \end{vmatrix}$

$= 9\begin{vmatrix} 14 & -1 \\ 0 & 2 \end{vmatrix} -7\begin{vmatrix} 28 & -1 \\ -4 & 2 \end{vmatrix} +0\begin{vmatrix} 28 & 14 \\ -4 & 0 \end{vmatrix}$

$= 9(28-0)-7(56-4)+0$

$= 9(28)-7(52)$

$= 252-364$

$= -112$

$D_y=\begin{vmatrix} 5 & 9 & 0 \\ 0 & 28 & -1 \\ 4 & -4 & 2 \end{vmatrix}$

$= 5\begin{vmatrix} 28 & -1 \\ -4 & 2 \end{vmatrix} -9\begin{vmatrix} 0 & -1 \\ 4 & 2 \end{vmatrix} +0\begin{vmatrix} 0 & 28 \\ 4 & -4 \end{vmatrix}$

$= 5(56-4)-9[0-(-4)]+0$

$= 5(52)-9(4)$

$= 260-36$

$= 224$

$D_z=\begin{vmatrix} 5 & 7 & 9 \\ 0 & 14 & 28 \\ 4 & 0 & -4 \end{vmatrix}$

$= 5\begin{vmatrix} 14 & 28 \\ 0 & -4 \end{vmatrix} -0\begin{vmatrix} 7 & 9 \\ 0 & -4 \end{vmatrix} +4\begin{vmatrix} 7 & 9 \\ 14 & 28 \end{vmatrix}$

$= 5(-56-0)-0+4(196-126)$

$= -280+4(70)$

$= -280+280$

$= 0$

$x=\dfrac{D_x}{D}=\dfrac{-112}{112}=-1, \quad y=\dfrac{D_y}{D}=\dfrac{224}{112}=2,$

$z=\dfrac{D_z}{D}=\dfrac{0}{112}=0$

The solution is (–1, 2, 0).

Chapter 4 Test

1. $\begin{vmatrix} 4 & -7 \\ 2 & 5 \end{vmatrix}=4(5)-(-7)(2)=20+14=34$

2. $\begin{vmatrix} 4 & 0 & 2 \\ 1 & -3 & 5 \\ 0 & -1 & 2 \end{vmatrix}$

$= 4\begin{vmatrix} -3 & 5 \\ -1 & 2 \end{vmatrix} -0\begin{vmatrix} 1 & 5 \\ 0 & 2 \end{vmatrix} +2\begin{vmatrix} 1 & -3 \\ 0 & -1 \end{vmatrix}$

$= 4[-6-(-5)]-0+2(-1-0)$

$= 4(-1)+2(-1)$

$= -4-2$

$= -6$

3. $\begin{cases} 2x - y = -1 \\ 5x + 4y = 17 \end{cases}$

Solve each equation for y.

$\begin{cases} y = 2x + 1 \\ y = -\dfrac{5}{4}x + \dfrac{17}{4} \end{cases}$

Graph $y_1 = 2x + 1$ and $y_2 = -\dfrac{5}{4}x + \dfrac{17}{4}$ and find

the point of intersection.

 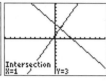

The solution is $(1, 3)$.

By elimination:
Multiply the first equation by 4 and add it to the second equation.

$8x - 4y = -4$

$\underline{5x + 4y = 17}$

$13x \qquad = 13$

$x = 1$

Replace x with 1 in the second equation.

$5(1) + 4y = 17$

$4y = 12$

$y = 3$

The solution is $(1, 3)$.

4. $\begin{cases} 7x - 14y = 5 \\ \qquad x = 2y \end{cases}$

Solve each equation for y.

$\begin{cases} y = \dfrac{1}{2}x - \dfrac{5}{14} \\ y = \dfrac{1}{2}x \end{cases}$

Graph $y_1 = \dfrac{1}{2}x - \dfrac{5}{14}$ and $y_2 = \dfrac{1}{2}x$ and find the

point of intersection.

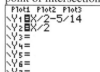 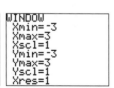

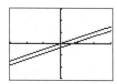

The two lines are parallel so there are no intersection points. The system is inconsistent so the solution is $\varnothing$.

By substitution:
Replace x with $2y$ in the first equation.

$7(2y) - 14y = 5$

$14y - 14y = 5$

$0 = 5$ False

The system is inconsistent. The solution is $\varnothing$.

5. $\begin{cases} 4x - 7y = 29 \\ 2x + 5y = -11 \end{cases}$

Multiply the second equation by -2 and add to the first equation.

$-4x - 10y = 22$

$\underline{4x - 7y = 29}$

$-17y = 51$

$y = -3$

Replace y with -3 in the first equation.

$4x - 7(-3) = 29$

$4x + 21 = 29$

$4x = 8$

$x = 2$

The solution is $(2, -3)$.

6. $\begin{cases} 15x + 6y = 15 \\ 10x + 4y = 10 \end{cases}$

Divide the first equation by 3 and the second equation by 2.

$\begin{cases} 5x + 2y = 5 \\ 5x + 2y = 5 \end{cases}$

The system is dependent.
The solution is $\{(x, y) \mid 10x + 4y = 10\}$.

7. $\begin{cases} 2x - 3y \quad = 4 \quad (1) \\ \quad 3y + 2z = 2 \quad (2) \\ x \quad\quad - z = -5 \quad (3) \end{cases}$

Add equation (1) and equation (2).
$2x + 2z = 6$ or $x + z = 3$ (4)

Add equation (3) and equation (4).

$x + z = 3$

$\underline{x - z = -5}$

$2x \quad = -2$

$x = -1$

Replace x with -1 in equation (3).

$$-1 - z = -5$$

$$-z = -4 \text{ so } z = 4$$

Replace x with -1 in equation (1).

$$2(-1) - 3y = 4$$

$$-2 - 3y = 4$$

$$-3y = 6$$

$$y = -2$$

The solution is $(-1, -2, 4)$.

8. $\begin{cases} 3x - 2y - z = -1 & (1) \\ 2x - 2y = 4 & (2) \\ 2x - 2z = -12 & (3) \end{cases}$

Multiply equation (2) by -1 and add to equation (1).

$$3x - 2y - z = -1$$

$$\underline{-2x + 2y = -4}$$

$$x \qquad - z = -5 \quad (4)$$

Multiply equation (4) by -2 and add to equation (3).

$$2x - 2z = -12$$

$$\underline{-2x + 2z = 10}$$

$$0 = -2 \text{ False}$$

The system is inconsistent. The solution is $\varnothing$.

9. $\begin{cases} \dfrac{x}{2} + \dfrac{y}{4} = -\dfrac{3}{4} \\ x + \dfrac{3}{4}y = -4 \end{cases}$

Clear fractions by multiplying both equations by 4.

$$\begin{cases} 2x + y = -3 \\ 4x + 3y = -16 \end{cases}$$

Multiply the first equation by -2 and add to the second equation.

$$-4x - 2y = 6$$

$$\underline{4x + 3y = -16}$$

$$y = -10$$

Replace y with -10 in the first equation.

$$2x + (-10) = -3$$

$$2x = 7 \text{ so } x = \frac{7}{2}$$

The solution is $\left(\dfrac{7}{2}, -10\right)$.

10. $\begin{cases} 3x - y = 7 \\ 2x + 5y = -1 \end{cases}$

$$D = \begin{vmatrix} 3 & -1 \\ 2 & 5 \end{vmatrix} = 3(5) - (-1)(2) = 15 + 2 = 17$$

$$D_x = \begin{vmatrix} 7 & -1 \\ -1 & 5 \end{vmatrix}$$

$$= 7(5) - (-1)(-1)$$

$$= 35 - 1$$

$$= 34$$

$$D_y = \begin{vmatrix} 3 & 7 \\ 2 & -1 \end{vmatrix}$$

$$= -1(3) - 7(2)$$

$$= -3 - 14$$

$$= -17$$

$$x = \frac{D_x}{D} = \frac{34}{17} = 2$$

$$y = \frac{D_y}{D} = \frac{-17}{17} = -1$$

The solution is $(2, -1)$.

11. $\begin{cases} x + y + z = 4 \\ 2x + 5y = 1 \\ x - y - 2z = 0 \end{cases}$

$$D = \begin{vmatrix} 1 & 1 & 1 \\ 2 & 5 & 0 \\ 1 & -1 & -2 \end{vmatrix}$$

$$= 1\begin{vmatrix} 2 & 5 \\ 1 & -1 \end{vmatrix} - 0\begin{vmatrix} 1 & 1 \\ 1 & -1 \end{vmatrix} + (-2)\begin{vmatrix} 1 & 1 \\ 2 & 5 \end{vmatrix}$$

$$= (-2 - 5) - 0 - 2(5 - 2)$$

$$= -7 - 2(3)$$

$$= -13$$

$$D_x = \begin{vmatrix} 4 & 1 & 1 \\ 1 & 5 & 0 \\ 0 & -1 & -2 \end{vmatrix}$$

$$= 4\begin{vmatrix} 5 & 0 \\ -1 & -2 \end{vmatrix} - 1\begin{vmatrix} 1 & 1 \\ -1 & -2 \end{vmatrix} + 0\begin{vmatrix} 1 & 1 \\ 5 & 0 \end{vmatrix}$$

$$= 4(-10 - 0) - [-2 - (-1)] + 0$$

$$= 4(-10) - (-1) + 0$$

$$= -40 + 1$$

$$= -39$$

$$D_y = \begin{vmatrix} 1 & 4 & 1 \\ 2 & 1 & 0 \\ 1 & 0 & -2 \end{vmatrix}$$

$$= 1\begin{vmatrix} 2 & 1 \\ 1 & 0 \end{vmatrix} - 0\begin{vmatrix} 1 & 4 \\ 1 & 0 \end{vmatrix} + (-2)\begin{vmatrix} 1 & 4 \\ 2 & 1 \end{vmatrix}$$

$$= (0-1) - 0 - 2(1-8)$$
$$= -1 - 2(-7)$$
$$= -1 + 14$$
$$= 13$$

$$D_z = \begin{vmatrix} 1 & 1 & 4 \\ 2 & 5 & 1 \\ 1 & -1 & 0 \end{vmatrix}$$

$$= 1\begin{vmatrix} 1 & 4 \\ 5 & 1 \end{vmatrix} - (-1)\begin{vmatrix} 1 & 4 \\ 2 & 1 \end{vmatrix} + 0\begin{vmatrix} 1 & 1 \\ 2 & 5 \end{vmatrix}$$

$$= (1-20) + (1-8) + 0$$
$$= -19 - 7$$
$$= -26$$

$$x = \frac{D_x}{D} = \frac{-39}{-13} = 3, \quad y = \frac{D_y}{D} = \frac{13}{-13} = -1,$$

$$z = \frac{D_z}{D} = \frac{-26}{-13} = 2$$

The solution is (3, –1, 2).

12. $\begin{cases} x - y = -2 \\ 3x - 3y = -6 \end{cases}$

$$\begin{bmatrix} 1 & -1 & | & -2 \\ 3 & -3 & | & -6 \end{bmatrix}$$

Multiply R1 by –3 and add to R2.

$$\begin{bmatrix} 1 & -1 & | & -2 \\ 0 & 0 & | & 0 \end{bmatrix}$$

This corresponds to

$$\begin{cases} x - y = -2 \\ 0 = 0. \end{cases}$$

This is a dependent system. The solution is $\{(x,\ y)\ |\ x - y = -2\}$.

13. $\begin{cases} x + 2y = -1 \\ 2x + 5y = -5 \end{cases}$

$$\begin{bmatrix} 1 & 2 & | & -1 \\ 2 & 5 & | & -5 \end{bmatrix}$$

Multiply R1 by –2 and add to R2.

$$\begin{bmatrix} 1 & 2 & | & -1 \\ 0 & 1 & | & -3 \end{bmatrix}$$

This corresponds to

$$\begin{cases} x + 2y = -1 \\ y = -3. \end{cases}$$

Now solve using back-substitution:

$$x + 2(-3) = -1$$
$$x - 6 = -1$$
$$x = 5$$

The solution is (5, –3).

14. $\begin{cases} x - y - z = 0 \\ 3x - y - 5z = -2 \\ 2x + 3y = -5 \end{cases}$

$$\begin{bmatrix} 1 & -1 & -1 & | & 0 \\ 3 & -1 & -5 & | & -2 \\ 2 & 3 & 0 & | & -5 \end{bmatrix}$$

Multiply R1 by –3 and add to R2.
Multiply R1 by –2 and add to R3.

$$\begin{bmatrix} 1 & -1 & -1 & | & 0 \\ 0 & 2 & -2 & | & -2 \\ 0 & 5 & 2 & | & -5 \end{bmatrix}$$

Divide R2 by 2.

$$\begin{bmatrix} 1 & -1 & -1 & | & 0 \\ 0 & 1 & -1 & | & -1 \\ 0 & 5 & 2 & | & -5 \end{bmatrix}$$

Multiply R2 by – and add to R3.

$$\begin{bmatrix} 1 & -1 & -1 & | & 0 \\ 0 & 1 & -1 & | & -1 \\ 0 & 0 & 7 & | & 0 \end{bmatrix}$$

Divide R3 by 7.

$$\begin{bmatrix} 1 & -1 & -1 & | & 0 \\ 0 & 1 & -1 & | & -1 \\ 0 & 0 & 1 & | & 0 \end{bmatrix}$$

This corresponds to

$$\begin{cases} x - y - z = 0 \\ y - z = -1 \\ z = 0. \end{cases}$$

Now solve using back-substitution:

$$y - 0 = -1$$
$$y = -1$$
$$x - (-1) - 0 = 0$$
$$x + 1 = 0$$
$$x = -1$$

The solution is (–1, –1, 0).

15. Let x = double occupancy rooms and
y = single occupancy rooms.
$$\begin{cases} x + y = 80 \\ 90x + 80y = 6930 \end{cases}$$
Multiply the first equation by –80 and add to the second equation.
$$-80x - 80y = -6400$$
$$\underline{90x + 80y = 6930}$$
$$10x \qquad = 530$$
$$x = 53$$
Replace x with 53 in the first equation.
$$53 + y = 80$$
$$y = 27$$
53 double-occupancy and 27 single-occupancy rooms are occupied.

16. Let x = gallons of 10% solution and
y = gallons of 20% solution.
$$\begin{cases} x + y = 20 \\ 0.10x + 0.20y = 0.175(20) \end{cases}$$
Multiply the first equation by –0.10 add to the second equation.
$$-0.10x - 0.10y = -2.0$$
$$\underline{0.10x + 0.20y = 3.5}$$
$$0.10y = 1.5$$
$$y = 15$$
Replace y with 15 in the first equation.
$$x + 15 = 20$$
$$x = 5$$
They should use 5 gallons of 10% fructose solution and 15 gallons of the 20% solution.

17. $R(x) = 4x$ and $C(x) = 1.5x + 2000$
Break even occurs when $R(x) = C(x)$.
$$4x = 1.5x + 2000$$
$$2.5x = 2000$$
$$x = 800$$
The company must sell 800 packages.

18. Let x = measure of the smallest angle. Then the largest angle has a measure of $5x - 3$, and the remaining angle has a measure of $2x - 1$. The sum of the three angles must add to 180° ::
$$a + b + c = 180$$
$$x + (5x - 3) + (2x - 1) = 180$$
$$x + 5x - 3 + 2x - 1 = 180$$
$$8x - 4 = 180$$
$$8x = 184$$
$$x = 23$$
$$5x - 3 = 5(23) - 3 = 115 - 3 = 112$$
$$2x - 1 = 2(23) - 1 = 46 - 1 = 45$$
The angle measures are 23°, 45°, and 112°.

Chapter 4 Cumulative Review

1. a. True
b. True

2. a. False
b. True

3. a. $11 + 2 - 7 = 6$
b. $-5 - 4 + 2 = -7$

4. a. $-7 - (-2) = -7 + 2 = -5$
b. $14 - 38 = -24$

5. a. The opposite of 8 is –8.
b. The opposite of $\frac{1}{5}$ is $-\frac{1}{5}$.
c. The opposite of –9.6 is 9.6.

6. a. The reciprocal of 5 is $\frac{1}{5}$.
b. The reciprocal of $-\frac{2}{3}$ is $-\frac{3}{2}$.

7. a. $3(2x + y) = 6x + 3y$
b. $-(3x - 1) = -3x + 1$
c. $0.7a(b - 2) = 0.7ab - 1.4a$

8. a. $7(3x - 2y + 4) = 21x - 14y + 28$

b. $-(-2s-3t) = 2s+3t$

9. a. $3x-5x+4 = (3-5)x+4 = -2x+4$

   b. $7yz + yz = (7+1)yz = 8yz$

   c. $4z+6.1 = 4z+6.1$

10. a. $5y^2 - 1 + 2(y^2+2) = 5y^2 - 1 + 2y^2 + 4$
$$= 7y^2 + 3$$

   b. $(7.8x-1.2)-(5.6x-2.4)$
$$= 7.8x - 1.2 - 5.6x + 2.4$$
$$= 2.2x + 1.2$$

11. $-6x-1+5x = 3$
$$-x-1 = 3$$
$$-x = 4$$
$$x = -4$$
The solution is –4.

12. $8y-14 = 6y-14$
$$2y = 0$$
$$y = 0$$
The solution is 0.

13. $0.3x+0.1 = 0.27x-0.02$
$$0.03x = -0.12$$
$$x = -4$$
The solution is –4.

14. $2(m-6)-m = 4(m-3)-3m$
$$2m-12-m = 4m-12-3m$$
$$m-12 = m-12$$
$$0 = 0 \quad \text{True}$$
The solution is all real numbers.

15. Let x = length of the third side, then
$2x+12$ = length of the two equal sides.
$$x + (2x+12) + (2x+12) = 149$$
$$5x + 24 = 149$$
$$5x = 125$$
$$x = 25$$
$$2(25) + 12 = 50 + 12 = 62$$
The sides are 25 cm, 62 cm, and 62 cm.

16. Let x = measure of the equal angles,
$x+10$ = measure of the third angle, and

$\frac{1}{2}x$ = measure of the fourth angle.

$$x + x + (x+10) + \frac{1}{2}x = 360$$
$$\frac{7}{2}x + 10 = 360$$
$$\frac{7}{2}x = 350$$
$$7x = 700$$
$$x = 100$$
$$x + 10 = 100 + 10 = 110$$
$$\frac{1}{2}x = \frac{1}{2}(100) = 50$$
The measures of the angles are 100°, 100°, 110°, and 50°.

17. $3x+4 \geq 2x-6$
$$x \geq -10$$
$$\{x \mid x \geq -10\}$$

18. $5(2x-1) > -5$
$$10x - 5 > -5$$
$$10x > 0$$
$$x > 0$$
$$(0, \infty)$$

19. $2 < 4-x < 7$
$$-2 < -x < 3$$
$$2 > x > -3$$
$$-3 < x < 2$$
$$(-3, 2)$$

20. $-1 < \dfrac{-2x-1}{3} < 1$
$$3(-1) < 3\left[\dfrac{-2x-1}{3}\right] < 3(1)$$
$$-3 < -2x-1 < 3$$
$$-2 < -2x < 4$$
$$1 > x > -2$$
$$-2 < x < 1$$
$$(-2, 1)$$

21. $|2x| + 5 = 7$

$\quad |2x| = 2$

$\quad 2x = 2 \ \text{ or } \ 2x = -2$

$\quad\quad x = 1 \ \text{ or } \quad x = -1$

The solution is $\{-1, 1\}$.

22. $|x - 5| = 4$

$\quad x - 5 = 4 \ \text{ or } \ x - 5 = -4$

$\quad\quad x = 9 \ \text{ or } \quad\quad x = 1$

The solution is $\{1, 9\}$.

23. $|m - 6| < 2$

$\quad -2 < m - 6 < 2$

$\quad\quad 4 < m < 8$

$\quad (4, 8)$

24. $|2x + 1| > 5$

$\quad 2x + 1 < -5 \ \text{ or } \ 2x + 1 > 5$

$\quad\quad 2x < -6 \ \text{ or } \quad 2x > 4$

$\quad\quad\quad x < -3 \ \text{ or } \quad\quad x > 2$

$\quad (-\infty, -3) \cup (2, \infty)$

25.

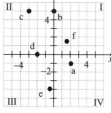

a. $(2, -1)$ is in Quadrant IV.

b. $(0, 5)$ is on the *y*-axis.

c. $(-3, 5)$ is in Quadrant II.

d. $(-2, 0)$ is on the *x*-axis.

e. $\left(-\dfrac{1}{2}, -4\right)$ is in Quadrant III.

f. $(1.5, 1.5)$ is in Quadrant I.

26. a. $(-1, -5)$ is in Quadrant III.

b. $(4, -2)$ is in Quadrant IV.

c. $(0, 2)$ is on the *y*-axis.

27. Yes. For each input, *x*, there is exactly one output, *y*.

28. $-2x + \dfrac{1}{2}y = -2$, or $y = 4x - 4$

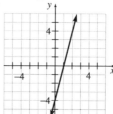

29. $f(x) = 7x^2 - 3x + 1$, $g(x) = 3x - 2$, $h(x) = x^2$

a. $f(1) = 7(1)^2 - 3(1) + 1 = 7 - 3 + 1 = 5$

b. $g(3) = 3(3) - 2 = 9 - 2 = 7$

c. $h(-2) = (-2)^2 = 4$

30. $f(x) = 3x^2$

a. $f(5) = 3(5)^2 = 3(25) = 75$

b. $f(-2) = 3(-2)^2 = 3(4) = 12$

31. a. $f(x) = \dfrac{1}{2}x + \dfrac{3}{7}$

This is a linear function written in slope-intercept form - $y = mx + b$. Therefore, the y-intercept is $\left(0, \dfrac{3}{7}\right)$.

b. $y = -2.5x - 3.2$

This is a linear equation that is written in slope-intercept form. Therefore, the y-intercept is $(0, -3.2)$.

32. $m = \dfrac{9 - 6}{0 - (-2)} = \dfrac{3}{2}$

33. $3x - 4y = 4$

$\quad -4y = -3x + 4$

$\quad\quad y = \dfrac{3}{4}x - 1$

$\quad m = \dfrac{3}{4}$, y-intercept $= (0, -1)$

34. $y = 2$

$m = 0$, y-intercept $= (0, 2)$

35. a. $3x + 7y = 4$

$7y = -3x + 4$

$y = -\dfrac{3}{7}x + \dfrac{4}{7}$

$m = -\dfrac{3}{7}$

$6x + 14y = 7$

$14y = -6x + 7$

$y = -\dfrac{3}{7}x + \dfrac{1}{2}$

$m = -\dfrac{3}{7}$

Parallel, since the slopes are equal and the y-intercepts are different.

b. $-x + 3y = 2$

$3y = x + 2$

$y = \dfrac{1}{3}x + \dfrac{2}{3}$ $\qquad m = \dfrac{1}{3}$

$2x + 6y = 5$

$6y = -2x + 5$

$y = -\dfrac{1}{3}x + \dfrac{5}{6}$ $\qquad m = -\dfrac{1}{3}$

$\dfrac{1}{3} \cdot \left(-\dfrac{1}{3}\right) = -\dfrac{1}{9}$

Neither, since the slopes are not equal and their product is not -1.

36. $y - (-9) = \dfrac{1}{5}(x - 0)$

$y + 9 = \dfrac{1}{5}x$

$y = \dfrac{1}{5}x - 9$

37. $m = \dfrac{-5 - 0}{-4 - 4} = \dfrac{-5}{-8} = \dfrac{5}{8}$

$y - 0 = \dfrac{5}{8}(x - 4)$

$y = \dfrac{5}{8}x - \dfrac{5}{2}$

$f(x) = \dfrac{5}{8}x - \dfrac{5}{2}$

38. $f(x) = \dfrac{1}{2}x - \dfrac{1}{3}$ or $y = \dfrac{1}{2}x - \dfrac{1}{3}$

$m = \dfrac{1}{2}$ so $m_\perp = -2$

$y - 6 = -2[x - (-2)]$

$y - 6 = -2(x + 2)$

$y - 6 = -2x - 4$

$y = -2x + 2$

39. $3x \geq y$, or $y \leq 3x$

Graph the boundary line $y = 3x$ with a solid line because the inequality symbol is $\leq$.

Test: $(0, 1)$

$3x \geq y$

$3(0) \geq 1$

$0 \geq 1$ False

Shade the half-plane that does not contain $(0, 1)$.

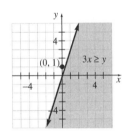

40. $x \geq 1$

Graph the boundary line $x = 1$ with a solid line because the inequality symbol is $\geq$.

Test: $(0, 0)$

$x \geq 1$

$0 \geq 1$ False

Shade the half-plane that does not contain $(0, 0)$.

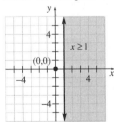

41. a.
$$\begin{cases} -x+y=2 \\ 2x-y=-3 \end{cases}$$
$$-(-1)+1=2 \qquad 2(-1)-(1)=-3$$
$$1+1=2 \qquad\qquad -2-1=-3$$
$$2=2 \ \text{True} \qquad -3=-3 \ \text{True}$$
Yes, (-1, 1) is a solution.

b.
$$\begin{cases} 5x+3y=-1 \\ x-y=1 \end{cases}$$
$$5(-2)+3(3)=-1$$
$$-10+9=-1 \qquad -2-3=-1$$
$$-1=-1 \ \text{True} \qquad -5=-1 \ \text{False}$$
No, (-2, 3) is not a solution.

42.
$$\begin{cases} 5x+y=-2 \\ 4x-2y=-10 \end{cases}$$
Multiply the first equation by 2 and add to the second equation.
$$10x+2y=-4$$
$$\underline{4x-2y=-10}$$
$$14x \quad\ =-14$$
$$x=-1$$
Replace x with -1 in the first equation.
$$5(-1)+y=-2$$
$$-5+y=-2$$
$$y=3$$
The solution is (-1, 3).

43.
$$\begin{cases} 3x-y+z=-15 \ (1) \\ x+2y-z=1 \quad (2) \\ 2x+3y-2z=0 \quad (3) \end{cases}$$
Add equation (1) and equation (2).
$$4x+y=-14 \ (4)$$
Multiply equation (1) by 2 and add equation (3).
$$6x-2y+2z=-30$$
$$\underline{2x+3y-2z=0}$$
$$8x+y \quad\ =-30 \ (5)$$
Form a new system using equations (4) and (5) and then solve the new system:
$$\begin{cases} 4x+y=-14 \ (4) \\ 8x+y=-30 \ (5) \end{cases}$$
Multiply equation (4) by -1 and add to equation (5).

$$-4x-y=14$$
$$\underline{8x+y=-30}$$
$$4x \quad\ =-16$$
$$x=-4$$
Replace x with -4 in equation (4).
$$4(-4)+y=-14$$
$$-16+y=-14$$
$$y=2$$

Replace x with -4 and y with 2 in equation (1).
$$3(-4)-(2)+z=-15$$
$$-12-2+z=-15$$
$$-14+z=-15$$
$$z=-1$$
The solution is (-4, 2, -1).

44.
$$\begin{cases} x-2y+z=0 \quad (1) \\ 3x-y-2z=-15 \ (2) \\ 2x-3y+3z=7 \quad (3) \end{cases}$$
Multiply equation (1) by 2 and add to equation (2).
$$2x-4y+2z=0$$
$$\underline{3x-y-2z=-15}$$
$$5x-5y \quad\ =-15 \ \text{or}\ x-y=-3 \ (4)$$
Multiply equation (1) by -3 and add to equation (3).
$$-3x+6y-3z=0$$
$$\underline{2x-3y+3z=7}$$
$$-x+3y \quad\ =7 \ (5)$$
Add equations (4) and (5).
$$2y=4$$
$$y=2$$
Replace y with 2 in equation (4).
$$x-2=-3$$
$$x=-1$$
Replace x with -1 and y with 2 in equation (1).
$$-1-2(2)+z=0$$
$$-5+z=0$$
$$z=5$$
The solution is (-1, 2, 5).

45. $\begin{cases} x+3y=5 \\ 2x-y=-4 \end{cases}$

$$\begin{bmatrix} 1 & 3 & | & 5 \\ 2 & -1 & | & -4 \end{bmatrix}$$

Multiply R1 by –2 and add to R2.

$$\begin{bmatrix} 1 & 3 & | & 5 \\ 0 & -7 & | & -14 \end{bmatrix}$$

Divide R2 by –7.

$$\begin{bmatrix} 1 & 3 & | & 5 \\ 0 & 1 & | & 2 \end{bmatrix}$$

This corresponds to

$$\begin{cases} x+3y=5 \\ \quad\ \ y=2. \end{cases}$$

Now solve using back-substitution:

$$x+3(2)=5$$
$$x+6=5$$
$$x=-1$$

The solution is (–1, 2).

46. $\begin{cases} -6x+8y=0 \\ 9x-12y=2 \end{cases}$

Divide the first equation by –2 and the second equation by 3.

$$\begin{cases} 3x-4y=0 \\ 3x-4y=\dfrac{2}{3} \end{cases}$$

This system is inconsistent. The solution is $\varnothing$.

Chapter 5

Mental Math 5.1

1. $5x^{-1}y^{-2} = \dfrac{5}{xy^2}$

2. $7xy^{-4} = \dfrac{7x}{y^4}$

3. $a^2b^{-1}c^{-5} = \dfrac{a^2}{bc^5}$

4. $a^{-4}b^2c^{-6} = \dfrac{b^2}{a^4c^6}$

5. $\dfrac{y^{-2}}{x^{-4}} = \dfrac{x^4}{y^2}$

6. $\dfrac{x^{-7}}{z^{-3}} = \dfrac{z^3}{x^7}$

Exercise Set 5.1

1. $4^2 \cdot 4^3 = 4^{2+3} = 4^5$

3. $x^5 \cdot x^3 = x^{5+3} = x^8$

5. $-7x^3 \cdot 20x^9 = -7 \cdot 20x^{3+9} = -140x^{12}$

7. $(4xy)(-5x) = -20x^{1+1}y = -20x^2y$

9. $(-4x^3p^2)(4y^3x^3) = -16x^{3+3}y^3p^2$
$$= -16x^6y^3p^2$$

11. $-8^0 = -(8^0) = -1$

13. $(4x+5)^0 = 1$

15. $(5x)^0 + 5x^0 = 1 + 5 \cdot 1 = 1 + 5 = 6$

17. Answers may vary. The difference is due to order of operations. -5^0 can be thought of as $-1 \cdot 5^0$. The exponent is done first ($5^0 = 1$) and then the result is multiplied by -1.

19. $\dfrac{a^5}{a^2} = a^{5-2} = a^3$

21. $\dfrac{x^9y^6}{x^8y^6} = x^{9-8}y^{6-6} = x^1y^0 = x$

23. $-\dfrac{26z^{11}}{2z^7} = -13z^{11-7} = -13z^4$

25. $\dfrac{-36a^5b^7c^{10}}{6ab^3c^4} = -6a^{5-1}b^{7-3}c^{10-4}$
$$= -6a^4b^4c^6$$

27. $4^{-2} = \dfrac{1}{4^2} = \dfrac{1}{16}$

29. $\dfrac{x^7}{x^{15}} = x^{7-15} = x^{-8} = \dfrac{1}{x^8}$

31. $5a^{-4} = \dfrac{5}{a^4}$

33. $\dfrac{x^{-2}}{x^5} = x^{-2-5} = x^{-7} = \dfrac{1}{x^7}$

35. $\dfrac{8r^4}{2r^{-4}} = 4r^{4-(-4)} = 4r^8$

37. $\dfrac{x^{-9}x^4}{x^{-5}} = \dfrac{x^{-9+4}}{x^{-5}} = \dfrac{x^{-5}}{x^{-5}} = x^{-5-(-5)} = x^0 = 1$

39. $4^{-1} + 3^{-2} = \dfrac{1}{4^1} + \dfrac{1}{3^2}$
$$= \dfrac{1}{4} + \dfrac{1}{9}$$
$$= \dfrac{9}{36} + \dfrac{4}{36}$$
$$= \dfrac{13}{36}$$

41. $4x^0 + 5 = 4(1) + 5 = 4 + 5 = 9$

43. $x^7 \cdot x^8 \cdot x = x^{7+8+1} = x^{16}$

45. $2x^3 \cdot 5x^7 = 2 \cdot 5x^{3+7} = 10x^{10}$

47. $\dfrac{z^{12}}{z^{15}} = z^{12-15} = z^{-3} = \dfrac{1}{z^3}$

49. $\dfrac{y^{-3}}{y^{-7}} = y^{-3-(-7)} = y^4$

51. $3x^{-1} = \dfrac{3}{x^1} = \dfrac{3}{x}$

53. $3^0 - 3t^0 = 1 - 3 \cdot 1 = 1 - 3 = -2$

55. $\dfrac{r^4}{r^{-4}} = r^{4-(-4)} = r^8$

57. $\dfrac{x^{-7}y^{-2}}{x^2 y^2} = x^{-7-2}y^{-2-2} = x^{-9}y^{-4} = \dfrac{1}{x^9 y^4}$

59. $\dfrac{2a^{-6}b^2}{18ab^{-5}} = \dfrac{a^{-6-1}b^{2-(-5)}}{9} = \dfrac{a^{-7}b^7}{9} = \dfrac{b^7}{9a^7}$

61. $\dfrac{(24x^8)(x)}{20x^{-7}} = \dfrac{6x^{8+1}}{5x^{-7}} = \dfrac{6x^{9-(-7)}}{5} = \dfrac{6x^{16}}{5}$

63. $31,250,000 = 3.125 \times 10^7$

65. $0.016 = 1.6 \times 10^{-2}$

67. $67,413 = 6.7413 \times 10^4$

69. $0.0125 = 1.25 \times 10^{-2}$

71. $0.000053 = 5.3 \times 10^{-5}$

73. $778,300,000 = 7.783 \times 10^8$

75. $737,000 = 7.37 \times 10^5$

77. $1,410,000,000 = 1.41 \times 10^9$

79. $0.001 = 1 \times 10^{-3}$

81. $3.6 \times 10^{-9} = 0.0000000036$

83. $9.3 \times 10^7 = 93,000,000$

85. $1.278 \times 10^6 = 1,278,000$

87. $7.35 \times 10^{12} = 7,350,000,000,000$

89. $4.03 \times 10^{-7} = 0.000000403$

91. $2.0 \times 10^8 = 200,000,000$

93. $4.9 \times 10^9 = 4,900,000,000$

95. $(5 \cdot 2)^2 = (10)^2 = 100$

97. $\left(\dfrac{3}{4}\right)^3 = \dfrac{3^3}{4^3} = \dfrac{27}{64}$

99. $(2^3)^2 = 8^2 = 64$

101. $(2^{-1})^4 = \left(\dfrac{1}{2}\right)^4 = \dfrac{1^4}{2^4} = \dfrac{1}{16}$

103. Answers may vary. See page 352 in the text.

105. a. $x^a \cdot x^a = x^{a+a} = x^{2a}$

 b. $x^a + x^a = 2x^a$

 c. $\dfrac{x^a}{x^b} = x^{a-b}$

 d. $x^a \cdot x^b = x^{a+b}$

 e. $x^a + x^b = x^a + x^b$

107. 7^{13}

109. 7^{-11}

111. $x^5 \cdot x^{7a} = x^{5+7a}$

113. $\dfrac{x^{3t-1}}{x^t} = x^{(3t-1)-t} = x^{2t-1}$

115. $x^{4a} \cdot x^7 = x^{4a+7}$

117. $\dfrac{z^{6x}}{z^7} = z^{6x-7}$

119. $\dfrac{x^{3t} \cdot x^{4t-1}}{x^t} = \dfrac{x^{3t+(4t-1)}}{x^t} = x^{7t-1-t} = x^{6t-1}$

121. $x^{9+b} \cdot x^{3a-b} = x^{(9+b)+(3a-b)} = x^{3a+9}$

Mental Math 5.2

1. $(x^4)^5 = x^{4(5)} = x^{20}$

2. $(5^6)^2 = 5^{6(2)} = 5^{12}$

3. $x^4 \cdot x^5 = x^{4+5} = x^9$

4. $x^7 \cdot x^8 = x^{7+8} = x^{15}$

5. $(y^6)^7 = y^{6(7)} = y^{42}$

6. $(x^3)^4 = x^{3(4)} = x^{12}$

7. $(z^4)^9 = z^{4(9)} = z^{36}$

8. $(z^3)^7 = z^{3(7)} = z^{21}$

9. $(z^{-6})^{-3} = z^{-6(-3)} = z^{18}$

10. $(y^{-4})^{-2} = y^{-4(-2)} = y^8$

Exercise Set 5.2

1. $(3^{-1})^2 = 3^{-1(2)} = 3^{-2} = \dfrac{1}{3^2} = \dfrac{1}{9}$

3. $(x^4)^{-9} = x^{4(-9)} = x^{-36} = \dfrac{1}{x^{36}}$

5. $(y)^{-5} = y^{-5} = \dfrac{1}{y^5}$

7. $(3x^2y^3)^2 = 3^2(x^2)^2(y^3)^2$
$= 9x^{2(2)}y^{3(2)}$
$= 9x^4y^6$

9. $\left(\dfrac{2x^5}{y^{-3}}\right)^4 = \dfrac{2^4(x^5)^4}{(y^{-3})^4}$
$= \dfrac{16x^{5(4)}}{y^{-3(4)}}$
$= \dfrac{16x^{20}}{y^{-12}}$
$= 16x^{20}y^{12}$

11. $(a^2bc^{-3})^{-6} = (a^2)^{-6}b^{-6}(c^{-3})^{-6}$
$= a^{2(-6)}b^{-6}c^{-3(-6)}$
$= a^{-12}b^{-6}c^{18}$
$= \dfrac{c^{18}}{a^{12}b^6}$

13. $\left(\dfrac{x^7y^{-3}}{z^{-4}}\right)^{-5} = \dfrac{(x^7)^{-5}(y^{-3})^{-5}}{(z^{-4})^{-5}}$
$= \dfrac{x^{-35}y^{15}}{z^{20}}$
$= \dfrac{y^{15}}{x^{35}z^{20}}$

15. $(5^{-1})^3 = 5^{-1(3)} = 5^{-3} = \dfrac{1}{5^3} = \dfrac{1}{125}$

17. $\left(\dfrac{x^{-9}}{x^{-4}}\right)^{-3} = \dfrac{(x^{-9})^{-3}}{(x^{-4})^{-3}} = \dfrac{x^{27}}{x^{12}} = x^{27-12} = x^{15}$

19. $\left(\dfrac{5x^7y^4}{10x^3y^{-2}}\right)^{-3} = \left(\dfrac{x^4y^6}{2}\right)^{-3}$
$= \dfrac{(x^4)^{-3}(y^6)^{-3}}{(2)^{-3}}$
$= (2)^3 x^{-12}y^{-18}$
$= \dfrac{8}{x^{12}y^{18}}$

21. $\dfrac{8^{-2}x^{-3}y^{11}}{x^2y^{-5}} = \dfrac{x^{-3-2}y^{11-(-5)}}{8^2} = \dfrac{x^{-5}y^{16}}{64} = \dfrac{y^{16}}{64x^5}$

23. $\left(\dfrac{4p^6}{p^9}\right)^3 = \left(\dfrac{4}{p^3}\right)^3 = \dfrac{4^3}{(p^3)^3} = \dfrac{64}{p^9}$

25. $(-xy^0x^2a^3)^{-3} = (-x^3a^3)^{-3}$
$= (-1)^{-3}(x^3)^{-3}(a^3)^{-3}$
$= -1x^{-9}a^{-9}$
$= -\dfrac{1}{x^9a^9}$

27. $\left(\dfrac{x^{-1}y^{-2}}{5^{-3}}\right)^{-5} = \dfrac{(x^{-1})^{-5}(y^{-2})^{-5}}{(5^{-3})^{-5}} = \dfrac{x^5y^{10}}{5^{15}}$

29. $(x^7)^{-9} = x^{7(-9)} = x^{-63} = \dfrac{1}{x^{63}}$

31. $\left(\dfrac{7}{8}\right)^3 = \dfrac{7^3}{8^3} = \dfrac{343}{512}$

33. $(4x^2)^2 = 4^2(x^2)^2 = 16x^4$

35. $(-2^{-2}y)^3 = (-1)^3(2^{-2})^3 y^3$

$\qquad = -2^{-6}y^3$

$\qquad = -\dfrac{y^3}{2^6}$

$\qquad = -\dfrac{y^3}{64}$

37. $\left(\dfrac{4^{-4}}{y^3 x}\right)^{-2} = \dfrac{(4^{-4})^{-2}}{(y^3)^{-2}x^{-2}} = \dfrac{4^8}{y^{-6}x^{-2}} = 4^8 x^2 y^6$

39. $\left(\dfrac{1}{4}\right)^{-3} = \dfrac{1^{-3}}{4^{-3}} = \dfrac{4^3}{1^3} = \dfrac{64}{1} = 64$

41. $\left(\dfrac{3x^5}{6x^4}\right)^4 = \left(\dfrac{x^{5-4}}{2}\right)^4 = \left(\dfrac{x}{2}\right)^4 = \dfrac{x^4}{2^4} = \dfrac{x^4}{16}$

43. $\dfrac{(y^3)^{-4}}{y^3} = \dfrac{y^{-12}}{y^3} = y^{-12-3} = y^{-15} = \dfrac{1}{y^{15}}$

45. $\left(\dfrac{2x^{-3}}{y^{-1}}\right)^{-3} = \dfrac{2^{-3}(x^{-3})^{-3}}{(y^{-1})^{-3}} = \dfrac{x^9}{2^3 y^3} = \dfrac{x^9}{8y^3}$

47. $\dfrac{3^{-2}a^{-5}b^6}{4^{-2}a^{-7}b^{-3}} = \dfrac{4^2 a^{-5-(-7)}b^{6-(-3)}}{3^2} = \dfrac{16a^2 b^9}{9}$

49. $(4x^6 y^5)^{-2}(6x^4 y^3)$

$\qquad = 4^{-2}(x^6)^{-2}(y^5)^{-2} \cdot 6x^4 y^3$

$\qquad = \dfrac{1}{4^2}x^{-12}y^{-10} \cdot 6x^4 y^3$

$\qquad = \dfrac{6}{16}x^{-12+4}y^{-10+3}$

$\qquad = \dfrac{3x^{-8}y^{-7}}{8} = \dfrac{3}{8x^8 y^7}$

51. $x^6(x^6 bc)^{-6} = x^6(x^6)^{-6}b^{-6}c^{-6}$

$\qquad = \dfrac{x^6 x^{-36}}{b^6 c^6}$

$\qquad = \dfrac{x^{-30}}{b^6 c^6}$

$\qquad = \dfrac{1}{x^{30}b^6 c^6}$

53. $\dfrac{2^{-3}x^2 y^{-5}}{5^{-2}x^7 y^{-1}} = \dfrac{5^2 x^{2-7}y^{-5-(-1)}}{2^3}$

$\qquad = \dfrac{25x^{-5}y^{-4}}{8}$

$\qquad = \dfrac{25}{8x^5 y^4}$

55. $\left(\dfrac{2x^2}{y^4}\right)^3\left(\dfrac{2x^5}{y}\right)^{-2} = \dfrac{2^3 x^{2(3)}2^{-2}x^{5(-2)}}{y^{4(3)}y^{-2}}$

$\qquad = \dfrac{8x^6 x^{-10}}{2^2 y^{12}y^{-2}}$

$\qquad = \dfrac{2x^{-4}}{y^{10}}$

$\qquad = \dfrac{2}{x^4 y^{10}}$

57. $(5\times10^{11})(2.9\times10^{-3}) = 5\times2.9\times10^{11+(-3)}$

$\qquad = 14.5\times10^8$

$\qquad = 1.45\times10^1\times10^8$

$\qquad = 1.45\times10^9$

59. $(2\times10^5)^3 = 2^3\times10^{5(3)} = 8\times10^{15}$

61. $\dfrac{3.6\times10^{-4}}{9\times10^2} = \dfrac{3.6}{9}\times10^{-4-2}$

$\qquad = 0.4\times10^{-6}$

$\qquad = 4\times10^{-1}\times10^{-6}$

$\qquad = 4\times10^{-7}$

63. $\dfrac{0.0069}{0.023} = \dfrac{6.9\times10^{-3}}{2.3\times10^{-2}}$

$\qquad = \dfrac{6.9}{2.3}\times10^{-3-(-2)}$

$\qquad = 3\times10^{-1}$

65. $\dfrac{18,200\times100}{91,000}=\dfrac{1.82\times10^4\times1\times10^2}{9.1\times10^4}$

$\quad=\dfrac{1.82\times10^6}{9.1\times10^4}$

$\quad=0.2\times10^{6-4}$

$\quad=2\times10^{-1}\times10^2$

$\quad=2\times10^{-1+2}$

$\quad=2\times10^1$

67. $\dfrac{6000\times0.006}{0.009\times400}=\dfrac{6\times10^3\times6\times10^{-3}}{9\times10^{-3}\times4\times10^2}$

$\quad=\dfrac{36\times10^0}{36\times10^{-1}}$

$\quad=1\times10^{0-(-1)}$

$\quad=1\times10^1$

69. $\dfrac{0.00064\times2000}{16,000}=\dfrac{6.4\times10^{-4}\times2\times10^3}{1.6\times10^4}$

$\quad=\dfrac{12.8\times10^{-1}}{1.6\times10^4}$

$\quad=8\times10^{-1-4}$

$\quad=8\times10^{-5}$

71. $\dfrac{66,000\times0.001}{0.002\times0.003}=\dfrac{6.6\times10^4\times1\times10^{-3}}{2\times10^{-3}\times3\times10^{-3}}$

$\quad=\dfrac{6.6\times10^1}{6\times10^{-6}}$

$\quad=1.1\times10^{1-(-6)}$

$\quad=1.1\times10^7$

73. $\dfrac{1.25\times10^{15}}{(2.2\times10^{-2})(6.4\times10^{-5})}$

$\quad=\dfrac{1.25\times10^{15}}{14.08\times10^{-7}}$

$\quad=0.0887784091\times10^{15-(-7)}$

$\quad=0.0887784091\times10^{22}$

$\quad=8.877840909\times10^{-2}\times10^{22}$

$\quad=8.877840909\times10^{20}$

75. $200,000\times10^{-8}=2\times10^5\times10^{-8}=2\times10^{-3}$ sec.

77. $(3.8\times10^{-6})(1.64\times10^{-5})$

$\quad=6.232\times10^{-11}$

The volume is 6.232×10^{-11} cubic meters.

79. $12m-14-15m-1=-3m-15$

81. $-9y-(5-6y)=-9y-5+6y=-3y-5$

83. $5(x-3)-4(2x-5)=5x-15-8x+20$

$\quad\quad=-3x+5$

85. $(x^{2b+7})^2=x^{(2b+7)\cdot2}=x^{4b+14}$

87. $\dfrac{x^{-5y+2}x^{2y}}{x}=\dfrac{x^{-5y+2+2y}}{x}$

$\quad=\dfrac{x^{-3y+2}}{x}$

$\quad=x^{-3y+2-1}$

$\quad=x^{-3y+1}$

89. $(c^{2a+3})^3=c^{(2a+3)\cdot3}=c^{6a+9}$

91. $\dfrac{(y^{4a})^7}{y^{2a-1}}=\dfrac{y^{28a}}{y^{2a-1}}=y^{28a-(2a-1)}=y^{26a+1}$

93. $\left(\dfrac{3y^{5a}}{y^{-a+1}}\right)^2=\dfrac{3^2y^{5a(2)}}{y^{(-a+1)\cdot2}}$

$\quad=\dfrac{9y^{10a}}{y^{-2a+2}}$

$\quad=9y^{10a-(-2a+2)}$

$\quad=9y^{12a-2}$

95. $\dfrac{(y^{3-a})^b}{(y^{1-b})^a}=\dfrac{y^{(3-a)\cdot b}}{y^{(1-b)\cdot a}}$

$\quad=\dfrac{y^{3b-ab}}{y^{a-ab}}$

$\quad=y^{3b-ab-(a-ab)}$

$\quad=y^{3b-a}$

97. $\dfrac{x^{-5-3a}y^{-2a-b}}{x^{-5+3b}y^{-2b-a}} = \left(\dfrac{x^{-5-3a}}{x^{-5+3b}}\right)\left(\dfrac{y^{-2a-b}}{y^{-2b-a}}\right)$

$\qquad = x^{-5-3a-(-5+3b)}y^{-2a-b-(-2b-a)}$

$\qquad = x^{-5-3a+5-3b}y^{-2a-b+2b+a}$

$\qquad = x^{-3a-3b}y^{b-a}$

99. $\left(\dfrac{3x^{-1}}{y^{-3}}\right)\left(5x^{-7}\right) = \dfrac{3 \cdot 5 x^{-1+(-7)}}{y^{-3}}$

$\qquad = \dfrac{15x^{-8}}{y^{-3}}$

$\qquad = \dfrac{15y^{3}}{x^{8}}$

The area is $\dfrac{15y^3}{x^8}$ square feet.

101. $D = \dfrac{M}{V}$

$3.12 \times 10^{-2} = \dfrac{M}{4.269 \times 10^{14}}$

$(3.12 \times 10^{-2})(4.269 \times 10^{14}) = M$

$3.12 \times 4.269 \times 10^{-2+14} = M$

$13.31928 \times 10^{12} = M$

$1.331928 \times 10^{1} \times 10^{12} = M$

$1.331928 \times 10^{13} = M$

The mass is 1.331928×10^{13} tons.

103. $a^{-2} = \dfrac{1}{a^2}$

Since both 1 and a^2 are both positive, their quotient cannot be negative. Therefore, no, there is no such a.

105. $D = \dfrac{2.927 \times 10^8}{3.536 \times 10^6}$

$\qquad = \dfrac{2.927}{3.536} \times 10^{8-6}$

$\qquad = 0.8277714932 \times 10^2$

$\qquad = 82.77714932$

$\qquad \approx 83$

The population density is about 83 people per square mile.

107. $\dfrac{1.27 \times 10^8}{3.22 \times 10^7} = \dfrac{1.27}{3.22} \times 10^{8-7}$

$\qquad = 0.3944099379 \times 10^1$

$\qquad = 3.944099379$

Japan's population was about 3.9 times greater than Oceania's.

109. $\dfrac{3.16 \times 10^9}{7.01 \times 10^8} = \dfrac{3.16}{7.01} \times 10^{9-8}$

$\qquad = 0.4507845934 \times 10^1$

$\qquad = 4.507845934$

Moscow's volume is about 4.5 times greater than São Paulo's.

Exercise Set 5.3

1. 4 has degree 0.

3. $5x^2$ has degree 2.

5. $-3xy^2$ has degree $1+2=3$.

7. $6x+3$ has degree 1 and is a binomial.

9. $3x^2 - 2x + 5$ has degree 2 and is a trinomial.

11. $-xyz$ has degree $1+1+1=3$ and is a monomial.

13. $x^2y - 4xy^2 + 5x + y$ has degree $2+1=3$ and is none of these.

15. Answers may vary. The degree of a term is found by adding the exponents on each variable in the term.

17. $P(x) = x^2 + x + 1$

$P(7) = 7^2 + 7 + 1 = 49 + 7 + 1 = 57$

19. $Q(x) = 5x^2 - 1$

$Q(-10) = 5(-10)^2 - 1$

$\qquad = 5(100) - 1$

$\qquad = 500 - 1$

$\qquad = 499$

21. $Q(x) = 5x^2 - 1$

$$Q\left(\frac{1}{4}\right) = 5\left(\frac{1}{4}\right)^2 - 1$$

$$= 5\left(\frac{1}{16}\right) - 1$$

$$= \frac{5}{16} - \frac{16}{16}$$

$$= -\frac{11}{16}$$

23. a. $y_1 = -16x^2 + 75$

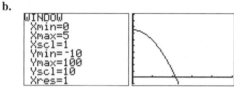

The y-values change from positive to negative between $x = 2$ and $x = 3$.

b.

The graph crosses the x-axis between $x = 2$ and $x = 3$.

25. $P(x) = -16x^2 + 525$

Let $y_1 = -16x^2 + 525$.

Construct a table of values starting at $x = 0$ and incrementing by 1. Scroll down the y_1 column and locate where $y_1 = 0$.

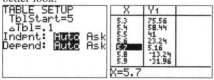

From the table, we see that the y-values change from positive to negative between $x = 5$ and $x = 6$. We can change the table settings to get a better look.

From the table, we see that the y-values change from positive to negative between 5.7 and 5.8. Since 5.16 is closer to 0 than -13.24, the object will hit the ground after about 5.7 seconds.

27. a. Let $y_1 = -16x^2 + 100$ and $y_2 = -16x^2 - 85x + 200$.

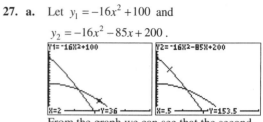

From the graph we can see that the second egg will hit the ground first.

b. The eggs are the same distance above the ground when the two graphs cross. Therefore, we need to find the x-coordinate of the intersection point.

The two eggs are the same height after about 1 second (to the nearest second).

29. $5y + y = 6y$

31. $4x + 7x - 3 = 11x - 3$

33. $4xy + 2x - 3xy - 1 = xy + 2x - 1$

35. $7x^2 - 2xy + 5y^2 - x^2 + xy + 11y^2$
$= 6x^2 - xy + 16y^2$

37. $(9y^2 - 8) + (9y^2 - 9) = 18y^2 - 17$

39.
$$\begin{array}{r} x^2 + xy - y^2 \\ 2x^2 - 4xy + 7y^2 \\ \hline 3x^2 - 3xy + 6y^2 \end{array}$$

41.
$$\begin{array}{r} x^2 - 6x + 3 \\ + (2x + 5) \\ \hline x^2 - 4x + 8 \end{array}$$

43. $(9y^2 - 7y + 5) - (8y^2 - 7y + 2)$
$= 9y^2 - 7y + 5 - 8y^2 + 7y - 2$
$= y^2 + 3$

45. $(4x^2 + 2x) - (6x^2 - 3x)$

$= 4x^2 + 2x - 6x^2 + 3x$

$= -2x^2 + 5x$

47.
$$\begin{array}{r} 3x^2 - 4x + 8 \\ -5x^2 \quad\;\; +7 \\ \hline -2x^2 - 4x + 15 \end{array}$$

49. $(5x - 11) + (-x - 2) = 5x - 11 - x - 2$

$\qquad\qquad\qquad\qquad = 4x - 13$

51. $(7x^2 + x + 1) - (6x^2 + x - 1)$

$= 7x^2 + x + 1 - 6x^2 - x + 1$

$= x^2 + 2$

53. $(7x^3 - 4x + 8) + (5x^3 + 4x + 8x)$

$= 7x^3 - 4x + 8 + 5x^3 + 4x + 8x$

$= 12x^3 + 8x + 8$

55.
$$\begin{array}{r} 9x^3 - 2x^2 + 4x - 7 \\ -2x^3 + 6x^2 + 4x - 3 \\ \hline 7x^3 + 4x^2 + 8x - 10 \end{array}$$

57. $(y^2 + 4yx + 7) + (-19y^2 + 7yx + 7)$

$= y^2 + 4yx + 7 - 19y^2 + 7yx + 7$

$= -18y^2 + 11yx + 14$

59. $(3x^3 - b + 2a - 6) + (-4x^3 + b + 6a - 6)$

$= 3x^3 - b + 2a - 6 - 4x^3 + b + 6a - 6$

$= -x^3 + 8a - 12$

61. $(4x^2 - 6x + 2) - (-x^2 + 3x + 5)$

$= 4x^2 - 6x + 2 + x^2 - 3x - 5$

$= 5x^2 - 9x - 3$

63. $(-3x + 8) + (-3x^2 + 3x - 5)$

$= -3x + 8 - 3x^2 + 3x - 5$

$= -3x^2 + 3$

65. $(-3 + 4x^2 + 7xy^2) + (2x^3 - x^2 + xy^2)$

$= -3 + 4x^2 + 7xy^2 + 2x^3 - x^2 + xy^2$

$= 2x^3 + 3x^2 + 8xy^2 - 3$

67.
$$\begin{array}{r} 6y^2 - 6y + 4 \\ y^2 + 6y - 7 \\ \hline 7y^2 \quad\quad - 3 \end{array}$$

69.
$$\begin{array}{r} 3x^2 + 15x + 8 \\ 2x^2 + 7x + 8 \\ \hline 5x^2 + 22x + 16 \end{array}$$

71.
$$\begin{array}{r} \frac{1}{2}x^2 - \frac{1}{3}x^2 y \qquad\quad + 2y^3 \\ \frac{1}{4}x^2 \qquad - \frac{8}{3}x^2 y^2 - \frac{1}{2}y^3 \\ \hline \frac{3}{4}x^2 - \frac{1}{3}x^2 y - \frac{8}{3}x^2 y^2 + \frac{3}{2}y^3 \end{array}$$

73. $(5q^4 - 2q^2 - 3q) + (-6q^4 + 3q^2 + 5)$

$= 5q^4 - 2q^2 - 3q - 6q^4 + 3q^2 + 5$

$= -q^4 + q^2 - 3q + 5$

75.
$$\begin{array}{r} 7x^2 + 4x + 9 \\ + \;\; 8x^2 + 7x - 8 \\ \hline 15x^2 + 11x + 1 \\ - \qquad\qquad 3x + 7 \\ \hline 15x^2 + 8x - 6 \end{array}$$

77. $(4x^4 - 7x^2 + 3) + (2 - 3x^4)$

$= 4x^4 - 7x^2 + 3 + 2 - 3x^4$

$= x^4 - 7x^2 + 5$

79. $\left(\frac{2}{3}x^2 - \frac{1}{6}x + \frac{5}{6}\right) - \left(\frac{1}{3}x^2 + \frac{5}{6}x - \frac{1}{6}\right)$

$= \frac{2}{3}x^2 - \frac{1}{6}x + \frac{5}{6} - \frac{1}{3}x^2 - \frac{5}{6}x + \frac{1}{6}$

$= \frac{1}{3}x^2 - x + 1$

Chapter 5: *Exponents, Polynomials, and Polynomial Functions*

81. If $L = 5$, $W = 4$, and $H = 9$, then
$$2HL + 2LW + 2HW$$
$$= 2(9)(5) + 2(5)(4) + 2(9)(4)$$
$$= 90 + 40 + 72$$
$$= 202$$
The surface area is 202 square inches.

83. $P(t) = -16t^2 + 300t$

t	$P(t)$

$Y_1 = -16X^2 + 300X$

a. From the table, $P(1) = 284$ feet

b. From the table, $P(2) = 536$ feet

c. From the table, $P(3) = 756$ feet

d. From the table, $P(4) = 944$ feet

e. Answers may vary. The projectile increases in height due to the initial force applied, but it slows down as time goes on. Eventually, as gravity takes over, the projectile will stop and then begin to fall back to the ground.

$Y_1 = 1064$ $Y_1 = -76$

f. From the table in part (**e**), $P(18) = 216$ and $P(19) = -76$. Since -76 is closer to 0 than 216, the time to hit the ground (to the nearest second) is 19 seconds.

85. $P(x) = 45x - 100,000$
$$P(4000) = 45(4000) - 100,000$$
$$= 80,000$$
The profit is \$80,000.

87. $R(x) = 2x$
$$R(20,000) = 2(20,000)$$
$$= 40,000$$
The revenue is \$40,000.

89. A

91. D

93. $5(3x - 2) = 15x - 10$

95. $-2(x^2 - 5x + 6) = -2x^2 + 10x - 12$

97. $(4x^{2a} - 3x^a + 0.5) - (x^{2a} - 5x^a - 0.2)$
$$= 4x^{2a} - 3x^a + 0.5 - x^{2a} + 5x^a + 0.2$$
$$= 3x^{2a} + 2x^a + 0.7$$

99. $(8x^{2y} - 7x^y + 3) + (-4x^{2y} + 9x^y - 14)$
$$= 8x^{2y} - 7x^y + 3 - 4x^{2y} + 9x^y - 14$$
$$= 4x^{2y} + 2x^y - 11$$

101. $P = 2l + 2w$
$$= 2(3x^2 - x + 2y) + 2(x + 5y)$$
$$= 6x^2 - 2x + 4y + 2x + 10y$$
$$= 6x^2 + 14y$$
The perimeter is $P = (6x^2 + 14y)$ units.

103. $P(x) + Q(x) = (3x + 3) + (4x^2 - 6x + 3)$
$$= 3x + 3 + 4x^2 - 6x + 3$$
$$= 4x^2 - 3x + 6$$

105. $Q(x) - R(x) = (4x^2 - 6x + 3) - (5x^2 - 7)$
$$= 4x^2 - 6x + 3 - 5x^2 + 7$$
$$= -x^2 - 6x + 10$$

107. $2[Q(x)] - R(x)$
$$= 2(4x^2 - 6x + 3) - (5x^2 - 7)$$
$$= 8x^2 - 12x + 6 - 5x^2 + 7$$
$$= 3x^2 - 12x + 13$$

109. $3[R(x)] + 4[P(x)]$
$$= 3(5x^2 - 7) + 4(3x + 3)$$
$$= 15x^2 - 21 + 12x + 12$$
$$= 15x^2 + 12x - 9$$

111. $P(x) = 2x - 3$

a. $P(a) = 2a - 3$

202

b. $P(-x) = 2(-x) - 3 = -2x - 3$

c. $P(x+h) = 2(x+h) - 3 = 2x + 2h - 3$

113. $P(x) = 4x$

    a. $P(a) = 4a$

    b. $P(-x) = 4(-x) = -4x$

    c. $P(x+h) = 4(x+h) = 4x + 4h$

115. $P(x) = 4x - 1$

    a. $P(a) = 4a - 1$

    b. $P(-x) = 4(-x) - 1 = -4x - 1$

    c. $P(x+h) = 4(x+h) - 1 = 4x + 4h - 1$

117. $f(x) = -246.7x^2 + 1887.9x + 1016.9$

    a. 1998 means that $x = 0$:
$$f(0) = -246.7(0)^2 + 1887.9(0) + 1016.9$$
$$= 1016.9$$
$$\approx 1017 \text{ stations}$$

    b. 2000 means that $x = 2$:
$$f(2) = -246.7(2)^2 + 1887.9(2) + 1016.9$$
$$= 3805.9$$
$$\approx 3806 \text{ stations}$$

    c. 2006 means $x = 8$:
$$f(8) = -246.7(8)^2 + 1887.9(8) + 1016.9$$
$$= 331.3$$
$$\approx 331 \text{ stations}$$

    d. Answers may vary. If the number of stations were increasing at a steady rate, the function would be linear and the number of stations would continue to increase over time. Since the value in part **c** is lower than for parts **a** and **b**, this is not the case.

119. $f(x) = 0.014x^2 + 0.12x + 0.85$

    a. 1999 means that $x = 9$:
$$f(9) = 0.014(9)^2 + 0.12(9) + 0.85$$
$$= 3.064$$
$$\approx 3.1 \text{ million SUV's}$$

    b. 2005 means that $x = 15$:
$$f(15) = 0.014(15)^2 + 0.12(15) + 0.85$$
$$= 5.8 \text{ million SUV's}$$

121. $f(x) = 1.4x^2 + 129.6x + 939$

    a. 1985 means that $x = 5$:
$$f(5) = 1.4(5)^2 + 129.6(5) + 939$$
$$= \$1622$$

    b. 1995 means that $x = 15$:
$$f(15) = 1.4(15)^2 + 129.6(15) + 939$$
$$= \$3198$$

    c. 2010 means $x = 30$:
$$f(30) = 1.4(30)^2 + 129.6(30) + 939$$
$$= \$6087$$

    d. No; $f(x)$ is not linear.

Exercise Set 5.4

1. $(-4x^3)(3x^2) = -4(3)x^5 = -12x^5$

3. $3x(4x+7) = 3x(4x) + 3x(7)$
$$= 12x^2 + 21x$$

5. $-6xy(4x+y) = -6xy(4x) - 6xy(y)$
$$= -24x^2y - 6xy^2$$

7. $-4ab(xa^2 + ya^2 - 3)$
$$= -4ab(xa^2) - 4ab(ya^2) - 4ab(-3)$$
$$= -4a^3bx - 4a^3by + 12ab$$

9.
$$\begin{array}{r} 2x + 4 \\ \times \quad x - 3 \\ \hline -6x - 12 \\ 2x^2 + 4x \\ \hline 2x^2 - 2x - 12 \end{array}$$

11. $(2x+3)(x^3 - x + 2)$
$$= 2x(x^3 - x + 2) + 3(x^3 - x + 2)$$
$$= 2x^4 - 2x^2 + 4x + 3x^3 - 3x + 6$$
$$= 2x^4 + 3x^3 - 2x^2 + x + 6$$

13.
$$
\begin{array}{r}
3x-2 \\
\times \quad 5x+1 \\
\hline
3x-2 \\
15x^2-10x \\
\hline
15x^2-7x-2
\end{array}
$$

15.
$$
\begin{array}{r}
3m^2+2m-1 \\
\times \quad 5m+2 \\
\hline
6m^2+4m-2 \\
15m^3+10m^2-5m \\
\hline
15m^3+16m^2-m-2
\end{array}
$$

17. Answers may vary. We multiply two polynomials by multiplying each term of one polynomial by each term of the other and simplifying.

19. $(x-3)(x+4) = x\cdot x+x(4)-3\cdot x-3(4)$
$$= x^2+4x-3x-12$$
$$= x^2+x-12$$

21. $(5x+8y)(2x-y)$
$$= 5x\cdot 2x+5x(-y)+8y(2x)+8y(-y)$$
$$= 10x^2-5xy+16xy-8y^2$$
$$= 10x^2+11xy-8y^2$$

23. $(3x-1)(x+3) = 3x\cdot x+3x\cdot 3-1\cdot x-1\cdot 3$
$$= 3x^2+9x-x-3$$
$$= 3x^2+8x-3$$

25. $\left(3x+\dfrac{1}{2}\right)\left(3x-\dfrac{1}{2}\right)$
$$= 3x(3x)+3x\left(-\dfrac{1}{2}\right)+\dfrac{1}{2}(3x)+\dfrac{1}{2}\left(-\dfrac{1}{2}\right)$$
$$= 9x^2-\dfrac{3}{2}x+\dfrac{3}{2}x-\dfrac{1}{4}$$
$$= 9x^2-\dfrac{1}{4}$$

27. $(x+4)^2 = x^2+2(x)(4)+4^2$
$$= x^2+8x+16$$

29. $(6y-1)(6y+1) = (6y)^2-1^2 = 36y^2-1$

31. $(3x-y)^2 = (3x)^2-2(3x)(y)+y^2$
$$= 9x^2-6xy+y^2$$

33. $(3b-6y)(3b+6y) = (3b)^2-(6y)^2$
$$= 9b^2-36y^2$$

35. $[3+(4b+1)]^2$
$$= 3^2+2(3)(4b+1)+(4b+1)^2$$
$$= 9+6(4b+1)+(4b)^2+2(4b)(1)+1^2$$
$$= 9+24b+6+16b^2+8b+1$$
$$= 16b^2+32b+16$$

37. $[(2s-3)-1][(2s-3)+1]$
$$= (2s-3)^2-1^2$$
$$= (2s)^2-2(2s)(3)+3^2-1$$
$$= 4s^2-12s+9-1$$
$$= 4s^2-12s+8$$

39. $[(xy+4)-6]^2$
$$= (xy+4)^2-2(xy+4)(6)+6^2$$
$$= (xy)^2+2(xy)(4)+4^2-12(xy+4)+36$$
$$= x^2y^2+8xy+16-12xy-48+36$$
$$= x^2y^2-4xy+4$$

41. Answers may vary. The FOIL method can be used to multiply two binomials together.

43. $(x+y)(2x-1)(x+1)$
$$= (x+y)(2x^2+2x-x-1)$$
$$= (x+y)(2x^2+x-1)$$
$$= x(2x^2+x-1)+y(2x^2+x-1)$$
$$= 2x^3+x^2-x+2x^2y+xy-y$$
$$= 2x^3+2x^2y+x^2+xy-x-y$$

45. $(x-2)^4 = (x-2)^2 (x-2)^2$

$\qquad = \left(x^2 - 4x + 4\right)\left(x^2 - 4x + 4\right)$

$$
\begin{array}{r}
x^2 - 4x + 4 \\
\times \qquad x^2 - 4x + 4 \\
\hline
4x^2 - 16x + 16 \\
-4x^3 + 16x^2 - 16x \\
x^4 - 4x^3 + 4x^2 \\
\hline
x^4 - 8x^3 + 24x^2 - 32x + 16
\end{array}
$$

47. $(x-5)(x+5)(x^2+25) = (x^2-25)(x^2+25)$

$\qquad = (x^2)^2 - 25^2$

$\qquad = x^4 - 625$

49. $(3x+1)(3x+5)$

$= (3x)^2 + 3x(5) + 1(3x) + 1(5)$

$= 9x^2 + 15x + 3x + 5$

$= 9x^2 + 18x + 5$

51. $(2x^3+5)(5x^2+4x+1)$

$= 2x^3(5x^2+4x+1) + 5(5x^2+4x+1)$

$= 10x^5 + 8x^4 + 2x^3 + 25x^2 + 20x + 5$

53. $(7x-3)(7x+3) = (7x)^2 - 3^2 = 49x^2 - 9$

55.
$$
\begin{array}{r}
3x^2 + 4x - 4 \\
\times \qquad 3x + 6 \\
\hline
18x^2 + 24x - 24 \\
9x^3 + 12x^2 - 12x \\
\hline
9x^3 + 30x^2 + 12x - 24
\end{array}
$$

57. $\left(4x + \dfrac{1}{3}\right)\left(4x - \dfrac{1}{2}\right)$

$= (4x)^2 + 4x\left(-\dfrac{1}{2}\right) + \dfrac{1}{3}(4x) + \dfrac{1}{3}\left(-\dfrac{1}{2}\right)$

$= 16x^2 - 2x + \dfrac{4}{3}x - \dfrac{1}{6}$

$= 16x^2 - \dfrac{2}{3}x - \dfrac{1}{6}$

59. $(6x+1)^2 = (6x)^2 + 2(6x)(1) + 1^2$

$\qquad = 36x^2 + 12x + 1$

61. $(x^2+2y)(x^2-2y) = (x^2)^2 - (2y)^2$

$\qquad = x^4 - 4y^2$

63.
$$
\begin{array}{r}
5a^2b^2 - 6a - 6b \\
\times \qquad -6a^2b^2 \\
\hline
-30a^4b^4 + 36a^3b^2 + 36a^2b^3
\end{array}
$$

65. $(a-4)(2a-4) = 2a^2 - 4a - 8a + 16$

$\qquad = 2a^2 - 12a + 16$

67. $(7ab+3c)(7ab-3c) = (7ab)^2 - (3c)^2$

$\qquad = 49a^2b^2 - 9c^2$

69. $(m-4)^2 = m^2 - 2(m)(4) + 4^2$

$\qquad = m^2 - 8m + 16$

71. $(3x+1)^2 = (3x)^2 + 2(3x)(1) + 1^2$

$\qquad = 9x^2 + 6x + 1$

73. $(y-4)(y-3) = y^2 - 3y - 4y + 12$

$\qquad = y^2 - 7y + 12$

75. $(x+y)(2x-1)(x+1)$

$= (x+y)(2x^2 + 2x - x - 1)$

$= (x+y)(2x^2 + x - 1)$

$= x(2x^2 + x - 1) + y(2x^2 + x - 1)$

$= 2x^3 + x^2 - x + 2x^2 y + xy - y$

$= 2x^3 + 2x^2 y + x^2 + xy - x - y$

77.
$$
\begin{array}{r}
3x^2 + 2x - 1 \\
\times \qquad 3x^2 + 2x - 1 \\
\hline
-3x^2 - 2x + 1 \\
6x^3 + 4x^2 - 2x \\
9x^4 + 6x^3 - 3x^2 \\
\hline
9x^4 + 12x^3 - 2x^2 - 4x + 1
\end{array}
$$

79.
$$
\begin{array}{r}
4x^2 - 2x + 5 \\
\times \qquad 3x + 1 \\
\hline
4x^2 - 2x + 5 \\
12x^3 - 6x^2 + 15x \\
\hline
12x^3 - 2x^2 + 13x + 5
\end{array}
$$

81. $f(x) = x^2 - 3x$

$f(a) = a^2 - 3a$

83. $f(x) = x^2 - 3x$

$f(a+h) = (a+h)^2 - 3(a+h)$

$ = a^2 + 2ah + h^2 - 3a - 3h$

85. $f(x) = x^2 - 3x$

$f(b-2) = (b-2)^2 - 3(b-2)$

$ = b^2 - 4b + 4 - 3b + 6$

$ = b^2 - 7b + 10$

87. $y = -2x + 7$

$m = -2$

89. $3x - 5y = 14$

$-5y = -3x + 14$

$y = \dfrac{3}{5}x - \dfrac{14}{5}$

$m = \dfrac{3}{5}$

91. Since any vertical line crosses the graph at most once, it is a function.

93. $F(x) = x^2 + 3x + 2$

a. $F(a+h) = (a+h)^2 + 3(a+h) + 2$

$ = a^2 + 2ah + h^2 + 3a + 3h + 2$

b. $F(a) = a^2 + 3a + 2$

c. $F(a+h) - F(a)$

$= a^2 + 2ah + h^2 + 3a + 3h + 2 - (a^2 + 3a + 2)$

$= 2ah + h^2 + 3h$

95. $5x^2 y^n (6y^{n+1} - 2)$

$= 5x^2 y^n (6y^{n+1}) + 5x^2 y^n (-2)$

$= 30x^2 y^{2n+1} - 10x^2 y^n$

97. $(x^a + 5)(x^{2a} - 3)$

$= x^a \cdot x^{2a} + x^a(-3) + 5(x^{2a}) + 5(-3)$

$= x^{3a} - 3x^a + 5x^{2a} - 15$

99. Area $= \pi r^2$

$= \pi(5x - 2)^2$

$= \pi(25x^2 - 20x + 4)$ square km

101. Area $= (3x - 2)^2 - x^2$

$= (9x^2 - 12x + 4) - x^2$

$= (8x^2 - 12x + 4)$ square inches

103. One operation is addition while the other is multiplication.

a. $(3x + 5) + (3x + 7) = 6x + 12$

b. $(3x + 5)(3x + 7)$

$= 9x^2 + 21x + 15x + 35$

$= 9x^2 + 36x + 35$

105. $P(x) \cdot R(x) = (5x)(x + 5)$

$= 5x \cdot x + 5x \cdot 5$

$= 5x^2 + 25x$

107. $[Q(x)]^2 = (x^2 - 2)^2$

$= (x^2)^2 - 2(x^2)(2) + 2^2$

$= x^4 - 4x^2 + 4$

109. $R(x) \cdot Q(x) = (x + 5)(x^2 - 2)$

$= x^3 - 2x + 5x^2 - 10$

$= x^3 + 5x^2 - 2x - 10$

Mental Math 5.5

1. $6 = 2 \cdot 3$

$12 = 2 \cdot 2 \cdot 3$

$\text{GCF} = 2 \cdot 3 = 6$

2. $9 = 3 \cdot 3$

$27 = 3 \cdot 3 \cdot 3$

$\text{GCF} = 3 \cdot 3 = 9$

3. $15x = 3 \cdot 5 \cdot x$

$10 = 2 \cdot 5$

$\text{GCF} = 5$

4. $9x = 3 \cdot 3 \cdot x$

$12 = 2 \cdot 2 \cdot 3$

GCF $= 3$

5. $13x = 13 \cdot x$

$2x = 2 \cdot x$

GCF $= x$

6. $4y = 4 \cdot y$

$5y = 5 \cdot y$

GCF $= y$

7. $7x = 7 \cdot x$

$14x = 2 \cdot 7 \cdot x$

GCF $= 7x$

8. $8z = 2 \cdot 2 \cdot 2 \cdot z$

$4z = 2 \cdot 2 \cdot z$

GCF $= 2 \cdot 2 \cdot z = 4z$

Exercise Set 5.5

1. a^8, a^5, and a^3 ; GCF $= a^3$

3. $x^2 y^3 z^3$, $y^2 z^3$, and $xy^2 z^2$; GCF $= y^2 z^2$

5. $6x^3 y$, $9x^2 y^2$, and $12x^2 y$; GCF $= 3x^2 y$

7. $10x^3 yz^3$, $20x^2 z^5$, $45xz^3$; GCF $= 5xz^3$

9. $18x - 12 = 6(3x - 2)$

11. $4y^2 - 16xy^3 = 4y^2(1 - 4xy)$

13. $6x^5 - 8x^4 + 2x^3 = 2x^3(3x^2 - 4x + 1)$

15. $8a^3 b^3 - 4a^2 b^2 + 4ab + 16ab^2$
$= 4ab(2a^2 b^2 - ab + 1 + 4b)$

17. $6(x+3) + 5a(x+3) = (x+3)(6+5a)$

19. $2x(z+7) + (z+7) = (z+7)(2x+1)$

21. $3x(x^2+5) - 2(x^2+5) = (x^2+5)(3x-2)$

23. Answers may vary. If we do not include the 1, we would not get the original expression when we distribute. That is,
$3(x^2 - 3x) = 3x^2 - 9x \neq 3x^2 - 9x + 3$

25. $ab + 3a + 2b + 6 = a(b+3) + 2(b+3)$
$= (a+2)(b+3)$

27. $ac + 4a - 2c - 8 = a(c+4) - 2(c+4)$
$= (a-2)(c+4)$

29. $2xy - 3x - 4y + 6 = x(2y-3) - 2(2y-3)$
$= (x-2)(2y-3)$

31. $12xy - 8x - 3y + 2 = 4x(3y-2) - 1(3y-2)$
$= (4x-1)(3y-2)$

33. $6x^3 + 9 = 3(2x^3 + 3)$

35. $x^3 + 3x^2 = x^2(x+3)$

37. $8a^3 - 4a = 4a(2a^2 - 1)$

39. $-20x^2 y + 16xy^3 = -4xy(5x - 4y^2)$

41. $10a^2 b^3 + 5ab^2 - 15ab^3 = 5ab^2(2ab + 1 - 3b)$

43. $9abc^2 + 6a^2 bc - 6ab + 3bc$
$= 3b(3ac^2 + 2a^2 c - 2a + c)$

45. $4x(y-2) - 3(y-2) = (y-2)(4x-3)$

47. $6xy + 10x + 9y + 15 = 2x(3y+5) + 3(3y+5)$
$= (2x+3)(3y+5)$

49. $xy + 3y - 5x - 15 = y(x+3) - 5(x+3)$
$= (x+3)(y-5)$

51. $6ab - 2a - 9b + 3 = 2a(3b-1) - 3(3b-1)$
$= (3b-1)(2a-3)$

53. $12xy + 18x + 2y + 3 = 6x(2y+3) + 1(2y+3)$
$= (6x+1)(2y+3)$

55. $2m(n-8) - (n-8) = (2m-1)(n-8)$

57. $15x^3y^2 - 18x^2y^2 = 3x^2y^2(5x - 6)$

59. $2x^2 + 3xy + 4x + 6y$
$= x(2x + 3y) + 2(2x + 3y)$
$= (2x + 3y)(x + 2)$

61. $5x^2 + 5xy - 3x - 3y = 5x(x + y) - 3(x + y)$
$= (x + y)(5x - 3)$

63. $x^3 + 3x^2 + 4x + 12 = x^2(x + 3) + 4(x + 3)$
$= (x + 3)(x^2 + 4)$

65. $x^3 - x^2 - 2x + 2 = x^2(x - 1) - 2(x - 1)$
$= (x - 1)(x^2 - 2)$

67. $(5x^2)(11x^5) = 5(11)x^2x^5 = 55x^7$

69. $(5x^2)^3 = 5^3(x^2)^3 = 125x^6$

71. $(x + 2)(x - 5) = x^2 - 5x + 2x - 10$
$= x^2 - 3x - 10$

73. $(x + 3)(x + 2) = x^2 + 3x + 2x + 6$
$= x^2 + 5x + 6$

75. $(y - 3)(y - 1) = y^2 - 1y - 3y + 3$
$= y^2 - 4y + 3$

77. None. Check by multiplying the binomials together.

   a. $(2 - x)(3 - y) = 6 - 2y - 3x + xy$
$= xy - 3x - 2y + 6$

   b. $(-2 + x)(-3 + y) = 6 - 2y - 3x + xy$
$= xy - 3x - 2y + 6$

   c. $(x - 2)(y - 3) = xy - 3x - 2y + 6$

   d. $(-x + 2)(-y + 3) = xy - 3x - 2y + 6$

79. **a** is correct.

81. $I(R_1 + R_2) = E$

83. $x^2 + 4(10x) = x^2 + 40x = x(x + 40)$ sq. in.

85. $h(t) = -16t^2 + 224$

   a. $h(t) = -16(t^2 - 14)$

   b. $h(2) = -16(2)^2 + 224$
$= -16(4) + 224$
$= -64 + 224$
$= 160$
$h(2) = -16(2^2 - 14)$
$= -16(4 - 14)$
$= -16(-10)$
$= 160$

   c. Answers may vary. The two expressions are equivalent even though they are in different forms.

87. $3y^n + 3y^{2n} + 5y^{8n} = y^n(3 + 3y^n + 5y^{7n})$

89. $3x^{5a} - 6x^{3a} + 9x^{2a} = 3x^{2a}(x^{3a} - 2x^a + 3)$

Mental Math 5.6

  1. $10 = 2 \cdot 5$
$7 = 2 + 5$
2 and 5

  2. $12 = 2 \cdot 2 \cdot 3 = 2 \cdot 6$
$8 = 2 + 6$
2 and 6

  3. $24 = 2 \cdot 2 \cdot 2 \cdot 3 = 8 \cdot 3$
$11 = 8 + 3$
8 and 3

  4. $30 = 2 \cdot 3 \cdot 5 = 10 \cdot 3$
$13 = 10 + 3$
10 and 3

Exercise Set 5.6

  1. $x^2 + 9x + 18 = (x + 6)(x + 3)$

  3. $x^2 - 12x + 32 = (x - 4)(x - 8)$

  5. $x^2 + 10x - 24 = (x + 12)(x - 2)$

7. $x^2 - 2x - 24 = (x-6)(x+4)$

9. Note that the GCF is 3, so that
$$3x^2 - 18x + 24 = 3(x^2 - 6x + 8)$$
$$= 3(x-2)(x-4).$$

11. Note that the GCF is $4z$, so that
$$4x^2z + 28xz + 40z = 4z(x^2 + 7x + 10)$$
$$= 4z(x+2)(x+5).$$

13. Note that the GCF is 2, so that
$$2x^2 + 30x - 108 = 2(x^2 + 15x - 54)$$
$$= 2(x+18)(x-3).$$

15. $x^2 + bx + 6$
$6 = 2 \cdot 3$ or $6 = (-2)(-3)$
$6 = 1 \cdot 6$ or $6 = (-1)(-6)$
$(x+2)(x+3) = x^2 + 5x + 6$
$(x-2)(x-3) = x^2 - 5x + 6$
$(x+1)(x+6) = x^2 + 7x + 6$
$(x-1)(x-6) = x^2 - 7x + 6$
$b = \pm 5$ and $b = \pm 7$

17. If r is an x-intercept of a polynomial function, then $(x-r)$ is a factor of the polynomial (see *Discover the Concept* on page 403 of the text). From the graph, the x-intercepts are $x = -5$ and $x = 3$. Therefore, the factors of the polynomial are $(x+5)$ and $(x-3)$.

19. If r is an x-intercept of a polynomial function, then $(x-r)$ is a factor of the polynomial (see *Discover the Concept* on page 403 of the text). From the graph, the x-intercepts are $x = 2$ and $x = 6$. Therefore, the factors of the polynomial are $(x-2)$ and $(x-6)$.

21. $2x^2 - 11x + 12 = (2x-3)(x-4)$

23. $2x^2 + 25x - 20$ is prime.

25. Note that the GCF is 2, so that
$$12x^2 + 10x - 50 = 2(6x^2 + 5x - 25)$$
$$= 2(3x-5)(2x+5).$$

27. Note that the GCF is y^2, so that
$$3y^4 - y^3 - 10y^2 = y^2(3y^2 - y - 10)$$
$$= y^2(3y+5)(y-2).$$

29. Note that the GCF is $2x$, so that
$$6x^3 + 8x^2 + 24x = 2x(3x^2 + 4x + 12)$$

31. $x^2 + 8xz + 7z^2 = (x+z)(x+7z)$

33. $2x^2 - 5xy - 3y^2 = (2x+y)(x-3y)$

35. $x^2 - x - 12$; $ac = -12$ so the two numbers are -4 and 3.
$$x^2 - x - 12 = x^2 - 4x + 3x - 12$$
$$= x(x-4) + 3(x-4)$$
$$= (x+3)(x-4)$$

37. Note that the GCF is 2, so that
$$28y^2 + 22y + 4 = 2(14y^2 + 11y + 2).$$
$ac = 28$; the two numbers are 4 and 7.
$$14y^2 + 11y + 2 = 14y^2 + 7y + 4y + 2$$
$$= 7y(2y+1) + 2(2y+1)$$
$$= (7y+2)(2y+1)$$
So, $28y^2 + 22y + 4 = 2(7y+2)(2y+1)$.

39. $2x^2 + 15x - 27$; $ac = -54$ so the two numbers are 18 and -3.
$$2x^2 + 15x - 27 = 2x^2 + 18x - 3x - 27$$
$$= 2x(x+9) - 3(x+9)$$
$$= (2x-3)(x+9)$$

41. $3x^2 + bx + 5$

$3 = 1 \cdot 3$ or $3 = (-1)(-3)$

$5 = 1 \cdot 5$ or $5 = (-1)(-5)$

$(3x+1)(x+5) = 3x^2 + 16x + 5$

$(3x-1)(x-5) = 3x^2 - 16x + 5$

$(-3x+1)(-x+5) = 3x^2 - 16x + 5$

$(-3x-1)(-x-5) = 3x^2 + 16x + 5$

$(3x+5)(x+1) = 3x^2 + 8x + 5$

$(3x-5)(x-1) = 3x^2 - 8x + 5$

$(-3x+5)(-x+1) = 3x^2 - 8x + 5$

$(-3x-5)(-x-1) = 3x^2 + 8x + 5$

$b = \pm 8$ and $b = \pm 16$

43. Let $y = x^2$. Then we have

$x^4 + x^2 - 6 = y^2 + y - 6 = (y+3)(y-2)$.

This yields $(x^2+3)(x^2-2)$.

45. Let $y = 5x + 1$. Then we have

$(5x+1)^2 + 8(5x+1) + 7 = y^2 + 8y + 7$
$= (y+1)(y+7)$.

This yields
$[(5x+1)+1][(5x+1)+7] = (5x+2)(5x+8)$.

47. Let $y = x^3$. Then we have

$x^6 - 7x^3 + 12 = y^2 - 7y + 12$
$= (y-4)(y-3)$.

This yields $(x^3-4)(x^3-3)$.

49. Let $y = a + 5$. Then we have

$(a+5)^2 - 5(a+5) - 24 = y^2 - 5y - 24$
$= (y-8)(y+3)$.

This yields
$[(a+5)-8][(a+5)+3] = (a-3)(a+8)$.

51. Note that the GCF is x, so that

$V(x) = 3x^3 - 2x^2 - 8x = x(3x^2 - 2x - 8)$
$= x(3x+4)(x-2)$.

53. $x^2 - 24x - 81 = (x-27)(x+3)$

55. $x^2 - 15x - 54 = (x-18)(x+3)$

57. $3x^2 - 6x + 3 = 3(x^2 - 2x + 1)$
$= 3(x-1)(x-1)$
$= 3(x-1)^2$

59. $3x^2 - 5x - 2 = (3x+1)(x-2)$

61. $8x^2 - 26x + 15 = (4x-3)(2x-5)$

63. $18x^4 + 21x^3 + 6x^2 = 3x^2(6x^2 + 7x + 2)$
$= 3x^2(3x+2)(2x+1)$

65. $3a^2 + 12ab + 12b^2 = 3(a^2 + 4ab + 4b^2)$
$= 3(a+2b)(a+2b)$
$= 3(a+2b)^2$

67. $x^2 + 4x + 5$ is prime.

69. Let $y = x + 4$. Then

$2(x+4)^2 + 3(x+4) - 5$
$= 2y^2 + 3y - 5$
$= (2y+5)(y-1)$
$= [2(x+4)+5][(x+4)-1]$
$= (2x+8+5)(x+3)$
$= (2x+13)(x+3)$

71. $6x^2 - 49x + 30 = (3x-2)(2x-15)$

73. $x^4 - 5x^2 - 6 = (x^2-6)(x^2+1)$

75. $6x^3 - x^2 - x = x(6x^2 - x - 1)$
$= x(3x+1)(2x-1)$

77. $12a^2 - 29ab + 15b^2 = (4a-3b)(3a-5b)$

79. $9x^2 + 30x + 25 = (3x+5)(3x+5)$
$= (3x+5)^2$

81. $3x^2y - 11xy + 8y = y(3x^2 - 11x + 8)$
$= y(3x-8)(x-1)$

83. $2x^2 + 2x - 12 = 2(x^2 + x - 6)$
$= 2(x+3)(x-2)$

85. $(x-4)^2 + 3(x-4) - 18$

$= [(x-4)+6][(x-4)-3]$

$= (x+2)(x-7)$

87. $2x^6 + 3x^3 - 9 = (2x^3 - 3)(x^3 + 3)$

89. $72xy^4 - 24xy^2z + 2xz^2$

$= 2x\left(36y^4 - 12y^2z + z^2\right)$

$= 2x\left(6y^2 - z\right)\left(6y^2 - z\right)$

$= 2x\left(6y^2 - z\right)^2$

91. $(x-3)(x+3) = x^2 - 3^3 = x^2 - 9$

93. $(2x+1)^2 = (2x)^2 + 2(2x)(1) + 1^2$

$= 4x^2 + 4x + 1$

95.

$$
\begin{array}{r}
x^2 + 2x + 4 \\
\times \qquad x - 2 \\
\hline
-2x^2 - 4x - 8 \\
x^3 + 2x^2 + 4x \qquad\ \\
\hline
x^3 \qquad\qquad\quad -8
\end{array}
$$

97. $h(t) = -16t^2 + 80t + 576$

a. $h(0) = -16(0)^2 + 80(0) + 576 = 576$ ft

$h(2) = -16(2)^2 + 80(2) + 576$

$= -16(4) + 160 + 576$

$= -64 + 160 + 576$

$= 672$ ft

$h(4) = -16(4)^2 + 80(4) + 576$

$= -16(16) + 320 + 576$

$= -256 + 320 + 576$

$= 640$ ft

$h(6) = -16(6)^2 + 80(6) + 576$

$= -16(36) + 480 + 576$

$= -576 + 480 + 576$

$= 480$ ft

b. Answers may vary. The object increases in height due to the initial force applied, but it slows down as time goes on. Eventually, as gravity takes over, the object will stop and then begin to fall back to the ground.

c. $h(t) = -16t^2 + 80t + 576$

$= -16(t^2 - 5t - 36)$

$= -16(t-9)(t+4)$

99. $x^{2n} + 10x^n + 16 = (x^n + 2)(x^n + 8)$

101. $x^{2n} - 3x^n - 18 = (x^n - 6)(x^n + 3)$

103. $2x^{2n} + 11x^n + 5 = \left(2x^n + 1\right)\left(x^n + 5\right)$

105. $4x^{2n} - 12x^n + 9 = (2x^n - 3)(2x^n - 3)$

$= (2x^n - 3)^2$

107. $x^4 + 6x^3 + 5x^2 = x^2(x^2 + 6x + 5)$

$= x^2(x+5)(x+1)$

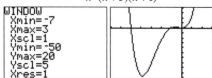

Tracing the graphs allows us to see that the two graphs are indeed coinciding. The factorization is correct.

109. $30x^3 + 9x^2 - 3x = 3x\left(10x^2 + 3x - 1\right)$

$= 3x(5x-1)(2x+1)$

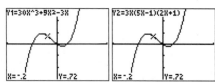

Tracing the graphs allows us to see that the two graphs are indeed coinciding. The factorization is correct.

Exercise Set 5.7

1. $x^2 + 6x + 9 = (x+3)^2$

3. $4x^2 - 12x + 9 = (2x-3)^2$

5. $3x^2 - 24x + 48 = 3(x^2 - 8x + 16)$
$$= 3(x-4)^2$$

7. $9y^2x^2 + 12yx^2 + 4x^2 = x^2(9y^2 + 12y + 4)$
$$= x^2(3y+2)^2$$

9. $x^2 - 25 = (x+5)(x-5)$

11. $9 - 4z^2 = (3+2z)(3-2z)$

13. $(y+2)^2 - 49 = [(y+2)+7][(y+2)-7]$
$$= (y+9)(y-5)$$

15. $64x^2 - 100 = 4(16x^2 - 25)$
$$= 4(4x+5)(4x-5)$$

17. $x^3 + 27 = x^3 + 3^3 = (x+3)(x^2 - 3x + 9)$

19. $z^3 - 1 = z^3 - 1^3 = (z-1)(z^2 + z + 1)$

21. $m^3 + n^3 = (m+n)(m^2 - mn + n^2)$

23. $x^3y^2 - 27y^2 = y^2(x^3 - 27)$
$$= y^2(x^3 - 3^3)$$
$$= y^2(x-3)(x^2 + 3x + 9)$$

25. $a^3b + 8b^4 = b(a^3 + 8b^3)$
$$= b\left[a^3 + (2b)^3\right]$$
$$= b(a+2b)(a^2 - 2ab + 4b^2)$$

27. $125y^3 - 8x^3 = (5y)^3 - (2x)^3$
$$= (5y-2x)(25y^2 + 10xy + 4x^2)$$

29. $(x^2 + 6x + 9) - y^2 = (x+3)^2 - y^2$
$$= (x+3+y)(x+3-y)$$

31. $(x^2 - 10x + 25) - y^2 = (x-5)^2 - y^2$
$$= (x-5+y)(x-5-y)$$

33. $(4x^2 + 4x + 1) - z^2$
$$= (2x+1)^2 - z^2$$
$$= (2x+1+z)(2x+1-z)$$

35. $9x^2 - 49 = (3x+7)(3x-7)$

37. $x^2 - 12x + 36 = (x-6)^2$

39. $x^4 - 81 = (x^2 + 9)(x^2 - 9)$
$$= (x^2 + 9)(x+3)(x-3)$$

41. $(x^2 + 8x + 16) - 4y^2$
$$= (x+4)^2 - (2y)^2$$
$$= (x+4+2y)(x+4-2y)$$

43. $(x+2y)^2 - 9 = (x+2y)^2 - 3^2$
$$= (x+2y+3)(x+2y-3)$$

45. $x^3 - 216 = x^3 - 6^3 = (x-6)(x^2 + 6x + 36)$

47. $x^3 + 125 = x^3 + 5^3 = (x+5)(x^2 - 5x + 25)$

49. $4x^2 + 25$ is prime.

51. $4a^2 + 12a + 9 = (2a+3)(2a+3)$
$$= (2a+3)^2$$

53. $18x^2y - 2y = 2y(9x^2 - 1)$
$$= 2y(3x+1)(3x-1)$$

55. $8x^3 + y^3 = (2x)^3 + y^3$
$$= (2x+y)(4x^2 - 2xy + y^2)$$

57. $x^6 - y^3 = (x^2)^3 - y^3$
$$= (x^2 - y)(x^4 + x^2y + y^2)$$

59. $(x^2 + 16x + 64) - x^4 = (x+8)^2 - (x^2)^2$
$$= (x+8+x^2)(x+8-x^2)$$

61. $3x^6 y^2 + 81y^2 = 3y^2(x^6 + 27)$

$\qquad = 3y^2\left[(x^2)^3 + 3^3\right]$

$\qquad = 3y^2(x^2 + 3)(x^4 - 3x^2 + 9)$

63. $(x+y)^3 + 125$

$\qquad = (x+y)^3 + 5^3$

$\qquad = [(x+y)+5][(x+y)^2 - 5(x+y) + 25]$

$\qquad = (x+y+5)(x^2 + 2xy + y^2 - 5x - 5y + 25)$

65. $(2x+3)^3 - 64$

$\qquad = (2x+3)^3 - 4^3$

$\qquad = [(2x+3)-4][(2x+3)^2 + 4(2x+3) + 16]$

$\qquad = (2x-1)(4x^2 + 12x + 9 + 8x + 12 + 16)$

$\qquad = (2x-1)(4x^2 + 20x + 37)$

67. $x - 5 = 0$

$\qquad x = 5$

69. $3x + 1 = 0$

$\qquad 3x = -1$

$\qquad x = -\dfrac{1}{3}$

71. $-2x = 0$

$\qquad x = 0$

73. $-5x + 25 = 0$

$\qquad -5x = -25$

$\qquad x = 5$

75. Area $= \pi R^2 - \pi r^2$

$\qquad = \pi(R^2 - r^2)$

$\qquad = \pi(R+r)(R-r)$ sq. units

77. Volume $= x^3 - y^2 x$

$\qquad = x(x^2 - y^2)$

$\qquad = x(x+y)(x-y)$ cubic units

79. $\dfrac{1}{2} \cdot b = \dfrac{1}{2} \cdot 6 = 3$ so $c = 3^2 = 9$

81. $\dfrac{1}{2} \cdot b = \dfrac{1}{2}(-14) = -7$ so $c = (-7)^2 = 49$

83. $\dfrac{1}{2} \cdot c = \dfrac{c}{2}$ so $\left(\dfrac{c}{2}\right)^2 = 16$

$\qquad \dfrac{c^2}{4} = 16$

$\qquad c^2 = 64$

$\qquad c = \pm 8$

85. $x^6 - 1$

    a. $(x^3)^2 - 1^2$

$\qquad = (x^3 + 1)(x^3 - 1)$

$\qquad = (x+1)(x^2 - x + 1)(x-1)(x^2 + x + 1)$

    b. $(x^2)^3 - 1^3$

$\qquad = (x^2 - 1)(x^4 + x^2 + 1)$

$\qquad = (x+1)(x-1)(x^4 + x^2 + 1)$

    c. Answers may vary. The two results are numerically equivalent, but they are not in the same factored form.

87. $x^{2n} - 36 = (x^n)^2 - 6^2 = (x^n + 6)(x^n - 6)$

89. $25x^{2n} - 81 = (5x^n)^2 - 9^2$

$\qquad = (5x^n + 9)(5x^n - 9)$

91. $x^{4n} - 625 = (x^{2n})^2 - 25^2$

$\qquad = (x^{2n} + 25)(x^{2n} - 25)$

$\qquad = (x^{2n} + 25)\left[(x^n)^2 - 5^2\right]$

$\qquad = (x^{2n} + 25)(x^n + 5)(x^n - 5)$

Integrated Review

1. $(-y^2 + 6y - 1) + (3y^2 - 4y - 10)$

$\qquad = -y^2 + 6y - 1 + 3y^2 - 4y - 10$

$\qquad = 2y^2 + 2y - 11$

2. $(5z^4 - 6z^2 + z + 1) - (7z^4 - 2z + 1)$

$\qquad = 5z^4 - 6z^2 + z + 1 - 7z^4 + 2z - 1$

$\qquad = -2z^4 - 6z^2 + 3z$

3. $(x^2 - 6x + 2) - (x - 5)$

$= x^2 - 6x + 2 - x + 5$

$= x^2 - 7x + 7$

4. $(2x^2 + 6x - 5) + (5x^2 - 10x)$

$= 7x^2 - 4x - 5$

5. $(5x - 3)^2 = (5x)^2 - 2(5x)(3) + 3^2$

$= 25x^2 - 30x + 9$

6. $(5x^2 - 14x - 3) \div (5x + 1) = x - 3$

7. $(2x^4 - 3x^2 + 5x - 2) \div (x + 2)$

$= 2x^3 - 4x^2 + 5x - 5 + \dfrac{8}{x + 2}$

8.

$$
\begin{array}{r}
x^2 - 3x - 2 \\
\times \qquad\qquad 4x - 1 \\
\hline
- x^2 + 3x + 2 \\
4x^3 - 12x^2 - 8x \\
\hline
4x^3 - 13x^2 - 5x + 2
\end{array}
$$

9. $x^2 - 8x + 16 - y^2 = (x - 4)^2 - y^2$

$= (x - 4 + y)(x - 4 - y)$

10. $12x^2 - 22x - 20 = 2(6x^2 - 11x - 10)$

$= 2(3x + 2)(2x - 5)$

11. $x^4 - x = x(x^3 - 1) = x(x - 1)(x^2 + x + 1)$

12. Let $y = 2x + 1$. Then

$(2x + 1)^2 - 3(2x + 1) + 2$

$= y^2 - 3y + 2$

$= (y - 2)(y - 1)$

$= [(2x + 1) - 2][(2x + 1) - 1]$

$= (2x - 1)(2x)$

$= 2x(2x - 1)$

13. $14x^2 y - 2xy = 2xy(7x - 1)$

14. $24ab^2 - 6ab = 6ab(4b - 1)$

15. $4x^2 - 16 = 4(x^2 - 4) = 4(x + 2)(x - 2)$

16. $9x^2 - 81 = 9(x^2 - 9) = 9(x + 3)(x - 3)$

17. $3x^2 - 8x - 11 = (3x - 11)(x + 1)$

18. $5x^2 - 2x - 3 = (5x + 3)(x - 1)$

19. $4x^2 + 8x - 12 = 4(x^2 + 2x - 3)$

$= 4(x + 3)(x - 1)$

20. $6x^2 - 6x - 12 = 6(x^2 - x - 2)$

$= 6(x - 2)(x + 1)$

21. $4x^2 + 36x + 81 = (2x + 9)(2x + 9)$

$= (2x + 9)^2$

22. $25x^2 + 40x + 16 = (5x + 4)(5x + 4)$

$= (5x + 4)^2$

23. $8x^3 + 125y^3 = (2x)^3 + (5y)^3$

$= (2x + 5y)(4x^2 - 10xy + 25y^2)$

24. $27x^3 - 64y^3 = (3x)^3 - (4y)^3$

$= (3x - 4y)(9x^2 + 12xy + 16y^2)$

25. $64x^2 y^3 - 8x^2 = 8x^2(8y^3 - 1)$

$= 8x^2[(2y)^3 - 1^3]$

$= 8x^2(2y - 1)(4y^2 + 2y + 1)$

26. $27x^5 y^4 - 216x^2 y$

$= 27x^2 y \left(x^3 y^3 - 8 \right)$

$= 27x^2 y \left((xy)^3 - 2^3 \right)$

$= 27x^2 y \left(xy - 2 \right)\left(x^2 y^2 + 2xy + 4 \right)$

27. $(x + 5)^3 + y^3$

$= [(x + 5) + y][(x + 5)^2 - (x + 5)y + y^2]$

$= (x + y + 5)(x^2 + 10x + 25 - xy - 5y + y^2]$

$= (x + y + 5)(x^2 + 10x - xy - 5y + y^2 + 25]$

28. $(y-1)^3 + 27x^3$

$= (y-1)^3 + (3x)^3$

$= [(y-1)+3x][(y-1)^2 - (y-1)(3x)+9x^2]$

$= (y-1+3x)(y^2-2y+1-3xy+3x+9x^2)$

29. Let $y = 5a-3$. Then

$(5a-3)^2 - 6(5a-3)+9$

$= y^2 - 6y + 9$

$= (y-3)(y-3)$

$= (y-3)^2$

$= [(5a-3)-3]^2$

$= (5a-6)^2$

30. Let $y = 4r+1$. Then

$(4r+1)^2 + 8(4r+1)+16$

$= y^2 + 8y + 16$

$= (y+4)(y+4)$

$= (y+4)^2$

$= [(4r+1)+4]^2$

$= (4r+5)^2$

31. $7x^2 - 63x = 7x(x-9)$

32. $20x^2 + 23x + 6 = (4x+3)(5x+2)$

33. $ab - 6a + 7b - 42 = a(b-6)+7(b-6)$

$= (a+7)(b-6)$

34. $20x^2 - 220x + 600 = 20(x^2 - 11x + 30)$

$= 20(x-6)(x-5)$

35. $x^4 - 1 = \left(x^2\right)^2 - 1^2$

$= \left(x^2+1\right)\left(x^2-1\right)$

$= \left(x^2+1\right)(x+1)(x-1)$

36. $15x^2 - 20x = 5x(3x-4)$

37. $10x^2 - 7x - 33 = (5x-11)(2x+3)$

38. $45m^3n^3 - 27m^2n^2 = 9m^2n^2(5mn-3)$

39. $5a^3b^3 - 50a^3b = 5a^3b(b^2-10)$

40. $x^4 + x = x(x^3+1) = x(x+1)(x^2-x+1)$

41. $16x^2 + 25$ is a prime polynomial.

42. $20x^3 + 20y^3 = 20(x^3 + y^3)$

$= 20(x+y)(x^2-xy+y^2)$

43. $10x^3 - 210x^2 + 1100x$

$= 10x(x^2 - 21x + 110)$

$= 10x(x-11)(x-10)$

44. $9y^2 - 42y + 49 = (3y-7)(3y-7)$

$= (3y-7)^2$

45. $64a^3b^4 - 27a^3b$

$= a^3b(64b^3 - 27)$

$= a^3b[(4b)^3 - 3^3]$

$= a^3b(4b-3)(16b^2+12b+9)$

46. $y^4 - 16 = (y^2)^2 - 4^2$

$= (y^2+4)(y^2-4)$

$= (y^2+4)(y+2)(y-2)$

47. $2x^3 - 54 = 2(x^3 - 27)$

$= 2(x^3 - 3^3)$

$= 2(x-3)(x^2+3x+9)$

48. $2sr + 10s - r - 5 = 2s(r+5)-1(r+5)$

$= (2s-1)(r+5)$

49. $3y^5 - 5y^4 + 6y - 10 = y^4(3y-5)+2(3y-5)$

$= (y^4+2)(3y-5)$

50. $64a^2 + b^2$ is a prime polynomial.

51. $100z^3 + 100 = 100(z^3+1)$

$= 100(z+1)(z^2-z+1)$

52. $250x^4 - 16x = 2x(125x^3 - 8)$
$$= 2x[(5x)^3 - 2^3]$$
$$= 2x(5x - 2)(25x^2 + 10x + 4)$$

53. $4b^2 - 36b + 81 = (2b - 9)(2b - 9)$
$$= (2b - 9)^2$$

54. $2a^5 - a^4 + 6a - 3 = a^4(2a - 1) + 3(2a - 1)$
$$= (a^4 + 3)(2a - 1)$$

55. Let $x = y - 6$. Then
$$(y - 6)^2 + 3(y - 6) + 2$$
$$= x^2 + 3x + 2$$
$$= (x + 2)(x + 1)$$
$$= [(y - 6) + 2][(y - 6) + 1]$$
$$= (y - 4)(y - 5)$$

56. Let $x = c + 2$. Then
$$(c + 2)^2 - 6(c + 2) + 5$$
$$= x^2 - 6x + 5$$
$$= (x - 5)(x - 1)$$
$$= [(c + 2) - 5][(c + 2) - 1]$$
$$= (c - 3)(c + 1)$$

57. Area $= 3^2 - 4x^2$
$$= (3 + 2x)(3 - 2x)$$

Mental Math 5.8

1. $(x - 3)(x + 5) = 0$
$x - 3 = 0$ or $x + 5 = 0$
$x = 3$ or $x = -5$
The solutions are $-5, 3$.

2. $(y + 5)(y + 3) = 0$
$y + 5 = 0$ or $y + 3 = 0$
$y = -5$ or $y = -3$
The solutions are $-5, -3$.

3. $(z - 3)(z + 7) = 0$
$z - 3 = 0$ or $z + 7 = 0$
$z = 3$ or $z = -7$
The solutions are $-7, 3$.

4. $(c - 2)(c - 4) = 0$
$c - 2 = 0$ or $c - 4 = 0$
$c = 2$ or $c = 4$
The solutions are $2, 4$.

5. $x(x - 9) = 0$
$x = 0$ or $x - 9 = 0$
$x = 9$
The solutions are $0, 9$.

6. $w(w + 7) = 0$
$w = 0$ or $w + 7 = 0$
$w = -7$
The solutions are $-7, 0$.

Exercise Set 5.8

1. $(x + 3)(3x - 4) = 0$
$x + 3 = 0$ or $3x - 4 = 0$
$x = -3$ or $3x = 4$
$$x = \frac{4}{3}$$
The solutions are $-3, \frac{4}{3}$.

3. $3(2x - 5)(4x + 3) = 0$
$2x - 5 = 0$ or $4x + 3 = 0$
$2x = 5$ or $4x = -3$
$x = \frac{5}{2}$ or $x = -\frac{3}{4}$
The solutions are $-\frac{3}{4}, \frac{5}{2}$.

5. $x^2 + 11x + 24 = 0$
$(x + 8)(x + 3) = 0$
$x + 8 = 0$ or $x + 3 = 0$
$x = -8$ or $x = -3$
The solutions are $-8, -3$.

7. $12x^2 + 5x - 2 = 0$

$(4x-1)(3x+2) = 0$

$4x - 1 = 0$ or $3x + 2 = 0$

$4x = 1$ or $\quad 3x = -2$

$x = \dfrac{1}{4}$ or $\quad x = -\dfrac{2}{3}$

The solutions are $-\dfrac{2}{3}, \dfrac{1}{4}$.

9. $z^2 + 9 = 10z$

$z^2 - 10z + 9 = 0$

$(z-9)(z-1) = 0$

$z - 9 = 0$ or $z - 1 = 0$

$z = 9$ or $\quad z = 1$

The solutions are 1, 9.

11. $x(5x + 2) = 3$

$5x^2 + 2x - 3 = 0$

$(5x-3)(x+1) = 0$

$5x - 3 = 0$ or $x + 1 = 0$

$5x = 3$ or $\quad x = -1$

$x = \dfrac{3}{5}$

The solutions are $-1, \dfrac{3}{5}$.

13. $x^2 - 6x = x(8 + x)$

$x^2 - 6x = 8x + x^2$

$-14x = 0$

$x = 0$

The solutions is 0.

15. $\dfrac{z^2}{6} - \dfrac{z}{2} - 3 = 0$

$z^2 - 3z - 18 = 0$

$(z-6)(z+3) = 0$

$z - 6 = 0$ or $z + 3 = 0$

$z = 6$ or $\quad z = -3$

The solutions are $-3, 6$.

17. $\dfrac{x^2}{2} + \dfrac{x}{20} = \dfrac{1}{10}$

$10x^2 + x = 2$

$10x^2 + x - 2 = 0$

$(5x-2)(2x+1) = 0$

$5x - 2 = 0$ or $2x + 1 = 0$

$5x = 2$ or $\quad 2x = -1$

$x = \dfrac{2}{5}$ or $\quad x = -\dfrac{1}{2}$

The solutions are $-\dfrac{1}{2}, \dfrac{2}{5}$.

19. $\dfrac{4t^2}{5} = \dfrac{t}{5} + \dfrac{3}{10}$

$8t^2 = 2t + 3$

$8t^2 - 2t - 3 = 0$

$(4t-3)(2t+1) = 0$

$4t - 3 = 0$ or $2t + 1 = 0$

$4t = 3$ or $\quad 2t = -1$

$t = \dfrac{3}{4}$ or $\quad t = -\dfrac{1}{2}$

The solutions are $-\dfrac{1}{2}, \dfrac{3}{4}$.

21. $(x+2)(x-7)(3x-8) = 0$

$x + 2 = 0$ or $x - 7 = 0$ or $3x - 8 = 0$

$x = -2$ or $\quad x = 7$ or $\quad 3x = 8$

$x = \dfrac{8}{3}$

The solutions are $-2, 7, \dfrac{8}{3}$.

23. $y^3 = 9y$

$y^3 - 9y = 0$

$y(y^2 - 9) = 0$

$y(y+3)(y-3) = 0$

$y = 0$ or $y + 3 = 0$ or $y - 3 = 0$

$y = -3$ or $\quad y = 3$

The solutions are $-3, 0, 3$.

25.
$$x^3 - x = 2x^2 - 2$$
$$x^3 - 2x^2 - x + 2 = 0$$
$$x^2(x-2) - 1(x-2) = 0$$
$$(x^2 - 1)(x-2) = 0$$
$$(x+1)(x-1)(x-2) = 0$$
$$x+1 = 0 \quad \text{or} \quad x-1 = 0 \quad \text{or} \quad x-2 = 0$$
$$x = -1 \quad \text{or} \quad x = 1 \quad \text{or} \quad x = 2$$
The solutions are –1, 1, 2.

27. Answers may vary. The expression $2x(x-3)(x-1)$ has an additional factor of x, and hence an additional solution.

29. $(2x+7)(x-10) = 0$
$$2x+7 = 0 \quad \text{or} \quad x-10 = 0$$
$$2x = -7 \quad \text{or} \quad x = 10$$
$$x = -\frac{7}{2}$$
The solutions are $-\frac{7}{2}, 10$.

31. $3x(x-5) = 0$
$$3x = 0 \quad \text{or} \quad x-5 = 0$$
$$x = 0 \quad \text{or} \quad x = 5$$
The solutions are 0, 5.

33. $x^2 - 2x - 15 = 0$
$$(x-5)(x+3) = 0$$
$$x-5 = 0 \quad \text{or} \quad x+3 = 0$$
$$x = 5 \quad \text{or} \quad x = -3$$
The solutions are –3, 5.

35.
$$12x^2 + 2x - 2 = 0$$
$$2(6x^2 + x - 1) = 0$$
$$2(3x-1)(2x+1) = 0$$
$$3x-1 = 0 \quad \text{or} \quad 2x+1 = 0$$
$$3x = 1 \quad \text{or} \quad 2x = -1$$
$$x = \frac{1}{3} \quad \text{or} \quad x = -\frac{1}{2}$$
The solutions are $-\frac{1}{2}, \frac{1}{3}$.

37.
$$w^2 - 5w = 36$$
$$w^2 - 5w - 36 = 0$$
$$(w-9)(w+4) = 0$$
$$w-9 = 0 \quad \text{or} \quad w+4 = 0$$
$$w = 9 \quad \text{or} \quad w = -4$$
The solutions are –4, 9.

39. $25x^2 - 40x + 16 = 0$
$$(5x-4)^2 = 0$$
$$5x-4 = 0$$
$$5x = 4$$
$$x = \frac{4}{5}$$
The solutions is $\frac{4}{5}$.

41.
$$2r^3 + 6r^2 = 20r$$
$$2r^3 + 6r^2 - 20r = 0$$
$$2r(r^2 + 3r - 10) = 0$$
$$2r(r+5)(r-2) = 0$$
$$2r = 0 \quad \text{or} \quad r+5 = 0 \quad \text{or} \quad r-2 = 0$$
$$r = 0 \quad \text{or} \quad r = -5 \quad \text{or} \quad r = 2$$
The solutions are –5, 0, 2.

43. $z(5z-4)(z+3) = 0$
$$z = 0 \quad \text{or} \quad 5z-4 = 0 \quad \text{or} \quad z+3 = 0$$
$$5z = 4 \quad \text{or} \quad z = -3$$
$$z = \frac{4}{5}$$
The solutions are $-3, 0, \frac{4}{5}$.

45. $2z(z+6) = 2z^2 + 12z - 8$
$$2z^2 + 12z = 2z^2 + 12z - 8$$
$$0 = -8 \text{ False}$$
No solution exist; $\varnothing$

47. $(x-1)(x+4) = 24$
$$x^2 + 3x - 4 = 24$$
$$x^2 + 3x - 28 = 0$$
$$(x+7)(x-4) = 0$$
$$x+7 = 0 \quad \text{or} \quad x-4 = 0$$
$$x = -7 \quad \text{or} \quad x = 4$$
The solutions are –7, 4.

49. $\dfrac{x^2}{4} - \dfrac{5}{2}x + 6 = 0$

$x^2 - 10x + 24 = 0$

$(x-6)(x-4) = 0$

$x - 6 = 0$ or $x - 4 = 0$

$x = 6$ or $\quad x = 4$

The solutions are 4, 6.

51. $\quad y^2 + \dfrac{1}{4} = -y$

$4y^2 + 1 = -4y$

$4y^2 + 4y + 1 = 0$

$(2y+1)^2 = 0$

$2y + 1 = 0$

$2y = -1$

$y = -\dfrac{1}{2}$

The solution is $-\dfrac{1}{2}$.

53. $\quad\quad y^3 + 4y^2 = 9y + 36$

$y^3 + 4y^2 - 9y - 36 = 0$

$y^2(y+4) - 9(y+4) = 0$

$(y^2 - 9)(y+4) = 0$

$(y+3)(y-3)(y+4) = 0$

$y + 3 = 0$ or $y - 3 = 0$ or $y + 4 = 0$

$y = -3$ or $\quad y = 3$ or $\quad y = -4$

The solutions are $-4, -3, 3$.

55. $\quad\quad 2x^3 = 50x$

$2x^3 - 50x = 0$

$2x(x^2 - 25) = 0$

$2x(x+5)(x-5) = 0$

$2x = 0$ or $x + 5 = 0$ or $x - 5 = 0$

$x = 0$ or $\quad x = -5$ or $\quad x = 5$

The solutions are $-5, 0, 5$.

57. $\quad x^2 + (x+1)^2 = 61$

$x^2 + x^2 + 2x + 1 = 61$

$2x^2 + 2x - 60 = 0$

$2(x^2 + x - 30) = 0$

$2(x+6)(x-5) = 0$

$x + 6 = 0$ or $x - 5 = 0$

$x = -6$ or $\quad x = 5$

The solutions are $-6, 5$.

59. $\quad m^2(3m-2) = m$

$3m^3 - 2m^2 = m$

$3m^3 - 2m^2 - m = 0$

$m(3m^2 - 2m - 1) = 0$

$m(3m+1)(m-1) = 0$

$m = 0$ or $3m + 1 = 0$ or $m - 1 = 0$

$3m = -1$ or $\quad m = 1$

$m = -\dfrac{1}{3}$

The solutions are $-\dfrac{1}{3}, 0, 1$.

61. $\quad\quad 3x^2 = -x$

$3x^2 + x = 0$

$x(3x+1) = 0$

$x = 0$ or $3x + 1 = 0$

$3x = -\dfrac{1}{3}$

The solutions are $-\dfrac{1}{3}, 0$.

63. $x(x-3) = x^2 + 5x + 7$

$x^2 - 3x = x^2 + 5x + 7$

$-8x = 7$

$x = -\dfrac{7}{8}$

The solution is $-\dfrac{7}{8}$.

65. $3(t-8)+2t = 7+t$

$3t-24+2t = 7+t$

$5t-24 = 7+t$

$4t = 31$

$t = \dfrac{31}{4}$

The solution is $\dfrac{31}{4}$.

67. $-3(x-4)+x = 5(3-x)$

$-3x+12+x = 15-5x$

$-2x+12 = 15-5x$

$3x = 3$

$x = 1$

The solution is 1.

69. **a** and **d** are incorrect because the right side of the equation is not zero.

71. Let n = the one number and $n+5$ = the other number.

$n(n+5) = 66$

$n^2+5n-66 = 0$

$(n+11)(n-6) = 0$

$n+11 = 0 \quad$ or $\quad n-6 = 0$

$n = -11 \quad$ or $\quad n = 6$

The two solutions are –11 and –6 or 6 and 11.

73. Let d = amount of cable needed. Then, from the Pythagorean theorem:

$d^2 = 45^2+60^2 = 5625$

so

$d = \sqrt{5625} = 75$ ft .

75. $C(x) = x^2-15x+50$

$9500 = x^2-15x+50$

$0 = x^2-15x-9450$

$0 = (x-105)(x+90)$

$x-105 = 0 \quad$ or $\quad x+90 = 0$

$x = 105 \quad$ or $\quad x = -90$

Disregard the negative. 105 units.

77. Let x = one leg of a right triangle and $x-3$ = the other leg of the right triangle.

$15^2 = x^2+(x-3)^2$

$225 = x^2+x^2-6x+9$

$225 = 2x^2-6x+9$

$0 = 2x^2-6x-216$

$0 = 2(x^2-3x-108)$

$0 = 2(x-12)(x+9)$

$x-12 = 0 \quad$ or $\quad x+9 = 0$

$x = 12 \quad$ or $\quad x = -9$

Disregarding the negative solution, we find that one leg of the right triangle is 12 cm and the other leg is 9 cm.

79. Note that the outer rectangle has dimensions of $2x+12$ and $2x+16$. Thus, the area of the border is $(2x+12)(2x+16)-12\cdot16$. Set this equal to 128 and solve for x.

$(2x+12)(2x+16)-12\cdot16 = 128$

$4x^2+56x+192-192 = 128$

$4x^2+56x = 128$

$4x^2+56x-128 = 0$

$x^2+14x-32 = 0$

$(x+16)(x-2) = 0$

$x+16 = 0 \quad$ or $\quad x-2 = 0$

$x = -16 \quad$ or $\quad x = 2$

Since x must be positive, we see that $x = 2$ inches.

81. The sunglasses will hit the ground when $h(t)$ equals 0.

$-16t^2+1600 = 0$

$-16(t^2-100) = 0$

$-16(t-10)(t+10) = 0$

$t-10 = 0 \quad$ or $\quad t+10 = 0$

$t = 10 \quad$ or $\quad t = -10$

The sunglasses will hit the ground 10 seconds after being dropped.

83. Let the width of the floor $= w$. Then the length is $2w - 3$ and so the area is

$$(2w - 3)w = 90$$

$$2w^2 - 3w - 90 = 0$$

$$(2w - 15)(w + 6) = 0$$

$$2w - 15 = 0 \quad \text{or} \quad w + 6 = 0$$

$$2w = 15 \quad \text{or} \quad w = -6$$

$$w = \frac{15}{2} = 7.5$$

Disregard –6.

$$2w - 3 = 2(7.5) - 3 = 15 - 3 = 12$$

The width is 7.5 ft and the length is 12 ft.

85.

$$0.5x^2 = 50$$

$$0.5x^2 - 50 = 0$$

$$5x^2 - 500 = 0$$

$$x^2 - 100 = 0$$

$$(x + 10)(x - 10) = 0$$

$$x + 10 = 0 \quad \text{or} \quad x - 10 = 0$$

$$x = -10 \quad \text{or} \quad x = 10$$

Disregard the negative solution. A 10-inch square tier is needed, provided each person has one serving.

87. The object will hit the ground when $h(t)$ equals 0.

$$-16t^2 + 80t + 576 = 0$$

$$-16(t^2 - 5t - 36) = 0$$

$$-16(t - 9)(t + 4) = 0$$

$$t - 9 = 0 \quad \text{or} \quad t + 4 = 0$$

$$t = 9 \quad \text{or} \quad t = -4$$

The object will hit the ground 9 seconds after being dropped.

89. E

91. F

93. B

95. (–3, 0), (0, 2); function

97. (–4, 0), (0, 2), (4, 0), (0, –2); not a function.

99. Answers may vary.

101. $(x^2 + x - 6)(3x^2 - 14x - 5) = 0$

$$x^2 + x - 6 = 0 \quad \text{or} \quad 3x^2 - 14x - 5 = 0$$

$$(x + 3)(x - 2) = 0 \quad \text{or} \quad (3x + 1)(x - 5) = 0$$

$$x + 3 = 0, \ x - 2 = 0, \ 3x + 1 = 0 \text{ or } x - 5 = 0$$

$$x = -3, \ x = 2, \ 3x = -1, \ x = 5$$

$$x = -\frac{1}{3}$$

The solutions are $-3, -\frac{1}{3}, 2, 5$.

103. No; answers may vary.

105. Answers may vary. For example:

$$f(x) = (x - 6)(x - 7) = x^2 - 13x + 42$$

107. Answers may vary. For example:

$$f(x) = (x - 4)(x + 3) = x^2 - x - 12$$

Chapter 5 Review

1. $(-2)^2 = (-2)(-2) = 4$

2. $(-3)^4 = (-3)(-3)(-3)(-3) = 81$

3. $-2^2 = -(2 \cdot 2) = -4$

4. $-3^4 = -(3 \cdot 3 \cdot 3 \cdot 3) = -81$

5. $8^0 = 1$

6. $-9^0 = -1$

7. $-4^{-2} = -\frac{1}{4^2} = -\frac{1}{16}$

8. $(-4)^{-2} = \frac{1}{(-4)^2} = \frac{1}{16}$

9. $-xy^2 \cdot y^3 \cdot xy^2 z = -x^{1+1} y^{2+3+2} z = -x^2 y^7 z$

10. $(-4xy)(-3xy^2 b) = 12x^2 y^3 b$

11. $a^{-14} a^5 = a^{-14+5} = a^{-9} = \frac{1}{a^9}$

12. $\dfrac{a^{16}}{a^{17}} = a^{16-17} = a^{-1} = \dfrac{1}{a}$

13. $\dfrac{x^{-7}}{x^4} = x^{-7-4} = x^{-11} = \dfrac{1}{x^{11}}$

14. $\dfrac{9a(a^{-3})}{18a^{15}} = \dfrac{a^{1-3-15}}{2} = \dfrac{a^{-17}}{2} = \dfrac{1}{2a^{17}}$

15. $\dfrac{y^{6p-3}}{y^{6p+2}} = y^{(6p-3)-(6p+2)}$

$\qquad\qquad = y^{6p-3-6p-2}$

$\qquad\qquad = y^{-5}$

$\qquad\qquad = \dfrac{1}{y^5}$

16. $36{,}890{,}000 = 3.689 \times 10^7$

17. $-0.000362 = -3.62 \times 10^{-4}$

18. $1.678 \times 10^{-6} = 0.000001678$

19. $4.1 \times 10^5 = 410{,}000$

20. $(8^5)^3 = 8^{5 \cdot 3} = 8^{15}$

21. $\left(\dfrac{a}{4}\right)^2 = \dfrac{a^2}{4^2} = \dfrac{a^2}{16}$

22. $(3x)^3 = 3^3 x^3 = 27x^3$

23. $(-4x)^{-2} = \dfrac{1}{(-4x)^2} = \dfrac{1}{(-4)^2 x^2} = \dfrac{1}{16x^2}$

24. $\left(\dfrac{6x}{5}\right)^2 = \dfrac{(6x)^2}{5^2} = \dfrac{36x^2}{25}$

25. $(8^6)^{-3} = 8^{6(-3)} = 8^{-18} = \dfrac{1}{8^{18}}$

26. $\left(\dfrac{4}{3}\right)^{-2} = \dfrac{4^{-2}}{3^{-2}} = \dfrac{3^2}{4^2} = \dfrac{9}{16}$

27. $(-2x^3)^{-3} = \dfrac{1}{(-2x^3)^3}$

$\qquad\qquad = \dfrac{1}{(-2)^3 (x^3)^3}$

$\qquad\qquad = \dfrac{1}{-8x^9}$

$\qquad\qquad = -\dfrac{1}{8x^9}$

28. $\left(\dfrac{8p^6}{4p^4}\right)^{-2} = (2p^2)^{-2} = 2^{-2}p^{-4} = \dfrac{1}{4p^4}$

29. $(-3x^{-2}y^2)^3 = (-3)^3 (x^{-2})^3 (y^2)^3$

$\qquad\qquad = -27x^{-6}y^6$

$\qquad\qquad = -\dfrac{27y^6}{x^6}$

30. $\left(\dfrac{x^{-5}y^{-3}}{z^3}\right)^{-5} = \dfrac{x^{25}y^{15}}{z^{-15}} = x^{25}y^{15}z^{15}$

31. $\dfrac{4^{-1}x^3 yz}{x^{-2}yx^4} = \dfrac{x^{3-(-2)-4}y^{1-1}z}{4} = \dfrac{x^{3+2-4}y^0 z}{4} = \dfrac{xz}{4}$

32. $(5xyz)^{-4}(x^{-2})^{-3} = \dfrac{1}{(5xyz)^4}x^6$

$\qquad\qquad = \dfrac{x^6}{5^4 x^4 y^4 z^4}$

$\qquad\qquad = \dfrac{x^2}{625y^4 z^4}$

33. $\dfrac{2(3yz)^{-3}}{y^{-3}} = \dfrac{2(3)^{-3}y^{-3}z^{-3}}{y^{-3}} = \dfrac{2}{3^3 z^3} = \dfrac{2}{27z^3}$

34. $x^{4a}(3x^{5a})^3 = x^{4a}(3^3 x^{15a})$

$\qquad\qquad = 27x^{4a+15a}$

$\qquad\qquad = 27x^{19a}$

35. $\dfrac{4y^{3x-3}}{2y^{2x+4}} = 2y^{(3x-3)-(2x+4)}$

$\qquad\qquad = 2y^{3x-3-2x-4}$

$\qquad\qquad = 2y^{x-7}$

36. $\dfrac{(0.00012)(144,000)}{0.0003} = \dfrac{(1.2\times10^{-4})(1.44\times10^{5})}{3\times10^{-4}}$

$$= 0.576\times10^{5}$$
$$= 5.76\times10^{4}$$

37. $\dfrac{(-0.00017)(0.00039)}{3000} = \dfrac{(-1.7\times10^{-4})(3.9\times10^{-4})}{3\times10^{3}}$

$$= -2.21\times10^{-4-4-3}$$
$$= -2.21\times10^{-11}$$

38. $\dfrac{27x^{-5}y^{5}}{18x^{-6}y^{2}}\cdot\dfrac{x^{4}y^{-2}}{x^{-2}y^{3}} = \dfrac{3x^{-5+4}y^{5-2}}{2x^{-6-2}y^{2+3}}$

$$= \dfrac{3x^{-1}y^{3}}{2x^{-8}y^{5}}$$
$$= \dfrac{3}{2}x^{-1-(-8)}y^{3-5}$$
$$= \dfrac{3}{2}x^{7}y^{-2}$$
$$= \dfrac{3x^{7}}{2y^{2}}$$

39. $\dfrac{3x^{5}}{y^{-4}}\cdot\dfrac{(3xy^{-3})^{-2}}{(z^{-3})^{-4}} = \dfrac{3x^{5}\cdot3^{-2}x^{-2}y^{6}}{y^{-4}z^{12}}$

$$= \dfrac{3^{1-2}x^{5-2}y^{6-(-4)}}{z^{12}}$$
$$= \dfrac{3^{-1}x^{3}y^{10}}{z^{12}}$$
$$= \dfrac{x^{3}y^{10}}{3z^{12}}$$

40. $\dfrac{(x^{w})^{2}}{(x^{w-4})^{-2}} = \dfrac{x^{2w}}{x^{-2(w-4)}}$

$$= \dfrac{x^{2w}}{x^{-2w+8}}$$
$$= x^{2w-(-2w+8)}$$
$$= x^{4w-8}$$

41. The degree of the polynomial
$x^{2}y-3xy^{3}z+5x+7y$ is the degree of the term
$-3xy^{3}z$ which is 5.

42. $3x+2$ has degree 1.

43. $4x+8x-6x^{2}-6x^{2}y = (4+8)x-6x^{2}-6x^{2}y$
$$= 12x-6x^{2}-6x^{2}y$$

44. $-8xy^{3}+4xy^{3}-3x^{3}y = (-8+4)xy^{3}-3x^{3}y$
$$= -4xy^{3}-3x^{3}y$$

45. $(3x+7y)+(4x^{2}-3x+7)+(y-1)$
$$= 3x+7y+4x^{2}-3x+7+y-1$$
$$= 4x^{2}+(3-3)x+(7+1)y+(7-1)$$
$$= 4x^{2}+8y+6$$

46. $(4x^{2}-6xy+9y^{2})-(8x^{2}-6xy-y^{2})$
$$= 4x^{2}-6xy+9y^{2}-8x^{2}+6xy+y^{2}$$
$$= (4-8)x^{2}+(-6+6)xy+(9+1)y^{2}$$
$$= -4x^{2}+10y^{2}$$

47. $(3x^{2}-4b+28)+(9x^{2}-30)-(4x^{2}-6b+20)$
$$= 3x^{2}-4b+28+9x^{2}-30-4x^{2}+6b-20$$
$$= (3+9-4)x^{2}+(-4+6)b+(28-30-20)$$
$$= 8x^{2}+2b-22$$

48. $(9xy+4x^{2}+18)+(7xy-4x^{3}-9x)$
$$= 9xy+4x^{2}+18+7xy-4x^{3}-9x$$
$$= -4x^{3}+4x^{2}+(9+7)xy-9x+18$$
$$= -4x^{3}+4x^{2}+16xy-9x+18$$

49. $(3x^{2}y-7xy-4)+(9x^{2}y+x)-(x-7)$
$$= 3x^{2}y-7xy-4+9x^{2}y+x-x+7$$
$$= (3+9)x^{2}y-7xy+(-4+7)$$
$$= 12x^{2}y-7xy+3$$

50.
$$\begin{array}{r} x^{2}-5x+7 \\ -\quad(x+4) \\ \hline x^{2}-6x+3 \end{array}$$

51.
$$\begin{array}{r} x^{3}\quad\ +2xy^{2}-y \\ +\quad(x-4xy^{2}\quad\ -7) \\ \hline x^{3}+x-2xy^{2}-y-7 \end{array}$$

52. $P(6) = 9(6)^2 - 7(6) + 8 = 290$

53. $P(-2) = 9(-2)^2 - 7(-2) + 8 = 58$

54. $P(-3) = 9(-3)^2 - 7(-3) + 8 = 110$

55. $P(x) + Q(x) = (2x - 1) + (x^2 + 2x - 5)$
$$= 2x - 1 + x^2 + 2x - 5$$
$$= x^2 + 4x - 6$$

56. $2[P(x)] - Q(x) = 2(2x - 1) - (x^2 + 2x - 5)$
$$= 4x - 2 - x^2 - 2x + 5$$
$$= -x^2 + 2x + 3$$

57. $2(2x^2 y - 6x + 1) + 2(x^2 y + 5)$
$$= 4x^2 y - 12x + 2 + 2x^2 y + 10$$
$$= (6x^2 y - 12x + 12) \text{ cm}$$

58. $-6x(4x^2 - 6x + 1) = -24x^3 + 36x^2 - 6x$

59. $-4ab^2(3ab^3 + 7ab + 1)$
$$= -4ab^2(3ab^3) - 4ab^2(7ab) - 4ab^2(1)$$
$$= -12a^2 b^5 - 28a^2 b^3 - 4ab^2$$

60. $(x - 4)(2x + 9) = 2x^2 + 9x - 8x - 36$
$$= 2x^2 + x - 36$$

61. $(-3xa + 4b)^2$
$$= (-3xa)^2 + 2(-3xa)(4b) + (4b)^2$$
$$= 9x^2 a^2 - 24xab + 16b^2$$

62.
$$\begin{array}{r} 9x^2 + 4x + 1 \\ \times \qquad 4x - 3 \\ \hline -27x^2 - 12x - 3 \\ 36x^3 + 16x^2 + 4x \\ \hline 36x^3 - 11x^2 - 8x - 3 \end{array}$$

63. $(5x - 9y)(3x + 9y)$
$$= 15x^2 + 45xy - 27xy - 81y^2$$
$$= 15x^2 + 18xy - 81y^2$$

64. $\left(x - \dfrac{1}{3}\right)\left(x + \dfrac{2}{3}\right) = x^2 + \dfrac{2}{3}x - \dfrac{1}{3}x - \dfrac{1}{3}\left(\dfrac{2}{3}\right)$
$$= x^2 + \dfrac{1}{3}x - \dfrac{2}{9}$$

65. $(x^2 + 9x + 1)^2$
$$= (x^2 + 9x + 1)(x^2 + 9x + 1)$$
$$= x^2(x^2 + 9x + 1) + 9x(x^2 + 9x + 1)$$
$$\quad + 1(x^2 + 9x + 1)$$
$$= x^4 + 9x^3 + x^2 + 9x^3 + 81x^2 + 9x$$
$$\quad + x^2 + 9x + 1$$
$$= x^4 + 18x^3 + 83x^2 + 18x + 1$$

66. $(3x - y)^2 = (3x)^2 - 2(3x)y + y^2$
$$= 9x^2 - 6xy + y^2$$

67. $(4x + 9)^2 = (4x)^2 + 2(4x)(9) + 9^2$
$$= 16x^2 + 72x + 81$$

68. $(x + 3y)(x - 3y) = x^2 - (3y)^2 = x^2 - 9y^2$

69. $[4 + (3a - b)][4 - (3a - b)]$
$$= 4^2 - (3a - b)^2$$
$$= 16 - [(3a)^2 - 2(3a)b + b^2]$$
$$= 16 - (9a^2 - 6ab + b^2)$$
$$= 16 - 9a^2 + 6ab - b^2$$

70. $P(x) \cdot Q(x)$
$$= (2x - 1)(x^2 + 2x - 5)$$
$$= 2x(x^2 + 2x - 5) - 1(x^2 + 2x - 5)$$
$$= 2x^3 + 4x^2 - 10x - x^2 - 2x + 5$$
$$= 2x^3 + 3x^2 - 12x + 5$$

71. $Area = lw$
$$= (3y + 7z)(3y - 7z)$$
$$= (3y)^2 - (7z)^2$$
$$= (9y^2 - 49z^2) \text{ square units}$$

72. $4a^b(3a^{b+2} - 7) = 4a^b(3a^{b+2}) + 4a^b(-7)$
$$= 12a^{b+b+2} - 28a^b$$
$$= 12a^{2b+2} - 28a^b$$

73. $(4xy^z - b)^2 = (4xy^z)^2 - 2(4xy^z)b + b^2$
$$= 4^2 x^2 (y^z)^2 - 8xy^z b + b^2$$
$$= 16x^2 y^{2z} - 8xy^z b + b^2$$

74. $(3x^a - 4)(3x^a + 4) = (3x^a)^2 - 4^2$
$$= 3^2 (x^a)^2 - 16$$
$$= 9x^{2a} - 16$$

75. $16x^3 - 24x^2 = 8x^2(2x - 3)$

76. $36y - 24y^2 = 12y(3 - 2y)$

77. $6ab^2 + 8ab - 4a^2 b^2 = 2ab(3b + 4 - 2ab)$

78. $14a^2 b^2 - 21ab^2 + 7ab$
$$= 7ab(2ab - 3b + 1)$$

79. $6a(a + 3b) - 5(a + 3b) = (6a - 5)(a + 3b)$

80. $4x(x - 2y) - 5(x - 2y) = (4x - 5)(x - 2y)$

81. $xy - 6y + 3x - 18 = y(x - 6) + 3(x - 6)$
$$= (y + 3)(x - 6)$$

82. $ab - 8b + 4a - 32 = b(a - 8) + 4(a - 8)$
$$= (b + 4)(a - 8)$$

83. $pq - 3p - 5q + 15 = p(q - 3) - 5(q - 3)$
$$= (p - 5)(q - 3)$$

84. $x^3 - x^2 - 2x + 2 = x^2(x - 1) - 2(x - 1)$
$$= (x^2 - 2)(x - 1)$$

85. Area $= 2xy - x^2 = x(2y - x)$ sq. units

86. $x^2 - 14x - 72 = (x - 18)(x + 4)$

87. $x^2 + 16x - 80 = (x - 4)(x + 20)$

88. $2x^2 - 18x + 28 = 2(x^2 - 9x + 14)$
$$= 2(x - 7)(x - 2)$$

89. $3x^2 + 33x + 54 = 3(x^2 + 11x + 18)$
$$= 3(x + 9)(x + 2)$$

90. $2x^3 - 7x^2 - 9x = x(2x^2 - 7x - 9)$
$$= x(2x - 9)(x + 1)$$

91. $3x^2 + 2x - 16 = (3x + 8)(x - 2)$

92. $6x^2 + 17x + 10 = (6x + 5)(x + 2)$

93. $15x^2 - 91x + 6 = (15x - 1)(x - 6)$

94. $4x^2 + 2x - 12 = 2(2x^2 + x - 6)$
$$= 2(2x - 3)(x + 2)$$

95. $9x^2 - 12x - 12 = 3(3x^2 - 4x - 4)$
$$= 3(3x + 2)(x - 2)$$

96. $y^2(x + 6)^2 - 2y(x + 6)^2 - 3(x + 6)^2$
$$= (x + 6)^2 (y^2 - 2y - 3)$$
$$= (x + 6)^2 (y - 3)(y + 1)$$

97. Let $y = x + 5$. Then
$$(x + 5)^2 + 6(x + 5) + 8$$
$$= y^2 + 6y + 8$$
$$= (y + 4)(y + 2)$$
$$= [(x + 5) + 4][(x + 5) + 2]$$
$$= (x + 9)(x + 7)$$

98. $x^4 - 6x^2 - 16 = (x^2 - 8)(x^2 + 2)$

99. $x^4 + 8x^2 - 20 = (x^2 + 10)(x^2 - 2)$

100. $x^2 - 100 = (x + 10)(x - 10)$

101. $x^2 - 81 = (x + 9)(x - 9)$

102. $2x^2 - 32 = 2(x^2 - 16) = 2(x + 4)(x - 4)$

103. $6x^2 - 54 = 6(x^2 - 9) = 6(x + 3)(x - 3)$

104. $81 - x^4 = (9 + x^2)(9 - x^2)$
$$= (9 + x^2)(3 + x)(3 - x)$$

105. $16 - y^4 = (4 + y^2)(4 - y^2)$
$$= (4 + y^2)(2 + y)(2 - y)$$

106. $(y+2)^2 - 25 = [(y+2)+5][(y+2)-5]$
$= (y+7)(y-3)$

107. $(x-3)^2 - 16 = [(x-3)+4][(x-3)-4]$
$= (x+1)(x-7)$

108. $x^3 + 216 = x^3 + 6^3$
$= (x+6)(x^2 - 6 \cdot x + 6^2)$
$= (x+6)(x^2 - 6x + 36)$

109. $y^3 + 512 = y^3 + 8^3$
$= (y+8)(y^2 - 8 \cdot y + 8^2)$
$= (y+8)(y^2 - 8y + 64)$

110. $8 - 27y^3 = 2^3 - (3y)^3$
$= (2-3y)(4 + 2 \cdot 3y + (3y)^2)$
$= (2-3y)(4 + 6y + 9y^2)$

111. $1 - 64y^3 = 1^3 - (4y)^3$
$= (1-4y)(1^2 + 1 \cdot 4y + (4y)^2)$
$= (1-4y)(1 + 4y + 16y^2)$

112. $6x^4y + 48xy = 6xy(x^3 + 8)$
$= 6xy(x^3 + 2^3)$
$= 6xy(x+2)(x^2 - 2x + 2^2)$
$= 6xy(x+2)(x^2 - 2x + 4)$

113. $2x^5 + 16x^2y^3$
$= 2x^2(x^3 + 8y^3)$
$= 2x^2(x^3 + (2y)^3)$
$= 2x^2(x+2y)(x^2 - x \cdot 2y + (2y)^2)$
$= 2x^2(x+2y)(x^2 - 2xy + 4y^2)$

114. $x^2 - 2x + 1 - y^2$
$= (x^2 - 2x + 1) - y^2$
$= (x-1)^2 - y^2$
$= [(x-1)+y][(x-1)-y]$
$= (x-1+y)(x-1-y)$

115. $x^2 - 6x + 9 - 4y^2$
$= (x^2 - 6x + 9) - 4y^2$
$= (x-3)^2 - (2y)^2$
$= [(x-3)+2y][(x-3)-2y]$
$= (x-3+2y)(x-3-2y)$

116. $4x^2 + 12x + 9 = (2x+3)(2x+3)$
$= (2x+3)^2$

117. $16a^2 - 40ab + 25b^2 = (4a-5b)(4a-5b)$
$= (4a-5b)^2$

118. $\text{Volume} = \pi R^2 h - \pi r^2 h$
$= \pi h(R^2 - r^2)$
$= \pi h(R+r)(R-r) \text{ cubic units}$

119. $(3x-1)(x+7) = 0$
$3x-1=0 \text{ or } x+7=0$
$x = \dfrac{1}{3} \text{ or } \quad x = -7$
The solutions are $-7, \dfrac{1}{3}$.

120. $3(x+5)(8x-3) = 0$
$x+5 = 0 \quad \text{or } 8x-3 = 0$
$x = -5 \text{ or } \quad x = \dfrac{3}{8}$
The solutions are $-5, \dfrac{3}{8}$.

121. $5x(x-4)(2x-9) = 0$
$5x = 0 \text{ or } x-4 = 0 \text{ or } 2x-9 = 0$
$x = 0 \text{ or } \quad x = 4 \text{ or } \quad x = \dfrac{9}{2}$
The solutions are $0, 4, \dfrac{9}{2}$.

122. $6(x+3)(x-4)(5x+1) = 0$
$x+3 = 0 \quad \text{or } x-4 = 0 \text{ or } 5x+1 = 0$
$x = -3 \text{ or } \quad x = 4 \text{ or } \quad 5x = -1$
$x = -\dfrac{1}{5}$
The solutions are $-\dfrac{1}{5}, -3, 4$.

123.
$$2x^2 = 12x$$
$$2x^2 - 12x = 0$$
$$2x(x-6) = 0$$
$$2x = 0 \text{ or } x - 6 = 0$$
$$x = 0 \text{ or } \quad x = 6$$
The solutions are 0, 6.

124.
$$4x^3 - 36x = 0$$
$$4x(x^2 - 9) = 0$$
$$4x(x+3)(x-3) = 0$$
$$4x = 0 \text{ or } x + 3 = 0 \quad \text{or } x - 3 = 0$$
$$x = 0 \text{ or } \quad x = -3 \text{ or } \quad x = 3$$
The solutions are $-3, 0, 3$.

125.
$$(1-x)(3x+2) = -4x$$
$$3x + 2 - 3x^2 - 2x = -4x$$
$$-3x^2 + x + 2 = -4x$$
$$-3x^2 + 5x + 2 = 0$$
$$3x^2 - 5x - 2 = 0$$
$$(3x+1)(x-2) = 0$$
$$3x + 1 = 0 \quad \text{or } x - 2 = 0$$
$$3x = -1 \text{ or } \quad x = 2$$
$$x = -\frac{1}{3}$$
The solutions are $-\frac{1}{3}, 2$.

126.
$$2x(x-12) = -40$$
$$2x^2 - 24x = -40$$
$$2x^2 - 24x + 40 = 0$$
$$2(x^2 - 12x + 20) = 0$$
$$2(x-10)(x-2) = 0$$
$$x - 10 = 0 \quad \text{or } x - 2 = 0$$
$$x = 10 \text{ or } \quad x = 2$$
The solutions are 2, 10.

127.
$$3x^2 + 2x = 12 - 7x$$
$$3x^2 + 9x - 12 = 0$$
$$3(x^2 + 3x - 4) = 0$$
$$3(x+4)(x-1) = 0$$
$$x + 4 = 0 \quad \text{or } x - 1 = 0$$
$$x = -4 \text{ or } \quad x = 1$$
The solutions are $-4, 1$.

128.
$$2x^2 + 3x = 35$$
$$2x^2 + 3x - 35 = 0$$
$$(2x-7)(x+5) = 0$$
$$2x - 7 = 0 \quad \text{or } x + 5 = 0$$
$$2x = 7 \text{ or } \quad x = -5$$
$$x = \frac{7}{2}$$
The solutions are $-5, \frac{7}{2}$.

129.
$$x^3 - 18x = 3x^2$$
$$x^3 - 3x^2 - 18x = 0$$
$$x(x^2 - 3x - 18) = 0$$
$$x(x-6)(x+3) = 0$$
$$x = 0 \text{ or } x - 6 = 0 \text{ or } x + 3 = 0$$
$$x = 6 \text{ or } \quad x = -3$$
The solutions are $-3, 0, 6$.

130.
$$19x^2 - 42x = -x^3$$
$$x^3 + 19x^2 - 42x = 0$$
$$x(x^2 + 19x - 42) = 0$$
$$x(x+21)(x-2) = 0$$
$$x = 0 \text{ or } x + 21 = 0 \quad \text{or } x - 2 = 0$$
$$x = -21 \text{ or } \quad x = 2$$
The solutions are $-21, 0, 2$.

131.
$$12x = 6x^3 + 6x^2$$
$$-6x^3 - 6x^2 + 12x = 0$$
$$-6x(x^2 + x - 2) = 0$$
$$-6x(x+2)(x-1) = 0$$
$$-6x = 0 \text{ or } x + 2 = 0 \quad \text{or } x - 1 = 0$$
$$x = 0 \text{ or } \quad x = -2 \text{ or } \quad x = 1$$
The solutions are $-2, 0, 1$.

132.
$$8x^3 + 10x^2 = 3x$$
$$8x^3 + 10x^2 - 3x = 0$$
$$x(8x^2 + 10x - 3) = 0$$
$$x(4x - 1)(2x + 3) = 0$$
$$x = 0 \quad \text{or} \quad 4x - 1 = 0 \quad \text{or} \quad 2x + 3 = 0$$
$$4x = 1 \quad \text{or} \quad 2x = -3$$
$$x = \frac{1}{4} \quad \text{or} \quad x = -\frac{3}{2}$$

The solutions are $-\frac{3}{2}, 0, \frac{1}{4}$.

133. Let $x =$ the number. Then
$$x + 2x^2 = 105$$
$$2x^2 + x - 105 = 0$$
$$(2x + 15)(x - 7) = 0$$
$$2x + 15 = 0 \quad \text{or} \quad x - 7 = 0$$
$$2x = -15 \quad \text{or} \quad x = 7$$
$$x = -\frac{15}{2}$$

The numbers are $-\frac{15}{2}$ and 7.

134. Let $x =$ width; then $2x - 5 =$ length.
$$x(2x - 5) = 33$$
$$2x^2 - 5x = 33$$
$$2x^2 - 5x - 33 = 0$$
$$(2x - 11)(x + 3) = 0$$
$$2x - 11 = 0 \quad \text{or} \quad x + 3 = 0$$
$$2x = 11 \quad \text{or} \quad x = -3$$
$$x = \frac{11}{2}$$

Disregard the negative.

Width $= \frac{11}{2} = 5\frac{1}{2}$ m

Length $= 2\left(\frac{11}{2}\right) - 5 = 6$ m

135. $h(t) = -16t^2 + 400$
$$0 = -16t^2 + 400$$
$$0 = -16(t^2 - 25)$$
$$0 = -16(t + 5)(t - 5)$$
$$t + 5 = 0 \quad \text{or} \quad t - 5 = 0$$
$$t = -5 \quad \text{or} \quad t = 5$$

Disregard the negative. The stunt dummy will reach the ground after 5 seconds.

Chapter 5 Test

1. $(-9x)^{-2} = \dfrac{1}{(-9x)^2} = \dfrac{1}{81x^2}$

2. $-3xy^{-2}(4xy^2)z = -12x^{1+1}y^{-2+2}z$
$$= -12x^2 z$$

3. $\dfrac{6^{-1}a^2b^{-3}}{3^{-2}a^{-5}b^2} = \dfrac{3^2 a^{2+5}}{6^1 b^{2+3}} = \dfrac{9a^7}{6b^5} = \dfrac{3a^7}{2b^5}$

4. $\left(\dfrac{-xy^{-5}z}{xy^3}\right)^{-5} = \dfrac{(-1)^{-5} x^{-5} y^{25} z^{-5}}{x^{-5} y^{-15}}$
$$= \dfrac{-x^{-5-(-5)} y^{25-(-15)}}{z^5}$$
$$= -\dfrac{y^{40}}{z^5}$$

5. $630,000,000 = 6.3 \times 10^8$

6. $0.01200 = 1.2 x 10^{-2}$

7. $5 \times 10^{-6} = 0.000005$

8. $\dfrac{(0.0024)(0.00012)}{0.00032} = \dfrac{(2.4 \times 10^{-3})(1.2 \times 10^{-4})}{3.2 \times 10^{-4}}$
$$= \dfrac{(2.4)(1.2)}{3.2} \times 10^{-3+(-4)-(-4)}$$
$$= 0.9 \times 10^{-3}$$
$$= 0.0009$$

9. $(4x^3 y - 3x - 4) - (9x^3 y + 8x + 5)$
$$= 4x^3 y - 3x - 4 - 9x^3 y - 8x - 5$$
$$= -5x^3 y - 11x - 9$$

10. $-3xy(4x + y) = -3xy(4x) - 3xy(y)$
$$= -12x^2 y - 3xy^2$$

11. $(3x + 4)(4x - 7) = 12x^2 - 21x + 16x - 28$
$$= 12x^2 - 5x - 28$$

12. $(5a - 2b)(5a + 2b) = (5a)^2 - (2b)^2$
$$= 25a^2 - 4b^2$$

13. $(6m+n)^2 = (6m)^2 + 2(6m)n + n^2$
$= 36m^2 + 12mn + n^2$

14.

$$\begin{array}{r} x^2 - 6x + 4 \\ \times \qquad\quad 2x - 1 \\ \hline -x^2 + 6x - 4 \\ 2x^3 - 12x^2 + 8x \\ \hline 2x^3 - 13x^3 + 14x - 4 \end{array}$$

15. $16x^3 y - 12x^2 y^4 = 4x^2 y(4x - 3y^3)$

16. $x^2 - 13x - 30 = (x-15)(x+2)$

17. $4y^2 + 20y + 25 = (2y+5)(2y+5)$
$= (2y+5)^2$

18. $6x^2 - 15x - 9 = 3(2x^2 - 5x - 3)$
$= 3(2x+1)(x-3)$

19. $4x^2 - 25 = (2x)^2 - 5^2 = (2x+5)(2x-5)$

20. $x^3 + 64 = x^3 + 4^3 = (x+4)(x^2 - 4x + 16)$

21. $3x^2 y - 27y^3 = 3y(x^2 - 9y^2)$
$= 3y(x^2 - (3y)^2)$
$= 3y(x+3y)(x-3y)$

22. $6x^2 + 24 = 6(x^2 + 4)$

23. $16y^3 - 2 = 2(8y^3 - 1)$
$= 2((2y)^3 - 1^3)$
$= 2(2y-1)(4y^2 + 2y + 1)$

24. $x^2 y - 9y - 3x^2 + 27 = y(x^2 - 9) - 3(x^2 - 9)$
$= (x^2 - 9)(y - 3)$
$= (x+3)(x-3)(y-3)$

25. $\quad 3n(7n - 20) = 96$
$21n^2 - 60n = 96$
$21n^2 - 60n - 96 = 0$
$3(7n^2 - 20n - 32) = 0$
$3(7n+8)(n-4) = 0$
$7n+8 = 0 \quad \text{or} \quad n - 4 = 0$
$7n = -8 \quad \text{or} \qquad n = 4$
$n = -\dfrac{8}{7}$

The solutions are $-\dfrac{8}{7}, 4$.

26. $(x+2)(x-2) = 5(x+4)$
$x^2 - 4 = 5x + 20$
$x^2 - 5x - 24 = 0$
$(x-8)(x+3) = 0$
$x - 8 = 0 \quad \text{or} \quad x + 3 = 0$
$x = 8 \quad \text{or} \qquad x = -3$
The solutions are 8, –3.

27. $\quad 2x^3 + 5x^2 = 8x + 20$
$2x^3 + 5x^2 - 8x - 20 = 0$
$x^2(2x+5) - 4(2x+5) = 0$
$(2x+5)(x^2 - 4) = 0$
$(2x+5)(x+2)(x-2) = 0$
$2x+5 = 0 \quad \text{or} \ x + 2 = 0 \quad \text{or} \ x - 2 = 0$
$2x = -5 \text{ or} \qquad x = -2 \text{ or} \qquad x = 2$
$x = -\dfrac{5}{2}$

The solutions are $-\dfrac{5}{2}, -2, 2$.

28. Area $= x^2 - (2y)^2$
$= (x+2y)(x-2y)$ square units

29. $h(t) = -16t^2 + 96t + 880$

a. $-16(1)^2 + 96(1) + 880 = -16 + 96 + 880$
$= 960$ feet

b. $-16(5.1)^2 + 96(5.1) + 880$
$= -416.16 + 489.6 + 880$
$= 953.44$ feet

c.
$$0 = -16t^2 + 96t + 880$$

$$16t^2 - 96t - 880 = 0$$

$$16(t^2 - 6t - 55) = 0$$

$$(t - 11)(t + 5) = 0$$

$$t - 11 = 0 \quad \text{or} \quad t + 5 = 0$$

$$t = 11 \quad \text{or} \qquad t = -5$$

Disregard the negative. The pebble will hit the ground in 11 seconds.

Chapter 5 Cumulative Review

1. a. $\sqrt[3]{27} = 3$

    b. $\sqrt[5]{1} = 1$

    c. $\sqrt[4]{16} = 2$

2. a. $\sqrt[3]{64} = 4$

    b. $\sqrt[4]{81} = 3$

    c. $\sqrt[5]{32} = 2$

3. $2(x - 3) = 5x - 9$

$$2x - 6 = 5x - 9$$

$$-3x = -3$$

$$x = 1$$

The solution is 1.

4. $0.3y + 2.4 = 0.1y + 4$

$$10(0.3y + 2.4) = 10(0.1y + 4)$$

$$3y + 24 = y + 40$$

$$2y = 16$$

$$y = 8$$

The solution is 8.

5. $A = 10,000\left(1 + \dfrac{0.05}{4}\right)^{4(3)}$

$$= 10,000(1.0125)^{12}$$

$$= 10,000(1.160754518)$$

$$= 11,607.54518$$

There will be \$11,607.55 in the account.

6. The area of the room is
$2(14 \cdot 8) + 2(18 \cdot 8) = 512$ sq ft. Two coats means
$2 \cdot 512 = 1024$ sq ft of wall needs paint.

$$\frac{1}{400} = \frac{x}{1024}$$

$$1024\left(\frac{1}{400}\right) = 1024\left(\frac{x}{512}\right)$$

$$2.56 = x$$

$$x \approx 3$$

3 gallons of paint are needed.

7. a. $\dfrac{1}{4}x \le \dfrac{3}{8}$

$$8\left(\frac{1}{4}x\right) \le 8\left(\frac{3}{8}\right)$$

$$2x \le 3$$

$$x \le \frac{3}{2}$$

$$\left\{x \,\middle|\, x \le \frac{3}{2}\right\}$$

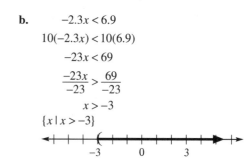

    b. $-2.3x < 6.9$

$$10(-2.3x) < 10(6.9)$$

$$-23x < 69$$

$$\frac{-23x}{-23} > \frac{69}{-23}$$

$$x > -3$$

$$\{x \mid x > -3\}$$

8. $x + 2 \le \dfrac{1}{4}(x - 7)$

$$4(x + 2) \le 4\left[\frac{1}{4}(x - 7)\right]$$

$$4x + 8 \le x - 7$$

$$3x \le -15$$

$$x \le -5$$

$$\{x \mid x \le -5\} \text{ or } \left(-\infty, -5\right]$$

9. $-1 \leq \frac{2x}{3} + 5 \leq 2$

$3(-1) \leq 3\left(\frac{2x}{3} + 5\right) \leq 3(2)$

$-3 \leq 2x + 15 \leq 6$

$-18 \leq 2x \leq -9$

$-9 \leq x \leq -\frac{9}{2}$ or $\left[-9, -\frac{9}{2}\right]$

10. $-\frac{1}{3} < \frac{3x+1}{6} \leq \frac{1}{3}$

$6\left(-\frac{1}{3}\right) < 6\left(\frac{3x+1}{6}\right) \leq 6\left(\frac{1}{3}\right)$

$-2 < 3x + 1 \leq 2$

$-3 < 3x \leq 1$

$-1 < x \leq \frac{1}{3}$ or $\left(-1, \frac{1}{3}\right]$

11. $|y| = 0$

$y = 0$

The solution is 0.

12. $8 + |4c| = 24$

$|4c| = 16$

$4c = 16$ or $4c = -16$

$c = 4$ or $c = -4$

The solutions are –4, 4.

13. $\left|2x - \frac{1}{10}\right| < -13$ is impossible.

The solution is $\varnothing$.

14. $|5x - 1| + 9 > 5$

$|5x - 1| > -4$ is always true.

All real numbers are solutions: $(-\infty, \infty)$

15. $y = -2x + 3$

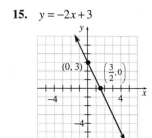

16. $y = 3x$

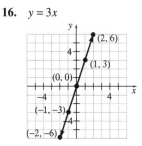

17. $x = y^2$ is not a function (of x). For a single x, it is possible to get more than 1 y. For example:

$1 = y^2$

$\pm 1 = y$

Since a value from the domain corresponds to more than one value from the range, the relation is not a function.

18. $f(x) = 3x^2 + 2x + 3$

$f(-3) = 3(-3)^2 + 2(-3) + 3$

$= 3(9) - 6 + 3$

$= 27 - 6 + 3$

$= 24$

19. $x = 2$

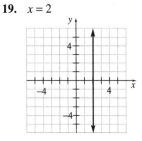

20. $y - 5 = 0$

$y = 5$

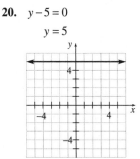

21. $y = 2$

$m = 0$

22. $f(x) = -2x - 3$

$m = -2$

231

23. $y = 3$

24. $x = -3$

25. $x + \dfrac{1}{2}y \geq -4 \qquad$ or $\ y \leq -2$

$\qquad \dfrac{1}{2}y \geq -x - 4 \quad$ or $\ y \leq -2$

$\qquad\quad y \geq -2x - 8 \ $ or $\ y \leq -2$

Graph each inequality. The union of the two inequalities is both shaded regions, as shown by the shading in the graph below.

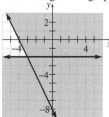

26. $y - 3 = 0[x - (-2)]$

$\quad y - 3 = 0$

$\qquad\quad y = 3$

27. $\begin{cases} y = x + 5 \\ 3x = 2y - 9 \end{cases}$

Substitute $x + 5$ for y in the second equation.

$3x = 2(x + 5) - 9$

$3x = 2x + 10 - 9$

$3x = 2x + 1$

$\ x = 1$

Replace 1 for x in the first equation.

$y = (1) + 5 = 6$

The solution is $(1, 6)$.

28. $\begin{cases} 4x - 2y = 8 \\ \quad\ y = 3x - 6 \end{cases}$

Substitute $3x - 6$ for y in the first equation.

$4x - 2(3x - 6) = 8$

$4x - 6x + 12 = 8$

$\qquad -2x = -4$

$\qquad\quad x = 2$

Replace 2 for x in the second equation.

$y = 3(2) - 6 = 6 - 6 = 0$

The solution is $(2, 0)$.

29. $\begin{cases} 2x + 4y \quad\ = 1 \quad (1) \\ 4x \quad\ - 4z = -1 \ (2) \\ \quad\ y - 4z = -3 \ (3) \end{cases}$

Multiply equation (2) by –1 and add to equation (3).

$-4x \quad\ + 4z = 1$

$\underline{\qquad\quad y - 4z = -3}$

$-4x + y \qquad = -2 \ (4)$

Multiply equation (1) by 2 and add to equation (4).

$4x + 8y = 2$

$\underline{-4x + y = -2}$

$\qquad 9y = 0$

$\qquad\ \ y = 0$

Replace y with 0 in equation (1).

$2x + 4(0) = 1$

$\qquad 2x = 1$

$\qquad\ \ x = \dfrac{1}{2}$

Replace y with 0 in equation (3).

$y - 4z = -3$

$\quad -4z = -3$

$\qquad z = \dfrac{3}{4}$

The solution is $\left(\dfrac{1}{2}, 0, \dfrac{3}{4} \right)$.

30. $\begin{cases} x + y - \dfrac{3}{2}z = \dfrac{1}{2} \quad (1) \\ \quad\ -y - 2z = 14 \quad (2) \\ x - \dfrac{2}{3}y \qquad = -\dfrac{1}{3} \ (3) \end{cases}$

Multiply equation (1) by 2 and equation (3) by 3 to clear fractions.

$\begin{cases} 2x + 2y - 3z = 1 \quad (1) \\ \quad\ -y - 2z = 14 \ (2) \\ 3x - 2y \qquad = -1 \ (3) \end{cases}$

Add equation (1) and equation (3).

$5x - 3z = 0 \ \ (4)$

Multiply equation (2) by 2 and add to equation (1).

$\quad -2y - 4z = 28$

$\underline{2x + 2y - 3z = 1}$

$2x - 7z = 29 \ (5)$

Use equations (4) and (5) to make a new system and then solve the new system.

$$\begin{cases} 5x - 3z = 0 & (4) \\ 2x - 7z = 29 & (5). \end{cases}$$

Multiply equation (4) by –2, multiply equation (5) by 5, and add.

$$-10x + 6z = 0$$
$$\underline{10x - 35z = 145}$$
$$-29z = 145$$
$$z = -5$$

Replace z with –5 in equation (4).

$$5x - 3(-5) = 0$$
$$5x + 15 = 0$$
$$5x = -15$$
$$x = -3$$

Replace z with 5 in equation (2).

$$-y - 2(-5) = 14$$
$$-y + 10 = 14$$
$$-y = 4$$
$$y = -4$$

The solution is (–3, –4, –5).

31. Let x = the first number and y = the second number.

$$\begin{cases} x = y - 4 \\ 4x = 2y + 6 \end{cases}$$

Multiply equation (1) by –4 and add to (2).

$$-4x = -4y + 16$$
$$\underline{4x = 2y + 6}$$
$$0 = -2y + 22$$
$$2y = 22$$
$$y = 11$$

Replace y with 11 in equation (1).

$$x = 11 - 4 = 7$$

The two numbers are 7 and 11.

32. Let x = ounces of 20% solution and y = ounces of 60% solution.

$$\begin{cases} x + y = 50 \\ 0.20x + 0.60y = 50(0.30) \end{cases}$$

Multiply the second equation by 100 to clear decimals.

$$\begin{cases} x + y = 50 \\ 20x + 60y = 1500 \end{cases}$$

Multiply the first equation by –20 and add to the second equation.

$$-20x - 20y = -1000$$
$$\underline{20x + 60y = 1500}$$
$$40y = 500$$
$$y = \frac{500}{40} = 12.5$$

Replace y with 12.5 in the first equation.

$$x + 12.5 = 50$$
$$x = 37.5$$

You should mix 37.5 ounces of the 20% solution and 12.5 ounces of the 60% solution.

33. $\begin{cases} 2x - y = 3 \\ 4x - 2y = 5 \end{cases}$

$$\begin{bmatrix} 2 & -1 & | & 3 \\ 4 & -2 & | & 5 \end{bmatrix}$$

Divide R1 by 2.

$$\begin{bmatrix} 1 & -\frac{1}{2} & | & \frac{3}{2} \\ 4 & -2 & | & 5 \end{bmatrix}$$

Multiply R1 by –4 and add to R2.

$$\begin{bmatrix} 1 & -\frac{1}{2} & | & \frac{3}{2} \\ 0 & 0 & | & -1 \end{bmatrix}$$

This corresponds to

$$\begin{cases} x - \frac{1}{2}y = \frac{3}{2} \\ 0 = -1 \text{ False} \end{cases}$$

The system is inconsistent. The solution is $\varnothing$.

34. $\begin{cases} 4y = 8 \\ x + y = 7 \end{cases}$

$$\begin{bmatrix} 0 & 4 & | & 8 \\ 1 & 1 & | & 7 \end{bmatrix}$$

Interchange R1 and R2.

$$\begin{bmatrix} 1 & 1 & | & 7 \\ 0 & 4 & | & 8 \end{bmatrix}$$

Divide R2 by 4.

$$\begin{bmatrix} 1 & 1 & | & 7 \\ 0 & 1 & | & 2 \end{bmatrix}$$

This corresponds to

$$\begin{cases} x + y = 7 \\ y = 2. \end{cases}$$

Replace y with 2 in the equation $x + y = 7$.

$$x + 2 = 7$$
$$x = 5$$

The solution is (5, 2).

35. $\begin{cases} x - 2y + z = 4 \\ 3x + y - 2z = 3 \\ 5x + 5y + 3z = -8 \end{cases}$

$D = \begin{vmatrix} 1 & -2 & 1 \\ 3 & 1 & -2 \\ 5 & 5 & 3 \end{vmatrix}$

$= 1\begin{vmatrix} 1 & -2 \\ 5 & 3 \end{vmatrix} - (-2)\begin{vmatrix} 3 & -2 \\ 5 & 3 \end{vmatrix} + 1\begin{vmatrix} 3 & 1 \\ 5 & 5 \end{vmatrix}$

$= [3 - (-10)] + 2[9 - (-10)] + (15 - 5)$

$= 13 + 2(19) + 10$

$= 61$

$D_x = \begin{vmatrix} 4 & -2 & 1 \\ 3 & 1 & -2 \\ -8 & 5 & 3 \end{vmatrix}$

$= 4\begin{vmatrix} 1 & -2 \\ 5 & 3 \end{vmatrix} - (-2)\begin{vmatrix} 3 & -2 \\ -8 & 3 \end{vmatrix} + 1\begin{vmatrix} 3 & 1 \\ -8 & 5 \end{vmatrix}$

$= 4[3 - (-10)] + 2(9 - 16) + [15 - (-8)]$

$= 4(13) + 2(-7) + 23$

$= 52 - 14 + 23$

$= 61$

$D_y = \begin{vmatrix} 1 & 4 & 1 \\ 3 & 3 & -2 \\ 5 & -8 & 3 \end{vmatrix}$

$= 1\begin{vmatrix} 3 & -2 \\ -8 & 3 \end{vmatrix} - 4\begin{vmatrix} 3 & -2 \\ 5 & 3 \end{vmatrix} + 1\begin{vmatrix} 3 & 3 \\ 5 & -8 \end{vmatrix}$

$= (9 - 16) - 4[9 - (-10)] + (-24 - 15)$

$= -7 - 4(19) + (-39)$

$= -7 - 76 - 39$

$= -122$

$D_z = \begin{vmatrix} 1 & -2 & 4 \\ 3 & 1 & 3 \\ 5 & 5 & -8 \end{vmatrix}$

$= 1\begin{vmatrix} 1 & 3 \\ 5 & -8 \end{vmatrix} - (-2)\begin{vmatrix} 3 & 3 \\ 5 & -8 \end{vmatrix} + 4\begin{vmatrix} 3 & 1 \\ 5 & 5 \end{vmatrix}$

$= (-8 - 15) + 2(-24 - 15) + 4(15 - 5)$

$= -23 + 2(-39) + 4(10)$

$= -23 - 78 + 40$

$= -61$

$x = \dfrac{D_x}{D} = \dfrac{61}{61} = 1, \quad y = \dfrac{D_y}{D} = \dfrac{-122}{61} = -2,$

$z = \dfrac{D_z}{D} = \dfrac{-61}{61} = -1$

The solution is $(1, -2, -1)$.

36. $\begin{cases} x + y + z = 0 \\ 2x - 3y + z = 5 \\ 2x + y + 2z = 2 \end{cases}$

$D = \begin{vmatrix} 1 & 1 & 1 \\ 2 & -3 & 1 \\ 2 & 1 & 2 \end{vmatrix}$

$= 1\begin{vmatrix} -3 & 1 \\ 1 & 2 \end{vmatrix} - 1\begin{vmatrix} 2 & 1 \\ 2 & 2 \end{vmatrix} + 1\begin{vmatrix} 2 & -3 \\ 2 & 1 \end{vmatrix}$

$= (-6 - 1) - (4 - 2) + [2 - (-6)]$

$= -7 - 2 + 8$

$= -1$

$D_x = \begin{vmatrix} 0 & 1 & 1 \\ 5 & -3 & 1 \\ 2 & 1 & 2 \end{vmatrix}$

$= 0\begin{vmatrix} -3 & 1 \\ 1 & 2 \end{vmatrix} - 1\begin{vmatrix} 5 & 1 \\ 2 & 2 \end{vmatrix} + 1\begin{vmatrix} 5 & -3 \\ 2 & 1 \end{vmatrix}$

$= -(10 - 2) + [5 - (-6)]$

$= -8 + 11$

$= 3$

$D_y = \begin{vmatrix} 1 & 0 & 1 \\ 2 & 5 & 1 \\ 2 & 2 & 2 \end{vmatrix}$

$= 1\begin{vmatrix} 5 & 1 \\ 2 & 2 \end{vmatrix} - 0\begin{vmatrix} 2 & 1 \\ 2 & 2 \end{vmatrix} + 1\begin{vmatrix} 2 & 5 \\ 2 & 2 \end{vmatrix}$

$= (10 - 2) + (4 - 10)$

$= 8 + (-6)$

$= 2$

$D_z = \begin{vmatrix} 1 & 1 & 0 \\ 2 & -3 & 5 \\ 2 & 1 & 2 \end{vmatrix}$

$= 1\begin{vmatrix} -3 & 5 \\ 1 & 2 \end{vmatrix} - 1\begin{vmatrix} 2 & 5 \\ 2 & 2 \end{vmatrix} + 0\begin{vmatrix} 2 & -3 \\ 2 & 1 \end{vmatrix}$

$= (-6 - 5) - (4 - 10)$

$= -11 - (-6)$

$= -11 + 6$

$= -5$

$x = \dfrac{D_x}{D} = \dfrac{3}{-1} = -3, \quad y = \dfrac{D_y}{D} = \dfrac{2}{-1} = -2,$

$z = \dfrac{D_z}{D} = \dfrac{-5}{-1} = 5$

The solution is (–3, –2, 5).

37. a. $730,000 = 7.3 \times 10^5$

b. $0.00000104 = 1.04 \times 10^{-6}$

38. a. $8,250,000 = 8.25 \times 10^6$

b. $0.0000346 = 3.46 \times 10^{-5}$

39. a. $(2x^0 y^{-3})^{-2} = 2^{-2}(1)^{-2}(y^{-3})^{-2} = \dfrac{y^6}{2^2} = \dfrac{y^6}{4}$

b. $\left(\dfrac{x^{-5}}{x^{-2}}\right)^{-3} = \dfrac{(x^{-5})^{-3}}{(x^{-2})^{-3}} = \dfrac{x^{15}}{x^6} = x^{15-6} = x^9$

c. $\left(\dfrac{2}{7}\right)^{-2} = \dfrac{2^{-2}}{7^{-2}} = \dfrac{7^2}{2^2} = \dfrac{49}{4}$

d. $\dfrac{5^{-2} x^{-3} y^{11}}{x^2 y^{-5}} = \dfrac{x^{-3-2} y^{11-(-5)}}{5^2}$

$\qquad = \dfrac{x^{-5} y^{16}}{25}$

$\qquad = \dfrac{y^{16}}{25x^5}$

40. a. $(4a^{-1}b^0)^{-3} = 4^{-3}(a^{-1})^{-3}(1)^{-3} = \dfrac{a^3}{4^3} = \dfrac{a^3}{64}$

b. $\left(\dfrac{a^{-6}}{a^{-8}}\right)^{-2} = \dfrac{(a^{-6})^{-2}}{(a^{-8})^{-2}} = \dfrac{a^{12}}{a^{16}} = a^{-4} = \dfrac{1}{a^4}$

c. $\left(\dfrac{2}{3}\right)^{-3} = \dfrac{2^{-3}}{3^{-3}} = \dfrac{3^3}{2^3} = \dfrac{27}{8}$

d. $\dfrac{3^{-2} a^{-2} b^{12}}{a^4 b^{-5}} = \dfrac{a^{-2-4} b^{12-(-5)}}{3^2}$

$\qquad = \dfrac{a^{-6} b^{17}}{9}$

$\qquad = \dfrac{b^{17}}{9a^6}$

41. The degree is the degree of the term $x^2 y^2$, which is $2 + 2 = 4$.

42. $(3x^2 - 2x) - (5x^2 + 3x)$

$\qquad = 3x^2 - 2x - 5x^2 - 3x$

$\qquad = -2x^2 - 5x$

43. a. $(2x^3)(5x^6) = 2(5)x^{3+6} = 10x^9$

b. $(7y^4 z^4)(-xy^{11} z^5) = -7xy^{4+11} z^{4+5}$

$\qquad\qquad = -7xy^{15} z^9$

44. a. $(3y^6)(4y^2) = 3(4)y^{6+2} = 12y^8$

b. $(6a^3 b^2)(-a^2 bc^4) = -6a^{3+2} b^{2+1} c^4$

$\qquad\qquad = -6a^5 b^3 c^4$

45. $17x^3 y^2 - 34x^4 y^2 = 17x^3 y^2 (1 - 2x)$

46. $12x^3 y - 3xy^3 = 3xy(4x^2 - y^2)$

$\qquad\qquad = 3xy((2x)^2 - y^2)$

$\qquad\qquad = 3xy(2x + y)(2x - y)$

47. $x^2 + 10x + 16 = (x + 8)(x + 2)$

48. $5a^2 + 14a - 3 = (5a - 1)(a + 3)$

49. $\quad 2x^2 + 9x - 5 = 0$

$\qquad (2x - 1)(x + 5) = 0$

$\qquad 2x - 1 = 0 \ \text{ or } \ x + 5 = 0$

$\qquad\quad 2x = 1 \ \text{ or } \qquad x = -5$

$\qquad\qquad x = \dfrac{1}{2}$

The solutions are $-5, \dfrac{1}{2}$.

50. $\quad 3x^2 - 10x - 8 = 0$

$\qquad (3x + 2)(x - 4) = 0$

$\qquad 3x + 2 = 0 \ \text{ or } x - 4 = 0$

$\qquad\quad 3x = -2 \ \text{ or } \qquad x = 4$

$\qquad\qquad x = -\dfrac{2}{3}$

The solutions are $-\dfrac{2}{3}, 4$.

Chapter 6

Exercise Set 6.1

1. $f(x) = \dfrac{x+8}{2x-1}$

$f(2) = \dfrac{2+8}{2(2)-1} = \dfrac{10}{4-1} = \dfrac{10}{3}$

$f(0) = \dfrac{0+8}{2(0)-1} = \dfrac{8}{-1} = -8$

$f(-1) = \dfrac{-1+8}{2(-1)-1} = \dfrac{7}{-3} = -\dfrac{7}{3}$

3. $g(x) = \dfrac{x^2+8}{x^3-25x}$

$g(3) = \dfrac{(3)^2+8}{(3)^3-25(3)}$

$\quad = \dfrac{9+8}{27-75}$

$\quad = \dfrac{17}{-48}$

$\quad = -\dfrac{17}{48}$

$g(-2) = \dfrac{(-2)^2+8}{(-2)^3-25(-2)}$

$\quad = \dfrac{4+8}{-8+50}$

$\quad = \dfrac{12}{42}$

$\quad = \dfrac{2}{7}$

$g(1) = \dfrac{(1)^2+8}{(1)^3-25(1)} = \dfrac{1+8}{1-25} = \dfrac{9}{-24} = -\dfrac{3}{8}$

5. $f(x) = \dfrac{5x-7}{4}$

Domain: $\{x \mid x \text{ is a real number}\}$

7. $s(t) = \dfrac{t^2+1}{2t}$

Undefined values when

$2t = 0$

$t = \dfrac{0}{2} = 0$

Domain: $\{t \mid t \text{ is a real number and } t \neq 0\}$

9. $f(x) = \dfrac{3x}{7-x}$

Undefined values when

$7-x = 0$

$\quad 7 = x$

Domain: $\{x \mid x \text{ is a real number and } x \neq 7\}$

11. $f(x) = \dfrac{x}{3x-1}$

Undefined values when

$3x-1 = 0$

$\quad 3x = 1$

$\quad x = \dfrac{1}{3}$

Domain: $\left\{x \mid x \text{ is a real number and } x \neq \dfrac{1}{3}\right\}$

13. $C(x) = \dfrac{3+2x}{x^3+x^2-2x}$

Undefined values when

$x^3+x^2-2x = 0$

$x(x^2+x-2) = 0$

$x(x+2)(x-1) = 0$

$x = 0 \text{ or } x+2 = 0 \quad \text{or } x-1 = 0$

$\qquad\qquad x = -2 \text{ or } \qquad x = 1$

Domain: $\{x \mid x \text{ is a real number and } x \neq -2,$
$x \neq 0,\ x \neq 1\}$

15. $C(x) = \dfrac{x+3}{x^2-4}$

Undefined values when

$x^2-4 = 0$

$(x+2)(x-2) = 0$

$x+2 = 0 \quad \text{or } x-2 = 0$

$\quad x = -2 \text{ or } \qquad x = 2$

Domain: $\{x \mid x \text{ is a real number and } x \neq -2,$
$x \neq 2\}$

17. Answers may vary. The domain of a rational function is all real numbers, except values that make the denominator equal 0.

19. $\dfrac{4x-8}{3x-6} = \dfrac{4(x-2)}{3(x-2)} = \dfrac{4}{3}$

21. $\dfrac{2x-14}{7-x} = \dfrac{2(x-7)}{-1(x-7)} = \dfrac{2}{-1} = -2$

23. $\dfrac{x^2-2x-3}{x^2-6x+9} = \dfrac{(x-3)(x+1)}{(x-3)^2} = \dfrac{x+1}{x-3}$

25. $\dfrac{2x^2+12x+18}{x^2-9} = \dfrac{2(x^2+6x+9)}{x^2-3^2}$

$\qquad = \dfrac{2(x+3)^2}{(x+3)(x-3)}$

$\qquad = \dfrac{2(x+3)}{x-3}$

27. $\dfrac{3x+6}{x^2+2x} = \dfrac{3(x+2)}{x(x+2)} = \dfrac{3}{x}$

29. $\dfrac{2x^2-x-3}{2x^3-3x^2+2x-3} = \dfrac{(2x-3)(x+1)}{x^2(2x-3)+1(2x-3)}$

$\qquad = \dfrac{(2x-3)(x+1)}{(2x-3)(x^2+1)}$

$\qquad = \dfrac{x+1}{x^2+1}$

31. $\dfrac{8q^2}{16q^3-16q^2} = \dfrac{8q^2}{16q^2(q-1)} = \dfrac{1}{2(q-1)}$

33. $\dfrac{x^2+6x-40}{10+x} = \dfrac{(x+10)(x-4)}{x+10} = x-4$

35. $\dfrac{x^3-125}{5-x} = \dfrac{(x-5)(x^2+5x+25)}{-1(x-5)}$

$\qquad = \dfrac{x^2+5x+25}{-1}$

$\qquad = -x^2-5x-25$

37. $\dfrac{8x^3-27}{4x-6} = \dfrac{(2x)^3-3^3}{2(2x-3)}$

$\qquad = \dfrac{(2x-3)(4x^2+6x+9)}{2(2x-3)}$

$\qquad = \dfrac{4x^2+6x+9}{2}$

39. $\dfrac{2+x}{x+2} = \dfrac{x+2}{x+2} = 1$; $\dfrac{5-x}{-x+5} = \dfrac{5-x}{5-x} = 1$;

$\qquad \dfrac{-x-y}{-y-x} = \dfrac{-y-x}{-y-x} = 1$; $\dfrac{x-3}{3-x} = \dfrac{(x-3)}{-1(x-3)} = -1$

Expression D does not simplify to 1.

41. $\dfrac{3xy^3}{4x^3y^2} \cdot \dfrac{-8x^3y^4}{9x^4y^7} = \dfrac{-24x^4y^7}{36x^7y^9} = -\dfrac{2}{3x^3y^2}$

43. $\dfrac{8a}{3a^4b^2} \div \dfrac{4b^5}{6a^2b} = \dfrac{8a}{3a^4b^2} \cdot \dfrac{6a^2b}{4b^5}$

$\qquad = \dfrac{48a^3b}{12a^4b^7}$

$\qquad = \dfrac{4}{ab^6}$

45. $\dfrac{a^2b}{a^2-b^2} \cdot \dfrac{a+b}{4a^3b} = \dfrac{a^2b(a+b)}{4a^3b(a+b)(a-b)}$

$\qquad = \dfrac{1}{4a(a-b)}$

47. $\dfrac{x^2-9}{4} \div \dfrac{x^2-6x+9}{x^2-x-6}$

$\qquad = \dfrac{x^2-9}{4} \cdot \dfrac{x^2-x-6}{x^2-6x+9}$

$\qquad = \dfrac{(x+3)(x-3)}{4} \cdot \dfrac{(x-3)(x+2)}{(x-3)^2}$

$\qquad = \dfrac{(x+3)(x+2)}{4}$

49. $\dfrac{9x+9}{4x+8} \cdot \dfrac{2x+4}{3x^2-3} = \dfrac{9(x+1)\cdot 2(x+2)}{4(x+2)\cdot 3(x^2-1)}$

$\qquad = \dfrac{18(x+1)(x+2)}{12(x+2)(x+1)(x-1)}$

$\qquad = \dfrac{3}{2(x-1)}$

51. $\dfrac{a+b}{ab} \div \dfrac{a^2-b^2}{4a^3b} = \dfrac{a+b}{ab} \cdot \dfrac{4a^3b}{a^2-b^2}$

$\qquad = \dfrac{4a^3b(a+b)}{ab(a+b)(a-b)}$

$\qquad = \dfrac{4a^2}{a-b}$

237

53. $\dfrac{2x^2-4x-30}{5x^2-40x-75} \div \dfrac{x^2-8x+15}{x^2-6x+9}$

$= \dfrac{2(x^2-2x-15)}{5(x^2-8x-15)} \cdot \dfrac{(x-3)^2}{(x-5)(x-3)}$

$= \dfrac{2(x-5)(x+3)(x-3)}{5(x^2-8x-15)(x-5)}$

$= \dfrac{2(x+3)(x-3)}{5(x^2-8x-15)}$

55. $\dfrac{2x^3-16}{6x^2+6x-36} \cdot \dfrac{9x+18}{3x^2+6x+12}$

$= \dfrac{2(x^3-8)\cdot 9(x+2)}{6(x^2+x-6)\cdot 3(x^2+2x+4)}$

$= \dfrac{18(x-2)(x^2+2x+4)(x+2)}{18(x+3)(x-2)(x^2+2x+4)}$

$= \dfrac{x+2}{x+3}$

57. $\dfrac{15b-3a}{b^2-a^2} \div \dfrac{a-5b}{ab+b^2} = \dfrac{3(5b-a)}{(b+a)(b-a)} \cdot \dfrac{b(a+b)}{-(5b-a)}$

$= \dfrac{3b(5b-a)(a+b)}{-(b+a)(b-a)(5b-a)}$

$= \dfrac{3b}{-(b-a)}$

$= \dfrac{3b}{a-b}$

59. $\dfrac{a^3+a^2b+a+b}{a^3+a} \cdot \dfrac{6a^2}{2a^2-2b^2}$

$= \dfrac{a^2(a+b)+1(a+b)}{a(a^2+1)} \cdot \dfrac{6a^2}{2(a^2-b^2)}$

$= \dfrac{6a^2(a+b)(a^2+1)}{2a(a^2+1)(a+b)(a-b)}$

$= \dfrac{3a}{a-b}$

61. $\dfrac{5a}{12} \cdot \dfrac{2}{25a^2} \cdot \dfrac{15a}{2} = \dfrac{1}{6} \cdot \dfrac{1}{5a} \cdot \dfrac{15a}{2}$

$= \dfrac{1}{6} \cdot \dfrac{1}{1} \cdot \dfrac{3}{2}$

$= \dfrac{3}{12}$

$= \dfrac{1}{4}$

63. $\dfrac{3x-x^2}{x^3-27} \div \dfrac{x}{x^2+3x+9}$

$= \dfrac{x(3-x)}{(x-3)(x^2+3x+9)} \cdot \dfrac{x^2+3x+9}{x}$

$= \dfrac{3-x}{x-3}$

$= -1$

65. $\dfrac{4a}{7} \div \left(\dfrac{a^2}{14} \cdot \dfrac{3}{a}\right) = \dfrac{4a}{7} \div \dfrac{3a}{14}$

$= \dfrac{4a}{7} \cdot \dfrac{14}{3a}$

$= \dfrac{4}{1} \cdot \dfrac{2}{3}$

$= \dfrac{8}{3}$

67. $\dfrac{8b+24}{3a+6} \div \dfrac{ab-2b+3a-6}{a^2-4a+4}$

$= \dfrac{8(b+3)}{3(a+2)} \cdot \dfrac{(a-2)^2}{b(a-2)+3(a-2)}$

$= \dfrac{8(b+3)}{3(a+2)} \cdot \dfrac{(a-2)^2}{(a-2)(b+3)}$

$= \dfrac{8(a-2)}{3(a+2)}$

69. $\dfrac{4}{x} \div \dfrac{3xy}{x^2} \cdot \dfrac{6x^2}{x^4} = \dfrac{4}{x} \cdot \dfrac{x^2}{3xy} \cdot \dfrac{6x^2}{x^4}$

$= \dfrac{24x^4}{3x^6 y}$

$= \dfrac{8}{x^2 y}$

71. $\dfrac{3x^2-5x-2}{y^2+y-2} \cdot \dfrac{y^2+4y-5}{12x^2+7x+1} \div \dfrac{5x^2-9x-2}{8x^2-2x-1}$

$= \dfrac{(3x+1)(x-2)(y+5)(y-1)(4x+1)(2x-1)}{(y+2)(y-1)(4x+1)(3x+1)(5x+1)(x-2)}$

$= \dfrac{(y+5)(2x-1)}{(y+2)(5x+1)}$

73. $\dfrac{5a^2-20}{3a^2-12a} \div \dfrac{a^3+2a^2}{2a^2-8a} \cdot \dfrac{9a^3+6a^2}{2a^2-4a}$

$= \dfrac{5(a^2-4)}{3a(a-4)} \cdot \dfrac{2a(a-4)}{a^2(a+2)} \cdot \dfrac{3a^2(3a+2)}{2a(a-2)}$

$= \dfrac{5(a+2)(a-2)(3a+2)}{a(a+2)(a-2)}$

$= \dfrac{5(3a+2)}{a}$

75. $\dfrac{5x^4+3x^2-2}{x-1} \cdot \dfrac{x+1}{x^4-1}$

$= \dfrac{(5x^2-2)(x^2+1)}{x-1} \cdot \dfrac{x+1}{(x^2+1)(x^2-1)}$

$= \dfrac{(5x^2-2)(x^2+1)}{x-1} \cdot \dfrac{x+1}{(x^2+1)(x+1)(x-1)}$

$= \dfrac{5x^2-2}{(x-1)^2}$

77. $\dfrac{4}{5}+\dfrac{3}{5}=\dfrac{4+3}{5}=\dfrac{7}{5}$

79. $\dfrac{5}{28}-\dfrac{2}{21}$

The LCD = 84.

$\dfrac{5}{28}\cdot\dfrac{3}{3}-\dfrac{2}{21}\cdot\dfrac{4}{4}=\dfrac{15}{84}-\dfrac{8}{84}$

$= \dfrac{7}{84}$

$= \dfrac{7\cdot1}{7\cdot12}$

$= \dfrac{1}{12}$

81. $\dfrac{3}{8}+\dfrac{1}{2}-\dfrac{3}{16}$

The LCD = 16.

$\dfrac{3}{8}\cdot\dfrac{2}{2}+\dfrac{1}{2}\cdot\dfrac{8}{8}-\dfrac{3}{16}=\dfrac{6}{16}+\dfrac{8}{16}-\dfrac{3}{16}$

$= \dfrac{6+8-3}{16}$

$= \dfrac{11}{16}$

83. $A = l \cdot w$

$= \dfrac{x+2}{x} \cdot \dfrac{5x}{x^2-4}$

$= \dfrac{x+2}{x} \cdot \dfrac{5x}{(x+2)(x-2)}$

$= \dfrac{5}{x-2}$ square meters

85. $f(x)=\dfrac{100,000x}{100-x}$

a. $\{x \mid 0 \le x < 100\}$

b. $f(30)=\dfrac{100,000(30)}{100-30}=\$42,857.14$

c. $f(60)=\dfrac{100,000(60)}{100-60}=\$150,000$

$f(80)=\dfrac{100,000(80)}{100-80}=\$400,000$

d. $f(90)=\dfrac{100,000(90)}{100-90}=\$900,000$

$f(95)=\dfrac{100,000(95)}{100-95}=\$1,900,000$

$f(99)=\dfrac{100,000(99)}{100-99}=\$9,900,000$

Answers may vary. As *x* approaches 100%, the cost increases at a continuously faster rate. For values near 100%, the cost will be extremely large.

87. Answers may vary. When dividing by a fraction, we multiply by the reciprocal of the divisor. This causes *R* to be in the denominator, so it cannot equal 0.

89. Since $A = b \cdot h$, we have $b = \dfrac{A}{h}$.

Now

$b = \dfrac{\dfrac{x^2+x-2}{x^3}}{\dfrac{x^2}{x-1}}$

$= \dfrac{(x+2)(x-1)}{x^3} \cdot \dfrac{x-1}{x^2}$

$= \dfrac{(x+2)(x-1)^2}{x^5}$ feet

91. $f(x) = \dfrac{20x}{100 - x}$

x	0	10	30	50	70	90	95	99
y	0	$\dfrac{20}{9}$	$\dfrac{60}{7}$	20	$\dfrac{140}{3}$	180	380	1980

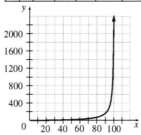

93. $\dfrac{x^{2n} - 4}{7x} \cdot \dfrac{14x^3}{x^n - 2} = \dfrac{(x^n + 2)(x^n - 2) \cdot 2x^2}{x^n - 2}$

$\qquad\qquad = 2x^2(x^n + 2)$

95. $\dfrac{y^{2n} + 9}{10y} \cdot \dfrac{y^n - 3}{y^{4n} - 81}$

$\quad = \dfrac{y^{2n} + 9}{10y} \cdot \dfrac{y^n - 3}{(y^{2n} + 9)(y^{2n} - 9)}$

$\quad = \dfrac{y^n - 3}{10y(y^n + 3)(y^n - 3)}$

$\quad = \dfrac{1}{10y(y^n + 3)}$

97. $\dfrac{y^{2n} - y^n - 2}{2y^n - 4} \div \dfrac{y^{2n} - 1}{1 + y^n}$

$\quad = \dfrac{(y^n - 2)(y^n + 1)}{2(y^n - 2)} \cdot \dfrac{1 + y^n}{(y^n + 1)(y^n - 1)}$

$\quad = \dfrac{1 + y^n}{2(y^n - 1)} \quad$ or $\quad \dfrac{y^n + 1}{2(y^n - 1)}$

Mental Math 6.2

1. A, B

2. D

3. C

4. A, C

5. $\dfrac{5}{y} + \dfrac{7}{y} = \dfrac{5 + 7}{y} = \dfrac{12}{y}$

6. $\dfrac{5}{y} - \dfrac{7}{y} = \dfrac{5 - 7}{y} = -\dfrac{2}{y}$

7. $\dfrac{5}{y} \cdot \dfrac{7}{y} = \dfrac{5 \cdot 7}{y \cdot y} = \dfrac{35}{y^2}$

8. $\dfrac{5}{y} \div \dfrac{7}{y} = \dfrac{5}{y} \cdot \dfrac{y}{7} = \dfrac{5}{7}$

Exercise Set 6.2

1. $\dfrac{2}{x} - \dfrac{5}{x} = \dfrac{2 - 5}{x} = -\dfrac{3}{x}$

3. $\dfrac{2}{x - 2} + \dfrac{x}{x - 2} = \dfrac{2 + x}{x - 2} = \dfrac{x + 2}{x - 2}$

5. $\dfrac{x^2}{x + 2} - \dfrac{4}{x + 2} = \dfrac{x^2 - 4}{x + 2}$

$\qquad\qquad = \dfrac{(x + 2)(x - 2)}{x + 2}$

$\qquad\qquad = x - 2$

7. $\dfrac{2x - 6}{x^2 + x - 6} + \dfrac{3 - 3x}{x^2 + x - 6} = \dfrac{-x - 3}{x^2 + x - 6}$

$\qquad\qquad = \dfrac{-(x + 3)}{(x + 3)(x - 2)}$

$\qquad\qquad = \dfrac{-1}{x - 2}$

$\qquad\qquad = \dfrac{1}{2 - x}$

9. $P = 4 \cdot s = 4\left(\dfrac{x}{x + 5}\right) = \dfrac{4x}{x + 5}$ feet

$\quad A = s^2 = \left(\dfrac{x}{x + 5}\right)^2$

$\qquad = \dfrac{x^2}{(x + 5)^2} = \dfrac{x^2}{x^2 + 10x + 25}$ sq. feet

11. $7 = 7$

$\quad 5x = 5 \cdot x$

$\quad \text{LCD} = 7 \cdot 5 \cdot x = 35x$

13. $x = x$

$x + 1 = x + 1$

$\text{LCD} = x(x+1)$

15. $x + 7 = x + 7$

$x - 7 = x - 7$

$\text{LCD} = (x+7)(x-7)$

17. $3x + 6 = 3(x+2)$

$2x - 4 = 2(x-2)$

$\text{LCD} = 2 \cdot 3 \cdot (x+2)(x-2)$

$\qquad = 6(x+2)(x-2)$

19. $(3x-1)(x+2) = (3x-1) \cdot (x+2)$

$3x - 1 = 3x - 1$

$\text{LCD} = (3x-1)(x+2)$

21. $a^2 - b^2 = (a+b)(a-b)$

$a^2 - 2ab + b^2 = (a-b)^2$

$\text{LCD} = (a+b)(a-b)^2$

23. $x^2 - 9 = (x+3)(x-3)$

$x = x$

$12 - 4x = 4(3-x) = -4(x-3)$

$\text{LCD} = -4x(x+3)(x-3)$

25. Answers may vary. The LCD will be the product of the denominators when the denominators have no common factors.

27. $\dfrac{4}{3x} + \dfrac{3}{2x} = \dfrac{4 \cdot 2}{3x \cdot 2} + \dfrac{3 \cdot 3}{2x \cdot 3} = \dfrac{8+9}{6x} = \dfrac{17}{6x}$

29. $\dfrac{5}{2y^2} - \dfrac{2}{7y} = \dfrac{5 \cdot 7}{2y^2 \cdot 7} - \dfrac{2 \cdot 2y}{7y \cdot 2y} = \dfrac{35 - 4y}{14y^2}$

31. $\dfrac{x-3}{x+4} - \dfrac{x+2}{x-4}$

$= \dfrac{(x-3)(x-4)}{(x+4)(x-4)} - \dfrac{(x+2)(x+4)}{(x-4)(x+4)}$

$= \dfrac{(x^2 - 7x + 12) - (x^2 + 6x + 8)}{(x+4)(x-4)}$

$= \dfrac{-13x + 4}{(x+4)(x-4)}$

33. $\dfrac{1}{x-5} + \dfrac{x}{x^2 - x - 20}$

$= \dfrac{1}{x-5} + \dfrac{x}{(x-5)(x+4)}$

$= \dfrac{1(x+4)}{(x-5)(x+4)} + \dfrac{x}{(x-5)(x+4)}$

$= \dfrac{x+4+x}{(x-5)(x+4)}$

$= \dfrac{2x+4}{(x-5)(x+4)}$

35. $\dfrac{1}{a-b} + \dfrac{1}{b-a} = \dfrac{1}{a-b} + \dfrac{1}{-(a-b)}$

$= \dfrac{1}{a-b} - \dfrac{1}{a-b}$

$= 0$

37. $\dfrac{x+1}{1-x} + \dfrac{1}{x-1} = \dfrac{x+1}{-(x-1)} + \dfrac{1}{x-1}$

$= \dfrac{-(x+1)+1}{x-1}$

$= \dfrac{-x}{x-1}$

$= -\dfrac{x}{x-1}$

39. $\dfrac{5}{x-2} + \dfrac{x+4}{2-x} = \dfrac{5}{x-2} + \dfrac{x+4}{-(x-2)}$

$= \dfrac{5}{x-2} - \dfrac{x+4}{x-2}$

$= \dfrac{5 - (x+4)}{x-2}$

$= \dfrac{5 - x - 4}{x-2}$

$= \dfrac{-x+1}{x-2}$

41. $\dfrac{y+1}{y^2-6y+8}-\dfrac{3}{y^2-16}$

$=\dfrac{y+1}{(y-4)(y-2)}-\dfrac{3}{(y+4)(y-4)}$

$=\dfrac{(y+1)(y+4)}{(y-4)(y-2)(y+4)}-\dfrac{3(y-2)}{(y+4)(y-4)(y-2)}$

$=\dfrac{(y^2+5y+4)-(3y-6)}{(y-4)(y+4)(y-2)}$

$=\dfrac{y^2+5y+4-3y+6}{(y-4)(y+4)(y-2)}$

$=\dfrac{y^2+2y+10}{(y-4)(y+4)(y-2)}$

43. $\dfrac{x+4}{3x^2+11x+6}+\dfrac{x}{2x^2+x-15}$

$=\dfrac{x+4}{(3x+2)(x+3)}+\dfrac{x}{(2x-5)(x+3)}$

$=\dfrac{(x+4)(2x-5)}{(3x+2)(x+3)(2x-5)}$

$\qquad+\dfrac{x(3x+2)}{(2x-5)(x+3)(3x+2)}$

$=\dfrac{2x^2+3x-20+(3x^2+2x)}{(3x+2)(x+3)(2x-5)}$

$=\dfrac{5x^2+5x-20}{(3x+2)(x+3)(2x-5)}$

$=\dfrac{5(x^2+x-4)}{(3x+2)(x+3)(2x-5)}$

45. $\dfrac{7}{x^2-x-2}+\dfrac{x}{x^2+4x+3}$

$=\dfrac{7}{(x-2)(x+1)}+\dfrac{x}{(x+3)(x+1)}$

$=\dfrac{7(x+3)+x(x-2)}{(x-2)(x+1)(x+3)}$

$=\dfrac{7x+21+x^2-2x}{(x-2)(x+1)(x+3)}$

$=\dfrac{x^2+5x+21}{(x-2)(x+1)(x+3)}$

47. $\dfrac{2}{x+1}-\dfrac{3x}{3x+3}+\dfrac{1}{2x+2}$

$=\dfrac{2}{x+1}-\dfrac{3x}{3(x+1)}+\dfrac{1}{2(x+1)}$

$=\dfrac{2}{x+1}-\dfrac{x}{x+1}+\dfrac{1}{2(x+1)}$

$=\dfrac{2\cdot2}{(x+1)\cdot2}-\dfrac{x\cdot2}{(x+1)\cdot2}+\dfrac{1}{2(x+1)}$

$=\dfrac{4-2x+1}{2(x+1)}$

$=\dfrac{-2x+5}{2(x+1)}$

49. $\dfrac{3}{x+3}+\dfrac{5}{x^2+6x+9}-\dfrac{x}{x^2-9}$

$=\dfrac{3}{x+3}+\dfrac{5}{(x+3)^2}-\dfrac{x}{(x+3)(x-3)}$

$=\dfrac{3(x+3)(x-3)}{(x+3)^2(x-3)}+\dfrac{5(x-3)}{(x+3)^2(x-3)}$

$\qquad-\dfrac{x(x+3)}{(x+3)^2(x-3)}$

$=\dfrac{3(x^2-9)+5x-15-(x^2+3x)}{(x+3)^2(x-3)}$

$=\dfrac{3x^2-27+5x-15-x^2-3x}{(x+3)^2(x-3)}$

$=\dfrac{2x^2+2x-42}{(x+3)^2(x-3)}$

$=\dfrac{2(x^2+x-21)}{(x+3)^2(x-3)}$

51. $\dfrac{4}{3x^2y^3}+\dfrac{5}{3x^2y^3}=\dfrac{4+5}{3x^2y^3}=\dfrac{9}{3x^2y^3}=\dfrac{3}{x^2y^3}$

53. $\dfrac{x-5}{2x}-\dfrac{x+5}{2x}=\dfrac{x-5-(x+5)}{2x}$

$=\dfrac{x-5-x-5}{2x}$

$=\dfrac{-10}{2x}$

$=-\dfrac{5}{x}$

55. $\dfrac{3}{2x+10}+\dfrac{8}{3x+15}$

$=\dfrac{3}{2(x+5)}+\dfrac{8}{3(x+5)}$

$=\dfrac{3\cdot 3}{2(x+5)\cdot 3}+\dfrac{8\cdot 2}{3(x+5)\cdot 2}$

$=\dfrac{9+16}{6(x+5)}$

$=\dfrac{25}{6(x+5)}$

57. $\dfrac{-2}{x^2-3x}-\dfrac{1}{x^3-3x^2}$

$=\dfrac{-2}{x(x-3)}-\dfrac{1}{x^2(x-3)}$

$=\dfrac{-2\cdot x}{x(x-3)\cdot x}-\dfrac{1}{x^2(x-3)}$

$=\dfrac{-2x-1}{x^2(x-3)}$

59. $\dfrac{ab}{a^2-b^2}+\dfrac{b}{a+b}$

$=\dfrac{ab}{(a+b)(a-b)}+\dfrac{b}{a+b}$

$=\dfrac{ab}{(a+b)(a-b)}+\dfrac{b(a-b)}{(a+b)(a-b)}$

$=\dfrac{ab+ba-b^2}{(a+b)(a-b)}$

$=\dfrac{2ab-b^2}{(a+b)(a-b)}$

61. $\dfrac{5}{x^2-4}-\dfrac{3}{x^2+4x+4}$

$=\dfrac{5}{(x+2)(x-2)}-\dfrac{3}{(x+2)^2}$

$=\dfrac{5(x+2)}{(x+2)^2(x-2)}-\dfrac{3(x-2)}{(x+2)^2(x-2)}$

$=\dfrac{5x+10-3x+6}{(x+2)^2(x-2)}$

$=\dfrac{2x+16}{(x+2)^2(x-2)}$

63. $\dfrac{2}{a^2+2a+1}+\dfrac{3}{a^2-1}$

$=\dfrac{2}{(a+1)^2}+\dfrac{3}{(a+1)(a-1)}$

$=\dfrac{2(a-1)}{(a+1)^2(a-1)}+\dfrac{3(a+1)}{(a+1)^2(a-1)}$

$=\dfrac{2a-2+3a+3}{(a+1)^2(a-1)}$

$=\dfrac{5a+1}{(a+1)^2(a-1)}$

65. Answers may vary. First determine the LCD. Then write equivalent rational expressions that have the LCD as their denominator. Add the numerators and keep the LCD as the denominator.

67. Answers may vary. Take the reciprocal of the divisor (i.e. invert it) and change the division to multiplication. Then multiply the expressions.

69. $\left(\dfrac{2}{3}-\dfrac{1}{x}\right)\cdot\left(\dfrac{3}{x}+\dfrac{1}{2}\right)=\left(\dfrac{2x}{3x}-\dfrac{3}{3x}\right)\cdot\left(\dfrac{6}{2x}+\dfrac{x}{2x}\right)$

$=\dfrac{2x-3}{3x}\cdot\dfrac{x+6}{2x}$

$=\dfrac{2x^2+9x-18}{6x^2}$

71. $\left(\dfrac{1}{x}+\dfrac{2}{3}\right)-\left(\dfrac{1}{x}-\dfrac{2}{3}\right)=\dfrac{1}{x}+\dfrac{2}{3}-\dfrac{1}{x}+\dfrac{2}{3}=\dfrac{4}{3}$

73. $\left(\dfrac{2a}{3}\right)^2\div\left(\dfrac{a^2}{a+1}-\dfrac{1}{a+1}\right)=\dfrac{4a^2}{9}\div\dfrac{a^2-1}{a+1}$

$=\dfrac{4a^2}{9}\cdot\dfrac{a+1}{(a+1)(a-1)}$

$=\dfrac{4a^2}{9(a-1)}$

75. $\left(\dfrac{2x}{3}\right)^2\div\left(\dfrac{x}{3}\right)^2=\dfrac{4x^2}{9}\div\dfrac{x^2}{9}=\dfrac{4x^2}{9}\cdot\dfrac{9}{x^2}=4$

77. $\dfrac{x}{x^2-9}+\dfrac{3}{x^2-6x+9}-\dfrac{1}{x+3}$

$=\dfrac{x}{(x+3)(x-3)}+\dfrac{3}{(x-3)^2}-\dfrac{1}{x+3}$

$=\dfrac{x(x-3)+3(x+3)-1(x-3)^2}{(x+3)(x-3)^2}$

$=\dfrac{x^2-3x+3x+9-(x^2-6x+9)}{(x+3)(x-3)^2}$

$=\dfrac{6x}{(x+3)(x-3)^2}$

79. $\left(\dfrac{x}{x+1}-\dfrac{x}{x-1}\right)\div\dfrac{x}{2x+2}$

$=\dfrac{x(x-1)-x(x+1)}{(x+1)(x-1)}\cdot\dfrac{2(x+1)}{x}$

$=\dfrac{x^2-x-x^2-x}{x-1}\cdot\dfrac{2}{x}$

$=\dfrac{-2x}{x-1}\cdot\dfrac{2}{x}$

$=-\dfrac{4}{x-1}$

81. $\dfrac{4}{x}\cdot\left(\dfrac{2}{x+2}-\dfrac{2}{x-2}\right)=\dfrac{4}{x}\cdot\dfrac{2(x-2)-2(x+2)}{(x+2)(x-2)}$

$=\dfrac{4}{x}\cdot\dfrac{2x-4-2x-4}{(x+2)(x-2)}$

$=\dfrac{4}{x}\cdot\dfrac{-8}{(x+2)(x-2)}$

$=-\dfrac{32}{x(x+2)(x-2)}$

83. $12\left(\dfrac{2}{3}+\dfrac{1}{6}\right)=\dfrac{24}{3}+\dfrac{12}{6}=8+2=10$

85. $x^2\left(\dfrac{4}{x^2}+1\right)=x^2\cdot\dfrac{4}{x^2}+x^2\cdot1=4+x^2$

87. $\sqrt{100}=10$

89. $\sqrt[3]{8}=2$

91. $\sqrt[4]{81}=3$

93. $a^2+b^2=c^2$

$3^2+4^2=c^2$

$9+16=c^2$

$25=c^2$

$c=5$ meters

95. $x^{-1}+(2x)^{-1}=\dfrac{1}{x}+\dfrac{1}{2x}=\dfrac{2}{2x}+\dfrac{1}{2x}=\dfrac{3}{2x}$

97. $4x^{-2}-3x^{-1}=\dfrac{4}{x^2}-\dfrac{3}{x}=\dfrac{4}{x^2}-\dfrac{3x}{x^2}=\dfrac{4-3x}{x^2}$

99. $x^{-3}(2x+1)-5x^{-2}=\dfrac{2x+1}{x^3}-\dfrac{5}{x^2}$

$=\dfrac{2x+1}{x^3}-\dfrac{5x}{x^3}$

$=\dfrac{2x+1-5x}{x^3}$

$=\dfrac{1-3x}{x^3}$

101. $\dfrac{2}{x-2}+\dfrac{x}{x-2}=\dfrac{x+2}{x-2}$

Let $y_1=\dfrac{2}{x-2}+\dfrac{x}{x-2}$ and $y_2=\dfrac{x+2}{x-2}$.

Graph both equations and trace to see that the graphs coincide.

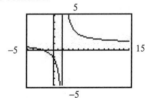

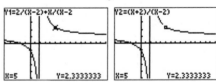

103. $\dfrac{x-3}{x+4}-\dfrac{x+2}{x-4}=\dfrac{-13x+4}{(x+4)(x-4)}$

Let $y_1=\dfrac{x-3}{x+4}-\dfrac{x+2}{x-4}$ and $y_2=\dfrac{-13x+4}{(x+4)(x-4)}$.

Graph both equations using a standard viewing window and trace to see that the graphs coincide.

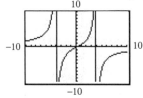

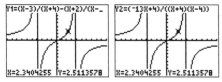

Exercise Set 6.3

1. $\dfrac{\dfrac{10}{3x}}{\dfrac{5}{6x}}=\dfrac{10}{3x}\cdot\dfrac{6x}{5}=\dfrac{2}{1}\cdot\dfrac{2}{1}=4$

3. $\dfrac{1+\dfrac{2}{5}}{2+\dfrac{3}{5}}=\dfrac{\left(1+\dfrac{2}{5}\right)5}{\left(2+\dfrac{3}{5}\right)5}=\dfrac{5+2}{10+3}=\dfrac{7}{13}$

5. $\dfrac{\dfrac{4}{x-1}}{\dfrac{x}{x-1}}=\dfrac{4}{x-1}\cdot\dfrac{x-1}{x}=\dfrac{4}{x}$

7. $\dfrac{1-\dfrac{2}{x}}{x+\dfrac{4}{9x}}=\dfrac{\left(1-\dfrac{2}{x}\right)9x}{\left(x+\dfrac{4}{9x}\right)9x}=\dfrac{9x-18}{9x^2+4}=\dfrac{9(x-2)}{9x^2+4}$

9. $\dfrac{\dfrac{4x^2-y^2}{xy}}{\dfrac{2}{y}-\dfrac{1}{x}}=\dfrac{\left(\dfrac{4x^2-y^2}{xy}\right)xy}{\left(\dfrac{2}{y}-\dfrac{1}{x}\right)xy}$

$=\dfrac{4x^2-y^2}{2x-y}$

$=\dfrac{(2x+y)(2x-y)}{2x-y}$

$=2x+y$

11. $\dfrac{\dfrac{x+1}{3}}{\dfrac{2x-1}{6}}=\dfrac{x+1}{3}\cdot\dfrac{6}{2x-1}$

$=\dfrac{x+1}{1}\cdot\dfrac{2}{2x-1}$

$=\dfrac{2(x+1)}{2x-1}$

13. $\dfrac{\dfrac{2}{x}+\dfrac{3}{x^2}}{\dfrac{4}{x^2}-\dfrac{9}{x}}=\dfrac{\left(\dfrac{2}{x}+\dfrac{3}{x^2}\right)x^2}{\left(\dfrac{4}{x^2}-\dfrac{9}{x}\right)x^2}=\dfrac{2x+3}{4-9x}$

15. $\dfrac{\dfrac{1}{x}+\dfrac{2}{x^2}}{x+\dfrac{8}{x^2}}=\dfrac{\left(\dfrac{1}{x}+\dfrac{2}{x^2}\right)x^2}{\left(x+\dfrac{8}{x^2}\right)x^2}$

$=\dfrac{x+2}{x^3+8}$

$=\dfrac{x+2}{(x+2)(x^2-2x+4)}$

$=\dfrac{1}{x^2-2x+4}$

17. $\dfrac{\dfrac{4}{5-x}+\dfrac{5}{x-5}}{\dfrac{2}{x}+\dfrac{3}{x-5}}=\dfrac{\dfrac{-4}{x-5}+\dfrac{5}{x-5}}{\dfrac{2(x-5)+3x}{x(x-5)}}$

$=\dfrac{\dfrac{1}{x-5}}{\dfrac{2x-10+3x}{x(x-5)}}$

$=\dfrac{1}{x-5}\cdot\dfrac{x(x-5)}{5x-10}$

$=\dfrac{x}{5x-10}$

19.
$$\frac{\frac{x+2}{x}-\frac{2}{x-1}}{\frac{x+1}{x}+\frac{x+1}{x-1}}=\frac{\left(\frac{x+2}{x}-\frac{2}{x-1}\right)x(x-1)}{\left(\frac{x+1}{x}+\frac{x+1}{x-1}\right)x(x-1)}$$

$$=\frac{(x+2)(x-1)-2x}{(x+1)(x-1)+x(x+1)}$$

$$=\frac{x^2+x-2-2x}{x^2-1+x^2+x}$$

$$=\frac{x^2-x-2}{2x^2+x-1}$$

$$=\frac{(x-2)(x+1)}{(2x-1)(x+1)}=\frac{x-2}{2x-1}$$

21.
$$\frac{\frac{2}{x}+3}{\frac{4}{x^2}-9}=\frac{\left(\frac{2}{x}+3\right)x^2}{\left(\frac{4}{x^2}-9\right)x^2}$$

$$=\frac{2x+3x^2}{4-9x^2}$$

$$=\frac{x(2+3x)}{(2+3x)(2-3x)}$$

$$=\frac{x}{2-3x}$$

23.
$$\frac{1-\frac{x}{y}}{\frac{x^2}{y^2}-1}=\frac{\left(1-\frac{x}{y}\right)y^2}{\left(\frac{x^2}{y^2}-1\right)y^2}$$

$$=\frac{y^2-xy}{x^2-y^2}$$

$$=\frac{y(y-x)}{(x+y)(x-y)}$$

$$=\frac{-y(x-y)}{(x+y)(x-y)}=-\frac{y}{x+y}$$

25.
$$\frac{\frac{-2x}{x-y}}{\frac{y}{x^2}}=\frac{-2x}{x-y}\cdot\frac{x^2}{y}=-\frac{2x^3}{y(x-y)}$$

27.
$$\frac{\frac{2}{x}+\frac{1}{x^2}}{\frac{y}{x^2}}=\frac{\left(\frac{2}{x}+\frac{1}{x^2}\right)x^2}{\left(\frac{y}{x^2}\right)x^2}=\frac{2x+1}{y}$$

29.
$$\frac{\frac{x}{9}-\frac{1}{x}}{1+\frac{3}{x}}=\frac{\left(\frac{x}{9}-\frac{1}{x}\right)9x}{\left(1+\frac{3}{x}\right)9x}$$

$$=\frac{x^2-9}{9x+27}$$

$$=\frac{(x+3)(x-3)}{9(x+3)}$$

$$=\frac{x-3}{9}$$

31.
$$\frac{\frac{x-1}{x^2-4}}{1+\frac{1}{x-2}}=\frac{\frac{x-1}{x^2-4}}{\frac{(x-2)+1}{x-2}}$$

$$=\frac{x-1}{(x+2)(x-2)}\cdot\frac{x-2}{x-1}$$

$$=\frac{1}{x+2}$$

33.
$$\frac{x^{-1}}{x^{-2}+y^{-2}}=\frac{\left(\frac{1}{x}\right)x^2y^2}{\left(\frac{1}{x^2}+\frac{1}{y^2}\right)x^2y^2}=\frac{xy^2}{x^2+y^2}$$

35.
$$\frac{2a^{-1}+3b^{-2}}{a^{-1}-b^{-1}}=\frac{\left(\frac{2}{a}+\frac{3}{b^2}\right)ab^2}{\left(\frac{1}{a}-\frac{1}{b}\right)ab^2}$$

$$=\frac{2b^2+3a}{b^2-ab}$$

$$=\frac{2b^2+3a}{b(b-a)}$$

37.
$$\frac{1}{x-x^{-1}}=\frac{1\cdot x}{\left(x-\frac{1}{x}\right)x}$$

$$=\frac{x}{x^2-1}$$

$$=\frac{x}{(x+1)(x-1)}$$

39.
$$\frac{a^{-1}+1}{a^{-1}-1}=\frac{\left(\frac{1}{a}+1\right)a}{\left(\frac{1}{a}-1\right)a}=\frac{1+a}{1-a}$$

41. $\dfrac{3x^{-1}+(2y)^{-1}}{x^{-2}} = \dfrac{\left(\frac{3}{x}+\frac{1}{2y}\right)2x^2y}{\left(\frac{1}{x^2}\right)2x^2y}$

$= \dfrac{6xy+x^2}{2y}$

$= \dfrac{x(6y+x)}{2y}$ or $\dfrac{x(x+6y)}{2y}$

43. $\dfrac{2a^{-1}+(2a)^{-1}}{a^{-1}+2a^{-2}} = \dfrac{\left(\frac{2}{a}+\frac{1}{2a}\right)2a^2}{\left(\frac{1}{a}+\frac{2}{a^2}\right)2a^2}$

$= \dfrac{4a+a}{2a+4}$

$= \dfrac{5a}{2a+4}$

45. $\dfrac{5x^{-1}+2y^{-1}}{x^{-2}y^{-2}} = \dfrac{\frac{5}{x}+\frac{2}{y}}{\frac{1}{x^2y^2}}$

$= \dfrac{\frac{5y+2x}{xy}}{\frac{1}{x^2y^2}}$

$= \dfrac{5y+2x}{xy}\cdot\dfrac{x^2y^2}{1}$

$= xy(5y+2x)$ or $5xy^2+2x^2y$

47. $\dfrac{5x^{-1}-2y^{-1}}{25x^{-2}-4y^{-2}} = \dfrac{\left(\frac{5}{x}-\frac{2}{y}\right)x^2y^2}{\left(\frac{25}{x^2}-\frac{4}{y^2}\right)x^2y^2}$

$= \dfrac{5xy^2-2x^2y}{25y^2-4x^2}$

$= \dfrac{xy(5y-2x)}{(5y+2x)(5y-2x)}$

$= \dfrac{xy}{2x+5y}$

49. $\dfrac{3x^3y^2}{12x} = \dfrac{x^{3-1}y^2}{4} = \dfrac{x^2y^2}{4}$

51. $\dfrac{144x^5y^5}{-16x^2y} = -9x^{5-2}y^{5-1} = -9x^3y^4$

53. $|x-5| = 9$

$x-5 = 9$ or $x-5 = -9$

$x = 14$ or $x = -4$

The solutions are –4, 14.

55. $\dfrac{a}{1-\frac{s}{770}} = \dfrac{a}{\frac{770}{770}-\frac{s}{770}}$

$= \dfrac{a}{\frac{770-s}{770}}$

$= a\cdot\dfrac{770}{770-s}$

$= \dfrac{770a}{770-s}$

57. $\dfrac{\frac{1}{x}}{\frac{3}{y}}$; a and b

59. $\dfrac{1}{1+(1+x)^{-1}} = \dfrac{1(1+x)}{\left(1+\frac{1}{1+x}\right)(1+x)}$

$= \dfrac{1+x}{(1+x)+1}$

$= \dfrac{1+x}{2+x}$

61. $\dfrac{x}{1-\frac{1}{1+\frac{1}{x}}} = \dfrac{x}{1-\frac{1}{\left(\frac{x+1}{x}\right)}} = \dfrac{x}{1-\frac{x}{x+1}}$

$= \dfrac{x(x+1)}{\left(1-\frac{x}{x+1}\right)(x+1)}$

$= \dfrac{x(x+1)}{x+1-x}$

$= x(x+1) = x^2+x$

63.
$$\frac{\frac{2}{y^2}-\frac{5}{xy}-\frac{3}{x^2}}{\frac{2}{y^2}+\frac{7}{xy}+\frac{3}{x^2}}=\frac{\left(\frac{2}{y^2}-\frac{5}{xy}-\frac{3}{x^2}\right)x^2y^2}{\left(\frac{2}{y^2}+\frac{7}{xy}+\frac{3}{x^2}\right)x^2y^2}$$
$$=\frac{2x^2-5xy-3y^2}{2x^2+7xy+3y^2}$$
$$=\frac{(2x+y)(x-3y)}{(2x+y)(x+3y)}$$
$$=\frac{x-3y}{x+3y}$$

65.
$$\frac{3(a+1)^{-1}+4a^{-2}}{(a^3+a^2)^{-1}}=\frac{\frac{3}{a+1}+\frac{4}{a^2}}{\frac{1}{a^3+a^2}}$$
$$=\frac{\frac{3a^2+4(a+1)}{a^2(a+1)}}{\frac{1}{a^2(a+1)}}$$
$$=\frac{3a^2+4a+4}{1}$$
$$=3a^2+4a+4$$

67. $f(x)=\frac{1}{x}$

   a. $f(a+h)=\frac{1}{a+h}$

   b. $f(a)=\frac{1}{a}$

   c. $\frac{f(a+h)-f(a)}{h}=\frac{\frac{1}{a+h}-\frac{1}{a}}{h}$

   d. $\frac{f(a+h)-f(a)}{h}=\frac{\left(\frac{1}{a+h}-\frac{1}{a}\right)a(a+h)}{h\cdot a(a+h)}$
$$=\frac{a-(a+h)}{ha(a+h)}$$
$$=\frac{-h}{ha(a+h)}$$
$$=\frac{-1}{a(a+h)}$$

69. $f(x)=\frac{3}{x+1}$

   a. $f(a+h)=\frac{3}{a+h+1}$

   b. $f(a)=\frac{3}{a+1}$

   c. $\frac{f(a+h)-f(a)}{h}=\frac{\frac{3}{a+h+1}-\frac{3}{a+1}}{h}$

   d. $\frac{f(a+h)-f(a)}{h}$
$$=\frac{\left(\frac{3}{a+h+1}-\frac{3}{a+1}\right)(a+h+1)(a+1)}{h\cdot(a+h+1)(a+1)}$$
$$=\frac{3(a+1)-3(a+h+1)}{h(a+h+1)(a+1)}$$
$$=\frac{3a+3-3a-3h-3}{h(a+h+1)(a+1)}$$
$$=\frac{-3h}{h(a+h+1)(a+1)}$$
$$=\frac{-3}{(a+h+1)(a+1)}$$

Exercise Set 6.4

1. $\frac{4a^2+8a}{2a}=\frac{4a^2}{2a}+\frac{8a}{2a}=2a+4$

3. $\frac{12a^5b^2+16a^4b}{4a^4b}=\frac{12a^5b^2}{4a^4b}+\frac{16a^4b}{4a^4b}$
$$=3ab+4$$

5. $\frac{4x^2y^2+6xy^2-4y^2}{2x^2y}$
$$=\frac{4x^2y^2}{2x^2y}+\frac{6xy^2}{2x^2y}-\frac{4y^2}{2x^2y}$$
$$=2y+\frac{3y}{x}-\frac{2y}{x^2}$$

7. $\frac{4x^2+8x+4}{4}=\frac{4x^2}{4}+\frac{8x}{4}+\frac{4}{4}$
$$=x^2+2x+1$$

9. $\dfrac{3x^4+6x^2-18}{3}=\dfrac{3x^4}{3}+\dfrac{6x^2}{3}-\dfrac{18}{3}$

$\qquad\qquad = (x^4+2x^2-6)$ meters

11.

$$\begin{array}{r} x+1 \\ x+2\overline{)x^2+3x+2} \\ \underline{x^2+2x} \\ x+2 \\ \underline{x+2} \\ 0 \end{array}$$

Answer: $x+1$

13.

$$\begin{array}{r} 2x-8 \\ x+1\overline{)2x^2-6x-7} \\ \underline{2x^2+2x} \\ -8x-7 \\ \underline{-8x-8} \\ 1 \end{array}$$

Answer: $2x-8+\dfrac{1}{x+1}$

15.

$$\begin{array}{r} x-\frac{1}{2} \\ 2x+4\overline{)2x^2+3x-2} \\ \underline{2x^2+4x} \\ -x-2 \\ \underline{-x-2} \\ 0 \end{array}$$

Answer: $x-\dfrac{1}{2}$

17.

$$\begin{array}{r} 2x^2-\frac{1}{2}x+5 \\ 2x+4\overline{)4x^3+7x^2+8x+20} \\ \underline{4x^3+8x^2} \\ -x^2+8x \\ \underline{-x^2-2x} \\ 10x+20 \\ \underline{10x+20} \\ 0 \end{array}$$

Answer: $2x^2-\dfrac{1}{2}x+5$

19. $A=l\cdot w$ so $w=\dfrac{A}{l}=\dfrac{15x^2-29x-14}{5x+2}$.

$$\begin{array}{r} 3x-7 \\ 5x+2\overline{)15x^2-29x-14} \\ \underline{15x^2+6x} \\ -35x-14 \\ \underline{-35x-14} \\ 0 \end{array}$$

The width is $(3x-7)$ in.

21. $\dfrac{25a^2b^{12}}{10a^5b^7}=\dfrac{5a^{2-5}b^{12-7}}{2}=\dfrac{5a^{-3}b^5}{2}=\dfrac{5b^5}{2a^3}$

23. $\dfrac{x^6y^6-x^3y^3}{x^3y^3}=\dfrac{x^6y^6}{x^3y^3}-\dfrac{x^3y^3}{x^3y^3}=x^3y^3-1$

25.

$$\begin{array}{r} a+3 \\ a+1\overline{)a^2+4a+3} \\ \underline{a^2+a} \\ 3a+3 \\ \underline{3a+3} \\ 0 \end{array}$$

Answer: $a+3$

27.

$$\begin{array}{r} 2x+5 \\ x-2\overline{)2x^2+x-10} \\ \underline{2x^2-4x} \\ 5x-10 \\ \underline{5x-10} \\ 0 \end{array}$$

Answer: $2x+5$

29. $\dfrac{-16y^3+24y^4}{-4y^2}=\dfrac{-16y^3}{-4y^2}+\dfrac{24y^4}{-4y^2}$

$\qquad\qquad = 4y-6y^2$

31.

$$\begin{array}{r} 2x+23 \\ x-5\overline{)2x^2+13x+15} \\ \underline{2x^2-10x} \\ 23x+15 \\ \underline{23x-115} \\ 130 \end{array}$$

Answer: $2x+23+\dfrac{130}{x-5}$

33. $\dfrac{20x^2y^3 + 6xy^4 - 12x^3y^5}{2xy^3}$

$= \dfrac{20x^2y^3}{2xy^3} + \dfrac{6xy^4}{2xy^3} - \dfrac{12x^3y^5}{2xy^3}$

$= 10x + 3y - 6x^2y^2$

35.

$$2x+4$$
$$3x+2\overline{\smash{\big)}\,6x^2+16x+8}$$
$$\underline{6x^2+\ 4x}$$
$$12x+8$$
$$\underline{12x+8}$$
$$0$$

Answer: $2x+4$

37.

$$y+5$$
$$2y-3\overline{\smash{\big)}\,2y^2+7y-15}$$
$$\underline{2y^2-3y}$$
$$10y-15$$
$$\underline{10y-15}$$
$$0$$

Answer: $y+5$

39.

$$2x+3$$
$$2x-3\overline{\smash{\big)}\,4x^2+0x-9}$$
$$\underline{4x^2-6x}$$
$$6x-9$$
$$\underline{6x-9}$$
$$0$$

Answer: $2x+3$

41.

$$2x^2-8x+38$$
$$x+4\overline{\smash{\big)}\,2x^3+0x^2+6x\ -4}$$
$$\underline{2x^3+8x^2}$$
$$-8x^2+\ 6x$$
$$\underline{-8x^2-32x}$$
$$38x-\ 4$$
$$\underline{38x+152}$$
$$-156$$

Answer: $2x^2-8x+38-\dfrac{156}{x+4}$

43.

$$3x+3$$
$$x-1\overline{\smash{\big)}\,3x^2+0x-4}$$
$$\underline{3x^2-3x}$$
$$3x-4$$
$$\underline{3x-3}$$
$$-1$$

Answer: $3x+3-\dfrac{1}{x-1}$

45.

$$-2x^3+3x^2-x+4$$
$$-x+5\overline{\smash{\big)}\,2x^4-13x^3+16x^2-9x+20}$$
$$\underline{2x^4-10x^3}$$
$$-3x^3+16x^2$$
$$\underline{-3x^3+15x^2}$$
$$x^2-9x$$
$$\underline{x^2-5x}$$
$$-4x+20$$
$$\underline{-4x+20}$$
$$0$$

Answer: $-2x^3+3x^2-x+4$

47.

$$3x^3\qquad\ +5x+4$$
$$x^2-2\overline{\smash{\big)}\,3x^5+0x^4-x^3+4x^2-12x-8}$$
$$\underline{3x^5\qquad-6x^3}$$
$$5x^3+4x^2-12x$$
$$\underline{5x^3+0x^2-10x}$$
$$4x^2-2x-8$$
$$\underline{4x^2+0x-8}$$
$$-2x$$

Answer: $3x^3+5x+4-\dfrac{2x}{x^2-2}$

49. $\dfrac{3x^3-5}{3x^2} = \dfrac{3x^3}{3x^2} - \dfrac{5}{3x^2} = x - \dfrac{5}{3x^2}$

51. $3^2 = (-3)^2$

53. $-2^3 = (-2)^3$

55. $|x+5| < 4$

$-4 < x+5 < 4$

$-9 < x < -1$

$(-9, -1)$

57. $|2x+7| \geq 9$

$2x+7 \leq -9$ or $2x+7 \geq 9$

$2x \leq -16$ or $2x \geq 2$

$x \leq -8$ or $x \geq 1$

$(-\infty, -8] \cup [1, \infty)$

59. $P(x) = 3x^3 + 2x^2 - 4x + 3$

$P(1) = 3(1)^3 + 2(1)^2 - 4(1) + 3$

$ = 3 + 2 - 4 + 3$

$ = 4$

$$\begin{array}{r} 3x^2 + 5x + 1 \\ x-1\overline{\smash{\big)}\,3x^3 + 2x^2 - 4x + 3} \\ \underline{3x^3 - 3x^2} \\ 5x^2 - 4x \\ \underline{5x^2 - 5x} \\ x + 3 \\ \underline{x - 1} \\ 4 \end{array}$$

Remainder: 4

61. $P(x) = 5x^4 - 2x^2 + 3x - 6$

$P(-3) = 5(-3)^4 - 2(-3)^2 + 3(-3) - 6$

$ = 5(81) - 2(9) - 9 - 6$

$ = 405 - 18 - 9 - 6$

$ = 372$

$$\begin{array}{r} 5x^3 - 15x^2 + 43x - 126 \\ x+3\overline{\smash{\big)}\,5x^4 + 0x^3 - 2x^2 + 3x - 6} \\ \underline{5x^4 + 15x^3} \\ -15x^3 - 2x^2 \\ \underline{-15x^3 - 45x^2} \\ 43x^2 + 3x \\ \underline{43x^2 + 129x} \\ -126x - 6 \\ \underline{-126x - 378} \\ 372 \end{array}$$

Remainder: 372

63. Answers may vary. The remainder when dividing by the linear factor $(x-c)$ is the same as the result when we evaluate the function at $x = c$. **Note:** $(x+3) = (x-(-3))$ so $c = -3$.

65.

$$\begin{array}{r} x^3 + \frac{5}{3}x^2 + \frac{5}{3}x + \frac{8}{3} \\ x-1\overline{\smash{\big)}\,x^4 + \frac{2}{3}x^3 + 0x^2 + x + 0} \\ \underline{x^4 - x^3} \\ \frac{5}{3}x^3 - 0x^2 \\ \underline{\frac{5}{3}x^3 - \frac{5}{3}x^2} \\ \frac{5}{3}x^2 + x \\ \underline{\frac{5}{3}x^2 - \frac{5}{3}x} \\ \frac{8}{3}x + 0 \\ \underline{\frac{8}{3}x - \frac{8}{3}} \\ \frac{8}{3} \end{array}$$

Answer: $x^3 + \frac{5}{3}x^2 + \frac{5}{3}x + \frac{8}{3} + \frac{8}{3(x-1)}$

67.

$$\begin{array}{r} \frac{3}{2}x^3 + \frac{1}{4}x^2 + \frac{1}{8}x - \frac{7}{16} \\ 2x-1\overline{\smash{\big)}\,3x^4 - x^3 + 0x^2 - x + \frac{1}{2}} \\ \underline{3x^4 - \frac{3}{2}x^3} \\ \frac{1}{2}x^3 + 0x^2 \\ \underline{\frac{1}{2}x^3 - \frac{1}{4}x^2} \\ \frac{1}{4}x^2 - x \\ \underline{\frac{1}{4}x^2 - \frac{1}{8}x} \\ -\frac{7}{8}x + \frac{1}{2} \\ \underline{-\frac{7}{8}x + \frac{7}{16}} \\ \frac{1}{16} \end{array}$$

Answer: $\frac{3}{2}x^3 + \frac{1}{4}x^2 + \frac{1}{8}x - \frac{7}{16} + \frac{1}{16(2x-1)}$

69.
$$\begin{array}{r} x^3 \quad\quad -\frac{2}{5}x \\ 5x+10\overline{\smash{\big)}\,5x^4+10x^3-2x^2-4x+\;\;0} \\ \underline{5x^4+10x^3} \\ -2x^2-4x \\ \underline{-2x^2-4x} \\ 0 \end{array}$$

Answer: $x^3 - \frac{2}{5}x$

71. $\dfrac{f(x)}{g(x)} = \dfrac{25x^2 - 5x + 30}{5x}$

$= \dfrac{25x^2}{5x} - \dfrac{5x}{5x} + \dfrac{30}{5x}$

$= 5x - 1 + \dfrac{6}{x}$

Setting the denominator equal to 0 we get

$5x = 0$

$x = 0.$

Thus, $x = 0$ is not in the domain of $\dfrac{f(x)}{g(x)}$.

73. $\dfrac{f(x)}{g(x)} = \dfrac{7x^4 - 3x^2 + 2}{x - 2}$

$$\begin{array}{r} 7x^3 + 14x^2 + 25x + 50 \\ x-2\overline{\smash{\big)}\,7x^4 + 0x^3 - \;\;3x^2 + \;\;0x + \;\;2} \\ \underline{7x^4 - 14x^3} \\ 14x^3 - \;\;3x^2 \\ \underline{14x^3 - 28x^2} \\ 25x^2 + \;\;0x \\ \underline{25x^2 - 50x} \\ 50x + \;\;2 \\ \underline{50x - 100} \\ 102 \end{array}$$

Therefore,

$\dfrac{f(x)}{g(x)} = \dfrac{7x^4 - 3x^2 + 2}{x - 2}$

$= 7x^3 + 14x^2 + 25x + 50 + \dfrac{102}{x - 2}$

Setting the denominator equal to 0 we get
$x - 2 = 0$, or $x = 2$.

Thus, $x = 2$ is not in the domain of $\dfrac{f(x)}{g(x)}$.

75. Answers may vary.

Exercise Set 6.5

1.
$$\begin{array}{r} 5\rfloor\;1 \quad\;\; 3 \quad -40 \\ \underline{5 \quad\;\; 40} \\ 1 \quad\;\; 8 \quad\;\; 0 \end{array}$$
$\left(x^2 + 3x - 40\right) \div \left(x - 5\right) = x + 8$

3.
$$\begin{array}{r} -6\rfloor\;1 \quad\;\; 5 \quad -6 \\ \underline{-6 \quad\;\; 6} \\ 1 \quad -1 \quad\;\; 0 \end{array}$$
$\left(x^2 + 5x - 6\right) \div \left(x + 6\right) = x - 1$

5.
$$\begin{array}{r} 2\rfloor\;1 \quad -7 \quad -13 \quad\;\; 5 \\ \underline{2 \quad -10 \quad -46} \\ 1 \quad -5 \quad -23 \quad -41 \end{array}$$
$\left(x^3 - 7x^2 - 13x + 5\right) \div \left(x - 2\right) = x^2 - 5x - 23 - \dfrac{41}{x - 2}$

7.
$$\begin{array}{r} 2\rfloor\;4 \quad\;\; 0 \quad -9 \\ \underline{8 \quad\;\; 16} \\ 4 \quad\;\; 8 \quad\;\; 7 \end{array}$$
$\left(4x^2 - 9\right) \div \left(x - 2\right) = 4x + 8 + \dfrac{7}{x - 2}$

9. a. $P(2) = 3(2)^2 - 4(2) - 1 = 12 - 8 - 1 = 3$

b.
$$\begin{array}{r} 2\rfloor\;3 \quad -4 \quad -1 \\ \underline{6 \quad\;\; 4} \\ 3 \quad\;\; 2 \quad\;\; 3 \end{array}$$
The remainder is 3 so $P(2) = 3$.

11. a. $P(-2) = 4(-2)^4 + 7(-2)^2 + 9(-2) - 1$
$= 64 + 28 - 18 - 1$
$= 73$

b.
$$\begin{array}{r} -2\rfloor\;4 \quad\;\; 0 \quad\;\; 7 \quad\;\; 9 \quad -1 \\ \underline{-8 \quad\;\; 16 \quad -46 \quad 74} \\ 4 \quad -8 \quad\;\; 23 \quad -37 \quad 73 \end{array}$$
The remainder is 73 so $P(-2) = 73$.

13. a. $P(-1) = (-1)^5 + 3(-1)^4 + 3(-1) - 7$
$= -1 + 3 - 3 - 7$
$= -8$

b.
$$\begin{array}{r|rrrrrr} -1 & 1 & 3 & 0 & 0 & 3 & -7 \\ & & -1 & -2 & 2 & -2 & -1 \\ \hline & 1 & 2 & -2 & 2 & 1 & -8 \end{array}$$
The remainder is -8 so $P(-1) = -8$.

15.
$$\begin{array}{r|rrrr} 3 & 1 & -3 & 0 & 2 \\ & & 3 & 0 & 0 \\ \hline & 1 & 0 & 0 & 2 \end{array}$$
$$\left(x^3 - 3x^2 + 2\right) \div (x - 3) = x^2 + \frac{2}{x-3}$$

17.
$$\begin{array}{r|rrr} -1 & 6 & 13 & 8 \\ & & -6 & -7 \\ \hline & 6 & 7 & 1 \end{array}$$
$$\left(6x^2 + 13x + 8\right) \div (x + 1) = 6x + 7 + \frac{1}{x+1}$$

19.
$$\begin{array}{r|rrrrr} 5 & 2 & -13 & 16 & -9 & 20 \\ & & 10 & -15 & 5 & -20 \\ \hline & 2 & -3 & 1 & -4 & 0 \end{array}$$
$$\left(2x^4 - 13x^3 + 16x^2 - 9x + 20\right) \div (x - 5)$$
$$= 2x^3 - 3x^2 + x - 4$$

21.
$$\begin{array}{r|rrr} -3 & 3 & 0 & -15 \\ & & -9 & 27 \\ \hline & 3 & -9 & 12 \end{array}$$
$$\left(3x^2 - 15\right) \div (x + 3) = 3x - 9 + \frac{12}{x+3}$$

23.
$$\begin{array}{r|rrrr} \frac{1}{2} & 3 & -6 & 4 & 5 \\ & & \frac{3}{2} & -\frac{9}{4} & \frac{7}{8} \\ \hline & 3 & -\frac{9}{2} & \frac{7}{4} & \frac{47}{8} \end{array}$$
$$\left(3x^3 - 6x^2 + 4x + 5\right) \div \left(x - \frac{1}{2}\right)$$
$$= 3x^2 - \frac{9}{2}x + \frac{7}{4} + \frac{47}{8\left(x - \frac{1}{2}\right)}$$

25.
$$\begin{array}{r|rrrr} \frac{1}{3} & 3 & 2 & -4 & 1 \\ & & 1 & 1 & -1 \\ \hline & 3 & 3 & -3 & 0 \end{array}$$
$$\left(3x^3 + 2x^2 - 4x + 1\right) \div \left(x - \frac{1}{3}\right) = 3x^2 + 3x - 3$$

27.
$$\begin{array}{r|rrrr} -1 & 3 & 7 & -4 & 12 \\ & & -3 & -4 & 8 \\ \hline & 3 & 4 & -8 & 20 \end{array}$$
$$\left(7x^2 - 4x + 12 + 3x^3\right) \div (x + 1) = 3x^2 + 4x - 8 + \frac{20}{x+1}$$

29.
$$\begin{array}{r|rrrr} 1 & 1 & 0 & 0 & -1 \\ & & 1 & 1 & 1 \\ \hline & 1 & 1 & 1 & 0 \end{array}$$
$$\left(x^3 - 1\right) \div (x - 1) = x^2 + x + 1$$

31.
$$\begin{array}{r|rrr} -6 & 1 & 0 & -36 \\ & & -6 & 36 \\ \hline & 1 & -6 & 0 \end{array}$$
$$\left(x^2 - 36\right) \div (x + 6) = x - 6$$

33.
$$\begin{array}{r|rrrr} 1 & 1 & 3 & -7 & 4 \\ & & 1 & 4 & -3 \\ \hline & 1 & 4 & -3 & 1 \end{array}$$
Thus, $P(1) = 1$.

35.
$$\begin{array}{r|rrrr} -3 & 3 & -7 & -2 & 5 \\ & & -9 & 48 & -138 \\ \hline & 3 & -16 & 46 & -133 \end{array}$$
Thus, $P(-3) = -133$.

37.
$$\begin{array}{r|rrrrr} -1 & 4 & 0 & 1 & 0 & -2 \\ & & -4 & 4 & -5 & 5 \\ \hline & 4 & -4 & 5 & -5 & 3 \end{array}$$
Thus, $P(-1) = 3$.

39.

$$\frac{1}{3}\bigg| \quad 2 \qquad 0 \qquad -3 \qquad 0 \qquad -2$$

$$\qquad \qquad \frac{2}{3} \qquad \frac{2}{9} \qquad -\frac{25}{27} \qquad -\frac{25}{81}$$

$$\overline{\quad 2 \qquad \frac{2}{3} \qquad -\frac{25}{9} \qquad -\frac{25}{27} \qquad -\frac{187}{81}}$$

Thus, $P\left(\dfrac{1}{3}\right) = -\dfrac{187}{81}$.

41.

$$\frac{1}{2}\bigg| \quad 1 \qquad 1 \qquad -1 \qquad 0 \qquad 0 \qquad 3$$

$$\qquad \qquad \frac{1}{2} \qquad \frac{3}{4} \qquad -\frac{1}{8} \qquad -\frac{1}{16} \qquad -\frac{1}{32}$$

$$\overline{\quad 1 \qquad \frac{3}{2} \qquad -\frac{1}{4} \qquad -\frac{1}{8} \qquad -\frac{1}{16} \qquad \frac{95}{32}}$$

Thus, $P\left(\dfrac{1}{2}\right) = \dfrac{95}{32}$.

43. Answers may vary.

45. $7x + 2 = x - 3$

$7x - x = -3 - 2$

$6x = -5$

$x = -\dfrac{5}{6}$

The solution is $-\dfrac{5}{6}$.

47.

$$x^2 = 4x - 4$$

$$x^2 - 4x + 4 = 0$$

$$(x-2)^2 = 0$$

$$x - 2 = 0$$

$$x = 2$$

The solution is 2.

49.

$$\frac{x}{3} - 5 = 13$$

$$3\left(\frac{x}{3} - 5\right) = (13) \cdot 3$$

$$x - 15 = 39$$

$$x = 54$$

The solution is 54.

51. $x^3 - 1 = x^3 - 1^3 = (x-1)(x^2 + x + 1)$

53. $125z^3 + 8 = (5z)^3 + 2^3$

$$= (5z + 2)(25z^2 - 10z + 4)$$

55. $xy + 2x + 3y + 6 = (xy + 2x) + (3y + 6)$

$$= x(y + 2) + 3(y + 2)$$

$$= (y + 2)(x + 3)$$

57. $x^3 - 9x = x(x^2 - 9) = x(x + 3)(x - 3)$

59.

$$-3\big| \quad 1 \qquad 3 \qquad 4 \qquad 12$$

$$\qquad \qquad -3 \qquad 0 \qquad -12$$

$$\overline{\quad 1 \qquad 0 \qquad 4 \qquad 0}$$

Remainder = 0 and

$$(x + 3)(x^2 + 4) = x^3 + 3x^2 + 4x + 12$$

61. $P(x)$ is equal to the remainder when $P(x)$ is divided by $x - c$. Therefore, $P(c) = 0$.

63. Multiply $(x^2 - x + 10)$ by $(x + 3)$ and add the remainder, -2.

$$(x^2 - x + 10)(x + 3) - 2$$

$$= (x^3 + 3x^2 - x^2 - 3x + 10x + 30) - 2$$

$$= x^3 + 2x^2 + 7x + 28$$

65. $V = lwh$ so $w = \dfrac{V}{lh}$

$$= \frac{x^4 + 6x^3 - 7x^2}{x^2(x+7)}$$

$$= \frac{x^4 + 6x^3 - 7x^2}{x^3 + 7x^2}$$

$$\begin{array}{r} x - 1 \\ x^3 + 7x^2 \overline{)\ x^4 + 6x^3 - 7x^2} \\ \underline{x^4 + 7x^3} \\ -x^3 - 7x^2 \\ \underline{-x^3 - 7x^2} \\ 0 \end{array}$$

The width is $(x - 1)$ meters.

Exercise Set 6.6

1. $\dfrac{x}{2} - \dfrac{x}{3} = 12$

$6\left(\dfrac{x}{2} - \dfrac{x}{3}\right) = 6(12)$

$3x - 2x = 72$

$x = 72$

3. $\dfrac{x}{3} = \dfrac{1}{6} + \dfrac{x}{4}$

$12\left(\dfrac{x}{3}\right) = 12\left(\dfrac{1}{6} + \dfrac{x}{4}\right)$

$4x = 2 + 3x$

$x = 2$

5. $\dfrac{2}{x} + \dfrac{1}{2} = \dfrac{5}{x}$

$2x\left(\dfrac{2}{x} + \dfrac{1}{2}\right) = 2x\left(\dfrac{5}{x}\right)$

$4 + x = 10$

$x = 6$

7. $\dfrac{x^2 + 1}{x} = \dfrac{5}{x}$

$x\left(\dfrac{x^2 + 1}{x}\right) = x\left(\dfrac{5}{x}\right)$

$x^2 + 1 = 5$

$x^2 - 4 = 0$

$x + 2 = 0 \quad \text{or} \quad x - 2 = 0$

$x = -2 \quad \text{or} \quad x = 2$

9. $\dfrac{x+5}{x+3} = \dfrac{2}{x+3}$

$(x+3) \cdot \dfrac{x+5}{x+3} = (x+3) \cdot \dfrac{2}{x+3}$

$x + 5 = 2$

$x = -3$

which we discard as extraneous.
No solution, or $\varnothing$.

11. $\dfrac{5}{x-2} - \dfrac{2}{x+4} = -\dfrac{4}{x^2 + 2x - 8}$

$\dfrac{5}{x-2} - \dfrac{2}{x+4} = -\dfrac{4}{(x+4)(x-2)}$

$5(x+4) - 2(x-2) = -4$

$5x + 20 - 2x + 4 = -4$

$3x + 24 = -4$

$3x = -28$

$x = -\dfrac{28}{3}$

13. $\dfrac{1}{x-1} = \dfrac{2}{x+1}$

$(x+1)(x-1) \cdot \dfrac{1}{x-1} = (x+1)(x-1) \cdot \dfrac{2}{x+1}$

$1(x+1) = 2(x-1)$

$x + 1 = 2x - 2$

$-x = -3$

$x = 3$

15. $\dfrac{x^2 - 23}{2x^2 - 5x - 3} + \dfrac{2}{x-3} = \dfrac{-1}{2x+1}$

$\dfrac{x^2 - 23}{(2x+1)(x-3)} + \dfrac{2}{x-3} = \dfrac{-1}{2x+1}$

$(x^2 - 23) + 2(2x+1) = -1(x-3)$

$x^2 - 23 + 4x + 2 = -x + 3$

$x^2 + 5x - 24 = 0$

$(x+8)(x-3) = 0$

$x + 8 = 0 \quad \text{or} \quad x - 3 = 0$

$x = -8 \quad \text{or} \quad x = 3$

We discard 3 as extraneous. $x = -8$ is the only solution.

17. $\dfrac{1}{x-4} - \dfrac{3x}{x^2 - 16} = \dfrac{2}{x+4}$

$\dfrac{1}{x-4} - \dfrac{3x}{(x+4)(x-4)} = \dfrac{2}{x+4}$

$1(x+4) - 3x = 2(x-4)$

$x + 4 - 3x = 2x - 8$

$-2x + 4 = 2x - 8$

$-4x = -12$

$x = 3$

19. $\dfrac{1}{x-4} = \dfrac{8}{x^2-16}$

$\dfrac{1}{x-4} = \dfrac{8}{(x+4)(x-4)}$

$1(x+4) = 8$

$x+4 = 8$

$x = -4$

which we discard as extraneous.
No solution, or $\varnothing$.

21. $\dfrac{1}{x-2} - \dfrac{2}{x^2-2x} = 1$

$\dfrac{1}{x-2} - \dfrac{2}{x(x-2)} = 1$

$x(x-2)\left[\dfrac{1}{x-2} - \dfrac{2}{x(x-2)}\right] = x(x-2)\cdot 1$

$x-2 = x(x-2)$

$x-2 = x^2 - 2x$

$0 = x^2 - 3x + 2$

$0 = (x-2)(x-1)$

$x-2 = 0 \text{ or } x-1 = 1$

$x = 2 \text{ or } \quad x = 1$

We discard 2 as extraneous. $x = 1$ is the only solution.

23. $\dfrac{5}{x} = \dfrac{20}{12}$

$12x\left(\dfrac{5}{x}\right) = 12x\left(\dfrac{20}{12}\right)$

$60 = 20x$

$3 = x$

25. $1 - \dfrac{4}{a} = 5$

$a\left(1 - \dfrac{4}{a}\right) = a(5)$

$a - 4 = 5a$

$-4 = 4a$

$-1 = a$

27. $\dfrac{x^2+5}{x} - 1 = \dfrac{5(x+1)}{x}$

$x\left(\dfrac{x^2+5}{x} - 1\right) = x\left[\dfrac{5(x+1)}{x}\right]$

$x^2 + 5 - x = 5x + 5$

$x^2 - 6x = 0$

$x(x-6) = 0$

$x = 0 \text{ or } x-6 = 0$

$x = 6$

We discard 0 as extraneous. $x = 6$ is the only solution.

29. $\dfrac{1}{2x} - \dfrac{1}{x+1} = \dfrac{1}{3x^2+3x}$

$\dfrac{1}{2x} - \dfrac{1}{x+1} = \dfrac{1}{3x(x+1)}$

$1\cdot 3(x+1) - 1\cdot 6x = 1\cdot 2$

$3x + 3 - 6x = 2$

$-3x + 3 = 2$

$-3x = -1$

$x = \dfrac{1}{3}$

31. $\dfrac{1}{x} - \dfrac{x}{25} = 0$

$25x\left(\dfrac{1}{x} - \dfrac{x}{25}\right) = 25x(0)$

$25 - x^2 = 0$

$-(x^2 - 25) = 0$

$-(x+5)(x-5) = 0$

$x+5 = 0 \quad \text{or } x-5 = 0$

$x = -5 \text{ or } \quad x = 5$

33. $5 - \dfrac{2}{2y-5} = \dfrac{3}{2y-5}$

$(2y-5)\left(5 - \dfrac{2}{2y-5}\right) = (2y-5)\cdot\dfrac{3}{2y-5}$

$5(2y-5) - 2 = 3$

$10y - 25 - 2 = 3$

$10y - 27 = 3$

$10y = 30$

$y = 3$

35. $\dfrac{x-1}{x+2} = \dfrac{2}{3}$

$3(x-1) = 2(x+2)$

$3x-3 = 2x+4$

$x = 7$

37. $\dfrac{x+3}{x+2} = \dfrac{1}{x+2}$

$x+3 = 1$

$x = -2$

which we discard as extraneous.
No solution, or $\varnothing$.

39. $\dfrac{1}{a-3} + \dfrac{2}{a+3} = \dfrac{1}{a^2-9}$

$\dfrac{1}{a-3} + \dfrac{2}{a+3} = \dfrac{1}{(a+3)(a-3)}$

$1(a+3) + 2(a-3) = 1$

$a+3+2a-6 = 1$

$3a-3 = 1$

$3a = 4$

$a = \dfrac{4}{3}$

41. $\dfrac{64}{x^2-16} + 1 = \dfrac{2x}{x-4}$

$\dfrac{64}{(x+4)(x-4)} + 1 = \dfrac{2x}{x-4}$

$64 + 1(x+4)(x-4) = 2x(x+4)$

$64 + (x^2-16) = 2x^2 + 8x$

$x^2 + 48 = 2x^2 + 8x$

$0 = x^2 + 8x - 48$

$0 = (x+12)(x-4)$

$x+12 = 0 \quad \text{or} \ x-4 = 0$

$x = -12 \ \text{or} \qquad x = 4$

We discard 4 as extraneous. $x = -12$ is the only solution.

43. $\dfrac{-15}{4y+1} + 4 = y$

$(4y+1)\left(\dfrac{-15}{4y+1} + 4\right) = (4y+1)y$

$-15 + 4(4y+1) = 4y^2 + y$

$-15 + 16y + 4 = 4y^2 + y$

$-11 + 16y = 4y^2 + y$

$0 = 4y^2 - 15y + 11$

$0 = (4y-11)(y-1)$

$4y-11 = 0 \quad \text{or} \ y-1 = 0$

$4y = 11 \ \text{or} \qquad y = 1$

$y = \dfrac{11}{4} \ \text{or} \qquad y = 1$

45. $\dfrac{28}{x^2-9} + \dfrac{2x}{x-3} + \dfrac{6}{x+3} = 0$

$\dfrac{28}{(x+3)(x-3)} + \dfrac{2x}{x-3} + \dfrac{6}{x+3} = 0$

$28 + 2x(x+3) + 6(x-3) = 0$

$28 + 2x^2 + 6x + 6x - 18 = 0$

$2x^2 + 12x + 10 = 0$

$2(x^2 + 6x + 5) = 0$

$2(x+5)(x+1) = 0$

$x+5 = 0 \quad \text{or} \ x+1 = 0$

$x = -5 \ \text{or} \qquad x = -1$

47. $\dfrac{x+2}{x^2+7x+10} = \dfrac{1}{3x+6} - \dfrac{1}{x+5}$

$\dfrac{x+2}{(x+5)(x+2)} = \dfrac{1}{3(x+2)} - \dfrac{1}{x+5}$

$3(x+2) = 1(x+5) - 1 \cdot 3(x+2)$

$3x+6 = x+5 - 3x - 6$

$3x+6 = -2x - 1$

$5x = -7$

$x = -\dfrac{7}{5}$

49. Let $x =$ the number.

$3x+4 = 19$

$3x = 15$

$x = 5$

The number is 5.

51. Let w = width. Then $w + 5$ = length.

$$2l + 2w = 50$$
$$2(w + 5) + 2w = 50$$
$$2w + 10 + 2w = 50$$
$$4w + 10 = 50$$
$$4w = 40$$
$$w = 10;$$
$$w + 5 = 10 + 5 = 15$$

The length is 15 inches and the width is 10 inches.

53. 10% (reading from the graph)

55. The tallest bars are for categories 25-29 years and 30-34 years.

57. 19% of 35,710
$$0.19(35,710) = 6784.9$$
We would expect approximately 6785 inmates 25-29 years old in 2001.

59. $f(x) = 20 + \dfrac{4000}{x}$

$$25 = 20 + \dfrac{4000}{x}$$
$$5 = \dfrac{4000}{x}$$
$$5x = 4000$$
$$x = 800$$

800 pencil sharpeners must be produced for the average cost to be $25.

61. $x^{-2} - 5x^{-1} - 36 = 0$

$$\dfrac{1}{x^2} - \dfrac{5}{x} - 36 = 0$$
$$1 - 5x - 36x^2 = 0$$
$$36x^2 + 5x - 1 = 0$$
$$(9x - 1)(4x + 1) = 0$$
$$9x - 1 = 0 \text{ or } 4x + 1 = 0$$
$$9x = 1 \text{ or } \quad 4x = -1$$
$$x = \dfrac{1}{9} \text{ or } \quad x = -\dfrac{1}{4}$$

63. $6p^{-2} - 5p^{-1} + 1 = 0$

$$\dfrac{6}{p^2} - \dfrac{5}{p} + 1 = 0$$
$$6 - 5p + p^2 = 0$$
$$p^2 - 5p + 6 = 0$$
$$(p - 2)(p - 3) = 0$$
$$p - 2 = 0 \text{ or } p - 3 = 0$$
$$p = 2 \text{ or } \quad p = 3$$

65. $\dfrac{-8.5}{x + 1.9} = \dfrac{5.7}{x - 3.6}$

$$-8.5(x - 3.6) = 5.7(x + 1.9)$$
$$-8.5x + 30.6 = 5.7x + 10.83$$
$$-14.2x = -19.77$$
$$x = 1.39$$

67. $\dfrac{12.2}{x} + 17.3 = \dfrac{9.6}{x} - 14.7$

$$x\left(\dfrac{12.2}{x} + 17.3\right) = x\left(\dfrac{9.6}{x} - 14.7\right)$$
$$12.2 + 17.3x = 9.6 - 14.7x$$
$$32x = -2.6$$
$$x = -0.08$$

69. $(4 - x)^2 - 5(4 - x) + 6 = 0$

Let $u = 4 - x$. The $u^2 = (4 - x)^2$ and
$$u^2 - 5u + 6 = 0$$
$$(u - 3)(u - 2) = 0$$
$$u = 3 \text{ or } \quad u = 2$$
$$4 - x = 3 \text{ or } 4 - x = 2$$
$$-x = -1 \text{ or } \quad -x = -2$$
$$x = 1 \text{ or } \quad x = 2$$

71. $\left(\dfrac{5}{2 + x}\right)^2 + \left(\dfrac{5}{2 + x}\right) - 20 = 0$

Let $u = \dfrac{5}{2 + x}$. Then $u^2 = \left(\dfrac{5}{2 + x}\right)^2$ and
$$u^2 + u - 20 = 0$$
$$(u + 5)(u - 4) = 0$$
$$u = -5 \qquad \text{or} \qquad u = 4$$
$$\dfrac{5}{2 + x} = -5 \qquad \text{or} \quad \dfrac{5}{2 + x} = 4$$

$$5 = -5(2+x) \quad \text{or} \quad 5 = 4(2+x)$$
$$5 = -10 - 5x \quad \text{or} \quad 5 = 8 + 4x$$
$$5x = -15 \quad \text{or} \quad -3 = 4x$$
$$x = -3 \quad \text{or} \quad -\frac{3}{4} = x$$

73. $\dfrac{2}{x} = \dfrac{10}{5}$

Let $y_1 = \dfrac{2}{x}$ and $y_2 = \dfrac{10}{5}$. Graph both equations and find the point of intersection. The x-coordinate of the intersection point is the solution to the equation.

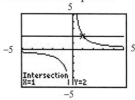

75. $\dfrac{6x+7}{2x+9} = \dfrac{5}{3}$

Let $y_1 = \dfrac{6x+7}{2x+9}$ and $y_2 = \dfrac{5}{3}$. Graph both equations and find the point of intersection. The x-coordinate of the intersection point is the solution to the equation.

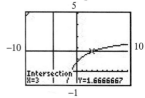

Integrated Review

1. $\dfrac{x}{2} = \dfrac{1}{8} + \dfrac{x}{4}$
$$8\left(\dfrac{x}{2}\right) = 8\left(\dfrac{1}{8} + \dfrac{x}{4}\right)$$
$$4x = 1 + 2x$$
$$2x = 1$$
$$x = \dfrac{1}{2}$$

2. $\dfrac{x}{4} = \dfrac{3}{2} + \dfrac{x}{10}$
$$20\left(\dfrac{x}{4}\right) = 20\left(\dfrac{3}{2} + \dfrac{x}{10}\right)$$
$$5x = 30 + 2x$$
$$3x = 30$$
$$x = 10$$

3. $\dfrac{1}{8} + \dfrac{x}{4} = \dfrac{1}{8} + \dfrac{x \cdot 2}{4 \cdot 2} = \dfrac{1}{8} + \dfrac{2x}{8} = \dfrac{1+2x}{8}$

4. $\dfrac{3}{2} + \dfrac{x}{10} = \dfrac{3 \cdot 5}{2 \cdot 5} + \dfrac{x}{10} = \dfrac{15}{10} + \dfrac{x}{10} = \dfrac{15+x}{10}$

5. $\dfrac{4}{x+2} - \dfrac{2}{x-1} = \dfrac{4(x-1)}{(x+2)(x-1)} - \dfrac{2(x+2)}{(x-1)(x+2)}$
$$= \dfrac{4x-4-2x-4}{(x+2)(x-1)}$$
$$= \dfrac{2x-8}{(x+2)(x-1)}$$
$$= \dfrac{2(x-4)}{(x+2)(x-1)}$$

6. $\dfrac{5}{x-2} - \dfrac{10}{x+4} = \dfrac{5(x+4)}{(x-2)(x+4)} - \dfrac{10(x-2)}{(x-2)(x+4)}$
$$= \dfrac{5x+20-10x+20}{(x-2)(x+4)}$$
$$= \dfrac{-5x+40}{(x-2)(x+4)}$$
$$= \dfrac{-5(x-8)}{(x-2)(x+4)}$$

7. $\dfrac{4}{x+2} = \dfrac{2}{x-1}$
$$4(x-1) = 2(x+2)$$
$$4x-4 = 2x+4$$
$$2x = 8$$
$$x = 4$$

8. $\dfrac{5}{x-2} = \dfrac{10}{x+4}$
$$5(x+4) = 10(x-2)$$
$$5x+20 = 10x-20$$
$$-5x = -40$$
$$x = 8$$

9.

$$\frac{2}{x^2-4} = \frac{1}{x+2} - \frac{3}{x-2}$$

$$\frac{2}{(x+2)(x-2)} = \frac{1}{x+2} - \frac{3}{x-2}$$

$$2 = 1(x-2) - 3(x+2)$$

$$2 = x - 2 - 3x - 6$$

$$2 = -2x - 8$$

$$2x = -10$$

$$x = -5$$

10.

$$\frac{3}{x^2-25} = \frac{1}{x+5} + \frac{2}{x-5}$$

$$\frac{3}{(x+5)(x-5)} = \frac{1}{x+5} + \frac{2}{x-5}$$

$$3 = 1(x-5) + 2(x+5)$$

$$3 = x - 5 + 2x + 10$$

$$3 = 3x + 5$$

$$-2 = 3x$$

$$-\frac{2}{3} = x$$

11. $\dfrac{5}{x^2-3x} + \dfrac{4}{2x-6} = \dfrac{5}{x(x-3)} + \dfrac{4}{2(x-3)}$

$$= \frac{5}{x(x-3)} + \frac{2}{(x-3)}$$

$$= \frac{5}{x(x-3)} + \frac{2 \cdot x}{(x-3) \cdot x}$$

$$= \frac{5+2x}{x(x-3)}$$

12. $\dfrac{5}{x^2-3x} \div \dfrac{4}{2x-6} = \dfrac{5}{x^2-3x} \cdot \dfrac{2x-6}{4}$

$$= \frac{5}{x(x-3)} \cdot \frac{2(x-3)}{4}$$

$$= \frac{5}{2x}$$

13.

$$\frac{x-1}{x+1} + \frac{x+7}{x-1} = \frac{4}{x^2-1}$$

$$\frac{x-1}{x+1} + \frac{x+7}{x-1} = \frac{4}{(x+1)(x-1)}$$

$$(x-1)^2 + (x+7)(x+1) = 4$$

$$x^2 - 2x + 1 + x^2 + 8x + 7 = 4$$

$$2x^2 + 6x + 8 = 4$$

$$2x^2 + 6x + 4 = 0$$

$$2(x^2 + 3x + 2) = 0$$

$$2(x+2)(x+1) = 0$$

$$x + 2 = 0 \quad \text{or} \quad x + 1 = 0$$

$$x = -2 \quad \text{or} \quad x = -1$$

We discard -1 as extraneous. $x = -2$ is the only solution.

14. $\left(1 - \dfrac{y}{x}\right) \div \left(1 - \dfrac{x}{y}\right) = \dfrac{x-y}{x} \div \dfrac{y-x}{y}$

$$= \frac{x-y}{x} \cdot \frac{y}{y-x}$$

$$= \frac{x-y}{x} \cdot \frac{y}{-(x-y)}$$

$$= -\frac{y}{x}$$

15. $\dfrac{a^2-9}{a-6} \cdot \dfrac{a^2-5a-6}{a^2-a-6}$

$$= \frac{(a+3)(a-3)}{a-6} \cdot \frac{(a-6)(a+1)}{(a-3)(a+2)}$$

$$= \frac{(a+3)(a+1)}{a+2}$$

16. $\dfrac{2}{a-6} + \dfrac{3a}{a^2-5a-6} - \dfrac{a}{5a+5}$

$$= \frac{2}{a-6} + \frac{3a}{(a-6)(a+1)} - \frac{a}{5(a+1)}$$

$$= \frac{2 \cdot 5(a+1) + 3a \cdot 5 - a(a-6)}{5(a-6)(a+1)}$$

$$= \frac{10a + 10 + 15a - a^2 + 6a}{5(a-6)(a+1)}$$

$$= \frac{-a^2 + 31a + 10}{5(a-6)(a+1)}$$

17.
$$\frac{2x+3}{3x-2} = \frac{4x+1}{6x+1}$$
$$(2x+3)(6x+1) = (4x+1)(3x-2)$$
$$12x^2 + 20x + 3 = 12x^2 - 5x - 2$$
$$20x + 3 = -5x - 2$$
$$25x = -5$$
$$x = -\frac{1}{5}$$

18.
$$\frac{5x-3}{2x} = \frac{10x+3}{4x+1}$$
$$(5x-3)(4x+1) = 2x(10x+3)$$
$$20x^2 - 7x - 3 = 20x^2 + 6x$$
$$-7x - 3 = 6x$$
$$-13x = 3$$
$$x = -\frac{3}{13}$$

19.
$$\frac{a}{9a^2-1} + \frac{2}{6a-2} = \frac{a}{(3a+1)(3a-1)} + \frac{2}{2(3a-1)}$$
$$= \frac{a}{(3a+1)(3a-1)} + \frac{1}{3a-1}$$
$$= \frac{a+(3a+1)}{(3a+1)(3a-1)}$$
$$= \frac{4a+1}{(3a+1)(3a-1)}$$

20.
$$\frac{3}{4a-8} - \frac{a+2}{a^2-2a} = \frac{3}{4(a-2)} - \frac{a+2}{a(a-2)}$$
$$= \frac{3a-4(a+2)}{4a(a-2)}$$
$$= \frac{3a-4a-8}{4a(a-2)}$$
$$= \frac{-a-8}{4a(a-2)} \quad \text{or} \quad -\frac{a+8}{4a(a-2)}$$

21.
$$-\frac{3}{x^2} - \frac{1}{x} + 2 = 0$$
$$x^2\left(-\frac{3}{x^2} - \frac{1}{x} + 2\right) = x^2(0)$$
$$-3 - x + 2x^2 = 0$$
$$2x^2 - x - 3 = 0$$
$$(2x-3)(x+1) = 0$$
$$2x-3 = 0 \quad \text{or} \quad x+1 = 0$$
$$2x = 3 \quad \text{or} \quad x = -1$$
$$x = \frac{3}{2} \quad \text{or} \quad x = -1$$

22.
$$\frac{x}{2x+6} + \frac{5}{x^2-9} = \frac{x}{2(x+3)} + \frac{5}{(x+3)(x-3)}$$
$$= \frac{x(x-3) + 5 \cdot 2}{2(x+3)(x-3)}$$
$$= \frac{x^2 - 3x + 10}{2(x+3)(x-3)}$$

23.
$$\frac{x-8}{x^2-x-2} + \frac{2}{x-2} = \frac{x-8}{(x-2)(x+1)} + \frac{2}{x-2}$$
$$= \frac{x-8+2(x+1)}{(x-2)(x+1)}$$
$$= \frac{x-8+2x+2}{(x-2)(x+1)}$$
$$= \frac{3x-6}{(x-2)(x+1)}$$
$$= \frac{3(x-2)}{(x-2)(x+1)}$$
$$= \frac{3}{x+1}$$

24.
$$\frac{x-8}{x^2-x-2} + \frac{2}{x-2} = \frac{3}{x+1}$$
$$\frac{x-8}{(x-2)(x+1)} + \frac{2}{x-2} = \frac{3}{x+1}$$
$$x-8+2(x+1) = 3(x-2)$$
$$x-8+2x+2 = 3x-6$$
$$3x-6 = 3x-6$$
$$-6 = -6$$
which is true for any real number.
Therefore, the solution is {x|x is a real number and $x \neq 2$, $x \neq -1$}.

25. $\dfrac{3}{a}-5=\dfrac{7}{a}-1$

$a\left(\dfrac{3}{a}-5\right)=a\left(\dfrac{7}{a}-1\right)$

$3-5a=7-a$

$-4a=4$

$a=-1$

26. $\dfrac{7}{3z-9}+\dfrac{5}{z}=\dfrac{7}{3(z-3)}+\dfrac{5}{z}$

$=\dfrac{7z}{3(z-3)\cdot z}+\dfrac{5\cdot3(z-3)}{z\cdot3(z-3)}$

$=\dfrac{7z+15z-45}{3z(z-3)}$

$=\dfrac{22z-45}{3z(z-3)}$

27. a. $\dfrac{x}{5}-\dfrac{x}{4}+\dfrac{1}{10}$ is an expression.

b. Write each rational term so that the denominator is the LCD, 20.

c. $\dfrac{x}{5}-\dfrac{x}{4}+\dfrac{1}{10}=\dfrac{x\cdot4}{5\cdot4}-\dfrac{x\cdot5}{4\cdot5}+\dfrac{1\cdot2}{10\cdot2}$

$=\dfrac{4x-5x+2}{20}$

$=\dfrac{-x+2}{20}$

28. a. $\dfrac{x}{5}-\dfrac{x}{4}=\dfrac{1}{10}$ is an equation.

b. Clear the equation of fractions by multiplying each term by the LCD, 20.

c. $\dfrac{x}{5}-\dfrac{x}{4}=\dfrac{1}{10}$

$20\left(\dfrac{x}{5}-\dfrac{x}{4}\right)=20\left(\dfrac{1}{10}\right)$

$4x-5x=2$

$-x=2$

$x=-2$

29. b

30. d

31. d

32. a

33. d

Exercise Set 6.7

1. $F=\dfrac{9}{5}C+32$

$F-32=\dfrac{9}{5}C$

$C=\dfrac{5}{9}(F-32)$

3. $Q=\dfrac{A-I}{L}$

$QL=L\left(\dfrac{A-I}{L}\right)$

$QL=A-I$

$I=A-QL$

5. $\dfrac{1}{R}=\dfrac{1}{R_1}+\dfrac{1}{R_2}$

$RR_1R_2\cdot\dfrac{1}{R}=RR_1R_2\left(\dfrac{1}{R_1}+\dfrac{1}{R_2}\right)$

$R_1R_2=RR_2+RR_1$

$R_1R_2=R(R_2+R_1)$

$R=\dfrac{R_1R_2}{R_1+R_2}$

7. $S=\dfrac{n(a+L)}{2}$

$2S=n(a+L)$

$n=\dfrac{2S}{a+L}$

9. $A=\dfrac{h(a+b)}{2}$

$2A=h(a+b)$

$2A=ah+bh$

$2A-ah=bh$

$b=\dfrac{2A-ah}{h}$

11. $\dfrac{P_1V_1}{T_1}=\dfrac{P_2V_2}{T_2}$

$T_1T_2\cdot\dfrac{P_1V_1}{T_1}=T_1T_2\cdot\dfrac{P_2V_2}{T_2}$

$P_1V_1T_2=P_2V_2T_1$

$T_2=\dfrac{P_2V_2T_1}{P_1V_1}$

13.
$$f = \frac{f_1 f_2}{f_1 + f_2}$$
$$(f_1 + f_2)f = f_1 f_2$$
$$f_1 f + f_2 f = f_1 f_2$$
$$f_1 f = f_1 f_2 - f_2 f$$
$$f_1 f = f_2(f_1 - f)$$
$$\frac{f_1 f}{(f_1 - f)} = f_2$$

15.
$$\lambda = \frac{2L}{n}$$
$$n\lambda = 2L$$
$$\frac{n\lambda}{2} = L$$

17.
$$\frac{\theta}{\omega} = \frac{2L}{c}$$
$$c\omega \cdot \frac{\theta}{\omega} = c\omega \cdot \frac{2L}{c}$$
$$c\theta = 2L\omega$$
$$c = \frac{2L\omega}{\theta}$$

19. Let n = the number. Then $\frac{1}{n}$ = the reciprocal of the number.
$$n + 5\left(\frac{1}{n}\right) = 6$$
$$n + \frac{5}{n} = 6$$
$$n\left(n + \frac{5}{n}\right) = 6n$$
$$n^2 + 5 = 6n$$
$$n^2 - 6n + 5 = 0$$
$$(n - 5)(n - 1) = 0$$
$$n - 5 = 0 \text{ or } n - 1 = 0$$
$$n = 5 \text{ or } \quad n = 1$$
The numbers are 1 and 5.

21. Let x = the number.
$$\frac{12 + x}{41 + 2x} = \frac{1}{3}$$
$$3(12 + x) = 1 \cdot (41 + 2x)$$
$$36 + 3x = 41 + 2x$$
$$x = 5$$
The number is 5.

23. Let a = amount of water in 3 minutes.
$$\frac{15}{10} = \frac{a}{3}$$
$$10a = 15(3)$$
$$10a = 45$$
$$a = 4.5$$
The camel can drink 4.5 gallons.

25. Let w = the number of women.
$$\frac{10.2}{100} = \frac{w}{35,712}$$
$$100w = 10.2(35,712)$$
$$10 \cdot 100w = 10 \cdot 10.2(35,712)$$
$$1000w = 102(35,712)$$
$$1000w = 3,642,624$$
$$w = 3642.624$$
There are about 3643 women.

27. Let x = number of hours needed working together.
$$\frac{1}{26} + \frac{1}{39} = \frac{1}{x}$$
$$78x\left(\frac{1}{26} + \frac{1}{39}\right) = 78x\left(\frac{1}{x}\right)$$
$$3x + 2x = 78$$
$$5x = 78$$
$$x = \frac{78}{5} = 15.6$$
The roofers together would take 15.6 hours.

29. Let x = time to sort the stack working together.
$$\frac{1}{20} + \frac{1}{30} + \frac{1}{60} = \frac{1}{x}$$
$$3x + 2x + x = 60$$
$$6x = 60$$
$$x = 10$$
It takes them 10 minutes to sort the mail when all three work together.

31. Let r = speed of the car. Then
$r + 150$ = speed of the plane.

$$t_{\text{plane}} = t_{\text{car}}$$

$$\frac{600}{r + 150} = \frac{150}{r}$$

$$600r = 150(r + 150)$$

$$600r = 150r + 22,500$$

$$450r = 22,500$$

$$r = \frac{22,500}{450} = 50$$

$$r + 150 = 50 + 150 = 200$$

The speed of the plane was 200 mph.

33. Let r = speed of the boat in still water.

$$t_{\text{downstream}} = t_{\text{upstream}}$$

$$\frac{20}{r + 5} = \frac{10}{r - 5}$$

$$20(r - 5) = 10(r + 5)$$

$$20r - 100 = 10r + 50$$

$$10r = 150$$

$$r = 15$$

The speed of the boat in still water is 15 mph.

35. Let x = the first integer. Then
$x + 1$ = the next integer.

$$\frac{1}{x} + \frac{1}{x + 1} = -\frac{15}{56}$$

$$56(x + 1) + 56x = -15x(x + 1)$$

$$56x + 56 + 56x = -15x^2 - 15x$$

$$112x + 56 = -15x^2 - 15x$$

$$15x^2 + 127x + 56 = 0$$

$$(15x + 7)(x + 8) = 0$$

$$15x + 7 = 0 \quad \text{or} \quad x + 8 = 0$$

$$15x = -7 \quad \text{or} \quad x = -8$$

$$x = \cancel{-\frac{7}{15}} \qquad x + 1 = -8 + 1 = -7$$

The integers are –8 and –7.

37. Let t = time for 2nd hose to fill the pond.

$$\frac{1}{45} + \frac{1}{t} = \frac{1}{20}$$

$$180t\left(\frac{1}{45} + \frac{1}{t}\right) = 180t \cdot \frac{1}{20}$$

$$4t + 180 = 9t$$

$$180 = 5t$$

$$36 = t$$

The second hose will take 36 minutes to fill the pond alone.

39. Let r = the speed of the first train. Then
$r + 15$ = the speed of the 2nd train.

$$d_{\text{train 1}} + d_{\text{train 2}} = 630$$

$$6r + 6(r + 15) = 630$$

$$6r + 6r + 90 = 630$$

$$12r = 540$$

$$r = 45$$

$$r + 15 = 45 + 15 = 60$$

The speed of the trains were 45 mph and 60 mph.

41. Let t = time to travel 1 mile.

$$\frac{0.17}{1} = \frac{1}{t}$$

$$0.17t = 1$$

$$100(0.17t) = 100(1)$$

$$17t = 100$$

$$t = \frac{100}{17} = 5.882352941$$

It would take 5.9 hours.

43. Let t = time to fill quota working together.

$$\frac{1}{5} + \frac{1}{6} + \frac{1}{7.5} = \frac{1}{t}$$

$$225t\left(\frac{1}{5} + \frac{1}{6} + \frac{1}{7.5}\right) = 225t \cdot \frac{1}{t}$$

$$45t + 37.5t + 30t = 225$$

$$112.5t = 225$$

$$t = 2$$

It would take 2 hours using all three machines.

45. Let r = the speed of plane in still air.

$$t_{\text{with}} = t_{\text{against}}$$

$$\frac{465}{r+20} = \frac{345}{r-20}$$

$$465(r-20) = 345(r+20)$$

$$465r - 9300 = 345r + 6900$$

$$120r = 16,200$$

$$r = 135$$

The planes speed in still air is 135 mph.

47. Let d = the distance of the run.

$$t_{\text{jogger 2}} = \frac{1}{2} + t_{\text{jogger 1}}$$

$$\frac{d}{6} = \frac{1}{2} + \frac{d}{8}$$

$$24\left(\frac{d}{6}\right) = 24\left(\frac{1}{2} + \frac{d}{8}\right)$$

$$4d = 12 + 3d$$

$$d = 12$$

The run was 12 miles.

49. Let t = time to complete the job working together.

$$\frac{1}{4} + \frac{1}{5} = \frac{1}{t}$$

$$20t\left(\frac{1}{4} + \frac{1}{5}\right) = 20t \cdot \frac{1}{t}$$

$$5t + 4t = 20$$

$$9t = 20$$

$$t = \frac{20}{9} = 2\frac{2}{9}$$

It would take them $2\frac{2}{9}$ hours.

51. Let n = numerator. Then

$n+1$ = the denominator, and $\dfrac{n}{n+1}$ = the fraction.

$$\frac{n-3}{(n+1)-3} = \frac{4}{5}$$

$$\frac{n-3}{n-2} = \frac{4}{5}$$

$$5(n-3) = 4(n-2)$$

$$5n - 15 = 4n - 8$$

$$n = 7$$

Thus, $\dfrac{n}{n+1} = \dfrac{7}{7+1} = \dfrac{7}{8}$ is the fraction.

53. Let t = time to move the cans working together.

$$\frac{1}{2} + \frac{1}{6} = \frac{1}{t}$$

$$6t\left(\frac{1}{2} + \frac{1}{6}\right) = 6t \cdot \frac{1}{t}$$

$$3t + t = 6$$

$$4t = 6$$

$$t = \frac{6}{4} = 1\frac{1}{2}$$

It would take them $1\frac{1}{2}$ minutes.

55. Let r = the speed in still air.

$$t_{\text{into wind}} = t_{\text{wind behind}}$$

$$\frac{10}{r-3} = \frac{11}{r+3}$$

$$10(r+3) = 11(r-3)$$

$$10r + 30 = 11r - 33$$

$$63 = r$$

The speed in still air is 63 mph.

57. Let r = the speed in still water.

$$t_{\text{downstream}} = t_{\text{upstream}}$$

$$\frac{9}{r+6} = \frac{3}{r-6}$$

$$9(r-6) = 3(r+6)$$

$$9r - 54 = 3r + 18$$

$$6r = 72$$

$$r = 12$$

Thus,

$$t = t_{\text{downstream}} + t_{\text{upstream}}$$

$$= \frac{9}{12+6} + \frac{3}{12-6}$$

$$= \frac{1}{2} + \frac{1}{2}$$

$$= 1$$

It takes him 1 hour to cover the 12 miles.

59. Let t = time if they worked together.

$$\frac{1}{3} + \frac{1}{6} = \frac{1}{t}$$

$$6t\left(\frac{1}{3} + \frac{1}{6}\right) = 6t \cdot \frac{1}{t}$$

$$2t + t = 6$$

$$3t = 6$$

$$t = 2$$

It would take them 2 hours.

61. $\dfrac{x}{4} = \dfrac{x+3}{6}$

$6x = 4(x+3)$

$6x = 4x + 12$

$2x = 12$

$x = 6$

63. $\dfrac{x-6}{4} = \dfrac{x-2}{5}$

$5(x-6) = 4(x-2)$

$5x - 30 = 4x - 8$

$x = 22$

65. Answers may vary.

$\dfrac{705w}{h^2} = 47$

$\dfrac{705(240)}{h^2} = 47$

$169,200 = 47h^2$

$3600 = h^2$

$0 = 3600 - h^2$

$0 = (60+h)(60-h)$

$60 + h = 0 \quad \text{or} \quad 60 - h = 0$

$h = -60 \quad \text{or} \quad 60 = h$

The patient is 60 inches, or 5 feet tall.

67. $\dfrac{1}{R} = \dfrac{1}{R_1} + \dfrac{1}{R_2}$

$\dfrac{1}{2} = \dfrac{1}{3} + \dfrac{1}{R_2}$

$6R_2\left(\dfrac{1}{2}\right) = 6R_2\left(\dfrac{1}{3} + \dfrac{1}{R_2}\right)$

$3R_2 = 2R_2 + 6$

$R_2 = 6$

The other resistance is 6 ohms.

69. $\dfrac{1}{R} = \dfrac{1}{R_1} + \dfrac{1}{R_2} + \dfrac{1}{R_3}$

$\dfrac{1}{R} = \dfrac{1}{5} + \dfrac{1}{6} + \dfrac{1}{2}$

$30R\left(\dfrac{1}{R}\right) = 30R\left(\dfrac{1}{5} + \dfrac{1}{6} + \dfrac{1}{2}\right)$

$30 = 6R + 5R + 15R$

$30 = 26R$

$R = \dfrac{30}{26} = \dfrac{15}{13}$

The combined resistance is $\dfrac{15}{13}$ ohms.

Mental Math 6.8

1. $y = 5x$ represents direct variation

2. $y = \dfrac{700}{x}$ represents inverse variation

3. $y = 5xz$ represents joint variation

4. $y = \dfrac{1}{2}abc$ represents joint variation

5. $y = \dfrac{9.1}{x}$ represents inverse variation

6. $y = 2.3x$ represents direct variation

7. $y = \dfrac{2}{3}x$ represents direct variation

8. $y = 3.1st$ represents joint variation

Exercise Set 6.8

1. $y = kx$

3. $a = \dfrac{k}{b}$

5. $y = kxz$

7. $y = \dfrac{k}{x^3}$

9. $y = \dfrac{kx}{p^2}$

11. $y = kx$

$4 = k(20)$

$k = \dfrac{1}{5}$

Therefore, $y = \dfrac{1}{5}x$

13. $y = kx$

$6 = k(4)$

$k = \dfrac{3}{2}$

Therefore, $y = \dfrac{3}{2}x$

15. $y = kx$

$7 = k\left(\dfrac{1}{2}\right)$

$k = 14$

Therefore, $y = 14x$

17. $y = kx$

$0.2 = k(0.8)$

$k = 0.25$

Therefore, $y = 0.25x$

19. $W = kr^3$

$1.2 = k(2)^3$

$1.2 = 8k$

$k = \dfrac{1.2}{8} = 0.15$

$W = 0.15r^3$

$= 0.15(3)^3$

$= 0.15(27)$

$= 4.05 \text{ lb}$

The weight of the larger ball is 4.05 pounds.

21. $P = kN$

$260,000 = k(450,000)$

$k = \dfrac{260,000}{450,000} = \dfrac{26}{45}$

$P = \dfrac{26}{45}N = \dfrac{26}{45}(980,000)$

$= 566,222 \text{ tons}$

We should expect St. Louis to produce 566,222 tons of pollutants.

23. $y = \dfrac{k}{x}$

$6 = \dfrac{k}{5}$

$k = 30$

Therefore, $y = \dfrac{30}{x}$

25. $y = \dfrac{k}{x}$

$100 = \dfrac{k}{7}$

$k = 700$

Therefore, $y = \dfrac{700}{x}$

27. $y = \dfrac{k}{x}$

$\dfrac{1}{8} = \dfrac{k}{16}$

$k = 2$

Therefore, $y = \dfrac{2}{x}$

29. $y = \dfrac{k}{x}$

$0.2 = \dfrac{k}{0.7}$

$k = 0.14$

Therefore, $y = \dfrac{0.14}{x}$

31. $R = \dfrac{k}{T}$

$45 = \dfrac{k}{6}$

$k = 45(6) = 270$

$R = \dfrac{270}{T} = \dfrac{270}{5} = 54 \text{ mph}$

The car is traveling at a rate of 54 mph.

33. $I = \dfrac{k}{R}$

$40 = \dfrac{k}{270}$

$k = 40(270) = 10,800$

$I = \dfrac{10,800}{R} = \dfrac{10,800}{150} = 72$ amps

The current is 72 amps.

35. $I_1 = \dfrac{k}{d^2}$

Replace d with $2d$.

$I_2 = \dfrac{k}{(2d)^2} = \dfrac{k}{4d^2} = \dfrac{1}{4} \cdot \dfrac{k}{d^2} = \dfrac{1}{4} I_1$

Thus, the intensity is divided by 4.

37. $x = kyz$

39. $r = kst^3$

41. $y = kx^3$

$9 = k(3)^3$

$9 = 27k$

$k = \dfrac{9}{27} = \dfrac{1}{3}$

Therefore, $y = \dfrac{1}{3} x^3$.

43. $y = k\sqrt{x}$

$0.4 = k\sqrt{4}$

$0.4 = 2k$

$k = \dfrac{0.4}{2} = 0.2$

Therefore, $y = 0.2\sqrt{x}$.

45. $y = \dfrac{k}{x^2}$

$0.052 = \dfrac{k}{(5)^2}$

$0.052 = \dfrac{k}{25}$

$k = 0.052(25) = 1.3$

Therefore, $y = \dfrac{1.3}{x^2}$.

47. $y = kxz^3$

$120 = k(5)(2)^3$

$120 = 40k$

$k = \dfrac{120}{40} = 3$

Therefore, $y = 3xz^3$.

49. $W = \dfrac{kwh^2}{l}$

$12 = \dfrac{k\left(\frac{1}{2}\right)\left(\frac{1}{3}\right)^2}{10}$

$120 = \dfrac{1}{18} k$

$k = 120(18) = 2160$

$W = \dfrac{2160wh^2}{l}$

$= \dfrac{2160\left(\frac{2}{3}\right)\left(\frac{1}{2}\right)^2}{16}$

$= \dfrac{360}{16}$

$= \dfrac{45}{2}$ tons or 22.5 tons

The beam could support 22.5 tons.

51. $V = kr^2 h$

$32\pi = k(4)^2(6)$

$32\pi = 96k$

$k = \dfrac{32\pi}{96} = \dfrac{\pi}{3}$

$V = \dfrac{\pi}{3} r^2 h = \dfrac{\pi}{3}(3)^2(5)$

$= \dfrac{45\pi}{3}$

$= 15\pi$ cu. in.

The cone would have a volume of 15π cubic inches.

53. $H = ksd^3$

$40 = k(120)(2)^3$

$40 = 960k$

$k = \dfrac{40}{960} = \dfrac{1}{24}$

$H = \dfrac{1}{24} sd^3 = \dfrac{1}{24}(80)(3)^3 = 90$ hp

90 horsepower could be safely transmitted.

55. $y = \dfrac{k}{x}$

$400 = \dfrac{k}{8}$

$k = 400(8) = 3200$

$y = \dfrac{3200}{x} = \dfrac{3200}{4} = 800$ millibars

The atmospheric pressure would be 800 millibars.

57. $r = 6$ cm

$C = 2\pi r = 2\pi(6) = 12\pi$ cm

$A = \pi r^2 = \pi(6)^2 = 36\pi$ sq. cm

59. $r = 7$ m

$C = 2\pi r = 2\pi(7) = 14\pi$ m

$A = \pi r^2 = \pi(7)^2 = 49\pi$ sq. m

61. $\sqrt{36} = 6$

63. $\sqrt{4} = 2$

65. $\sqrt{\dfrac{1}{25}} = \dfrac{1}{5}$

67. $\sqrt{\dfrac{25}{121}} = \dfrac{5}{11}$

69. $V_1 = khr^2$

$V_2 = k\left(\dfrac{1}{2}h\right)(2r)^2$

$\quad = k\left(\dfrac{1}{2}h\right)(4r^2) = 2(khr^2) = 2V_1$

The volume is multiplied by 2.

71. $y_1 = kx^2$

$y_2 = k(2x)^2 = k(4x^2) = 4(kx^2) = 4y_1$

If x is doubled, then y is multiplied by 4.

73.

x	$\dfrac{1}{4}$	$\dfrac{1}{2}$	1	2	4
$y = \dfrac{3}{x}$	12	6	3	$\dfrac{3}{2}$	$\dfrac{3}{4}$

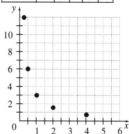

75.

x	$\dfrac{1}{4}$	$\dfrac{1}{2}$	1	2	4
$y = \dfrac{1}{2x}$	2	1	$\dfrac{1}{2}$	$\dfrac{1}{4}$	$\dfrac{1}{8}$

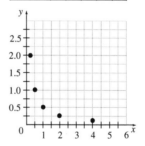

Chapter 6 Review

1. $f(x) = \dfrac{3 - 5x}{7}$

Domain $\{x \mid x$ is a real number$\}$

2. $g(x) = \dfrac{2x + 4}{11}$

Domain $\{x \mid x$ is a real number$\}$

3. $F(x) = \dfrac{-3x^2}{x - 5}$

Undefined values when

$x - 5 = 0$

$\quad x = 5$

Domain $\{x \mid x$ is a real number and $x \neq 5\}$

4. $h(x) = \dfrac{4x}{3x-12}$

Undefined values when

$3x - 12 = 0$

$\qquad 3x = 12$

$\qquad\quad x = 4$

Domain $\{x \mid x \text{ is a real number and } x \neq 4\}$

5. $f(x) = \dfrac{x^3+2}{x^2+8x}$

Undefined values when

$x^2 + 8x = 0$

$x(x+8) = 0$

$x = 0 \;\text{ or }\; x+8 = 0$

$\qquad\qquad\qquad x = -8$

Domain

$\{x \mid x \text{ is a real number and } x \neq 0,\ x \neq -8\}$

6. $G(x) = \dfrac{20}{3x^2-48}$

Undefined values when

$\qquad 3x^2 - 48 = 0$

$\qquad 3(x^2 - 16) = 0$

$3(x+4)(x-4) = 0$

$x + 4 = 0 \;\text{ or }\; x - 4 = 0$

$\quad x = -4 \;\text{ or }\qquad x = 4$

Domain

$\{x \mid x \text{ is a real number and } x \neq -4,\ x \neq 4\}$

7. $\dfrac{15x^4}{45x^2} = \dfrac{15x^{4-2}}{45} = \dfrac{x^2}{3}$

8. $\dfrac{x+2}{2+x} = \dfrac{x+2}{x+2} = 1$

9. $\dfrac{18m^6 p^2}{10m^4 p} = \dfrac{2 \cdot 9m^{6-4}p^{2-1}}{2 \cdot 5} = \dfrac{9m^2 p}{5}$

10. $\dfrac{x-12}{12-x} = \dfrac{x-12}{-1(x-12)} = \dfrac{1}{-1} = -1$

11. $\dfrac{5x-15}{25x-75} = \dfrac{5(x-3)}{5 \cdot 5(x-3)} = \dfrac{1}{5}$

12. $\dfrac{22x+8}{11x+4} = \dfrac{2(11x+4)}{11x+4} = 2$

13. $\dfrac{2x}{2x^2-2x} = \dfrac{2x}{2x(x-1)} = \dfrac{1}{x-1}$

14. $\dfrac{x+7}{x^2-49} = \dfrac{x+7}{(x+7)(x-7)} = \dfrac{1}{x-7}$

15. $\dfrac{2x^2+4x-30}{x^2+x-20} = \dfrac{2(x^2+2x-15)}{(x+5)(x-4)}$

$\qquad\qquad\qquad = \dfrac{2(x+5)(x-3)}{(x+5)(x-4)}$

$\qquad\qquad\qquad = \dfrac{2(x-3)}{x-4}$

16. $\dfrac{xy-3x+2y-6}{x^2+4x+4} = \dfrac{x(y-3)+2(y-3)}{(x+2)^2}$

$\qquad\qquad\qquad = \dfrac{(y-3)(x+2)}{(x+2)^2} = \dfrac{y-3}{x+2}$

17. $C(x) = \dfrac{35x+4200}{x}$

   a. $C(50) = \dfrac{35(50)+4200}{50} = \$119$

   b. $C(100) = \dfrac{35(100)+4200}{100} = \$77$

   c. Decrease

18. $\dfrac{5}{x^3} \cdot \dfrac{x^2}{15} = \dfrac{1}{3x}$

19. $\dfrac{3x^4 yz^3}{15x^2 y^2} \cdot \dfrac{10xy}{z^6} = \dfrac{30x^{4+1}y^{1+1}z^3}{15x^2 y^2 z^6}$

$\qquad\qquad\qquad = \dfrac{2x^5 y^2 z^3}{x^2 y^2 z^6}$

$\qquad\qquad\qquad = 2x^{5-2}y^{2-2}z^{3-6}$

$\qquad\qquad\qquad = \dfrac{2x^3}{z^3}$

20. $\dfrac{4-x}{5} \cdot \dfrac{15}{2x-8} = \dfrac{-1(x-4)}{5} \cdot \dfrac{15}{2(x-4)} = -\dfrac{3}{2}$

21. $\dfrac{x^2-6x+9}{2x^2-18}\cdot\dfrac{4x+12}{5x-15}$

$=\dfrac{(x-3)^2}{2(x^2-9)}\cdot\dfrac{4(x+3)}{5(x-3)}$

$=\dfrac{x-3}{(x+3)(x-3)}\cdot\dfrac{2(x+3)}{5}=\dfrac{2}{5}$

22. $\dfrac{a-4b}{a^2+ab}\cdot\dfrac{b^2-a^2}{8b-2a}$

$=\dfrac{a-4b}{a(a+b)}\cdot\dfrac{(b-a)(b+a)}{2(4b-a)}$

$=\dfrac{-1(4b-a)}{a}\cdot\dfrac{b-a}{2(4b-a)}$

$=\dfrac{-(b-a)}{2a}$

$=\dfrac{a-b}{2a}$

23. $\dfrac{x^2-x-12}{2x^2-32}\cdot\dfrac{x^2+8x+16}{3x^2+21x+36}$

$=\dfrac{(x-4)(x+3)}{2(x^2-16)}\cdot\dfrac{(x+4)^2}{3(x^2+7x+12)}$

$=\dfrac{(x-4)(x+3)}{2(x+4)(x-4)}\cdot\dfrac{(x+4)^2}{3(x+4)(x+3)}=\dfrac{1}{6}$

24. $\dfrac{2x^3+54}{5x^2+5x-30}\cdot\dfrac{6x+12}{3x^2-9x+27}$

$=\dfrac{2(x^3+27)}{5(x^2+x-6)}\cdot\dfrac{6(x+2)}{3(x^2-3x+9)}$

$=\dfrac{2(x+3)(x^2-3x+9)}{5(x+3)(x-2)}\cdot\dfrac{2(x+2)}{x^2-3x+9}$

$=\dfrac{4(x+2)}{5(x-2)}$

25. $\dfrac{3}{4x}\div\dfrac{8}{2x^2}=\dfrac{3}{4x}\cdot\dfrac{2x^2}{8}=\dfrac{3x}{16}$

26. $\dfrac{4x+8y}{3}\div\dfrac{5x+10y}{9}=\dfrac{4x+8y}{3}\cdot\dfrac{9}{5x+10y}$

$=\dfrac{4(x+2y)\cdot9}{3\cdot5(x+2y)}$

$=\dfrac{12}{5}$

27. $\dfrac{5ab}{14c^3}\div\dfrac{10a^4b^2}{6ac^5}=\dfrac{5ab}{14c^3}\cdot\dfrac{6ac^5}{10a^4b^2}$

$=\dfrac{30a^2bc^5}{140a^4b^2c^3}$

$=\dfrac{3a^{2-4}b^{1-2}c^{5-3}}{14}$

$=\dfrac{3a^{-2}b^{-1}c^2}{14}$

$=\dfrac{3c^2}{14a^2b}$

28. $\dfrac{2}{5x}\div\dfrac{4-18x}{6-27x}=\dfrac{2}{5x}\cdot\dfrac{6-27x}{4-18x}$

$=\dfrac{2\cdot3(2-9x)}{5x\cdot2(2-9x)}$

$=\dfrac{3}{5x}$

29. $\dfrac{x^2-25}{3}\div\dfrac{x^2-10x+25}{x^2-x-20}$

$=\dfrac{x^2-25}{3}\cdot\dfrac{x^2-x-20}{x^2-10x+25}$

$=\dfrac{(x+5)(x-5)}{3}\cdot\dfrac{(x-5)(x+4)}{(x-5)^2}$

$=\dfrac{(x+5)(x+4)}{3}$

30. $\dfrac{a-4b}{a^2+ab}\div\dfrac{20b-5a}{b^2-a^2}$

$=\dfrac{a-4b}{a(a+b)}\cdot\dfrac{(b+a)(b-a)}{5(4b-a)}$

$=\dfrac{-1(4b-a)(b-a)}{5a(4b-a)}$

$=\dfrac{a-b}{5a}$

31. $\dfrac{7x+28}{2x+4}\div\dfrac{x^2+2x-8}{x^2-2x-8}$

$=\dfrac{7(x+4)}{2(x+2)}\cdot\dfrac{(x-4)(x+2)}{(x+4)(x-2)}$

$=\dfrac{7(x-4)}{2(x-2)}$

32. $\dfrac{3x+3}{x-1} \div \dfrac{x^2-6x-7}{x^2-1}$

$\quad = \dfrac{3(x+1)}{x-1} \cdot \dfrac{(x+1)(x-1)}{(x-7)(x+1)}$

$\quad = \dfrac{3(x+1)}{x-7}$

33. $\dfrac{2x-x^2}{x^3-8} \div \dfrac{x^2}{x^2+2x+4}$

$\quad = \dfrac{x(2-x)}{(x-2)(x^2+2x+4)} \cdot \dfrac{x^2+2x+4}{x^2}$

$\quad = \dfrac{-(x-2)}{x(x-2)}$

$\quad = -\dfrac{1}{x}$

34. $\dfrac{5a^2-20}{a^3+2a^2+a+2} \div \dfrac{7a}{a^3+a}$

$\quad = \dfrac{5(a^2-4)}{a^2(a+2)+1(a+2)} \cdot \dfrac{a(a^2+1)}{7a}$

$\quad = \dfrac{5(a+2)(a-2)(a^2+1)}{7(a+2)(a^2+1)} = \dfrac{5(a-2)}{7}$

35. $\dfrac{2a}{21} \div \dfrac{3a^2}{7} \cdot \dfrac{4}{a} = \dfrac{2a}{21} \cdot \dfrac{7}{3a^2} \cdot \dfrac{4}{a} = \dfrac{8}{9a^2}$

36. $\dfrac{5x-15}{3-x} \cdot \dfrac{x+2}{10x+20} \cdot \dfrac{x^2-9}{x^2-x-6}$

$\quad = \dfrac{5(x-3)}{-1(x-3)} \cdot \dfrac{x+2}{10(x+2)} \cdot \dfrac{(x+3)(x-3)}{(x-3)(x+2)}$

$\quad = -\dfrac{x+3}{2(x+2)}$

37. $\dfrac{4a+8}{5a^2-20} \cdot \dfrac{3a^2-6a}{a+3} \div \dfrac{2a^2}{5a+15}$

$\quad = \dfrac{4(a+2)}{5(a^2-4)} \cdot \dfrac{3a(a-2)}{a+3} \cdot \dfrac{5(a+3)}{2a^2}$

$\quad = \dfrac{2(a+2)}{(a+2)(a-2)} \cdot \dfrac{3(a-2)}{1} \cdot \dfrac{1}{a} = \dfrac{6}{a}$

38. The denominators have no common factors.
LCD = (9)(2) = 18.

39. $4x^2y^5 = 2 \cdot 2 \cdot x^2 \cdot y^5$

$\quad 10x^2y^4 = 2 \cdot 5 \cdot x^2 \cdot y^4$

$\quad 6y^4 = 2 \cdot 3 \cdot y^4$

$\quad$ LCD $= 2 \cdot 2 \cdot 3 \cdot 5 \cdot x^2 \cdot y^5 = 60x^2y^5$

40. The denominators have no common factors.
LCD $= 2x(x-2)$

41. The denominators have no common factors.
LCD $= 5x(x-5)$

42. $5x^3 = 5 \cdot x^3$

$\quad x^2+3x-28 = (x-4)(x+7)$

$\quad 10x^2-30x = 10x(x-3) = 2 \cdot 5 \cdot x \cdot (x-3)$

$\quad$ The LCD $= 2 \cdot 5 \cdot x^3 \cdot (x-4) \cdot (x+7) \cdot (x-3)$.

$\quad\quad = 10x^3(x-4)(x+7)(x-3)$

43. $\dfrac{2}{15} + \dfrac{4}{15} = \dfrac{2+4}{15} = \dfrac{6}{15} = \dfrac{2}{5}$

44. $\dfrac{4}{x-4} + \dfrac{x}{x-4} = \dfrac{4+x}{x-4}$

45. $\dfrac{4}{3x^2} + \dfrac{2}{3x^2} = \dfrac{4+2}{3x^2} = \dfrac{6}{3x^2} = \dfrac{2}{x^2}$

46. $\dfrac{1}{x-2} - \dfrac{1}{4-2x} = \dfrac{1}{x-2} - \dfrac{1}{-2(x-2)}$

$\quad\quad = \dfrac{1 \cdot 2}{(x-2) \cdot 2} + \dfrac{1}{2(x-2)}$

$\quad\quad = \dfrac{2+1}{2(x-2)}$

$\quad\quad = \dfrac{3}{2(x-2)}$

47. $\dfrac{2x+1}{x^2+x-6} + \dfrac{2-x}{x^2+x-6} = \dfrac{2x+1+(2-x)}{x^2+x-6}$

$\quad\quad = \dfrac{x+3}{(x+3)(x-2)}$

$\quad\quad = \dfrac{1}{x-2}$

48. $\dfrac{7}{2x} + \dfrac{5}{6x} = \dfrac{7 \cdot 3}{2x \cdot 3} + \dfrac{5}{6x}$

$\quad\quad = \dfrac{21}{6x} + \dfrac{5}{6x} = \dfrac{26}{6x} = \dfrac{13}{3x}$

49. $\dfrac{1}{3x^2 y^3} - \dfrac{1}{5x^4 y} = \dfrac{5x^2}{15x^4 y^3} - \dfrac{3y^2}{15x^4 y^3}$

$= \dfrac{5x^2 - 3y^2}{15x^4 y^3}$

50. $\dfrac{1}{10-x} + \dfrac{x-1}{x-10} = \dfrac{-1}{x-10} + \dfrac{x-1}{x-10}$

$= \dfrac{-1+x-1}{x-10} = \dfrac{x-2}{x-10}$

51. $\dfrac{x-2}{x+1} - \dfrac{x-3}{x-1}$

$= \dfrac{(x-2)(x-1) - (x-3)(x+1)}{(x+1)(x-1)}$

$= \dfrac{x^2 - 3x + 2 - (x^2 - 2x - 3)}{(x+1)(x-1)}$

$= \dfrac{x^2 - 3x + 2 - x^2 + 2x + 3}{(x+1)(x-1)}$

$= \dfrac{-x+5}{(x+1)(x-1)}$

52. $\dfrac{x}{9-x^2} - \dfrac{2}{5x-15}$

$= \dfrac{x}{(3+x)(3-x)} - \dfrac{2}{5(x-3)}$

$= \dfrac{-5x}{5(3+x)(x-3)} - \dfrac{2(3+x)}{5(3+x)(x-3)}$

$= \dfrac{-5x - 6 - 2x}{5(x+3)(x-3)}$

$= \dfrac{-7x - 6}{5(x+3)(x-3)}$

53. $2x + 1 - \dfrac{1}{x-3} = \dfrac{(2x+1)(x-3) - 1}{x-3}$

$= \dfrac{2x^2 - 5x - 3 - 1}{x-3}$

$= \dfrac{2x^2 - 5x - 4}{x-3}$

54. $\dfrac{2}{a^2 - 2a + 1} + \dfrac{3}{a^2 - 1}$

$= \dfrac{2}{(a-1)^2} + \dfrac{3}{(a+1)(a-1)}$

$= \dfrac{2(a+1) + 3(a-1)}{(a-1)^2 (a+1)}$

$= \dfrac{2a + 2 + 3a - 3}{(a+1)^2 (a-1)}$

$= \dfrac{5a - 1}{(a-1)^2 (a+1)}$

55. $\dfrac{x}{9x^2 + 12x + 16} - \dfrac{3x+4}{27x^3 - 64}$

$= \dfrac{x}{9x^2 + 12x + 16} - \dfrac{3x+4}{(3x-4)(9x^2 + 12x + 16)}$

$= \dfrac{x(3x-4) - (3x+4)}{(3x-4)(9x^2 + 12x + 16)}$

$= \dfrac{3x^2 - 4x - 3x - 4}{(3x-4)(9x^2 + 12x + 16)}$

$= \dfrac{3x^2 - 7x - 4}{(3x-4)(9x^2 + 12x + 16)}$

56. $\dfrac{2}{x-1} - \dfrac{3x}{3x-3} + \dfrac{1}{2x-2}$

$= \dfrac{2}{x-1} - \dfrac{3x}{3(x-1)} + \dfrac{1}{2(x-1)}$

$= \dfrac{2 \cdot 6 - 3x \cdot 2 + 1 \cdot 3}{6(x-1)}$

$= \dfrac{15 - 6x}{6(x-1)}$

$= \dfrac{3(5 - 2x)}{6(x-1)} = \dfrac{5 - 2x}{2(x-1)}$

57. $\dfrac{3}{2x} \cdot \left(\dfrac{2}{x+1} - \dfrac{2}{x-3} \right)$

$= \dfrac{3}{2x} \cdot \dfrac{2(x-3) - 2(x+1)}{(x+1)(x-3)}$

$= \dfrac{3}{2x} \cdot \dfrac{-8}{(x+1)(x-3)}$

$= -\dfrac{12}{x(x+1)(x-3)}$

58. $\left(\dfrac{2}{x} - \dfrac{1}{5} \right) \cdot \left(\dfrac{2}{x} + \dfrac{1}{3} \right) = \left(\dfrac{10-x}{5x} \right) \left(\dfrac{6+x}{3x} \right)$

$= \dfrac{(10-x)(6+x)}{15x^2}$

59. $\dfrac{2}{x^2-16} - \dfrac{3x}{x^2+8x+16} + \dfrac{3}{x+4}$

$= \dfrac{2}{(x+4)(x-4)} - \dfrac{3x}{(x+4)^2} + \dfrac{3}{x+4}$

$= \dfrac{2(x+4)}{(x+4)^2(x-4)} - \dfrac{3x(x-4)}{(x+4)^2(x-4)}$

$\quad + \dfrac{3(x+4)(x-4)}{(x+4)^2(x-4)}$

$= \dfrac{2x+8-3x^2+12x+3x^2-48}{(x+4)^2(x-4)}$

$= \dfrac{14x-40}{(x+4)^2(x-4)}$

60. $P = \dfrac{1}{x} + \dfrac{1}{x} + \dfrac{1}{x} + \dfrac{2}{x} + \dfrac{5}{2x} + \dfrac{2}{x} + \dfrac{3}{2x}$

$= \dfrac{1+1+1+2+2}{x} + \dfrac{5+3}{2x}$

$= \dfrac{7}{x} + \dfrac{8}{2x}$

$= \dfrac{7\cdot 2}{x\cdot 2} + \dfrac{8}{2x}$

$= \dfrac{14}{2x} + \dfrac{8}{2x} = \dfrac{22}{2x} = \dfrac{11}{x}$

61. $\dfrac{\frac{2}{5}}{\frac{3}{5}} = \dfrac{2}{5}\cdot\dfrac{5}{3} = \dfrac{2}{3}$

62. $\dfrac{1-\frac{3}{4}}{2+\frac{1}{4}} = \dfrac{\left(1-\frac{3}{4}\right)4}{\left(2+\frac{1}{4}\right)4} = \dfrac{4-3}{8+1} = \dfrac{1}{9}$

63. $\dfrac{\frac{1}{x}-\frac{2}{3x}}{\frac{5}{2x}-\frac{1}{3}} = \dfrac{\left(\frac{1}{x}-\frac{2}{3x}\right)6x}{\left(\frac{5}{2x}-\frac{1}{3}\right)6x} = \dfrac{6-4}{15-2x} = \dfrac{2}{15-2x}$

64. $\dfrac{\frac{x^2}{15}}{\frac{x+1}{5x}} = \dfrac{x^2}{15}\cdot\dfrac{5x}{x+1} = \dfrac{x^3}{3(x+1)}$

65. $\dfrac{\frac{3}{y^2}}{\frac{6}{y^3}} = \dfrac{3}{y^2}\cdot\dfrac{y^3}{6} = \dfrac{y}{2}$

66. $\dfrac{\frac{x+2}{3}}{\frac{5}{x-2}} = \dfrac{x+2}{3}\cdot\dfrac{x-2}{5} = \dfrac{(x+2)(x-2)}{15}$

67. $\dfrac{2-\frac{3}{2x}}{x-\frac{2}{5x}} = \dfrac{\left(2-\frac{3}{2x}\right)10x}{\left(x-\frac{2}{5x}\right)10x} = \dfrac{20x-15}{10x^2-4}$

68. $\dfrac{1+\frac{x}{y}}{\frac{x^2}{y^2}-1} = \dfrac{\left(1+\frac{x}{y}\right)y^2}{\left(\frac{x^2}{y^2}-1\right)y^2}$

$= \dfrac{y^2+xy}{x^2-y^2}$

$= \dfrac{y(y+x)}{(x+y)(x-y)}$

$= \dfrac{y}{x-y}$

69. $\dfrac{\frac{5}{x}+\frac{1}{xy}}{\frac{3}{x^2}} = \dfrac{\frac{5y}{xy}+\frac{1}{xy}}{\frac{3}{x^2}}$

$= \dfrac{\frac{5y+1}{xy}}{\frac{3}{x^2}}$

$= \dfrac{5y+1}{xy}\cdot\dfrac{x^2}{3}$

$= \dfrac{x(5y+1)}{3y} \quad \text{or} \quad \dfrac{5xy+x}{3y}$

70. $\dfrac{\frac{x}{3}-\frac{3}{x}}{1+\frac{3}{x}} = \dfrac{\left(\frac{x}{3}-\frac{3}{x}\right)3x}{\left(1+\frac{3}{x}\right)3x}$

$= \dfrac{x^2-9}{3x+9}$

$= \dfrac{(x+3)(x-3)}{3(x+3)}$

$= \dfrac{x-3}{3}$

71.
$$\frac{\frac{1}{x-1}+1}{\frac{1}{x+1}-1}=\frac{\left(\frac{1}{x-1}+1\right)(x+1)(x-1)}{\left(\frac{1}{x+1}-1\right)(x+1)(x-1)}$$

$$=\frac{(x+1)+(x+1)(x-1)}{(x-1)-(x+1)(x-1)}$$

$$=\frac{x+1+x^2-1}{x-1-(x^2-1)}$$

$$=\frac{x^2+x}{-x^2+x}$$

$$=\frac{x(x+1)}{-x(x-1)}$$

$$=-\frac{x+1}{x-1}\quad\text{or}\quad\frac{1+x}{1-x}$$

72.
$$\frac{2}{1-\frac{2}{x}}=\frac{2\cdot x}{\left(1-\frac{2}{x}\right)x}=\frac{2x}{x-2}$$

73.
$$\frac{1}{1+\frac{2}{1-\frac{1}{x}}}=\frac{1}{1+\frac{2}{\frac{x-1}{x}}}=\frac{1}{1+\frac{2x}{x-1}}$$

$$=\frac{1(x-1)}{\left(1+\frac{2x}{x-1}\right)(x-1)}$$

$$=\frac{x-1}{x-1+2x}$$

$$=\frac{x-1}{3x-1}$$

74.
$$\frac{\frac{x^2+5x-6}{4x+3}}{\frac{(x+6)^2}{8x+6}}=\frac{x^2+5x-6}{4x+3}\cdot\frac{8x+6}{(x+6)^2}$$

$$=\frac{(x+6)(x-1)}{4x+3}\cdot\frac{2(4x+3)}{(x+6)^2}$$

$$=\frac{2(x-1)}{x+6}$$

75.
$$\frac{\frac{x-3}{x+3}+\frac{x+3}{x-3}}{\frac{x-3}{x+3}-\frac{x+3}{x-3}}=\frac{\left(\frac{x-3}{x+3}+\frac{x+3}{x-3}\right)(x+3)(x-3)}{\left(\frac{x-3}{x+3}-\frac{x+3}{x-3}\right)(x+3)(x-3)}$$

$$=\frac{(x-3)^2+(x+3)^2}{(x-3)^2-(x+3)^2}$$

$$=\frac{x^2-6x+9+x^2+6x+9}{x^2-6x+9-x^2-6x-9}$$

$$=\frac{2x^2+18}{-12x}$$

$$=-\frac{2(x^2+9)}{12x}$$

$$=-\frac{x^2+9}{6x}$$

76.
$$\frac{\frac{3}{x-1}-\frac{2}{1-x}}{\frac{2}{x-1}-\frac{2}{x}}=\frac{\frac{3}{x-1}+\frac{2}{x-1}}{\frac{2}{x-1}-\frac{2}{x}}$$

$$=\frac{\frac{5}{x-1}}{\frac{2x-2(x-1)}{x(x-1)}}$$

$$=\frac{5}{x-1}\cdot\frac{x(x-1)}{2}$$

$$=\frac{5x}{2}$$

77. $f(x)=\dfrac{3}{x}$

   a. $f(a+h)=\dfrac{3}{a+h}$

   b. $f(a)=\dfrac{3}{a}$

   c. $\dfrac{f(a+h)-f(a)}{h}=\dfrac{\frac{3}{a+h}-\frac{3}{a}}{h}$

   d. $\dfrac{f(a+h)-f(a)}{h}=\dfrac{\frac{3}{a+h}-\frac{3}{a}}{h}$

$$=\frac{\left(\frac{3}{a+h}-\frac{3}{a}\right)a(a+h)}{h\cdot a(a+h)}$$

$$=\frac{3a-3(a+h)}{ha(a+h)}$$

$$=\frac{-3h}{ha(a+h)}$$

$$=\frac{-3}{a(a+h)}$$

78. $\dfrac{3x^5yb^9}{9xy^7} = \dfrac{x^{5-1}y^{1-7}b^9}{3} = \dfrac{x^4y^{-6}b^9}{3} = \dfrac{x^4b^9}{3y^6}$

79. $\dfrac{-9xb^4z^3}{-4axb^2} = \dfrac{9b^{4-2}x^{1-1}z^3}{4a} = \dfrac{9b^2z^3}{4a}$

80. $\dfrac{4xy+2x^2-9}{4xy} = \dfrac{4xy}{4xy} + \dfrac{2x^2}{4xy} - \dfrac{9}{4xy}$

$= 1 + \dfrac{x}{2y} - \dfrac{9}{4xy}$

81. $\dfrac{12xb^2+16xb^4}{4xb^3} = \dfrac{12xb^2}{4xb^3} + \dfrac{16xb^4}{4xb^3}$

$= \dfrac{3}{b} + 4b$

82.

$$
\begin{array}{r}
3x^3+9x^2+2x+6 \\
x-3{\overline{\smash{\big)}\,3x^4+0x^3-25x^2+0x-20}} \\
\underline{3x^4-9x^3} \\
9x^3-25x^2 \\
\underline{9x^3-27x^2} \\
2x^2+0x \\
\underline{2x^2-6x} \\
6x-20 \\
\underline{6x-18} \\
-2
\end{array}
$$

Answer: $3x^3+9x^2+2x+6-\dfrac{2}{x-3}$

83.

$$
\begin{array}{r}
2x^3-4x^2+7x-9 \\
x+2{\overline{\smash{\big)}\,2x^4+0x^3-x^2+5x-12}} \\
\underline{2x^4+4x^3} \\
-4x^3-x^2 \\
\underline{-4x^3-8x^2} \\
7x^2+5x \\
\underline{7x^2+14x} \\
-9x-12 \\
\underline{-9x-18} \\
6
\end{array}
$$

Answer: $2x^3-4x^2+7x-9+\dfrac{6}{x+2}$

84.

$$
\begin{array}{r}
x^3+x-1 \\
2x-1{\overline{\smash{\big)}\,2x^4-x^3+2x^2-3x+1}} \\
\underline{2x^4-x^3} \\
2x^2-3x \\
\underline{2x^2-x} \\
-2x+1 \\
\underline{-2x+1} \\
0
\end{array}
$$

Answer: x^3+x-1

85.

$$
\begin{array}{r}
x^2-1 \\
2x+3{\overline{\smash{\big)}\,2x^3+3x^2-2x+2}} \\
\underline{2x^3+3x^2} \\
-2x+2 \\
\underline{-2x-3} \\
5
\end{array}
$$

Answer: $x^2-1+\dfrac{5}{2x+3}$

86.

$$
\begin{array}{r}
3x^2+2x-1 \\
x^2+x+2{\overline{\smash{\big)}\,3x^4+5x^3+7x^2+3x-2}} \\
\underline{3x^4+3x^3+6x^2} \\
2x^3+x^2+3x \\
\underline{2x^3+2x^2+4x} \\
-x^2-x-2 \\
\underline{-x^2-x-2} \\
0
\end{array}
$$

Answer: $3x^2+2x-1$

87.

$$
\begin{array}{r}
3x^2\qquad+6 \\
3x^2-2x-5{\overline{\smash{\big)}\,9x^4-6x^3+3x^2-12x-30}} \\
\underline{9x^4-6x^3-15x^2} \\
18x^2-12x-30 \\
\underline{18x^2-12x-30} \\
0
\end{array}
$$

Answer: $3x^2+6$

88. $\underline{2|}\ 3 \quad 0 \quad 12 \quad -4$

$6 \quad 12 \quad 48$

$3 \quad 6 \quad 24 \quad 44$

Answer: $3x^2 + 6x + 24 + \dfrac{44}{x-2}$

89. $-\dfrac{3}{2}\bigg|\ 3 \quad 2 \quad -4 \quad -1$

$\phantom{-\frac{3}{2}|\ 3 \quad}-\dfrac{9}{2} \quad \dfrac{15}{4} \quad \dfrac{3}{8}$

$\phantom{-\frac{3}{2}|\ }3 \quad -\dfrac{5}{2} \quad -\dfrac{1}{4} \quad -\dfrac{5}{8}$

Answer: $3x^2 - \dfrac{5}{2}x - \dfrac{1}{4} - \dfrac{5}{8\left(x+\frac{3}{2}\right)}$

90. $\underline{-1|}\ 1 \quad 0 \quad 0 \quad 0 \quad 0 \quad -1$

$-1 \quad 1 \quad -1 \quad 1 \quad -1$

$1 \quad -1 \quad 1 \quad -1 \quad 1 \quad -2$

Answer: $x^4 - x^3 + x^2 - x + 1 - \dfrac{2}{x+1}$

91. $\underline{3|}\ 1 \quad 0 \quad 0 \quad -81$

$3 \quad 9 \quad 27$

$1 \quad 3 \quad 9 \quad -54$

Answer: $x^2 + 3x + 9 - \dfrac{54}{x-3}$

92. $\underline{4|}\ 3 \quad 1 \quad -1 \quad 0 \quad -2$

$12 \quad 52 \quad 204 \quad 816$

$3 \quad 13 \quad 51 \quad 204 \quad 814$

Answer: $3x^3 + 13x^2 + 51x + 204 + \dfrac{814}{x-4}$

93. $\underline{-2|}\ 3 \quad 0 \quad -2 \quad 0 \quad 10$

$-6 \quad 12 \quad -20 \quad 40$

$3 \quad -6 \quad 10 \quad -20 \quad 50$

Answer: $3x^3 - 6x^2 + 10x - 20 + \dfrac{50}{x+2}$

94. $\underline{4|}\ 3 \quad 0 \quad 0 \quad 0 \quad -9 \quad 7$

$12 \quad 48 \quad 192 \quad 768 \quad 3036$

$3 \quad 12 \quad 48 \quad 192 \quad 759 \quad 3043$

Thus, $P(4) = 3043$.

95. $\underline{-5|}\ 3 \quad 0 \quad 0 \quad 0 \quad -9 \quad 7$

$-15 \quad 75 \quad -375 \quad 1875 \quad -9330$

$3 \quad -15 \quad 75 \quad -375 \quad 1866 \quad -9323$

Thus, $P(-5) = -9323$.

96. $\dfrac{2}{3}\bigg|\ 3 \quad 0 \quad 0 \quad 0 \quad -9 \quad 7$

$\phantom{\frac{2}{3}|\ 3 \quad}2 \quad \dfrac{4}{3} \quad \dfrac{8}{9} \quad \dfrac{16}{27} \quad -\dfrac{454}{81}$

$\phantom{\frac{2}{3}|\ }3 \quad 2 \quad \dfrac{4}{3} \quad \dfrac{8}{9} \quad -\dfrac{227}{27} \quad \dfrac{113}{81}$

Thus, $P\left(\dfrac{2}{3}\right) = \dfrac{113}{81}$.

97. $-\dfrac{1}{2}\bigg|\ 3 \quad 0 \quad 0 \quad 0 \quad -9 \quad 7$

$\phantom{-\frac{1}{2}|\ 3 \quad}-\dfrac{3}{2} \quad \dfrac{3}{4} \quad -\dfrac{3}{8} \quad \dfrac{3}{16} \quad \dfrac{141}{32}$

$\phantom{-\frac{1}{2}|\ }3 \quad -\dfrac{3}{2} \quad \dfrac{3}{4} \quad -\dfrac{3}{8} \quad -\dfrac{141}{16} \quad \dfrac{365}{32}$

Thus, $P\left(-\dfrac{1}{2}\right) = \dfrac{365}{32}$.

98. $\underline{3|}\ 1 \quad -1 \quad -6 \quad -6 \quad 18$

$3 \quad 6 \quad 0 \quad -18$

$1 \quad 2 \quad 0 \quad -6 \quad 0$

length $= (x^3 + 2x^2 - 6)$ miles

99. $\dfrac{2}{5} = \dfrac{x}{15}$

$5x = 2(15)$

$5x = 30$

$x = 6$

100. $\dfrac{3}{x} + \dfrac{1}{3} = \dfrac{5}{x}$

$3x\left(\dfrac{3}{x} + \dfrac{1}{3}\right) = 3x \cdot \dfrac{5}{x}$

$9 + x = 15$

$x = 6$

101. $4 + \dfrac{8}{x} = 8$

$x\left(4 + \dfrac{8}{x}\right) = x \cdot 8$

$4x + 8 = 8x$

$8 = 4x$

$2 = x$

102. $\dfrac{2x+3}{5x-9} = \dfrac{3}{2}$

$3(5x-9) = 2(2x+3)$

$15x-27 = 4x+6$

$11x = 33$

$x = 3$

103. $\dfrac{1}{x-2} - \dfrac{3x}{x^2-4} = \dfrac{2}{x+2}$

$\dfrac{1}{x-2} - \dfrac{3x}{(x+2)(x-2)} = \dfrac{2}{x+2}$

$(x+2)-3x = 2(x-2)$

$-2x+2 = 2x-4$

$-4x = -6$

$x = \dfrac{-6}{-4} = \dfrac{3}{2}$

104. $\dfrac{7}{x} - \dfrac{x}{7} = 0$

$\dfrac{7}{x} = \dfrac{x}{7}$

$x^2 = 49$

$x^2 - 49 = 0$

$(x+7)(x-7) = 0$

$x+7 = 0 \quad \text{or} \quad x-7 = 0$

$x = -7 \quad \text{or} \quad x = 7$

105. $\dfrac{x-2}{x^2-7x+10} = \dfrac{1}{5x-10} - \dfrac{1}{x-5}$

$\dfrac{x-2}{(x-5)(x-2)} = \dfrac{1}{5(x-2)} - \dfrac{1}{x-5}$

$5(x-2) = 1(x-5) - 1 \cdot 5(x-2)$

$5x-10 = x-5-5x+10$

$5x-10 = -4x+5$

$9x = 15$

$x = \dfrac{15}{9} = \dfrac{5}{3}$

106. $\dfrac{5}{x^2-7x} + \dfrac{4}{2x-14} = \dfrac{5}{x(x-7)} + \dfrac{2}{x-7}$

$= \dfrac{5+2\cdot x}{x(x-7)}$

$= \dfrac{2x+5}{x(x-7)}$

107. $3 - \dfrac{5}{x} - \dfrac{2}{x^2} = 0$

$3x^2 - 5x - 2 = 0$

$(3x+1)(x-2) = 0$

$3x+1 = 0 \quad \text{or} \quad x-2 = 0$

$3x = -1 \quad \text{or} \quad x = 2$

$x = -\dfrac{1}{3}$

The solutions are $-\dfrac{1}{3}$ and 2.

108. $\dfrac{4}{3-x} - \dfrac{7}{2x-6} + \dfrac{5}{x}$

$= \dfrac{-4}{x-3} - \dfrac{7}{2(x-3)} + \dfrac{5}{x}$

$= \dfrac{-4(2x) - 7x + 5 \cdot 2(x-3)}{2x(x-3)}$

$= \dfrac{-8x - 7x + 10x - 30}{2x(x-3)}$

$= \dfrac{-5x - 30}{2x(x-3)}$

109. $A = \dfrac{h(a+b)}{2}$

$2A = h(a+b)$

$2A = ah + bh$

$2A - bh = ah$

$\dfrac{2A-bh}{h} = a$

110. $\dfrac{1}{R} = \dfrac{1}{R_1} + \dfrac{1}{R_2}$

$RR_1R_2\left(\dfrac{1}{R}\right) = RR_1R_2\left(\dfrac{1}{R_1} + \dfrac{1}{R_2}\right)$

$R_1R_2 = RR_2 + RR_1$

$R_1R_2 - RR_2 = RR_1$

$R_2(R_1 - R) = RR_1$

$R_2 = \dfrac{RR_1}{R_1 - R}$

111. $I = \dfrac{E}{R+r}$

$I(R+r) = E$

$IR + Ir = E$

$IR = E - Ir$

$R = \dfrac{E-Ir}{I}$

112.
$$A = P + Prt$$
$$A - P = Prt$$
$$\frac{A - P}{Pt} = r$$

113.
$$H = \frac{kA(T_1 - T_2)}{L}$$
$$HL = kA(T_1 - T_2)$$
$$\frac{HL}{k(T_1 - T_2)} = A$$

114. Let x = the number.
$$x + 2\left(\frac{1}{x}\right) = 3$$
$$x\left(x + \frac{2}{x}\right) = 3x$$
$$x^2 + 2 = 3x$$
$$x^2 - 3x + 2 = 0$$
$$(x - 2)(x - 1) = 0$$
$$x - 2 = 0 \text{ or } x - 1 = 0$$
$$x = 2 \text{ or } \quad x = 1$$
The number is either 1 or 2.

115. Let x = the number added to the numerator.
Then $2x$ = the number added to the denominator.
Thus,
$$\frac{3 + x}{7 + 2x} = \frac{10}{21}$$
$$21(3 + x) = 10(7 + 2x)$$
$$63 + 21x = 70 + 20x$$
$$x = 7$$
The number is 7.

116. Let x = the numerator. Then
$x + 2$ = the denominator.
$$\frac{x - 3}{(x + 2) + 5} = \frac{2}{3}$$
$$\frac{x - 3}{x + 7} = \frac{2}{3}$$
$$3(x - 3) = 2(x + 7)$$
$$3x - 9 = 2x + 14$$
$$x = 23; \; x + 2 = 23 + 2 = 25$$

The original fraction was $\frac{23}{25}$.

117. Let n = the first even integer. Then
$n + 2$ = the next even integer.
$$\frac{1}{n} + \frac{1}{n + 2} = -\frac{9}{40}$$
$$40n(n + 2)\left(\frac{1}{n} + \frac{1}{n + 2}\right) = 40n(n + 2)\left(-\frac{9}{40}\right)$$
$$40(n + 2) + 40n = -9n(n + 2)$$
$$40n + 80 + 40n = -9n^2 - 18n$$
$$9n^2 + 98n + 80 = 0$$
$$(9n + 8)(n + 10) = 0$$
$$9n + 8 = 0 \quad \text{or} \quad n + 10 = 0$$
$$9n = -8 \text{ or} \qquad n = -10$$
$$n = -\frac{8}{9} \qquad n + 2 = -10 + 2 = -8$$

Discard the non-integer solution $-\frac{8}{9}$.

The two integers are –10 and –8.

118. Let t = time for all three to paint room.
$$\frac{1}{4} + \frac{1}{5} + \frac{1}{6} = \frac{1}{t}$$
$$60t\left(\frac{1}{4} + \frac{1}{5} + \frac{1}{6}\right) = 60t\left(\frac{1}{t}\right)$$
$$15t + 12t + 10t = 60$$
$$37t = 60$$
$$t = \frac{60}{37} = 1\frac{23}{37} \text{ hours}$$

119. Let t = time for Tom to type labels alone.
$$\frac{1}{6} + \frac{1}{t} = \frac{1}{4}$$
$$12t\left(\frac{1}{6} + \frac{1}{t}\right) = 12t\left(\frac{1}{4}\right)$$
$$2t + 12 = 3t$$
$$12 = t$$
Tom can type the mailing labels in 12 hours.

120. Let t = time to empty a full tank.
$$\frac{1}{2} - \frac{1}{2.5} = \frac{1}{t}$$
$$10t\left(\frac{1}{2} - \frac{1}{2.5}\right) = 10t\left(\frac{1}{t}\right)$$
$$5t - 4t = 10$$
$$t = 10 \text{ hours}$$

121. Let r = the speed of the car. Then $r + 430$ = the speed of the jet.

$$t_{driving} = t_{flying}$$

$$\frac{210}{r} = \frac{1715}{r+430}$$

$$1715r = 210(r+430)$$

$$1715r = 210r + 90,300$$

$$1505r = 90,300$$

$$r = 60;$$

$$r + 430 = 60 + 430 = 490$$

The speed of the jet is 490 mph.

122.

$$\frac{1}{R} = \frac{1}{R_1} + \frac{1}{R_2}$$

$$\frac{1}{\frac{30}{11}} = \frac{1}{5} + \frac{1}{R_2}$$

$$30R_2\left(\frac{11}{30}\right) = 30R_2\left(\frac{1}{5} + \frac{1}{R_2}\right)$$

$$11R_2 = 6R_2 + 30$$

$$5R_2 = 30$$

$$R_2 = 6 \text{ ohms}$$

123. Let r = the speed of the current.

$$t_{upstream} = t_{downstream}$$

$$\frac{72}{32-r} = \frac{120}{32+r}$$

$$72(32+r) = 120(32-r)$$

$$2304 + 72r = 3840 - 120r$$

$$192r = 1536$$

$$r = 8$$

The speed of the current is 8 mph.

124. Let r = the speed of the wind.

$$t_{with\ wind} = t_{against\ wind}$$

$$\frac{445}{400+r} = \frac{355}{400-r}$$

$$445(400-r) = 355(400+r)$$

$$178,000 - 445r = 142,000 + 355r$$

$$36,000 = 800r$$

$$45 = r$$

The speed of the wind is 45 mph.

125. Let r = the speed of the walker. Then $r + 3$ = the speed of the jogger.

$$t_{jogging} = t_{walking}$$

$$\frac{14}{r+3} = \frac{8}{r}$$

$$14r = 8(r+3)$$

$$14r = 8r + 24$$

$$6r = 24$$

$$r = 4$$

The speed of the walker is 4 mph.

126. Let r = speed of the faster train. Then $r - 18$ = speed of the slower train.

$$t_{faster\ train} = t_{slower\ train}$$

$$\frac{378}{r} = \frac{270}{r-18}$$

$$378(r-18) = 270r$$

$$378r - 6804 = 270r$$

$$108r = 6804$$

$$r = 63;$$

$$r - 18 = 63 - 18 = 45$$

The speeds of the trains are 63 mph and 45 mph.

127. $A = kB$

$$6 = k(14)$$

$$k = \frac{6}{14} = \frac{3}{7}$$

$$A = \frac{3}{7}B = \frac{3}{7}(21) = 3(3) = 9$$

128. $C = \dfrac{k}{D}$

$$12 = \frac{k}{8}$$

$$96 = k$$

$$C = \frac{96}{D}$$

$$C = \frac{96}{24} = 4$$

129. $P = \dfrac{k}{V}$

$1250 = \dfrac{k}{2}$

$k = 1250(2) = 2500$

$P = \dfrac{2500}{V}$

$800 = \dfrac{2500}{V}$

$V = \dfrac{2500}{800} = 3.125$ cu. ft.

The volume would be 3.125 cubic feet.

130. $A = kr^2$

$36\pi = k(3)^2$

$36\pi = 9k$

$4\pi = k$

$A = 4\pi r^2$

$A = 4\pi(4)^2 = 64\pi$ sq. in.

The surface area would be 64π square inches.

Chapter 6 Test

1. $f(x) = \dfrac{5x^2}{1-x}$

Undefined values when

$1 - x = 0$

$1 = x$

Domain $\{x \mid x$ is a real number and $x \neq 1\}$

2. $f(x) = \dfrac{9x^2 - 9}{x^2 + 4x + 3}$

Undefined values when

$x^2 + 4x + 3 = 0$

$(x+3)(x+1) = 0$

$x + 3 = 0$ or $x + 1 = 0$

$x = -3$ or $x = -1$

Domain $\{x \mid x$ is a real number and $x \neq -3, x \neq -1\}$

3. $\dfrac{7x - 21}{24 - 8x} = \dfrac{7(x-3)}{8(3-x)} = \dfrac{7(x-3)}{-8(x-3)} = -\dfrac{7}{8}$

4. $\dfrac{x^2 - 4x}{x^2 + 5x - 36} = \dfrac{x(x-4)}{(x+9)(x-4)} = \dfrac{x}{x+9}$

5. $\dfrac{2x^3 + 16}{6x^2 + 12x} \cdot \dfrac{5}{x^2 - 2x + 4}$

$= \dfrac{2(x^3 + 8)}{6x(x+2)} \cdot \dfrac{5}{x^2 - 2x + 4}$

$= \dfrac{2(x+2)(x^2 - 2x + 4) \cdot 5}{6x(x+2)(x^2 - 2x + 4)} = \dfrac{5}{3x}$

6. $\dfrac{3x^2 - 12}{x^2 + 2x - 8} \div \dfrac{6x + 18}{x + 4}$

$= \dfrac{3(x^2 - 4)}{(x+4)(x-2)} \cdot \dfrac{x+4}{6(x+3)}$

$= \dfrac{(x+2)(x-2)}{2(x-2)(x+3)}$

$= \dfrac{x+2}{2(x+3)}$

7. $\dfrac{4x - 12}{2x - 9} \div \dfrac{3 - x}{4x^2 - 81} \cdot \dfrac{x+3}{5x + 15}$

$= \dfrac{4(x-3)}{2x - 9} \cdot \dfrac{(2x+9)(2x-9)}{-1(x-3)} \cdot \dfrac{x+3}{5(x+3)}$

$= -\dfrac{4(2x+9)}{5}$

8. $\dfrac{3 + 2x}{10 - x} + \dfrac{13 + x}{x - 10} = \dfrac{3 + 2x}{-1(x - 10)} + \dfrac{13 + x}{x - 10}$

$= \dfrac{-3 - 2x + 13 + x}{x - 10}$

$= \dfrac{10 - x}{x - 10}$

$= \dfrac{-1(x - 10)}{x - 10}$

$= -1$

9. $\dfrac{3}{x^2 - x - 6} + \dfrac{2}{x^2 - 5x + 6}$

$= \dfrac{3}{(x-3)(x+2)} + \dfrac{2}{(x-3)(x-2)}$

$= \dfrac{3(x-2) + 2(x+2)}{(x-3)(x+2)(x-2)}$

$= \dfrac{3x - 6 + 2x + 4}{(x-3)(x+2)(x-2)}$

$= \dfrac{5x - 2}{(x-3)(x+2)(x-2)}$

10.

$$\frac{5}{x-7}-\frac{2x}{3x-21}+\frac{x}{2x-14}$$

$$=\frac{5}{x-7}-\frac{2x}{3(x-7)}+\frac{x}{2(x-7)}$$

$$=\frac{5(6)-2x(2)+3x}{6(x-7)}$$

$$=\frac{30-4x+3x}{6(x-7)}$$

$$=\frac{30-x}{6(x-7)}\quad\text{or}\quad\frac{-x+30}{6(x-7)}$$

11.

$$\frac{3x}{5}\cdot\left(\frac{5}{x}-\frac{5}{2x}\right)=\frac{3x}{5}\cdot\left(\frac{5(2)-5}{2x}\right)$$

$$=\frac{3x}{5}\cdot\left(\frac{5}{2x}\right)$$

$$=\frac{3x\cdot5}{5\cdot2x}$$

$$=\frac{3}{2}$$

12.

$$\frac{\dfrac{4x}{13}}{\dfrac{20x}{13}}=\frac{4x}{13}\cdot\frac{13}{20x}=\frac{1}{5}$$

13.

$$\frac{\dfrac{5}{x}-\dfrac{7}{3x}}{\dfrac{9}{8x}-\dfrac{1}{x}}=\frac{\left(\dfrac{5}{x}-\dfrac{7}{3x}\right)24x}{\left(\dfrac{9}{8x}-\dfrac{1}{x}\right)24x}=\frac{120-56}{27-24}=\frac{64}{3}$$

14.

$$\frac{4x^2y+9x+3xz}{3xz}=\frac{4x^2y}{3xz}+\frac{9x}{3xz}+\frac{3xz}{3xz}$$

$$=\frac{4xy}{3z}+\frac{3}{z}+1$$

15.

$$\begin{array}{r}2x^2-x-2\\2x+1\overline{\smash{\big)}\,4x^3+0x^2-5x+0}\\\underline{4x^3+2x^2}\\-2x^2-5x\\\underline{-2x^2-\ x}\\-4x+0\\\underline{-4x-2}\\2\end{array}$$

Answer: $2x^2-x-2+\dfrac{2}{2x+1}$

16.

$$\begin{array}{r|rrrrr}-3 & 4 & -3 & 0 & -1 & -1\\ & & -12 & 45 & -135 & 408\\\hline & 4 & -15 & 45 & -136 & 407\end{array}$$

Answer: $4x^3-15x^2+45x-136+\dfrac{407}{x+3}$

17.

$$\begin{array}{r|rrrrr}-2 & 4 & 0 & 7 & -2 & -5\\ & & -8 & 16 & -46 & 96\\\hline & 4 & -8 & 23 & -48 & 91\end{array}$$

Thus, $P(-2)=91$.

18.

$$\frac{3}{x+2}-\frac{1}{5x}=\frac{2}{5x^2+10x}$$

$$\frac{3}{x+2}-\frac{1}{5x}=\frac{2}{5x(x+2)}$$

$$3(5x)-1(x+2)=2$$

$$15x-x-2=2$$

$$14x=4$$

$$x=\frac{4}{14}=\frac{2}{7}$$

19.

$$\frac{x^2+8}{x}-1=\frac{2(x+4)}{x}$$

$$x\left(\frac{x^2+8}{x}-1\right)=x\left(\frac{2(x+4)}{x}\right)$$

$$(x^2+8)-x=2(x+4)$$

$$x^2-x+8=2x+8$$

$$x^2-3x=0$$

$$x(x-3)=0$$

$$x=0\ \text{ or }\ x-3=0$$

$$x=3$$

Discard the answer 0 as extraneous. $x=3$ is the only solution.

20.

$$\frac{x+b}{a}=\frac{4x-7a}{b}$$

$$ab\left(\frac{x+b}{a}\right)=ab\left(\frac{4x-7a}{b}\right)$$

$$b(x+b)=a(4x-7a)$$

$$xb+b^2=4ax-7a^2$$

$$b^2+7a^2=4ax-xb$$

$$b^2+7a^2=x(4a-b)$$

$$x=\frac{7a^2+b^2}{4a-b}$$

21. Let x = the number.

$$(x+1) \cdot \frac{2}{x} = \frac{12}{5}$$

$$\frac{2(x+1)}{x} = \frac{12}{5}$$

$$\frac{2x+2}{x} = \frac{12}{5}$$

$$5(2x+2) = 12x$$

$$10x+10 = 12x$$

$$10 = 2x$$

$$5 = x$$

The number is 5.

22. Let t = time to weed garden together.

Note that 1 hr and 30 min = $\frac{3}{2}$ hours.

$$\frac{1}{2} + \frac{1}{3} = \frac{1}{t}$$
$$\frac{}{\frac{3}{2}}$$

$$\frac{1}{2} + \frac{2}{3} = \frac{1}{t}$$

$$6t\left(\frac{1}{2} + \frac{2}{3}\right) = 6t\left(\frac{1}{t}\right)$$

$$3t + 4t = 6$$

$$7t = 6$$

$$t = \frac{6}{7}$$

It takes them $\frac{6}{7}$ hour.

23. $W = \frac{k}{V}$

$$20 = \frac{k}{12}$$

$$k = 20(12) = 240$$

$$W = \frac{240}{V} = \frac{240}{15} = 16$$

24. $Q = kRS^2$

$$24 = k(3)(4)^2$$

$$24 = 48k$$

$$k = \frac{24}{48} = \frac{1}{2}$$

$$Q = \frac{1}{2}RS^2 = \frac{1}{2}(2)(3)^2 = 9$$

25. $S = k\sqrt{d}$

$$160 = k\sqrt{400}$$

$$160 = 20k$$

$$k = \frac{160}{20} = 8$$

$$S = 8\sqrt{d}$$

$$128 = 8\sqrt{d}$$

$$\sqrt{d} = \frac{128}{8}$$

$$\sqrt{d} = 16$$

$$d = 256$$

The height of the cliff is 256 feet.

Chapter 6 Cumulative Review

1. a. $8x$

   b. $8x+3$

   c. $x \div (-7)$ or $\frac{x}{-7}$

   d. $2x - 1\frac{6}{10} = 2x - 1.6$

2. a. $x - \frac{1}{3}$

   b. $5x - 6$

   c. $8x + 3$

   d. $\frac{7}{2-x}$

3. $\frac{y}{3} - \frac{y}{4} = \frac{1}{6}$

$$12\left(\frac{y}{3} - \frac{y}{4}\right) = 12\left(\frac{1}{6}\right)$$

$$4y - 3y = 2$$

$$y = 2$$

4. $\dfrac{x}{7} + \dfrac{x}{5} = \dfrac{12}{5}$

$35\left(\dfrac{x}{7} + \dfrac{x}{5}\right) = 35\left(\dfrac{12}{5}\right)$

$5x + 7x = 84$

$12x = 84$

$x = 7$

5. $c < 200$

$-14.25t + 598.69 < 200$

$-14.25t < -398.69$

$t > 27.98 \approx 28$

$1985 + 28 = 2013$

The consumption of cigarettes will be less than 200 billion per year in 2013 and after.

6. Let x = score on final exam.

$\dfrac{78 + 65 + 82 + 79 + 2x}{6} \geq 78$

$\dfrac{304 + 2x}{6} \geq 78$

$6\left(\dfrac{304 + 2x}{6}\right) \geq 6(78)$

$304 + 2x \geq 468$

$2x \geq 164$

$x \geq 82$

The minimum score she can make on her final exam is 82.

7. $\left|\dfrac{3x+1}{2}\right| = -2$ is impossible.

The solution is $\varnothing$.

8. $\left|\dfrac{2x-1}{3}\right| + 6 = 3$

$\left|\dfrac{2x-1}{3}\right| = -3$, which is impossible.

The solution is $\varnothing$.

9. $\left|\dfrac{2(x+1)}{3}\right| \leq 0$

$\dfrac{2(x+1)}{3} = 0$

$2(x+1) = 0$

$2x + 2 = 0$

$2x = -2$

$x = -1$

The solution is -1.

10. $\left|\dfrac{3(x-1)}{4}\right| \geq 2$

$\dfrac{3(x-1)}{4} \leq -2$ or $\dfrac{3(x-1)}{4} \geq 2$

$\dfrac{3x-3}{4} \leq -2$ or $\dfrac{3x-3}{4} \geq 2$

$3x - 3 \leq -8$ or $3x - 3 \geq 8$

$3x \leq -5$ or $3x \geq 11$

$x \leq -\dfrac{5}{3}$ or $x \geq \dfrac{11}{3}$

$\left(-\infty, -\dfrac{5}{3}\right] \cup \left[\dfrac{11}{3}, \infty\right)$

11. $y = -2x + 3$

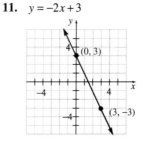

12. $y = -x + 3$

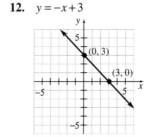

13. a. Function

b. Not a function

c. Function

14. $f(x) = -x^2 + 3x - 2$

a. $f(0) = -(0)^2 + 3(0) - 2 = -2$

b. $f(-3) = -(-3)^2 + 3(-3) - 2$

$= -9 - 9 - 2$

$= -20$

c. $f\left(\frac{1}{3}\right) = -\left(\frac{1}{3}\right)^2 + 3\left(\frac{1}{3}\right) - 2$

$= -\frac{1}{9} + 1 - 2$

$= -\frac{1}{9} + \frac{9}{9} - \frac{18}{9}$

$= \frac{-1 + 9 - 18}{9}$

$= -\frac{10}{9}$

15. $x - 3y = 6$

$-3y = -x + 6$

$y = \frac{1}{3}x - 2$

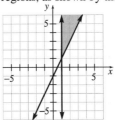

16. $3x - y = 6$

$-y = -3x + 6$

$y = 3x - 6$

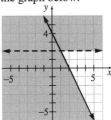

17. $y - (-5) = -3(x - 1)$

$y + 5 = -3x + 3$

$y = -3x - 2$

18. $y - 3 = \frac{1}{2}(x - (-1))$

$y - 3 = \frac{1}{2}(x + 1)$

$y - 3 = \frac{1}{2}x + \frac{1}{2}$

$y = \frac{1}{2}x + \frac{1}{2} + 3$

$y = \frac{1}{2}x + \frac{7}{2}$

$f(x) = \frac{1}{2}x + \frac{7}{2}$

19. $x \geq 1$ and $y \geq 2x - 1$

Graph each inequality. The intersection of the two inequalities is the overlap of the two shaded regions, as shown by the graph below.

20. $2x + y \leq 4$ or $y > 2$

Graph each inequality. The union of the two inequalities is both shaded regions, as shown by the graph below.

21. $\begin{cases} 3x - 2y = 10 \\ 4x - 3y = 15 \end{cases}$

Multiply the first equation by –4 and the second equation by 3, and add.

$-12x + 8y = -40$

$\underline{12x - 9y = 45}$

$-y = 5$

$y = -5$

Replace *y* with –5 in the first equation.

$$3x - 2(-5) = 10$$
$$3x + 10 = 10$$
$$3x = 0$$
$$x = 0$$

The solution is (0, –5).

22. $\begin{cases} -2x + 3y = 6 \\ 3x - y = 5 \end{cases}$

Solve the second equation for y: $y = 3x - 5$.

Replace y with $3x - 5$ in the first equation.
$$-2x + 3(3x - 5) = 6$$
$$-2x + 9x - 15 = 6$$
$$7x = 21$$
$$x = 3$$

Replace x with 3 in the equation $y = 3x - 5$.
$$y = 3(3) - 5 = 9 - 5 = 4$$

The solution is (3, 4).

23. $\begin{cases} 2x - 4y + 8z = 2 \ (1) \\ -x - 3y + z = 11 \ (2) \\ x - 2y + 4z = 0 \ (3) \end{cases}$

Add equation (2) and equation (3).
$$-5y + 5z = 11 \ (4)$$

Multiply equation (2) by 2 and add to equation (1).

$$-2x - 6y + 2z = 22$$
$$\underline{2x - 4y + 8z = 2}$$
$$-10y + 10z = 24 \ (5)$$

Use equations (4) and (5) to make a new system and then solve the new system

$\begin{cases} -5y + 5z = 11 \ (4) \\ -10y + 10z = 24 \ (5). \end{cases}$

Multiply equation (4) by –2 and add to equation (5).

$$10y - 10z = -22$$
$$\underline{-10y + 10z = 24}$$
$$0 = 2, \text{ which is impossible.}$$

The solution is $\varnothing$.

24. $\begin{cases} 2x - 2y + 4z = 6 \ (1) \\ -4x - y + z = -8 \ (2) \\ 3x - y + z = 6 \ (3) \end{cases}$

Multiply equation (2) by –1 and add to equation (3).
$$4x + y - z = 8$$
$$\underline{3x - y + z = 6}$$
$$7x \qquad = 14$$
$$x = 2$$

Multiply equation (2) by –2 and add to equation (1).
$$8x + 2y - 2z = 16$$
$$\underline{2x - 2y + 4z = 6}$$
$$10x \qquad + 2z = 22 \text{ or } 5x + z = 11$$

Replace x with 2 in the equation $5x + z = 11$.
$$5(2) + z = 11$$
$$10 + z = 11$$
$$z = 1$$

Replace x with 2 and z with 1 in equation (3).
$$3(2) - y + 1 = 6$$
$$7 - y = 6$$
$$-y = -1$$
$$y = 1$$

The solution is (2, 1, 1).

25. Let x = measure of the smallest angle, y = measure of the largest angle and, z = measure of the remaining angle.

$\begin{cases} x + y + z = 180 \qquad (1) \\ y = x + 80 \ (2) \\ z = x + 10 \ (3) \end{cases}$

Substitute $x + 80$ for y and $x + 10$ for z in equation (1).
$$x + (x + 80) + (x + 10) = 180$$
$$3x + 90 = 180$$
$$3x = 90$$
$$x = 30$$

Replace x with 30 in equation (2) and equation (3).
$$y = 30 + 80 = 110$$
$$z = 30 + 10 = 40$$

The angles measure 30°, 110°, and 40°.

26. Let x = the price of a ream of paper and y = the price of a box of manila folders.
$$\begin{cases} 3x+2y = 21.90 \ (1) \\ 5x+ \ y = 24.25 \ (2) \end{cases}$$
Multiply equation (2) by -2 and add to equation (1).
$$-10x-2y = -48.50$$
$$\underline{\ \ 3x+2y = 21.90}$$
$$-7x \ \ \ \ \ = -26.60$$
$$x = 3.80$$
Replace x with 3.80 in equation (2).
$$5(3.80)+y = 24.25$$
$$19+y = 24.25$$
$$y = 5.25$$
A ream of paper cost \$3.80 and a box of manila folders cost \$5.25.

27. $\begin{cases} x+2y+ \ z = 2 \\ -2x- \ y+2z = 5 \\ x+3y-2z = -8 \end{cases}$

$$\begin{bmatrix} 1 & 2 & 1 & | & 2 \\ -2 & -1 & 2 & | & 5 \\ 1 & 3 & -2 & | & -8 \end{bmatrix}$$
Multiply R1 by 2 and add to R2.
Multiply R1 by -1 and add to R3.
$$\begin{bmatrix} 1 & 2 & 1 & | & 2 \\ 0 & 3 & 4 & | & 9 \\ 0 & 1 & -3 & | & -10 \end{bmatrix}$$
Interchange R2 and R3.
$$\begin{bmatrix} 1 & 2 & 1 & | & 2 \\ 0 & 1 & -3 & | & -10 \\ 0 & 3 & 4 & | & 9 \end{bmatrix}$$
Mutiply R2 by -3 and add to R3.
$$\begin{bmatrix} 1 & 2 & 1 & | & 2 \\ 0 & 1 & -3 & | & -10 \\ 0 & 0 & 13 & | & 39 \end{bmatrix}$$
Divide R3 by 13.
$$\begin{bmatrix} 1 & 2 & 1 & | & 2 \\ 0 & 1 & -3 & | & -10 \\ 0 & 0 & 1 & | & 3 \end{bmatrix}$$
This corresponds to
$$\begin{cases} x+2y+ \ z = 2 \\ y-3z = -10 \\ z = 3. \end{cases}$$

$$y-3z = -10$$
$$y-3(3) = -10$$
$$y-9 = -10$$
$$y = -1$$
and so
$$x+2(-1)+(3) = 2$$
$$x-2+3 = 2$$
$$x+1 = 2$$
$$x = 1$$
The solution is $(1, -1, 3)$.

28. $\begin{cases} x+ \ y+ z = 9 \\ 2x-2y+3z = 2 \\ -3x+ \ y- z = 1 \end{cases}$

$$\begin{bmatrix} 1 & 1 & 1 & | & 9 \\ 2 & -2 & 3 & | & 2 \\ -3 & 1 & -1 & | & 1 \end{bmatrix}$$
Multiply R1 by -2 and add to R2.
Multiply R1 by 3 and add to R3.
$$\begin{bmatrix} 1 & 1 & 1 & | & 9 \\ 0 & -4 & 1 & | & -16 \\ 0 & 4 & 2 & | & 28 \end{bmatrix}$$
Divide R2 by -4.
$$\begin{bmatrix} 1 & 1 & 1 & | & 9 \\ 0 & 1 & -\frac{1}{4} & | & 4 \\ 0 & 4 & 2 & | & 28 \end{bmatrix}$$
Multiply R2 by -4 and add to R3.
$$\begin{bmatrix} 1 & 1 & 1 & | & 9 \\ 0 & 1 & -\frac{1}{4} & | & 4 \\ 0 & 0 & 3 & | & 12 \end{bmatrix}$$
Divide R3 by 3.
$$\begin{bmatrix} 1 & 1 & 1 & | & 9 \\ 0 & 1 & -\frac{1}{4} & | & 4 \\ 0 & 0 & 1 & | & 4 \end{bmatrix}$$
This corresponds to
$$\begin{cases} x+y+ \ z = 9 \\ y-\frac{1}{4}z = 4 \\ z = 4. \end{cases}$$

$$y - \frac{1}{4}(4) = 4$$

$$y - 1 = 4$$

$$y = 5$$

and so

$$x + 5 + 4 = 9$$

$$x + 9 = 9$$

$$x = 0$$

The solution is $(0, 5, 4)$.

29. a. $7^0 = 1$

b. $-7^0 = -1 \cdot 7^0 = -1 \cdot 1 = -1$

c. $(2x + 5)^0 = 1$

d. $2x^0 = 2 \cdot x^0 = 2 \cdot 1 = 2$

30. a. $2^{-2} + 3^{-1} = \dfrac{1}{2^2} + \dfrac{1}{3}$

$$= \frac{1}{4} + \frac{1}{3}$$

$$= \frac{3}{12} + \frac{4}{12}$$

$$= \frac{7}{12}$$

b. $-6a^0 = -6 \cdot a^0 = -6 \cdot 1 = -6$

c. $\dfrac{x^{-5}}{x^{-2}} = x^{-5-(-2)} = x^{-3} = \dfrac{1}{x^3}$

31. a. $x^{-b}(2x^b)^2 = \dfrac{2^2(x^b)^2}{x^b}$

$$= \frac{4x^{2b}}{x^b}$$

$$= 4x^{2b-b}$$

$$= 4x^b$$

b. $\dfrac{(y^{3a})^2}{y^{a-6}} = \dfrac{y^{6a}}{y^{a-6}} = y^{6a-(a-6)} = y^{5a+6}$

32. a. $3x^{4a}(4x^{-a})^2 = 3x^{4a} \cdot 16x^{-2a}$

$$= 48x^{4a+(-2a)}$$

$$= 48x^{2a}$$

b. $\dfrac{(y^{4b})^3}{y^{2b-3}} = \dfrac{y^{12b}}{y^{2b-3}}$

$$= y^{12b-(2b-3)}$$

$$= y^{12b-2b+3}$$

$$= y^{10b+3}$$

33. a. $3x^2$ has degree = 2

b. $-2^3x^5 = -8x^5$ has degree = 5

c. y has degree = 1

d. $12x^2yz^3$ has degree = $2 + 1 + 3 = 6$

e. 5 has degree = 0

34. $(2x^2 + 8x - 3) - (2x - 7)$

$$= 2x^2 + 8x - 3 - 2x + 7$$

$$= 2x^2 + 6x + 4$$

35. $[3 + (2a + b)]^2$

$$= 3^2 + 2(3)(2a + b) + (2a + b)^2$$

$$= 9 + 6(2a + b) + (4a^2 + 2(2a)b + b^2)$$

$$= 9 + 12a + 6b + 4a^2 + 4ab + b^2$$

36. $[4 + (3x - y)]^2$

$$= 4^2 + 2(4)(3x - y) + (3x - y)^2$$

$$= 16 + 8(3x - y) + (9x^2 - 2(3x)y + y^2)$$

$$= 16 + 24x - 8y + 9x^2 - 6xy + y^2$$

37. $ab - 6a + 2b - 12 = a(b - 6) + 2(b - 6)$

$$= (b - 6)(a + 2)$$

38. $xy + 2x - 5y - 10 = x(y + 2) - 5(y + 2)$

$$= (y + 2)(x - 5)$$

39. $2n^2 - 38n + 80 = 2(n^2 - 19n + 40)$

40. $6x^2 - x - 35 = (2x - 5)(3x + 7)$

41. $x^2 + 4x + 4 - y^2$

$= (x^2 + 4x + 4) - y^2$

$= (x + 2)^2 - y^2$

$= [(x + 2) + y][(x + 2) - y]$

$= (x + 2 + y)(x + 2 - y)$

42. $4x^2 - 4x + 1 - 9y^2$

$= (4x^2 - 4x + 1) - 9y^2$

$= (2x - 1)^2 - (3y)^2$

$= [(2x - 1) + 3y][(2x - 1) - 3y]$

$= (2x - 1 + 3y)(2x - 1 - 3y)$

43. $(x + 2)(x - 6) = 0$

$x + 2 = 0 \quad \text{or} \quad x - 6 = 0$

$x = -2 \quad \text{or} \quad x = 6$

The solutions are -2 and 6.

44. $2x(3x + 1)(x - 3) = 0$

$\underline{x = 0} \quad \text{or} \quad 3x + 1 = 0 \quad \text{or} \quad \underline{x = 3}$

$3x = -1 \quad \text{or} \quad \underline{x = 3}$

$\underline{x = -\dfrac{1}{3}}$

The solutions are $-\dfrac{1}{3}, 0, 3$.

45. $\dfrac{2x^2}{10x^3 - 2x^2} = \dfrac{2x^2}{2x^2(5x - 1)} = \dfrac{1}{5x - 1}$

46. a. Domain: $(-\infty, \infty)$; Range: $[-4, \infty)$

b. x-intercepts: $(-2, 0), (2, 0)$
y-intercept: $(0, -4)$

c. There is no such point.

d. The point with the least y-value is $(0, -4)$.

e. $-2, 2$

f. Between $x = -2$ and $x = 2$, or $(-2, 2)$.

g. The solutions are -2 and 2.

47. $\dfrac{5k}{k^2 - 4} - \dfrac{2}{k^2 + k - 2}$

$= \dfrac{5k}{(k + 2)(k - 2)} - \dfrac{2}{(k + 2)(k - 1)}$

$= \dfrac{5k(k - 1) - 2(k - 2)}{(k + 2)(k - 2)(k - 1)}$

$= \dfrac{5k^2 - 5k - 2k + 4}{(k + 2)(k - 2)(k - 1)}$

$= \dfrac{5k^2 - 7k + 4}{(k + 2)(k - 2)(k - 1)}$

48. $\dfrac{5a}{a^2 - 4} - \dfrac{3}{2 - a}$

$= \dfrac{5a}{(a + 2)(a - 2)} + \dfrac{3}{a - 2}$

$= \dfrac{5a + 3(a + 2)}{(a + 2)(a - 2)}$

$= \dfrac{5a + 3a + 6}{(a + 2)(a - 2)}$

$= \dfrac{8a + 6}{(a + 2)(a - 2)}$

49. $\dfrac{3}{x} - \dfrac{x + 21}{3x} = \dfrac{5}{3}$

$3x\left(\dfrac{3}{x} - \dfrac{x + 21}{3x}\right) = 3x\left(\dfrac{5}{3}\right)$

$9 - (x + 21) = 5x$

$9 - x - 21 = 5x$

$-x - 12 = 5x$

$-12 = 6x$

$-2 = x$

The solution is -2.

50. $\dfrac{3x - 4}{2x} = -\dfrac{8}{x}$

$x(3x - 4) = -8(2x)$

$3x^2 - 4x = -16x$

$3x^2 + 12x = 0$

$3x(x + 4) = 0$

$3x = 0 \quad \text{or} \quad x + 4 = 0$

$x = 0 \quad \text{or} \quad x = -4$

Discard the answer 0 as extraneous.

$x = -4$ is the only solution.

Chapter 7

Mental Math 7.1

1. D

2. A, C

3. D

4. C

Exercise Set 7.1

1. $\sqrt{100} = 10$ because $10^2 = 100$.

3. $\sqrt{\dfrac{1}{4}} = \dfrac{1}{2}$ because $\left(\dfrac{1}{2}\right)^2 = \dfrac{1}{4}$.

5. $\sqrt{0.0001} = 0.01$ because $(0.01)^2 = 0.0001$.

7. $-\sqrt{36} = -1 \cdot \sqrt{36} = -1 \cdot 6 = -6$ because $6^2 = 36$.

9. $\sqrt{x^{10}} = x^5$ because $(x^5)^2 = x^{10}$.

11. $\sqrt{16y^6} = 4y^3$ because $(4y^3)^2 = 16y^6$.

13. $\sqrt{7} \approx 2.646$
    Since $4 < 7 < 9$, then $\sqrt{4} < \sqrt{7} < \sqrt{9}$, or
    $2 < \sqrt{7} < 3$. The approximation is between 2 and
    3 and thus is reasonable.

15. $\sqrt{38} \approx 6.164$
    Since $36 < 38 < 49$, then $\sqrt{36} < \sqrt{38} < \sqrt{49}$, or
    $6 < \sqrt{38} < 7$. The approximation is between 6
    and 7 and thus is reasonable.

17. $\sqrt{200} \approx 14.142$
    Since $196 < 200 < 225$, then
    $\sqrt{196} < \sqrt{200} < \sqrt{225}$, or $14 < \sqrt{200} < 15$. The
    approximation is between 14 and 15 and thus is
    reasonable.

19. $\sqrt[3]{64} = 4$ because $4^3 = 64$.

21. $\sqrt[3]{\dfrac{1}{8}} = \dfrac{1}{2}$ because $\left(\dfrac{1}{2}\right)^3 = \dfrac{1}{8}$.

23. $\sqrt[3]{-1} = -1$ because $(-1)^3 = -1$.

25. $\sqrt[3]{x^{12}} = x^4$ because $(x^4)^3 = x^{12}$.

27. $\sqrt[3]{-27x^9} = -3x^3$ because $(-3x^3)^3 = -27x^9$.

29. $-\sqrt[4]{16} = -2$ because $2^4 = 16$.

31. $\sqrt[4]{-16}$ is not a real number. There is no real
    number that, when raised to the fourth power, is
    -16.

33. $\sqrt[5]{-32} = -2$ because $(-2)^5 = -32$.

35. $\sqrt[5]{x^{20}} = x^4$ because $(x^4)^5 = x^{20}$.

37. $\sqrt[6]{64x^{12}} = 2x^2$ because $(2x^2)^6 = 64x^{12}$.

39. $\sqrt{81x^4} = 9x^2$ because $(9x^2)^2 = 81x^4$.

41. $\sqrt[4]{256x^8} = 4x^2$ because $(4x^2)^4 = 256x^8$.

43. $\sqrt{(-8)^2} = |-8| = 8$

45. $\sqrt[3]{(-8)^3} = -8$

47. $\sqrt{4x^2} = 2|x|$

49. $\sqrt[3]{x^3} = x$

51. $\sqrt{(x-5)^2} = |x-5|$

53. $\sqrt{x^2 + 4x + 4} = \sqrt{(x+2)^2} = |x+2|$

55. $-\sqrt{121} = -11$

57. $\sqrt[3]{8x^3} = 2x$

59. $\sqrt{y^{12}} = y^6$

61. $\sqrt{25a^2b^{20}} = 5ab^{10}$

63. $\sqrt[3]{-27x^{12}y^9} = -3x^4y^3$

65. $\sqrt[4]{a^{16}b^4} = a^4b$

67. $\sqrt[5]{-32x^{10}y^5} = -2x^2y$

69. $\sqrt{\dfrac{25}{49}} = \dfrac{5}{7}$

71. $\sqrt{\dfrac{x^2}{4y^2}} = \dfrac{x}{2y}$

73. $-\sqrt[3]{\dfrac{z^{21}}{27x^3}} = -\dfrac{z^7}{3x}$

75. $\sqrt[4]{\dfrac{x^4}{16}} = \dfrac{x}{2}$

77. $f(x) = \sqrt{2x+3}$
$f(0) = \sqrt{2(0)+3} = \sqrt{3}$

79. $g(x) = \sqrt[3]{x-8}$
$g(7) = \sqrt[3]{7-8} = \sqrt[3]{-1} = -1$

81. $g(x) = \sqrt[3]{x-8}$
$g(-19) = \sqrt[3]{-19-8} = \sqrt[3]{-27} = -3$

83. $f(x) = \sqrt{2x+3}$
$f(2) = \sqrt{2(2)+3} = \sqrt{7}$

85. $f(x) = \sqrt{x}+2$
Domain: $[0, \infty)$

Using a graphing calculator, define $y_1 = \sqrt{x}+2$ and graph it using a $[-3, 10, 1]$ by $[-2, 10, 1]$ window.

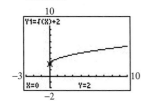 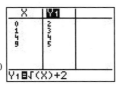

87. $f(x) = \sqrt{x-3}$
Domain: $[3, \infty)$

x	$f(x) = \sqrt{x-3}$
3	$\sqrt{3-3} = \sqrt{0} = 0$
4	$\sqrt{4-3} = \sqrt{1} = 1$
7	$\sqrt{7-3} = \sqrt{4} = 2$
12	$\sqrt{12-3} = \sqrt{9} = 3$

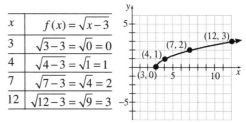

Using a graphing calculator, define $y_1 = \sqrt{x-3}$ and graph it using a $[-2, 12, 1]$ by $[-2, 10, 1]$ window.

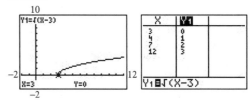

89. The graph of $f(x) = \sqrt{x}+2$ will look the same as the graph of $y = \sqrt{x}$ but shifted upward 2 units. Thus, the answer is C.

91. The graph of $f(x) = \sqrt{x-3}$ will look the same as the graph of $y = \sqrt{x}$ but shifted to the right 3 units. Thus, the answer is D.

93. The graph of $f(x) = \sqrt[3]{x}+1$ will look the same as the graph of $y = \sqrt[3]{x}$ but shifted upward 1unit. Thus, the answer is A.

95. The graph of $f(x) = \sqrt[3]{x-1}$ will look the same as the graph of $y = \sqrt[3]{x}$ but shifted to the right 1unit. Thus, the answer is B.

97. $f(x) = \sqrt[3]{x}+1$
Domain: $(-\infty, \infty)$

Using a graphing calculator, define $y_1 = \sqrt[3]{x}+1$ and graph it using a $[-30, 30, 5]$ by $[-5, 5, 1]$ window.

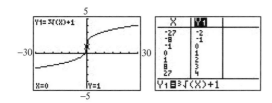

99. $g(x) = \sqrt[3]{x-1}$

Domain: $(-\infty, \infty)$

x	$g(x) = \sqrt[3]{x-1}$
1	$\sqrt[3]{1-1} = \sqrt[3]{0} = 0$
2	$\sqrt[3]{2-1} = \sqrt[3]{1} = 1$
0	$\sqrt[3]{0-1} = \sqrt[3]{-1} = -1$
9	$\sqrt[3]{9-1} = \sqrt[3]{8} = 2$
-7	$\sqrt[3]{-7-1} = \sqrt[3]{-8} = -2$

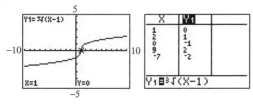

Using a graphing calculator, define $y_1 = \sqrt[3]{x-1}$
and graph it using a $[-10, 10, 1]$ by $[-5, 5, 1]$
window.

101. $(-2x^3 y^2)^5 = (-2)^5 x^{3\cdot 5} y^{2\cdot 5} = -32x^{15} y^{10}$

103. $(-3x^2 y^3 z^5)(20x^5 y^7) = -3(20)x^{2+5} y^{3+7} z^5$
$= -60x^7 y^{10} z^5$

105. $\dfrac{7x^{-1} y}{14(x^5 y^2)^{-2}} = \dfrac{7x^{-1} y}{14x^{-10} y^{-4}} = \dfrac{x^9 y^5}{2}$

107. Answers may vary. One possibility follows: It is
not possible for the square of a real number to
equal -64.

109. $44 < 160 < 169$ so $\sqrt{144} < \sqrt{160} < \sqrt{169}$, or
$12 < \sqrt{160} < 13$. Thus $\sqrt{160}$ is between 12 and
13. Therefore, the answer is B.

111. $\sqrt{30} \approx 5$, $\sqrt{10} \approx 3$, and $\sqrt{90} \approx 10$ so
$P = \sqrt{30} + \sqrt{10} + \sqrt{90} \approx 5 + 3 + 10 = 18$.
Therefore, the answer is B.

113. $B = \sqrt{\dfrac{hw}{3131}} = \sqrt{\dfrac{66 \cdot 135}{3131}} = \sqrt{\dfrac{8910}{3131}} \approx 1.69$ sq. m

115. Answers may vary. One possibility follows: If
$\sqrt{13} \approx 5.7$ were true, then 5.7^2 would
approximately equal 13. However, since
$5 < 5.7 < 6$, then $5^2 < 5.7^2 < 6^2$ which means
$25 < 5.7^2 < 36$. Now since 13 is not between 25
and 36, $\sqrt{13}$ cannot equal 5.7.

Mental Math 7.2

1. A

2. B

3. C

4. A

5. B

6. B

7. B

8. C

9. B

10. B

Exercise Set 7.2

1. $49^{1/2} = \sqrt{49} = 7$

3. $27^{1/3} = \sqrt[3]{27} = 3$

5. $\left(\dfrac{1}{16}\right)^{1/4} = \sqrt[4]{\dfrac{1}{16}} = \dfrac{1}{2}$

7. $169^{1/2} = \sqrt{169} = 13$

9. $2m^{1/3} = 2\sqrt[3]{m}$

11. $(9x^4)^{1/2} = \sqrt{9x^4} = 3x^2$

13. $(-27)^{1/3} = \sqrt[3]{-27} = -3$

15. $-16^{1/4} = -\sqrt[4]{16} = -2$

17. $16^{3/4} = \left(\sqrt[4]{16}\right)^3 = 2^3 = 8$

19. $(-64)^{2/3} = \left(\sqrt[3]{-64}\right)^2 = (-4)^2 = 16$

21. $(-16)^{3/4} = \left(\sqrt[4]{-16}\right)^3$ is not a real number.

23. $(2x)^{3/5} = \sqrt[5]{(2x)^3}$ or $\left(\sqrt[5]{2x}\right)^3$

25. $(7x+2)^{2/3} = \sqrt[3]{(7x+2)^2}$ or $\left(\sqrt[3]{7x+2}\right)^2$

27. $\left(\dfrac{16}{9}\right)^{3/2} = \left(\sqrt{\dfrac{16}{9}}\right)^3 = \left(\dfrac{4}{3}\right)^3 = \dfrac{64}{27}$

29. $8^{-4/3} = \dfrac{1}{8^{4/3}} = \dfrac{1}{\left(\sqrt[3]{8}\right)^4} = \dfrac{1}{2^4} = \dfrac{1}{16}$

31. $(-64)^{-2/3} = \dfrac{1}{(-64)^{2/3}} = \dfrac{1}{\left(\sqrt[3]{-64}\right)^2} = \dfrac{1}{(-4)^2} = \dfrac{1}{16}$

33. $(-4)^{-3/2} = \dfrac{1}{(-4)^{3/2}} = \dfrac{1}{\left(\sqrt{-4}\right)^3}$ is not a real number.

35. $x^{-1/4} = \dfrac{1}{x^{1/4}}$

37. $\dfrac{1}{a^{-2/3}} = a^{2/3}$

39. $\dfrac{5}{7x^{-3/4}} = \dfrac{5x^{3/4}}{7}$

41. Answers may vary. One possibility follows: In both cases, to write the expression with positive exponents, we write 1 over x to the opposite of the existing negative exponent. That is,
$$x^{-7} = \dfrac{1}{x^{-(-7)}} = \dfrac{1}{x^7} \text{ and } x^{-1/4} = \dfrac{1}{x^{-(-1/4)}} = \dfrac{1}{x^{1/4}}.$$

43. $a^{2/3}a^{5/3} = a^{2/3+5/3} = a^{7/3}$

45. $x^{-2/5} \cdot x^{7/5} = x^{-\frac{2}{5}+\frac{7}{5}} = x^{5/5} = x$

47. $3^{1/4} \cdot 3^{3/8} = 3^{\frac{1}{4}+\frac{3}{8}} = 3^{\frac{2}{8}+\frac{3}{8}} = 3^{5/8}$

49. $\dfrac{y^{1/3}}{y^{1/6}} = y^{\frac{1}{3}-\frac{1}{6}} = y^{\frac{2}{6}-\frac{1}{6}} = y^{1/6}$

51. $(4u^2)^{3/2} = 4^{3/2}u^{2(3/2)} = \left(\sqrt{4}\right)^3 u^3 = 2^3 u^3 = 8u^3$

53. $\dfrac{b^{1/2}b^{3/4}}{-b^{1/4}} = -b^{\frac{1}{2}+\frac{3}{4}-\frac{1}{4}} = -b^{\frac{2}{4}+\frac{3}{4}-\frac{1}{4}} = -b^1 = -b$

55. $\dfrac{(3x^{1/4})^3}{x^{1/12}} = \dfrac{3^3 x^{3/4}}{x^{1/12}}$
$$= 27x^{\frac{3}{4}-\frac{1}{12}}$$
$$= 27x^{\frac{9}{12}-\frac{1}{12}}$$
$$= 27x^{8/12}$$
$$= 27x^{2/3}$$

57. $y^{1/2}(y^{1/2} - y^{2/3}) = y^{1/2}y^{1/2} - y^{1/2}y^{2/3}$
$$= y^{1/2+1/2} - y^{1/2+2/3}$$
$$= y^1 - y^{7/6}$$
$$= y - y^{7/6}$$

59. $x^{2/3}(2x-2) = 2xx^{2/3} - 2x^{2/3}$
$$= 2x^{1+2/3} - 2x^{2/3}$$
$$= 2x^{5/3} - 2x^{2/3}$$

61. $(2x^{1/3}+3)(2x^{1/3}-3) = (2x^{1/3})^2 - 3^2$
$$= 2^2(x^{1/3})^2 - 9$$
$$= 4x^{2/3} - 9$$

63. $x^{8/3} + x^{10/3} = x^{8/3}(1) + x^{8/3}(x^{2/3})$
$$= x^{8/3}(1 + x^{2/3})$$

65. $x^{2/5} - 3x^{1/5} = x^{1/5}(x^{1/5}) - x^{1/5}(3)$
$$= x^{1/5}(x^{1/5} - 3)$$

67. $5x^{-1/3} + x^{2/3} = x^{-1/3}(5) + x^{-1/3}(x^{3/3})$
$$= x^{-1/3}(5 + x)$$

69. $\sqrt[6]{x^3} = x^{3/6} = x^{1/2} = \sqrt{x}$

71. $\sqrt[6]{4} = 4^{1/6} = (2^2)^{1/6} = 2^{1/3} = \sqrt[3]{2}$

73. $\sqrt[4]{16x^2} = (16x^2)^{1/4} = 16^{1/4}x^{2/4} = 2x^{1/2} = 2\sqrt{x}$

75. $\sqrt[8]{x^4 y^4} = (x^4 y^4)^{1/8}$
$= x^{4/8} y^{4/8}$
$= x^{1/2} y^{1/2}$
$= (xy)^{1/2}$
$= \sqrt{xy}$

77. $\sqrt[3]{y} \cdot \sqrt[5]{y^2} = y^{1/3} \cdot y^{2/5}$
$= y^{\frac{5}{15} + \frac{6}{15}}$
$= y^{11/15}$
$= \sqrt[15]{y^{11}}$

79. $\dfrac{\sqrt[3]{b^2}}{\sqrt[4]{b}} = \dfrac{b^{2/3}}{b^{1/4}} = b^{\frac{2}{3} - \frac{1}{4}} = b^{\frac{8}{12} - \frac{3}{12}} = b^{5/12} = \sqrt[12]{b^5}$

81. $\dfrac{\sqrt[3]{a^2}}{\sqrt[6]{a}} = \dfrac{a^{2/3}}{a^{1/6}} = a^{\frac{2}{3} - \frac{1}{6}} = a^{\frac{4}{6} - \frac{1}{6}} = a^{3/6} = a^{1/2} = \sqrt{a}$

83. $\sqrt{3} \cdot \sqrt[3]{4} = 3^{1/2} \cdot 4^{1/3}$
$= 3^{3/6} \cdot 4^{2/6}$
$= (3^3 \cdot 4^2)^{1/6}$
$= (432)^{1/6}$
$= \sqrt[6]{432}$

85. $\sqrt[5]{7} \cdot \sqrt[3]{y} = 7^{1/5} \cdot y^{1/3}$
$= 7^{3/15} \cdot y^{5/15}$
$= (7^3 \cdot y^5)^{1/15}$
$= (343 y^5)^{1/15}$
$= \sqrt[15]{343 y^5}$

87. $75 = 25 \cdot 3$

89. $48 = 4 \cdot 12$ or $16 \cdot 3$

91. $16 = 8 \cdot 2$

93. $54 = 27 \cdot 2$

95. $B(w) = 70 w^{3/4}$
$B(60) = 70(60)^{3/4}$
≈ 1509 calories

97. $f(x) = 1.54 x^{9/5}$
$f(10) = 1.54(10)^{9/5}$
≈ 97.2 million subscriptions

99. $\square \cdot a^{2/3} = a^{3/3}$
$\square = \dfrac{a^{3/3}}{a^{2/3}}$
$\square = a^{3/3 - 2/3}$
$\square = a^{1/3}$

101. $\dfrac{\square}{x^{-2/5}} = x^{3/5}$
$x^{-2/5} \left(\dfrac{\square}{x^{-2/5}} \right) = x^{3/5} \cdot x^{-2/5}$
$\square = x^{3/5 - 2/5}$
$\square = x^{1/5}$

103. $8^{1/4} \approx 1.6818$

105. $18^{3/5} \approx 5.6645$

107. $\dfrac{\sqrt{t}}{\sqrt{u}} = \dfrac{t^{1/2}}{u^{1/2}}$

Exercise Set 7.3

1. $\sqrt{7} \cdot \sqrt{2} = \sqrt{7 \cdot 2} = \sqrt{14}$

3. $\sqrt[4]{8} \cdot \sqrt[4]{2} = \sqrt[4]{8 \cdot 2} = \sqrt[4]{16} = 2$

5. $\sqrt[3]{4} \cdot \sqrt[3]{9} = \sqrt[3]{4 \cdot 9} = \sqrt[3]{36}$

7. $\sqrt{2} \cdot \sqrt{3x} = \sqrt{2 \cdot 3x} = \sqrt{6x}$

9. $\sqrt{\dfrac{7}{x}} \cdot \sqrt{\dfrac{2}{y}} = \sqrt{\dfrac{7}{x} \cdot \dfrac{2}{y}} = \sqrt{\dfrac{14}{xy}}$

11. $\sqrt[4]{4x^3} \cdot \sqrt[4]{5} = \sqrt[4]{4x^3 \cdot 5} = \sqrt[4]{20x^3}$

13. $\sqrt{\dfrac{6}{49}} = \dfrac{\sqrt{6}}{\sqrt{49}} = \dfrac{\sqrt{6}}{7}$

15. $\sqrt{\dfrac{2}{49}} = \dfrac{\sqrt{2}}{\sqrt{49}} = \dfrac{\sqrt{2}}{7}$

17. $\sqrt[4]{\dfrac{x^3}{16}} = \dfrac{\sqrt[4]{x^3}}{\sqrt[4]{16}} = \dfrac{\sqrt[4]{x^3}}{2}$

19. $\sqrt[3]{\dfrac{4}{27}} = \dfrac{\sqrt[3]{4}}{\sqrt[3]{27}} = \dfrac{\sqrt[3]{4}}{3}$

21. $\sqrt[4]{\dfrac{8}{x^8}} = \dfrac{\sqrt[4]{8}}{\sqrt[4]{x^8}} = \dfrac{\sqrt[4]{8}}{x^2}$

23. $\sqrt[3]{\dfrac{2x}{81y^{12}}} = \dfrac{\sqrt[3]{2x}}{\sqrt[3]{81y^{12}}} = \dfrac{\sqrt[3]{2x}}{\sqrt[3]{27y^{12}} \cdot \sqrt[3]{3}} = \dfrac{\sqrt[3]{2x}}{3y^4\sqrt[3]{3}}$

25. $\sqrt{\dfrac{x^2 y}{100}} = \dfrac{\sqrt{x^2 y}}{\sqrt{100}} = \dfrac{\sqrt{x^2}\sqrt{y}}{10} = \dfrac{x\sqrt{y}}{10}$

27. $\sqrt{\dfrac{5x^2}{4y^2}} = \dfrac{\sqrt{5x^2}}{\sqrt{4y^2}} = \dfrac{\sqrt{5}\sqrt{x^2}}{2y} = \dfrac{\sqrt{5}x}{2y}$

29. $-\sqrt[3]{\dfrac{z^7}{27x^3}} = -\dfrac{\sqrt[3]{z^7}}{\sqrt[3]{27x^3}} = -\dfrac{\sqrt[3]{z^6 z}}{3x} = -\dfrac{z^2\sqrt[3]{z}}{3x}$

31. $\sqrt{32} = \sqrt{16 \cdot 2} = \sqrt{16} \cdot \sqrt{2} = 4\sqrt{2}$

33. $\sqrt[3]{192} = \sqrt[3]{64 \cdot 3} = \sqrt[3]{64} \cdot \sqrt[3]{3} = 4\sqrt[3]{3}$

35. $5\sqrt{75} = 5\sqrt{25 \cdot 3} = 5\sqrt{25} \cdot \sqrt{3} = 5(5)\sqrt{3} = 25\sqrt{3}$

37. $\sqrt{24} = \sqrt{4 \cdot 6} = \sqrt{4} \cdot \sqrt{6} = 2\sqrt{6}$

39. $\sqrt{100x^5} = \sqrt{100x^4 \cdot x} = \sqrt{100x^4} \cdot \sqrt{x} = 10x^2\sqrt{x}$

41. $\sqrt[3]{16y^7} = \sqrt[3]{8y^6 \cdot 2y} = \sqrt[3]{8y^6} \cdot \sqrt[3]{2y} = 2y^2\sqrt[3]{2y}$

43. $\sqrt[4]{a^8 b^7} = \sqrt[4]{a^8 b^4 \cdot b^3} = \sqrt[4]{a^8 b^4} \cdot \sqrt[4]{b^3} = a^2 b\sqrt[4]{b^3}$

45. $\sqrt{y^5} = \sqrt{y^4 \cdot y} = \sqrt{y^4} \cdot \sqrt{y} = y^2\sqrt{y}$

47. $\sqrt{25a^2 b^3} = \sqrt{25a^2 b^2 \cdot b} = \sqrt{25a^2 b^2} \cdot \sqrt{b} = 5ab\sqrt{b}$

49. $\sqrt[5]{-32x^{10}y} = \sqrt[5]{-32x^{10} \cdot y}$
$= \sqrt[5]{-32x^{10}} \cdot \sqrt[5]{y}$
$= -2x^2\sqrt[5]{y}$

51. $\sqrt[3]{50x^{14}} = \sqrt[3]{x^{12} \cdot 50x^2}$
$= \sqrt[3]{x^{12}} \cdot \sqrt[3]{50x^2}$
$= x^4\sqrt[3]{50x^2}$

53. $-\sqrt{32a^8 b^7} = -\sqrt{16a^8 b^6 \cdot 2b}$
$= -\sqrt{16a^8 b^6} \cdot \sqrt{2b}$
$= -4a^4 b^3\sqrt{2b}$

55. $\sqrt{9x^7 y^9} = \sqrt{9x^6 y^8 \cdot xy}$
$= \sqrt{9x^6 y^8} \cdot \sqrt{xy}$
$= 3x^3 y^4\sqrt{xy}$

57. $\sqrt[3]{125r^9 s^{12}} = 5r^3 s^4$

59. $\dfrac{\sqrt{14}}{\sqrt{7}} = \sqrt{\dfrac{14}{7}} = \sqrt{2}$

61. $\dfrac{\sqrt[3]{24}}{\sqrt[3]{3}} = \sqrt[3]{\dfrac{24}{3}} = \sqrt[3]{8} = 2$

63. $\dfrac{5\sqrt[4]{48}}{\sqrt[4]{3}} = 5\sqrt[4]{\dfrac{48}{3}} = 5\sqrt[4]{16} = 5(2) = 10$

65. $\dfrac{\sqrt{x^5 y^3}}{\sqrt{xy}} = \sqrt{\dfrac{x^5 y^3}{xy}} = \sqrt{x^4 y^2} = x^2 y$

67. $\dfrac{8\sqrt[3]{54m^7}}{\sqrt[3]{2m}} = 8\sqrt[3]{\dfrac{54m^7}{2m}}$
$= 8\sqrt[3]{27m^6}$
$= 8(3m^2)$
$= 24m^2$

69. $\dfrac{3\sqrt{100x^2}}{2\sqrt{2x^{-1}}} = \dfrac{3}{2}\sqrt{\dfrac{100x^2}{2x^{-1}}}$
$= \dfrac{3}{2}\sqrt{50x^3}$
$= \dfrac{3}{2}\sqrt{25x^2 \cdot 2}$
$= \dfrac{3}{2}(5x)\sqrt{2}$
$= \dfrac{15x}{2}\sqrt{2}$

71. $\dfrac{\sqrt[4]{96a^{10}b^3}}{\sqrt[4]{3a^2 b^3}} = \sqrt[4]{\dfrac{96a^{10}b^3}{3a^2 b^3}}$
$= \sqrt[4]{32a^8}$
$= \sqrt[4]{16a^8 \cdot 2}$
$= 2a^2\sqrt[4]{2}$

73. $6x + 8x = 14x$

75. $(2x+3)(x-5) = 2x^2 - 10x + 3x - 15$
$= 2x^2 - 7x - 15$

77. $9y^2 - 8y^2 = 1y^2 = y^2$

79. $-3(x+5) = -3x - 3(5) = -3x - 15$

81. $(x-4)^2 = x^2 - 2(x)(4) + 4^2$
$= x^2 - 8x + 16$

83. $A = \pi r \sqrt{r^2 + h^2}$

    a. $A = \pi(4)\sqrt{4^2 + 3^2}$
        $= 4\pi\sqrt{16 + 9}$
        $= 4\pi\sqrt{25}$
        $= 4\pi(5)$
        $= 20\pi$ sq. centimeters

    b. $A = \pi(6.8)\sqrt{(6.8)^2 + (7.2)^2}$
        $= 6.8\pi\sqrt{46.24 + 51.84}$
        $= 6.8\pi\sqrt{98.08}$
        ≈ 211.57 sq. feet

85. $F(x) = 0.6\sqrt{49 - x^2}$

    a. $F(3) = 0.6\sqrt{49 - 3^2}$
        $= 0.6\sqrt{49 - 9}$
        $= 0.6\sqrt{40} \approx 3.8$ times

    b. $F(5) = 0.6\sqrt{49 - 5^2}$
        $= 0.6\sqrt{49 - 25}$
        $= 0.6\sqrt{24} \approx 2.9$ times

    c. Answers may vary. One possibility follows:
The owner can use the equation to predict the general demand depending on his or her two-day rental price. Based on this demand (and perhaps taking other factors into consideration) he or she can determine the number of copies of each tape that should be kept in stock.

Mental Math 7.4

1. $2\sqrt{3} + 4\sqrt{3} = (2+4)\sqrt{3} = 6\sqrt{3}$

2. $5\sqrt{7} + 3\sqrt{7} = (5+3)\sqrt{7} = 8\sqrt{7}$

3. $8\sqrt{x} - 5\sqrt{x} = (8-5)\sqrt{x} = 3\sqrt{x}$

4. $3\sqrt{y} + 10\sqrt{y} = (3+10)\sqrt{y} = 13\sqrt{y}$

5. $7\sqrt[3]{x} + 5\sqrt[3]{x} = (7+5)\sqrt[3]{x} = 12\sqrt[3]{x}$

6. $8\sqrt[3]{z} - 2\sqrt[3]{z} = (8-2)\sqrt[3]{z} = 6\sqrt[3]{z}$

7. $\sqrt{11} + \sqrt{11} = (1+1)\sqrt{11} = 2\sqrt{11}$

8. $\sqrt{11} + \sqrt[3]{11}$ cannot be combined.

9. $9\sqrt{13} - \sqrt{13} = (9-1)\sqrt{13} = 8\sqrt{13}$

10. $9\sqrt{13} - \sqrt[4]{13}$ cannot be combined.

11. $8\sqrt[3]{2x} + 3\sqrt[3]{2x} - \sqrt[3]{2x} = (8+3-1)\sqrt[3]{2x} = 10\sqrt[3]{2x}$

12. $8\sqrt[3]{2x} + 3\sqrt[3]{2x^2} - \sqrt[3]{2x} = 8\sqrt[3]{2x} - \sqrt[3]{2x} + 3\sqrt[3]{2x^2}$
                        $= (8-1)\sqrt[3]{2x} + 3\sqrt[3]{2x^2}$
                        $= 7\sqrt[3]{2x} + 3\sqrt[3]{2x^2}$

Exercise Set 7.4

1. $\sqrt{8} - \sqrt{32} = \sqrt{4 \cdot 2} - \sqrt{16 \cdot 2}$
               $= \sqrt{4} \cdot \sqrt{2} - \sqrt{16} \cdot \sqrt{2}$
               $= 2\sqrt{2} - 4\sqrt{2}$
               $= -2\sqrt{2}$

3. $2\sqrt{2x^3} + 4x\sqrt{8x}$
    $= 2\sqrt{x^2 \cdot 2x} + 4x\sqrt{4 \cdot 2x}$
    $= 2\sqrt{x^2} \cdot \sqrt{2x} + 4x\sqrt{4} \cdot \sqrt{2x}$
    $= 2x\sqrt{2x} + 4x(2)\sqrt{2x}$
    $= 2x\sqrt{2x} + 8x\sqrt{2x}$
    $= 10x\sqrt{2x}$

5. $2\sqrt{50} - 3\sqrt{125} + \sqrt{98}$
    $= 2\sqrt{25 \cdot 2} - 3\sqrt{25 \cdot 5} + \sqrt{49 \cdot 2}$
    $= 2\sqrt{25} \cdot \sqrt{2} - 3\sqrt{25} \cdot \sqrt{5} + \sqrt{49} \cdot \sqrt{2}$
    $= 2(5)\sqrt{2} - 3(5)\sqrt{5} + 7\sqrt{2}$
    $= 10\sqrt{2} - 15\sqrt{5} + 7\sqrt{2}$
    $= 17\sqrt{2} - 15\sqrt{5}$

7. $\sqrt[3]{16x} - \sqrt[3]{54x} = \sqrt[3]{8 \cdot 2x} - \sqrt[3]{27 \cdot 2x}$
                   $= \sqrt[3]{8} \cdot \sqrt[3]{2x} - \sqrt[3]{27} \cdot \sqrt[3]{2x}$
                   $= 2\sqrt[3]{2x} - 3\sqrt[3]{2x}$
                   $= -\sqrt[3]{2x}$

9. $\sqrt{9b^3} - \sqrt{25b^3} + \sqrt{49b^3}$

$= \sqrt{9b^2 \cdot b} - \sqrt{25b^2 \cdot b} + \sqrt{49b^2 \cdot b}$

$= \sqrt{9b^2} \cdot \sqrt{b} - \sqrt{25b^2} \cdot \sqrt{b} + \sqrt{49b^2} \cdot \sqrt{b}$

$= 3b\sqrt{b} - 5b\sqrt{b} + 7b\sqrt{b}$

$= 5b\sqrt{b}$

11. $\dfrac{5\sqrt{2}}{3} + \dfrac{2\sqrt{2}}{5} = \dfrac{5\left(5\sqrt{2}\right) + 3\left(2\sqrt{2}\right)}{3(5)}$

$= \dfrac{25\sqrt{2} + 6\sqrt{2}}{15}$

$= \dfrac{31\sqrt{2}}{15}$

13. $\sqrt[3]{\dfrac{11}{8}} - \dfrac{\sqrt[3]{11}}{6} = \dfrac{\sqrt[3]{11}}{\sqrt[3]{8}} - \dfrac{\sqrt[3]{11}}{6}$

$= \dfrac{\sqrt[3]{11}}{2} - \dfrac{\sqrt[3]{11}}{6}$

$= \dfrac{3\sqrt[3]{11} - \sqrt[3]{11}}{6}$

$= \dfrac{2\sqrt[3]{11}}{6}$

$= \dfrac{\sqrt[3]{11}}{3}$

15. $\dfrac{\sqrt{20x}}{9} + \sqrt{\dfrac{5x}{9}} = \dfrac{\sqrt{4 \cdot 5x}}{9} + \dfrac{\sqrt{5x}}{\sqrt{9}}$

$= \dfrac{2\sqrt{5x}}{9} + \dfrac{\sqrt{5x}}{3}$

$= \dfrac{2\sqrt{5x} + 3\sqrt{5x}}{9}$

$= \dfrac{5\sqrt{5x}}{9}$

17. $7\sqrt{9} - 7 + \sqrt{3} = 7(3) - 7 + \sqrt{3}$

$= 21 - 7 + \sqrt{3}$

$= 14 + \sqrt{3}$

19. $2 + 3\sqrt{y^2} - 6\sqrt{y^2} + 5 = 2 + 3y - 6y + 5$

$= 7 - 3y$

21. $3\sqrt{108} - 2\sqrt{18} - 3\sqrt{48}$

$= 3\sqrt{36 \cdot 3} + 2\sqrt{9 \cdot 2} - 3\sqrt{16 \cdot 3}$

$= 3\sqrt{36} \cdot \sqrt{3} + 2\sqrt{9} \cdot \sqrt{2} - 3\sqrt{16} \cdot \sqrt{3}$

$= 3(6)\sqrt{3} + 2(3)\sqrt{2} - 3(4)\sqrt{3}$

$= 18\sqrt{3} + 6\sqrt{2} - 12\sqrt{3}$

$= 6\sqrt{3} + 6\sqrt{2}$

23. $-5\sqrt[3]{625} + \sqrt[3]{40} = -5\sqrt[3]{125 \cdot 5} + \sqrt[3]{8 \cdot 5}$

$= -5(5)\sqrt[3]{5} + 2\sqrt[3]{5}$

$= -25\sqrt[3]{5} + 2\sqrt[3]{5}$

$= -23\sqrt[3]{5}$

25. $\sqrt{9b^3} - \sqrt{25b^3} + \sqrt{16b^3}$

$= \sqrt{9b^2 \cdot b} - \sqrt{25b^2 \cdot b} + \sqrt{16b^2 \cdot b}$

$= 3b\sqrt{b} - 5b\sqrt{b} + 4b\sqrt{b}$

$= 2b\sqrt{b}$

27. $5y\sqrt{8y} + 2\sqrt{50y^3} = 5y\sqrt{4 \cdot 2y} + 2\sqrt{25y^2 \cdot 2y}$

$= 5y(2)\sqrt{2y} + 2(5y)\sqrt{2y}$

$= 10y\sqrt{2y} + 10y\sqrt{2y}$

$= 20y\sqrt{2y}$

29. $\sqrt[3]{54xy^3} - 5\sqrt[3]{2xy^3} + y\sqrt[3]{128x}$

$= \sqrt[3]{27y^3 \cdot 2x} - 5\sqrt[3]{y^3 \cdot 2x} + y\sqrt[3]{64 \cdot 2x}$

$= 3y\sqrt[3]{2x} - 5y\sqrt[3]{2x} + 4y\sqrt[3]{2x}$

$= 2y\sqrt[3]{2x}$

31. $6\sqrt[3]{11} + 8\sqrt{11} - 12\sqrt{11} = 6\sqrt[3]{11} - 4\sqrt{11}$

33. $-2\sqrt[4]{x^7} + 3\sqrt[4]{16x^7} = -2\sqrt[4]{x^4 \cdot x^3} + 3\sqrt[4]{8x^4 \cdot x^3}$

$= -2x\sqrt[4]{x^3} + 3(2x)\sqrt[4]{x^3}$

$= -2x\sqrt[4]{x^3} + 6x\sqrt[4]{x^3}$

$= 4x\sqrt[4]{x^3}$

35. $\dfrac{4\sqrt{3}}{3} - \dfrac{\sqrt{12}}{3} = \dfrac{4\sqrt{3}}{3} - \dfrac{\sqrt{4 \cdot 3}}{3}$

$= \dfrac{4\sqrt{3} - 2\sqrt{3}}{3}$

$= \dfrac{2\sqrt{3}}{3}$

37. $\dfrac{\sqrt[3]{8x^4}}{7} + \dfrac{3x\sqrt[3]{x}}{7} = \dfrac{\sqrt[3]{8x^3 \cdot x}}{7} + \dfrac{3x\sqrt[3]{x}}{7}$

$= \dfrac{2x\sqrt[3]{x} + 3x\sqrt[3]{x}}{7}$

$= \dfrac{5x\sqrt[3]{x}}{7}$

39.
$$\sqrt{\frac{28}{x^2}} + \sqrt{\frac{7}{4x^2}} = \frac{\sqrt{4 \cdot 7}}{x} + \frac{\sqrt{7}}{2x}$$
$$= \frac{2\sqrt{7}}{x} + \frac{\sqrt{7}}{2x}$$
$$= \frac{2(2\sqrt{7}) + \sqrt{7}}{2x}$$
$$= \frac{4\sqrt{7} + \sqrt{7}}{2x}$$
$$= \frac{5\sqrt{7}}{2x}$$

41.
$$\sqrt[3]{\frac{16}{27}} - \frac{\sqrt[3]{54}}{6} = \frac{\sqrt[3]{8 \cdot 2}}{\sqrt[3]{27}} - \frac{\sqrt[3]{27 \cdot 2}}{6}$$
$$= \frac{2\sqrt[3]{2}}{3} - \frac{3\sqrt[3]{2}}{6}$$
$$= \frac{2(2\sqrt[3]{2}) - 3\sqrt[3]{2}}{6}$$
$$= \frac{4\sqrt[3]{2} - 3\sqrt[3]{2}}{6}$$
$$= \frac{\sqrt[3]{2}}{6}$$

43.
$$-\frac{\sqrt[3]{2x^4}}{9} + \sqrt[3]{\frac{250x^4}{27}} = -\frac{\sqrt[3]{x^3 \cdot 2x}}{9} + \frac{\sqrt[3]{125x^3 \cdot 2x}}{\sqrt[3]{27}}$$
$$= \frac{-x\sqrt[3]{2x}}{9} + \frac{5x\sqrt[3]{2x}}{3}$$
$$= \frac{-x\sqrt[3]{2x} + 3(5x\sqrt[3]{2x})}{9}$$
$$= \frac{-x\sqrt[3]{2x} + 15x\sqrt[3]{2x}}{9}$$
$$= \frac{14x\sqrt[3]{2x}}{9}$$

45.
$$P = 2\sqrt{12} + \sqrt{12} + 2\sqrt{27} + 3\sqrt{3}$$
$$= 2\sqrt{4 \cdot 3} + \sqrt{4 \cdot 3} + 2\sqrt{9 \cdot 3} + 3\sqrt{3}$$
$$= 2(2)\sqrt{3} + 2\sqrt{3} + 2(3)\sqrt{3} + 3\sqrt{3}$$
$$= 4\sqrt{3} + 2\sqrt{3} + 6\sqrt{3} + 3\sqrt{3}$$
$$= 15\sqrt{3} \text{ inches}$$

47.
$$\sqrt{7}\left(\sqrt{5} + \sqrt{3}\right) = \sqrt{7}\sqrt{5} + \sqrt{7}\sqrt{3}$$
$$= \sqrt{35} + \sqrt{21}$$

49.
$$\left(\sqrt{5} - \sqrt{2}\right)^2 = \left(\sqrt{5}\right)^2 - 2\sqrt{5}\sqrt{2} + \left(\sqrt{2}\right)^2$$
$$= 5 - 2\sqrt{10} + 2$$
$$= 7 - 2\sqrt{10}$$

51.
$$\sqrt{3x}\left(\sqrt{3} - \sqrt{x}\right) = \sqrt{3x}\sqrt{3} - \sqrt{3x}\sqrt{x}$$
$$= \sqrt{9x} - \sqrt{3x^2}$$
$$= 3\sqrt{x} - x\sqrt{3}$$

53.
$$\left(2\sqrt{x} - 5\right)\left(3\sqrt{x} + 1\right)$$
$$= 2\sqrt{x}\left(3\sqrt{x}\right) + 2\sqrt{x} \cdot 1 - 5\left(3\sqrt{x}\right) - 5(1)$$
$$= 6x + 2\sqrt{x} - 15\sqrt{x} - 5$$
$$= 6x - 13\sqrt{x} - 5$$

55.
$$\left(\sqrt[3]{a} - 4\right)\left(\sqrt[3]{a} + 5\right)$$
$$= \sqrt[3]{a}\left(\sqrt[3]{a}\right) + \sqrt[3]{a} \cdot 5 - 4\sqrt[3]{a} - 4(5)$$
$$= \sqrt[3]{a^2} + 5\sqrt[3]{a} - 4\sqrt[3]{a} - 20$$
$$= \sqrt[3]{a^2} + \sqrt[3]{a} - 20$$

57.
$$6\left(\sqrt{2} - 2\right) = 6\sqrt{2} - 6(2)$$
$$= 6\sqrt{2} - 12$$

59.
$$\sqrt{2}\left(\sqrt{2} + x\sqrt{6}\right) = \sqrt{2}\sqrt{2} + \sqrt{2}\left(x\sqrt{6}\right)$$
$$= 2 + x\sqrt{12}$$
$$= 2 + x\sqrt{4 \cdot 3}$$
$$= 2 + 2x\sqrt{3}$$

61.
$$\left(2\sqrt{7} + 3\sqrt{5}\right)\left(\sqrt{7} - 2\sqrt{5}\right)$$
$$= 2\sqrt{7}\sqrt{7} + 2\sqrt{7}\left(-2\sqrt{5}\right) + 3\sqrt{5}\sqrt{7} + 3\sqrt{5}\left(-2\sqrt{5}\right)$$
$$= 2(7) - 4\sqrt{35} + 3\sqrt{35} - 6(5)$$
$$= 14 - \sqrt{35} - 30$$
$$= -16 - \sqrt{35}$$

63.
$$\left(\sqrt{x} - y\right)\left(\sqrt{x} + y\right) = \left(\sqrt{x}\right)^2 - y^2$$
$$= x - y^2$$

65.
$$\left(\sqrt{3} + x\right)^2 = \left(\sqrt{3}\right)^2 + 2\sqrt{3} \cdot x + x^2$$
$$= 3 + 2x\sqrt{3} + x^2$$

67.
$$\left(\sqrt{5x} - 3\sqrt{2}\right)\left(\sqrt{5x} - 3\sqrt{3}\right)$$
$$= \left(\sqrt{5x}\right)^2 + \sqrt{5x}\left(-3\sqrt{3}\right)$$
$$\qquad - 3\sqrt{2}\left(\sqrt{5x}\right) - 3\sqrt{2}\left(-3\sqrt{3}\right)$$
$$= 5x - 3\sqrt{15x} - 3\sqrt{10x} + 9\sqrt{6}$$

69. $\left(\sqrt[3]{4}+2\right)\left(\sqrt[3]{2}-1\right)$

$=\sqrt[3]{4}\left(\sqrt[3]{2}\right)+\sqrt[3]{4}\cdot(-1)+2\sqrt[3]{2}+2(-1)$

$=\sqrt[3]{8}-\sqrt[3]{4}+2\sqrt[3]{2}-2$

$=2-\sqrt[3]{4}+2\sqrt[3]{2}-2$

$=2\sqrt[3]{2}-\sqrt[3]{4}$

71. $\left(\sqrt[3]{x}+1\right)\left(\sqrt[3]{x}-4\sqrt{x}+7\right)$

$=\left(\sqrt[3]{x}\right)^{2}+\sqrt[3]{x}\left(-4\sqrt{x}\right)+\sqrt[3]{x}\cdot 7$

$\qquad +1\left(\sqrt[3]{x}\right)+1\left(-4\sqrt{x}\right)+1(7)$

$=\sqrt[3]{x^{2}}-4x^{1/3}x^{1/2}+8\sqrt[3]{x}-4\sqrt{x}+7$

$=\sqrt[3]{x^{2}}-4x^{5/6}+8\sqrt[3]{x}-4\sqrt{x}+7$

$=\sqrt[3]{x^{2}}-4\sqrt[6]{x^{5}}+8\sqrt[3]{x}-4\sqrt{x}+7$

73. $\left(\sqrt{x-1}+5\right)^{2}=\sqrt{x-1}^{2}+2\sqrt{x-1}\cdot 5+5^{2}$

$=(x-1)+10\sqrt{x-1}+25$

$=x+10\sqrt{x-1}+24$

75. $\left(\sqrt{2x+5}-1\right)^{2}=\sqrt{2x+5}^{2}-2\sqrt{2x+5}\cdot 1+1^{2}$

$=(2x+5)-2\sqrt{2x+5}+1$

$=2x-2\sqrt{2x+5}+6$

77. $\dfrac{2x-14}{2}=\dfrac{2(x-7)}{2}=x-7$

79. $\dfrac{7x-7y}{x^{2}-y^{2}}=\dfrac{7(x-y)}{(x+y)(x-y)}=\dfrac{7}{x+y}$

81. $\dfrac{6a^{2}b-9ab}{3ab}=\dfrac{3ab(2a-3)}{3ab}=2a-3$

83. $\dfrac{-4+2\sqrt{3}}{6}=\dfrac{2\left(-2+\sqrt{3}\right)}{6}=\dfrac{-2+\sqrt{3}}{3}$

85. $P=2l+2w=2\left(3\sqrt{20}\right)+2\left(\sqrt{125}\right)$

$=6\sqrt{4\cdot 5}+2\sqrt{25\cdot 5}$

$=6(2)\sqrt{5}+2(5)\sqrt{5}$

$=12\sqrt{5}+10\sqrt{5}$

$=22\sqrt{5}$ feet

$A=lw=\left(3\sqrt{20}\right)\left(\sqrt{125}\right)$

$=3\sqrt{4\cdot 5}\sqrt{25\cdot 5}$

$=3(2)\sqrt{5}\cdot 5\sqrt{5}$

$=30\cdot 5$

$=150$ square feet

87. a. $\sqrt{3}+\sqrt{3}=2\sqrt{3}$

b. $\sqrt{3}\cdot\sqrt{3}=\sqrt{9}=3$

c. Answers may vary. One possibility follows: In part **a.**, we are adding, so we combine the like radicals. The result will still contain a radical. In part **b.**, we are multiplying a radical by itself. The result will no longer contain a radical.

89. Answer may vary. One possibility follows. On simplifying the expression $2x+3x$, we can combine the two term because they are "like terms": $2x+3x=(2+3)x=5x$ Likewise, on simplifying the expression $2\sqrt{x}+3\sqrt{x}$, we can combine the two radical terms because they are "like radicals": $2\sqrt{x}+3\sqrt{x}=(2+3)\sqrt{x}=5\sqrt{x}$.

Mental Math 7.5

1. The conjugate of $\sqrt{2}+x$ is $\sqrt{2}-x$.

2. The conjugate of $\sqrt{3}+y$ is $\sqrt{3}-y$.

3. The conjugate of $5-\sqrt{a}$ is $5+\sqrt{a}$.

4. The conjugate of $6-\sqrt{b}$ is $6-\sqrt{b}$.

5. The conjugate of $7\sqrt{5}+8\sqrt{x}$ is $7\sqrt{5}-8\sqrt{x}$.

6. The conjugate of $9\sqrt{2}-6\sqrt{y}$ is $9\sqrt{2}+6\sqrt{y}$.

Exercise Set 7.5

1. $\dfrac{\sqrt{2}}{\sqrt{7}}=\dfrac{\sqrt{2}\cdot\sqrt{7}}{\sqrt{7}\cdot\sqrt{7}}=\dfrac{\sqrt{14}}{\sqrt{49}}=\dfrac{\sqrt{14}}{7}$

3. $\sqrt{\dfrac{1}{5}}=\dfrac{\sqrt{1}}{\sqrt{5}}=\dfrac{1\cdot\sqrt{5}}{\sqrt{5}\cdot\sqrt{5}}=\dfrac{\sqrt{5}}{5}$

5. $\sqrt[3]{\dfrac{3}{4}}=\dfrac{\sqrt[3]{3}}{\sqrt[3]{4}}=\dfrac{\sqrt[3]{3}\cdot\sqrt[3]{2}}{\sqrt[3]{4}\cdot\sqrt[3]{2}}=\dfrac{\sqrt[3]{6}}{\sqrt[3]{8}}=\dfrac{\sqrt[3]{6}}{2}$

7. $\dfrac{4}{\sqrt[3]{3}}=\dfrac{4\cdot\sqrt[3]{9}}{\sqrt[3]{3}\cdot\sqrt[3]{9}}=\dfrac{4\sqrt[3]{9}}{\sqrt[3]{27}}=\dfrac{4\sqrt[3]{9}}{3}$

9. $\dfrac{3}{\sqrt{8x}} = \dfrac{3 \cdot \sqrt{2x}}{\sqrt{8x} \cdot \sqrt{2x}} = \dfrac{3\sqrt{2x}}{\sqrt{16x^2}} = \dfrac{3\sqrt{2x}}{4x}$

11. $\dfrac{3}{\sqrt[3]{4x^2}} = \dfrac{3 \cdot \sqrt[3]{2x}}{\sqrt[3]{4x^2} \cdot \sqrt[3]{2x}} = \dfrac{3\sqrt[3]{2x}}{\sqrt[3]{8x^3}} = \dfrac{3\sqrt[3]{2x}}{2x}$

13. $\sqrt{\dfrac{4}{x}} = \dfrac{\sqrt{4}}{\sqrt{x}} = \dfrac{2 \cdot \sqrt{x}}{\sqrt{x} \cdot \sqrt{x}} = \dfrac{2\sqrt{x}}{\sqrt{x^2}} = \dfrac{2\sqrt{x}}{x}$

15. $\dfrac{9}{\sqrt{3a}} = \dfrac{9 \cdot \sqrt{3a}}{\sqrt{3a} \cdot \sqrt{3a}} = \dfrac{9\sqrt{3a}}{3a} = \dfrac{3\sqrt{3a}}{a}$

17. $\dfrac{3}{\sqrt[3]{2}} = \dfrac{3 \cdot \sqrt[3]{4}}{\sqrt[3]{2} \cdot \sqrt[3]{4}} = \dfrac{3\sqrt[3]{4}}{\sqrt[3]{8}} = \dfrac{3\sqrt[3]{4}}{2}$

19. $\dfrac{2\sqrt{3}}{\sqrt{7}} = \dfrac{2\sqrt{3} \cdot \sqrt{7}}{\sqrt{7} \cdot \sqrt{7}} = \dfrac{2\sqrt{21}}{\sqrt{49}} = \dfrac{2\sqrt{21}}{7}$

21. $\sqrt{\dfrac{2x}{5y}} = \dfrac{\sqrt{2x}}{\sqrt{5y}} = \dfrac{\sqrt{2x} \cdot \sqrt{5y}}{\sqrt{5y} \cdot \sqrt{5y}} = \dfrac{\sqrt{10xy}}{5y}$

23. $\sqrt[4]{\dfrac{81}{8}} = \dfrac{\sqrt[4]{81}}{\sqrt[4]{8}} = \dfrac{3 \cdot \sqrt[4]{2}}{\sqrt[4]{8} \cdot \sqrt[4]{2}} = \dfrac{3\sqrt[4]{2}}{\sqrt[4]{16}} = \dfrac{3\sqrt[4]{2}}{2}$

25. $\sqrt[4]{\dfrac{16}{9x^7}} = \dfrac{\sqrt[4]{16}}{\sqrt[4]{9x^7}} = \dfrac{2 \cdot \sqrt[4]{9x}}{\sqrt[4]{9x^7} \cdot \sqrt[4]{9x}} = \dfrac{2\sqrt[4]{9x}}{\sqrt[4]{81x^8}} = \dfrac{2\sqrt[4]{9x}}{3x^2}$

27. $\dfrac{5a}{\sqrt[5]{8a^9b^{11}}} = \dfrac{5a \cdot \sqrt[5]{4ab^4}}{\sqrt[5]{8a^9b^{11}} \cdot \sqrt[5]{4ab^4}}$

$= \dfrac{5a\sqrt[5]{4ab^4}}{\sqrt[5]{32a^{10}b^{15}}}$

$= \dfrac{5a\sqrt[5]{4ab^4}}{2a^2b^3}$

29. $\dfrac{6}{2-\sqrt{7}} = \dfrac{6(2+\sqrt{7})}{(2-\sqrt{7})(2+\sqrt{7})}$

$= \dfrac{6(2+\sqrt{7})}{2^2 - (\sqrt{7})^2}$

$= \dfrac{6(2+\sqrt{7})}{4-7}$

$= \dfrac{6(2+\sqrt{7})}{-3}$

$= -2(2+\sqrt{7})$

31. $\dfrac{-7}{\sqrt{x}-3} = \dfrac{-7(\sqrt{x}+3)}{(\sqrt{x}-3)(\sqrt{x}+3)}$

$= \dfrac{-7(\sqrt{x}+3)}{(\sqrt{x})^2 - (3)^2}$

$= \dfrac{-7(\sqrt{x}+3)}{x-9}$ or $\dfrac{7(\sqrt{x}+3)}{9-x}$

33. $\dfrac{\sqrt{2}-\sqrt{3}}{\sqrt{2}+\sqrt{3}} = \dfrac{(\sqrt{2}-\sqrt{3})(\sqrt{2}-\sqrt{3})}{(\sqrt{2}+\sqrt{3})(\sqrt{2}-\sqrt{3})}$

$= \dfrac{(\sqrt{2})^2 - 2\sqrt{2}\sqrt{3} + (\sqrt{3})^2}{(\sqrt{2})^2 - (\sqrt{3})^2}$

$= \dfrac{2 - 2\sqrt{6} + 3}{2-3}$

$= \dfrac{5 - 2\sqrt{6}}{-1}$

$= -5 + 2\sqrt{6}$

35. $\dfrac{\sqrt{a}+1}{2\sqrt{a}-\sqrt{b}} = \dfrac{(\sqrt{a}+1)(2\sqrt{a}+\sqrt{b})}{(2\sqrt{a}-\sqrt{b})(2\sqrt{a}+\sqrt{b})}$

$= \dfrac{\sqrt{a} \cdot 2\sqrt{a} + \sqrt{a}\sqrt{b} + 1 \cdot 2\sqrt{a} + 1 \cdot \sqrt{b}}{(2\sqrt{a})^2 - (\sqrt{b})^2}$

$= \dfrac{2a + \sqrt{ab} + 2\sqrt{a} + \sqrt{b}}{4a - b}$

37. $\dfrac{8}{1+\sqrt{10}} = \dfrac{8(1-\sqrt{10})}{(1+\sqrt{10})(1-\sqrt{10})}$

$= \dfrac{8(1-\sqrt{10})}{1^2 - (\sqrt{10})^2}$

$= \dfrac{8(1-\sqrt{10})}{1-10}$

$= -\dfrac{8(1-\sqrt{10})}{9}$

39.
$$\frac{\sqrt{x}}{\sqrt{x}+\sqrt{y}} = \frac{\sqrt{x}\left(\sqrt{x}-\sqrt{y}\right)}{\left(\sqrt{x}+\sqrt{y}\right)\left(\sqrt{x}-\sqrt{y}\right)}$$
$$= \frac{\sqrt{x}\cdot\sqrt{x}-\sqrt{x}\cdot\sqrt{y}}{\left(\sqrt{x}\right)^2-\left(\sqrt{y}\right)^2}$$
$$= \frac{x-\sqrt{xy}}{x-y}$$

41.
$$\frac{2\sqrt{3}+\sqrt{6}}{4\sqrt{3}-\sqrt{6}} = \frac{\left(2\sqrt{3}+\sqrt{6}\right)\left(4\sqrt{3}+\sqrt{6}\right)}{\left(4\sqrt{3}-\sqrt{6}\right)\left(4\sqrt{3}+\sqrt{6}\right)}$$
$$= \frac{8\cdot3+2\sqrt{18}+4\sqrt{18}+6}{\left(4\sqrt{3}\right)^2-\left(\sqrt{6}\right)^2}$$
$$= \frac{30+6\sqrt{18}}{16\cdot3-6}$$
$$= \frac{30+6(3)\sqrt{2}}{42}$$
$$= \frac{30+18\sqrt{2}}{42}$$
$$= \frac{6\left(5+3\sqrt{2}\right)}{42}$$
$$= \frac{5+3\sqrt{2}}{7}$$

43. $\sqrt{\frac{5}{3}} = \frac{\sqrt{5}}{\sqrt{3}} = \frac{\sqrt{5}\cdot\sqrt{5}}{\sqrt{3}\cdot\sqrt{5}} = \frac{\sqrt{25}}{\sqrt{15}} = \frac{5}{\sqrt{15}}$

45.
$$\sqrt{\frac{18}{5}} = \frac{\sqrt{18}}{\sqrt{5}}$$
$$= \frac{\sqrt{9}\cdot\sqrt{2}}{\sqrt{5}}$$
$$= \frac{3\sqrt{2}}{\sqrt{5}}$$
$$= \frac{3\sqrt{2}\cdot\sqrt{2}}{\sqrt{5}\cdot\sqrt{2}}$$
$$= \frac{3\cdot2}{\sqrt{10}}$$
$$= \frac{6}{\sqrt{10}}$$

47. $\frac{\sqrt{4x}}{7} = \frac{2\sqrt{x}}{7} = \frac{2\sqrt{x}\cdot\sqrt{x}}{7\cdot\sqrt{x}} = \frac{2\sqrt{x^2}}{7\sqrt{x}} = \frac{2x}{7\sqrt{x}}$

49. $\frac{\sqrt[3]{5y^2}}{\sqrt[3]{4x}} = \frac{\sqrt[3]{5y^2}\cdot\sqrt[3]{5^2 y}}{\sqrt[3]{4x}\cdot\sqrt[3]{5^2 y}} = \frac{\sqrt[3]{5^3 y^3}}{\sqrt[3]{100xy}} = \frac{5y}{\sqrt[3]{100xy}}$

51. $\sqrt{\frac{2}{5}} = \frac{\sqrt{2}}{\sqrt{5}} = \frac{\sqrt{2}\cdot\sqrt{2}}{\sqrt{5}\cdot\sqrt{2}} = \frac{\sqrt{4}}{\sqrt{10}} = \frac{2}{\sqrt{10}}$

53. $\frac{\sqrt{2x}}{11} = \frac{\sqrt{2x}\cdot\sqrt{2x}}{11\cdot\sqrt{2x}} = \frac{\sqrt{4x^2}}{11\sqrt{2x}} = \frac{2x}{11\sqrt{2x}}$

55. $\sqrt[3]{\frac{7}{8}} = \frac{\sqrt[3]{7}}{\sqrt[3]{8}} = \frac{\sqrt[3]{7}}{2} = \frac{\sqrt[3]{7}\cdot\sqrt[3]{7^2}}{2\cdot\sqrt[3]{7^2}} = \frac{\sqrt[3]{7^3}}{2\sqrt[3]{49}} = \frac{7}{2\sqrt[3]{49}}$

57.
$$\frac{\sqrt[3]{3x^5}}{10} = \frac{\sqrt[3]{x^3\cdot3x^2}}{10}$$
$$= \frac{x\sqrt[3]{3x^2}\cdot\sqrt[3]{3^2 x}}{10\cdot\sqrt[3]{3^2 x}}$$
$$= \frac{x\sqrt[3]{3^3 x^3}}{10\sqrt[3]{9x}}$$
$$= \frac{x\cdot3x}{10\sqrt[3]{9x}}$$
$$= \frac{3x^2}{10\sqrt[3]{9x}}$$

59.
$$\sqrt{\frac{18x^4 y^6}{3z}} = \frac{\sqrt{18x^4 y^6}}{\sqrt{3z}}$$
$$= \frac{\sqrt{9x^4 y^6\cdot2}}{\sqrt{3z}}$$
$$= \frac{3x^2 y^3\sqrt{2}}{\sqrt{3z}}$$
$$= \frac{3x^2 y^3\sqrt{2}\cdot\sqrt{2}}{\sqrt{3z}\cdot\sqrt{2}}$$
$$= \frac{3x^2 y^3\cdot2}{\sqrt{6z}}$$
$$= \frac{6x^2 y^3}{\sqrt{6z}}$$

61. Answers may vary. One possibility follows:

When rationalizing the denominator of $\frac{\sqrt{5}}{\sqrt{7}}$, we multiply both the numerator and the denominator by $\sqrt{7}$. By doing this, we are really multiplying the expression by 1, so that the overall value of the expression says the same.

63. $\dfrac{2-\sqrt{11}}{6} = \dfrac{\left(2-\sqrt{11}\right)\left(2+\sqrt{11}\right)}{6\left(2+\sqrt{11}\right)}$

$= \dfrac{4-11}{12+6\sqrt{11}}$

$= \dfrac{-7}{12+6\sqrt{11}}$

65. $\dfrac{2-\sqrt{7}}{-5} = \dfrac{\left(2-\sqrt{7}\right)\left(2+\sqrt{7}\right)}{-5\left(2+\sqrt{7}\right)}$

$= \dfrac{4-7}{-5\left(2+\sqrt{7}\right)}$

$= \dfrac{-3}{-10-5\sqrt{7}}$

$= \dfrac{3}{10+5\sqrt{7}}$

67. $\dfrac{\sqrt{x}+3}{\sqrt{x}} = \dfrac{\left(\sqrt{x}+3\right)\left(\sqrt{x}-3\right)}{\sqrt{x}\left(\sqrt{x}-3\right)}$

$= \dfrac{\sqrt{x^2}-9}{\sqrt{x^2}-3\sqrt{x}}$

$= \dfrac{x-9}{x-3\sqrt{x}}$

69. $\dfrac{\sqrt{2}-1}{\sqrt{2}+1} = \dfrac{\left(\sqrt{2}-1\right)\left(\sqrt{2}+1\right)}{\left(\sqrt{2}+1\right)\left(\sqrt{2}+1\right)}$

$= \dfrac{\sqrt{4}-1}{\sqrt{4}+2\sqrt{2}+1}$

$= \dfrac{2-1}{2+2\sqrt{2}+1}$

$= \dfrac{1}{3+2\sqrt{2}}$

71. $\dfrac{\sqrt{x}+1}{\sqrt{x}-1} = \dfrac{\left(\sqrt{x}+1\right)\left(\sqrt{x}-1\right)}{\left(\sqrt{x}-1\right)\left(\sqrt{x}-1\right)}$

$= \dfrac{\sqrt{x^2}-1}{\sqrt{x^2}-2\sqrt{x}+1}$

$= \dfrac{x-1}{x-2\sqrt{x}+1}$

73. $2x-7 = 3(x-4)$
$2x-7 = 3x-12$
$-x-7 = -12$
$-x = -5$
$x = 5$
The solution is 5.

75. $(x-6)(2x+1) = 0$
$x-6 = 0$ or $2x+1 = 0$
$x = 6$ or $2x = -1$
$x = -\dfrac{1}{2}$
The solutions are $\left\{-\dfrac{1}{2}, 6\right\}$.

77. $x^2 - 8x = -12$
$x^2 - 8x + 12 = 0$
$(x-6)(x-2) = 0$
$x-6 = 0$ or $x-2 = 0$
$x = 6$ or $x = 2$
The solutions are $\{2, 6\}$.

79. $r = \sqrt{\dfrac{A}{4\pi}}$

$= \dfrac{\sqrt{A}}{\sqrt{4\pi}}$

$= \dfrac{\sqrt{A}}{2\sqrt{\pi}}$

$= \dfrac{\sqrt{A}\cdot\sqrt{\pi}}{2\sqrt{\pi}\cdot\sqrt{\pi}} = \dfrac{\sqrt{A\pi}}{2\pi}$

81. Answers may vary. One possibility follows. When we multiply both the numerator and denominator by the same thing, we are really multiplying the expression by 1. Thus, the overall value of the expression does not change.

Integrated Review

1. $\sqrt{81} = 9$

2. $\sqrt[3]{-8} = -2$

3. $\sqrt[4]{\dfrac{1}{16}} = \dfrac{1}{2}$

4. $\sqrt{x^6} = x^3$

5. $\sqrt[3]{y^9} = y^3$

6. $\sqrt{4y^{10}} = 2y^5$

7. $\sqrt[5]{-32y^5} = -2y$

8. $\sqrt[4]{81b^{12}} = 3b^3$

9. $36^{1/2} = \sqrt{36} = 6$

10. $(3y)^{1/4} = \sqrt[4]{3y}$

11. $64^{-2/3} = \dfrac{1}{64^{2/3}} = \dfrac{1}{\left(\sqrt[3]{64}\right)^2} = \dfrac{1}{(4)^2} = \dfrac{1}{16}$

12. $(x+1)^{3/5} = \sqrt[5]{(x+1)^3}$

13. $y^{-1/6} \cdot y^{7/6} = y^{-1/6+7/6} = y^{6/6} = y^1 = y$

14. $\dfrac{(2x^{1/3})^4}{x^{5/6}} = \dfrac{2^4 x^{4/3}}{x^{5/6}}$
$= 16x^{\frac{4}{3}-\frac{5}{6}}$
$= 16x^{\frac{8}{6}-\frac{5}{6}}$
$= 16x^{3/6}$
$= 16x^{1/2}$

15. $\dfrac{x^{1/4}x^{3/4}}{x^{-1/4}} = x^{\frac{1}{4}+\frac{3}{4}-\left(-\frac{1}{4}\right)} = x^{\frac{1+3+1}{4}} = x^{5/4}$

16. $4^{1/3} \cdot 4^{2/5} = 4^{\frac{1}{3}+\frac{2}{5}} = 4^{\frac{5+6}{15}} = 4^{11/15}$

17. $\sqrt[3]{8x^6} = (8x^6)^{1/3} = (2^3 x^6)^{1/3} = 2^{3(1/3)} x^{6(1/3)} = 2x^2$

18. $\sqrt[12]{a^9 b^6} = (a^9 b^6)^{1/12}$
$= a^{9(1/12)} b^{6(1/12)}$
$= a^{3/4} b^{1/2}$
$= a^{3/4} b^{2/4}$
$= (a^3 b^2)^{1/4}$
$= \sqrt[4]{a^3 b^2}$

19. $\sqrt[4]{x} \cdot \sqrt{x} = x^{1/4} \cdot x^{1/2} = x^{\frac{1}{4}+\frac{1}{2}} = x^{\frac{1+2}{4}} = x^{3/4} = \sqrt[4]{x^3}$

20. $\sqrt{5} \cdot \sqrt[3]{2} = 5^{1/2} \cdot 2^{1/3}$
$= 5^{3/6} \cdot 2^{2/6}$
$= (5^3 \cdot 2^2)^{1/6}$
$= \sqrt[6]{125 \cdot 4}$
$= \sqrt[6]{500}$

21. $\sqrt{40} = \sqrt{4 \cdot 10} = \sqrt{4} \cdot \sqrt{10} = 2\sqrt{10}$

22. $\sqrt[4]{16x^7 y^{10}} = \sqrt[4]{16x^4 y^8 \cdot x^3 y^2}$
$= \sqrt[4]{16x^4 y^8} \cdot \sqrt[4]{x^3 y^2}$
$= 2xy^2 \sqrt[4]{x^3 y^2}$

23. $\sqrt[3]{54x^4} = \sqrt[3]{27x^3 \cdot 2x} = \sqrt[3]{27x^3} \cdot \sqrt[3]{2x} = 3x\sqrt[3]{2x}$

24. $\sqrt[5]{-64b^{10}} = \sqrt[5]{-32b^{10} \cdot 2} = -2b^5 \sqrt[5]{2}$

25. $\sqrt{5} \cdot \sqrt{x} = \sqrt{5x}$

26. $\sqrt[3]{8x} \cdot \sqrt[3]{8x^2} = \sqrt[3]{64x^3} = 4x$

27. $\dfrac{\sqrt{98y^6}}{\sqrt{2y}} = \sqrt{\dfrac{98y^6}{2y}} = \sqrt{49y^5} = \sqrt{49y^4 \cdot y} = 7y^2\sqrt{y}$

28. $\dfrac{\sqrt[4]{48a^9 b^3}}{\sqrt[4]{ab^3}} = \sqrt[4]{\dfrac{48a^9 b^3}{ab^3}}$
$= \sqrt[4]{48a^8}$
$= \sqrt[4]{16a^8 \cdot 3}$
$= 2a^2 \sqrt[4]{3}$

29. $\sqrt{20} - \sqrt{75} + 5\sqrt{7} = \sqrt{4 \cdot 5} - \sqrt{25 \cdot 3} + 5\sqrt{7}$
$= 2\sqrt{5} - 5\sqrt{3} + 5\sqrt{7}$

30. $\sqrt[3]{54y^4} - y\sqrt[3]{16y} = \sqrt[3]{27y^3 \cdot 2y} - y\sqrt[3]{8 \cdot 2y}$
$= 3y\sqrt[3]{2y} - 2y\sqrt[3]{2y}$
$= y\sqrt[3]{2y}$

31. $\sqrt{3}\left(\sqrt{5} - \sqrt{2}\right) = \sqrt{3}\sqrt{5} - \sqrt{3}\sqrt{2}$
$= \sqrt{15} - \sqrt{6}$

32. $\left(\sqrt{7} + \sqrt{3}\right)^2 = \left(\sqrt{7}\right)^2 + 2\sqrt{7}\sqrt{3} + \left(\sqrt{3}\right)^2$
$= 7 + 2\sqrt{21} + 3$
$= 10 + 2\sqrt{21}$

303

33. $\left(2x-\sqrt{5}\right)\left(2x+\sqrt{5}\right) = (2x)^2 - \left(\sqrt{5}\right)^2$

$$= 4x^2 - 5$$

34. $\left(\sqrt{x+1}-1\right)^2 = \sqrt{x+1}^2 - 2\sqrt{x+1}\cdot 1 + 1^2$

$$= x+1-2\sqrt{x+1}+1$$
$$= x+2-2\sqrt{x+1}$$

35. $\sqrt{\dfrac{7}{3}} = \dfrac{\sqrt{7}}{\sqrt{3}} = \dfrac{\sqrt{7}\cdot\sqrt{3}}{\sqrt{3}\cdot\sqrt{3}} = \dfrac{\sqrt{21}}{\sqrt{9}} = \dfrac{\sqrt{21}}{3}$

36. $\dfrac{5}{\sqrt[3]{2x^2}} = \dfrac{5\cdot\sqrt[3]{2^2 x}}{\sqrt[3]{2x^2}\cdot\sqrt[3]{2^2 x}} = \dfrac{5\sqrt[3]{4x}}{\sqrt[3]{2^3 x^3}} = \dfrac{5\sqrt[3]{4x}}{2x}$

37. $\dfrac{\sqrt{3}-\sqrt{7}}{2\sqrt{3}+\sqrt{7}} = \dfrac{\left(\sqrt{3}-\sqrt{7}\right)\left(2\sqrt{3}-\sqrt{7}\right)}{\left(2\sqrt{3}+\sqrt{7}\right)\left(2\sqrt{3}-\sqrt{7}\right)}$

$$= \dfrac{2\sqrt{9}-\sqrt{3}\sqrt{7}-\sqrt{7}\cdot 2\sqrt{3}+\sqrt{49}}{\left(2\sqrt{3}\right)^2 - \left(\sqrt{7}\right)^2}$$

$$= \dfrac{2(3)-\sqrt{21}-2\sqrt{21}+7}{4\cdot 3-7}$$

$$= \dfrac{6-3\sqrt{21}+7}{12-7}$$

$$= \dfrac{13-3\sqrt{21}}{5}$$

38. $\sqrt{\dfrac{7}{3}} = \dfrac{\sqrt{7}}{\sqrt{3}} = \dfrac{\sqrt{7}\cdot\sqrt{7}}{\sqrt{3}\cdot\sqrt{7}} = \dfrac{\sqrt{49}}{\sqrt{21}} = \dfrac{7}{\sqrt{21}}$

39. $\sqrt[3]{\dfrac{9y}{11}} = \dfrac{\sqrt[3]{9y}}{\sqrt[3]{11}} = \dfrac{\sqrt[3]{9y}\cdot\sqrt[3]{3y^2}}{\sqrt[3]{11}\cdot\sqrt[3]{3y^2}} = \dfrac{\sqrt[3]{27y^3}}{\sqrt[3]{33y^2}} = \dfrac{3y}{\sqrt[3]{33y^2}}$

40. $\dfrac{\sqrt{x}-2}{\sqrt{x}} = \dfrac{\left(\sqrt{x}-2\right)\left(\sqrt{x}+2\right)}{\sqrt{x}\left(\sqrt{x}+2\right)}$

$$= \dfrac{\left(\sqrt{x}\right)^2 - 2^2}{\sqrt{x^2}+2\sqrt{x}}$$

$$= \dfrac{x-4}{x+2\sqrt{x}}$$

Exercise Set 7.6

1. $\sqrt{2x} = 4$

$\left(\sqrt{2x}\right)^2 = 4^2$

$2x = 16$

$x = 8$

The solution is 8.

3. $\sqrt{x-3} = 2$

$\left(\sqrt{x-3}\right)^2 = 2^2$

$x-3 = 4$

$x = 7$

The solution is 7.

5. $\sqrt{2x} = -4$

No solution since a principle square root does not yield a negative number. The solution set is $\varnothing$.

7. $\sqrt{4x-3} - 5 = 0$

$\sqrt{4x-3} = 5$

$\left(\sqrt{4x-3}\right)^2 = 5^2$

$4x-3 = 25$

$4x = 28$

$x = 7$

The solution is 7.

9. $\sqrt{2x-3} - 2 = 1$

$\sqrt{2x-3} = 3$

$\left(\sqrt{2x-3}\right)^2 = 3^2$

$2x-3 = 9$

$2x = 12$

$x = 6$

The solution is 6.

11. $\sqrt[3]{6x} = -3$

$\left(\sqrt[3]{6x}\right)^3 = (-3)^3$

$6x = -27$

$x = -\dfrac{27}{6} = -\dfrac{9}{2}$

The solution is $-\dfrac{9}{2}$.

13. $\sqrt[3]{x-2} - 3 = 0$

$\sqrt[3]{x-2} = 3$

$\left(\sqrt[3]{x-2}\right)^3 = 3^2$

$x - 2 = 27$

$x = 29$

The solution is 29.

15. $\sqrt{13-x} = x-1$

$\left(\sqrt{13-x}\right)^2 = (x-1)^2$

$13 - x = x^2 - 2x + 1$

$0 = x^2 - x - 12$

$0 = (x-4)(x+3)$

$x - 4 = 0 \ \text{ or } \ x + 3 = 0$

$x = 4 \ \text{ or } \quad x = -3$

We discard -3 as extraneous. The solution is 4.

17. $x - \sqrt{4-3x} = -8$

$x + 8 = \sqrt{4-3x}$

$(x+8)^2 = \left(\sqrt{4-3x}\right)^2$

$x^2 + 16x + 64 = 4 - 3x$

$x^2 + 19x + 60 = 0$

$(x+4)(x+15) = 0$

$x + 4 = 0 \quad \text{ or } \ x + 15 = 0$

$x = -4 \ \text{ or } \qquad x = -15$

We discard -15 as extraneous. The solution is -4.

19. $\sqrt{y+5} = 2 - \sqrt{y-4}$

$\left(\sqrt{y+5}\right)^2 = \left(2 - \sqrt{y-4}\right)^2$

$y + 5 = 4 - 4\sqrt{y-4} + (y-4)$

$y + 5 = y - 4\sqrt{y-4}$

$5 = -4\sqrt{y-4}$

$5^2 = \left(-4\sqrt{y-4}\right)^2$

$25 = 16(y-4)$

$25 = 16y - 64$

$89 = 16y$

$\dfrac{89}{16} = y$

which we discard as extraneous. There is no solution. The solution set is $\varnothing$.

21. $\sqrt{x-3} + \sqrt{x+2} = 5$

$\sqrt{x-3} = 5 - \sqrt{x+2}$

$\left(\sqrt{x-3}\right)^2 = \left(5 - \sqrt{x+2}\right)^2$

$x - 3 = 25 - 10\sqrt{x+2} + (x+2)$

$x - 3 = 27 - 10\sqrt{x+2} + x$

$-30 = -10\sqrt{x+2}$

$3 = \sqrt{x+2}$

$3^2 = \left(\sqrt{x+2}\right)^2$

$9 = x + 2$

$7 = x$

The solution is 7.

23. $\sqrt{3x-2} = 5$

$\left(\sqrt{3x-2}\right)^2 = 5^2$

$3x - 2 = 25$

$3x = 27$

$x = 9$

The solution is 9.

25. $-\sqrt{2x} + 4 = -6$

$10 = \sqrt{2x}$

$10^2 = \left(\sqrt{2x}\right)^2$

$100 = 2x$

$50 = x$

The solution is 50.

27. $\sqrt{3x+1} + 2 = 0$

$\sqrt{3x+1} = -2$

No solution since a principle square root does not yield a negative number. The solution set is $\varnothing$.

29. $\sqrt[4]{4x+1} - 2 = 0$

$\sqrt[4]{4x+1} = 2$

$\left(\sqrt[4]{4x+1}\right)^4 = 2^4$

$4x + 1 = 16$

$4x = 15$

$x = \dfrac{15}{4}$

The solution is $\dfrac{15}{4}$.

31.
$$\sqrt{4x-3} = 7$$
$$\left(\sqrt{4x-3}\right)^2 = 7^2$$
$$4x-3 = 49$$
$$4x = 52$$
$$x = 13$$
The solution is 13.

33.
$$\sqrt[3]{6x-3} - 3 = 0$$
$$\sqrt[3]{6x-3} = 3$$
$$\left(\sqrt[3]{6x-3}\right)^3 = 3^3$$
$$6x-3 = 27$$
$$6x = 30$$
$$x = 5$$
The solution is 5.

35.
$$\sqrt[3]{2x-3} - 2 = -5$$
$$\sqrt[3]{2x-3} = -3$$
$$\left(\sqrt[3]{2x-3}\right)^3 = (-3)^3$$
$$2x-3 = -27$$
$$2x = -24$$
$$x = -12$$
The solution is –12.

37.
$$\sqrt{x+4} = \sqrt{2x-5}$$
$$\left(\sqrt{x+4}\right)^2 = \left(\sqrt{2x-5}\right)^2$$
$$x+4 = 2x-5$$
$$-x = -9$$
$$x = 9$$
The solution is 9.

39.
$$x - \sqrt{1-x} = -5$$
$$x+5 = \sqrt{1-x}$$
$$(x+5)^2 = \left(\sqrt{1-x}\right)^2$$
$$x^2 + 10x + 25 = 1-x$$
$$x^2 + 11x + 24 = 0$$
$$(x+8)(x+3) = 0$$
$$x+8 = 0 \quad \text{or} \quad x+3 = 0$$
$$x = -8 \quad \text{or} \quad x = -3$$
We discard –8 as extraneous. The solution is –3.

41.
$$\sqrt[3]{-6x-1} = \sqrt[3]{-2x-5}$$
$$\left(\sqrt[3]{-6x-1}\right)^3 = \left(\sqrt[3]{-2x-5}\right)^3$$
$$-6x-1 = -2x-5$$
$$-4x = -4$$
$$x = 1$$
The solution is 1.

43.
$$\sqrt{5x-1} - \sqrt{x+2} = 3$$
$$\sqrt{5x-1} = \sqrt{x}+1$$
$$\left(\sqrt{5x-1}\right)^2 = \left(\sqrt{x}+1\right)^2$$
$$5x-1 = x + 2\sqrt{x} + 1$$
$$4x-2 = 2\sqrt{x}$$
$$2x-1 = \sqrt{x}$$
$$(2x-1)^2 = \left(\sqrt{x}\right)^2$$
$$4x^2 - 4x + 1 = x$$
$$4x^2 - 5x + 1 = 0$$
$$(4x-1)(x-1) = 0$$
$$4x-1 = 0 \quad \text{or} \quad x-1 = 0$$
$$4x = 1 \quad \text{or} \quad x = 1$$
$$x = \frac{1}{4}$$
We discard $\frac{1}{4}$ as extraneous. The solution is 1.

45.
$$\sqrt{2x-1} = \sqrt{1-2x}$$
$$\left(\sqrt{2x-1}\right)^2 = \left(\sqrt{1-2x}\right)^2$$
$$2x-1 = 1-2x$$
$$4x = 2$$
$$x = \frac{2}{4} = \frac{1}{2}$$
The solution is $\frac{1}{2}$.

47.
$$\sqrt{3x+4} - 1 = \sqrt{2x+1}$$
$$\sqrt{3x+4} = \sqrt{2x+1} + 1$$
$$\left(\sqrt{3x+4}\right)^2 = \left(\sqrt{2x+1}+1\right)^2$$
$$3x+4 = (2x+1) + 2\sqrt{2x+1} + 1$$
$$3x+4 = 2x+2 + 2\sqrt{2x+1}$$
$$x+2 = 2\sqrt{2x+1}$$
$$(x+2)^2 = \left(2\sqrt{2x+1}\right)^2$$
$$x^2 + 4x + 4 = 4(2x+1)$$
$$x^2 + 4x + 4 = 8x + 4$$
$$x^2 - 4x = 0$$
$$x(x-4) = 0$$
$$x = 0 \quad \text{or} \quad x-4 = 0$$
$$x = 4$$
The solutions are 0 and 4.

49.
$$\sqrt{y+3} - \sqrt{y-3} = 1$$
$$\sqrt{y+3} = 1 + \sqrt{y-3}$$
$$\left(\sqrt{y+3}\right)^2 = \left(1+\sqrt{y-3}\right)^2$$
$$y+3 = 1 + 2\sqrt{y-3} + (y-3)$$
$$y+3 = -2 + 2\sqrt{y-3} + y$$
$$5 = 2\sqrt{y-3}$$
$$(5)^2 = \left(2\sqrt{y-3}\right)^2$$
$$25 = 4(y-3)$$
$$25 = 4y - 12$$
$$37 = 4y$$
$$\frac{37}{4} = y$$

The solution is $\frac{37}{4}$.

51. Let c = length of the hypotenuse.
$$6^2 + 3^2 = c^2$$
$$36 + 9 = c^2$$
$$45 = c^2$$
$$\sqrt{45} = \sqrt{c^2}$$
$$\sqrt{9 \cdot 5} = c$$
$$3\sqrt{5} = c \text{ so } c = 3\sqrt{5} \text{ feet}$$

53. Let b = length of the unknown leg.
$$3^2 + b^2 = 7^2$$
$$9 + b^2 = 49$$
$$b^2 = 40$$
$$\sqrt{b^2} = \sqrt{40}$$
$$b = \sqrt{4 \cdot 10}$$
$$b = 2\sqrt{10} \text{ meters}$$

55. Let b = length of the unknown leg.
$$9^2 + b^2 = \left(11\sqrt{5}\right)^2$$
$$81 + b^2 = 121 \cdot 5$$
$$81 + b^2 = 605$$
$$b^2 = 525$$
$$\sqrt{b^2} = \sqrt{524}$$
$$b = \sqrt{4 \cdot 131}$$
$$b = 2\sqrt{131} \approx 22.9 \text{ meters}$$

57. Let c = length of the hypotenuse.
$$7^2 + 7.2^2 = c^2$$
$$49 + 51.84 = c^2$$
$$100.84 = c^2$$
$$\sqrt{100.84} = \sqrt{c^2}$$
$$c = \sqrt{100.84}$$
$$c \approx 10.0 \text{ mm}$$

59. Let c = amount of cable needed.
$$15^2 + 8^2 = c^2$$
$$225 + 64 = c^2$$
$$289 = c^2$$
$$\sqrt{289} = \sqrt{c^2}$$
$$17 = c$$
Thus, 17 feet of cable is needed.

61. Let c = length of the ladder.
$$12^2 + 5^2 = c^2$$
$$144 + 25 = c^2$$
$$169 = c^2$$
$$\sqrt{169} = \sqrt{c^2}$$
$$13 = c$$
A 13-foot ladder is needed.

63.
$$r = \sqrt{\frac{A}{4\pi}}$$
$$1080 = \sqrt{\frac{A}{4\pi}}$$
$$(1080)^2 = \left(\sqrt{\frac{A}{4\pi}}\right)^2$$
$$1,166,400 = \frac{A}{4\pi}$$
$$14,657,415 \approx A$$
The surface area is 14,657,415 sq. miles.

65.
$$v = \sqrt{2gh}$$
$$80 = \sqrt{2(32)h}$$
$$(80)^2 = \left(\sqrt{64h}\right)^2$$
$$6400 = 64h$$
$$100 = h$$
The object fell 100 feet.

67.
$$S = 2\sqrt{I} - 9$$
$$11 = 2\sqrt{I} - 9$$
$$20 = 2\sqrt{I}$$
$$10 = \sqrt{I}$$
$$10^2 = \left(\sqrt{I}\right)^2$$
$$100 = I$$
The estimated IQ is 100.

69.
$$P = 2\pi\sqrt{\frac{l}{32}}$$
$$= 2\pi\sqrt{\frac{2}{32}}$$
$$= 2\pi\sqrt{\frac{1}{16}}$$
$$= 2\pi\left(\frac{1}{4}\right)$$
$$= \frac{\pi}{2} \text{ sec} \approx 1.57 \text{ sec}$$

71.
$$P = 2\pi\sqrt{\frac{l}{32}}$$
$$4 = 2\pi\sqrt{\frac{l}{32}}$$
$$\frac{4}{2\pi} = \sqrt{\frac{l}{32}}$$
$$\left(\frac{2}{\pi}\right)^2 = \left(\sqrt{\frac{l}{32}}\right)^2$$
$$\frac{4}{\pi^2} = \frac{l}{32}$$
$$l = 32\left(\frac{4}{\pi^2}\right) \approx 12.97 \text{ feet}$$

73. Answers may vary. One possibility follows:
The longer the pendulum length is, the greater
the period is.

75.
$$s = \frac{1}{2}(6 + 10 + 14) = \frac{1}{2}(30) = 15$$
$$A = \sqrt{s(s-a)(s-b)(s-c)}$$
$$= \sqrt{15(15-6)(15-10)(15-14)}$$
$$= \sqrt{15(9)(5)(1)}$$
$$= \sqrt{675}$$
$$= \sqrt{225 \cdot 3}$$
$$= 15\sqrt{3} \text{ sq. mi} \approx 25.98 \text{ sq. mi.}$$

77. Answers may vary. One possibility follows:
When we cannot easily measure both the base
and the height of the triangle, Heron's formula
will be useful. It is easier to obtain the measures
of the lengths of the three sides than it is to
obtain the measure of the height.

79.
$$D(h) = 111.7\sqrt{h}$$
$$80 = 111.7\sqrt{h}$$
$$\frac{80}{111.7} = \sqrt{h}$$
$$\left(\frac{80}{111.7}\right)^2 = \left(\sqrt{h}\right)^2$$
$$0.5129483389 = h$$
$$h \approx 0.51 \text{ km}$$

81. Function

83. Function

85. Not a function

87. $\dfrac{\dfrac{x}{6}}{\dfrac{2x}{3} + \dfrac{1}{2}} = \dfrac{\left(\dfrac{x}{6}\right)6}{\left(\dfrac{2x}{3} + \dfrac{1}{2}\right)6} = \dfrac{x}{4x + 3}$

89. $\dfrac{\dfrac{z}{5} + \dfrac{1}{10}}{\dfrac{z}{20} - \dfrac{z}{5}} = \dfrac{\left(\dfrac{z}{5} + \dfrac{1}{10}\right)20}{\left(\dfrac{z}{20} - \dfrac{z}{5}\right)20}$
$$= \frac{4z + 2}{z - 4z}$$
$$= \frac{4z + 2}{-3z}$$
$$= -\frac{4z + 2}{3z}$$

91.
$$\sqrt{\sqrt{x+3} + \sqrt{x}} = \sqrt{3}$$
$$\left(\sqrt{\sqrt{x+3} + \sqrt{x}}\right)^2 = \left(\sqrt{3}\right)^2$$
$$\sqrt{x+3} + \sqrt{x} = 3$$
$$\sqrt{x+3} = 3 - \sqrt{x}$$
$$\left(\sqrt{x+3}\right)^2 = \left(3 - \sqrt{x}\right)^2$$
$$x + 3 = 9 - 6\sqrt{x} + x$$
$$-6 = -6\sqrt{x}$$
$$(-6)^2 = \left(-6\sqrt{x}\right)^2$$
$$36 = 36x$$
$$1 = x$$

93. $C(x) = 80\sqrt[3]{x} + 500$

$1620 = 80\sqrt[3]{x} + 500$

$1120 = 80\sqrt[3]{x}$

$14 = \sqrt[3]{x}$

$14^3 = \left(\sqrt[3]{x}\right)^3$

$2744 = x$

Thus, 2743 deliveries will keep overhead below $1620.

95. $3\sqrt{x^2 - 8x} = x^2 - 8x$

Let $t = x^2 - 8x$. Then

$3\sqrt{t} = t$

$\left(3\sqrt{t}\right)^2 = t^2$

$9t = t^2$

$0 = t^2 - 9t$

$0 = t(t - 9)$

$t = 0$ or $t = 9$

Replace t with $x^2 - 8x$.

$x^2 - 8x = 0$ or $x^2 - 8x = 9$

$x(x - 8) = 0$ $x^2 - 8x - 9 = 0$

$x = 0$ or $x = 8$ $(x - 9)(x + 1) = 0$

                      $x = 9$ or $x = -1$

The solutions are -1, 0, 8, and 9.

97. $7 - (x^2 - 3x) = \sqrt{(x^2 - 3x) + 5}$

Let $t = x^2 - 3x$. Then

$7 - t = \sqrt{t + 5}$

$(7 - t)^2 = \left(\sqrt{t + 5}\right)^2$

$49 - 14t + t^2 = t + 5$

$t^2 - 15t + 44 = 0$

$(t - 11)(t - 4) = 0$

$t = 11$ or $t = 4$

Replace t with $x^2 - 3x$.

$x^2 - 3x = 11$ or $x^2 - 3x = 4$

$x^2 - 3x - 11 = 0$ $x^2 - 3x - 4 = 0$

Can't factor $(x - 4)(x + 1) = 0$

                     $x = 4$ or $x = -1$

The solutions are -1 and 4.

[Note: This equation $x^2 - 3x - 11 = 0$ actually has two irrational solutions. We will learn to find such solutions in Chapter 8. As it turns out the two irrational solutions are extraneous and thus are discarded, so the overall solutions are only -1 and 4.]

Mental Math 7.7

1. $\sqrt{-81} = 9i$

2. $\sqrt{-49} = 7i$

3. $\sqrt{-7} = i\sqrt{7}$

4. $\sqrt{-3} = i\sqrt{3}$

5. $-\sqrt{16} = -4$

6. $-\sqrt{4} = -2$

7. $\sqrt{-64} = 8i$

8. $\sqrt{-100} = 10i$

Exercise Set 7.7

1. $\sqrt{-24} = \sqrt{-1 \cdot 24} = \sqrt{-1}\sqrt{4 \cdot 6} = i \cdot 2\sqrt{6} = 2i\sqrt{6}$

3. $-\sqrt{-36} = -\sqrt{-1 \cdot 36} = -\sqrt{-1}\sqrt{36} = -i \cdot 6 = -6i$

5. $8\sqrt{-63} = 8\sqrt{-1 \cdot 63}$

$= 8\sqrt{-1}\sqrt{9 \cdot 7}$

$= 8i \cdot 3\sqrt{7}$

$= 24i\sqrt{7}$

7. $-\sqrt{54} = -\sqrt{9 \cdot 6} = -3\sqrt{6}$

9. $\sqrt{-2} \cdot \sqrt{-7} = i\sqrt{2} \cdot i\sqrt{7}$

$= i^2\sqrt{14}$

$= (-1)\sqrt{14}$

$= -\sqrt{14}$

11. $\sqrt{-5} \cdot \sqrt{-10} = i\sqrt{5} \cdot i\sqrt{10}$

$= i^2\sqrt{50}$

$= (-1)\sqrt{25 \cdot 2}$

$= -5\sqrt{2}$

13. $\sqrt{16} \cdot \sqrt{-1} = 4i$

15. $\dfrac{\sqrt{-9}}{\sqrt{3}} = \dfrac{i\sqrt{9}}{\sqrt{3}} = \dfrac{3i}{\sqrt{3}} = \dfrac{3i \cdot \sqrt{3}}{\sqrt{3} \cdot \sqrt{3}} = \dfrac{3i\sqrt{3}}{3} = i\sqrt{3}$

17. $\dfrac{\sqrt{-80}}{\sqrt{-10}} = \dfrac{i\sqrt{80}}{i\sqrt{10}} = \sqrt{\dfrac{80}{10}} = \sqrt{8} = \sqrt{4 \cdot 2} = 2\sqrt{2}$

19. $(4 - 7i) + (2 + 3i) = (4 + 2) + (-7 + 3)i$
$= 6 + (-4)i$
$= 6 - 4i$

21. $(6 + 5i) - (8 - i) = 6 + 5i - 8 + i$
$= (6 - 8) + (5 + 1)i$
$= -2 + 6i$

23. $6 - (8 + 4i) = 6 - 8 - 4i$
$= (6 - 8) - 4i$
$= -2 - 4i$

25. $6i(2 - 3i) = 12i - 18i^2$
$= 12i - 18(-1)$
$= 18 + 12i$

27. $\left(\sqrt{3} + 2i\right)\left(\sqrt{3} - 2i\right)$
$= \sqrt{3} \cdot \sqrt{3} - \sqrt{3} \cdot 2i + \sqrt{3} \cdot 2i - 4i^2$
$= 3 - 4(-1)$
$= 3 + 4$
$= 7$

29. $\left(4 - 2i\right)^2 = (4 - 2i)(4 - 2i)$
$= 16 - 4 \cdot 2i - 4 \cdot 2i + 4i^2$
$= 16 - 8i - 8i + 4(-1)$
$= 16 - 16i - 4$
$= 12 - 16i$

31. $\dfrac{4}{i} = \dfrac{4(-i)}{i(-i)} = \dfrac{-4i}{-i^2} = \dfrac{-4i}{-(-1)} = -4i$

33. $\dfrac{7}{4 + 3i} = \dfrac{7(4 - 3i)}{(4 + 3i)(4 - 3i)}$
$= \dfrac{28 - 21i}{4^2 - 9i^2}$
$= \dfrac{28 - 21i}{16 + 9}$
$= \dfrac{28 - 21i}{25}$
$= \dfrac{28}{25} - \dfrac{21}{25}i$

35. $\dfrac{3 + 5i}{1 + i} = \dfrac{(3 + 5i)(1 - i)}{(1 + i)(1 - i)}$
$= \dfrac{3 - 3i + 5i - 5i^2}{1^2 - i^2}$
$= \dfrac{3 + 2i + 5}{1 + 1}$
$= \dfrac{8 + 2i}{2}$
$= 4 + i$

37. $\dfrac{5 - i}{3 - 2i} = \dfrac{(5 - i)(3 + 2i)}{(3 - 2i)(3 + 2i)}$
$= \dfrac{15 + 10i - 3i - 2i^2}{3^2 - 4i^2}$
$= \dfrac{15 + 7i + 2}{9 + 4}$
$= \dfrac{17 + 7i}{13}$
$= \dfrac{17}{13} + \dfrac{7}{13}i$

39. $(7i)(-9i) = -63i^2 = -63(-1) = 63$

41. $(6 - 3i) - (4 - 2i) = 6 - 3i - 4 + 2i = 2 - i$

43. $(6 - 2i)(3 + i) = 18 + 6i - 6i - 2i^2 = 18 + 2 = 20$

45. $(8 - 3i) + (2 + 3i) = 8 - 3i + 2 + 3i = 10$

47. $(1 - i) + (1 + i) = 1 + i - i - i^2 = 1 + 1 = 2$

49. $\dfrac{16 + 15i}{-3i} = \dfrac{(16 + 15i)(3i)}{-3i(3i)}$
$= \dfrac{48i + 45i^2}{-9i^2}$
$= \dfrac{-45 + 48i}{9}$
$= \dfrac{-45}{9} + \dfrac{48}{9}i$
$= -5 + \dfrac{16}{3}i$

51. $(9 + 8i)^2 = 9^2 + 2(9)(8i) + (8i)^2$
$= 81 + 144i + 64i^2$
$= 81 + 144i - 64$
$= 17 + 144i$

53. $\dfrac{2}{3+i} = \dfrac{2(3-i)}{(3+i)(3-i)}$

$= \dfrac{6-2i}{3^2-i^2}$

$= \dfrac{6-2i}{9+1}$

$= \dfrac{6-2i}{10}$

$= \dfrac{6}{10} - \dfrac{2}{10}i$

$= \dfrac{3}{5} - \dfrac{1}{5}i$

55. $(5-6i) - 4i = 5 - 6i - 4i = 5 - 10i$

57. $\dfrac{2-3i}{2+i} = \dfrac{(2-3i)(2-i)}{(2+i)(2-i)}$

$= \dfrac{4-2i-6i+3i^2}{2^2-i^2}$

$= \dfrac{4-8i-3}{4+1}$

$= \dfrac{1-8i}{5}$

$= \dfrac{1}{5} - \dfrac{8}{5}i$

59. $(2+4i) + (6-5i) = 2 + 4i + 6 - 5i = 8 - i$

61. $i^8 = (i^4)^2 = 1^2 = 1$

63. $i^{21} = i^{20} \cdot i = (i^4)^5 \cdot i = 1^5 \cdot i = i$

65. $i^{11} = i^8 \cdot i^3 = (i^4)^2 \cdot i^3 = 1^2 \cdot (-i) = -i$

67. $i^{-6} = \dfrac{1}{i^6} = \dfrac{1}{i^4 \cdot i^2} = \dfrac{1}{1 \cdot (-1)} = -1$

69. $(2i)^6 = 2^6 i^6 = 64i^4 \cdot i^2 = 64(1)(-1) = -64$

71. $(-3i)^5 = (-3)^5 i^5 = -243 i^4 \cdot i = -243(1)i = -243i$

73. $x + 50° + 90° = 180°$

$x + 140° = 180°$

$x = 40°$

75.
$$\begin{array}{r|rrrr} 1 & 1 & -6 & 3 & -4 \\ & & 1 & -5 & -2 \\ \hline & 1 & -5 & -2 & -6 \end{array}$$

Answer: $x^2 - 5x - 2 - \dfrac{6}{x-1}$

77. 5 people

79. $5 + 9 = 14$ people

81. $\dfrac{5 \text{ people}}{30 \text{ people}} = \dfrac{1}{6} \approx 0.1666$

About 16.7% of the people reported an average checking balance of $201 to $300.

83. $i^3 + i^4 = -i + 1 = 1 - i$

85. $i^6 + i^8 = i^4 \cdot i^2 + (i^4)^2$

$= 1(-1) + 1^2$

$= -1 + 1$

$= 0$

87. $2 + \sqrt{-9} = 2 + i\sqrt{9} = 2 + 3i$

89. $\dfrac{6 + \sqrt{-18}}{3} = \dfrac{6 + i\sqrt{9 \cdot 2}}{3}$

$= \dfrac{6 + 3i\sqrt{2}}{3}$

$= \dfrac{6}{3} + \dfrac{3\sqrt{2}}{3}i$

$= 2 + i\sqrt{2}$

91. $\dfrac{5 - \sqrt{-75}}{10} = \dfrac{5 - i\sqrt{25 \cdot 3}}{10}$

$= \dfrac{5 - 5i\sqrt{3}}{10}$

$= \dfrac{5}{10} - \dfrac{5\sqrt{3}}{10}i$

$= \dfrac{1}{2} - \dfrac{\sqrt{3}}{2}i$

93. Answers may vary. One possibility follows: On using the FOIL method, the product of the "firsts" will be real. The product of the "lasts" will be real. The products of the "outers" and "inners" will be imaginary with opposite signs. Thus, when we simplify, the "outers" and "inners" cancel out leaving only the sum of the "firsts" and "lasts," which again must be real.

95. $\left(8 - \sqrt{-4}\right) - \left(2 + \sqrt{-16}\right) = 8 - 2i - 2 - 4i$
$$= 6 - 6i$$

97.
$$x^2 + 2x = -2$$
$$(-1+i)^2 + 2(-1+i) \overset{?}{=} -2$$
$$(1 - 2i + i^2) - 2 + 2i \overset{?}{=} -2$$
$$1 - 1 - 2 \overset{?}{=} -2$$
$$-2 = -2, \text{ which is true.}$$
Yes, $-1 + i$ is a solution.

Chapter 7 Review

1. $\sqrt{81} = 9$ because $9^2 = 81$.

2. $\sqrt[4]{81} = 3$ because $3^4 = 81$.

3. $\sqrt[3]{-8} = -2$ because $(-2)^4 = -8$.

4. $\sqrt[4]{16} = 2$ because $2^4 = 16$.

5. $-\sqrt{\dfrac{1}{49}} = -\dfrac{1}{7}$ because $\left(\dfrac{1}{7}\right)^2 = \dfrac{1}{49}$.

6. $\sqrt{x^{64}} = x^{32}$ because $(x^{32})^2 = x^{32 \cdot 2} = x^{64}$.

7. $-\sqrt{36} = -6$ because $6^2 = 36$.

8. $\sqrt[3]{64} = 4$ because $4^3 = 64$.

9. $\sqrt[3]{-a^6 b^9} = \sqrt[3]{-1}\sqrt[3]{a^6}\sqrt[3]{b^9} = -1a^2 b^3 = -a^2 b^3$

10. $\sqrt{16a^4 b^{12}} = \sqrt{16}\sqrt{a^4}\sqrt{b^{12}} = 4a^2 b^6$

11. $\sqrt[5]{32a^5 b^{10}} = \sqrt[5]{32}\sqrt[5]{a^5}\sqrt[5]{b^{10}} = 2ab^2$

12. $\sqrt[5]{-32x^{15} y^{20}} = \sqrt[5]{-32}\sqrt[5]{x^{15}}\sqrt[5]{y^{20}} = -2x^3 y^4$

13. $\sqrt{\dfrac{x^{12}}{36y^2}} = \dfrac{\sqrt{x^{12}}}{\sqrt{36y^2}} = \dfrac{x^6}{6y}$

14. $\sqrt[3]{\dfrac{27y^3}{z^{12}}} = \dfrac{\sqrt[3]{27y^3}}{\sqrt[3]{z^{12}}} = \dfrac{3y}{z^4}$

15. $\sqrt{(-x)^2} = |-x|$

16. $\sqrt[4]{(x^2 - 4)^4} = |x^2 - 4|$

17. $\sqrt[3]{(-27)^3} = -27$

18. $\sqrt[5]{(-5)^5} = -5$

19. $-\sqrt[5]{x^5} = -x$

20. $\sqrt[4]{16(2y + z)^{12}} = \sqrt[4]{16}\sqrt[4]{(2y + z)^{12}}$
$$= 2\left|(2y + z)^3\right|$$

21. $\sqrt{25(x - y)^{10}} = \sqrt{25}\sqrt{(x - y)^{10}}$
$$= 5\left|(x - y)^5\right|$$

22. $\sqrt[5]{-y^5} = \sqrt[5]{-1}\sqrt[5]{y^5} = -1y = -y$

23. $\sqrt[9]{-x^9} = \sqrt[9]{-1}\sqrt[9]{x^9} = -1x = -x$

24. $f(x) = \sqrt{x} + 3$
Domain: $[0, \infty)$

Using a graphing calculator, define $y_1 = \sqrt{x} + 3$ and graph it using a $[-3, 10, 1]$ by $[-2, 10, 1]$ window.

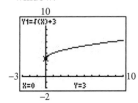

25. $g(x) = \sqrt[3]{x} - 3$
Domain: $(-\infty, \infty)$

x	$g(x) = \sqrt[3]{x} - 3$
-5	$\sqrt[3]{-5} - 3 = \sqrt[3]{-8} = -2$
2	$\sqrt[3]{2} - 3 = \sqrt[3]{-1} = -1$
3	$\sqrt[3]{3} - 3 = \sqrt[3]{0} = 0$
4	$\sqrt[3]{4} - 3 = \sqrt[3]{1} = 1$
11	$\sqrt[3]{11} - 3 = \sqrt[3]{8} = 2$

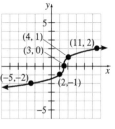

Using a graphing calculator, define $y_1 = \sqrt[3]{x} - 3$ and graph it using a $[-10, 15, 1]$ by $[-5, 5, 1]$ window.

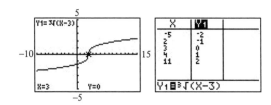

26. $\left(\dfrac{1}{81}\right)^{1/4} = \dfrac{1}{81^{1/4}} = \dfrac{1}{\sqrt[4]{81}} = \dfrac{1}{3}$

27. $\left(-\dfrac{1}{27}\right)^{1/3} = -\dfrac{1}{27^{1/3}} = -\dfrac{1}{\sqrt[3]{27}} = -\dfrac{1}{3}$

28. $(-27)^{-1/3} = \dfrac{1}{(-27)^{1/3}} = \dfrac{1}{\sqrt[3]{-27}} = \dfrac{1}{-3} = -\dfrac{1}{3}$

29. $(-64)^{-1/3} = \dfrac{1}{(-64)^{1/3}} = \dfrac{1}{\sqrt[3]{-64}} = \dfrac{1}{-4} = -\dfrac{1}{4}$

30. $-9^{3/2} = -\left(\sqrt{9}\right)^3 = -3^3 = -27$

31. $64^{-1/3} = \dfrac{1}{64^{1/3}} = \dfrac{1}{\sqrt[3]{64}} = \dfrac{1}{4}$

32. $(-25)^{5/2} = \left(\sqrt{-25}\right)^5$ is not a real number, since there is no real number whose 4th power is negative.

33. $\left(\dfrac{25}{49}\right)^{-3/2} = \dfrac{1}{\left(\dfrac{25}{49}\right)^{3/2}} = \dfrac{1}{\left(\sqrt{\dfrac{25}{49}}\right)^3} = \dfrac{1}{\left(\dfrac{5}{7}\right)^3} = \dfrac{1}{\dfrac{125}{343}} = \dfrac{343}{125}$

34. $\left(\dfrac{8}{27}\right)^{-2/3} = \dfrac{1}{\left(\dfrac{8}{27}\right)^{2/3}} = \dfrac{1}{\left(\sqrt[3]{\dfrac{8}{27}}\right)^2} = \dfrac{1}{\left(\dfrac{2}{3}\right)^2} = \dfrac{1}{\dfrac{4}{9}} = \dfrac{9}{4}$

35. $\left(-\dfrac{1}{36}\right)^{-1/4} = \dfrac{1}{\left(-\dfrac{1}{36}\right)^{1/4}} = \dfrac{1}{\sqrt[4]{-\dfrac{1}{36}}}$

is not a real number, since there is no real number whose 4th power is negative.

36. $\sqrt[3]{x^2} = x^{2/3}$

37. $\sqrt[5]{5x^2 y^3} = (5x^2 y^3)^{1/5}$
$= 5^{1/5}(x^2)^{1/5}(y^3)^{1/5}$
$= 5^{1/5} x^{2/5} y^{3/5}$

38. $y^{4/5} = \sqrt[5]{y^4}$

39. $5(xy^2 z^5)^{1/3} = 5\sqrt[3]{xy^2 z^5}$

40. $(x+2y)^{-1/2} = \dfrac{1}{(x+2y)^{1/2}} = \dfrac{1}{\sqrt{x+2y}}$

41. $a^{1/3}a^{4/3}a^{1/2} = a^{\frac{1}{3}+\frac{4}{3}+\frac{1}{2}} = a^{\frac{2}{6}+\frac{8}{6}+\frac{3}{6}} = a^{13/6}$

42. $\dfrac{b^{1/3}}{b^{4/3}} = b^{1/3-4/3} = b^{-3/3} = b^{-1} = \dfrac{1}{b}$

43. $(a^{1/2}a^{-2})^3 = (a^{1/2-2})^3$
$= (a^{1/2-4/2})^3$
$= (a^{-3/2})^3$
$= a^{-9/2}$
$= \dfrac{1}{a^{9/2}}$

44. $(x^{-3} y^6)^{1/3} = (x^{-3})^{1/3}(y^6)^{1/3} = x^{-1} y^2 = \dfrac{y^2}{x}$

45. $\left(\dfrac{b^{3/4}}{a^{-1/2}}\right)^8 = (a^{1/2}b^{3/4})^8 = (a^{1/2})^8 (b^{3/4})^8 = a^4 b^6$

46. $\dfrac{x^{1/4}x^{-1/2}}{x^{2/3}} = x^{1/4+(-1/2)-2/3}$
$= x^{\frac{3}{12}-\frac{6}{12}-\frac{8}{12}}$
$= x^{-11/12}$
$= \dfrac{1}{x^{11/12}}$

47. $\left(\dfrac{49c^{5/3}}{a^{-1/4}b^{5/6}}\right)^{-1} = \dfrac{49^{-1}c^{-5/3}}{a^{1/4}b^{-5/6}} = \dfrac{b^{5/6}}{49a^{1/4}c^{5/3}}$

48. $a^{-1/4}(a^{5/4} - a^{9/4}) = a^{-1/4}(a^{5/4}) - a^{-1/4}(a^{9/4})$
$= a^{-1/4+5/4} - a^{-1/4+9/4}$
$= a^{4/4} - a^{8/4}$
$= a - a^2$

49. $\sqrt{20} \approx 4.472$

50. $\sqrt[3]{-39} \approx -3.391$

51. $\sqrt[4]{726} \approx 5.191$

52. $56^{1/3} \approx 3.826$

53. $-78^{3/4} \approx -26.246$

54. $105^{-2/3} \approx 0.045$

55. $\sqrt[3]{2} \cdot \sqrt{7} = 2^{1/3} \cdot 7^{1/2}$
$= 2^{2/6} \cdot 7^{3/6}$
$= (2^2 \cdot 7^3)^{1/6}$
$= \sqrt[6]{1372}$

56. $\sqrt[3]{3} \cdot \sqrt[4]{x} = 3^{1/3} \cdot x^{1/4}$
$= 3^{4/12} \cdot x^{3/12}$
$= (3^4 \cdot x^3)^{1/12}$
$= \sqrt[12]{81x^3}$

57. $\sqrt{3} \cdot \sqrt{8} = \sqrt{24} = \sqrt{4 \cdot 6} = 2\sqrt{6}$

58. $\sqrt[3]{7y} \cdot \sqrt[3]{x^2 z} = \sqrt[3]{7y \cdot x^2 z} = \sqrt[3]{7x^2 yz}$

59. $\dfrac{\sqrt{44x^3}}{\sqrt{11x}} = \sqrt{\dfrac{44x^3}{11x}} = \sqrt{4x^2} = 2x$

60. $\dfrac{\sqrt[4]{a^6 b^{13}}}{\sqrt[4]{a^2 b}} = \sqrt[4]{\dfrac{a^6 b^{13}}{a^2 b}} = \sqrt[4]{a^4 b^{12}} = ab^3$

61. $\sqrt{60} = \sqrt{4 \cdot 15} = 2\sqrt{15}$

62. $-\sqrt{75} = -\sqrt{25 \cdot 3} = -5\sqrt{3}$

63. $\sqrt[3]{162} = \sqrt[3]{27 \cdot 6} = 3\sqrt[3]{6}$

64. $\sqrt[3]{-32} = \sqrt[3]{-8 \cdot 4} = -2\sqrt[3]{4}$

65. $\sqrt{36x^7} = \sqrt{36x^6 \cdot x} = 6x^3 \sqrt{x}$

66. $\sqrt[3]{24a^5 b^7} = \sqrt[3]{8a^3 b^6 \cdot 3a^2 b^2} = 2ab^2 \sqrt[3]{3a^2 b^2}$

67. $\sqrt{\dfrac{p^{17}}{121}} = \dfrac{\sqrt{p^{17}}}{\sqrt{121}} = \dfrac{\sqrt{p^{16} \cdot p}}{11} = \dfrac{p^8 \sqrt{p}}{11}$

68. $\sqrt[3]{\dfrac{y^5}{27x^6}} = \dfrac{\sqrt[3]{y^5}}{\sqrt[3]{27x^6}} = \dfrac{\sqrt[3]{y^3 y^2}}{\sqrt[3]{27x^6}} = \dfrac{y\sqrt[3]{y^2}}{3x^2}$

69. $\sqrt[4]{\dfrac{xy^6}{81}} = \dfrac{\sqrt[4]{xy^6}}{\sqrt[4]{81}} = \dfrac{\sqrt[4]{y^4 \cdot xy^2}}{3} = \dfrac{y\sqrt[4]{xy^2}}{3}$

70. $\sqrt{\dfrac{2x^3}{49y^4}} = \dfrac{\sqrt{2x^3}}{\sqrt{49y^4}} = \dfrac{\sqrt{x^2 \cdot 2x}}{7y^2} = \dfrac{x\sqrt{2x}}{7y^2}$

71. $r = \sqrt{\dfrac{A}{\pi}}$

a. $r = \sqrt{\dfrac{25}{\pi}} = \dfrac{\sqrt{25}}{\sqrt{\pi}} = \dfrac{5}{\sqrt{\pi}}$ meters, or
$r = \dfrac{5}{\sqrt{\pi}} = \dfrac{5\sqrt{\pi}}{\sqrt{\pi}\sqrt{\pi}} = \dfrac{5\sqrt{\pi}}{\pi}$ meters

b. $r = \sqrt{\dfrac{104}{\pi}} \approx 5.75$ inches

72. $x\sqrt{75xy} - \sqrt{27x^3 y}$
$= x\sqrt{25 \cdot 3xy} - \sqrt{9x^2 \cdot 3xy}$
$= x \cdot 5\sqrt{3xy} - 3x\sqrt{3xy}$
$= 2x\sqrt{3xy}$

73. $2\sqrt{32x^2 y^3} - xy\sqrt{98y}$
$= 2\sqrt{16x^2 y^2 \cdot 2y} - xy\sqrt{49 \cdot 2y}$
$= 2 \cdot 4xy\sqrt{2y} - xy \cdot 7\sqrt{2y}$
$= 8xy\sqrt{2y} - 7xy\sqrt{2y}$
$= xy\sqrt{2y}$

74. $\sqrt[3]{128} + \sqrt[3]{250} = \sqrt[3]{64 \cdot 2} + \sqrt[3]{125 \cdot 2}$
$= 4\sqrt[3]{2} + 5\sqrt[3]{2}$
$= 9\sqrt[3]{2}$

75. $3\sqrt[4]{32a^5} - a\sqrt[4]{162a}$
$= 3\sqrt[4]{16a^4 \cdot 2a} - a\sqrt[4]{81 \cdot 2a}$
$= 3 \cdot 2a\sqrt[4]{2a} - 3a\sqrt[4]{2a}$
$= 6a\sqrt[4]{2a} - 3a\sqrt[4]{2a}$
$= 3a\sqrt[4]{2a}$

76. $\dfrac{5}{\sqrt{4}} + \dfrac{\sqrt{3}}{3} = \dfrac{5}{2} + \dfrac{\sqrt{3}}{3} = \dfrac{5 \cdot 3 + 2\sqrt{3}}{6} = \dfrac{15 + 2\sqrt{3}}{6}$

77. $\sqrt{\dfrac{8}{x^2}} - \sqrt{\dfrac{50}{16x^2}} = \dfrac{\sqrt{8}}{\sqrt{x^2}} - \dfrac{\sqrt{50}}{\sqrt{16x^2}}$
$= \dfrac{\sqrt{4 \cdot 2}}{x} - \dfrac{\sqrt{25 \cdot 2}}{4x}$
$= \dfrac{2\sqrt{2} \cdot 4}{x \cdot 4} - \dfrac{5\sqrt{2}}{4x}$
$= \dfrac{8\sqrt{2} - 5\sqrt{2}}{4x}$
$= \dfrac{3\sqrt{2}}{4x}$

78.
$$2\sqrt{50}-3\sqrt{125}+\sqrt{98}$$
$$=2\sqrt{25\cdot2}-3\sqrt{25\cdot5}+\sqrt{49\cdot2}$$
$$=2\cdot5\sqrt{2}-3\cdot5\sqrt{5}+7\sqrt{2}$$
$$=10\sqrt{2}-15\sqrt{5}+7\sqrt{2}$$
$$=17\sqrt{2}-15\sqrt{5}$$

79.
$$2a\sqrt[4]{32b^5}-3b\sqrt[4]{162a^4b}+\sqrt[4]{2a^4b^5}$$
$$=2a\sqrt[4]{16b^4\cdot2b}-3b\sqrt[4]{81a^4\cdot2b}+\sqrt[4]{a^4b^4\cdot2b}$$
$$=2a\cdot2b\sqrt[4]{2b}-3b\cdot3a\sqrt[4]{2b}+ab\sqrt[4]{2b}$$
$$=4ab\sqrt[4]{2b}-9ab\sqrt[4]{2b}+ab\sqrt[4]{2b}$$
$$=-4ab\sqrt[4]{2b}$$

80.
$$\sqrt{3}\left(\sqrt{27}-\sqrt{3}\right)=\sqrt{3}\left(\sqrt{9\cdot3}-\sqrt{3}\right)$$
$$=\sqrt{3}\left(3\sqrt{3}-\sqrt{3}\right)$$
$$=\sqrt{3}\left(2\sqrt{3}\right)$$
$$=2\sqrt{9}$$
$$=2(3)$$
$$=6$$

81.
$$\left(\sqrt{x}-3\right)^2=\left(\sqrt{x}\right)^2-2\cdot\sqrt{x}\cdot3+3^2$$
$$=x-6\sqrt{x}+9$$

82.
$$\left(\sqrt{5}-5\right)\left(2\sqrt{5}+2\right)=2\sqrt{25}+2\sqrt{5}-10\sqrt{5}-10$$
$$=2(5)-8\sqrt{5}-10$$
$$=10-8\sqrt{5}-10$$
$$=-8\sqrt{5}$$

83.
$$\left(2\sqrt{x}-3\sqrt{y}\right)\left(2\sqrt{x}+3\sqrt{y}\right)=\left(2\sqrt{x}\right)^2-\left(3\sqrt{y}\right)^2$$
$$=2^2\left(\sqrt{x}\right)^2-3^2\left(\sqrt{y}\right)^2$$
$$=4x-9y$$

84.
$$\left(\sqrt{a}-3\right)\left(\sqrt{a}+3\right)=\left(\sqrt{a}\right)^2-(3)^2$$
$$=a-9$$

85.
$$\left(\sqrt[3]{a}+2\right)^2=\left(\sqrt[3]{a}\right)^2+2\cdot\sqrt[3]{a}\cdot2+2^2$$
$$=\sqrt[3]{a^2}+4\sqrt[3]{a}+4$$

86.
$$\left(\sqrt[3]{5x}+9\right)\left(\sqrt[3]{5x}-9\right)=\left(\sqrt[3]{5x}\right)^2-9^2$$
$$=\sqrt[3]{(5x)^2}-81$$
$$=\sqrt[3]{25x^2}-81$$

87.
$$\left(\sqrt[3]{a}+4\right)\left(\sqrt[3]{a^2}-4\sqrt[3]{a}+16\right)$$
$$=\left(\sqrt[3]{a}\right)\left(\sqrt[3]{a^2}\right)-4\cdot\left(\sqrt[3]{a}\right)^2+16\sqrt[3]{a}$$
$$\qquad\qquad+4\sqrt[3]{a^2}-16\sqrt[3]{a}+64$$
$$=\sqrt[3]{a^3}-4\sqrt[3]{a^2}+4\sqrt[3]{a^2}+64$$
$$=a+64$$

88.
$$\frac{3}{\sqrt{7}}=\frac{3\cdot\sqrt{7}}{\sqrt{7}\cdot\sqrt{7}}=\frac{3\sqrt{7}}{7}$$

89.
$$\sqrt{\frac{x}{12}}=\frac{\sqrt{x}}{\sqrt{12}}$$
$$=\frac{\sqrt{x}}{\sqrt{4\cdot3}}=\frac{\sqrt{x}}{2\sqrt{3}}=\frac{\sqrt{x}\cdot\sqrt{3}}{2\sqrt{3}\cdot\sqrt{3}}=\frac{\sqrt{3x}}{2\cdot3}=\frac{\sqrt{3x}}{6}$$

90.
$$\frac{5}{\sqrt[3]{4}}=\frac{5\cdot\sqrt[3]{2}}{\sqrt[3]{4}\cdot\sqrt[3]{2}}=\frac{5\sqrt[3]{2}}{\sqrt[3]{8}}=\frac{5\sqrt[3]{2}}{2}$$

91.
$$\sqrt{\frac{24x^5}{3y^2}}=\sqrt{\frac{8x^5}{y^2}}=\frac{\sqrt{8x^5}}{\sqrt{y^2}}=\frac{\sqrt{4x^4\cdot2x}}{y}=\frac{2x^2\sqrt{2x}}{y}$$

92.
$$\sqrt[3]{\frac{15x^6y^7}{z^2}}=\frac{\sqrt[3]{15x^6y^7}}{\sqrt[3]{z^2}}$$
$$=\frac{\sqrt[3]{15x^6y^7}\cdot\sqrt[3]{z}}{\sqrt[3]{z^2}\cdot\sqrt[3]{z}}$$
$$=\frac{\sqrt[3]{15x^6y^7z}}{\sqrt[3]{z^3}}$$
$$=\frac{\sqrt[3]{15x^6y^6\cdot yz}}{z}$$
$$=\frac{x^2y^2\sqrt[3]{15yz}}{z}$$

93.
$$\frac{5}{2-\sqrt{7}}=\frac{5\left(2+\sqrt{7}\right)}{\left(2-\sqrt{7}\right)\left(2+\sqrt{7}\right)}$$
$$=\frac{5\left(2+\sqrt{7}\right)}{2^2-\left(\sqrt{7}\right)^2}$$
$$=\frac{10+5\sqrt{7}}{4-7}$$
$$=\frac{10+5\sqrt{7}}{-3}$$
$$=-\frac{10+5\sqrt{7}}{3}$$

94.
$$\frac{3}{\sqrt{y}-2} = \frac{3\left(\sqrt{y}+2\right)}{\left(\sqrt{y}-2\right)\left(\sqrt{y}+2\right)}$$
$$= \frac{3\left(\sqrt{y}+2\right)}{\left(\sqrt{y}\right)^2 - 2^2}$$
$$= \frac{3\sqrt{y}+6}{y-4}$$

95.
$$\frac{\sqrt{2}-\sqrt{3}}{\sqrt{2}+\sqrt{3}} = \frac{\left(\sqrt{2}-\sqrt{3}\right)\left(\sqrt{2}-\sqrt{3}\right)}{\left(\sqrt{2}+\sqrt{3}\right)\left(\sqrt{2}-\sqrt{3}\right)}$$
$$= \frac{2-\sqrt{2}\sqrt{3}-\sqrt{3}\sqrt{2}+3}{\left(\sqrt{2}\right)^2 - \left(\sqrt{3}\right)^2}$$
$$= \frac{5-2\sqrt{6}}{-1}$$
$$= -5+2\sqrt{6}$$

96.
$$\frac{\sqrt{11}}{3} = \frac{\sqrt{11}\cdot\sqrt{11}}{3\cdot\sqrt{11}} = \frac{11}{3\sqrt{11}}$$

97.
$$\sqrt{\frac{18}{y}} = \frac{\sqrt{18}}{\sqrt{y}} = \frac{3\sqrt{2}}{\sqrt{y}} = \frac{3\sqrt{2}\cdot\sqrt{2}}{\sqrt{y}\cdot\sqrt{2}} = \frac{3\cdot 2}{\sqrt{2y}} = \frac{6}{\sqrt{2y}}$$

98.
$$\frac{\sqrt[3]{9}}{7} = \frac{\sqrt[3]{9}\cdot\sqrt[3]{3}}{7\cdot\sqrt[3]{3}} = \frac{\sqrt[3]{27}}{7\sqrt[3]{3}} = \frac{3}{7\sqrt[3]{3}}$$

99.
$$\sqrt{\frac{24x^5}{3y^2}} = \sqrt{\frac{8x^5}{y^2}}$$
$$= \frac{\sqrt{4x^4\cdot 2x}}{\sqrt{y^2}}$$
$$= \frac{2x^2\sqrt{2x}}{y}$$
$$= \frac{2x^2\sqrt{2x}\cdot\sqrt{2x}}{y\cdot\sqrt{2x}}$$
$$= \frac{2x^2\cdot 2x}{y\sqrt{2x}}$$
$$= \frac{4x^3}{y\sqrt{2x}}$$

100.
$$\sqrt[3]{\frac{xy^2}{10z}} = \frac{\sqrt[3]{xy^2}}{\sqrt[3]{10z}}$$
$$= \frac{\sqrt[3]{xy^2}\cdot\sqrt[3]{x^2y}}{\sqrt[3]{10z}\cdot\sqrt[3]{x^2y}}$$
$$= \frac{\sqrt[3]{x^3y^3}}{\sqrt[3]{10x^2yz}}$$
$$= \frac{xy}{\sqrt[3]{10x^2yz}}$$

101.
$$\frac{\sqrt{x}+5}{-3} = \frac{\left(\sqrt{x}+5\right)\left(\sqrt{x}-5\right)}{-3\left(\sqrt{x}-5\right)}$$
$$= \frac{\left(\sqrt{x}\right)^2 - 5^2}{-3\sqrt{x}+15}$$
$$= \frac{x-25}{-3\sqrt{x}+15}$$

102.
$$\sqrt{y-7} = 5$$
$$\left(\sqrt{y-7}\right)^2 = 5^2$$
$$y-7 = 25$$
$$y = 32$$
The solution is 32.

103.
$$\sqrt{2x}+10 = 4$$
$$\sqrt{2x} = -6$$
No solution exist since the principle square root of a number is not negative. The solution set is $\varnothing$.

104.
$$\sqrt[3]{2x-6} = 4$$
$$\left(\sqrt[3]{2x-6}\right)^3 = 4^3$$
$$2x-6 = 64$$
$$2x = 70$$
$$x = 35$$
The solution is 35.

105.
$$\sqrt{x+6} = \sqrt{x+2}$$
$$\left(\sqrt{x+6}\right)^2 = \left(\sqrt{x+2}\right)^2$$
$$x+6 = x+2$$
$$6 = 2, \text{ which is false.}$$
There is no solution. The solution set is $\varnothing$.

106.
$$2x - 5\sqrt{x} = 3$$
$$2x - 3 = 5\sqrt{x}$$
$$(2x-3)^2 = \left(5\sqrt{x}\right)^2$$
$$4x^2 - 12x + 9 = 25x$$
$$4x^2 - 37x + 9 = 0$$
$$(4x-1)(x-9) = 0$$
$$4x - 1 = 0 \ \text{ or } \ x - 9 = 0$$
$$4x = 1 \ \text{ or } \quad x = 9$$
$$x = \frac{1}{4}$$

Discard the solution $\frac{1}{4}$ as extraneous. The solution is 3.

107.
$$\sqrt{x+9} = 2 + \sqrt{x-7}$$
$$\left(\sqrt{x+9}\right)^2 = \left(2 + \sqrt{x-7}\right)^2$$
$$x + 9 = 4 + 4\sqrt{x-7} + (x-7)$$
$$x + 9 = x - 3 + 4\sqrt{x-7}$$
$$12 = 4\sqrt{x-7}$$
$$3 = \sqrt{x-7}$$
$$3^2 = \left(\sqrt{x-7}\right)^2$$
$$9 = x - 7$$
$$16 = x$$
The solution is 16.

108. Let c = length of the hypotenuse.
$$3^2 + 3^2 = c^2$$
$$18 = c^2$$
$$\sqrt{18} = \sqrt{c^2}$$
$$3\sqrt{2} = c$$

109. Let c = length of the hypotenuse.
$$7^2 + \left(8\sqrt{3}\right)^2 = c^2$$
$$49 + 64 \cdot 3 = c^2$$
$$241 = c^2$$
$$\sqrt{241} = \sqrt{c^2}$$
$$\sqrt{241} = c$$

110. Let b = width of the lake.
$$a^2 + b^2 = c^2$$
$$40^2 + b^2 = 65^2$$
$$1600 + b^2 = 4225$$
$$b^2 = 2625$$
$$\sqrt{b^2} = \sqrt{2625}$$
$$b = 51.23475$$
The width is about 51.2 feet.

111. Let c = length of the shortest pipe.
$$a^2 + b^2 = c^2$$
$$3^2 + 3^2 = c^2$$
$$18 = c^2$$
$$\sqrt{18} = \sqrt{c^2}$$
$$4.24264 = c$$
The shortest possible pipe is 4.24 feet.

112. $\sqrt{-8} = i\sqrt{4\cdot2} = 2i\sqrt{2}$

113. $-\sqrt{-6} = -i\sqrt{6}$

114. $\sqrt{-4} + \sqrt{-16} = 2i + 4i = 6i$

115. $\sqrt{-2}\cdot\sqrt{-5} = i\sqrt{2}\cdot i\sqrt{5}$
$$= i^2\sqrt{10}$$
$$= -1\cdot\sqrt{10}$$
$$= -\sqrt{10}$$

116. $(12-6i)+(3+2i) = (12+3)+(-6+2)i$
$$= 15 + (-4)i$$
$$= 15 - 4i$$

117. $(-8-7i)-(5-4i) = -8-7i-5+4i$
$$= -13 - 3i$$

118. $\left(\sqrt{3}+\sqrt{2}\right)+\left(3\sqrt{2}-\sqrt{-8}\right)$
$$= \sqrt{3}+\sqrt{2}+3\sqrt{2}-i\sqrt{4\cdot2}$$
$$= \sqrt{3}+4\sqrt{2}-2i\sqrt{2}$$

119. $2i(2-5i) = 4i - 10i^2$
$$= 4i - 10(-1)$$
$$= 10 + 4i$$

120. $-3i(6-4i) = -18i + 12i^2$
$$= -18i + 12(-1)$$
$$= -12 - 18i$$

121. $(3+2i)(1+i) = 3+3i+2i+2i^2$
$= 3+5i+2(-1)$
$= 1+5i$

122. $(2-3i)^2 = 4-12i+9i^2$
$= 4-12i+9(-1)$
$= -5-12i$

123. $\left(\sqrt{6}-9i\right)\left(\sqrt{6}+9i\right) = \left(\sqrt{6}\right)^2 - (9i)^2$
$= 6-81i^2$
$= 6+81$
$= 87$

124. $\dfrac{2+3i}{2i} = \dfrac{(2+3i)\cdot(-2i)}{2i\cdot(-2i)}$
$= \dfrac{-4i-6i^2}{-4i^2}$
$= \dfrac{-4i+6}{4}$
$= \dfrac{6}{4}-\dfrac{4}{4}i$
$= \dfrac{3}{2}-i$

125. $\dfrac{1+i}{-3i} = \dfrac{(1+i)\cdot(3i)}{-3i\cdot(3i)}$
$= \dfrac{3i+3i^2}{-9i^2}$
$= \dfrac{3i-3}{9}$
$= \dfrac{-3}{9}-\dfrac{3}{9}i$
$= -\dfrac{1}{3}+\dfrac{1}{3}i$

Chapter 7 Test

1. $\sqrt{216} = \sqrt{36\cdot 6} = 6\sqrt{6}$

2. $-\sqrt[4]{x^{64}} = -x^{16}$

3. $\left(\dfrac{1}{125}\right)^{1/3} = \dfrac{1}{125^{1/3}} = \dfrac{1}{\sqrt[3]{125}} = \dfrac{1}{5}$

4. $\left(\dfrac{1}{125}\right)^{-1/3} = \dfrac{1}{\left(\dfrac{1}{125}\right)^{1/3}} = \dfrac{1}{\sqrt[3]{\dfrac{1}{125}}} = \dfrac{1}{\dfrac{1}{5}} = 5$

5. $\left(\dfrac{8x^3}{27}\right)^{2/3} = \dfrac{(8x^3)^{2/3}}{27^{2/3}}$
$= \dfrac{\left(\sqrt[3]{8x^3}\right)^2}{\left(\sqrt[3]{27}\right)^2}$
$= \dfrac{(2x)^2}{3^3}$
$= \dfrac{4x^2}{9}$

6. $\sqrt[3]{-a^{18}b^9} = \sqrt[3]{-1a^{18}b^9} = (-1)a^6b^3 = -a^6b^3$

7. $\left(\dfrac{64c^{4/3}}{a^{-2/3}b^{5/6}}\right)^{1/2} = \left(\dfrac{64a^{2/3}c^{4/3}}{b^{5/6}}\right)^{1/2}$
$= \dfrac{64^{1/2}(a^{2/3})^{1/2}(c^{4/3})^{1/2}}{(b^{5/6})^{1/2}}$
$= \dfrac{\sqrt{64}a^{1/3}c^{2/3}}{b^{5/12}}$
$= \dfrac{8a^{1/3}c^{2/3}}{b^{5/12}}$

8. $a^{-2/3}(a^{5/4} - a^3) = a^{-2/3}a^{5/4} - a^{-2/3}a^3$
$= a^{-\frac{2}{3}+\frac{5}{4}} - a^{-\frac{2}{3}+3}$
$= a^{-\frac{8}{12}+\frac{15}{12}} - a^{-\frac{2}{3}+\frac{9}{3}}$
$= a^{7/12} - a^{7/3}$

9. $\sqrt[4]{(4xy)^4} = |4xy| = 4|xy|$

10. $\sqrt[3]{(-27)^3} = -27$

11. $\sqrt{\dfrac{9}{y}} = \dfrac{\sqrt{9}}{\sqrt{y}} = \dfrac{3}{\sqrt{y}} = \dfrac{3\cdot\sqrt{y}}{\sqrt{y}\cdot\sqrt{y}} = \dfrac{3\sqrt{y}}{y}$

12. $\dfrac{4-\sqrt{x}}{4+2\sqrt{x}} = \dfrac{4-\sqrt{x}}{2\left(2+\sqrt{x}\right)}$
$= \dfrac{\left(4-\sqrt{x}\right)\left(2-\sqrt{x}\right)}{2\left(2+\sqrt{x}\right)\left(2-\sqrt{x}\right)}$
$= \dfrac{8-4\sqrt{x}-2\sqrt{x}+x}{2\left[2^2 - \left(\sqrt{x}\right)^2\right]}$
$= \dfrac{8-6\sqrt{x}+x}{2(4-x)}$ or $\dfrac{8-6\sqrt{x}+x}{8-2x)}$

13. $\dfrac{\sqrt[3]{ab}}{\sqrt[3]{ab^2}} = \sqrt[3]{\dfrac{ab}{ab^2}} = \sqrt[3]{\dfrac{1}{b}} = \dfrac{1}{\sqrt[3]{b}} = \dfrac{1 \cdot \sqrt[3]{b^2}}{\sqrt[3]{b} \cdot \sqrt[3]{b^2}} = \dfrac{\sqrt[3]{b^2}}{b}$

14. $\dfrac{\sqrt{6}+x}{8} = \dfrac{\left(\sqrt{6}+x\right)\left(\sqrt{6}-x\right)}{8\left(\sqrt{6}-x\right)}$

$= \dfrac{\left(\sqrt{6}\right)^2 - x^2}{8\left(\sqrt{6}-x\right)}$

$= \dfrac{6-x^2}{8\left(\sqrt{6}-x\right)}$

15. $\sqrt{125x^3} - 3\sqrt{20x^3} = \sqrt{25x^2 \cdot 5x} - 3\sqrt{4x^2 \cdot 5x}$

$= 5x\sqrt{5x} - 3 \cdot 2x\sqrt{5x}$

$= 5x\sqrt{5x} - 6x\sqrt{5x}$

$= -x\sqrt{5x}$

16. $\sqrt{3}\left(\sqrt{16}-\sqrt{2}\right) = \sqrt{3}\left(4-\sqrt{2}\right)$

$= 4\sqrt{3} - \sqrt{3}\sqrt{2}$

$= 4\sqrt{3} - \sqrt{6}$

17. $\left(\sqrt{x}+1\right)^2 = \left(\sqrt{x}\right)^2 + 2\sqrt{x} + 1^2$

$= x + 2\sqrt{x} + 1$

18. $\left(\sqrt{2}-4\right)\left(\sqrt{3}+1\right) = \sqrt{2}\sqrt{3} + 1 \cdot \sqrt{2} - 4\sqrt{3} - 4$

$= \sqrt{6} + \sqrt{2} - 4\sqrt{3} - 4$

19. $\left(\sqrt{5}+5\right)\left(\sqrt{5}-5\right) = \left(\sqrt{5}\right)^2 - 5^2$

$= 5 - 25$

$= -20$

20. $\sqrt{561} \approx 23.685$

21. $386^{-2/3} \approx 0.019$

22. $x = \sqrt{x-2} + 2$

$x - 2 = \sqrt{x-2}$

$(x-2)^2 = \left(\sqrt{x-2}\right)^2$

$x^2 - 4x + 4 = x - 2$

$x^2 - 5x + 6 = 0$

$(x-2)(x-3) = 0$

$x = 2$ or $x = 3$

The solutions are $\{2, 3\}$.

23. $\sqrt{x^2 - 7} + 3 = 0$

$\sqrt{x^2 - 7} = -3$

No solution exists since the principle square root of a number is not negative. The solution set is $\varnothing$.

24. $\sqrt[3]{x+5} = \sqrt[3]{2x-1}$

$\left(\sqrt[3]{x+5}\right)^3 = \left(\sqrt[3]{2x-1}\right)^3$

$x + 5 = 2x - 1$

$-x = -6$

$x = 6$

The solution is 6.

25. $\sqrt{-2} = i\sqrt{2}$

26. $-\sqrt{-8} = -i\sqrt{4 \cdot 2} = -2i\sqrt{2}$

27. $(12 - 6i) - (12 - 3i) = 12 - 6i - 12 + 3i$

$= -3i$

28. $(6 - 2i)(6 + 2i) = 6^2 - (2i)^2$

$= 36 - 4i^2$

$= 36 + 4$

$= 40$

29. $(4 + 3i)^2 = 4^2 + 2 \cdot 4 \cdot 3i + (3i)^2$

$= 16 + 24i + 9i^2$

$= 16 + 24i - 9$

$= 7 + 24i$

30. $\dfrac{1+4i}{1-i} = \dfrac{(1+4i)(1+i)}{(1-i)(1+i)}$

$= \dfrac{1 + i + 4i + 4i^2}{1^2 - i^2}$

$= \dfrac{1 + 5i - 4}{1 - (-1)}$

$= \dfrac{-3 + 5i}{2}$

$= -\dfrac{3}{2} + \dfrac{5}{2}i$

31. $x^2 + x^2 = 5^2$

$2x^2 = 25$

$x^2 = \dfrac{25}{2}$

$\sqrt{x^2} = \sqrt{\dfrac{25}{2}}$

$x = \dfrac{5}{\sqrt{2}} = \dfrac{5 \cdot \sqrt{2}}{\sqrt{2} \cdot \sqrt{2}} = \dfrac{5\sqrt{2}}{2}$

32. $g(x) = \sqrt{x+2}$

Domain: $[-2, \infty)$

Using a graphing calculator, define $y_1 = \sqrt{x+2}$ and graph it using a $[-10, 10, 1]$ by $[-5, 5, 1]$ window.

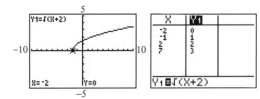

33. $V(r) = \sqrt{2.5r}$

$V(300) = \sqrt{2.5(300)} \approx 27$ mph

34. $V(r) = \sqrt{2.5r}$

$30 = \sqrt{2.5r}$

$30^2 = \left(\sqrt{2.5r}\right)^2$

$900 = 2.5r$

$r = \dfrac{900}{2.5} = 360$ feet

Chapter 7 Cumulative Review

1. a. $3xy - 2xy + 5 - 7 + xy = 2xy - 2$

b. $7x^2 + 3 - 5(x^2 - 4)$
$= 7x^2 + 3 - 5x^2 + 20$
$= 2x^2 + 23$

c. $(2.1x - 5.6) - (-x - 5.3)$
$= 2.1x - 5.6 + x + 5.3$
$= 3.1x - 0.3$

d. $\dfrac{1}{2}(4a - 6b) - \dfrac{1}{3}(9a + 12b - 1) + \dfrac{1}{4}$
$= 2a - 3b - 3a - 4b + \dfrac{1}{3} + \dfrac{1}{4}$
$= 2a - 3a - 3b - 4b + \dfrac{4}{12} + \dfrac{3}{12}$
$= -a - 7b + \dfrac{7}{12}$

2. a. $2(x - 3) + (5x + 3) = 2x - 6 + 5x + 3$
$= 7x - 3$

b. $4(3x + 2) - 3(5x - 1) = 12x + 8 - 15x + 3$
$= -3x + 11$

c. $7x + 2(x - 7) - 3x = 7x + 2x - 14 - 3x$
$= 6x - 14$

3. $\dfrac{x+5}{2} + \dfrac{1}{2} = 2x - \dfrac{x-3}{8}$

$8\left(\dfrac{x+5}{2} + \dfrac{1}{2}\right) = 8\left(2x - \dfrac{x-3}{8}\right)$

$4(x+5) + 4 = 16x - (x-3)$

$4x + 20 + 4 = 16x - x + 3$

$4x + 24 = 15x + 3$

$-11x = -21$

$x = \dfrac{21}{11}$

4. $\dfrac{a-1}{2} + a = 2 - \dfrac{2a+7}{8}$

$8\left(\dfrac{a-1}{2} + a\right) = 8\left(2 - \dfrac{2a+7}{8}\right)$

$4(a-1) + 8a = 16 - (2a+7)$

$4a - 4 + 8a = 16 - 2a - 7$

$12a - 4 = 9 - 2a$

$14a = 13$

$a = \dfrac{13}{14}$

5. Let x = the sales needed.

$600 + 0.20x > 1500$

$0.20x > 900$

$x > \dfrac{900}{0.20}$

$x > 4500$

They need sales of at least $4500.

6. Let r = their average speed.

$t_{\text{going}} + t_{\text{returning}} = 4.5$ hrs

$\dfrac{121.5}{r} + \dfrac{121.5}{r} = 4.5$

$\dfrac{243}{r} = 4.5$

$243 = 4.5r$

$r = \dfrac{243}{4.5} = 54$

Their average speed was 54 mph.

7. $2|x| + 25 = 23$

$2|x| = -2$

$|x| = -1$, which is impossible.

The solution set is $\varnothing$.

8. $|3x-2|+5=5$
$$|3x-2|=0$$
$$3x-2=0$$
$$3x=2$$
$$x=\frac{2}{3}$$

9. $\left|\dfrac{x}{3}-1\right|-7 \geq -5$

$$\left|\dfrac{x}{3}-1\right| \geq 2$$

$$\dfrac{x}{3}-1 \leq -2 \quad \text{or} \quad \dfrac{x}{3}-1 \geq 2$$

$$\dfrac{x}{3} \leq -1 \quad \text{or} \quad \dfrac{x}{3} \geq 3$$

$$x \leq -3 \quad \text{or} \quad x \geq 9$$

The solution set is $(-\infty, -3] \cup [9, \infty)$

10. $\left|\dfrac{x}{2}-1\right| \leq 0$

$\left|\dfrac{x}{2}-1\right|$ cannot be negative, so the only possible

solution comes from:

$$\left|\dfrac{x}{2}-1\right|=0$$

$$\dfrac{x}{2}-1=0$$

$$\dfrac{x}{2}=1$$

$$x=2$$

The solution set is $\{2\}$.

11. $y=|x|$

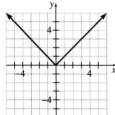

12. $y=|x-2|$

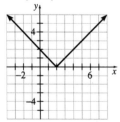

13. a. Domain: $\{2, 0, 3\}$
Range: $\{3, 4, -1\}$

   b. Domain: $\{-4, -3, -2, -1, 0, 1, 2, 3\}$
   Range: $\{1\}$

   c. Domain: $\{$Erie, Escondido, Gary, Miami, Waco,$\}$
   Range: $\{104, 109, 117, 359\}$

14. a. Domain: $(-\infty, 0]$
   Range: $(-\infty, \infty)$
   Not a function

   b. Domain: $(-\infty, \infty)$
   Range: $(-\infty, \infty)$
   Function

   c. Domain: $(-\infty, -2] \cup [2, \infty)$
   Range: $(-\infty, \infty)$
   Not a function

15. $y=-3$

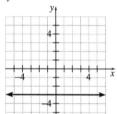

16. $f(x)=-2$
$$y=-2$$

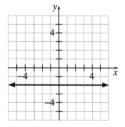

17. $x=-5$ is a vertical line. Thus, the slope is undefined.

18. $y=-3$ is a horizontal line. Thus, the slope is 0.

19.
$$\begin{cases} -\dfrac{x}{6}+\dfrac{y}{2}=\dfrac{1}{2} & (1) \\ \dfrac{x}{3}-\dfrac{y}{6}=-\dfrac{3}{4} & (2) \end{cases}$$

Multiply equation (1) by 6 and equation (2) by 12 to clear fractions.

$$\begin{cases} -x+3y=3 & (1) \\ 4x-2y=-9 & (2) \end{cases}$$

Solve the new equation (1) for x.

$-x=-3y+3$

$x=3y-3$

Replace x with $3y-3$ in the new equation (2).

$4(3y-3)-2y=-9$

$12y-12-2y=-9$

$10y=3$

$y=\dfrac{3}{10}$

Replace y with $\dfrac{3}{10}$ in the equation $x=3y-3$.

$x=3\left(\dfrac{3}{10}\right)-3=\dfrac{9}{10}-\dfrac{30}{10}=-\dfrac{21}{10}$

The solution is $\left(-\dfrac{21}{10},\dfrac{3}{10}\right)$.

20.
$$\begin{cases} \dfrac{x}{6}-\dfrac{y}{2}=1 & (1) \\ \dfrac{x}{3}-\dfrac{y}{4}=2 & (2) \end{cases}$$

Multiply equation (1) by 6 and equation (2) by 12 to clear fractions.

$$\begin{cases} x-3y=6 & (1) \\ 4x-3y=24 & (2) \end{cases}$$

Solve the new equation (1) for x.

$x=3y+6$

Replace x with $3y+6$ in the new equation (2).

$4(3y+6)-3y=24$

$12y+24-3y=24$

$9y=0$

$y=0$

Replace y with 0 in the equation $x=3y+6$:

$x=3(0)+6=6$

The solution is $(6, 0)$.

21. a. $2^2\cdot2^5=2^{2+5}=2^7$

b. $x^7x^3=x^{7+3}=x^{10}$

c. $y\cdot y^2\cdot y^4=y^{1+2+4}=y^7$

22. Let x = number of tee-shirts

y = number of shorts.

$$\begin{cases} x+y=9 & (1) \\ 3.50x+4.25y=33.75 & (2) \end{cases}$$

Solve equation (1) for y: $y=9-x$.

Replace y with $9-x$ in equation (2):

$3.50x+4.25(9-x)=33.75$

$3.50x+38.25-4.25x=33.75$

$-0.75x=-4.5$

$x=6$

Replace x with 6 in the equation $y=9-x$:

$y=9-6=3$

She bought 6 tee-shirts and 3 shorts.

23. $\dfrac{2000\times0.000021}{700}=\dfrac{(2\times10^3)\times(2.1\times10^{-5})}{7\times10^2}$

$=\dfrac{2\times2.1}{7}\times10^{3+(-5)-2}$

$=0.6\times10^{-4}$

$=6\times10^{-5}$

24. $\dfrac{0.0000035\times4000}{0.28}$

$=\dfrac{(3.5\times10^{-6})\times(4\times10^3)}{2.8\times10^{-1}}$

$=\dfrac{3.5\times4}{2.8}\times10^{-6+3-(-1)}$

$=5\times10^{-2}$

25. $P(x)=3x^2-2x-5$

a. $P(1)=3(1)^2-2(1)-5=3-2-5=-4$

b. $P(-2)=3(-2)^2-2(-2)-5$

$=3(4)+4-5$

$=12+4-5$

$=11$

26. $[(5x^2-3x+6)+(4x^2+5x-3)]-(2x-5)$

$=(9x^2+2x+3)-(2x-5)$

$=9x^2+2x+3-2x+5$

$=9x^2+8$

27. a. $(x+3)(2x+5)=2x^2+5x+6x+15$

$=2x^2+11x+15$

b. $(2x-3)(5x^2-6x+7)$

$=10x^3-12x^2+14x$

$\qquad -15x^2+18x-21$

$=10x^3-27x^2+32x-21$

28. a. $(y-2)(3y+4) = 3y^2 + 4y - 6y - 8$
$= 3y^2 - 2y - 8$

b. $(3y-1)(2y^2 + 3y - 1)$
$= 6y^3 + 9y^2 - 3y$
$\quad - 2y^2 - 3y + 1$
$= 6y^3 + 7y^2 - 6y + 1$

29. $20x^3 y = 2^2 \cdot 5x^3 y$
$10x^2 y^2 = 2 \cdot 5x^2 y^2$
$35x^3 = 5 \cdot 7x^3$
$GCF = 5x^2$

30. $x^3 - x^2 + 4x - 4 = (x^3 - x^2) + (4x - 4)$
$= x^2(x-1) + 4(x-1)$
$= (x-1)(x^2 + 4)$

31. a. $\dfrac{x^3 + 8}{2 + x} = \dfrac{x^3 + 2^3}{x + 2}$
$= \dfrac{(x+2)(x^2 - 2x + 4)}{x+2}$
$= x^2 - 2x + 4$

b. $\dfrac{2y^2 + 2}{y^3 - 5y^2 + y - 5} = \dfrac{2(y^2 + 1)}{y^2(y-5) + 1(y-5)}$
$= \dfrac{2(y^2 + 1)}{(y-5)(y^2 + 1)}$
$= \dfrac{2}{y-5}$

32. a. $\dfrac{a^3 - 8}{2 - a} = \dfrac{a^3 - 2^3}{2 - a}$
$= \dfrac{(a-2)(a^2 + 2a + 4)}{2 - a}$
$= -1(a^2 + 2a + 4)$
$= -a^2 - 2a - 4$

b. $\dfrac{3a^2 - 3}{a^3 + 5a^2 - a - 5} = \dfrac{3(a^2 - 1)}{a^2(a+5) - 1(a+5)}$
$= \dfrac{3(a^2 - 1)}{(a+5)(a^2 - 1)}$
$= \dfrac{3}{a+5}$

33. a. $\dfrac{2}{x^2 y} + \dfrac{5}{3x^3 y} = \dfrac{2 \cdot 3x}{x^2 y \cdot 3x} + \dfrac{5}{3x^3 y} = \dfrac{6x + 5}{3x^3 y}$

b. $\dfrac{3x}{x+2} + \dfrac{2x}{x-2} = \dfrac{3x(x-2) + 2x(x+2)}{(x+2)(x-2)}$
$= \dfrac{3x^2 - 6x + 2x^2 + 4x}{(x+2)(x-2)}$
$= \dfrac{5x^2 - 2x}{(x+2)(x-2)}$

c. $\dfrac{x}{x-1} - \dfrac{4}{1-x} = \dfrac{x}{x-1} + \dfrac{4}{x-1} = \dfrac{x+4}{x-1}$

34. a. $\dfrac{3}{xy^2} - \dfrac{2}{3x^2 y} = \dfrac{3 \cdot 3x}{xy^2 \cdot 3x} - \dfrac{2 \cdot y}{3x^2 y \cdot y} = \dfrac{9x - 2y}{3x^2 y^2}$

b. $\dfrac{5x}{x+3} - \dfrac{2x}{x-3} = \dfrac{5x(x-3) - 2x(x+3)}{(x+3)(x-3)}$
$= \dfrac{5x^2 - 15x - 2x^2 - 6x}{(x+3)(x-3)}$
$= \dfrac{3x^2 - 21x}{(x+3)(x-3)}$
$\text{or } \dfrac{3x(x-7)}{(x+3)(x-3)}$

c. $\dfrac{x}{x-2} - \dfrac{5}{2-x} = \dfrac{x}{x-2} + \dfrac{5}{x-2} = \dfrac{x+5}{x-2}$

35. a. $\dfrac{\dfrac{5x}{x+2}}{\dfrac{10}{x-2}} = \dfrac{5x}{x+2} \cdot \dfrac{x-2}{10} = \dfrac{x(x-2)}{2(x+2)}$

b. $\dfrac{\dfrac{x}{y^2} + \dfrac{1}{y}}{\dfrac{y}{x^2} + \dfrac{1}{x}} = \dfrac{\left(\dfrac{x}{y^2} + \dfrac{1}{y}\right)x^2 y^2}{\left(\dfrac{y}{x^2} + \dfrac{1}{x}\right)x^2 y^2}$
$= \dfrac{x^3 + x^2 y}{y^3 + xy^2}$
$= \dfrac{x^2(x+y)}{y^2(y+x)}$
$= \dfrac{x^2}{y^2}$

36. a. $\dfrac{\dfrac{y-2}{16}}{\dfrac{2y+3}{12}} = \dfrac{y-2}{16} \cdot \dfrac{12}{2y+3} = \dfrac{3(y-2)}{4(2y+3)}$

b. $\dfrac{\dfrac{x}{16}-\dfrac{1}{x}}{1-\dfrac{4}{x}}=\dfrac{\left(\dfrac{x}{16}-\dfrac{1}{x}\right)16x}{\left(1-\dfrac{4}{x}\right)16x}$

$=\dfrac{x^2-16}{16x-64}$

$=\dfrac{(x+4)(x-4)}{16(x-4)}$

$=\dfrac{x+4}{16}$

37. $\dfrac{10x^3-5x^2+20x}{5x}=\dfrac{10x^3}{5x}-\dfrac{5x^2}{5x}+\dfrac{20x}{5x}$

$\qquad\qquad\qquad\quad =2x^2-x+4$

38. $x-2\overline{\smash{\big)}\,x^3-2x^2+3x-6}$ quotient x^2+3

$\qquad\quad \underline{x^3-2x^2}$

$\qquad\qquad\qquad 3x-6$

$\qquad\qquad\qquad \underline{3x-6}$

$\qquad\qquad\qquad\qquad 0$

Answer: x^2+3

39. $3\rfloor\;\;2\quad -1\quad -13\quad\;\; 1$

$\qquad\qquad\quad\;\; 6\qquad 15\qquad 6$

$\qquad\overline{\;\;\;2\qquad 5\qquad\;\; 2\qquad 7}$

Answer: $2x^2+5x+2+\dfrac{7}{x-3}$

40. $3\rfloor\;\;4\quad -12\quad -1\quad 12$

$\qquad\qquad\quad\;\; 12\qquad 0\quad -3$

$\qquad\overline{\;\;\;4\qquad\;\; 0\quad -1\qquad 9}$

Answer: $4y^2-1+\dfrac{9}{y-3}$

41. $\dfrac{x+6}{x-2}=\dfrac{2(x+2)}{x-2}$

$(x-2)\left(\dfrac{x+6}{x-2}\right)=(x-2)\left[\dfrac{2(x+2)}{x-2}\right]$

$\qquad\qquad x+6=2(x+2)$

$\qquad\qquad x+6=2x+4$

$\qquad\qquad\quad -x=-2$

$\qquad\qquad\qquad\;\; x=2$

which we discard as extraneous. There is no solution. The solution set is $\varnothing$.

42. $\dfrac{28}{9-a^2}=\dfrac{2a}{a-3}+\dfrac{6}{a+3}$

$\dfrac{28}{-(a^2-9)}=\dfrac{2a}{a-3}+\dfrac{6}{a+3}$

$\dfrac{-28}{(a+3)(a-3)}=\dfrac{2a}{a-3}+\dfrac{6}{a+3}$

$-28=2a(a+3)+6(a-3)$

$-28=2a^2+6a+6a-18$

$0=2a^2+12a+10$

$0=2(a^2+6a+5)$

$0=2(a+5)(a+1)$

$a=-5$ or $a=-1$

The solutions are -5 and -1.

43. $\dfrac{1}{x}+\dfrac{1}{y}=\dfrac{1}{z}$

$xyz\left(\dfrac{1}{x}+\dfrac{1}{y}\right)=xyz\left(\dfrac{1}{z}\right)$

$yz+xz=xy$

$yz=xy-xz$

$yz=x(y-z)$

$x=\dfrac{yz}{y-z}$

44. $A=\dfrac{h(a+b)}{2}$

$2A=h(a+b)$

$2A=ah+bh$

$2A-bh=ah$

$\dfrac{2A-bh}{h}=a$

45. $u=\dfrac{k}{w}$

$3=\dfrac{k}{5}$

$k=3(5)=15$

The inverse variation equation is $u=\dfrac{15}{w}$.

46. $y=kx$

$0.51=k(3)$

$k=\dfrac{0.51}{3}=0.17$

The direct variation equation is $y=0.17x$.

47. a. $16^{-3/4}=\dfrac{1}{16^{3/4}}=\dfrac{1}{\left(\sqrt[4]{16}\right)^3}=\dfrac{1}{(2)^3}=\dfrac{1}{8}$

b. $(-27)^{-2/3} = \dfrac{1}{(-27)^{2/3}} = \dfrac{1}{\left(\sqrt[3]{-27}\right)^2} = \dfrac{1}{(-3)^2} = \dfrac{1}{9}$

48. a. $81^{-3/4} = \dfrac{1}{81^{3/4}} = \dfrac{1}{\left(\sqrt[4]{81}\right)^3} = \dfrac{1}{(3)^3} = \dfrac{1}{27}$

b. $(-125)^{-2/3} = \dfrac{1}{(-125)^{2/3}}$

$$= \dfrac{1}{\left(\sqrt[3]{-125}\right)^2}$$

$$= \dfrac{1}{(-5)^2}$$

$$= \dfrac{1}{25}$$

49. $\dfrac{\sqrt{x}+2}{5} = \dfrac{\left(\sqrt{x}+2\right)\left(\sqrt{x}-2\right)}{5\left(\sqrt{x}-2\right)}$

$$= \dfrac{\left(\sqrt{x}\right)^2 - 2^2}{5\left(\sqrt{x}-2\right)}$$

$$= \dfrac{x-4}{5\left(\sqrt{x}-2\right)}$$

50. a. $\sqrt{36a^3} - \sqrt{144a^3} + \sqrt{4a^3}$

$$= \sqrt{36a^2 \cdot a} - \sqrt{144a^2 \cdot a} + \sqrt{4a^2 \cdot a}$$

$$= 6a\sqrt{a} - 12a\sqrt{a} + 2a\sqrt{a}$$

$$= -4a\sqrt{a}$$

b. $\sqrt[3]{128ab^3} - 3\sqrt[3]{2ab^3} + b\sqrt[3]{16a}$

$$= \sqrt[3]{64b^3 \cdot 2a} - 3\sqrt[3]{b^3 \cdot 2a} + b\sqrt[3]{8 \cdot 2a}$$

$$= 4b\sqrt[3]{2a} - 3b\sqrt[3]{2a} + 2b\sqrt[3]{2a}$$

$$= 3b\sqrt[3]{2a}$$

c. $\dfrac{\sqrt[3]{81}}{10} + \sqrt[3]{\dfrac{192}{125}} = \dfrac{\sqrt[3]{27 \cdot 3}}{10} + \dfrac{\sqrt[3]{192}}{\sqrt[3]{125}}$

$$= \dfrac{3\sqrt[3]{3}}{10} + \dfrac{\sqrt[3]{64 \cdot 3}}{5}$$

$$= \dfrac{3\sqrt[3]{3}}{10} + \dfrac{4\sqrt[3]{3}}{5}$$

$$= \dfrac{3\sqrt[3]{3}}{10} + \dfrac{4\sqrt[3]{3} \cdot 2}{5 \cdot 2}$$

$$= \dfrac{11\sqrt[3]{3}}{10}$$

Chapter 8

Exercise Set 8.1

1. $x^2 = 16$

$\quad x = \pm\sqrt{16}$

$\quad x = \pm 4$

Check:

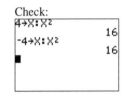

3. $x^2 - 7 = 0$

$\quad x^2 = 7$

$\quad x = \pm\sqrt{7}$

Check:

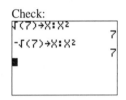

5. $x^2 = 18$

$\quad x = \pm\sqrt{18}$

$\quad x = \pm\sqrt{9 \cdot 2}$

$\quad x = \pm 3\sqrt{2}$

Check:

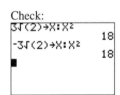

7. $3z^2 - 30 = 0$

$\quad 3z^2 = 30$

$\quad z^2 = 10$

$\quad z = \pm\sqrt{10}$

Check:

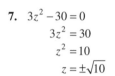

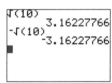

9. $(x+5)^2 = 9$

$\quad x + 5 = \pm\sqrt{9}$

$\quad x + 5 = \pm 3$

$\quad x = -5 \pm 3$

$\quad x = -8 \text{ or } x = -2$

Check:

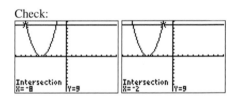

11. $(z-6)^2 = 18$

$\quad z - 6 = \pm\sqrt{18}$

$\quad z - 6 = \pm 3\sqrt{2}$

$\quad z = 6 \pm 3\sqrt{2}$

Check:

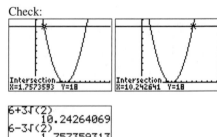

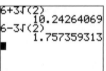

13. $(2x-3)^2 = 8$

$$2x-3 = \pm\sqrt{8}$$
$$2x-3 = \pm 2\sqrt{2}$$
$$2x = 3 \pm 2\sqrt{2}$$
$$x = \frac{3 \pm 2\sqrt{2}}{2}$$

Check:

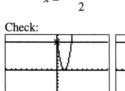 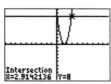

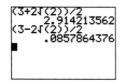

15. $x^2 + 9 = 0$

$$x^2 = -9$$
$$x = \pm\sqrt{-9}$$
$$x = \pm 3i$$

Check: $(3i)^2 + 9 \overset{?}{=} 0 \qquad (-3i)^2 + 9 \overset{?}{=} 0$

$$9i^2 + 9 \overset{?}{=} 0 \qquad 9i^2 + 9 \overset{?}{=} 0$$
$$-9 + 9 \overset{?}{=} 0 \qquad -9 + 9 \overset{?}{=} 0$$
$$0 = 0 \ \text{True} \qquad 0 = 0 \ \text{True}$$

17. $x^2 - 6 = 0$

$$x^2 = 6$$
$$x = \pm\sqrt{6}$$

Check:

$$\left(\sqrt{6}\right)^2 - 6 \overset{?}{=} 0$$
$$6 - 6 \overset{?}{=} 0$$
$$0 = 0 \ \text{True}$$
$$\left(-\sqrt{6}\right)^2 - 6 \overset{?}{=} 0$$
$$6 - 6 \overset{?}{=} 0$$
$$0 = 0 \ \text{True}$$

19. $2z^2 + 16 = 0$

$$2z^2 = -16$$
$$z^2 = -8$$
$$z = \pm\sqrt{-8}$$
$$z = \pm i\sqrt{8}$$
$$z = \pm 2i\sqrt{2}$$

Check:

$$2\left(2i\sqrt{2}\right)^2 + 16 \overset{?}{=} 0$$
$$2\left(8i^2\right) + 16 \overset{?}{=} 0$$
$$-16 + 16 \overset{?}{=} 0$$
$$0 = 0 \ \text{True}$$

$$2\left(-2i\sqrt{2}\right)^2 + 16 \overset{?}{=} 0$$
$$2\left(8i^2\right) + 16 \overset{?}{=} 0$$
$$-16 + 16 \overset{?}{=} 0$$
$$0 = 0 \ \text{True}$$

21. $(x-1)^2 = -16$

$$x-1 = \pm\sqrt{-16}$$
$$x-1 = \pm 4i$$
$$x = 1 \pm 4i$$

Check:

$$\left(1 + 4i - 1\right)^2 \overset{?}{=} -16$$
$$\left(4i\right)^2 \overset{?}{=} -16$$
$$-16 = -16 \ \text{True}$$
$$\left(1 - 4i - 1\right)^2 \overset{?}{=} -16$$
$$\left(-4i\right)^2 \overset{?}{=} -16$$
$$-16 = -16 \ \text{True}$$

23. $(z+7)^2 = 5$

$z + 7 = \pm\sqrt{5}$

$z = -7 + \sqrt{5}$

Check:

$\left(-7 + \sqrt{5} + 7\right)^2 \overset{?}{=} 5$

$\left(\sqrt{5}\right)^2 \overset{?}{=} 5$

$5 = 5$ True

$\left(-7 - \sqrt{5} + 7\right)^2 \overset{?}{=} 5$

$\left(\sqrt{5}\right)^2 \overset{?}{=} 5$

$5 = 5$ True

25. $(x+3)^2 = -8$

$x + 3 = \pm\sqrt{-8}$

$x + 3 = \pm i\sqrt{8}$

$x + 3 = \pm 2i\sqrt{2}$

$x = -3 \pm 2i\sqrt{2}$

Check.

$\left(-3 + 2i\sqrt{2} + 3\right)^2 \overset{?}{=} -8$

$\left(2i\sqrt{2}\right)^2 \overset{?}{=} -8$

$-8 = -8$ True

$\left(-3 - 2i\sqrt{2} + 3\right)^2 \overset{?}{=} -8$

$\left(-2i\sqrt{2}\right)^2 \overset{?}{=} -8$

$-8 = -8$ True

27. $x^2 + 16x + \left(\dfrac{16}{2}\right)^2 = x^2 + 16x + 64$

$= (x+8)^2$

29. $z^2 - 12z + \left(\dfrac{-12}{2}\right)^2 = z^2 - 12z + 36$

$= (z-6)^2$

31. $p^2 + 9p + \left(\dfrac{9}{2}\right)^2 = p^2 + 9p + \dfrac{81}{4}$

$= \left(p + \dfrac{9}{2}\right)^2$

33. $x^2 + x + \left(\dfrac{1}{2}\right)^2 = x^2 + x + \dfrac{1}{4}$

$= \left(x + \dfrac{1}{2}\right)^2$

35. $x^2 + 8x = -15$

$x^2 + 8x + \left(\dfrac{8}{2}\right)^2 = -15 + 16$

$x^2 + 8x + 16 = 1$

$(x+4)^2 = 1$

$x + 4 = \pm\sqrt{1}$

$x = -4 \pm 1$

$x = -5 \text{ or } x = -3$

Check:

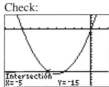 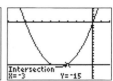

37. $x^2 + 6x + 2 = 0$

$x^2 + 6x = -2$

$x^2 + 6x + \left(\dfrac{6}{2}\right)^2 = -2 + 9$

$x^2 + 6x + 9 = 7$

$(x+3)^2 = 7$

$x + 3 = \pm\sqrt{7}$

$x = -3 \pm \sqrt{7}$

Check:

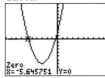 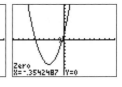

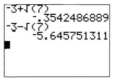

39.

$$x^2 + x - 1 = 0$$
$$x^2 + x = 1$$
$$x^2 + x + \left(\frac{1}{2}\right)^2 = 1 + \frac{1}{4}$$
$$x^2 + x + \frac{1}{4} = \frac{5}{4}$$
$$\left(x + \frac{1}{2}\right)^2 = \frac{5}{4}$$
$$x + \frac{1}{2} = \pm\sqrt{\frac{5}{4}}$$
$$x = -\frac{1}{2} \pm \frac{\sqrt{5}}{2}$$
$$x = \frac{-1 \pm \sqrt{5}}{2}$$

Check:

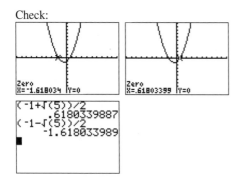

41.

$$x^2 + 2x - 5 = 0$$
$$x^2 + 2x = 5$$
$$x^2 + 2x + \left(\frac{2}{2}\right)^2 = 5 + 1$$
$$x^2 + 2x + 1 = 6$$
$$(x + 1)^2 = 6$$
$$x + 1 = \pm\sqrt{6}$$
$$x = -1 \pm \sqrt{6}$$

Check:

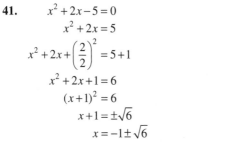

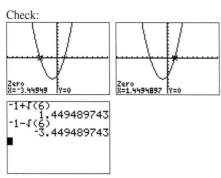

43.

$$3p^2 - 12p + 2 = 0$$
$$3p^2 - 12p = -2$$
$$p^2 - 4p = -\frac{2}{3}$$
$$p^2 - 4p + \left(\frac{-4}{2}\right)^2 = -\frac{2}{3} + 4$$
$$(p - 2)^2 = \frac{10}{3}$$
$$p - 2 = \pm\sqrt{\frac{10}{3}}$$
$$p - 2 = \pm\frac{\sqrt{10} \cdot \sqrt{3}}{\sqrt{3} \cdot \sqrt{3}}$$
$$p - 2 = \pm\frac{\sqrt{30}}{3}$$
$$p = 2 \pm \frac{\sqrt{30}}{3}$$
$$p = \frac{6 \pm \sqrt{30}}{3}$$

Check:

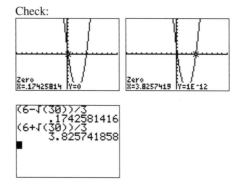

45.
$$4y^2 - 12y - 2 = 0$$
$$4y^2 - 12y = 2$$
$$y^2 - 3y = \frac{1}{2}$$
$$y^2 - 3y + \left(\frac{-3}{2}\right)^2 = \frac{1}{2} + \frac{9}{4}$$
$$y^2 - 3y + \frac{9}{4} = \frac{11}{4}$$
$$\left(y - \frac{3}{2}\right)^2 = \frac{11}{4}$$
$$y - \frac{3}{2} = \pm\sqrt{\frac{11}{4}}$$
$$y = \frac{3}{2} \pm \frac{\sqrt{11}}{2}$$
$$= \frac{3 \pm \sqrt{11}}{2}$$

Check:

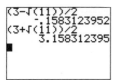

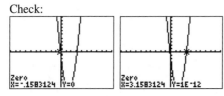

47.
$$2x^2 + 7x = 4$$
$$x^2 + \frac{7}{2}x = 2$$
$$x^2 + \frac{7}{2}x + \left(\frac{\frac{7}{2}}{2}\right)^2 = 2 + \frac{49}{16}$$
$$x^2 + \frac{7}{2}x + \frac{49}{16} = \frac{81}{16}$$
$$\left(x + \frac{7}{4}\right)^2 = \frac{81}{16}$$
$$x + \frac{7}{4} = \pm\sqrt{\frac{81}{16}}$$
$$x = -\frac{7}{4} \pm \frac{9}{4}$$
$$x = \frac{-7 \pm 9}{4}$$
$$x = -4, \frac{1}{2}$$

Check:

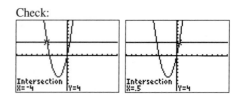

49.
$$x^2 - 4x - 5 = 0$$
$$x^2 - 4x = 5$$
$$x^2 - 4x + \left(\frac{-4}{2}\right)^2 = 5 + 4$$
$$x^2 - 4x + 4 = 9$$
$$(x - 2)^2 = 9$$
$$x = 2 \pm 3$$
$$x = -1, 5$$

Check:

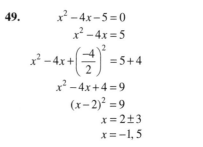

51.
$$x^2 + 8x + 1 = 0$$
$$x^2 + 8x = -1$$
$$x^2 + 8x + \left(\frac{8}{2}\right)^2 = -1 + 16$$
$$x^2 + 8x + 16 = 15$$
$$(x + 4)^2 = 15$$
$$x + 4 = \pm\sqrt{15}$$
$$x = -4 \pm \sqrt{15}$$

Check:

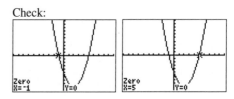

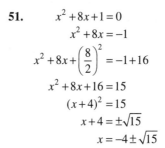

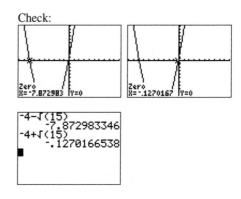

53.
$$3y^2 + 6y - 4 = 0$$
$$3y^2 + 6y = 4$$
$$y^2 + 2y = \frac{4}{3}$$
$$y^2 + 2y + \left(\frac{2}{2}\right)^2 = \frac{4}{3} + 1$$
$$y^2 + 2y + 1 = \frac{7}{3}$$
$$(y+1)^2 = \frac{7}{3}$$
$$y + 1 = \pm\sqrt{\frac{7}{3}}$$
$$y + 1 = \pm\frac{\sqrt{7} \cdot \sqrt{3}}{\sqrt{3} \cdot \sqrt{3}}$$
$$y + 1 = \pm\frac{\sqrt{21}}{3}$$
$$y = -1 \pm \frac{\sqrt{21}}{3}$$
$$y = \frac{-3 \pm \sqrt{21}}{3}$$

Check:

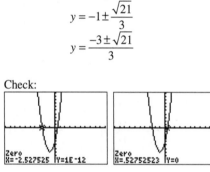

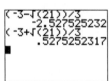

55.
$$2x^2 - 3x - 5 = 0$$
$$2x^2 - 3x = 5$$
$$x^2 - \frac{3}{2}x = \frac{5}{2}$$
$$x^2 - \frac{3}{2}x + \left(\frac{\frac{3}{2}}{2}\right)^2 = \frac{5}{2} + \frac{9}{16}$$
$$x^2 - \frac{3}{2}x + \frac{9}{16} = \frac{49}{16}$$
$$\left(x - \frac{3}{4}\right)^2 = \frac{49}{16}$$
$$x - \frac{3}{4} = \pm\sqrt{\frac{49}{16}}$$
$$x = \frac{3}{4} \pm \frac{7}{4}$$
$$x = \frac{3 \pm 7}{4}$$
$$x = -1, \frac{5}{2}$$

Check:

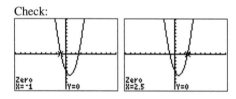

57.
$$y^2 + 2y + 2 = 0$$
$$y^2 + 2y = -2$$
$$y^2 + 2y + \left(\frac{2}{2}\right)^2 = -2 + 1$$
$$y^2 + 2y + 1 = -1$$
$$(y+1)^2 = -1$$
$$y + 1 = \pm\sqrt{-1}$$
$$y = -1 \pm i$$

Check:

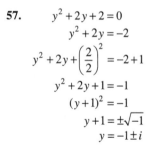

59.
$$x^2 - 6x + 3 = 0$$
$$x^2 - 6x = -3$$
$$x^2 - 6x + \left(\frac{-6}{2}\right)^2 = -3 + 9$$
$$x^2 - 6x + 9 = 6$$
$$(x-3)^2 = 6$$
$$x - 3 = \pm\sqrt{6}$$
$$x = 3 \pm \sqrt{6}$$

Check:

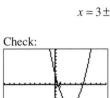 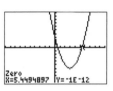

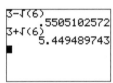

61.
$$2a^2 + 8a = -12$$
$$a^2 + 4a = -6$$
$$a^2 + 4a + \left(\frac{4}{2}\right)^2 = -6 + 4$$
$$a^2 + 4a + 4 = -2$$
$$(a+2)^2 = -2$$
$$a + 2 = \pm\sqrt{-2}$$
$$a + 2 = \pm i\sqrt{2}$$
$$a = -2 \pm i\sqrt{2}$$

Check:

63.
$$5x^2 + 15x - 1 = 0$$
$$5x^2 + 15x = 1$$
$$x^2 + 3x = \frac{1}{5}$$
$$x^2 + 3x + \left(\frac{3}{2}\right)^2 = \frac{1}{5} + \frac{9}{4}$$
$$x^2 + 3x + \frac{9}{4} = \frac{49}{20}$$

$$\left(x + \frac{3}{2}\right)^2 = \frac{49}{20}$$
$$x + \frac{3}{2} = \pm\sqrt{\frac{49}{20}}$$
$$x + \frac{3}{2} = \pm\frac{7}{\sqrt{20}}$$
$$x + \frac{3}{2} = \pm\frac{7}{2\sqrt{5}}$$
$$x + \frac{3}{2} = \pm\frac{7 \cdot \sqrt{5}}{2\sqrt{5} \cdot \sqrt{5}}$$
$$x + \frac{3}{2} = \pm\frac{7\sqrt{5}}{10}$$
$$x = -\frac{3}{2} \pm \frac{7\sqrt{5}}{10}$$
$$x = \frac{-15 \pm 7\sqrt{5}}{10}$$

Check:

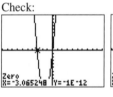 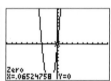

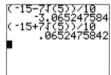

65.
$$2x^2 - x + 6 = 0$$
$$2x^2 - x = -6$$
$$x^2 - \frac{1}{2}x = -3$$
$$x^2 - \frac{1}{2}x + \left(\frac{-\frac{1}{2}}{2}\right)^2 = -3 + \frac{1}{16}$$
$$x^2 - \frac{1}{2}x + \frac{1}{16} = -\frac{47}{16}$$
$$\left(x - \frac{1}{4}\right)^2 = -\frac{47}{16}$$
$$x - \frac{1}{4} = \pm\sqrt{-\frac{47}{16}}$$
$$x - \frac{1}{4} = \pm\frac{\sqrt{47}}{4}i$$
$$x = \frac{1}{4} \pm \frac{\sqrt{47}}{4}i$$
$$x = \frac{1 \pm i\sqrt{47}}{4}$$

Check:

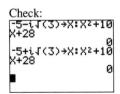

67.
$$x^2 + 10x + 28 = 0$$
$$x^2 + 10x = -28$$
$$x^2 + 10x + \left(\frac{10}{2}\right)^2 = -28 + 25$$
$$(x + 5)^2 = -3$$
$$x + 5 = \pm\sqrt{-3}$$
$$x = -5 \pm i\sqrt{3}$$

Check:

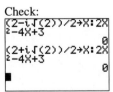

69.
$$z^2 + 3z - 4 = 0$$
$$z^2 + 3z = 4$$
$$z^2 + 3z + \left(\frac{3}{2}\right)^2 = 4 + \frac{9}{4}$$
$$z^2 + 3z + \frac{9}{4} = \frac{25}{4}$$
$$\left(z + \frac{3}{2}\right)^2 = \frac{25}{4}$$
$$z + \frac{3}{2} = \pm\sqrt{\frac{25}{4}}$$
$$z = -\frac{3}{2} \pm \frac{5}{2}$$
$$z = -4, 1$$

Check:

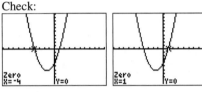

71.
$$2x^2 - 4x + 3 = 0$$
$$2x^2 - 4x = -3$$
$$x^2 - 2x = -\frac{3}{2}$$
$$x^2 - 2x + \left(\frac{-2}{2}\right)^2 = -\frac{3}{2} + 1$$
$$x^2 - 2x + 1 = -\frac{1}{2}$$
$$(x - 1)^2 = -\frac{1}{2}$$
$$x - 1 = \pm\sqrt{-\frac{1}{2}}$$
$$x - 1 = \pm\frac{1}{\sqrt{2}}i$$
$$x - 1 = \pm\frac{1 \cdot \sqrt{2}}{\sqrt{2} \cdot \sqrt{2}}i$$
$$x - 1 = \pm\frac{\sqrt{2}}{2}i$$
$$x = 1 \pm \frac{\sqrt{2}}{2}i \quad \text{or} \quad \frac{2 \pm i\sqrt{2}}{2}$$

Check:

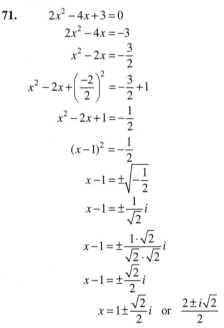

73.
$$3x^2 + 3x = 5$$
$$x^2 + x = \frac{5}{3}$$
$$x^2 + x + \left(\frac{1}{2}\right)^2 = \frac{5}{3} + \frac{1}{4}$$
$$x^2 + x + \frac{1}{4} = \frac{23}{12}$$
$$\left(x + \frac{1}{2}\right)^2 = \frac{23}{12}$$
$$x + \frac{1}{2} = \pm\sqrt{\frac{23}{12}}$$
$$x + \frac{1}{2} = \pm\frac{\sqrt{23}}{2\sqrt{3}}$$
$$x + \frac{1}{2} = \pm\frac{\sqrt{23} \cdot \sqrt{3}}{2\sqrt{3} \cdot \sqrt{3}}$$
$$x + \frac{1}{2} = \pm\frac{\sqrt{69}}{6}$$
$$x = -\frac{1}{2} \pm \frac{\sqrt{69}}{6}$$
$$x = \frac{-3 \pm \sqrt{69}}{6}$$

Check:

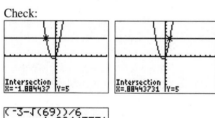

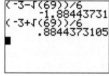

75. The graph crosses the x-axis two times. Therefore, there will be two real solutions to the equation.

77. The graph does not cross the x-axis. Therefore, there will be no real solutions to the equation.

79.
$$A = P(1+r)^t$$
$$4320 = 3000(1+r)^2$$
$$\frac{4320}{3000} = (1+r)^2$$
$$1.44 = (1+r)^2$$
$$\pm\sqrt{1.44} = 1 + r$$
$$\pm 1.2 = 1 + r$$
$$-1 \pm 1.2 = r$$
$$-2.2 = r \text{ or } 0.2 = r$$

Rate cannot be negative, so the rate is
$r = 0.2 = 20\%$.

81.
$$A = P(1+r)^t$$
$$1000 = 810(1+r)^2$$
$$\frac{1000}{810} = (1+r)^2$$
$$\frac{100}{81} = (1+r)^2$$
$$\pm\sqrt{\frac{100}{81}} = 1 + r$$
$$\pm\frac{10}{9} = 1 + r$$
$$-1 \pm \frac{10}{9} = r$$
$$-\frac{19}{9} = r \text{ or } \frac{1}{9} = r$$

Rate cannot be negative, so the rate is
$r = \frac{1}{9}$, or $11\frac{1}{9}\%$.

83. Answers may vary. For simple interest, the accrued interest is computed once at the end of the loan/investment period. For compound interest, interest accrues several times during the loan period. The effect is that compound interest involves paying interest on interest already received, thereby resulting in more overall interest at the end of the loan/investment period.

85. We would prefer to have simple interest. Compounding results in more overall interest than with simple interest. Since we would be paying the interest, we want the method that will yield the least interest overall.

87. $\dfrac{3}{5} + \sqrt{\dfrac{16}{25}} = \dfrac{3}{5} + \dfrac{4}{5} = \dfrac{7}{5}$

89. $\dfrac{9}{10} - \sqrt{\dfrac{49}{100}} = \dfrac{9}{10} - \dfrac{7}{10} = \dfrac{2}{10} = \dfrac{1}{5}$

91. $\dfrac{10-20\sqrt{3}}{2} = \dfrac{10}{2} - \dfrac{20\sqrt{3}}{2} = 5 - 10\sqrt{3}$

93. $\dfrac{12-8\sqrt{7}}{16} = \dfrac{12}{16} - \dfrac{8\sqrt{7}}{16}$

$\qquad = \dfrac{3}{4} - \dfrac{\sqrt{7}}{2}$

$\qquad = \dfrac{3}{4} - \dfrac{2\sqrt{7}}{4}$

$\qquad = \dfrac{3-2\sqrt{7}}{4}$

95. $\sqrt{b^2-4ac} = \sqrt{(6)^2-4(1)(2)}$

$\qquad = \sqrt{36-8}$

$\qquad = \sqrt{28}$

$\qquad = \sqrt{4\cdot 7}$

$\qquad = 2\sqrt{7}$

97. $\sqrt{b^2-4ac} = \sqrt{(-3)^2-4(1)(-1)}$

$\qquad = \sqrt{9+4}$

$\qquad = \sqrt{13}$

99. $y^2 + \underline{} + 9$

$\left(\dfrac{b}{2}\right)^2 = 9$

$\dfrac{b}{2} = \pm\sqrt{9}$

$\dfrac{b}{2} = \pm 3$

$b = \pm 6$

Answer: $\pm 6y$

101. $x^2 + \underline{} + \dfrac{1}{4}$

$\left(\dfrac{b}{2}\right)^2 = \dfrac{1}{4}$

$\dfrac{b}{2} = \pm\sqrt{\dfrac{1}{4}}$

$\dfrac{b}{2} = \pm\dfrac{1}{2}$

$b = \pm 1$

Answer: $\pm x$

103. $s(t) = 16t^2$

$1053 = 16t^2$

$t^2 = \dfrac{1053}{16}$

$t = \pm\sqrt{\dfrac{1053}{16}}$

$t \approx 8.11$ or -8.11 (disregard)

It would take 8.11 seconds for an object to hit the ground.

105. $s(t) = 16t^2$

$725 = 16t^2$

$t^2 = \dfrac{725}{16}$

$t = \pm\sqrt{\dfrac{725}{16}}$

$t \approx 6.73$ or -6.73 (disregard)

It would take 6.73 seconds for an object to fall from the top to the base of the dam.

107. $A = \pi r^2$

$36\pi = \pi r^2$

$r^2 = \dfrac{36\pi}{\pi}$

$r^2 = 36$

$r = \pm\sqrt{36}$

$r = 6$ or -6 (disregard)

The radius of the circle is 6 inches.

109. $a^2 + b^2 = c^2$

$(4x)^2 + (3x)^2 = 27^2$

$16x^2 + 9x^2 = 729$

$25x^2 = 729$

$x^2 = \dfrac{729}{25}$

$x = \pm\sqrt{\dfrac{729}{25}} = \pm\dfrac{27}{5}$

$x = 5.4$ or -5.4 (disregard)

$3x = 3(5.4) = 16.2$

$4x = 4(5.4) = 21.6$

The sides of the picture measure 16.2 in. and 21.6 in.

111. $p = -x^2 + 15$
$7 = -x^2 + 15$
$x^2 = 8$
$x = \pm\sqrt{8}$
$x \approx \pm 2.828$
Demand cannot be negative. Therefore, the demand is approximately 2.828 thousand (or 2828) units when the price is $7 per lamp.

Check:

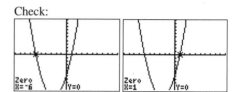

Mental Math 8.2

1. $x^2 + 3x + 1$
$a = 1, b = 3, c = 1$

2. $2x^2 - 5x - 7$
$a = 2, b = -5, c = -7$

3. $7x^2 - 4 = 0$
$a = 7, b = 0, c = -4$

4. $x^2 + 9 = 0$
$a = 1, b = 0, c = 9$

5. $6x^2 - x = 0$
$a = 6, b = -1, c = 0$

6. $5x^2 + 3x = 0$
$a = 5, b = 3, c = 0$

Exercise Set 8.2

1. $m^2 + 5m - 6 = 0$
$a = 1, b = 5, c = -6$

$$m = \frac{-5 \pm \sqrt{(5)^2 - 4(1)(-6)}}{2(1)}$$
$$= \frac{-5 \pm \sqrt{25 + 24}}{2}$$
$$= \frac{-5 \pm \sqrt{49}}{2}$$
$$= \frac{-5 \pm 7}{2}$$
$m = -6$ or 1
The solutions are -6 and 1.

3. $2y = 5y^2 - 3$
$5y^2 - 2y - 3 = 0$
$a = 5, b = -2, c = -3$

$$y = \frac{2 \pm \sqrt{(-2)^2 - 4(5)(-3)}}{2(5)}$$
$$= \frac{2 \pm \sqrt{4 + 60}}{10}$$
$$= \frac{2 \pm \sqrt{64}}{10}$$
$$= \frac{2 \pm 8}{10}$$
$y = -\frac{3}{5}$ or 1

The solutions are $-\frac{3}{5}$ and 1.

Check:

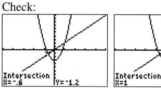

5. $x^2 - 6x + 9 = 0$
$a = 1, b = -6, c = 9$

$$x = \frac{6 \pm \sqrt{(-6)^2 - 4(1)(9)}}{2(1)}$$
$$= \frac{6 \pm \sqrt{36 - 36}}{2}$$
$$= \frac{6 \pm \sqrt{0}}{2}$$
$$= \frac{6}{2}$$
$$= 3$$
The solution is 3.

Check:

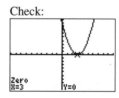

7. $x^2 + 7x + 4 = 0$

$a = 1, b = 7, c = 4$

$$x = \frac{-7 \pm \sqrt{(7)^2 - 4(1)(4)}}{2(1)}$$

$$= \frac{-7 \pm \sqrt{49 - 16}}{2}$$

$$= \frac{-7 \pm \sqrt{33}}{2}$$

The solutions are $\dfrac{-7 + \sqrt{33}}{2}$ and $\dfrac{-7 - \sqrt{33}}{2}$.

Check:

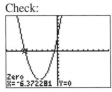 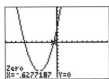

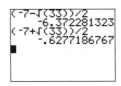

9. $8m^2 - 2m = 7$

$8m^2 - 2m - 7 = 0$

$a = 8, b = -2, c = -7$

$$m = \frac{2 \pm \sqrt{(-2)^2 - 4(8)(-7)}}{2(8)}$$

$$= \frac{2 \pm \sqrt{4 + 224}}{16}$$

$$= \frac{2 \pm \sqrt{228}}{16}$$

$$= \frac{2 \pm \sqrt{4 \cdot 57}}{16}$$

$$= \frac{2 \pm 2\sqrt{57}}{16}$$

$$= \frac{1 \pm \sqrt{57}}{8}$$

The solutions are $\dfrac{1 + \sqrt{57}}{8}$ and $\dfrac{1 - \sqrt{57}}{8}$.

Check:

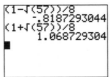

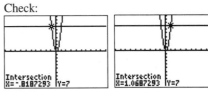

11. $3m^2 - 7m = 3$

$3m^2 - 7m - 3 = 0$

$a = 3, b = -7, c = -3$

$$m = \frac{7 \pm \sqrt{(-7)^2 - 4(3)(-3)}}{2(3)}$$

$$= \frac{7 \pm \sqrt{49 + 36}}{6}$$

$$= \frac{7 \pm \sqrt{85}}{6}$$

The solutions are $\dfrac{7 + \sqrt{85}}{6}$ and $\dfrac{7 - \sqrt{85}}{6}$.

Check:

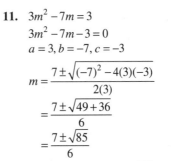

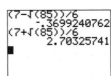

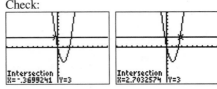

337

13. $\dfrac{1}{2}x^2 - x - 1 = 0$

$x^2 - 2x - 2 = 0$

$a = 1, b = -2, c = -2$

$x = \dfrac{2 \pm \sqrt{(-2)^2 - 4(1)(-2)}}{2(1)}$

$= \dfrac{2 \pm \sqrt{4+8}}{2}$

$= \dfrac{2 \pm \sqrt{12}}{2}$

$= \dfrac{2 \pm 2\sqrt{3}}{2}$

$= 1 \pm \sqrt{3}$

The solutions are $1 + \sqrt{3}$ and $1 - \sqrt{3}$.

Check:

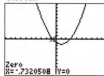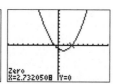

15. $\dfrac{2}{5}y^2 + \dfrac{1}{5}y = \dfrac{3}{5}$

$2y^2 + y - 3 = 0$

$a = 2, b = 1, c = -3$

$y = \dfrac{-1 \pm \sqrt{(1)^2 - 4(2)(-3)}}{2(2)}$

$= \dfrac{-1 \pm \sqrt{1+24}}{4}$

$= \dfrac{-1 \pm \sqrt{25}}{4}$

$= \dfrac{-1 \pm 5}{4}$

$y = -\dfrac{3}{2}$ or 1

The solutions are $-\dfrac{3}{2}$ and 1

Check:

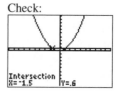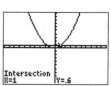

17. $\dfrac{1}{3}y^2 - y - \dfrac{1}{6} = 0$

$2y^2 - 6y - 1 = 0$

$a = 2, b = -6, c = -1$

$x = \dfrac{6 \pm \sqrt{(-6)^2 - 4(2)(-1)}}{2(2)}$

$= \dfrac{6 \pm \sqrt{36+8}}{4}$

$= \dfrac{6 \pm \sqrt{44}}{4}$

$= \dfrac{6 \pm 2\sqrt{11}}{4}$

$= \dfrac{3 \pm \sqrt{11}}{2}$

The solutions are $\dfrac{3 + \sqrt{11}}{2}$ and $\dfrac{3 - \sqrt{11}}{2}$.

Check:

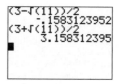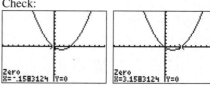

19. $m^2 + 5m - 6 = 0$

$(m + 6)(m - 1) = 0$

$m + 6 = 0$ or $m - 1 = 0$

$m = -6$ or $m = 1$

The results are the same. Answers may vary.

21.
$$6 = -4x^2 + 3x$$
$$4x^2 - 3x + 6 = 0$$
$$a = 4, b = -3, c = 6$$
$$x = \frac{3 \pm \sqrt{(-3)^2 - 4(4)(6)}}{2(4)}$$
$$= \frac{3 \pm \sqrt{9 - 96}}{8}$$
$$= \frac{3 \pm \sqrt{-87}}{8}$$
$$= \frac{3 \pm i\sqrt{87}}{8}$$

The solutions are $\dfrac{3 + i\sqrt{87}}{8}$ and $\dfrac{3 - i\sqrt{87}}{8}$.

Check:

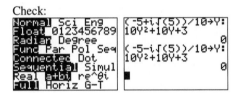

23. $(x + 5)(x - 1) = 2$
$$x^2 + 4x - 5 = 2$$
$$x^2 + 4x - 7 = 0$$
$$a = 1, b = 4, c = -7$$
$$x = \frac{-4 \pm \sqrt{(4)^2 - 4(1)(-7)}}{2(1)}$$
$$= \frac{-4 \pm \sqrt{16 + 28}}{2}$$
$$= \frac{-4 \pm \sqrt{44}}{2}$$
$$= \frac{-4 \pm 2\sqrt{11}}{2}$$
$$= -2 \pm \sqrt{11}$$

The solutions are $-2 + \sqrt{11}$ and $-2 - \sqrt{11}$.

Check:

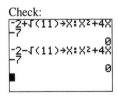

25. $10y^2 + 10y + 3 = 0$
$$a = 10, b = 10, c = 3$$
$$y = \frac{-10 \pm \sqrt{(10)^2 - 4(10)(3)}}{2(10)}$$
$$= \frac{-10 \pm \sqrt{100 - 120}}{20}$$
$$= \frac{-10 \pm \sqrt{-20}}{20}$$
$$= \frac{-10 \pm i\sqrt{4 \cdot 5}}{20}$$
$$= \frac{-10 \pm 2i\sqrt{5}}{20}$$
$$= \frac{-5 \pm i\sqrt{5}}{10}$$

The solutions are $\dfrac{-5 + i\sqrt{5}}{10}$ and $\dfrac{-5 - i\sqrt{5}}{10}$.

Check:

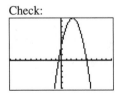

27. $9x - 2x^2 + 5 = 0$
$$-2x^2 + 9x + 5 = 0$$
$$a = -2, b = 9, c = 5$$
$$b^2 - 4ac = 9^2 - 4(-2)(5)$$
$$= 81 + 40$$
$$= 121 > 0$$

Therefore, there are two real solutions.

Check:

29.
$$4x^2 + 12x = -9$$
$$4x^2 + 12x + 9 = 0$$
$$a = 4, b = 12, c = 9$$
$$b^2 - 4ac = 12^2 - 4(4)(9)$$
$$= 144 - 144$$
$$= 0$$
Therefore, there is one real solution.

Check:

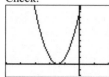

31.
$$3x = -2x^2 + 7$$
$$2x^2 + 3x - 7 = 0$$
$$a = 2, b = 3, c = -7$$
$$b^2 - 4ac = 3^2 - 4(2)(-7)$$
$$= 9 + 56$$
$$= 65 > 0$$
Therefore, there are two real solutions.

Check:

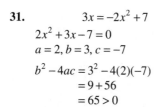

33.
$$6 = 4x - 5x^2$$
$$5x^2 - 4x + 6 = 0$$
$$a = 5, b = -4, c = 6$$
$$b^2 - 4ac = (-4)^2 - 4(5)(6)$$
$$= 16 - 120$$
$$= -104 < 0$$
Therefore, there are two complex but not real solutions.

Check:

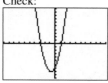

35.
$$x^2 + 5x = -2$$
$$x^2 + 5x + 2 = 0$$
$$a = 1, b = 5, c = 2$$
$$x = \frac{-5 \pm \sqrt{(5)^2 - 4(1)(2)}}{2(1)}$$
$$= \frac{-5 \pm \sqrt{25 - 8}}{2}$$
$$= \frac{-5 \pm \sqrt{17}}{2}$$
The solutions are $\dfrac{-5 + \sqrt{17}}{2}$ and $\dfrac{-5 - \sqrt{17}}{2}$.

37.
$$(m + 2)(2m - 6) = 5(m - 1) - 12$$
$$2m^2 - 6m + 4m - 12 = 5m - 5 - 12$$
$$2m^2 - 7m + 5 = 0$$
$$a = 2, b = -7, c = 5$$
$$m = \frac{7 \pm \sqrt{(-7)^2 - 4(2)(5)}}{2(2)}$$
$$= \frac{7 \pm \sqrt{49 - 40}}{4}$$
$$= \frac{7 \pm \sqrt{9}}{4}$$
$$= \frac{7 \pm 3}{4}$$
$$m = 1 \text{ or } \frac{5}{2}$$

The solutions are 1 and $\dfrac{5}{2}$.

39.
$$\frac{x^2}{3} - x = \frac{5}{3}$$
$$x^2 - 3x = 5$$
$$x^2 - 3x - 5 = 0$$
$$a = 1, b = -3, c = -5$$
$$x = \frac{3 \pm \sqrt{(-3)^2 - 4(1)(-5)}}{2(1)}$$
$$= \frac{3 \pm \sqrt{9 + 20}}{2}$$
$$= \frac{3 \pm \sqrt{29}}{2}$$
The solutions are $\dfrac{3 + \sqrt{29}}{2}$ and $\dfrac{3 - \sqrt{29}}{2}$.

41. $x(6x+2)-3=0$

$6x^2+2x-3=0$

$a=6, b=2, c=-3$

$x=\dfrac{-2\pm\sqrt{(2)^2-4(6)(-3)}}{2(6)}$

$=\dfrac{-2\pm\sqrt{4+72}}{12}$

$=\dfrac{-2\pm\sqrt{76}}{12}$

$=\dfrac{-2\pm\sqrt{4\cdot19}}{12}$

$=\dfrac{-2\pm2\sqrt{19}}{12}$

$=\dfrac{-1\pm\sqrt{19}}{6}$

The solutions are $\dfrac{-1+\sqrt{19}}{6}$ and $\dfrac{-1-\sqrt{19}}{6}$.

43. $x^2+6x+13=0$

$a=1, b=6, c=13$

$x=\dfrac{-6\pm\sqrt{(6)^2-4(1)(13)}}{2(1)}$

$=\dfrac{-6\pm\sqrt{36-52}}{2}$

$=\dfrac{-6\pm\sqrt{-16}}{2}$

$=\dfrac{-6\pm4i}{2}$

$=-3\pm2i$

The solutions are $-3+2i$ and $-3-2i$.

45. $\dfrac{2}{5}y^2+\dfrac{1}{5}y+\dfrac{3}{5}=0$

$2y^2+y+3=0$

$a=2, b=1, c=3$

$y=\dfrac{-1\pm\sqrt{(1)^2-4(2)(3)}}{2(2)}$

$=\dfrac{-1\pm\sqrt{1-24}}{4}$

$=\dfrac{-1\pm\sqrt{-23}}{4}$

$=\dfrac{-1\pm i\sqrt{23}}{4}$

The solutions are $\dfrac{-1+i\sqrt{23}}{4}$ and $\dfrac{-1-i\sqrt{23}}{4}$.

47. $\dfrac{1}{2}y^2=y-\dfrac{1}{2}$

$y^2=2y-1$

$y^2-2y+1=0$

$a=1, b=-2, c=1$

$y=\dfrac{2\pm\sqrt{(-2)^2-4(1)(1)}}{2(1)}$

$=\dfrac{2\pm\sqrt{4-4}}{2}$

$=\dfrac{2\pm\sqrt{0}}{2}$

$=1$

The solution is 1.

49. $(n-2)^2=15n$

$n^2-4n+4=15n$

$n^2-19n+4=0$

$a=1, b=-19, c=4$

$n=\dfrac{19\pm\sqrt{(-19)^2-4(1)(4)}}{2(1)}$

$=\dfrac{19\pm\sqrt{361-16}}{2}$

$=\dfrac{19\pm\sqrt{345}}{2}$

The solutions are $\dfrac{19+\sqrt{345}}{2}$ and $\dfrac{19-\sqrt{345}}{2}$.

51. a. The graph crosses the x-axis twice. Therefore, there are two distinct real solutions.

b. The graph touches the x-axis at one point. Therefore, there is one real solution.

53. $(x+8)^2+x^2=36^2$

$(x^2+16x+64)+x^2=1296$

$2x^2+16x-1232=0$

$a=2, b=16, c=-1232$

$x=\dfrac{-16\pm\sqrt{(16)^2-4(2)(-1232)}}{2(2)}$

$=\dfrac{-16\pm\sqrt{10,112}}{4}$

$x\approx21$ or $x\approx-29$ (disregard)

$x+(x+8)=21+21+8=50$

$50-36=14$

They saved about 14 feet of walking distance.

55. Let x = length of leg. Then $x+2$ = length of hypotenuse

$$x^2 + x^2 = (x+2)^2$$
$$2x^2 = x^2 + 4x + 4$$
$$x^2 - 4x - 4 = 0$$
$$a = 1, b = -4, c = -4$$

$$x = \frac{4 \pm \sqrt{(-4)^2 - 4(1)(-4)}}{2(1)}$$

$$= \frac{4 \pm \sqrt{32}}{2}$$

$$= \frac{4 \pm 4\sqrt{2}}{2}$$

$$= 2 \pm 2\sqrt{2} \text{ (disregard the negative)}$$

$$= 2 + 2\sqrt{2}$$

The sides measure $2+2\sqrt{2}$ cm, $2+2\sqrt{2}$ cm, and $4+2\sqrt{2}$ cm.

57. Let x = width; then $x+10$ = length.

Area = length · width
$$400 = (x+10)x$$
$$0 = x^2 + 10x - 400$$
$$a = 1, b = 10, c = -400$$

$$x = \frac{-10 \pm \sqrt{(10)^2 - 4(1)(-400)}}{2(1)}$$

$$= \frac{-10 \pm \sqrt{1700}}{2}$$

$$= \frac{-10 \pm 10\sqrt{17}}{2}$$

$$= -5 \pm 5\sqrt{17}$$

Disregard the negative length. The width is $-5+5\sqrt{17}$ ft and the length is $5+5\sqrt{17}$ ft.

59. a. Let x = length.

$$x^2 + x^2 = 100^2$$
$$2x^2 - 10,000 = 0$$
$$a = 2, b = 0, c = -10,000$$

$$x = \frac{0 \pm \sqrt{(0)^2 - 4(2)(-10,000)}}{2(2)}$$

$$= \frac{\pm\sqrt{80,000}}{4}$$

$$= \frac{\pm 200\sqrt{2}}{4}$$

$$= \pm 50\sqrt{2}$$

Disregard the negative length. The side measures $50\sqrt{2}$ meters.

b. Area $= s^2$
$$= \left(50\sqrt{2}\right)^2$$
$$= 2500(2)$$
$$= 5000$$
The area is 5000 square meters.

61. Let w = width; then $w+1.1$ = height.

Area = length · width
$$1439.9 = (w+1.1)w$$
$$0 = w^2 + 1.1w - 1439.9$$
$$a = 1, b = 1.1, c = -1439.9$$

$$w = \frac{-1.1 \pm \sqrt{(1.1)^2 - 4(1)(-1439.9)}}{2(1)}$$

$$= \frac{-1.1 \pm \sqrt{5760.81}}{2}$$

$$= 37.4 \text{ or } -3.608 \text{ (disregard)}$$

The door's width is 37.4 feet and its height is 38.5 feet.

63.
$$\frac{x-1}{1} = \frac{1}{x}$$
$$x(x-1) = 1$$
$$x^2 - x - 1 = 0$$
$$a = 1, b = -1, c = -1$$

$$x = \frac{1 \pm \sqrt{(-1)^2 - 4(1)(-1)}}{2(1)}$$

$$= \frac{1 \pm \sqrt{5}}{2} \text{ (disregard the negative)}$$

The value is $\frac{1+\sqrt{5}}{2}$.

65. $h(t) = -16t^2 + 20t + 1100$
$$0 = -16t^2 + 20t + 1100$$
$$a = -16, b = 20, c = 1100$$

$$t = \frac{-20 \pm \sqrt{(20)^2 - 4(-16)(1100)}}{2(-16)}$$

$$= \frac{-20 \pm \sqrt{70,800}}{-32}$$

$$\approx 8.9 \text{ or } -7.7 \text{ (disregard)}$$

It will take about 8.9 seconds for the pebble to hit the ground.

67. $h(t) = -16t^2 - 20t + 180$

$0 = -16t^2 - 20t + 180$

$a = -16, b = -20, c = 180$

$t = \dfrac{20 \pm \sqrt{(-20)^2 - 4(-16)(180)}}{2(-16)}$

$= \dfrac{20 \pm \sqrt{11,920}}{-32}$

≈ 2.8 or -4.0 (disregard)

It will take about 2.8 seconds for the ball to strike the ground.

69. $\sqrt{5x-2} = 3$

$\left(\sqrt{5x-2}\right)^2 = 3^2$

$5x - 2 = 9$

$5x = 11$

$x = \dfrac{11}{5}$

71. $\dfrac{1}{x} + \dfrac{2}{5} = \dfrac{7}{x}$

$5x\left(\dfrac{1}{x} + \dfrac{2}{5}\right) = 5x\left(\dfrac{7}{x}\right)$

$5 + 2x = 35$

$2x = 30$

$x = 15$

73. $x^4 + x^2 - 20 = (x^2 + 5)(x^2 - 4)$

$= (x^2 + 5)(x+2)(x-2)$

75. $z^4 - 13z^2 + 36$

$= (z^2 - 9)(z^2 - 4)$

$= (z+3)(z-3)(z+2)(z-2)$

77. $2x^2 - 6x + 3 = 0$

$a = 2, b = -6, c = 3$

$x = \dfrac{6 \pm \sqrt{(-6)^2 - 4(2)(3)}}{2(2)}$

$= \dfrac{6 \pm \sqrt{12}}{4}$

```
(6+√(12))/4
       2.366025404
(6-√(12))/4
       .6339745962
■
```

The solutions are roughly 0.6 and 2.4.

79. The greatest decrease in low temperature occurred from Sunday to Monday.

81. The lowest low temperature occurred on Wednesday.

83. $f(x) = 3x^2 - 18x + 56$

Thursday is four days from Sunday, so $x = 4$.

$f(4) = 3(4)^2 - 18(4) + 56 = 32$

This answer appears to agree with the graph.

85. $f(x) = 112.5x^2 + 498.7x + 5454$

a. $x = 2002 - 2000 = 2$

$f(2) = 112.5(2)^2 + 498.7(2) + 5454$

$= 6901.4$

Their net income was $6901.4 million in the year 2002.

b. $15,000 = 112.5x^2 + 498.7x + 5454$

$0 = 112.5x^2 + 498.7x - 9546$

$a = 112.5, b = 498.7, c = -9546$

$x = \dfrac{-498.7 \pm \sqrt{(498.7)^2 - 4(112.5)(-9546)}}{2(112.5)}$

$= \dfrac{-498.7 \pm \sqrt{4,544,401.69}}{225}$

≈ 7.26 or -11.69 (disregard)

Their income will be $15,000 million in the year 2007.

87. $\dfrac{-b + \sqrt{b^2 - 4ac}}{2a} + \dfrac{-b - \sqrt{b^2 - 4ac}}{2a}$

$= \dfrac{-b + \sqrt{b^2 - 4ac} - b - \sqrt{b^2 - 4ac}}{2a}$

$= \dfrac{-2b}{2a}$

$= -\dfrac{b}{a}$

89. $3x^2 - \sqrt{12}\,x + 1 = 0$

$a = 3, b = -\sqrt{12}, c = 1$

$$x = \frac{\sqrt{12} \pm \sqrt{\left(-\sqrt{12}\right)^2 - 4(3)(1)}}{2(3)}$$

$$= \frac{\sqrt{12} \pm \sqrt{12 - 12}}{6}$$

$$= \frac{\sqrt{4 \cdot 3} \pm \sqrt{0}}{6}$$

$$= \frac{2\sqrt{3}}{6}$$

$$= \frac{\sqrt{3}}{3}$$

The solution is $\dfrac{\sqrt{3}}{3}$.

91. $x^2 + \sqrt{2}\,x + 1 = 0$

$a = 1, b = \sqrt{2}, c = 1$

$$x = \frac{-\sqrt{2} \pm \sqrt{\left(\sqrt{2}\right)^2 - 4(1)(1)}}{2(1)}$$

$$= \frac{-\sqrt{2} \pm \sqrt{2 - 4}}{2}$$

$$= \frac{-\sqrt{2} \pm \sqrt{-2}}{2}$$

$$= \frac{-\sqrt{2} \pm i\sqrt{2}}{2}$$

The solutions are $\dfrac{-\sqrt{2} + i\sqrt{2}}{2}$ and $\dfrac{-\sqrt{2} - i\sqrt{2}}{2}$.

93. $2x^2 - \sqrt{3}\,x - 1 = 0$

$a = 2, b = -\sqrt{3}, c = -1$

$$x = \frac{\sqrt{3} \pm \sqrt{\left(-\sqrt{3}\right)^2 - 4(2)(-1)}}{2(2)}$$

$$= \frac{\sqrt{3} \pm \sqrt{3 + 8}}{4}$$

$$= \frac{\sqrt{3} \pm \sqrt{11}}{4}$$

The solutions are $\dfrac{\sqrt{3} + \sqrt{11}}{4}$ and $\dfrac{\sqrt{3} - \sqrt{11}}{4}$.

Exercise Set 8.3

1.
$$2x = \sqrt{10 + 3x}$$
$$4x^2 = 10 + 3x$$
$$4x^2 - 3x - 10 = 0$$
$$(4x + 5)(x - 2) = 0$$
$$4x + 5 = 0 \quad \text{or } x - 2 = 0$$
$$x = -\frac{5}{4} \quad \text{or} \quad x = 2$$

Discard $-\dfrac{5}{4}$ since it is an extraneous solution.

The solution is 2.

3.
$$x - 2\sqrt{x} = 8$$
$$x - 8 = 2\sqrt{x}$$
$$(x - 8)^2 = \left(2\sqrt{x}\right)^2$$
$$x^2 - 16x + 64 = 4x$$
$$x^2 - 20x + 64 = 0$$
$$(x - 16)(x - 4) = 0$$
$$x - 16 = 0 \quad \text{or } x - 4 = 0$$
$$x = 16 \quad \text{or} \quad x = 4 \text{ (discard)}$$

The solution is 16.

5.
$$\sqrt{9x} = x + 2$$
$$\left(\sqrt{9x}\right)^2 = (x + 2)^2$$
$$9x = x^2 + 4x + 4$$
$$0 = x^2 - 5x + 4$$
$$0 = (x - 4)(x - 1)$$
$$x - 4 = 0 \quad \text{or } x - 1 = 0$$
$$x = 4 \quad \text{or} \quad x = 1$$

The solutions are 1 and 4.

7. $\dfrac{2}{x}+\dfrac{3}{x-1}=1$

Multiply each term by $x(x-1)$.

$2(x-1)+3x=x(x-1)$

$2x-2+3x=x^2-x$

$0=x^2-6x+2$

$x=\dfrac{6\pm\sqrt{(-6)^2-4(1)(2)}}{2(1)}$

$=\dfrac{6\pm\sqrt{28}}{2}$

$=\dfrac{6\pm2\sqrt{7}}{2}$

$=3\pm\sqrt{7}$

The solutions are $3+\sqrt{7}$ and $3-\sqrt{7}$.

9. $\dfrac{3}{x}+\dfrac{4}{x+2}=2$

Multiply each term by $x(x+2)$.

$3(x+2)+4x=2x(x+2)$

$3x+6+4x=2x^2+4x$

$0=2x^2-3x-6$

$x=\dfrac{3\pm\sqrt{(-3)^2-4(2)(-6)}}{2(2)}$

$=\dfrac{3\pm\sqrt{57}}{4}$

The solutions are $\dfrac{3+\sqrt{57}}{4}$ and $\dfrac{3-\sqrt{57}}{4}$.

11. $\dfrac{7}{x^2-5x+6}=\dfrac{2x}{x-3}-\dfrac{x}{x-2}$

$\dfrac{7}{(x-3)(x-2)}=\dfrac{2x}{x-3}-\dfrac{x}{x-2}$

Multiply each term by $(x-3)(x-2)$.

$7=2x(x-2)-x(x-3)$

$7=2x^2-4x-x^2+3x$

$0=x^2-x-7$

$x=\dfrac{1\pm\sqrt{(-1)^2-4(1)(-7)}}{2(1)}$

$=\dfrac{1\pm\sqrt{29}}{2}$

The solutions are $\dfrac{1+\sqrt{29}}{2}$ and $\dfrac{1-\sqrt{29}}{2}$.

13. $p^4-16=0$

$(p^2-4)(p^2+4)=0$

$(p+2)(p-2)(p^2+4)=0$

$p+2=0$ or $p-2=0$ or $p^2+4=0$

$p=-2$ or $\quad p=2$ or $\quad p^2=-4$

$p=\pm\sqrt{-4}$

$p=\pm2i$

The solutions are -2, 2, $-2i$, and $2i$.

15. $4x^4+11x^2=3$

$4x^2+11x^2-3=0$

$(4x^2-1)(x^2+3)=0$

$(2x+1)(2x-1)(x^2+3)=0$

$2x+1=0$ or $2x-1=0$ or $x^2+3=0$

$2x=-1$ $\qquad 2x=1$ $\qquad x^2=-3$

$x=-\dfrac{1}{2}$ $\qquad x=\dfrac{1}{2}$ $\qquad x=\pm\sqrt{-3}$

$x=\pm i\sqrt{3}$

The solutions are $-\dfrac{1}{2},\dfrac{1}{2},-i\sqrt{3}$, and $i\sqrt{3}$.

17. $z^4-13z^2+36=0$

$(z^2-9)(z^2-4)=0$

$(z+3)(z-3)(z+2)(z-2)=0$

$z=-3,\,z=3,\,z=-2,\,z=2$

The solutions are -3, 3, -2, and 2.

19. $x^{2/3}-3x^{1/3}-10=0$

Let $y=x^{1/3}$. Then $y^2=x^{2/3}$ and

$y^2-3y-10=0$

$(y-5)(y+2)=0$

$y-5=0$ or $y+2=0$

$y=5$ or $\quad y=-2$

$x^{1/3}=5$ or $\quad x^{1/3}=-2$

$x=125$ or $\quad x=-8$

The solutions are -8 and 125.

21. $(5n+1)^2 + 2(5n+1) - 3 = 0$

Let $y = 5n + 1$. Then $y^2 = (5n+1)^2$ and

$y^2 + 2y - 3 = 0$
$(y+3)(y-1) = 0$
$y+3 = 0 \quad \text{or} \quad y-1 = 0$
$\quad y = -3 \quad \text{or} \quad\quad y = 1$
$5n+1 = -3 \quad \text{or} \quad 5n+1 = 1$
$\quad 5n = -4 \quad \text{or} \quad\quad 5n = 0$
$\quad n = -\dfrac{4}{5} \quad \text{or} \quad\quad n = 0$

The solutions are $-\dfrac{4}{5}$ and 0.

23. $2x^{2/3} - 5x^{1/3} = 3$

Let $y = x^{1/3}$. Then $y^2 = x^{2/3}$ and

$2y^2 - 5y = 3$
$2y^2 - 5y - 3 = 0$
$(2y+1)(y-3) = 0$
$2y+1 = 0 \quad \text{or} \quad y-3 = 0$
$\quad y = -\dfrac{1}{2} \quad \text{or} \quad\quad y = 3$
$\quad x^{1/3} = -\dfrac{1}{2} \quad \text{or} \quad x^{1/3} = 3$
$\quad x = -\dfrac{1}{8} \quad \text{or} \quad\quad x = 27$

The solutions are $-\dfrac{1}{8}$ and 27.

25.
$$1 + \frac{2}{3t-2} = \frac{8}{(3t-2)^2}$$
$(3t-2)^2 + 2(3t-2) = 8$
$(3t-2)^2 + 2(3t-2) - 8 = 0$

Let $y = 3t - 2$. Then $y^2 = (3t-2)^2$ and

$y^2 + 2y - 8 = 0$
$(y+4)(y-2) = 0$
$y+4 = 0 \quad \text{or} \quad y-2 = 0$
$\quad y = -4 \quad \text{or} \quad\quad y = 2$
$3t-2 = -4 \quad \text{or} \quad 3t-2 = 2$
$\quad 3t = -2 \quad \text{or} \quad\quad 3t = 4$
$\quad t = -\dfrac{2}{3} \quad \text{or} \quad\quad t = \dfrac{4}{3}$

The solutions are $-\dfrac{2}{3}$ and $\dfrac{4}{3}$.

27. $20x^{2/3} - 6x^{1/3} - 2 = 0$

Let $y = x^{1/3}$. Then $y^2 = x^{2/3}$ and

$20y^2 - 6y - 2 = 0$
$2(10y^2 - 3y - 1) = 0$
$2(5y+1)(2y-1) = 0$
$5y+1 = 0 \quad\quad \text{or} \quad 2y-1 = 0$
$\quad y = -\dfrac{1}{5} \quad \text{or} \quad\quad y = \dfrac{1}{2}$
$\quad x^{1/3} = -\dfrac{1}{5} \quad \text{or} \quad x^{1/3} = \dfrac{1}{2}$
$\quad x = -\dfrac{1}{125} \quad \text{or} \quad\quad x = \dfrac{1}{8}$

The solutions are $\dfrac{1}{8}$ and $-\dfrac{1}{125}$.

29.
$$a^4 - 5a^2 + 6 = 0$$
$(a^2-3)(a^2-2) = 0$
$a^2-3 = 0 \quad \text{or} \quad a^2-2 = 0$
$\quad a^2 = 3 \quad \text{or} \quad\quad a^2 = 2$
$\quad a = \pm\sqrt{3} \quad \text{or} \quad\quad a = \pm\sqrt{2}$

The solutions are $-\sqrt{3}, \sqrt{3}, -\sqrt{2},$ and $\sqrt{2}$.

31. $\dfrac{2x}{x-2} + \dfrac{x}{x+3} = -\dfrac{5}{x+3}$

Multiply each term by $(x+3)(x-2)$.

$2x(x+3) + x(x-2) = -5(x-2)$
$2x^2 + 6x + x^2 - 2x = -5x + 10$
$3x^2 + 9x - 10 = 0$
$$x = \frac{-9 \pm \sqrt{(9)^2 - 4(3)(-10)}}{2(3)}$$
$$= \frac{-9 \pm \sqrt{201}}{6}$$

The solutions are $\dfrac{-9+\sqrt{201}}{6}$ and $\dfrac{-9-\sqrt{201}}{6}$.

33.
$$(p+2)^2 = 9(p+2) - 20$$
$(p+2)^2 - 9(p+2) + 20 = 0$

Let $x = p + 2$. Then $x^2 = (p+2)^2$ and

$x^2 - 9x + 20 = 0$
$(x-5)(x-4) = 0$
$\quad x = 5 \quad \text{or} \quad\quad x = 4$
$p+2 = 5 \quad \text{or} \quad p+2 = 4$
$\quad p = 3 \quad \text{or} \quad\quad p = 2$

The solutions are 2 and 3.

35.
$$2x = \sqrt{11x+3}$$
$$(2x)^2 = \left(\sqrt{11x+3}\right)^2$$
$$4x^2 = 11x+3$$
$$4x^2 - 11x - 3 = 0$$
$$(4x+1)(x-3) = 0$$
$$x = -\frac{1}{4} \text{ (extraneous)} \text{ or } x = 3$$
The solution is 3.

37. $x^{2/3} - 8x^{1/3} + 15 = 0$
Let $y = x^{1/3}$. Then $y^2 = x^{2/3}$ and
$$y^2 - 8y + 15 = 0$$
$$(y-5)(y-3) = 0$$
$$y = 5 \quad \text{or} \quad y = 3$$
$$x^{1/3} = 5 \quad \text{or} \quad x^{1/3} = 3$$
$$x = 125 \text{ or} \quad x = 27$$
The solutions are 27 and 125.

39.
$$y^3 + 9y - y^2 - 9 = 0$$
$$y(y^2+9) - 1(y^2+9) = 0$$
$$(y^2+9)(y-1) = 0$$
$$y^2 + 9 = 0 \quad \text{or } y - 1 = 0$$
$$y^2 = -9 \quad \text{or} \quad y = 1$$
$$y = \pm\sqrt{-9}$$
$$y = \pm 3i$$
The solutions are 1, $-3i$, and $3i$.

41. $2x^{2/3} + 3x^{1/3} - 2 = 0$
Let $y = x^{1/3}$. Then $y^2 = x^{2/3}$ and
$$2y^2 + 3y - 2 = 0$$
$$(2y-1)(y+2) = 0$$
$$y = \frac{1}{2} \quad \text{or} \quad y = -2$$
$$x^{1/3} = \frac{1}{2} \quad \text{or } x^{1/3} = -2$$
$$x = \frac{1}{8} \quad \text{or} \quad x = -8$$
The solutions are -8 and $\frac{1}{8}$.

43. $x^{-2} - x^{-1} - 6 = 0$
Let $y = x^{-1}$. Then $y^2 = x^{-2}$ and
$$y^2 - y - 6 = 0$$
$$(y-3)(y+2) = 0$$
$$y = 3 \quad \text{or} \quad y = -2$$
$$x^{-1} = 3 \quad \text{or} \quad x^{-1} = -2$$
$$\frac{1}{x} = 3 \quad \text{or} \quad \frac{1}{x} = -2$$
$$x = \frac{1}{3} \quad \text{or} \quad x = -\frac{1}{2}$$
The solutions are $-\frac{1}{2}$ and $\frac{1}{3}$.

45.
$$x - \sqrt{x} = 2$$
$$x - 2 = \sqrt{x}$$
$$(x-2)^2 = x$$
$$x^2 - 4x + 4 = x$$
$$x^2 - 5x + 4 = 0$$
$$(x-4)(x-1) = 0$$
$$x = 4 \text{ or } x = 1 \text{ (extraneous)}$$
The solution is 4.

47.
$$\frac{x}{x-1} + \frac{1}{x+1} = \frac{2}{x^2-1}$$
$$\frac{x}{x-1} + \frac{1}{x+1} = \frac{2}{(x+1)(x-1)}$$
$$x(x+1) + (x-1) = 2$$
$$x^2 + x + x - 1 = 2$$
$$x^2 + 2x - 3 = 0$$
$$(x+3)(x-1) = 0$$
$$x = -3 \text{ or } x = 1 \text{ (extraneous)}$$
The solution is -3.

49.
$$p^4 - p^2 - 20 = 0$$
$$(p^2 - 5)(p^2 + 4) = 0$$
$$p^2 - 5 = 0 \quad \text{or } p^2 + 4 = 0$$
$$p^2 = 5 \quad \text{or} \quad p^2 = -4$$
$$p = \pm\sqrt{5} \quad \text{or} \quad p = \pm 2i$$
The solutions are $-\sqrt{5}, \sqrt{5}, -2i,$ and $2i$.

51.
$$2x^3 = -54$$
$$x^3 = -27$$
$$x^3 + 27 = 0$$
$$(x+3)(x^2 - 3x + 9) = 0$$
$$x + 3 = 0 \quad \text{or} \quad x^2 - 3x + 9 = 0$$
$$x = -3 \quad \text{or} \quad x = \frac{3 \pm \sqrt{(-3)^2 - 4(1)(9)}}{2(1)}$$
$$= \frac{3 \pm \sqrt{-27}}{2}$$
$$= \frac{3 \pm 3i\sqrt{3}}{2}$$

The solutions are -3, $\dfrac{3+3i\sqrt{3}}{2}$, and $\dfrac{3-3i\sqrt{3}}{2}$.

53.
$$1 = \frac{4}{x-7} + \frac{5}{(x-7)^2}$$
$$(x-7)^2 - 4(x-7) - 5 = 0$$
Let $y = x - 7$.
Then $y^2 = (x-7)^2$ and
$$y^2 - 4y - 5 = 0$$
$$(y-5)(y+1) = 0$$
$$y = 5 \quad \text{or} \quad y = -1$$
$$x - 7 = 5 \quad \text{or} \quad x - 7 = -1$$
$$x = 12 \quad \text{or} \quad x = 6$$
The solutions are 6 and 12.

55.
$$27y^4 + 15y^2 = 2$$
$$27y^4 + 15y^2 - 2 = 0$$
$$(9y^2 - 1)(3y^2 + 2) = 0$$
$$(3y+1)(3y-1)(3y^2 + 2) = 0$$
$$y = -\frac{1}{3} \quad \text{or} \quad y = \frac{1}{3} \quad \text{or} \quad y^2 = -\frac{2}{3}$$
$$y = \pm\sqrt{-\frac{2}{3}}$$
$$y = \pm\frac{\sqrt{6}}{3}i$$

The solutions are $-\dfrac{1}{3}, \dfrac{1}{3}, -\dfrac{\sqrt{6}}{3}i$, and $\dfrac{\sqrt{6}}{3}i$.

57. Let $x =$ speed on the first part.
Then $x - 1 =$ speed on the second part.
$$d = rt \quad \Rightarrow \quad t = \frac{d}{r}$$
$$t_{\text{on first part}} + t_{\text{on second part}} = 1\frac{3}{5}$$
$$\frac{3}{x} + \frac{4}{x-1} = \frac{8}{5}$$
$$3 \cdot 5(x-1) + 4 \cdot 5x = 8x(x-1)$$
$$15x - 15 + 20x = 8x^2 - 8x$$
$$0 = 8x^2 - 43x + 15$$
$$0 = (8x - 3)(x - 5)$$
$$8x - 3 = 0 \quad \text{or} \quad x - 5 = 0$$
$$x = \frac{3}{8} \quad \text{or} \quad x = 5$$
$$x - 1 = 4$$

Discard $\dfrac{3}{8}$ since $x - 1$ must be positive. The jogger's initial speed was 5 mph and her final speed was 4 mph.

59. Let $x =$ time for hose alone.
Then $x - 1 =$ time for the inlet pipe alone.
$$\frac{1}{x} + \frac{1}{x-1} = \frac{1}{8}$$
$$8(x-1) + 8x = x(x-1)$$
$$8x - 8 + 8x = x^2 - x$$
$$0 = x^2 - 17x + 8$$
$$x = \frac{17 \pm \sqrt{(-17)^2 - 4(1)(8)}}{2(1)}$$
$$= \frac{17 \pm \sqrt{257}}{2}$$
$$x \approx 0.5 \quad \text{or} \quad x \approx 16.5$$
$$x - 1 \approx 15.5$$

Discard 0.5 since $x - 1$ must be positive.
The hose can complete the job in 16.5 hours and the inlet pipe can complete the job in 15.5 hours.

61. Let x = original speed.
Then $x + 11$ = return speed.

$$d = rt \;\Rightarrow\; t = \frac{d}{r}$$

$$t_{\text{return}} = t_{\text{original}} - 1$$

$$\frac{330}{x+11} = \frac{330}{x} - 1$$

$$330x = 330(x+11) - x(x+11)$$

$$330x = 330x + 3630 - x^2 - 11x$$

$$x^2 + 11x - 3630 = 0$$

$$x = \frac{-11 \pm \sqrt{(11)^2 - 4(1)(-3630)}}{2(1)}$$

$$= \frac{-11 \pm \sqrt{14,641}}{2}$$

$$= \frac{-11 \pm 121}{2}$$

$$x = 55 \quad\text{or}\quad x = -66$$

Discard -66 since x must be positive.
$x + 11 = 55 + 11 = 66$
Original speed: 55 mph
Return speed: 66 mph

63. Let x = time for son alone.
Then $x - 1$ = time for dad alone.

$$\frac{1}{x} + \frac{1}{x-1} = \frac{1}{4}$$

$$4(x-1) + 4x = x(x-1)$$

$$4x - 4 + 4x = x^2 - x$$

$$0 = x^2 - 9x + 4$$

$$x = \frac{9 \pm \sqrt{(-9)^2 - 4(1)(4)}}{2(1)}$$

$$= \frac{9 \pm \sqrt{65}}{2}$$

$$x \approx 0.5 \quad\text{or}\quad x \approx 8.5$$

Discard 0.5 since $x - 1$ must be positive. It takes his son about 8.5 hours to clean the house alone.

65. Let x = the number.

$$x(x-4) = 96$$

$$x^2 - 4x - 96 = 0$$

$$(x-12)(x+8) = 0$$

$$x = 12 \quad\text{or}\quad x = -8$$

The number is 12 or -8.

67. a. length $= x - 3 - 3 = x - 6$ inches
(note that 3 inches are cut off of each end)

b. $V = lwh$

$$300 = (x-6)(x-6) \cdot 3$$

c. $300 = 3(x-6)^2$

$$100 = x^2 - 12x + 36$$

$$0 = x^2 - 12x - 64$$

$$0 = (x-16)(x+4)$$

$$x = 16 \quad\text{or}\quad x = -4 \text{ (discard)}$$

The sheet is 16 cm by 16 cm.

Check: $V = 3(x-6)(x-6)$

$$= 3(16-6)(16-6)$$

$$= 3(10)(10)$$

$$= 300 \text{ cubic cm}$$

69. Let x = length of the side of the square.

$$\text{Area} = x^2$$

$$920 = x^2$$

$$\sqrt{920} = x$$

Adding another radial line to an adjacent corner would yield a right triangle with legs r and hypotenuse x.

$$r^2 + r^2 = x^2$$

$$2r^2 = \left(\sqrt{920}\right)^2$$

$$2r^2 = 920$$

$$r^2 = 460$$

$$r = \pm\sqrt{460} = \pm 21.4476$$

Disregard the negative. The smallest whole number radius would be 22 feet.

71. $\dfrac{5x}{3} + 2 \le 7$

$$\frac{5x}{3} \le 5$$

$$5x \le 15$$

$$x \le 3$$

$$(-\infty, 3]$$

73. $\dfrac{y-1}{15} > -\dfrac{2}{5}$

$$15\left(\frac{y-1}{15}\right) > 15\left(-\frac{2}{5}\right)$$

$$y - 1 > -6$$

$$y > -5$$

$$(-5, \infty)$$

75. Domain: $\{x \mid x \text{ is a real number}\}$ or $(-\infty, \infty)$
Range: $\{y \mid y \text{ is a real number}\}$ or $(-\infty, \infty)$
It is a function since it passes the vertical line test.

77. Domain: $\{x \mid x \text{ is a real number}\}$ or $(-\infty, \infty)$

Range: $\{y \mid y \geq -1\}$ or $[-1, \infty)$

It is a function since it passes the vertical line test.

79. Answers may vary. One possibility:

$$(x-2)(x-5)(x+7) = 0$$

81. a. Let x = Dominguez's fastest lap speed and
$x + 0.88$ = Fernandez's fastest lap speed.

Using $t = \dfrac{d}{r}$, we have

$$t_{\text{Dominguez}} = t_{\text{Fernandez}} + 0.38$$

$$\frac{7920}{x} = \frac{7920}{x+0.88} + 0.38$$

$$7920(x+0.88) = 7920x + 0.38x(x+0.88)$$

$$7920x + 6969.6 = 7920x + 0.38x^2 + 0.3344x$$

$$0 = 0.38x^2 + 0.3344x - 6969.6$$

$$x = \frac{-0.3344 \pm \sqrt{(0.3344)^2 - 4(0.38)(-6969.6)}}{2(0.38)}$$

Using the positive square root, $x \approx 134.99$ feet per second.

b. $x + 0.88 = 134.99 + 0.88$

$= 135.87$ feet per second

c. 5280 ft = 1 mile, and 3600 sec = 1 hr.

Dominguez:

$$\frac{134.99 \text{ ft}}{\text{sec}} \cdot \frac{3600 \text{ sec}}{\text{hr}} \cdot \frac{1 \text{ mile}}{5280 \text{ ft}} \approx 92.0 \text{ mph}$$

Fernandez:

$$\frac{135.87 \text{ ft}}{\text{sec}} \cdot \frac{3600 \text{ sec}}{\text{hr}} \cdot \frac{1 \text{ mile}}{5280 \text{ ft}} \approx 92.6 \text{ mph}$$

Integrated Review

1. $x^2 - 10 = 0$

$$x^2 = 10$$

$$x = \pm\sqrt{10}$$

The solution set is $\left\{-\sqrt{10}, \sqrt{10}\right\}$.

2. $x^2 - 14 = 0$

$$x^2 = 14$$

$$x = \pm\sqrt{14}$$

The solution set is $\left\{-\sqrt{14}, \sqrt{14}\right\}$.

3. $(x-1)^2 = 8$

$$x - 1 = \pm\sqrt{8}$$

$$x - 1 = \pm 2\sqrt{2}$$

$$x = 1 \pm 2\sqrt{2}$$

The solution set is $\left\{1 - 2\sqrt{2}, 1 + 2\sqrt{2}\right\}$.

4. $(x+5)^2 = 12$

$$x + 5 = \pm\sqrt{12}$$

$$x + 5 = \pm 2\sqrt{3}$$

$$x = -5 \pm 2\sqrt{3}$$

The solution set is $\left\{-5 - 2\sqrt{3}, -5 + 2\sqrt{3}\right\}$.

5. $x^2 + 2x - 12 = 0$

$$x^2 + 2x + \left(\frac{2}{2}\right)^2 = 12 + 1$$

$$x^2 + 2x + 1 = 13$$

$$(x+1)^2 = 13$$

$$x + 1 = \pm\sqrt{13}$$

$$x = -1 \pm \sqrt{13}$$

The solution set is $\left\{-1 - \sqrt{13}, -1 + \sqrt{13}\right\}$.

6. $x^2 - 12x + 11 = 0$

$$x^2 - 12x + \left(\frac{-12}{2}\right)^2 = -11 + 36$$

$$x^2 - 12x + 36 = 25$$

$$(x-6)^2 = \pm\sqrt{25}$$

$$x - 6 = \pm 5$$

$$x = 6 \pm 5$$

$$x = 1 \text{ or } x = 11$$

The solution set is $\{1, 11\}$.

7.

$$3x^2 + 3x = 5$$

$$x^2 + x = \frac{5}{3}$$

$$x^2 + x + \left(\frac{1}{2}\right)^2 = \frac{5}{3} + \frac{1}{4}$$

$$x^2 + x + \frac{1}{4} = \frac{23}{12}$$

$$\left(x + \frac{1}{2}\right)^2 = \frac{23}{12}$$

$$x + \frac{1}{2} = \pm\sqrt{\frac{23}{12}}$$

$$x + \frac{1}{2} = \pm\frac{\sqrt{23}}{2\sqrt{3}}$$

$$x + \frac{1}{2} = \pm\frac{\sqrt{23} \cdot \sqrt{3}}{2\sqrt{3} \cdot \sqrt{3}}$$

$$x + \frac{1}{2} = \pm\frac{\sqrt{69}}{6}$$

$$x = -\frac{1}{2} \pm \frac{\sqrt{69}}{6}$$

$$x = \frac{-3 \pm \sqrt{69}}{6}$$

The solution set is $\left\{\dfrac{-3 - \sqrt{69}}{6}, \dfrac{-3 + \sqrt{69}}{6}\right\}$.

8.

$$16y^2 + 16y = 1$$

$$y^2 + y = \frac{1}{16}$$

$$y^2 + y + \left(\frac{1}{2}\right)^2 = \frac{1}{16} + \frac{1}{4}$$

$$y^2 + y + \frac{1}{4} = \frac{5}{16}$$

$$\left(y + \frac{1}{2}\right)^2 = \frac{5}{16}$$

$$y + \frac{1}{2} = \pm\sqrt{\frac{5}{16}}$$

$$y + \frac{1}{2} = \pm\frac{\sqrt{5}}{4}$$

$$y = -\frac{1}{2} \pm \frac{\sqrt{5}}{4}$$

$$y = \frac{-2 \pm \sqrt{5}}{4}$$

The solution set is $\left\{\dfrac{-2 - \sqrt{5}}{4}, \dfrac{-2 + \sqrt{5}}{4}\right\}$.

9.

$$2x^2 - 4x + 1 = 0$$

$$a = 2, b = -4, c = 1$$

$$x = \frac{4 \pm \sqrt{(-4)^2 - 4(2)(1)}}{2(2)}$$

$$= \frac{4 \pm \sqrt{8}}{4}$$

$$= \frac{4 \pm 2\sqrt{2}}{4}$$

$$= \frac{2 \pm \sqrt{2}}{2}$$

The solution set is $\left\{\dfrac{2 - \sqrt{2}}{2}, \dfrac{2 + \sqrt{2}}{2}\right\}$.

10.

$$\frac{1}{2}x^2 + 3x + 2 = 0$$

$$x^2 + 6x + 4 = 0$$

$$a = 1, b = 6, c = 4$$

$$x = \frac{-6 \pm \sqrt{(6)^2 - 4(1)(4)}}{2(1)}$$

$$= \frac{-6 \pm \sqrt{20}}{2}$$

$$= \frac{-6 \pm 2\sqrt{5}}{2}$$

$$= -3 \pm \sqrt{5}$$

The solution set is $\left\{-3 - \sqrt{5}, -3 + \sqrt{5}\right\}$.

11.

$$x^2 + 4x = -7$$

$$x^2 + 4x + 7 = 0$$

$$a = 1, b = 4, c = 7$$

$$x = \frac{-4 \pm \sqrt{(4)^2 - 4(1)(7)}}{2(1)}$$

$$= \frac{-4 \pm \sqrt{-12}}{2}$$

$$= \frac{-4 \pm i\sqrt{4 \cdot 3}}{2}$$

$$= \frac{-4 \pm 2i\sqrt{3}}{2}$$

$$= -2 \pm i\sqrt{3}$$

The solution set is $\left\{-2 - i\sqrt{3}, -2 + i\sqrt{3}\right\}$.

12. $x^2 + x = -3$
$x^2 + x + 3 = 0$
$a = 1, b = 1, c = 3$
$$x = \frac{-1 \pm \sqrt{(1)^2 - 4(1)(3)}}{2(1)}$$
$$= \frac{-1 \pm \sqrt{-11}}{2}$$
$$= \frac{-1 \pm i\sqrt{11}}{2}$$
The solution set is $\left\{\frac{-1-i\sqrt{11}}{2}, \frac{-1+i\sqrt{11}}{2}\right\}$.

13. $x^2 + 3x + 6 = 0$
$a = 1, b = 3, c = 6$
$$x = \frac{-3 \pm \sqrt{(3)^2 - 4(1)(6)}}{2(1)}$$
$$= \frac{-3 \pm \sqrt{-15}}{2}$$
$$= \frac{-3 \pm i\sqrt{15}}{2}$$
The solution set is $\left\{\frac{-3-i\sqrt{15}}{2}, \frac{-3+i\sqrt{15}}{2}\right\}$.

14. $2x^2 + 18 = 0$
$2x^2 = -18$
$x^2 = -9$
$x = \pm\sqrt{-9}$
$x = \pm 3i$
The solution set is $\{-3i, 3i\}$.

15. $x^2 + 17x = 0$
$x(x + 17) = 0$
$x = 0$ or $x + 17 = 0$
$x = -17$
The solution set is $\{-17, 0\}$.

16. $4x^2 - 2x - 3 = 0$
$a = 4, b = -2, c = -3$
$$x = \frac{2 \pm \sqrt{(-2)^2 - 4(4)(-3)}}{2(4)}$$
$$= \frac{2 \pm \sqrt{52}}{8}$$
$$= \frac{2 \pm 2\sqrt{13}}{8}$$
$$= \frac{1 \pm \sqrt{13}}{4}$$
The solution set is $\left\{\frac{1-\sqrt{13}}{4}, \frac{1+\sqrt{13}}{4}\right\}$.

17. $(x - 2)^2 = 27$
$x - 2 = \pm\sqrt{27}$
$x - 2 = \pm 3\sqrt{3}$
$x = 2 \pm 3\sqrt{3}$
The solution set is $\{2 - 3\sqrt{3}, 2 + 3\sqrt{3}\}$.

18. $\frac{1}{2}x^2 - 2x + \frac{1}{2} = 0$
$x^2 - 4x + 1 = 0$
$x^2 - 4x + \left(\frac{-4}{2}\right)^2 = -1 + 4$
$x^2 - 4x + 4 = 3$
$(x - 2)^2 = 3$
$x - 2 = \pm\sqrt{3}$
$x = 2 \pm \sqrt{3}$
The solution set is $\{2 - \sqrt{3}, 2 + \sqrt{3}\}$.

19. $3x^2 + 2x = 8$
$3x^2 + 2x - 8 = 0$
$(3x - 4)(x + 2) = 0$
$3x - 4 = 0$ or $x + 2 = 0$
$x = \frac{4}{3}$ or $x = -2$
The solution set is $\left\{-2, \frac{4}{3}\right\}$.

20.
$$2x^2 = -5x - 1$$
$$2x^2 + 5x + 1 = 0$$
$$a = 2, b = 5, c = 1$$
$$x = \frac{-5 \pm \sqrt{(5)^2 - 4(2)(1)}}{2(2)}$$
$$= \frac{-5 \pm \sqrt{17}}{4}$$
The solution set is $\left\{ \dfrac{-5 - \sqrt{17}}{4}, \dfrac{-5 + \sqrt{17}}{4} \right\}$.

21.
$$x(x - 2) = 5$$
$$x^2 - 2x = 5$$
$$x^2 - 2x + \left(\frac{-2}{2}\right)^2 = 5 + 1$$
$$x^2 - 2x + 1 = 6$$
$$(x - 1)^2 = 6$$
$$x - 1 = \pm\sqrt{6}$$
$$x = 1 \pm \sqrt{6}$$
The solution set is $\left\{ 1 - \sqrt{6}, 1 + \sqrt{6} \right\}$.

22. $x^2 - 31 = 0$
$$x^2 = 31$$
$$x = \pm\sqrt{31}$$
The solution set is $\left\{ -\sqrt{31}, \sqrt{31} \right\}$.

23. $5x^2 - 55 = 0$
$$5x^2 = 55$$
$$x^2 = 11$$
$$x = \pm\sqrt{11}$$
The solution set is $\left\{ -\sqrt{11}, \sqrt{11} \right\}$.

24. $5x^2 + 55 = 0$
$$5x^2 = -55$$
$$x^2 = -11$$
$$x = \pm\sqrt{-11}$$
$$x = \pm i\sqrt{11}$$
The solution set is $\left\{ -i\sqrt{11}, i\sqrt{11} \right\}$.

25.
$$x(x + 5) = 66$$
$$x^2 + 5x = 66$$
$$x^2 + 5x - 66 = 0$$
$$(x + 11)(x - 6) = 0$$
$$x + 11 = 0 \quad \text{or} \quad x - 6 = 0$$
$$x = -11 \quad \text{or} \quad x = 6$$
The solution set is $\left\{ -11, 6 \right\}$.

26. $5x^2 + 6x - 2 = 0$
$$a = 5, b = 6, c = -2$$
$$x = \frac{-6 \pm \sqrt{(6)^2 - 4(5)(-2)}}{2(5)}$$
$$= \frac{-6 \pm \sqrt{76}}{10}$$
$$= \frac{-6 \pm \sqrt{4 \cdot 19}}{10}$$
$$= \frac{-6 \pm 2\sqrt{19}}{10}$$
$$= \frac{-3 \pm \sqrt{19}}{5}$$
The solution set is $\left\{ \dfrac{-3 - \sqrt{19}}{5}, \dfrac{-3 + \sqrt{19}}{5} \right\}$.

27.
$$2x^2 + 3x = 1$$
$$2x^2 + 3x - 1 = 0$$
$$a = 2, b = 3, c = -1$$
$$x = \frac{-3 \pm \sqrt{(3)^2 - 4(2)(-1)}}{2(2)}$$
$$= \frac{-3 \pm \sqrt{17}}{4}$$
The solution set is $\left\{ \dfrac{-3 - \sqrt{17}}{4}, \dfrac{-3 + \sqrt{17}}{4} \right\}$.

28. $a^2 + b^2 = c^2$
$$x^2 + x^2 = 20^2$$
$$2x^2 = 400$$
$$x^2 = 200$$
$$x = \pm\sqrt{200}$$
$$= \pm 10\sqrt{2} \approx 14.1421$$
Disregard the negative. A side of the room is $10\sqrt{2}$ feet ≈ 14.1 feet.

29. Let x = time for Jack alone.
Then $x - 2$ = time for Lucy alone.

$$\frac{1}{x} + \frac{1}{x-2} = \frac{1}{4}$$

$$4(x-2) + 4x = x(x-2)$$

$$4x - 8 + 4x = x^2 - 2x$$

$$0 = x^2 - 10x + 8$$

$$x = \frac{10 \pm \sqrt{(-10)^2 - 4(1)(8)}}{2(1)}$$

$$= \frac{10 \pm \sqrt{68}}{2}$$

$x \approx 9.1$ or $x \approx 0.9$

Discard 0.9 $x - 2$ must be positive.

$x - 2 = 9.1 - 2 = 7.1$

It would take Jack 9.1 hours and Lucy 7.1 hours to prepare the crawfish boil.

30. Let x = initial speed.
Then $x + 1$ = increased speed.

$$t_1 + t_2 = \frac{4}{3}$$

$$\frac{5}{x} + \frac{2}{x+1} = \frac{4}{3}$$

$$5 \cdot 3(x+1) + 2 \cdot 3x = 4x(x+1)$$

$$15x + 15 + 6x = 4x^2 + 4x$$

$$0 = 4x^2 - 17x - 15$$

$$0 = (4x+3)(x-5)$$

$x = -\dfrac{4}{3}$ (discard) or $x = 5$

$x + 1 = 5 + 1 = 6$

Diane's initial speed was 5 mph, which she later increases to 6 mph.

Exercise Set 8.4

1. $(x+1)(x+5) > 0$

$x + 1 = 0$ or $x + 5 = 0$

$x = -1$ or $x = -5$

Region	Test Point	$(x+1)(x+5) > 0$ Result
A: $(-\infty, -5)$	-6	$(-5)(-11) > 0$ True
B: $(-5, -1)$	-2	$(-1)(3) > 0$ False
C: $(-1, \infty)$	0	$(1)(5) > 0$ True

Solution: $(-\infty, -5) \cup (-1, \infty)$

3. $(x-3)(x+4) \le 0$

$x - 3 = 0$ or $x + 4 = 0$

$x = 3$ or $x = -4$

Region	Test Point	$(x-3)(x+4) \le 0$ Result
A: $(-\infty, -4)$	-5	$(-8)(-1) \le 0$ False
B: $(-4, 3)$	0	$(-3)(4) \le 0$ True
C: $(3, \infty)$	4	$(1)(8) \le 0$ False

Solution: $[-4, 3]$

5. $x^2 - 7x + 10 \le 0$

$(x-5)(x-2) \le 0$

$x - 5 = 0$ or $x - 2 = 0$

$x = 5$ or $x = 2$

Region	Test Point	$(x-5)(x-2) \le 0$ Result
A: $(-\infty, 2)$	0	$(-5)(-2) \le 0$ False
B: $(2, 5)$	4	$(-1)(2) \le 0$ True
C: $(5, \infty)$	6	$(1)(4) \le 0$ False

Solution: $[2, 5]$

7. $3x^2 + 16x < -5$

$3x^2 + 16x + 5 < 0$

$(3x+1)(x+5) < 0$

$3x+1 = 0$ or $x+5 = 0$

$x = -\dfrac{1}{3}$ or $x = -5$

Region	Test Point	$(3x+1)(x+5) < 0$ Result
A: $(-\infty, -5)$	-6	$(-17)(-1) < 0$ False
B: $\left(-5, -\dfrac{1}{3}\right)$	-1	$(-2)(4) < 0$ True
C: $\left(-\dfrac{1}{3}, \infty\right)$	0	$(1)(5) < 0$ False

Solution: $\left(-5, -\dfrac{1}{3}\right)$

9. $(x-6)(x-4)(x-2) > 0$

$x-6 = 0$ or $x-4 = 0$ or $x-2 = 0$

$x = 6$ or $x = 4$ or $x = 2$

Region	Test Point	$(x-6)(x-4)(x-2) > 0$ Result
A: $(-\infty, 2)$	0	$(-6)(-4)(-2) > 0$ False
B: $(2, 4)$	3	$(-3)(-1)(1) > 0$ True
C: $(4, 6)$	5	$(-1)(1)(3) > 0$ False
D: $(6, \infty)$	7	$(1)(3)(5) > 0$ True

Solution: $(2, 4) \cup (6, \infty)$

11. $x(x-1)(x+4) \le 0$

$x = 0$ or $x-1 = 0$ or $x+4 = 0$

$x = 1$ or $x = -4$

Region	Test Point	$x(x-1)(x+4) \le 0$ Result
A: $(-\infty, -4)$	-5	$(-5)(-6)(-1) \le 0$ True
B: $(-4, 0)$	-1	$(-1)(-2)(3) \le 0$ False
C: $(0, 1)$	$\dfrac{1}{2}$	$\left(\dfrac{1}{2}\right)\left(-\dfrac{1}{2}\right)\left(\dfrac{9}{2}\right) \le 0$ True
D: $(1, \infty)$	2	$(2)(1)(6) \le 0$ False

Solution: $(-\infty, -4] \cup [0, 1]$

13.   Since we are solving the inequality

$$\left(x^2 - 9\right)\left(x^2 - 4\right) \le 0$$

we want to determine the values of x where the graph of the left hand side is on or below the x-axis. From the graph, we see that the solution set should be: $[-3, -2] \cup [2, 3]$

15. $\dfrac{x+7}{x-2} < 0$

$x+7 = 0$ or $x-2 = 0$

$x = -7$ or $x = 2$

Since the denominator equals 0 when $x = 2$, this value cannot be in the solution.

Region	Test Point	$\dfrac{x+7}{x-2} < 0$; Result
A: $(-\infty, -7)$	-8	$\dfrac{-1}{-10} < 0$; False
B: $(-7, 2)$	0	$\dfrac{7}{-2} < 0$; True
C: $(2, \infty)$	3	$\dfrac{10}{1} < 0$; False

Solution: $(-7, 2)$

17. $\dfrac{5}{x+1} > 0$

$x + 1 = 0$

$x = -1$

Since the denominator equals 0 when $x = -1$, this value cannot be in the solution.

Region	Test Point	$\dfrac{5}{x+1} > 0$; Result
A: $(-\infty, -1)$	-2	$\dfrac{5}{-1} > 0$; False
B: $(-1, \infty)$	0	$\dfrac{5}{1} > 0$; True

Solution: $(-1, \infty)$

19. Since we are solving the inequality

$\dfrac{x+1}{x-4} \geq 0$

we want to determine the values of x where the graph of the left hand side is on or above the x-axis. From the graph, we see that the solution set should be: $(-\infty, -1] \cup (4, \infty)$

21. $\dfrac{3}{x-2} < 4$

The denominator is equal to 0 when $x - 2 = 0$, or $x = 2$.

$\dfrac{3}{x-2} = 4$

$3 = 4x - 8$

$11 = 4x$

$\dfrac{11}{4} = x$

Region	Test Point	$\dfrac{3}{x-2} < 4$; Result
A: $(-\infty, 2)$	0	$\dfrac{3}{-2} < 4$; True
B: $\left(2, \dfrac{11}{4}\right)$	$\dfrac{5}{2}$	$\dfrac{3}{\frac{1}{2}} = 6 < 4$; False
C: $\left(\dfrac{11}{4}, \infty\right)$	3	$\dfrac{3}{1} < 4$; True

Solution: $(-\infty, 2) \cup \left(\dfrac{11}{4}, \infty\right)$

23. $\dfrac{x^2 + 6}{5x} \geq 1$

The denominator is equal to 0 when $5x = 0$, or $x = 0$.

$\dfrac{x^2 + 6}{5x} = 1$

$x^2 + 6 = 5x$

$x^2 - 5x + 6 = 0$

$(x-2)(x-3) = 0$

$x - 2 = 0$ or $x - 3 = 0$

$x = 2$ or $x = 3$

Region	Test Point	$\dfrac{x^2+6}{5x} \geq 1$; Result
A: $(-\infty, 0)$	-1	$\dfrac{7}{-5} \geq 1$; False
B: $(0, 2)$	1	$\dfrac{7}{5} \geq 1$; True
C: $(2, 3)$	$\dfrac{5}{2}$	$\dfrac{49/4}{25/2} = \dfrac{49}{50} \geq 1$; False
D: $(3, \infty)$	4	$\dfrac{22}{20} \geq 1$; True

Solution: $(0, 2] \cup [3, \infty)$

25. $(x-8)(x+7) > 0$

$x - 8 = 0$ or $x + 7 = 0$

$x = 8$ or $x = -7$

Region	Test Point	$(x-8)(x+7) > 0$ Result
A: $(-\infty, -7)$	-8	$(-16)(-1) > 0$ True
B: $(-7, 8)$	0	$(-8)(7) > 0$ False
C: $(8, \infty)$	9	$(1)(16) > 0$ True

Solution: $(-\infty, -7) \cup (8, \infty)$

27. $(2x-3)(4x+5) \le 0$

$2x-3=0$ or $4x+5=0$

$x = \dfrac{3}{2}$ or $\quad x = -\dfrac{5}{4}$

Region	Test Point	$(2x-3)(4x+5) \le 0$ Result
A: $\left(-\infty, -\dfrac{5}{4}\right)$	-2	$(-7)(-3) \le 0$ False
B: $\left(-\dfrac{5}{4}, \dfrac{3}{2}\right)$	0	$(-3)(5) \le 0$ True
C: $\left(\dfrac{3}{2}, \infty\right)$	2	$(1)(13) \le 0$ False

Solution: $\left[-\dfrac{5}{4}, \dfrac{3}{2}\right]$

29. $x^2 > x$

$x^2 - x > 0$

$x(x-1) > 0$

$x=0$ or $x-1=0$

$\qquad x=1$

Region	Test Point	$x(x-1) > 0$ Result
A: $(-\infty, 0)$	-1	$(-1)(-2) > 0$ True
B: $(0,1)$	$\dfrac{1}{2}$	$\left(\dfrac{1}{2}\right)\left(-\dfrac{1}{2}\right) > 0$ False
C: $(1, \infty)$	2	$(2)(1) > 0$ True

Solution: $(-\infty, 0) \cup (1, \infty)$

31. $(2x-8)(x+4)(x-6) \le 0$

$2x-8=0$ or $x+4=0$ or $x-6=0$

$x=4 \qquad x=-4$ or $\quad x=6$

Region	Test Point	$(2x-8)(x+4)(x-6) \le 0$ Result
A: $(-\infty, -4)$	-5	$(-18)(-1)(-11) \le 0$ True
B: $(-4, 4)$	0	$(-8)(4)(-6) \le 0$ False
C: $(4, 6)$	5	$(2)(9)(-1) \le 0$ True
D: $(6, \infty)$	7	$(6)(11)(1) \le 0$ False

Solution: $(-\infty, -4] \cup [4, 6]$

33. $\qquad 6x^2 - 5x \ge 6$

$6x^2 - 5x - 6 \ge 0$

$(3x+2)(2x-3) \ge 0$

$3x+2=0$ or $2x-3=0$

$x = -\dfrac{2}{3}$ or $\qquad x = \dfrac{3}{2}$

Region	Test Point	$(3x+2)(2x-3) \ge 0$ Result
A: $\left(-\infty, -\dfrac{2}{3}\right)$	-1	$(-1)(-5) \ge 0$ True
B: $\left(-\dfrac{2}{3}, \dfrac{3}{2}\right)$	0	$(2)(-3) \ge 0$ False
C: $\left(\dfrac{3}{2}, \infty\right)$	2	$(8)(1) \ge 0$ True

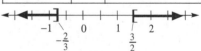

Solution: $\left(-\infty, -\dfrac{2}{3}\right] \cup \left[\dfrac{3}{2}, \infty\right)$

35. $4x^3 + 16x^2 - 9x - 36 > 0$

$4x^2(x+4) - 9(x+4) > 0$

$(x+4)(4x^2 - 9) > 0$

$(x+4)(2x+3)(2x-3) > 0$

$x+4 = 0$ or $2x+3 = 0$ or $2x-3 = 0$

$x = -4$ or $x = -\dfrac{3}{2}$ or $x = \dfrac{3}{2}$

Region	Test Point	$(x+4)(2x+3)(2x-3) > 0$ Result
A: $(-\infty, -4)$	-5	$(-1)(-7)(-13) > 0$ False
B: $\left(-4, -\dfrac{3}{2}\right)$	-2	$(2)(-1)(-7) > 0$ True
C: $\left(-\dfrac{3}{2}, \dfrac{3}{2}\right)$	0	$(4)(3)(-3) > 0$ False
D: $\left(\dfrac{3}{2}, \infty\right)$	2	$(6)(7)(1) > 0$ True

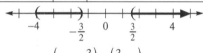

Solution: $\left(-4, -\dfrac{3}{2}\right) \cup \left(\dfrac{3}{2}, \infty\right)$

37. $x^4 - 26x^2 + 25 \geq 0$

$(x^2 - 25)(x^2 - 1) \geq 0$

$(x+5)(x-5)(x+1)(x-1) \geq 0$

$x = -5$ or $x = 5$ or $x = -1$ or $x = 1$

Region	Test Point	$(x+5)(x-5)(x+1)(x-1) \geq 0$ Result
A: $(-\infty, -5)$	-6	$(-1)(-11)(-5)(-7) \geq 0$ True
B: $(-5, -1)$	-2	$(3)(-7)(-1)(-3) \geq 0$ False
C: $(-1, 1)$	0	$(5)(-5)(1)(-1) \geq 0$ True
D: $(1, 5)$	2	$(7)(-3)(3)(1) \geq 0$ False
E: $(5, \infty)$	6	$(11)(1)(7)(5) \geq 0$ True

Solution: $(-\infty, -5] \cup [-1, 1] \cup [5, \infty)$

39. $(2x-7)(3x+5) > 0$

$2x - 7 = 0$ or $3x + 5 = 0$

$x = \dfrac{7}{2}$ or $x = -\dfrac{5}{3}$

Region	Test Point	$(2x-7)(3x+5) > 0$ Result
A: $\left(-\infty, -\dfrac{5}{3}\right)$	-2	$(-11)(-1) > 0$ True
B: $\left(-\dfrac{5}{3}, \dfrac{7}{2}\right)$	0	$(-7)(5) > 0$ False
C: $\left(\dfrac{7}{2}, \infty\right)$	4	$(1)(17) > 0$ True

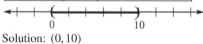

Solution: $\left(-\infty, -\dfrac{5}{3}\right) \cup \left(\dfrac{7}{2}, \infty\right)$

41. $\dfrac{x}{x-10} < 0$

$x = 0$ or $x - 10 = 0$

$x = 10$

Region	Test Point	$\dfrac{x}{x-10} < 0$; Result
A: $(-\infty, 0)$	-1	$\dfrac{-1}{-11} < 0$; False
B: $(0, 10)$	1	$\dfrac{1}{-9} < 0$; True
C: $(10, \infty)$	11	$\dfrac{11}{1} < 0$; False

Solution: $(0, 10)$

43. $\dfrac{x-5}{x+4} \geq 0$

$x - 5 = 0$ or $x + 4 = 0$

$x = 5$ or $x = -4$

Region	Test Point	$\dfrac{x-5}{x+4} \geq 0$; Result
A: $(-\infty, -4)$	-5	$\dfrac{-10}{-1} \geq 0$; True
B: $(-4, 5)$	0	$\dfrac{-5}{4} \geq 0$; False
C: $(5, \infty)$	6	$\dfrac{1}{10} \geq 0$; True

Solution: $(-\infty, -4) \cup [5, \infty)$

45. $\dfrac{x(x+6)}{(x-7)(x+1)} \ge 0$

$x = 0$ or $x+6=0$ or $x-7=0$ or $x+1=0$

$\qquad\qquad x=-6$ or $\quad x=7 \quad$ or $x=-1$

Region	Test Point	$\dfrac{x(x+6)}{(x-7)(x+1)} \ge 0$; Result
A: $(-\infty,-6)$	-7	$\dfrac{(-7)(-1)}{(-14)(-6)} \ge 0$; True
B: $(-6,-1)$	-2	$\dfrac{(-2)(4)}{(-9)(-1)} \ge 0$; False
C: $(-1,0)$	$-\dfrac{1}{2}$	$\dfrac{\left(-\frac{1}{2}\right)\left(\frac{11}{2}\right)}{\left(-\frac{15}{2}\right)\left(\frac{1}{2}\right)} \ge 0$; True
D: $(0,7)$	1	$\dfrac{(1)(7)}{(-6)(2)} \ge 0$; False
E: $(7,\infty)$	8	$\dfrac{(8)(14)}{(1)(9)} \ge 0$; True

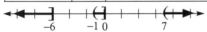

Solution: $(-\infty, -6] \cup (-1, 0] \cup (7, \infty)$

47. $\dfrac{-1}{x-1} > -1$

The denominator is equal to 0 when

$x-1=0$, or $x=1$.

$\dfrac{-1}{x-1} = -1$

$-1 = -1(x-1)$

$-1 = -x+1$

$x = 2$

Region	Test Point	$\dfrac{-1}{x-1} > -1$; Result
A: $(-\infty,1)$	0	$\dfrac{-1}{-1} = 1 > -1$; True
B: $(1,2)$	$\dfrac{3}{2}$	$\dfrac{-1}{\frac{1}{2}} = -2 > -1$; False
C: $(2,\infty)$	3	$\dfrac{-1}{2} > -1$; True

Solution: $(-\infty, 1) \cup (2, \infty)$

49. $\dfrac{x}{x+4} \le 2$

The denominator is equal to 0 when

$x+4=0$, or $x=-4$.

$\dfrac{x}{x+4} = 2$

$x = 2x+8$

$-x = 8$

$x = -8$

Region	Test Point	$\dfrac{x}{x+4} \le 2$; Result
A: $(-\infty,-8)$	-9	$\dfrac{-9}{-5} \le 2$; True
B: $(-8,-4)$	-5	$\dfrac{-5}{-1} \le 2$; False
C: $(-4,\infty)$	0	$\dfrac{0}{4} \le 2$; True

Solution: $(-\infty, -8] \cup (-4, \infty)$

51. $\dfrac{z}{z-5} \ge 2z$

The denominator is equal to 0 when $z=5$.

$\dfrac{z}{z-5} = 2z$

$z = 2z(z-5)$

$z = 2z^2 - 10z$

$0 = 2z^2 - 11z$

$0 = z(2z-11)$

$z = 0$ or $2z-11=0$

$\qquad\qquad z = \dfrac{11}{2}$

Region	Test Point	$\dfrac{z}{z-5} \ge 2z$; Result
A: $(-\infty,0)$	-1	$\dfrac{-1}{-6} \ge -2$; True
B: $(0,5)$	1	$\dfrac{1}{-4} \ge 2$; False
C: $\left(5,\dfrac{11}{2}\right)$	$\dfrac{21}{4}$	$\dfrac{21/4}{1/4} = 21 \ge \dfrac{21}{2}$; True
D: $\left(\dfrac{11}{2},\infty\right)$	6	$\dfrac{6}{1} \ge 12$; False

Solution: $(-\infty, 0] \cup \left(5, \dfrac{11}{2}\right]$

53. $\dfrac{(x+1)^2}{5x} > 0$

The denominator is equal to 0 when
$5x = 0,$ or $x = 0$.

$$\dfrac{(x+1)^2}{5x} = 0$$

$$(x+1)^2 = 0$$

$$x + 1 = 0$$

$$x = -1$$

Region	Test Point	$\dfrac{(x+1)^2}{5x} > 0;$ Result
A: $(-\infty,-1)$	-2	$\dfrac{1}{-10} > 0;$ False
B: $(-1,0)$	$-\dfrac{1}{2}$	$\dfrac{1/4}{-5/2} > 0;$ False
C: $(0,\infty)$	1	$\dfrac{4}{5} > 0;$ True

Solution: $(0, \infty)$

55. $g(x) = |x| + 2$

The graph of g is the same as the graph of
$y = |x|$, but the graph is shifted up two units.

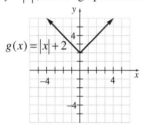

57. $F(x) = |x| - 1$

The graph of F is the same as the graph of
$y = |x|$, but the graph is shifted down one unit.

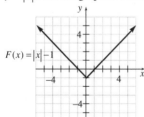

59. $F(x) = x^2 - 3$

The graph of F is the same as the graph of
$y = x^2$, but the graph is shifted down 3 units.

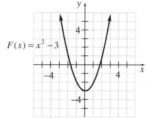

61. $H(x) = x^2 + 1$

The graph of H is the same as the graph of
$y = x^2$, but the graph is shifted up 1 unit.

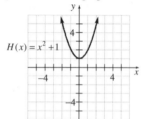

63. Answers may vary.

65. Let $x =$ the number.

Then $\dfrac{1}{x} =$ the reciprocal of the number.

$$x - \dfrac{1}{x} < 0$$

$$\dfrac{x^2 - 1}{x} < 0$$

$$\dfrac{(x+1)(x-1)}{x} < 0$$

$x + 1 = 0$ or $x - 1 = 0$ or $x = 0$

$x = -1$ or $x = 1$

Region	Test Point	$\dfrac{(x+1)(x-1)}{x} < 0;$ Result
A: $(-\infty,-1)$	-2	$\dfrac{(-1)(-3)}{-2} < 0;$ True
B: $(-1,0)$	$-\dfrac{1}{2}$	$\dfrac{\left(\frac{1}{2}\right)\left(-\frac{3}{2}\right)}{\left(-\frac{1}{2}\right)} < 0;$ False
C: $(0,1)$	$\dfrac{1}{2}$	$\dfrac{\left(\frac{3}{2}\right)\left(-\frac{1}{2}\right)}{\left(\frac{1}{2}\right)} < 0;$ True
D: $(1,\infty)$	2	$\dfrac{(3)(1)}{2} < 0;$ False

The numbers are any number less than -1 or
between 0 and 1. That is, $(-\infty,-1) \cup (0,1)$.

67. $P(x) = -2x^2 + 26x - 44$

$-2x^2 + 26x - 44 > 0$

$-2(x^2 + 13x - 22) > 0$

$-2(x - 11)(x - 2) > 0$

$x - 11 = 0$ or $x - 2 = 0$

$x = 11$ or $\quad x = 2$

Region	Test Point	$-2(x-11)(x-2) > 0$ Result
A: $(-\infty, 2)$	0	$-2(-11)(-2) > 0$ False
B: $(2, 11)$	3	$-2(-8)(1) > 0$ True
C: $(11, \infty)$	12	$-2(1)(10) > 0$ False

The company makes a profit when x is between 2 and 11.

69. $(x - 8)(x + 7) > 0$

Solution: $(-\infty, -7) \cup (8, \infty)$

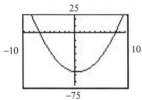

71. $x^4 - 26x^2 + 25 \geq 0$

Solution: $(-\infty, -5] \cup [-1, 1] \cup [5, \infty)$

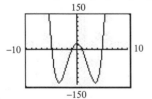

Mental Math 8.5

1. $f(x) = x^2$; vertex: (0, 0)

2. $f(x) = -5x^2$; vertex: (0, 0)

3. $g(x) = (x - 2)^2$; vertex: (2, 0)

4. $g(x) = (x + 5)^2$; vertex: (−5, 0)

5. $f(x) = 2x^2 + 3$; vertex: (0, 3)

6. $h(x) = x^2 - 1$; vertex: (0, −1)

7. $g(x) = (x + 1)^2 + 5$; vertex: (−1, 5)

8. $h(x) = (x - 10)^2 - 7$; vertex: (10, −7)

Exercise Set 8.5

1. The graph of $f(x) = x^2 - 1$ is the graph of $y = x^2$ shifted down 1 unit. The vertex is then $(0, -1)$, and the axis of symmetry is $x = 0$.

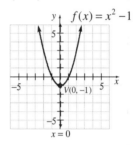

3. The graph of $h(x) = x^2 + 5$ is the graph of $y = x^2$ shifted up 5 units. The vertex is then $(0, 5)$, and the axis of symmetry is $x = 0$.

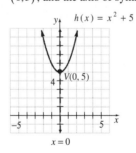

5. The graph of $g(x) = x^2 + 7$ is the graph of $y = x^2$ shifted up 7 units. The vertex is then $(0,7)$, and the axis of symmetry is $x = 0$.

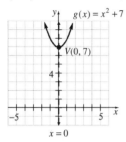

7. The graph of $f(x) = (x-5)^2$ is the graph of $y = x^2$ shifted right 5 units. The vertex is then $(5,0)$, and the axis of symmetry is $x = 5$.

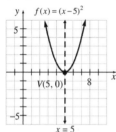

9. The graph of $h(x) = (x+2)^2$ is the graph of $y = x^2$ shifted left 2 units. The vertex is then $(-2,0)$, and the axis of symmetry is $x = -2$.

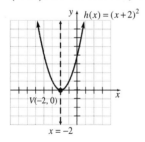

11. The graph of $G(x) = (x+3)^2$ is the graph of $y = x^2$ shifted left 3 units. The vertex is then $(-3,0)$, and the axis of symmetry is $x = -3$.

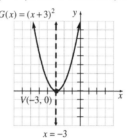

13. The graph of $f(x) = (x-2)^2 + 5$ is the graph of $y = x^2$ shifted right 2 units, and up 5 units. The vertex is then $(2,5)$, and the axis of symmetry is $x = 2$.

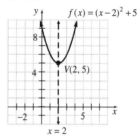

15. The graph of $h(x) = (x+1)^2 + 4$ is the graph of $y = x^2$ shifted left 1 unit, and up 4 units. The vertex is then $(-1,4)$, and the axis of symmetry is $x = -1$.

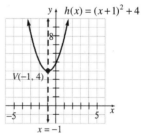

17. The graph of $g(x) = (x+2)^2 - 5$ is the graph of $y = x^2$ shifted left 2 units, and down 5 units. The vertex is then $(-2, -5)$, and the axis of symmetry is $x = -2$.

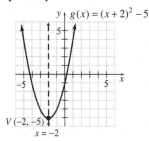

19. The graph of $g(x) = -x^2$ is the graph of $y = x^2$, but open down because $a < 0$. The vertex is then $(0, 0)$, and the axis of symmetry is $x = 0$.

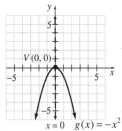

21. The graph of $h(x) = \frac{1}{3}x^2$ is the graph of $y = x^2$, but wider because $|a| < 1$. The vertex is then $(0, 0)$, and the axis of symmetry is $x = 0$.

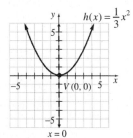

23. The graph of $H(x) = 2x^2$ is the graph of $y = x^2$, but narrower because $|a| > 1$. The vertex is then $(0, 0)$, and the axis of symmetry is $x = 0$.

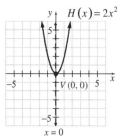

25. The graph of $f(x) = 2(x-1)^2 + 3$ is the graph of $y = x^2$ shifted right 1 unit, made narrower because $|a| > 1$, and shifted up 3 units. The vertex is then $(1, 3)$, and the axis of symmetry is $x = 1$.

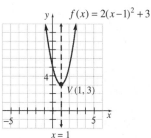

27. The graph of $h(x) = -3(x+3)^2 + 1$ is the graph of $y = x^2$ shifted left 3 units, made narrower because $|a| > 1$, opening down because $a < 0$, and shifted up 1 unit. The vertex is then $(-3, 1)$, and the axis of symmetry is $x = -3$.

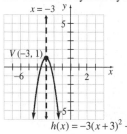

29. The graph of $H(x) = \frac{1}{2}(x-6)^2 - 3$ is the graph of $y = x^2$ shifted right 6 units, made wider because $|a| < 1$, and shifted down 3 units. The vertex is then $(6, -3)$, and the axis of symmetry is $x = 6$.

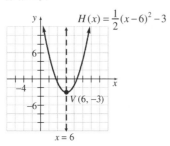

31. The graph of $f(x) = -(x-2)^2$ is the graph of $y = x^2$ shifted right 2 units, and opening down because $a < 0$. The vertex is then $(2, 0)$, and the axis of symmetry is $x = 2$.

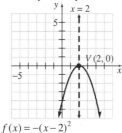

33. The graph of $F(x) = -x^2 + 4$ is the graph of $y = x^2$ opening down because $a < 0$, and shifted up 4 units. The vertex is then $(0, 4)$, and the axis of symmetry is $x = 0$.

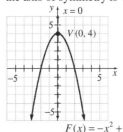

35. The graph of $F(x) = 2x^2 - 5$ is the graph of $y = x^2$ made narrower because $|a| > 1$, and shifted down 5 units. The vertex is then $(0, -5)$, and the axis of symmetry is $x = 0$.

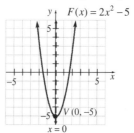

37. The graph of $h(x) = (x-6)^2 + 4$ is the graph of $y = x^2$ shifted right 6 units, and up 4 units. The vertex is then $(6, 4)$, and the axis of symmetry is $x = 6$.

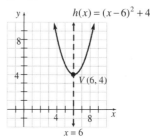

39. The graph of $F(x) = \left(x + \frac{1}{2}\right)^2 - 2$ is the graph of $y = x^2$ shifted left $\frac{1}{2}$ unit, and down 2 units. The vertex is then $\left(-\frac{1}{2}, -2\right)$, and the axis of symmetry is $x = -\frac{1}{2}$.

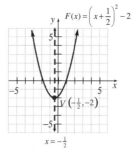

41. The graph of $F(x) = \frac{3}{2}(x+7)^2 + 1$ is the graph

of $y = x^2$ shifted left 7 units, made narrower

because $|a| > 1$, and shifted up 1 unit. The vertex

is then $(-7, 1)$, and the axis of symmetry is

$x = -7$.

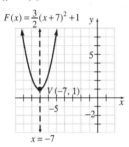

43. The graph of $f(x) = \frac{1}{4}x^2 - 9$ is the graph of

$y = x^2$ made wider because $|a| < 1$, and shifted

down 9 units. The vertex is then $(0, -9)$, and the

axis of symmetry is $x = 0$.

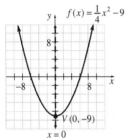

45. The graph of $G(x) = 5\left(x + \frac{1}{2}\right)^2$ is the graph of

$y = x^2$ shifted left $\frac{1}{2}$ unit, and made narrower

because $|a| > 1$. The vertex is then $\left(-\frac{1}{2}, 0\right)$, and

the axis of symmetry is $x = -\frac{1}{2}$.

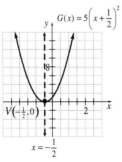

47. The graph of $h(x) = -(x-1)^2 - 1$ is the graph of

$y = x^2$ shifted right 1 unit, opening down

because $a < 0$, and shifted down 1 unit. The

vertex is then $(1, -1)$, and the axis of symmetry

is $x = 1$.

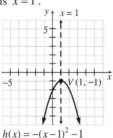

49. The graph of $g(x) = \sqrt{3}(x+5)^2 + \frac{3}{4}$ is the graph

of $y = x^2$ shifted left 5 units, made narrower

because $|a| > 1$, and shifted up $\frac{3}{4}$ units. The

vertex is then $\left(-5, \frac{3}{4}\right)$, and the axis of symmetry

is $x = -5$.

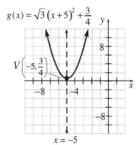

51. The graph of $h(x) = 10(x+4)^2 - 6$ is the graph

of $y = x^2$ shifted left 4 units, made narrower

because $|a| > 1$, and shifted down 6 units. The

vertex is then $(-4, -6)$, and the axis of

symmetry is $x = -4$.

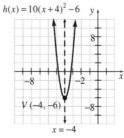

365

53. The graph of $f(x) = -2(x-4)^2 + 5$ is the graph of $y = x^2$ shifted right 4 units, made narrower because $|a| > 1$, opening down because $a < 0$, and shifted up 5 units. The vertex is then $(4,5)$, and the axis of symmetry is $x = 4$.

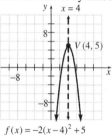

$$f(x) = -2(x-4)^2 + 5$$

55. $x^2 + 8x$
$$\left[\frac{1}{2}(8)\right]^2 = (4)^2 = 16$$
$$x^2 + 8x + 16$$

57. $z^2 - 16z$
$$\left[\frac{1}{2}(-16)\right]^2 = (-8)^2 = 64$$
$$z^2 - 16z + 64$$

59. $y^2 + y$
$$\left[\frac{1}{2}(1)\right]^2 = \left(\frac{1}{2}\right)^2 = \frac{1}{4}$$
$$y^2 + y + \frac{1}{4}$$

61.
$$x^2 + 4x = 12$$
$$x^2 + 4x + \left(\frac{4}{2}\right)^2 = 12 + 4$$
$$x^2 + 4x + 4 = 16$$
$$(x+2)^2 = 16$$
$$x + 2 = \pm\sqrt{16}$$
$$x + 2 = \pm 4$$
$$x = -2 \pm 4$$
$$x = -6 \ \text{or} \ 2$$

63.
$$z^2 + 10z - 1 = 0$$
$$z^2 + 10z = 1$$
$$z^2 + 10z + \left(\frac{10}{2}\right)^2 = 1 + 25$$
$$z^2 + 10z + 25 = 26$$
$$(z+5)^2 = 26$$
$$z + 5 = \pm\sqrt{26}$$
$$z = -5 \pm \sqrt{26}$$

65.
$$z^2 - 8z = 2$$
$$z^2 - 8z + \left(\frac{-8}{2}\right)^2 = 2 + 16$$
$$z^2 - 8z + 16 = 18$$
$$(z-4)^2 = 18$$
$$z - 4 = \pm\sqrt{18}$$
$$z - 4 = \pm 3\sqrt{2}$$
$$z = 4 \pm 3\sqrt{2}$$

67. We need a function with the form:
$$f(x) = 5(x-h)^2 + k$$
Since the vertex is $(h,k) = (2,3)$, we get:
$$f(x) = 5(x-2)^2 + 3$$

69. We need a function with the form:
$$f(x) = 5(x-h)^2 + k$$
Since the vertex is $(h,k) = (-3,6)$, we get:
$$f(x) = 5[x-(-3)]^2 + 6$$
$$= 5(x+3)^2 + 6$$

71. $y = f(x) + 1$

73. $y = f(x-3)$

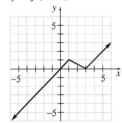

75. $y = f(x+2)+2$

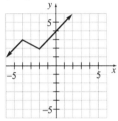

Exercise Set 8.6

1. $f(x) = x^2 + 8x + 7$

$-\dfrac{b}{2a} = \dfrac{-8}{2(1)} = -4$ and

$f(-4) = (-4)^2 + 8(-4) + 7$

$= 16 - 32 + 7$

$= -9$

Thus, the vertex is $(-4, -9)$.

3. $f(x) = -x^2 + 10x + 5$

$-\dfrac{b}{2a} = \dfrac{-10}{2(-1)} = 5$ and

$f(5) = -(5)^2 + 10(5) + 5$

$= -25 + 50 + 5$

$= 30$

Thus, the vertex is $(5, 30)$.

5. $f(x) = 5x^2 - 10x + 3$

$-\dfrac{b}{2a} = \dfrac{-(-10)}{2(5)} = 1$ and

$f(1) = 5(1)^2 - 10(1) + 3$

$= 5 - 10 + 3$

$= -2$

Thus, the vertex is $(1, -2)$.

7. $f(x) = -x^2 + x + 1$

$-\dfrac{b}{2a} = \dfrac{-1}{2(-1)} = \dfrac{1}{2}$ and

$f\left(\dfrac{1}{2}\right) = -\left(\dfrac{1}{2}\right)^2 + \left(\dfrac{1}{2}\right) + 1$

$= -\dfrac{1}{4} + \dfrac{1}{2} + 1$

$= \dfrac{5}{4}$

Thus, the vertex is $\left(\dfrac{1}{2}, \dfrac{5}{4}\right)$.

9. $f(x) = x^2 - 4x + 3$

$-\dfrac{b}{2a} = \dfrac{-(-4)}{2(1)} = 2$ and

$f(2) = (2)^2 - 4(2) + 3 = -1$

The vertex is $(2, -1)$, so the graph is D.

11. $f(x) = x^2 - 2x - 3$

$-\dfrac{b}{2a} = \dfrac{-(-2)}{2(1)} = 1$ and

$f(1) = (1)^2 - 2(1) - 3 = -4$

The vertex is $(1, -4)$ so the graph is B.

13. $f(x) = x^2 + 4x - 5$

$-\dfrac{b}{2a} = \dfrac{-4}{2(1)} = -2$ and

$f(-2) = (-2)^2 + 4(-2) - 5 = -9$

Thus, the vertex is $(-2, -9)$. The graph opens upward ($a = 1 > 0$).

$x^2 + 4x - 5 = 0$

$(x+5)(x-1) = 0$

$x+5 = 0$ or $x-1 = 0$

$x = -5$ or $x = 1$

x-intercepts: $(-5, 0)$ and $(1, 0)$.

$f(0) = -5$, so the y-intercept is $(0, -5)$.

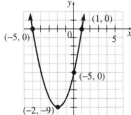

15. $f(x) = -x^2 + 2x - 1$

$-\dfrac{b}{2a} = \dfrac{-2}{2(-1)} = 1$ and

$f(1) = -(1)^2 + 2(1) - 1 = 0$

Thus, the vertex is (1, 0).

The graph opens downward ($a = -1 < 0$).

$-x^2 + 2x - 1 = 0$

$x^2 - 2x + 1 = 0$

$(x - 1)^2 = 0$

$x - 1 = 0$

$x = 1$

x-intercept: (1, 0).

$f(0) = -1$, so the y-intercept is (0, –1).

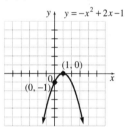

17. $f(x) = x^2 - 4$

$-\dfrac{b}{2a} = \dfrac{-0}{2(1)} = 0$ and

$f(0) = (0)^2 - 4 = -4$

Thus, the vertex is (0, –4).

The graph opens upward ($a = 1 > 0$).

$x^2 - 4 = 0$

$(x + 2)(x - 2) = 0$

$x + 2 = 0$ or $x - 2 = 0$

$x = -2$ or $x = 2$

x-intercepts: (–2, 0) and (2, 0).

$f(0) = -4$, so the y-intercept is (0, –4).

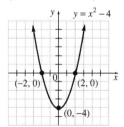

19. $f(x) = 4x^2 + 4x - 3$

$-\dfrac{b}{2a} = \dfrac{-4}{2(4)} = -\dfrac{1}{2}$ and

$f\left(-\dfrac{1}{2}\right) = 4\left(-\dfrac{1}{2}\right)^2 + 4\left(-\dfrac{1}{2}\right) - 3 = -4$

Thus, the vertex is $\left(-\dfrac{1}{2}, -4\right)$.

The graph opens upward ($a = 4 > 0$).

$4x^2 + 4x - 3 = 0$

$(2x + 3)(2x - 1) = 0$

$2x + 3 = 0$ or $2x - 1 = 0$

$x = -\dfrac{3}{2}$ or $x = \dfrac{1}{2}$

x-intercepts: $\left(-\dfrac{3}{2}, 0\right)$ and $\left(\dfrac{1}{2}, 0\right)$.

$f(0) = -3$, so the y-intercept is (0, –3).

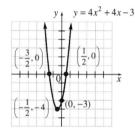

21. $f(x) = x^2 + 8x + 15$

$y = x^2 + 8x + 15$

$y - 15 = x^2 + 8x$

$y - 15 + 16 = x^2 + 8x + 16$

$y - 1 = (x + 4)^2$

$y = (x + 4)^2 + 1$

$f(x) = (x + 4)^2 + 1$

Thus, the vertex is (–4, 1).

The graph opens upward ($a = 1 > 0$).

$x^2 + 8x + 15 = 0$

$(x + 5)(x + 3) = 0$

$x + 5 = 0$ or $x + 3 = 0$

$x = -5$ or $x = -3$

x-intercepts: (–5, 0) and (–3, 0).

$f(0) = 15$, so the y-intercept is $(0, 15)$.

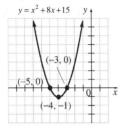

23. $f(x) = x^2 - 6x + 5$

$$y = x^2 - 6x + 5$$
$$y - 5 = x^2 - 6x$$
$$y - 5 + 9 = x^2 - 6x + 9$$
$$y + 4 = (x - 3)^2$$
$$y = (x - 3)^2 - 4$$
$$f(x) = (x - 3)^2 - 4$$

Thus, the vertex is $(3, -4)$.
The graph opens upward ($a = 1 > 0$).
$$x^2 - 6x + 5 = 0$$
$$(x - 5)(x - 1) = 0$$
$$x = 5 \ \text{ or } \ x = 1$$
x-intercepts: $(5, 0)$ and $(1, 0)$.
$f(0) = 5$, so the y-intercept is $(0, 5)$.

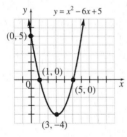

25. $f(x) = x^2 - 4x + 5$

$$y = x^2 - 4x + 5$$
$$y - 5 = x^2 - 4x$$
$$y - 5 + 4 = x^2 - 4x + 4$$
$$y - 1 = (x - 2)^2$$
$$y = (x - 2)^2 + 1$$
$$f(x) = (x - 2)^2 + 1$$

Thus, the vertex is $(2, 1)$.
The graph opens upward ($a = 1 > 0$).

$$x^2 - 4x + 5 = 0$$
$$x = \frac{4 \pm \sqrt{(-4)^2 - 4(1)(5)}}{2(1)} = \frac{4 \pm \sqrt{-4}}{2}$$

which give non-real solutions.
Hence, there are no x-intercepts.
$f(0) = 5$, so the y-intercept is $(0, 5)$.

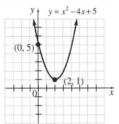

27. $f(x) = 2x^2 + 4x + 5$

$$y = 2x^2 + 4x + 5$$
$$y - 5 = 2(x^2 + 2x)$$
$$y - 5 + 2(1) = 2(x^2 + 2x + 1)$$
$$y - 3 = 2(x + 1)^2$$
$$y = 2(x + 1)^2 + 3$$
$$f(x) = 2(x + 1)^2 + 3$$

Thus, the vertex is $(-1, 3)$.
The graph opens upward ($a = 2 > 0$).
$$2x^2 + 4x + 5 = 0$$

$$x = \frac{-4 \pm \sqrt{(4)^2 - 4(2)(5)}}{2(2)} = \frac{-4 \pm \sqrt{-24}}{4}$$

which give non-real solutions.
Hence, there are no x-intercepts.
$f(0) = 5$, so the y-intercept is $(0, 5)$.

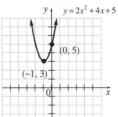

29.
$$f(x) = -2x^2 + 12x$$
$$y = -2(x^2 - 6x)$$
$$y + [-2(9)] = -2(x^2 - 6x + 9)$$
$$y - 18 = -2(x - 3)^2$$
$$y = -2(x - 3)^2 + 18$$
$$f(x) = -2(x - 3)^2 + 18$$
Thus, the vertex is (3, 18).
The graph opens downward ($a = -2 < 0$).
$$-2x^2 + 12x = 0$$
$$-2x(x - 6) = 0$$
$$x = 0 \text{ or } x - 6 = 0$$
$$x = 6$$
x-intercepts: (0, 0) and (6, 0)
$f(0) = 0$, so the y-intercept is (0, 0).

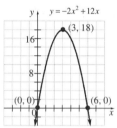

31. $f(x) = x^2 + 1$
$$x = -\frac{b}{2a} = -\frac{0}{2(1)} = 0$$
$$f(0) = (0)^2 + 1 = 1$$
Thus, the vertex is (0, 1).
The graph opens upward ($a = 1 > 0$).
$$x^2 + 1 = 0$$
$$x^2 = -1$$
which give non-real solutions.
Hence, there are no x-intercepts.
$f(0) = 1$, so the y-intercept is (0, 1).

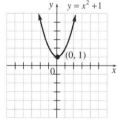

33.
$$f(x) = x^2 - 2x - 15$$
$$y = x^2 - 2x - 15$$
$$y + 15 = x^2 - 2x$$
$$y + 15 + 1 = x^2 - 2x + 1$$
$$y + 16 = (x - 1)^2$$
$$y = (x - 1)^2 - 16$$
$$f(x) = (x - 1)^2 - 16$$
Thus, the vertex is (1, −16).
The graph opens upward ($a = 1 > 0$).
$$x^2 - 2x - 15 = 0$$
$$(x - 5)(x + 3) = 0$$
$$x = 5 \text{ or } x = -3$$
x-intercepts: (−3, 0) and (5, 0).
$f(0) = -15$ so the y-intercept is (0, −15).

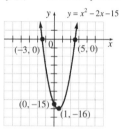

35. $f(x) = -5x^2 + 5x$
$$x = -\frac{b}{2a} = \frac{-5}{2(-5)} = \frac{1}{2} \text{ and}$$
$$f\left(\frac{1}{2}\right) = -5\left(\frac{1}{2}\right)^2 + 5\left(\frac{1}{2}\right) = -\frac{5}{4} + \frac{5}{2} = \frac{5}{4}$$
Thus, the vertex is $\left(\frac{1}{2}, \frac{5}{4}\right)$.
The graph opens downward ($a = -5 < 0$).
$$-5x^2 + 5x = 0$$
$$-5x(x - 1) = 0$$
$$x = 0 \text{ or } x - 1 = 0$$
$$x = 1$$
x-intercepts: (0, 0) and (1, 0)
$f(0) = 0$, so the y-intercept is (0, 0).

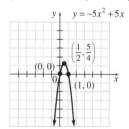

37. $f(x) = -x^2 + 2x - 12$

$x = -\dfrac{b}{2a} = \dfrac{-2}{2(-1)} = 1$ and

$f(1) = -(1)^2 + 2(1) - 12 = -11$

Thus, the vertex is $(1, -11)$.

The graph opens downward ($a = -1 < 0$).

$-x^2 + 2x - 12 = 0$

$x^2 - 2x + 12 = 0$

$x = \dfrac{2 \pm \sqrt{(-2)^2 - 4(1)(12)}}{2(1)} = \dfrac{2 \pm \sqrt{-44}}{2}$

which yields non-real solutions.

Hence, there are no x-intercepts.

$f(0) = -12$ so the y-intercept is $(0, -12)$.

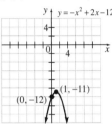

39. $f(x) = 3x^2 - 12x + 15$

$x = -\dfrac{b}{2a} = \dfrac{-(-12)}{2(3)} = \dfrac{12}{6} = 2$ and

$f(2) = 3(2)^2 - 12(2) + 15$

$= 12 - 24 + 15 = 3$

Thus, the vertex is $(2, 3)$.

The graph opens upward ($a = 3 > 0$).

$3x^2 - 12x + 15 = 0$

$x^2 - 4x + 5 = 0$

$x = \dfrac{4 \pm \sqrt{(-4)^2 - 4(1)(5)}}{2(1)} = \dfrac{4 \pm \sqrt{-4}}{2}$

which yields non-real solutions.

Hence, there are no x-intercepts.

$f(0) = 15$, so the y-intercept is $(0, 15)$.

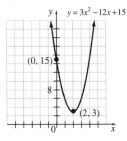

41. $f(x) = x^2 + x - 6$

$x = -\dfrac{b}{2a} = \dfrac{-1}{2(1)} = -\dfrac{1}{2}$ and

$f\left(-\dfrac{1}{2}\right) = \left(-\dfrac{1}{2}\right)^2 + \left(-\dfrac{1}{2}\right) - 6$

$= \dfrac{1}{4} - \dfrac{1}{2} - 6 = -\dfrac{25}{4}$

Thus, the vertex is $\left(-\dfrac{1}{2}, -\dfrac{25}{4}\right)$.

The graph opens upward ($a = 1 > 0$).

$x^2 + x - 6 = 0$

$(x + 3)(x - 2) = 0$

$x = -3$ or $x = 2$

x-intercepts: $(-3, 0)$ and $(2, 0)$.

$f(0) = -6$ so the y-intercept is $(0, -6)$.

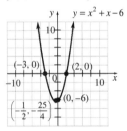

43. $f(x) = -2x^2 - 3x + 35$

$x = -\dfrac{b}{2a} = \dfrac{-(-3)}{2(-2)} = -\dfrac{3}{4}$ and

$f\left(-\dfrac{3}{4}\right) = -2\left(-\dfrac{3}{4}\right)^2 - 3\left(-\dfrac{3}{4}\right) + 35$

$= -\dfrac{9}{8} + \dfrac{9}{4} + 35 = \dfrac{289}{8}$

Thus, the vertex is $\left(-\dfrac{3}{4}, \dfrac{289}{8}\right)$.

The graph opens downward ($a = -2 < 0$).

$-2x^2 - 3x + 35 = 0$

$2x^2 + 3x - 35 = 0$

$(2x - 7)(x + 5) = 0$

$2x - 7 = 0$ or $x + 5 = 0$

$x = \dfrac{7}{2}$ or $x = -5$

x-intercepts: $(-5, 0)$ and $\left(\dfrac{7}{2}, 0\right)$.

$f(0) = 35$ so the y-intercept is $(0, 35)$.

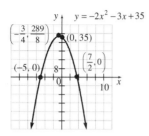

45. $h(t) = -16t^2 + 96t$

$t = -\dfrac{b}{2a} = \dfrac{-96}{2(-16)} = \dfrac{96}{32} = 3$ and

$$h(3) = -16(3)^2 + 96(3)$$
$$= -144 + 288$$
$$= 144$$

The maximum height is 144 feet.

47. $h(t) = -16t^2 + 32t$

$t = -\dfrac{b}{2a} = \dfrac{-32}{2(-16)} = \dfrac{32}{32} = 1$ and

$$h(1) = -16(1)^2 + 32(1)$$
$$= -16 + 32$$
$$= 16$$

The maximum height is 16 feet.

49. Let $x =$ one number. Then
$60 - x =$ the other number.
$$f(x) = x(60 - x)$$
$$= 60x - x^2$$
$$= -x^2 + 60x$$
The maximum will occur at the vertex.
$$x = -\dfrac{b}{2a} = \dfrac{-60}{2(-1)} = 30$$
$60 - x = 60 - 30 = 30$
The numbers are 30 and 30.

51. Let $x =$ one number.
Then $10 + x =$ the other number.
$$f(x) = x(10 + x)$$
$$= 10x + x^2$$
$$= x^2 + 10x$$
The minimum will occur at the vertex.

$$x = -\dfrac{b}{2a} = \dfrac{-10}{2(1)} = -5$$
$10 + x = 10 + (-5) = 5$
The numbers are -5 and 5.

53. Let $x =$ width.
Then $40 - x =$ the length.
Area = length · width
$$A(x) = (40 - x)x$$
$$= 40x - x^2$$
$$= -x^2 + 40x$$
The maximum will occur at the vertex.
$$x = -\dfrac{b}{2a} = \dfrac{-40}{2(-1)} = 20$$
$40 - x = 40 - 20 = 20$
The maximum area will occur when the length and width are 20 units each.

55. The graph of $f(x) = x^2 + 2$ is the graph of $y = x^2$ shifted up 2 units. The vertex is then $(0, 2)$, and the axis of symmetry is $x = 0$.

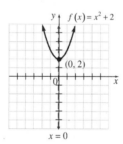

57. The graph of $g(x) = x + 2$ is the graph of $y = x$ shifted up 2 units. The slope is $m = 1$ and the y-intercept is $(0, b) = (0, 2)$.

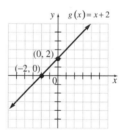

59. The graph of $f(x) = (x+5)^2 + 2$ is the graph of $y = x^2$ shifted left 5 units, and up 2 units. The vertex is then $(-5, 2)$, and the axis of symmetry is $x = -5$. The graph opens up because $a > 0$.

$f(0) = (0+5)^2 + 2 = 27$

The y-intercept is $(0, 27)$.

Since the graph opens up and the vertex is above the x-axis, there are no x-intercepts.

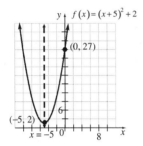

61. The graph of $f(x) = 3(x-4)^2 + 1$ is the graph of $y = x^2$ shifted right 4 units, made narrower because $|a| > 1$, and shifted up 1 unit. The vertex is then $(4, 1)$, and the axis of symmetry is $x = 4$. The graph opens up because $a > 0$.

$f(0) = 3(0-4)^2 + 1$
$= 3(4)^2 + 1$
$= 3(16) + 1$
$= 49$

The y-intercept is $(0, 49)$.

Since the graph opens up and the vertex is above the x-axis, there are no x-intercepts.

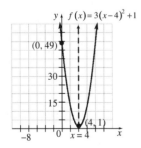

63. The graph of $f(x) = -(x-4)^2 + \frac{3}{2}$ is the graph of $y = x^2$ shifted right 4 units, opening down, and shifted up $\frac{3}{2}$ units. The vertex is then $\left(4, \frac{3}{2}\right)$, and the axis of symmetry is $x = 4$.

$f(0) = -(0-4)^2 + \frac{3}{2} = -\frac{29}{2}$ so the y-intercept is $\left(0, -\frac{29}{2}\right)$.

The graph opens down because $a < 0$.

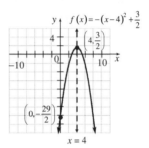

65. $f(x) = x^2 + 10x + 15$

$x = -\frac{b}{2a} = \frac{-10}{2(1)} = -5$ and

$f(-5) = (-5)^2 + 10(-5) + 15 = -10$
Thus, the vertex is $(-5, -10)$.
The graph opens upward ($a = 1 > 0$).
$f(0) = 15$ so the y-intercept is $(0, 15)$.

$x^2 + 10x + 15 = 0$

$x = \frac{-10 \pm \sqrt{(10)^2 - 4(1)(15)}}{2(1)}$

$= \frac{-10 \pm \sqrt{40}}{2} \approx -8.2 \text{ or } -1.8$

The x-intercepts are approximately $(-8.2, 0)$ and $(-1.8, 0)$.

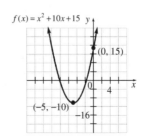

67. $f(x) = 3x^2 - 6x + 7$

$x = -\dfrac{b}{2a} = \dfrac{-(-6)}{2(3)} = 1$ and

$f(1) = 3(1)^2 - 6(1) + 7 = 4$

Thus, the vertex is $(1, 4)$.

The graph opens upward ($a = 3 > 0$).

$f(0) = 7$ so the y-intercept is $(0, 7)$.

$3x^2 - 6x + 7 = 0$

$x = \dfrac{6 \pm \sqrt{(-6)^2 - 4(3)(7)}}{2(1)} = \dfrac{6 \pm \sqrt{-48}}{2}$

which yields non-real solutions.

Hence, there are no x-intercepts.

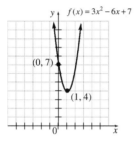

69. $f(x) = 2.3x^2 - 6.1x + 3.2$

minimum ≈ -0.84

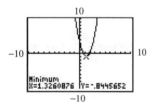

71. $f(x) = -1.9x^2 + 5.6x - 2.7$

maximum ≈ 1.43

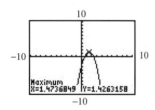

73. $p(x) = -x^2 + 93x + 1128$

a. It will have a maximum; answers may vary. Since the leading coefficient (the coefficient on x^2) is negative, the graph will open down.

b. $x = -\dfrac{b}{2a} = \dfrac{-93}{2(-1)} = 46.5$

$1990 + 46.5 = 2036.5$

The number of inmates in custody would be a maximum in the year 2036.

c. $p(46.5) = -(46.5)^2 + 93(46.5) + 1128$

$\quad = 3290.25$ thousand inmates,

The maximum number of inmates is predicted to be 3,290,250 inmates.

Exercise Set 8.7

1. The data appears to be linear.

3. The data appears to be neither linear nor quadratic.

5. The data appears to be linear.

7. The data points appear to have some curvature. A quadratic model would likely fit the data well.

9. Begin by graphing the data.

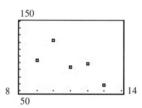

With so few data points, it is difficult to determine which model is best. The data is not linear or quadratic.

11. Begin by graphing the data.

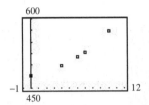

Linear model:

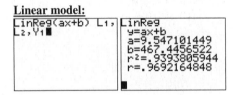

The linear model would be
$y = 9.547x + 467.446$

To predict the median weekly earnings in 2010, we evaluate the model for $x = 20$ (20 years after 1990).

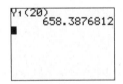

The linear model predicts the median weekly earnings in 2010 to be $658.39.

Quadratic model:

The quadratic model would be
$y = 0.710x^2 + 2.630x + 476.247$

To predict the median weekly earnings in 2010, we evaluate the model for $x = 20$.

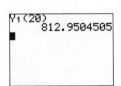

The quadratic model predicts the median weekly earnings in 2010 to be $812.95.

13. From Example 4, the regression equation is
$y = -3.43x + 55.52$
where x is the number of years since 1990 and y is the VCR unit sales in millions.
For 2007, we have $x = 17$.

$y = -3.43(17) + 55.52$

$\quad = -2.79$

The predicted number of units sold is negative. Explanations may vary. This may be occurring because we are trying to predict beyond the scope of the available data. We assume that the linear model will still hold, but this may not be the case.

15. Based on the graph in Exercise 8, a quadratic model appears to fit the data best.

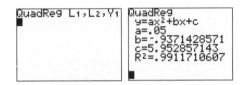

The quadratic model is
$y = 0.05x^2 - 0.937x + 5.953$

Use the model to predict Barbie doll sales when $x = 19$ (the year 2009).

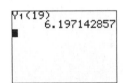

The model predicts that Barbie doll sales in 2009 will be about $6.197 billion.

17. a.

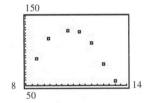

Based on the graph, it appears that a quadratic model would best fit the data.

b.

The quadratic model is

$$y = -13.010x^2 + 1727.626x - 37,489.948$$

c.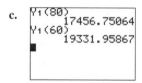

If the shoes are sold for \$80, the projected profit is about \$17,457. If the shoes are sold for \$60, the projected profit is about \$19,332.

d. If the shoes are sold for \$105, the profit would be \$1500. This is not a good selling price since the profit is much lower than what could be obtained with a lower selling price.

e. Graph the quadratic model and use the *maximum* option from the CALC menu to find the price that yields the maximum profit.

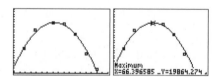

The shoes should be sold for about \$66 to achieve the maximum profit.

19.

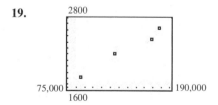

The data appears to be linear so we will fit a linear model.

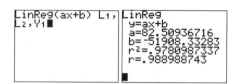

The linear model of best fit is
$$y = 82.509x - 51,908.333 .$$

21. The model from Exercise 19 is
$$y = 82.509x - 51,908.333$$
Evaluate this model when $x = 2400$.
$$y = 82.509(2400) - 51,908.333$$
$$= 198,021.6 - 51,908.333$$
$$= 146,113.267$$
The linear model predicts that a house with 2400 square feet will cost about \$146,113.

23.

The linear model for the data is
$$y = -29.3x + 60248.2 .$$

Since the equation is stored as y_1, we can use a table of values to get the predicted consumption per person.

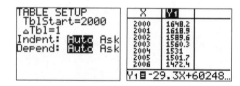

x (year)	Actual (per person)	Predicted (per person)	Difference
2000	1637	1648.2	-11.2
2001	1626	1618.9	7.1
2002	1609	1589.6	19.4
2003	1545	1560.5	-15.5

25. Begin by graphing the data.

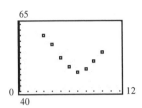

Based on the graph, it appears that a quadratic model would best fit the data.

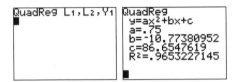

The quadratic model of best fit is
$y = 0.75x^2 - 10.774x + 86.655$.

Answers may vary. Since temperature is typically cyclical, the quadratic model is limited because the predicted temperature will continue to rise as the value of x increases instead of oscillating like the actual temperatures.

27. Since the commission is given as a constant rate, a linear model would best fit the relationship.

29. Since computing the area of a circle involves squaring the radius, the relationship would best be described with a quadratic model.

31. The temperatures will decline more quickly at first and then decrease more slowly as the oven temperature approaches the room temperature. This implies that the data will have some curvature, so the relationship would be described better by a quadratic model.

33. The distance-traveled formula indicates that distance is directly related to time $(d = r \cdot t)$.

Therefore, assuming a constant rate of travel, the relationship would best be described by a linear model.

35. $(x-1)(x+19) = 0$
$x - 1 = 0$ or $x + 19 = 0$
$x = 1$ or $x = -19$
The solution set is $\{-19, 1\}$.

37. $6x^2 + 13x - 5 = 0$
$a = 6, b = 13, c = -5$

$x = \dfrac{-13 \pm \sqrt{13^2 - 4(6)(-5)}}{2(6)}$

$= \dfrac{-13 \pm \sqrt{169 + 120}}{12}$

$= \dfrac{-13 \pm \sqrt{289}}{12}$

$= \dfrac{-13 \pm 17}{12}$

$x = -\dfrac{30}{12} = -\dfrac{5}{2}$ or $x = \dfrac{4}{12} = \dfrac{1}{3}$

The solution set is $\left\{-\dfrac{5}{2}, \dfrac{1}{3}\right\}$.

39. $4(2x + 7) = 2(x - 4)$
$8x + 28 = 2x - 8$
$6x + 28 = -8$
$6x = -36$
$x = -6$
The solution set is $\{-6\}$.

41. $f(x) = 2x^3 + x^2 - 7x + 12$

To find the y-intercept, we evaluate the function when $x = 0$.

$f(0) = 2(0)^3 + (0)^2 - 7(0) + 12 = 12$

The y-intercept is $(0, 12)$.

43. $g(x) = 3x^2 - 5x - 10$

To find the y-intercept, we evaluate the function when $x = 0$.

$g(0) = 3(0)^2 - 5(0) - 10 = -10$

The y-intercept is $(0, -10)$.

Chapter 8 Review

1. $x^2 - 15x + 14 = 0$
$(x-14)(x-1) = 0$
$x-14 = 0$ or $x-1 = 0$
$x = 14$ or $x = 1$
The solutions are 1 and 14.

2. $x^2 - x - 30 = 0$
$(x+5)(x-6) = 0$
$x+5 = 0$ or $x-6 = 0$
$x = -5$ or $x = 6$
The solutions are –5 and 6.

3. $10x^2 = 3x + 4$
$10x^2 - 3x - 4 = 0$
$(5x-4)(2x+1) = 0$
$5x-4 = 0$ or $2x+1 = 0$
$5x = 4$ or $2x = -1$
$x = \dfrac{4}{5}$ or $x = -\dfrac{1}{2}$
The solutions are $-\dfrac{1}{2}$ and $\dfrac{4}{5}$.

4. $7a^2 = 29a + 30$
$7a^2 - 29a - 30 = 0$
$(7a+6)(a-5) = 0$
$7a+6 = 0$ or $a-5 = 0$
$7a = -6$ or $a = 5$
$a = -\dfrac{6}{7}$
The solutions are $-\dfrac{6}{7}$ and 5.

5. $4m^2 = 196$
$m^2 = 49$
$m = \pm\sqrt{49}$
$m = \pm 7$
The solutions are –7 and 7.

6. $9y^2 = 36$
$y^2 = 4$
$y = \pm\sqrt{4}$
$y = \pm 2$
The solutions are –2 and 2.

7. $(9n+1)^2 = 9$
$9n+1 = \pm\sqrt{9}$
$9n+1 = \pm 3$
$9n = -1 \pm 3$
$n = \dfrac{-1 \pm 3}{9}$
The solutions are $-\dfrac{4}{9}$ and $\dfrac{2}{9}$.

8. $(5x-2)^2 = 2$
$5x-2 = \pm\sqrt{2}$
$5x = 2 \pm \sqrt{2}$
$x = \dfrac{2 \pm \sqrt{2}}{5}$
The solutions are $\dfrac{2 + \sqrt{2}}{5}$ and $\dfrac{2 - \sqrt{2}}{5}$.

9. $z^2 + 3z + 1 = 0$
$z^2 + 3z = -1$
$z^2 + 3z + \left(\dfrac{3}{2}\right)^2 = -1 + \dfrac{9}{4}$
$\left(z + \dfrac{3}{2}\right)^2 = \dfrac{5}{4}$
$z + \dfrac{3}{2} = \pm\sqrt{\dfrac{5}{4}}$
$z + \dfrac{3}{2} = \pm\dfrac{\sqrt{5}}{2}$
$z = -\dfrac{3}{2} \pm \dfrac{\sqrt{5}}{2}$
The solutions are $\dfrac{-3 + \sqrt{5}}{2}$ and $\dfrac{-3 - \sqrt{5}}{2}$.

10.
$$x^2 + x + 7 = 0$$
$$x^2 + x = -7$$
$$x^2 + x + \left(\frac{1}{2}\right)^2 = -7 + \frac{1}{4}$$
$$\left(x + \frac{1}{2}\right)^2 = -\frac{27}{4}$$
$$x + \frac{1}{2} = \pm\sqrt{-\frac{27}{4}}$$
$$x + \frac{1}{2} = \pm\frac{\sqrt{9 \cdot 3}}{2}i$$
$$x + \frac{1}{2} = \pm\frac{3\sqrt{3}}{2}i$$
$$x = -\frac{1}{2} \pm \frac{3\sqrt{3}}{2}i$$

The solutions are $\dfrac{-1 + 3i\sqrt{3}}{2}$ and $\dfrac{-1 - 3i\sqrt{3}}{2}$.

11.
$$(2x + 1)^2 = x$$
$$4x^2 + 4x + 1 = x$$
$$4x^2 + 3x = -1$$
$$x^2 + \frac{3}{4}x = -\frac{1}{4}$$
$$x^2 + \frac{3}{4}x + \left(\frac{\frac{3}{4}}{2}\right)^2 = -\frac{1}{4} + \frac{9}{64}$$
$$\left(x + \frac{3}{8}\right)^2 = -\frac{7}{64}$$
$$x + \frac{3}{8} = \pm\sqrt{-\frac{7}{64}}$$
$$x + \frac{3}{8} = \pm\frac{\sqrt{7}}{8}i$$
$$x = -\frac{3}{8} \pm \frac{\sqrt{7}}{8}i$$

The solutions are $\dfrac{-3 + i\sqrt{7}}{8}$ and $\dfrac{-3 - i\sqrt{7}}{8}$.

12.
$$(3x - 4)^2 = 10x$$
$$9x^2 - 24x + 16 = 10x$$
$$9x^2 - 34x = -16$$
$$x^2 - \frac{34}{9}x = -\frac{16}{9}$$
$$x^2 - \frac{34}{9}x + \left(\frac{-\frac{34}{9}}{2}\right)^2 = -\frac{16}{9} + \frac{289}{81}$$
$$\left(x - \frac{17}{9}\right)^2 = \frac{145}{81}$$
$$x - \frac{17}{9} = \pm\sqrt{\frac{145}{81}}$$
$$x - \frac{17}{9} = \pm\frac{\sqrt{145}}{9}$$
$$x = \frac{17 \pm \sqrt{145}}{9}$$

The solutions are $\dfrac{17 + \sqrt{145}}{9}$ and $\dfrac{17 - \sqrt{145}}{9}$.

13.
$$A = P(1 + r)^2$$
$$2717 = 2500(1 + r)^2$$
$$\frac{2717}{2500} = (1 + r)^2$$
$$(1 + r)^2 = 1.0868$$
$$1 + r = \pm\sqrt{1.0868}$$
$$r = -1 \pm \sqrt{1.0868}$$
$$r \approx -1 \pm 1.0425$$
$$= 0.0425 \text{ or } -2.0425$$

We can't have a negative interest rate, so we ignore the negative solution. The interest rate is 4.25%.

14. Let x = distance traveled.
Since the travel at the same rate, they travel the same distance for a given time period.
$$a^2 + b^2 = c^2$$
$$x^2 + x^2 = (150)^2$$
$$2x^2 = 22,500$$
$$x^2 = 11,250$$
$$x = \pm 75\sqrt{2} \approx \pm 106.1$$

Disregard the negative answer since distance is never negative.

The ships each traveled $75\sqrt{2} \approx 106.1$ miles.

15. Two complex but not real solutions exist.

16. Two real solutions exist.

17. Two real solutions exist.

18. One real solution exists.

19. $x^2 - 16x + 64 = 0$
$a = 1, b = -16, c = 64$
$$x = \frac{16 \pm \sqrt{(-16)^2 - 4(1)(64)}}{2(1)}$$
$$= \frac{16 \pm \sqrt{256 - 256}}{2} = \frac{16 \pm \sqrt{0}}{2} = 8$$
The solution is 8.

20. $x^2 + 5x = 0$
$a = 1, b = 5, c = 0$
$$x = \frac{-5 \pm \sqrt{(5)^2 - 4(1)(0)}}{2(1)}$$
$$= \frac{-5 \pm \sqrt{25}}{2}$$
$$= \frac{-5 \pm 5}{2}$$
The solutions are −5 and 0.

21. $x^2 + 11 = 0$
$a = 1, b = 0, c = 11$
$$x = \frac{0 \pm \sqrt{(0)^2 - 4(1)(11)}}{2(1)}$$
$$= \frac{\pm \sqrt{-44}}{2}$$
$$= \frac{\pm 2i\sqrt{11}}{2}$$
$$= \pm i\sqrt{11}$$
The solutions are $-i\sqrt{11}$ and $i\sqrt{11}$.

22. $2x^2 + 3x = 5$
$2x^2 + 3x - 5 = 0$
$a = 2, b = 3, c = -5$
$$x = \frac{-3 \pm \sqrt{(3)^2 - 4(2)(-5)}}{2(2)}$$
$$= \frac{-3 \pm \sqrt{49}}{4}$$
$$= \frac{-3 \pm 7}{4}$$
The solutions are $-\frac{5}{2}$ and 1.

23. $6x^2 + 7 = 5x$
$6x^2 - 5x + 7 = 0$
$a = 6, b = -5, c = 7$
$$x = \frac{5 \pm \sqrt{(-5)^2 - 4(6)(7)}}{2(6)}$$
$$= \frac{5 \pm \sqrt{25 - 168}}{12}$$
$$= \frac{5 \pm \sqrt{-143}}{12}$$
$$= \frac{5 \pm i\sqrt{143}}{12}$$
The solutions are $\frac{5 + i\sqrt{143}}{12}$ and $\frac{5 - i\sqrt{143}}{12}$.

24. $9a^2 + 4 = 2a$
$9a^2 - 2a + 4 = 0$
$$a = \frac{2 \pm \sqrt{(-2)^2 - 4(9)(4)}}{2(9)}$$
$$= \frac{2 \pm \sqrt{-140}}{18}$$
$$= \frac{2 \pm i\sqrt{4 \cdot 35}}{18}$$
$$= \frac{2 \pm 2i\sqrt{35}}{18}$$
$$= \frac{1 \pm i\sqrt{35}}{9}$$
The solutions are $\frac{1 + i\sqrt{35}}{9}$ and $\frac{1 - i\sqrt{35}}{9}$.

25. $(5a - 2)^2 - a = 0$
$25a^2 - 20a + 4 - a = 0$
$25a^2 - 21a + 4 = 0$
$$a = \frac{21 \pm \sqrt{(-21)^2 - 4(25)(4)}}{2(25)}$$
$$= \frac{21 \pm \sqrt{441 - 400}}{50}$$
$$= \frac{21 \pm \sqrt{41}}{50}$$
The solutions are $\frac{21 + \sqrt{41}}{50}$ and $\frac{21 - \sqrt{41}}{50}$.

26.
$$(2x-3)^2 = x$$
$$4x^2 -12x+9-x = 0$$
$$4x^2 -13x+9 = 0$$
$$a = 4, b = -13, c = 9$$
$$x = \frac{13\pm\sqrt{(-13)^2 - 4(4)(9)}}{2(4)}$$
$$= \frac{13\pm\sqrt{169-144}}{8}$$
$$= \frac{13\pm\sqrt{25}}{8}$$
$$= \frac{13\pm 5}{8}$$

The solutions are 1 and $\frac{9}{4}$.

27. $d(t) = -16t^2 + 30t + 6$

a. $d(1) = -16(1)^2 + 30(1) + 6$
$$= -16 + 30 + 6$$
$$= 20 \text{ feet}$$
After 1 second, the cadet's hat will be 20 feet above the ground.

b. $-16t^2 + 30t + 6 = 0$
$$8t^2 - 15t - 3 = 0$$
$$a = 8, b = -15, c = -3$$
$$t = \frac{15\pm\sqrt{(-15)^2 - 4(8)(-3)}}{2(8)}$$
$$= \frac{15\pm\sqrt{225+96}}{16}$$
$$= \frac{15\pm\sqrt{321}}{16}$$
Disregarding the negative, we have
$$t = \frac{15+\sqrt{321}}{16} \text{ seconds} \approx 2.1 \text{ seconds}.$$
It will take about 2.1 seconds for the cadet's hat to hit the ground.

28. Let x = length of the legs.
Then $x + 6$ = length of the hypotenuse.
$$x^2 + x^2 = (x+6)^2$$
$$2x^2 = x^2 + 12x + 36$$
$$x^2 - 12x - 36 = 0$$
$$a = 1, b = -12, c = -36$$

$$x = \frac{12\pm\sqrt{(-12)^2 - 4(1)(-36)}}{2(1)}$$
$$= \frac{12\pm\sqrt{144+144}}{2}$$
$$= \frac{12\pm\sqrt{144\cdot 2}}{2}$$
$$= \frac{12\pm 12\sqrt{2}}{2}$$
$$= 6\pm 6\sqrt{2}$$
Disregard the negative.
The length of each leg is $\left(6+6\sqrt{2}\right)$ cm.

29.
$$x^3 = 27$$
$$x^3 - 27 = 0$$
$$(x-3)(x^2 + 3x + 9) = 0$$
$$x - 3 = 0 \text{ or } x^2 + 3x + 9 = 0$$
$$x = 3 \qquad a = 1, b = 3, c = 9$$
$$x = \frac{-3\pm\sqrt{(3)^2 - 4(1)(9)}}{2(1)}$$
$$= \frac{-3\pm\sqrt{9-36}}{2}$$
$$= \frac{-3\pm\sqrt{-27}}{2}$$
$$= \frac{-3\pm 3i\sqrt{3}}{2}$$
The solutions are 3, $\frac{-3+3i\sqrt{3}}{2}$, and $\frac{-3-3i\sqrt{3}}{2}$.

30.
$$y^3 = -64$$
$$y^3 + 64 = 0$$
$$(y+4)(y^2 - 4y + 16) = 0$$
$$y + 4 = 0 \text{ or } y^2 - 4y + 16 = 0$$
$$y = -4 \qquad a = 1, b = -4, c = 16$$
$$y = \frac{4\pm\sqrt{(-4)^2 - 4(1)(16)}}{2(1)}$$
$$= \frac{4\pm\sqrt{16-64}}{2}$$
$$= \frac{4\pm\sqrt{-48}}{2}$$
$$= \frac{4\pm 4i\sqrt{3}}{2}$$
$$= 2\pm 2i\sqrt{3}$$
The solutions are -4, $2+2i\sqrt{3}$, and $2-2i\sqrt{3}$.

31.
$$\frac{5}{x}+\frac{6}{x-2}=3$$
$$x(x-2)\left(\frac{5}{x}+\frac{6}{x-2}\right)=3x(x-2)$$
$$5(x-2)+6x=3x^2-6x$$
$$5x-10+6x=3x^2-6x$$
$$0=3x^2-17x+10$$
$$0=(3x-2)(x-5)$$
$$3x-2=0 \text{ or } x-5=0$$
$$x=\frac{2}{3} \text{ or } \quad x=5$$

The solutions are $\frac{2}{3}$ and 5.

32.
$$\frac{7}{8}=\frac{8}{x^2}$$
$$7x^2=64$$
$$x^2=\frac{64}{7}$$
$$x=\pm\sqrt{\frac{64}{7}}$$
$$x=\pm\frac{8}{\sqrt{7}}$$
$$=\pm\frac{8\cdot\sqrt{7}}{\sqrt{7}\cdot\sqrt{7}}$$
$$=\pm\frac{8\sqrt{7}}{7}$$

The solutions are $-\frac{8\sqrt{7}}{7}$ and $\frac{8\sqrt{7}}{7}$.

33.
$$x^4-21x^2-100=0$$
$$(x^2-25)(x^2+4)=0$$
$$(x+5)(x-5)(x^2+4)=0$$
$$x+5=0 \text{ or } x-5=0 \text{ or } x^2+4=0$$
$$x=-5 \text{ or } \quad x=5 \text{ or } \quad x^2=-4$$
$$x=\pm 2i$$

The solutions are -5, 5, $-2i$, and $2i$.

34.
$$5(x+3)^2-19(x+3)=4$$
$$5(x+3)^2-19(x+3)-4=0$$

Let $y=x+3$. Then $y^2=(x+3)^2$ and

$$5y^2-19y-4=0$$
$$(5y+1)(y-4)=0$$
$$5y+1=0 \quad \text{ or } y-4=0$$
$$y=-\frac{1}{5} \text{ or } \quad y=4$$
$$x+3=-\frac{1}{5} \text{ or } x+3=4$$
$$x=-\frac{16}{5} \text{ or } \quad x=1$$

The solutions are $-\frac{16}{5}$ and 1.

35. $x^{2/3}-6x^{1/3}+5=0$

Let $y=x^{1/3}$. Then $y^2=x^{2/3}$ and

$$y^2-6y+5=0$$
$$(y-5)(y-1)=0$$
$$y-5=0 \quad \text{ or } y-1=0$$
$$y=5 \quad \text{ or } \quad y=1$$
$$x^{1/3}=5 \quad \text{ or } x^{1/3}=1$$
$$x=125 \text{ or } \quad x=1$$

The solutions are 1 and 125.

36. $x^{2/3}-6x^{1/3}=-8$
$$x^{2/3}-6x^{1/3}+8=0$$

Let $y=x^{1/3}$. Then $y^2=x^{2/3}$ and

$$y^2-6y+8=0$$
$$(y-4)(y-2)=0$$
$$y-4=0 \quad \text{ or } y-2=0$$
$$y=4 \quad \text{ or } \quad y=2$$
$$x^{1/3}=4 \quad \text{ or } x^{1/3}=2$$
$$x=64 \text{ or } \quad x=8$$

The solutions are 8 and 64.

37.
$$a^6-a^2=a^4-1$$
$$a^6-a^4-a^2+1=0$$
$$a^4(a^2-1)-1(a^2-1)=0$$
$$(a^2-1)(a^4-1)=0$$
$$(a+1)(a-1)(a^2+1)(a^2-1)=0$$
$$(a+1)(a-1)(a^2+1)(a+1)(a-1)=0$$
$$(a+1)^2(a-1)^2(a^2+1)=0$$
$$(a+1)^2=0 \text{ or } (a-1)^2=0 \text{ or } a^2+1=0$$
$$a+1=0 \quad \text{ or } \quad a-1=0 \text{ or } \quad a^2=-1$$
$$a=-1 \text{ or } \quad \quad a=1 \text{ or } \quad a=\pm i$$

The solutions are -1, 1, $-i$, and i.

38.
$$y^{-2} + y^{-1} = 20$$
$$\frac{1}{y^2} + \frac{1}{y} = 20$$
$$y^2\left(\frac{1}{y^2} + \frac{1}{y}\right) = y^2(20)$$
$$1 + y = 20y^2$$
$$0 = 20y^2 - y - 1$$
$$0 = (5y + 1)(4y - 1)$$
$$5y + 1 = 0 \quad \text{or} \quad 4y - 1 = 0$$
$$y = -\frac{1}{5} \quad \text{or} \qquad y = \frac{1}{4}$$

The solutions are $-\frac{1}{5}$ and $\frac{1}{4}$.

39. Let x = time for Jerome alone.
Then $x - 1$ = time for Tim alone.
$$\frac{1}{x} + \frac{1}{x-1} = \frac{1}{5}$$
$$5x(x-1)\left(\frac{1}{x} + \frac{1}{x-1}\right) = 5x(x-1)\left(\frac{1}{5}\right)$$
$$5(x-1) + 5x = x(x-1)$$
$$5x - 5 + 5x = x^2 - x$$
$$0 = x^2 - 11x + 5$$
$$a = 1, b = -11, c = 5$$
$$x = \frac{11 \pm \sqrt{(-11)^2 - 4(1)(5)}}{2(1)}$$
$$= \frac{11 \pm \sqrt{101}}{2}$$
$$x \approx 0.475 \text{ or } 10.525$$

Disregard $x = 0.475$ since Jerome's time alone cannot be less than the combined time.
Jerome can sort the mail alone in 10.5 hours and Tim can sort the mail alone in 9.5 hours.

40. Let x = the number.
Then $\frac{1}{x}$ = the reciprocal of the number.
$$x - \frac{1}{x} = -\frac{24}{5}$$
$$5x\left(x - \frac{1}{x}\right) = 5x\left(-\frac{24}{5}\right)$$
$$5x^2 - 5 = -24x$$
$$5x^2 + 24x - 5 = 0$$
$$(5x - 1)(x + 5) = 0$$
$$5x - 1 = 0 \text{ or } x + 5 = 0$$
$$x = \frac{1}{5} \text{ or } \qquad x = -5$$

Disregard the positive value since the number is supposed to be negative. The number is –5.

41.
$$2x^2 - 50 \le 0$$
$$2(x^2 - 25) \le 0$$
$$2(x+5)(x-5) \le 0$$
$$x + 5 = 0 \quad \text{or } x - 5 = 0$$
$$x = -5 \text{ or} \qquad x = 5$$

Region	Test Point	$2(x+5)(x-5) \le 0$ Result
A: $(-\infty, -5)$	-6	$2(-1)(-11) \le 0$ False
B: $(-5, 5)$	0	$2(5)(-5) \le 0$ True
C: $(5, \infty)$	6	$2(11)1 \le 0$ False

Solution: $[-5, 5]$

42.
$$\frac{1}{4}x^2 < \frac{1}{16}$$
$$x^2 < \frac{1}{4}$$
$$x^2 - \frac{1}{4} < 0$$
$$\left(x + \frac{1}{2}\right)\left(x - \frac{1}{2}\right) < 0$$
$$x + \frac{1}{2} = 0 \quad \text{or } x - \frac{1}{2} = 0$$
$$x = -\frac{1}{2} \text{ or} \qquad x = \frac{1}{2}$$

Region	Test Point	$\left(x+\frac{1}{2}\right)\left(x-\frac{1}{2}\right)<0$ Result
A: $\left(-\infty,-\frac{1}{2}\right)$	-1	$\left(-\frac{1}{2}\right)\left(-\frac{3}{2}\right)<0$ False
B: $\left(-\frac{1}{2},\frac{1}{2}\right)$	0	$\left(\frac{1}{2}\right)\left(-\frac{1}{2}\right)<0$ True
C: $\left(\frac{1}{2},\infty\right)$	1	$\left(\frac{3}{2}\right)\left(\frac{1}{2}\right)<0$ False

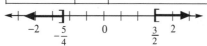

Solution: $\left(-\frac{1}{2},\frac{1}{2}\right)$

43. $(2x-3)(4x+5)\geq 0$

$2x-3=0$ or $4x+5=0$

$x=\frac{3}{2}$ or $\qquad x=-\frac{5}{4}$

Region	Test Point	$(2x-3)(4x+5)\geq 0$ Result
A: $\left(-\infty,-\frac{5}{4}\right)$	-2	$(-7)(-3)\geq 0$ True
B: $\left(-\frac{5}{4},\frac{3}{2}\right)$	0	$(-3)(5)\geq 0$ False
C: $\left(\frac{3}{2},\infty\right)$	2	$(1)(13)\geq 0$ True

Solution: $\left(-\infty,-\frac{5}{4}\right]\cup\left[\frac{3}{2},\infty\right)$

44. $\qquad (x^2-16)(x^2-1)>0$

$(x+4)(x-4)(x+1)(x-1)>0$

$x+4=0$ or $x-4=0$ or $x+1=0$ or $x-1=0$

$x=-4$ or $\quad x=4$ or $\quad x=-1$ or $\quad x=1$

Region	Test Point	$(x+4)(x-4)(x+1)(x-1)>0$ Result
A: $(-\infty,-4)$	-5	$(-1)(-9)(-4)(-6)>0$ True
B: $(-4,-1)$	-2	$(2)(-6)(-1)(-3)>0$ False
C: $(-1,1)$	0	$(4)(-4)(1)(-1)>0$ True
D: $(1,4)$	2	$(6)(-2)(3)(1)>0$ False
E: $(4,\infty)$	5	$(9)(1)(6)(4)>0$ True

Solution: $(-\infty,-4)\cup(-1,1)\cup(4,\infty)$

45. $\dfrac{x-5}{x-6}<0$

$x-5=0$ or $x-6=0$

$x=5$ or $\quad x=6$

Region	Test Point	$\dfrac{x-5}{x-6}<0$; Result
A: $(-\infty,5)$	0	$\dfrac{-5}{-6}<0$; False
B: $(5,6)$	$\dfrac{11}{2}$	$\dfrac{1/2}{-1/2}=-1<0$; True
C: $(6,\infty)$	7	$\dfrac{2}{1}<0$; False

Solution: $(5, 6)$

46. $\dfrac{x(x+5)}{4x-3} \geq 0$

$x = 0$ or $x+5 = 0$ or $4x-3 = 0$

$\qquad\qquad x = -5$ or $\qquad x = \dfrac{3}{4}$

Region	Test Point	$\dfrac{x(x+5)}{4x-3} \geq 0$; Result
A: $(-\infty, -5]$	-6	$\dfrac{-6(-1)}{-27} \geq 0$; False
B: $(-5, 0)$	-1	$\dfrac{-1(4)}{-7} \geq 0$; True
C: $\left(0, \dfrac{3}{4}\right)$	$\dfrac{1}{2}$	$\dfrac{\frac{1}{2}\left(\frac{11}{2}\right)}{-1} \geq 0$; False
D: $\left(\dfrac{3}{4}, \infty\right)$	1	$\dfrac{1(6)}{1} \geq 0$; True

Solution: $[-5, 0] \cup \left(\dfrac{3}{4}, \infty\right)$

47. $\dfrac{(4x+3)(x-5)}{x(x+6)} > 0$

$4x+3 = 0,\ x-5 = 0,\ x = 0,$ or $x+6 = 0$

$x = -\dfrac{3}{4},\ x = 5,\ x = 0,$ or $x = -6$

Region	Test Point	$\dfrac{(4x+3)(x-5)}{x(x+6)} > 0$; Result
A: $(-\infty, -6)$	-7	$\dfrac{(-25)(-12)}{-7(-1)} > 0$; True
B: $\left(-6, -\dfrac{3}{4}\right)$	-1	$\dfrac{(-1)(-6)}{-1(5)} > 0$; False
C: $\left(-\dfrac{3}{4}, 0\right)$	$-\dfrac{1}{2}$	$\dfrac{(1)\left(-\frac{11}{2}\right)}{-\frac{1}{2}\left(\frac{11}{2}\right)} > 0$; True
D: $(0, 5)$	1	$\dfrac{(7)(-4)}{1(7)} > 0$; False
E: $(5, \infty)$	6	$\dfrac{(27)(1)}{6(12)} > 0$; True

Solution: $(-\infty, -6) \cup \left(-\dfrac{3}{4}, 0\right) \cup (5, \infty)$

48. $(x+5)(x-6)(x+2) \leq 0$

$x+5 = 0$ or $x-6 = 0$ or $x+2 = 0$

$\quad x = -5$ or $\quad x = 6$ or $\quad x = -2$

Region	Test Point	$(x+5)(x-6)(x+2) \leq 0$ Result
A: $(-\infty, -5)$	-6	$(-1)(-12)(-4) \leq 0$ True
B: $(-5, -2)$	-3	$(2)(-9)(-1) \leq 0$ False
C: $(-2, 6)$	0	$(5)(-6)(2) \leq 0$ True
D: $(6, \infty)$	7	$(12)(1)(9) \leq 0$ False

Solution: $(-\infty, -5] \cup [-2, 6]$

49. $x^3 + 3x^2 - 25x - 75 > 0$

$x^2(x+3) - 25(x+3) > 0$

$(x+3)(x^2 - 25) > 0$

$(x+3)(x+5)(x-5) > 0$

$x+3 = 0$ or $x+5 = 0$ or $x-5 = 0$

$\quad x = -3$ or $\quad x = -5$ or $\quad x = 5$

Region	Test Point	$(x+3)(x+5)(x-5) > 0$ Result
A: $(-\infty, -5)$	-6	$(-3)(-1)(-11) > 0$ False
B: $(-5, -3)$	-4	$(-1)(1)(-9) > 0$ True
C: $(-3, 5)$	0	$(3)(5)(-5) > 0$ False
D: $(5, \infty)$	6	$(9)(11)(1) > 0$ True

Solution: $(-5, -3) \cup (5, \infty)$

50. $\dfrac{x^2+4}{3x} \le 1$

The denominator equals 0 when
$3x = 0$, or $x = 0$.

$$\dfrac{x^2+4}{3x} = 1$$
$$x^2+4 = 3x$$
$$x^2-3x+4 = 0$$
$$x = \dfrac{3 \pm \sqrt{(-3)^2 - 4(1)(4)}}{2(1)} = \dfrac{3 \pm \sqrt{-7}}{2(1)}$$

which yields non-real solutions.

Region	Test Point	$\dfrac{x^2+4}{3x} \le 1$; Result
A: $(-\infty, 0)$	-1	$\dfrac{5}{-3} \le 1$; True
B: $(0, \infty)$	1	$\dfrac{5}{3} \le 1$; False

Solution: $(-\infty, 0)$

51. $\dfrac{(5x+6)(x-3)}{x(6x-5)} < 0$

$x = -\dfrac{6}{5}$ or $x = 3$ or $x = 0$ or $x = \dfrac{5}{6}$

Region	Test Point	$\dfrac{(5x+6)(x-3)}{x(6x-5)} < 0$ Result
A: $\left(-\infty, -\dfrac{6}{5}\right)$	-2	$\dfrac{(-4)(-5)}{-2(-17)} < 0$; False
B: $\left(-\dfrac{6}{5}, 0\right)$	-1	$\dfrac{(1)(-4)}{-1(-11)} < 0$; True
C: $\left(0, \dfrac{5}{6}\right)$	$\dfrac{1}{2}$	$\dfrac{\left(\dfrac{17}{2}\right)\left(-\dfrac{5}{2}\right)}{\dfrac{1}{2}(-2)} < 0$; False
D: $\left(\dfrac{5}{6}, 3\right)$	2	$\dfrac{(16)(-1)}{2(7)} < 0$; True
E: $(3, \infty)$	4	$\dfrac{(26)(1)}{4(19)} < 0$; False

Solution: $\left(-\dfrac{6}{5}, 0\right) \cup \left(\dfrac{5}{6}, 3\right)$

52. $\dfrac{3}{x-2} > 2$

The denominator is equal to 0 when
$x-2 = 0$, or $x = 2$.

$$\dfrac{3}{x-2} = 2$$
$$3 = 2(x-2)$$
$$3 = 2x-4$$
$$7 = 2x$$
$$\dfrac{7}{2} = x$$

Region	Test Point	$\dfrac{3}{x-2} > 2$; Result
A: $(-\infty, 2)$	0	$\dfrac{3}{-2} > 2$; False
B: $\left(2, \dfrac{7}{2}\right)$	3	$\dfrac{3}{1} > 2$; True
C: $\left(\dfrac{7}{2}, \infty\right)$	5	$\dfrac{3}{3} > 2$; False

Solution: $\left(2, \dfrac{7}{2}\right)$

53. $f(x) = x^2 - 4$

$$x = -\dfrac{b}{2a} = \dfrac{-0}{2(1)} = 0$$
$$f(0) = (0)^2 - 4 = -4$$

Vertex: $(0, -4)$
Axis of symmetry: $x = 0$

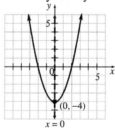

386

54. $g(x) = x^2 + 7$

$x = -\dfrac{b}{2a} = \dfrac{-0}{2(1)} = 0$

$f(0) = (0)^2 + 7 = 7$

Vertex: $(0, 7)$

Axis of symmetry: $x = 0$

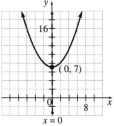

55. $H(x) = 2x^2$

$x = -\dfrac{b}{2a} = \dfrac{-0}{2(2)} = 0$

$f(0) = 2(0)^2 = 0$

Vertex: $(0, 0)$

Axis of symmetry: $x = 0$

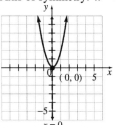

56. $h(x) = -\dfrac{1}{3}x^2$

$x = -\dfrac{b}{2a} = \dfrac{-0}{2\left(-\frac{1}{3}\right)} = 0$

$f(0) = -\dfrac{1}{3}(0)^2 = 0$

Vertex: $(0, 0)$

Axis of symmetry: $x = 0$

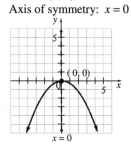

57. $F(x) = (x-1)^2$

Vertex: $(1, 0)$

Axis of symmetry: $x = 1$

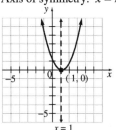

58. $G(x) = (x+5)^2$

Vertex: $(-5, 0)$

Axis of symmetry: $x = -5$

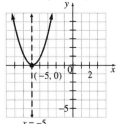

59. $f(x) = (x-4)^2 - 2$

Vertex: $(4, -2)$

Axis of symmetry: $x = 4$

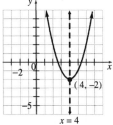

60. $f(x) = -3(x-1)^2 + 1$

Vertex: $(1, 1)$

Axis of symmetry: $x = 1$

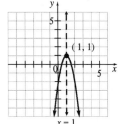

61. $f(x) = x^2 + 10x + 25$

$x = -\dfrac{b}{2a} = \dfrac{-10}{2(1)} = -5$

$f(-5) = (-5)^2 + 10(-5) + 25 = 0$

Vertex: $(-5, 0)$

$x^2 + 10x + 25 = 0$

$(x + 5)^2 = 0$

$x + 5 = 0$

$x = -5$

x-intercept: $(-5, 0)$

$f(0) = 25$ so the y-intercept is $(0, 25)$.

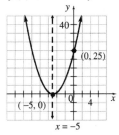

62. $f(x) = -x^2 + 6x - 9$

$x = -\dfrac{b}{2a} = \dfrac{-6}{2(-1)} = 3$

$f(3) = -(3)^2 + 6(3) - 9 = 0$

Vertex: $(3, 0)$

The vertex is on the x-axis, so the x-intercept must be $(3, 0)$.

$f(0) = -9$

y-intercept: $(0, -9)$.

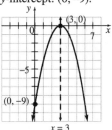

63. $f(x) = 4x^2 - 1$

$x = -\dfrac{b}{2a} = \dfrac{-0}{2(4)} = 0$

$f(0) = 4(0)^2 - 1 = -1$

Vertex: $(0, -1)$

$4x^2 - 1 = 0$

$(2x + 1)(2x - 1) = 0$

$x = -\dfrac{1}{2}$ or $x = \dfrac{1}{2}$

x-intercepts: $\left(-\dfrac{1}{2}, 0\right), \left(\dfrac{1}{2}, 0\right)$

$f(0) = -1$

y-intercept: $(0, -1)$.

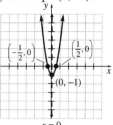

64. $f(x) = -5x^2 + 5$

$x = -\dfrac{b}{2a} = \dfrac{-0}{2(-5)} = 0$

$f(0) = -5(0)^2 + 5 = 5$

Vertex: $(0, 5)$

$-5x^2 + 5 = 0$

$-5x^2 = -5$

$x^2 = 1$

$x = \pm 1$

x-intercepts: $(-1, 0), (1, 0)$

$f(0) = 5$

y-intercept: $(0, 5)$.

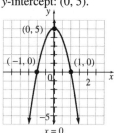

65. $f(x) = -3x^2 - 5x + 4$

$x = -\dfrac{b}{2a} = \dfrac{-(-5)}{2(-3)} = -\dfrac{5}{6}$

$f\left(-\dfrac{5}{6}\right) = -3\left(-\dfrac{5}{6}\right)^2 - 5\left(-\dfrac{5}{6}\right) + 4 = \dfrac{73}{12}$

Vertex: $\left(-\dfrac{5}{6}, \dfrac{73}{12}\right)$

The graph opens downward $(a = -3 < 0)$.

$f(0) = 4 \Rightarrow$ y-intercept: $(0, 4)$

$-3x^2 - 5x + 4 = 0$

$x = \dfrac{5 \pm \sqrt{(-5)^2 - 4(-3)(4)}}{2(-3)}$

$= \dfrac{5 \pm \sqrt{73}}{-6} \approx -2.2573$ or 0.5907

x-intercepts: $(-2.3, 0), (0.6, 0)$

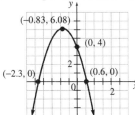

66. $h(t) = -16t^2 + 120t + 300$

a. $350 = -16t^2 + 120t + 300$

$16t^2 - 120t + 50 = 0$

$8t^2 - 60t + 25 = 0$

$a = 8, b = -60, c = 25$

$t = \dfrac{60 \pm \sqrt{(-60)^2 - 4(8)(25)}}{2(8)}$

$= \dfrac{60 \pm \sqrt{2800}}{16}$

$t \approx 0.4$ seconds or 7.1 seconds

The object will be 350 feet above the ground after roughly 0.4 seconds and 7.1 seconds.

b. The object will be at 350 feet on the way up and on the way down.

67. Let $x =$ one number; then

$420 - x =$ the other number.

Let $f(x)$ represent their product.

$f(x) = x(420 - x)$

$= 420x - x^2$

$= -x^2 + 420x$

$x = -\dfrac{b}{2a} = \dfrac{-420}{2(-1)} = 210;$

$420 - x = 420 - 210 = 210$

Therefore, the numbers are both 210.

68. $y = a(x - h)^2 + k$

vertex $(-3, 7)$ gives $y = a(x + 3)^2 + 7$

Passing through the origin gives

$0 = a(0 + 3)^2 + 7$

$-7 = 9a$

$-\dfrac{7}{9} = a$

Thus, $y = -\dfrac{7}{9}(x + 3)^2 + 7$.

69. Start by graphing the data.

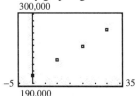

Based on the graph, it appears that a linear model would best fit the data.

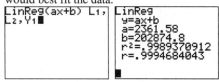

The linear model of best fit is

$y = 2361.58x + 202,874.8$

To predict the population in 2005, we evaluate the model for $x = 35$.

$y = 2361.58(35) + 202,874.8$

$= 82,655.3 + 202,874.8$

$= 285,530.1$

The linear model predicts that the population of the United States in 2005 will be 285,530.1 thousand (i.e. 285,530,100).

70. Start by finding the quadratic model of best fit.

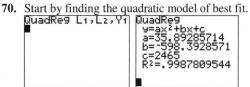

The quadratic model of best fit is

$$y = 35.893x^2 - 598.393x + 2465$$

To predict the amount of sales for 2006, we evaluate the model for $x = 16$.

$$y = 35.893(16)^2 - 598.393(16) + 2465$$
$$= 9188.608 - 9574.288 + 2465$$
$$= 2079.32$$

The quadratic model predicts that the amount of sales of online music in 2006 will be about $2079.3 million.

Chapter 8 Test

1.
$$5x^2 - 2x = 7$$
$$5x^2 - 2x - 7 = 0$$
$$(5x - 7)(x + 1) = 0$$
$$5x - 7 = 0 \quad \text{or} \quad x + 1 = 0$$
$$x = \frac{7}{5} \quad \text{or} \quad x = -1$$

The solutions are -1 and $\frac{7}{5}$.

2. $(x+1)^2 = 10$
$$x + 1 = \pm\sqrt{10}$$
$$x = -1 \pm \sqrt{10}$$

The solutions are $-1 + \sqrt{10}$ and $-1 - \sqrt{10}$.

3. $m^2 - m + 8 = 0$
$$a = 1, b = -1, c = 8$$
$$m = \frac{1 \pm \sqrt{(-1)^2 - 4(1)(8)}}{2(1)}$$
$$= \frac{1 \pm \sqrt{1 - 32}}{2}$$
$$= \frac{1 \pm \sqrt{-31}}{2}$$
$$= \frac{1 \pm i\sqrt{31}}{2}$$

The solutions are $\frac{1 + i\sqrt{31}}{2}$ and $\frac{1 - i\sqrt{31}}{2}$.

4.
$$y^2 - 3y = 5$$
$$y^2 - 3y - 5 = 0$$
$$a = 1, b = -3, c = -5$$
$$y = \frac{3 \pm \sqrt{(-3)^2 - 4(1)(-5)}}{2(1)}$$
$$= \frac{3 \pm \sqrt{9 + 20}}{2}$$
$$= \frac{3 \pm \sqrt{29}}{2}$$

The solutions are $\frac{3 + \sqrt{29}}{2}$ and $\frac{3 - \sqrt{29}}{2}$.

5.
$$\frac{4}{x+2} + \frac{2x}{x-2} = \frac{6}{x^2 - 4}$$
$$\frac{4}{x+2} + \frac{2x}{x-2} = \frac{6}{(x+2)(x-2)}$$
$$4(x-2) + 2x(x+2) = 6$$
$$4x - 8 + 2x^2 + 4x = 6$$
$$2x^2 + 8x - 14 = 0$$
$$x^2 + 4x - 7 = 0$$
$$a = 1, b = 4, c = -7$$
$$x = \frac{-4 \pm \sqrt{(4)^2 - 4(1)(-7)}}{2(1)}$$
$$= \frac{-4 \pm \sqrt{16 + 28}}{2}$$
$$= \frac{-4 \pm \sqrt{44}}{2}$$
$$= \frac{-4 \pm 2\sqrt{11}}{2}$$
$$= -2 \pm \sqrt{11}$$

The solutions are $-2 + \sqrt{11}$ and $-2 - \sqrt{11}$.

6.
$$x^5 + 3x^4 = x + 3$$
$$x^5 + 3x^4 - x - 3 = 0$$
$$x^4(x+3) - 1(x+3) = 0$$
$$(x+3)(x^4 - 1) = 0$$
$$(x+3)(x^2 + 1)(x^2 - 1) = 0$$
$$x + 3 = 0 \quad \text{or} \quad x^2 + 1 = 0 \quad \text{or} \quad x^2 - 1 = 0$$
$$x = -3 \quad \text{or} \quad x^2 = -1 \quad \text{or} \quad x^2 = 1$$
$$x = \pm i \quad \text{or} \quad x = \pm 1$$

The solutions are $-3, -1, 1, -i,$ and i.

7. $(x+1)^2 - 15(x+1) + 56 = 0$

Let $y = x+1$. Then $y^2 = (x+1)^2$ and

$y^2 - 15y + 56 = 0$
$(y-8)(y-7) = 0$
$\quad y = 8 \quad$ or $\quad y = 7$
$x+1 = 8$ or $x+1 = 7$
$\quad x = 7$ or $\quad x = 6$

The solutions are 6 and 7.

8. $\qquad x^2 - 6x = -2$

$x^2 - 6x + \left(\dfrac{-6}{2}\right)^2 = -2 + 9$

$\qquad x^2 - 6x + 9 = 7$

$\qquad\qquad (x-3)^2 = 7$

$\qquad\qquad x - 3 = \pm\sqrt{7}$

$\qquad\qquad\quad x = 3 \pm \sqrt{7}$

The solutions are $3 + \sqrt{7}$ and $3 - \sqrt{7}$.

9. $\qquad\qquad 2a^2 + 5 = 4a$

$\qquad\qquad 2a^2 - 4a = -5$

$\qquad\qquad a^2 - 2a = -\dfrac{5}{2}$

$a^2 - 2a + \left(\dfrac{-2}{2}\right)^2 = -\dfrac{5}{2} + 1$

$\qquad a^2 - 2a + 1 = -\dfrac{3}{2}$

$\qquad\qquad (a-1)^2 = -\dfrac{3}{2}$

$\qquad\qquad a - 1 = \pm\sqrt{-\dfrac{3}{2}}$

$\qquad\qquad a - 1 = \pm\dfrac{\sqrt{3}}{\sqrt{2}}i$

$\qquad\qquad a - 1 = \pm\dfrac{\sqrt{6}}{2}i$

$\qquad\qquad\quad a = 1 \pm \dfrac{\sqrt{6}}{2}i$

$\qquad\qquad\qquad = \dfrac{2 \pm i\sqrt{6}}{2}$

The solutions are $\dfrac{2 + i\sqrt{6}}{2}$ and $\dfrac{2 - i\sqrt{6}}{2}$.

10. $2x^2 - 7x > 15$
$2x^2 - 7x - 15 > 0$
$(2x+3)(x-5) > 0$
$2x + 3 = 0 \quad$ or $\quad x - 5 = 0$
$\qquad x = -\dfrac{3}{2} \quad$ or $\qquad x = 5$

Region	Test Point	$(2x+1)(x-5) > 0$ Result
A: $\left(-\infty, -\dfrac{3}{2}\right)$	-2	$(-3)(-7) > 0$ True
B: $\left(-\dfrac{3}{2}, 5\right)$	0	$(1)(-5) > 0$ False
C: $(5, \infty)$	6	$(13)(1) > 0$ True

Solution: $\left(-\infty, -\dfrac{3}{2}\right) \cup (5, \infty)$

11. $\qquad\qquad (x^2 - 16)(x^2 - 25) \ge 0$
$(x+4)(x-4)(x+5)(x-5) \ge 0$
$x + 4 = 0 \;$ or $\; x - 4 = 0 \;$ or $\; x + 5 = 0 \;$ or $\; x - 5 = 0$
$\quad x = -4$ or $\quad x = 4$ or $\quad x = -5$ or $\quad x = 5$

Region	Test Point	$(x+4)(x-4)(x+5)(x-5) \ge 0$ Result
A: $(-\infty, -5)$	-6	$(-2)(-10)(-1)(-11) \ge 0$ True
B: $(-5, -4)$	$-\dfrac{9}{2}$	$\left(-\dfrac{1}{2}\right)\left(-\dfrac{17}{2}\right)\left(\dfrac{1}{2}\right)\left(-\dfrac{19}{2}\right) \ge 0$ False
C: $(-4, 4)$	0	$(4)(-4)(5)(-5) \ge 0$ True
D: $(4, 5)$	$\dfrac{9}{2}$	$\left(\dfrac{17}{2}\right)\left(\dfrac{1}{2}\right)\left(\dfrac{19}{2}\right)\left(-\dfrac{1}{2}\right) \ge 0$ False
E: $(5, \infty)$	6	$(10)(2)(11)(1) \ge 0$ True

Solution: $(-\infty, -5] \cup [-4, 4] \cup [5, \infty)$

12. $\dfrac{5}{x+3} < 1$

The denominator is equal to 0 when
$x + 3 = 0$, or $x = -3$.

$\dfrac{5}{x+3} = 1$

$5 = x + 3$ so $x = 2$

Region	Test Point	$\dfrac{5}{x+3} < 1$; Result
A: $(-\infty, -3)$	-4	$\dfrac{5}{-1} < 1$; True
B: $(-3, 2)$	0	$\dfrac{5}{3} < 1$; False
C: $(2, \infty)$	3	$\dfrac{5}{6} < 1$; True

Solution: $(-\infty, -3) \cup (2, \infty)$

13. $\dfrac{7x - 14}{x^2 - 9} \le 0$

$\dfrac{7(x - 2)}{(x+3)(x-3)} \le 0$

$x - 2 = 0$ or $x + 3 = 0$ or $x - 3 = 0$
$x = 2$ or $x = -3$ or $x = 3$

Region	Test Point	$\dfrac{7(x-2)}{(x+3)(x-3)} \le 0$; Result
A: $(-\infty, -3)$	-4	$\dfrac{7(-6)}{(-1)(-7)} \le 0$; True
B: $(-3, 2)$	0	$\dfrac{7(-2)}{(3)(-3)} \le 0$; False
C: $(2, 3)$	$\dfrac{5}{2}$	$\dfrac{7\left(\frac{1}{2}\right)}{\left(\frac{11}{2}\right)\left(-\frac{1}{2}\right)} \le 0$; True
D: $(3, \infty)$	4	$\dfrac{7(2)}{(7)(1)} \le 0$; False

Solution: $(-\infty, -3) \cup [2, 3)$

14. $f(x) = 3x^2$

Vertex: $(0, 0)$

15. $G(x) = -2(x-1)^2 + 5$

Vertex: $(1, 5)$

16. $h(x) = x^2 - 4x + 4$

$x = -\dfrac{b}{2a} = \dfrac{-(-4)}{2(1)} = 2$

$h(2) = (2)^2 - 4(2) + 4 = 0$

Vertex: $(2, 0)$

$h(0) = 4 \Rightarrow$ *y*-intercept: $(0, 4)$

x-intercept: $(2, 0)$

17. $F(x) = 2x^2 - 8x + 9$

$x = -\dfrac{b}{2a} = \dfrac{-(-8)}{2(2)} = 2$

$F(2) = 2(2)^2 - 8(2) + 9 = 1$

Vertex: (2, 1)

$F(0) = 9 \Rightarrow$ *y*-intercept: (0, 9)

$2x^2 - 8x + 9 = 0$

$a = 2, b = -8, c = 9$

$x = \dfrac{8 \pm \sqrt{(-8)^2 - 4(2)(9)}}{2(2)}$

$= \dfrac{8 \pm \sqrt{-8}}{4}$

which yields non-real solutons.

Therefore, there are no *x*-intercepts.

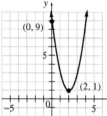

18. Let t = time for Sandy alone.

Then $t - 2$ = time for Dave alone.

$\dfrac{1}{t} + \dfrac{1}{t-2} = \dfrac{1}{4}$

$4(t-2) + 4t = t(t-2)$

$4t - 8 + 4t = t^2 - 2t$

$0 = t^2 - 10t + 8$

$a = 1, b = -10, c = 8$

$t = \dfrac{10 \pm \sqrt{(-10)^2 - 4(1)(8)}}{2(1)}$

$= \dfrac{10 \pm \sqrt{68}}{2}$

$= \dfrac{10 \pm 2\sqrt{17}}{2}$

$= 5 \pm \sqrt{17}$

≈ 9.12 or 0.88

Discard $t = 0.88$ since $t - 2$ must be positive.

It takes her about 9.12 hours.

19. $s(t) = -16t^2 + 32t + 256$

a. $t = -\dfrac{b}{2a} = \dfrac{-32}{2(-16)} = 1$

$s(1) = -16(1)^2 + 32(1) + 256 = 272$

Vertex: (1, 272)

The maximum height is 272 feet.

b. $-16t^2 + 32t + 256 = 0$

$t^2 - 2t - 16 = 0$

$a = 1, b = -2, c = -16$

$t = \dfrac{2 \pm \sqrt{(-2)^2 - 4(1)(-16)}}{2(1)}$

$= \dfrac{2 \pm \sqrt{68}}{2}$

$= \dfrac{2 \pm 2\sqrt{17}}{2}$

$= 1 \pm \sqrt{17} \approx -3.12$ and 5.12

Disregard the negative. It will hit the water in about 5.12 seconds.

20.
$a^2 + b^2 = c^2$

$x^2 + (x+8)^2 = (20)^2$

$x^2 + (x^2 + 16x + 64) = 400$

$2x^2 + 16x - 336 = 0$

$x^2 + 8x - 168 = 0$

$a = 1, b = 8, c = -168$

$x = \dfrac{-8 \pm \sqrt{(8)^2 - 4(1)(-168)}}{2(1)}$

$= \dfrac{-8 \pm \sqrt{736}}{2}$

≈ -17.565 or 9.565

Disregard the negative.

$x \approx 9.6$

$x + 8 \approx 9.6 + 8 = 17.6$

$17.6 + 9.6 = 27.2$

$27.2 - 20 = 7.2$

They would save about 7 feet.

21. a. Since it appears that there is some curvature in the graph, a quadratic model seems to fit better than a linear model.

b. Let x = the number of years after 1990.

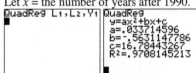

The quadratic model of best fit is

$y = 0.034x^2 - 0.563x + 16.784$

To predict the birth rate for 2009, we evaluate the model for $x = 19$.

$$y = 0.034(19)^2 - 0.563(19) + 16.784$$
$$= 12.274 - 10.697 + 16.784$$
$$= 18.361$$

The quadratic model predicts that the birth rate for 2009 will be about 18.36 per 1000 population. (**note:** if you use the regression equation without rounding the coefficients to three decimal places, the result will be 18.26 per 1000 population).

Chapter 8 Cumulative Review

1. a. $5 + y \geq 7$

b. $11 \neq z$

c. $20 < 5 - 2x$

2. $|3x - 2| = -5$ which is impossible.

Thus, there is no solution, or $\varnothing$.

3. $m = \dfrac{5 - 3}{2 - 0} = \dfrac{2}{2} = 1$

The y-intercept is $(0, 3)$ so $b = 3$.

$y = 1 \cdot x + 3$

$y = x + 3$

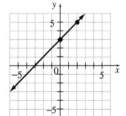

4. $\begin{cases} -6x + y = 5 \\ 4x - 2y = 6 \end{cases}$

Multiply the first equation by 2 and add to the second equation.

$$-12x + 2y = 10$$
$$\underline{4x - 2y = 6}$$
$$-8x = 16$$
$$x = -2$$

Replace x with –2 in the first equation.

$$-6(-2) + y = 5$$
$$12 + y = 5$$
$$y = -7$$

The solution is (–2, –7).

5. $\begin{cases} x - 5y = -12 \\ -x + y = 4 \end{cases}$

Add the two equations.

$$-4y = -8$$
$$y = 2$$

Replace y with 2 in the first equation.

$$x - 5(2) = -12$$
$$x - 10 = -12$$
$$x = -2$$

The solution is (–2, 2).

6. a. $(a^{-2}bc^3)^{-3} = (a^{-2})^{-3}b^{-3}(c^3)^{-3}$
$$= a^6 b^{-3} c^{-9}$$
$$= \dfrac{a^6}{b^3 c^9}$$

b. $\left(\dfrac{a^{-4}b^2}{c^3} \right)^{-2} = \dfrac{(a^{-4})^{-2}(b^2)^{-2}}{(c^3)^{-2}}$
$$= \dfrac{a^8 b^{-4}}{c^{-6}}$$
$$= \dfrac{a^8 c^6}{b^4}$$

c. $\left(\dfrac{3a^8 b^2}{12a^5 b^5} \right)^{-2} = \left(\dfrac{a^3}{4b^3} \right)^{-2}$
$$= \dfrac{(a^3)^{-2}}{4^{-2}(b^3)^{-2}}$$
$$= \dfrac{4^2 a^{-6}}{b^{-6}}$$
$$= \dfrac{16b^6}{a^6}$$

7. a. $(2x-7)(3x-4)=6x^2-8x-21x+28$
$$=6x^2-29x+28$$

b. $(3x+y)(5x-2y)=15x^2-6xy+5xy-2y^2$
$$=15x^2-xy-2y^2$$

8. a. $(4a-3)(7a-2)=28a^2-8a-21a+6$
$$=28a^2-29a+6$$

b. $(2a+b)(3a-5b)=6a^2-10ab+3ab-5b^2$
$$=6a^2-7ab-5b^2$$

9. a. $8x^2+4=4(2x^2+1)$

b. $5y-2z^4$ is a prime polynomial.

c. $6x^2-3x^3=3x^2(2-x)$

10. a. $9x^3+27x^2-15x=3x(3x^2+9x-5)$

b. $2x(3y-2)-5(3y-2)=(3y-2)(2x-5)$

c. $2xy+6x-y-3=2x(y+3)-1(y+3)$
$$=(y+3)(2x-1)$$

11. $x^2-12x+35=(x-5)(x-7)$

12. $x^2-2x-48=(x+6)(x-8)$

13. $3a^2x-12ax+12b^2x=3x(a^2-4a+4b^2)$
$$=3x(a-2b)(a-2b)$$
$$=3x(a-2b)^2$$

14. $2ax^2-12axy+18ay^2=2a(x^2-6xy+9y^2)$
$$=2a(x-3y)(x-3y)$$
$$=2a(x-3y)^2$$

15. $3(x^2+4)+5=-6(x^2+2x)+13$
$$3x^2+12+5=-6x^2-12x+13$$
$$9x^2+12x+4=0$$
$$(3x+2)^2=0$$
$$3x+2=0$$
$$3x=-2$$
$$x=-\frac{2}{3}$$
The solution is $-\frac{2}{3}$.

16. $2(a^2+2)-8=-2a(a-2)-5$
$$2a^2+4-8=-2a^2+4a-5$$
$$4a^2-4a+1=0$$
$$(2a-1)^2=0$$
$$2a-1=0$$
$$2a=1$$
$$a=\frac{1}{2}$$
The solution is $\frac{1}{2}$.

17.
$$x^3=4x$$
$$x^3-4x=0$$
$$x(x^2-4)=0$$
$$x(x+2)(x-2)=0$$
$$x=0 \text{ or } x+2=0 \quad \text{ or } x-2=0$$
$$x=-2 \text{ or } \quad x=2$$
The solutions are –2, 0, and 2.

18. $f(x)=x^2+x-12$
$$x=-\frac{b}{2a}=\frac{-1}{2(1)}=-\frac{1}{2}$$
$$f\left(-\frac{1}{2}\right)=\left(-\frac{1}{2}\right)^2+\left(-\frac{1}{2}\right)-12$$
$$=\frac{1}{4}-\frac{1}{2}-12$$
$$=-\frac{49}{4}$$
Vertex: $\left(-\frac{1}{2},-\frac{49}{4}\right)$
y-intercept:
$$f(0)=0^2+0-12=-12$$
The y-intercept is $(0,-12)$.
x-intercepts:
$$f(x)=0$$
$$x^2+x-12=0$$
$$(x+4)(x-3)=0$$
$$x=-4 \text{ or } x=3$$
The x-intercepts are $(-4,0)$ and $(3,0)$.

19. $\dfrac{2x^2}{10x^3 - 2x^2} = \dfrac{2x^2}{2x^2(5x-1)} = \dfrac{1}{5x-1}$

20. $\dfrac{x^2 - 4x + 4}{2-x} = \dfrac{(x-2)^2}{-(x-2)} = \dfrac{x-2}{-1} = 2-x$

21. $\dfrac{2x-1}{2x^2 - 9x - 5} + \dfrac{x+3}{6x^2 - x - 2}$

$= \dfrac{2x-1}{(2x+1)(x-5)} + \dfrac{x+3}{(2x+1)(3x-2)}$

$= \dfrac{(2x-1)(3x-2) + (x+3)(x-5)}{(2x+1)(x-5)(3x-2)}$

$= \dfrac{(6x^2 - 4x - 3x + 2) + (x^2 - 5x + 3x - 15)}{(2x+1)(x-5)(3x-2)}$

$= \dfrac{7x^2 - 9x - 13}{(2x+1)(x-5)(3x-2)}$

22. $\dfrac{a+1}{a^2 - 6a + 8} - \dfrac{3}{16 - a^2}$

$= \dfrac{a+1}{(a-4)(a-2)} - \dfrac{3}{(4+a)(4-a)}$

$= \dfrac{a+1}{(a-4)(a-2)} + \dfrac{3}{(4+a)(a-4)}$

$= \dfrac{(a+1)(a+4) + 3(a-2)}{(a-4)(a-2)(a+4)}$

$= \dfrac{(a^2 + 4a + a + 4) + 3a - 6}{(a-4)(a-2)(a+4)}$

$= \dfrac{a^2 + 8a - 2}{(a-4)(a-2)(a+4)}$

23. $\dfrac{x^{-1} + 2xy^{-1}}{x^{-2} - x^{-2}y^{-1}} = \dfrac{\dfrac{1}{x} + \dfrac{2x}{y}}{\dfrac{1}{x^2} - \dfrac{1}{x^2 y}}$

$= \dfrac{\left(\dfrac{1}{x} + \dfrac{2x}{y}\right) x^2 y}{\left(\dfrac{1}{x^2} - \dfrac{1}{x^2 y}\right) x^2 y}$

$= \dfrac{xy + 2x^3}{y-1}$

24. $\dfrac{(2a)^{-1} + b^{-1}}{a^{-1} + (2b)^{-1}} = \dfrac{\dfrac{1}{2a} + \dfrac{1}{b}}{\dfrac{1}{a} + \dfrac{1}{2b}}$

$= \dfrac{\left(\dfrac{1}{2a} + \dfrac{1}{b}\right) 2ab}{\left(\dfrac{1}{a} + \dfrac{1}{2b}\right) 2ab}$

$= \dfrac{b + 2a}{2b + a}$

$= \dfrac{2a + b}{a + 2b}$

25. $\dfrac{3x^5 y^2 - 15x^3 y - x^2 y - 6x}{x^2 y}$

$= \dfrac{3x^5 y^2}{x^2 y} - \dfrac{15x^3 y}{x^2 y} - \dfrac{x^2 y}{x^2 y} - \dfrac{6x}{x^2 y}$

$= 3x^3 y - 15x - 1 - \dfrac{6}{xy}$

26.

$$\begin{array}{r} x^2 - 6x + 8 \\ x+3 \overline{\smash{\big)}\ x^3 - 3x^2 - 10x + 24} \\ \underline{x^3 + 3x^2} \\ -6x^2 - 10x \\ \underline{-6x^2 - 18x} \\ 8x + 24 \\ \underline{8x + 24} \\ 0 \end{array}$$

Answer: $x^2 - 6x + 8$

27. $P(x) = 2x^3 - 4x^2 + 5$

a. $P(2) = 2(2)^3 - 4(2)^2 + 5$

$= 2(8) - 4(4) + 5$

$= 16 - 16 + 5$

$= 5$

b.

$$\begin{array}{r|rrrr} 2 & 2 & -4 & 0 & 5 \\ & & 4 & 0 & 0 \\ \hline & 2 & 0 & 0 & 5 \end{array}$$

Thus, $P(2) = 5$.

28. $P(x) = 4x^3 - 2x^2 + 3$

    a. $P(-2) = 4(-2)^3 - 2(-2)^2 + 3$
$$= 4(-8) - 2(4) + 3$$
$$= -32 - 8 + 3$$
$$= -37$$

    b.

-2⌋	4	-2	0	3
		-8	20	-40
	4	-10	20	-37

    Thus, $P(-2) = -37$.

29. $\dfrac{4x}{5} + \dfrac{3}{2} = \dfrac{3x}{10}$
$$10\left(\dfrac{4x}{5} + \dfrac{3}{2}\right) = 10\left(\dfrac{3x}{10}\right)$$
$$2(4x) + 5(3) = 3x$$
$$8x + 15 = 3x$$
$$5x = -15$$
$$x = -3$$
The solution is -3.

30. $\dfrac{x+3}{x^2+5x+6} = \dfrac{3}{2x+4} - \dfrac{1}{x+3}$
$$\dfrac{x+3}{(x+3)(x+2)} = \dfrac{3}{2(x+2)} - \dfrac{1}{x+3}$$
$$2(x+3) = 3(x+3) - 2(x+2)$$
$$2x+6 = 3x+9 - 2x - 4$$
$$2x+6 = x+5$$
$$x = -1$$

31. Let x = the number.
$$\dfrac{9-x}{19+x} = \dfrac{1}{3}$$
$$3(9-x) = 1(19+x)$$
$$27 - 3x = 19 + x$$
$$-4x = -8$$
$$x = 2$$
The number is 2.

32. Let t = time to roof the house together.
$$\dfrac{1}{24} + \dfrac{1}{40} = \dfrac{1}{t}$$
$$120t\left(\dfrac{1}{24} + \dfrac{1}{40}\right) = 120t\left(\dfrac{1}{t}\right)$$
$$5t + 3t = 120$$
$$8t = 120$$
$$t = \dfrac{120}{8} = 15$$
It would take them 15 hours to roof the house working together.

33. $y = kx$
$$5 = k(30)$$
$$k = \dfrac{5}{30} = \dfrac{1}{6} \text{ and } y = \dfrac{1}{6}x$$

34. $y = \dfrac{k}{x}$
$$8 = \dfrac{k}{24}$$
$$k = 8(24) = 192 \text{ and } y = \dfrac{192}{x}$$

35. **a.** $\sqrt{(-3)^2} = |-3| = 3$

    b. $\sqrt{x^2} = |x|$

    c. $\sqrt[4]{(x-2)^4} = |x-2|$

    d. $\sqrt[3]{(-5)^3} = -5$

    e. $\sqrt[5]{(2x-7)^5} = 2x-7$

    f. $\sqrt{25x^2} = \sqrt{25} \cdot \sqrt{x^2} = 5|x|$

    g. $\sqrt{x^2+2x+1} = \sqrt{(x+1)^2} = |x+1|$

36. **a.** $\sqrt{(-2)^2} = |-2| = 2$

    b. $\sqrt{y^2} = |y|$

    c. $\sqrt[4]{(a-3)^4} = |a-3|$

    d. $\sqrt[3]{(-6)^3} = -6$

    e. $\sqrt[5]{(3x-1)^5} = 3x-1$

37. **a.** $\sqrt[8]{x^4} = x^{4/8} = x^{1/2} = \sqrt{x}$

    b. $\sqrt[6]{25} = (25)^{1/6} = (5^2)^{1/6} = 5^{2/6} = 5^{1/3} = \sqrt[3]{5}$

    c. $\sqrt[4]{r^2 s^6} = (r^2 s^6)^{1/4}$
$$= r^{2/4} s^{6/4}$$
$$= r^{1/2} s^{3/2}$$
$$= (rs^3)^{1/2} = \sqrt{rs^3}$$

38. a. $\sqrt[4]{5^2} = 5^{2/4} = 5^{1/2} = \sqrt{5}$

b. $\sqrt[12]{x^3} = x^{3/12} = x^{1/4} = \sqrt[4]{x}$

c. $\sqrt[6]{x^2 y^4} = (x^2 y^4)^{1/6}$
$$= x^{2/6} y^{4/6}$$
$$= x^{1/3} y^{2/3}$$
$$= (xy^2)^{1/3} = \sqrt[3]{xy^2}$$

39. a. $\sqrt{25x^3} = \sqrt{25x^2 \cdot x} = 5x\sqrt{x}$

b. $\sqrt[3]{54x^6 y^8} = \sqrt[3]{27x^6 y^6 \cdot 2y^2}$
$$= 3x^2 y^2 \sqrt[3]{2y^2}$$

c. $\sqrt[4]{81z^{11}} = \sqrt[4]{81z^8 \cdot z^3} = 3z^2 \sqrt[4]{z^3}$

40. a. $\sqrt{64a^5} = \sqrt{64a^4 \cdot a} = 8a^2 \sqrt{a}$

b. $\sqrt[3]{24a^7 b^9} = \sqrt[3]{8a^6 b^9 \cdot 3a}$
$$= 2a^2 b^3 \sqrt[3]{3a}$$

c. $\sqrt[4]{48x^9} = \sqrt[4]{16x^8 \cdot 3x} = 2x^2 \sqrt[4]{3x}$

41. a. $\dfrac{2}{\sqrt{5}} = \dfrac{2 \cdot \sqrt{5}}{\sqrt{5} \cdot \sqrt{5}} = \dfrac{2\sqrt{5}}{5}$

b. $\dfrac{2\sqrt{16}}{\sqrt{9x}} = \dfrac{2 \cdot 4}{3\sqrt{x}} = \dfrac{8 \cdot \sqrt{x}}{3\sqrt{x} \cdot \sqrt{x}} = \dfrac{8\sqrt{x}}{3x}$

c. $\sqrt[3]{\dfrac{1}{2}} = \dfrac{\sqrt[3]{1}}{\sqrt[3]{2}} = \dfrac{1}{\sqrt[3]{2}} = \dfrac{1 \cdot \sqrt[3]{2^2}}{\sqrt[3]{2} \cdot \sqrt[3]{2^2}} = \dfrac{\sqrt[3]{4}}{2}$

42. a. $\left(\sqrt{3} - 4\right)\left(2\sqrt{3} + 2\right)$
$$= \sqrt{3} \cdot 2\sqrt{3} + 2\sqrt{3} - 4 \cdot 2\sqrt{3} - 4 \cdot 2$$
$$= 2(3) + 2\sqrt{3} - 8\sqrt{3} - 8$$
$$= 6 - 6\sqrt{3} - 8$$
$$= -2 - 6\sqrt{3}$$

b. $\left(\sqrt{5} - x\right)^2 = \left(\sqrt{5}\right)^2 - 2 \cdot \sqrt{5} \cdot x + x^2$
$$= 5 - 2x\sqrt{5} + x^2$$

c. $\left(\sqrt{a} + b\right)\left(\sqrt{a} - b\right) = \left(\sqrt{a}\right)^2 - b^2$
$$= a - b^2$$

43. $\sqrt{2x+5} + \sqrt{2x} = 3$
$$\sqrt{2x+5} = 3 - \sqrt{2x}$$
$$\left(\sqrt{2x+5}\right)^2 = \left(3 - \sqrt{2x}\right)^2$$
$$2x + 5 = 9 - 6\sqrt{2x} + 2x$$
$$-4 = -6\sqrt{2x}$$
$$(-4)^2 = \left(-6\sqrt{2x}\right)^2$$
$$16 = 36(2x)$$
$$16 = 72x$$
$$x = \frac{16}{72} = \frac{2}{9}$$

The solution is $\dfrac{2}{9}$.

44. $\sqrt{x-2} = \sqrt{4x+1} - 3$
$$\left(\sqrt{x-2}\right)^2 = \left(\sqrt{4x+1} - 3\right)^2$$
$$x - 2 = (4x+1) - 6\sqrt{4x+1} + 9$$
$$6\sqrt{4x+1} = 3x + 12$$
$$2\sqrt{4x+1} = x + 4$$
$$\left(2\sqrt{4x+1}\right)^2 = (x+4)^2$$
$$4(4x+1) = x^2 + 8x + 16$$
$$16x + 4 = x^2 + 8x + 16$$
$$0 = x^2 - 8x + 12$$
$$0 = (x-6)(x-2)$$
$$x - 6 = 0 \ \text{ or } \ x - 2 = 0$$
$$x = 6 \ \text{ or } \qquad x = 2$$

The solutions are 2 and 6.

45. a. $\dfrac{2+i}{1-i} = \dfrac{(2+i) \cdot (1+i)}{(1-i) \cdot (1+i)}$
$$= \dfrac{2 + 2i + 1i + i^2}{1^2 - i^2}$$
$$= \dfrac{2 + 3i - 1}{1 + 1}$$
$$= \dfrac{1 + 3i}{2} \ \text{ or } \ \dfrac{1}{2} + \dfrac{3}{2}i$$

b. $\dfrac{7}{3i} = \dfrac{7 \cdot (-3i)}{3i \cdot (-3i)} = \dfrac{-21i}{-9i^2} = \dfrac{-21i}{9} = -\dfrac{7}{3}i$

book

SSM: Intermediate Algebra A Graphing Approach, 3e

46. a. $3i(5-2i)=15i-6i^2$
$$=15i+6$$
$$=6+15i$$

b. $(6-5i)^2=6^2-2(6)(5i)+(5i)^2$
$$=36-60i+25i^2$$
$$=36-60i-25$$
$$=11-60i$$

c. $\left(\sqrt{3}+2i\right)\left(\sqrt{3}-2i\right)=\left(\sqrt{3}\right)^2-(2i)^2$
$$=3-4i^2$$
$$=3+4$$
$$=7$$

47. $(x+1)^2=12$
$$x+1=\pm\sqrt{12}$$
$$x+1=\pm2\sqrt{3}$$
$$x=-1\pm2\sqrt{3}$$
The solutions are $-1+2\sqrt{3}$ and $-1-2\sqrt{3}$.

48. $(y-1)^2=24$
$$y-1=\pm\sqrt{24}$$
$$y-1=\pm2\sqrt{6}$$
$$y=1\pm2\sqrt{6}$$
The solutions are $1+2\sqrt{6}$ and $1-2\sqrt{6}$.

49. $x-\sqrt{x}-6=0$
Let $y=\sqrt{x}$. Then $y^2=x$ and
$$y^2-y-6=0$$
$$(y-3)(y+2)=0$$
$$y-3=0 \text{ or } y+2=0$$
$$y=3 \text{ or } y=-2$$
$$\sqrt{x}=3 \text{ or } \sqrt{x}=-2 \text{ (not a real number)}$$
$$x=9$$
The solution is 9.

50. $m^2=4m+8$
$$m^2-4m-8=0$$
$$a=1, b=-4, c=-8$$
$$x=\frac{4\pm\sqrt{(-4)^2-4(1)(-8)}}{2(1)}$$
$$=\frac{4\pm\sqrt{48}}{2}$$
$$=\frac{4\pm4\sqrt{3}}{2}$$
$$=2\pm2\sqrt{3}$$
The solutions are $2+2\sqrt{3}$ and $2-2\sqrt{3}$.

399

Chapter 9

Mental Math 9.1

1. C

2. E

3. F

4. A

5. D

6. B

Exercise Set 9.1

1. **a.** $(f + g)(x) = x - 7 + 2x + 1 = 3x - 6$

   b. $(f - g)(x) = x - 7 - (2x + 1)$
   $= x - 7 - 2x - 1$
   $= -x - 8$

   c. $(f \cdot g)(x) = (x - 7)(2x + 1) = 2x^2 - 13x - 7$

   d. $\left(\dfrac{f}{g}\right)(x) = \dfrac{x - 7}{2x + 1}$, where $x \neq \dfrac{1}{2}$

3. **a.** $(f + g)(x) = x^2 + 5x + 1$

   b. $(f - g)(x) = x^2 - 5x + 1$

   c. $(f \cdot g)(x) = (x^2 + 1)(5x) = 5x^3 + 5x$

   d. $\left(\dfrac{f}{g}\right)(x) = \dfrac{x^2 + 1}{5x}$, where $x \neq 0$

5. **a.** $(f + g)(x) = \sqrt{x} + x + 5$

   b. $(f - g)(x) = \sqrt{x} - x - 5$

   c. $(f \cdot g)(x) = \sqrt{x}(x + 5) = x\sqrt{x} + 5\sqrt{x}$

   d. $\left(\dfrac{f}{g}\right)(x) = \dfrac{\sqrt{x}}{x + 5}$, where $x \neq -5$.

7. **a.** $(f + g)(x) = -3x + 5x^2 = 5x^2 - 3x$

   b. $(f - g)(x) = -3x - 5x^2 = -5x^2 - 3x$

c. $(f \cdot g)(x) = -3x\left(5x^2\right) = -15x^3$

d. $\left(\dfrac{f}{g}\right)(x) = \dfrac{-3x}{5x^2} = -\dfrac{3}{5x}$, where $x \neq 0$.

9. $(f \circ g)(2) = f(g(2))$
   $= f(-4)$
   $= (-4)^2 - 6(-4) + 2$
   $= 16 + 24 + 2$
   $= 42$

11. $(g \circ f)(-1) = g(f(-1)) = g(9) = -2(9) = -18$

13. $(g \circ h)(0) = g(h(0)) = g(0) = -2(0) = 0$

15. $(f \circ g)(x) = f(g(x))$
    $= f(5x)$
    $= (5x)^2 + 1$
    $= 25x^2 + 1$
    $(g \circ f)(x) = g(f(x))$
    $= g(x^2 + 1)$
    $= 5(x^2 + 1)$
    $= 5x^2 + 5$

17. $(f \circ g)(x) = f(g(x))$
    $= f(x + 7)$
    $= 2(x + 7) - 3$
    $= 2x + 14 - 3$
    $= 2x + 11$
    $(g \circ f)(x) = g(f(x))$
    $= g(2x - 3)$
    $= (2x - 3) + 7$
    $= 2x + 4$

19. $(f \circ g)(x) = f(g(x))$
    $= f(-2x)$
    $= (-2x)^3 + (-2x) - 2$
    $= -8x^3 - 2x - 2$
    $(g \circ f)(x) = g(f(x))$
    $= g(x^3 + x - 2)$
    $= -2(x^3 + x - 2)$
    $= -2x^3 - 2x + 4$

21. $(f \circ g)(x) = f(g(x))$
    $= f(-5x + 2)$
    $= \sqrt{-5x + 2} = f(-5x + 2)$
    $= \sqrt{-5x + 2}$

400

$$(g \circ f)(x) = g(f(x))$$
$$= g\left(\sqrt{x}\right)$$
$$= -5\sqrt{x} + 2$$

23. $H(x) = (g \circ h)(x)$
$$= g(h(x))$$
$$= g(x^2 + 2)$$
$$= \sqrt{x^2 + 2}$$

25. $F(x) = (h \circ f)(x)$
$$= h(f(x))$$
$$= h(3x)$$
$$= (3x)^2 + 2$$
$$= 9x^2 + 2$$

27. $G(x) = (f \circ g)(x)$
$$= f(g(x))$$
$$= f\left(\sqrt{x}\right)$$
$$= 3\sqrt{x}$$

29. Answers may vary. One possibility follows: $g(x) = x + 2$ and $f(x) = x^2$.

31. Answers may vary. One possibility follows: $g(x) = x + 5$ and $f(x) = \sqrt{x} + 2$.

33. Answers may vary. One possibility follows: $g(x) = 2x - 3$ and $f(x) = \dfrac{1}{x}$.

35. $x = y + 2$
$x - 2 = y$

37. $x = 3y$
$\dfrac{x}{3} = y$

39. $x = -2y - 7$
$2y + x = -7$
$2y = -x - 7$
$y = \dfrac{-x - 7}{2}$ or $y = -\dfrac{x + 7}{2}$

41. We are given $f(2) = 7$ and $g(2) = -1$, so
$(f + g)(2) = f(2) + g(2) = 7 + (-1) = 6$

43. We are given $g(2) = -1$ and $f(-1) = 4$, so
$(f \circ g)(2) = f(g(2)) = f(-1) = 4$

45. We are given $f(7) = 1$ and $g(7) = 4$, so
$(f \cdot g)(7) = f(7) \cdot g(7) = 1 \cdot 4 = 4$

47. We are given $f(-1) = 4$ and $g(-1) = -4$, so
$$\left(\dfrac{f}{g}\right)(-1) = \dfrac{f(-1)}{g(-1)} = \dfrac{4}{-4} = -1$$

49. Answers may vary. One possibility follows: To find $(f \circ g)(x)$, substitute $g(x)$ for x in the f function and simplify the result. To find $(g \circ f)(x)$, substitute $f(x)$ for x in the g function and simplify the result.

51. $P(x) = R(x) - C(x)$

Exercise Set 9.2

1. $f = \{(-1, -1), (1, 1), (0, 2), (2, 0)\}$ is a one-to-one function since each y-value corresponds to only one x-value. $f^{-1} = \{(-1, -1), (1, 1), (2, 0), (0, 2)\}$.

3. $h = \{(10, 10)\}$ is a one-to-one function since each y-value corresponds to only one x-value. $h^{-1} = \{(10, 10)\}$

5. $f = \{(11, 12), (4, 3), (3, 4), (6, 6)\}$ is a one-to-one function since each y-value corresponds to only one x-value. $f^{-1} = \{(12, 11), (3, 4), (4, 3), (6, 6)\}$

7. This function is not one-to-one because there are two months with the same output: (January, 282) and (May, 282).

9. This function is one-to-one since each output corresponds to only one input. The inverse function is the following table.

Rank in Pop. (Input)	1	49	12	2	46
State(Output)	CA	VT	VA	TX	SD

11. $f(x) = x^3 + 2$

  a. $f(1) = 1^3 + 2 = 3$

  b. $f^{-1}(3) = 1$

13. $f(x) = x^3 + 2$

   a. $f(-1) = (-1)^3 + 2 = 1$

   b. $f^{-1}(1) = -1$

15. The graph represents a one-to-one function because it passes the horizontal line test.

17. The graph does not represent a one-to-one function because it does not pass the horizontal line test.

19. The graph does not represent a one-to-one function because it does not pass the horizontal line test.

21. The graph does not represent a one-to-one function because it does not pass the horizontal line test.

23. $f(x) = x + 4$
$$y = x + 4$$
$$x = y + 4$$
$$y = x - 4$$
$$f^{-1}(x) = x - 4$$

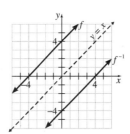

25. $f(x) = 2x - 3$
$$y = 2x - 3$$
$$x = 2y - 3$$
$$2y = x + 3$$
$$y = \frac{x+3}{2}$$
$$f^{-1}(x) = \frac{x+3}{2}$$

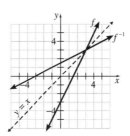

27. $f(x) = \frac{1}{2}x - 1$
$$y = \frac{1}{2}x - 1$$
$$x = \frac{1}{2}y - 1$$
$$\frac{1}{2}y = x + 1$$
$$y = 2x + 2$$
$$f^{-1}(x) = 2x + 2$$

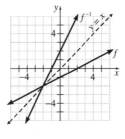

29. $f(x) = x^3$
$$y = x^3$$
$$x = y^3$$
$$y = \sqrt[3]{x}$$
$$f^{-1}(x) = \sqrt[3]{x}$$

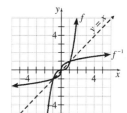

31. $f(x) = 5x + 2$
$$y = 5x + 2$$
$$x = 5y + 2$$
$$5y = x - 2$$
$$y = \frac{x-2}{5}$$
$$f^{-1}(x) = \frac{x-2}{5}$$

33. $f(x) = \frac{x-2}{5}$
$$y = \frac{x-2}{5}$$
$$x = \frac{y-2}{5}$$
$$5x = y - 2$$
$$y = 5x + 2$$
$$f^{-1}(x) = 5x + 2$$

35. $f(x) = \sqrt[3]{x}$
$$y = \sqrt[3]{x}$$
$$x = \sqrt[3]{y}$$
$$x^3 = y$$
$$f^{-1}(x) = x^3$$

37. $f(x) = \frac{5}{3x+1}$
$$y = \frac{5}{3x+1}$$
$$x = \frac{5}{3y+1}$$
$$3y + 1 = \frac{5}{x}$$
$$3y = \frac{5}{x} - 1$$
$$3y = \frac{5-x}{x}$$
$$y = \frac{5-x}{3x}$$
$$f^{-1}(x) = \frac{5-x}{3x}$$

39. $f(x) = (x+2)^3$
$$y = (x+2)^3$$
$$x = (y+2)^3$$
$$\sqrt[3]{x} = y+2$$
$$\sqrt[3]{x} - 2 = y$$
$$f^{-1}(x) = \sqrt[3]{x} - 2$$

41.

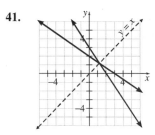

43.

45.

47. $(f \circ f^{-1})(x) = f(f^{-1}(x))$
$$= f\left(\frac{x-1}{2}\right)$$
$$= 2\left(\frac{x-1}{2}\right) + 1$$
$$= x - 1 + 1$$
$$= x$$

$(f^{-1} \circ f)(x) = f^{-1}(f(x))$
$$= f^{-1}(2x+1)$$
$$= \frac{(2x+1)-1}{2}$$
$$= \frac{2x}{2}$$
$$= x$$

49. $(f \circ f^{-1})(x) = f(f^{-1}(x))$
$$= f\left(\sqrt[3]{x-6}\right)$$
$$= \left(\sqrt[3]{x-6}\right)^3 + 6$$
$$= x - 6 + 6$$
$$= x$$

$(f^{-1} \circ f)(x) = f^{-1}(f(x))$
$$= f^{-1}(x^3 + 6)$$
$$= \sqrt[3]{(x^3 + 6) - 6}$$
$$= \sqrt[3]{x^3}$$
$$= x$$

51. $25^{1/2} = \sqrt{25} = 5$

53. $16^{3/4} = \left(\sqrt[4]{16}\right)^3 = (2)^3 = 8$

55. $9^{-3/2} = \dfrac{1}{9^{3/2}} = \dfrac{1}{\left(\sqrt{9}\right)^3} = \dfrac{1}{(3)^3} = \dfrac{1}{27}$

57. $f(x) = 3^x$; $f(2) = 3^2 = 9$

59. $f(x) = 3^x$; $f\left(\dfrac{1}{2}\right) = 3^{1/2} = \sqrt{3} \approx 1.73$

61. a. $\left(-2, \dfrac{1}{4}\right), \left(-1, \dfrac{1}{2}\right), (0,1), (1,2), (2,5)$

b. $\left(\dfrac{1}{4}, -2\right), \left(\dfrac{1}{2}, -1\right), (1,0), (2,1), (5,2)$

c.

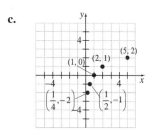

d.

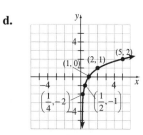

63. Answers may vary. One possibility follows. Every function will have an inverse. However, that inverse may not be a function. To determine whether the inverse will be a function, apply the horizontal line test to the original function. If every horizontal line intersects the graph of the original function at most once, then the function is one-to-one and its inverse will be a function.

65. $f(x) = 3x + 1$
$$y = 3x + 1$$
$$x = 3y + 1$$
$$x - 1 = 3y$$
$$y = \frac{x-1}{3}$$
$$f^{-1}(x) = \frac{x-1}{3}$$

Define $y_1 = 3x + 1$ and $y_2 = \frac{x-1}{3}$, and graph in a $[-6, 6, 1]$ by $[-4, 4, 1]$ window.

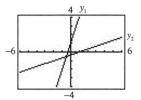

67. $f(x) = \sqrt[3]{x+1}$
$$y = \sqrt[3]{x+1}$$
$$x = \sqrt[3]{y+1}$$
$$x^3 = y + 1$$
$$y = x^3 - 1$$
$$f^{-1}(x) = x^3 - 1$$

Define $y_1 = \sqrt[3]{x+1}$ and $y_2 = x^3 - 1$, and graph in a $[-6, 6, 1]$ by $[-4, 4, 1]$ window.

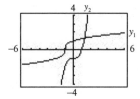

Exercise Set 9.3

1. $y = 4^x$

To graph the function, find and plot a few ordered pair solutions. Then connect the points with a smooth curve.

x	-2	-1	0	1
y	$\frac{1}{16}$	$\frac{1}{4}$	1	4

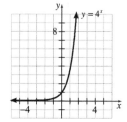

3. $y = 2^x + 1$

To graph the function, find and plot a few ordered pair solutions. Then connect the points with a smooth curve.

x	-2	-1	0	1	2
y	$\frac{5}{4}$	$\frac{3}{2}$	2	3	5

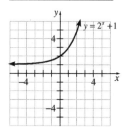

5. $y = \left(\frac{1}{4}\right)^x$

To graph the function, find and plot a few ordered pair solutions. Then connect the points with a smooth curve.

x	-1	0	1	2
y	4	1	$\frac{1}{4}$	$\frac{1}{16}$

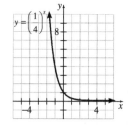

7. $y = \left(\dfrac{1}{2}\right)^x - 2$

To graph the function, find and plot a few ordered pair solutions. Then connect the points with a smooth curve.

x	-3	-2	-1	0	1	2
y	6	2	0	-1	$-\dfrac{3}{2}$	$-\dfrac{7}{4}$

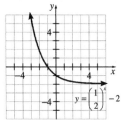

9. $y = -2^x$

To graph the function, find and plot a few ordered pair solutions. Then connect the points with a smooth curve.

x	-2	-1	0	1	2
y	$-\dfrac{1}{4}$	$-\dfrac{1}{2}$	-1	-2	-4

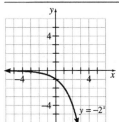

11. $y = -\left(\dfrac{1}{4}\right)^x$

To graph the function, find and plot a few ordered pair solutions. Then connect the points with a smooth curve.

x	-1	0	1	2
y	-4	-1	$-\dfrac{1}{4}$	$-\dfrac{1}{16}$

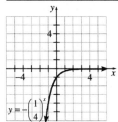

13. $f(x) = 2^{x+1}$

To graph the function, find and plot a few ordered pair solutions. Then connect the points with a smooth curve.

x	-3	-2	-1	0	1	2
$f(x)$	$\dfrac{1}{4}$	$\dfrac{1}{2}$	1	2	4	8

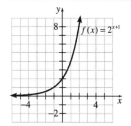

15. $f(x) = 4^{x-2}$

To graph the function, find and plot a few ordered pair solutions. Then connect the points with a smooth curve.

x	0	1	2	3
$f(x)$	$\dfrac{1}{16}$	$\dfrac{1}{4}$	1	4

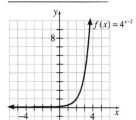

17. C

19. D

21. $3^x = 27$
$3^x = 3^3$
$x = 3$
The solution is 3.

23. $16^x = 8$
$(2^4)^x = 2^3$
$2^{4x} = 2^3$
$4x = 3$
$x = \dfrac{3}{4}$

The solution is $\dfrac{3}{4}$.

25.
$$32^{2x-3} = 2$$
$$(2^5)^{2x-3} = 2^1$$
$$10x - 15 = 1$$
$$10x = 16$$
$$x = \frac{8}{5}$$

The solution is $\frac{8}{5}$.

27.
$$\frac{1}{4} = 2^{3x}$$
$$2^{-2} = 2^{3x}$$
$$3x = -2$$
$$x = -\frac{2}{3}$$

The solution is $-\frac{2}{3}$.

29. $5^x = 625$
$$5^x = 5^4$$
$$x = 4$$
The solution is 4.

31.
$$4^x = 8$$
$$(2^2)^x = 2^3$$
$$2^{2x} = 2^3$$
$$2x = 3$$
$$x = \frac{3}{2}$$

The solution is $\frac{3}{2}$.

33.
$$27^{x+1} = 9$$
$$(3^3)^{x+1} = 3^2$$
$$3^{3x+3} = 3^2$$
$$3x + 3 = 2$$
$$3x = -1$$
$$x = -\frac{1}{3}$$

The solution is $-\frac{1}{3}$.

35.
$$81^{x-1} = 27^{2x}$$
$$(3^4)^{x-1} = (3^3)^{2x}$$
$$3^{4x-4} = 3^{6x}$$
$$4x - 4 = 6x$$
$$-4 = 2x$$
$$x = -2$$
The solution is -2.

37. $t = 50$; $y = 30(2.7)^{-0.004t}$
$$= 30(2.7)^{-(0.004)(50)}$$
$$= 30(2.7)^{-0.2}$$
$$\approx 24.6$$
Approximately 24.6 pounds of uranium will remain after 50 days.

39. $t = 10$; $y = 260(2.7)^{0.025t}$
$$= 260(2.7)^{0.025(10)}$$
$$= 260(2.7)^{0.25}$$
$$= 333$$
Approximately 333 bison should be in the park in 10 years.

41. $t = 10$; $y = 5(2.7)^{-0.15t}$
$$= 5(2.7)^{-0.15(10)}$$
$$= 5(2.7)^{-1.5}$$
$$\approx 1.1$$
Approximately 1.1 grams of the isotope will remain after 10 seconds.

43. a. $t = 1$; $y = 42.1(1.56)^t$
$$= 42.1(1.56)^1$$
$$\approx 65.7$$
We predict that approximately \$65.7 billion in retail revenues was expected in 2001.

b. $t = 9$; $y = 42.1(1.56)^t$
$$= 42.1(1.56)^9$$
$$\approx 2303.6$$
We predict that approximately \$2,303.6 billion (or \$2.3036 trillion) in Internet shopping revenues will occur in 2009.

45. a. $t = 40$; $y = 120.882(1.012)^x$
$$= 120.882(1.012)^{40}$$
$$\approx 194.8$$
We estimate that the population of the U. S. was 194.8 million people in 1970.

b. $t = 90$; $y = 120.882(1.012)^x$
$$= 120.882(1.012)^{90}$$
$$\approx 353.7$$
We predict that the population of the U. S. will be 353.7 million people in 2020.

47. $P = 6000$, $r = 0.08$, $t = 3$, and $n = 12$.
$$A = P\left(1 + \frac{r}{n}\right)^{nt}$$
$$= 6000\left(1 + \frac{0.08}{12}\right)^{12(3)}$$
$$= 6000(1.006)^{36}$$
$$\approx 7621.42$$
Erica would owe \$7621.42 after 3 years.

49. $P = 2000$, $r = 0.06$, $n = 2$, and $t = 12$.

$$A = P\left(1+\frac{r}{n}\right)^{nt}$$
$$= 2000\left(1+\frac{0.06}{2}\right)^{2(12)}$$
$$= 2000(1.03)^{24}$$
$$= 4065.59$$

Janina has approximately \$4065.59 in her savings account.

51. $y = 34(1.254)^x$
$$= 34(1.254)^{13}$$
$$\approx 645$$

We predict that there will be approximately 645 million cellular phone users in 2005.

53. $5x - 2 = 18$
$$5x = 20$$
$$x = 4$$
The solution is 4.

55. $3x - 4 = 3(x+1)$
$$3x - 4 = 3x + 3$$
$$-4 = 3 \quad \text{False}$$
The equation has not solution. The solution set is $\varnothing$.

57.
$$x^2 + 6 = 5x$$
$$x^2 - 5x + 6 = 0$$
$$(x-2)(x-3) = 0$$
$$x - 2 = 0 \ \text{ or } \ x - 3 = 0$$
$$x = 2 \ \text{ or } \quad x = 3$$
The solution set is $\{2, 3\}$.

59. $2^x = 8$
$$2^x = 2^3$$
$$x = 3$$
The solution is 3.

61. $5^x = \dfrac{1}{5}$
$$5^x = 5^{-1}$$
$$x = -1$$
The solution is -1.

63. Answers may vary. One possibility follows:
The graph of $y = b^x$ contains the point $(1, b)$ because if $x = 1$, then $y = b^1 = b$.

65. $y = \left|3^x\right|$

To graph the function, find and plot a few ordered pair solutions. Then connect the points with a smooth curve.

x	-2	-1	0	1	2
y	$\dfrac{1}{9}$	$\dfrac{1}{3}$	1	3	9

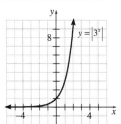

67. $y = 3^{|x|}$

To graph the function, find and plot a few ordered pair solutions. Then connect the points with a smooth curve.

x	-2	-1	0	1	2
y	9	3	1	3	9

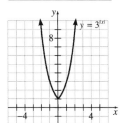

69. Define $y_1 = 2^x$ and $y_2 = \left(\dfrac{1}{2}\right)^{-x}$, and graph in a standard viewing window.

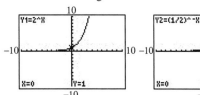

The graphs are the same since $\left(\dfrac{1}{2}\right)^{-x} = 2^x$.

Exercise Set 9.4

1. $\log_6 36 = 2$ means $6^2 = 36$.

3. $\log_3 \dfrac{1}{27} = -3$ means $3^{-3} = \dfrac{1}{27}$.

5. $\log_{10} 1000 = 3$ means $10^3 = 1000$.

7. $\log_e x = 4$ means $e^4 = x$.

9. $\log_e \dfrac{1}{e^2} = -2$ means $e^{-2} = \dfrac{1}{e^2}$.

11. $\log_7 \sqrt{7} = \dfrac{1}{2}$ means $7^{1/2} = \sqrt{7}$.

13. $2^4 = 16$ means $\log_2 16 = 4$.

15. $10^2 = 100$ means $\log_{10} 100 = 2$.

17. $e^3 = x$ means $\log_e x = 3$.

19. $10^{-1} = \dfrac{1}{10}$ means $\log_{10} \dfrac{1}{10} = -1$.

21. $4^{-2} = \dfrac{1}{16}$ means $\log_4 \dfrac{1}{16} = -2$.

23. $5^{1/2} = \sqrt{25}$ means $\log_5 \sqrt{5} = \dfrac{1}{2}$.

25. $\log_2 8 = 3$ because $2^3 = 8$.

27. $\log_3 \dfrac{1}{9} = -2$ because $3^{-2} = \dfrac{1}{9}$.

29. $\log_{25} 5 = \dfrac{1}{2}$ because $25^{1/2} = 5$.

31. $\log_{1/2} 2 = -1$ because $\left(\dfrac{1}{2}\right)^{-1} = 2$.

33. $\log_7 1 = 0$ from Property 1 (p. 705).

35. $\log_2 2^4 = 4$ from Property 2 (p. 705).

37. $\log_{10} 100 = 2$ because $10^2 = 100$

39. $3^{\log_3 5} = 5$ from Property 3 (p. 705).

41. $\log_3 81 = 4$ because $3^4 = 81$.

43. $\log_4 \left(\dfrac{1}{64}\right) = -3$ because $4^{-3} = \dfrac{1}{64}$.

45. Answers may vary.

47. $\log_3 9 = x$
$$3^x = 9$$
$$3^x = 3^2$$
$$x = 2$$
The solution is 2.

49. $\log_3 x = 4$
$$x = 3^4$$
$$x = 81$$
The solution is 81.

51. $\log_x 49 = 2$
$$x^2 = 49$$
$$x = \pm 7$$
Because the base cannot be negative, we discard -7. The solution is 7.

53. $\log_2 \dfrac{1}{8} = x$
$$2^x = \dfrac{1}{8}$$
$$2^x = 2^{-3}$$
$$x = -3$$
The solution is -3.

55. $\log_3 \left(\dfrac{1}{27}\right) = x$
$$3^x = \dfrac{1}{27}$$
$$3^x = 3^{-3}$$
$$x = -3$$
The solution is -3.

57. $\log_8 x = \dfrac{1}{3}$
$$8^{1/3} = x$$
$$x = \sqrt[3]{8} = 2$$
The solution is 2.

59. $\log_4 16 = x$
$$4^x = 16$$
$$4^x = 4^2$$
$$x = 2$$
The solution is 2.

61. $\log_{3/4} x = 3$

$$\left(\frac{3}{4}\right)^3 = x$$

$$x = \frac{27}{64}$$

The solution is $\frac{27}{64}$.

63. $\log_x 100 = 2$

$$x^2 = 100$$

$$x = \pm 10$$

Because the base cannot be negative, we discard -10. The solution is 10.

65. $\log_5 5^3 = 3$ from Property 2 (p. 705).

67. $2^{\log_2 3} = 3$ from Property 3 (p. 705).

69. $\log_9 9 = 1$ because $9^1 = 9$.

71. $y = \log_3 x$

To graph the logarithmic function, first write it in the exponential form $x = 3^y$. Then find and plot a few ordered pair solutions. Finally, connect the points with a smooth curve.

x	$\frac{1}{9}$	$\frac{1}{3}$	1	3
y	-2	-1	0	1

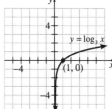

73. $f(x) = \log_{1/4} x$ or $y = \log_{1/4} x$

To graph the logarithmic function, first write it in the exponential form $x = \left(\frac{1}{4}\right)^y$. Then find and plot a few ordered pair solutions. Finally, connect the points with a smooth curve.

x	4	1	$\frac{1}{4}$	$\frac{1}{16}$
y	-1	0	1	2

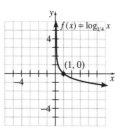

75. $f(x) = \log_5 x$ or $y = \log_5 x$

To graph the logarithmic function, first write it in the exponential form $x = 5^y$. Then find and plot a few ordered pair solutions. Finally, connect the points with a smooth curve.

x	$\frac{1}{25}$	$\frac{1}{5}$	1	5
y	-2	-1	0	1

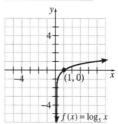

77. $f(x) = \log_{1/16} x$ or $y = \log_{1/16} x$

To graph the logarithmic function, first write it in the exponential form $x = \left(\frac{1}{16}\right)^y$. Then find and plot a few ordered pair solutions. Finally, connect the points with a smooth curve.

x	16	4	1	$\frac{1}{16}$
y	-1	$-\frac{1}{2}$	0	1

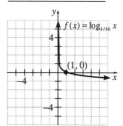

79. $\frac{x+3}{3+x} = 1$, for $x \neq -3$.

81. $\dfrac{x^2 - 8x + 16}{2x - 8} = \dfrac{(x-4)^2}{2(x-4)} = \dfrac{x-4}{2}$, for $x \neq 4$

83. $\dfrac{2}{x} + \dfrac{3}{x^2} = \dfrac{2x}{x^2} + \dfrac{3}{x^2} = \dfrac{2x+3}{x^2}$

85. $\dfrac{m^2}{m+1} - \dfrac{1}{m+1} = \dfrac{m^2-1}{m+1} = \dfrac{(m+1)(m-1)}{m+1} = m-1$,

for $m \neq -1$

87. $\log_7 (5x - 2) = 1$

$5x - 2 = 7^1$

$5x - 2 = 7$

$5x = 9$

$x = \dfrac{9}{5}$

89. $\log_3 \left(\log_5 125\right) = \log_3 (3) = 1$

91. $y = 4^x$; $y = \log_4 x$

To graph the function $y = 4^x$, find and plot a few ordered pair solutions. Then connect the points with a smooth curve.

x	-2	-1	0	1
y	$\dfrac{1}{16}$	$\dfrac{1}{4}$	1	4

To graph the function $y = \log_4 x$, reverse the coordinates of the ordered pairs found above, plot the points, and connect them with smooth curve.

x	$\dfrac{1}{16}$	$\dfrac{1}{4}$	1	4
y	-2	-1	0	1

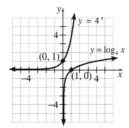

93. $y = \left(\dfrac{1}{3}\right)^x$; $y = \log_{1/3} x$ To graph the function

$y = \left(\dfrac{1}{3}\right)^x$, find and plot a few ordered pair

solutions. Then connect the points with a smooth curve.

x	-1	0	1	2
y	3	1	$\dfrac{1}{3}$	$\dfrac{1}{9}$

To graph the function $y = \log_{1/3} x$, reverse the coordinates of the ordered pairs found above, plot the points, and connect them with smooth curve.

x	3	1	$\dfrac{1}{3}$	$\dfrac{1}{9}$
y	-1	0	1	2

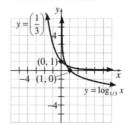

95. $\log_{10}(1 - k) = \dfrac{-0.3}{H}$, $H = 8$

$\log_{10}(1 - k) = \dfrac{-0.3}{8}$

$\log_{10}(1 - k) = -0.0375$

$1 - k = 10^{-0.0375}$

$1 - 10^{-0.0375} = k$

$k \approx 0.0827$

97. $\log_3 10$ is between 2 and 3 because 10 is between $3^2 = 9$ and $3^3 = 27$.

Mental Math 9.5

1. A

2. C

3. B

4. C

5. A

6. B

Exercise Set 9.5

1. $\log_5 2 + \log_5 7 = \log_5 (2 \cdot 7) = \log_5 14$

3. $\log_4 9 + \log_4 x = \log_4 9x$

5. $\log_{10} 5 + \log_{10} 2 + \log_{10} (x^2 + 2)$
$= \log_{10} \left[5 \cdot 2 (x^2 + 2) \right]$
$= \log_{10} (10x^2 + 20)$

7. $\log_5 12 - \log_5 4 = \log_5 \left(\dfrac{12}{4} \right) = \log_5 3$

9. $\log_2 x - \log_2 y = \log_2 \dfrac{x}{y}$

11. $\log_4 2 + \log_4 10 - \log_4 5 = \log_4 2 \cdot 10 - \log_4 5$
$= \log_4 \left(\dfrac{20}{5} \right)$
$= \log_4 4$
$= 1$

13. $\log_3 x^2 = 2 \log_3 x$

15. $\log_4 5^{-1} = -1 \cdot \log_4 5 = -\log_4 5$

17. $\log_5 \sqrt{y} = \log_5 y^{1/2} = \dfrac{1}{2} \log_5 y$

19. $2 \log_2 5 = \log_2 5^2 = \log_2 25$

21. $3 \log_5 x + 6 \log_5 z = \log_5 x^3 + \log_5 z^6 = \log_5 x^3 z^6$

23. $\log_{10} x - \log_{10} (x + 1) + \log_{10} (x^2 - 2)$
$= \log_{10} \dfrac{x}{x+1} + \log_{10} (x^2 - 2)$
$= \log_{10} \dfrac{x(x^2 - 2)}{x+1}$
$= \log_{10} \dfrac{x^3 - 2x}{x+1}$

25. $\log_4 5 + \log_4 7 = \log_4 (5 \cdot 7) = \log_4 35$

27. $\log_3 8 - \log_3 2 = \log_3 \left(\dfrac{8}{2} \right) = \log_3 4$

29. $\log_7 6 + \log_7 3 - \log_7 4 = \log_7 (6 \cdot 3) - \log_7 4$
$= \log_7 \left(\dfrac{18}{4} \right)$
$= \log_7 \dfrac{9}{2}$

31. $3 \log_4 2 + \log_4 6 = \log_4 2^3 + \log_4 6$
$= \log_4 8 + \log_4 6$
$= \log_4 (8 \cdot 6)$
$= \log_4 48$

33. $3 \log_2 x + \dfrac{1}{2} \log_2 x - 2 \log_2 (x+1)$
$= \log_2 x^3 + \log_2 x^{1/2} - \log_2 (x+1)^2$
$= \log_2 (x^3 \cdot x^{1/2}) - \log_2 (x+1)^2$
$= \log_2 x^{7/2} - \log_2 (x+1)^2$
$= \log_2 \dfrac{x^{7/2}}{(x+1)^2}$

35. $2 \log_8 x - \dfrac{2}{3} \log_8 x + \log_8 x = \left(2 - \dfrac{2}{3} + 4 \right) \log_8 x$
$= \dfrac{16}{3} \log_8 x$
$= \log_8 x^{16/3}$

37. $\log_2 \dfrac{7 \cdot 11}{3} = \log_2 (7 \cdot 11) - \log_2 3$
$= \log_2 7 + \log_2 11 - \log_2 3$

39. $\log_3 \left(\dfrac{4y}{5} \right) = \log_3 4y - \log_3 5$
$= \log_3 4 + \log_3 y - \log_3 5$

41. $\log_2 \left(\dfrac{x^3}{y} \right) = \log_2 x^3 - \log_2 y = 3 \log_2 x - \log_2 y$

43. $\log_b \sqrt{7x} = \log_b (7x)^{1/2}$
$= \dfrac{1}{2} \log_b (7x)$
$= \dfrac{1}{2} \left[\log_b 7 + \log_b x \right]$
$= \dfrac{1}{2} \log_b 7 + \dfrac{1}{2} \log_b x$

45. $\log_7 \left(\dfrac{5x}{4} \right) = \log_7 5x - \log_7 4$
$= \log_7 5 + \log_7 x - \log_7 4$

47. $\log_5 x^3(x+1) = \log_5 x^3 + \log_5(x+1)$
$\qquad\qquad = 3\log_5 x + \log_5(x+1)$

49. $\log_6 \dfrac{x^2}{x+3} = \log_6 x^2 - \log_6(x+3)$
$\qquad\qquad = 2\log_6 x - \log_6(x+3)$

51. $\log_b\left(\dfrac{5}{3}\right) = \log_b 5 - \log_b 3$
$\qquad\qquad = 0.7 - 0.5$
$\qquad\qquad = 0.2$

53. $\log_b 15 = \log_b(5 \cdot 3)$
$\qquad\quad = \log_b 5 + \log_b 3$
$\qquad\quad = 0.7 + 0.5$
$\qquad\quad = 1.2$

55. $\log_b \sqrt[3]{5} = \log_b 5^{1/3}$
$\qquad\quad = \dfrac{1}{3}\log_b 5$
$\qquad\quad = \dfrac{1}{3}(0.7)$
$\qquad\quad \approx 0.233$

57. $\log_b 8 = \log_b 2^3$
$\qquad\quad = 3\log_b 2$
$\qquad\quad = 3(0.43)$
$\qquad\quad = 1.29$

59. $\log_b\left(\dfrac{3}{9}\right) = \log_b\left(\dfrac{1}{3}\right)$
$\qquad\qquad = \log_b 3^{-1}$
$\qquad\qquad = (-1)\log_b 3$
$\qquad\qquad = -(0.68)$
$\qquad\qquad = -0.68$

61. $\log_b \sqrt{\dfrac{2}{3}} = \log_b\left(\dfrac{2}{3}\right)^{1/2}$
$\qquad\qquad = \dfrac{1}{2}\log_b \dfrac{2}{3}$
$\qquad\qquad = \dfrac{1}{2}\left(\log_b 2 - \log_b 3\right)$
$\qquad\qquad = \dfrac{1}{2}(0.43 - 0.68)$
$\qquad\qquad = \dfrac{1}{2}(-0.25)$
$\qquad\qquad = -0.125$

63. $y = 10^x$; $y = \log_{10} x$

To graph the function $y = 10^x$, find and plot a few ordered pair solutions. Then connect the points with a smooth curve.

x	-1	0	1
y	$\dfrac{1}{10}$	1	10

To graph the function $y = \log_{10} x$, reverse the coordinates of the ordered pairs found above, plot the points, and connect them with smooth curve.

x	$\dfrac{1}{10}$	1	10
y	-1	0	1

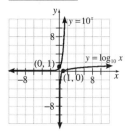

65. $\log_{10} \dfrac{1}{10} = \log_{10} 10^{-1} = -1$

67. $\log_7 \sqrt{7} = \log_7 7^{1/2} = \dfrac{1}{2}$

69. False

71. True

73. False

Integrated Review

1. $(f+g)(x) = (x-6) + (x^2+1) = x^2 + x - 5$

2. $(f-g)(x) = (x-6) - (x^2+1)$
$\qquad\qquad = x - 6 - x^2 - 1$
$\qquad\qquad = -x^2 + x - 7$

3. $(f \cdot g)(x) = (x-6)(x^2+1) = x^3 - 6x^2 + x - 6$

4. $\left(\dfrac{f}{g}\right)(x) = \dfrac{x-6}{x^2+1}$

5. $(f \circ g)(x) = f\big(g(x)\big) = \sqrt{g(x)} = \sqrt{3x-1}$

6. $(g \circ f)(x) = g\big(f(x)\big) = 3 \cdot g(x) - 1 = 3\sqrt{x} - 1$

7. $f = \{(-2,6),(4,8),(2,-6),(3,3)\}$ is a one-to-one function since each *y*-value corresponds to only one *x*-value. $f^{-1} = \{(6,-2),(8,4),(-6,2),(3,3)\}$.

8. $g = \{(4,2),(-1,3),(5,3),(7,1)\}$ is not one-to-one because there are two *x*-coordinates with the same *y*-coordinate: $(-1,3)$ and $(5,3)$.

9. This function is not one-to-one because it fails the horizontal line test.

10. This function is one-to-one because it passes the horizontal line test.

11. This function is not one-to-one because it fails the horizontal line test.

12. $f(x) = 3x$
$y = 3x$
$x = 3y$
$\dfrac{x}{3} = y$
$f^{-1}(x) = \dfrac{x}{3}$

13. $f(x) = x + 4$
$y = x + 4$
$x = y + 4$
$x - 4 = y$
$f^{-1}(x) = x - 4$

14. $f(x) = 5x - 1$
$y = 5x - 1$
$x = 5y - 1$
$x + 1 = 5y$
$\dfrac{x+1}{5} = y$
$f^{-1}(x) = \dfrac{x+1}{5}$

15. $f(x) = 3x + 2$
$y = 3x + 2$
$x = 3y + 2$
$x - 2 = 3y$
$\dfrac{x-2}{3} = y$
$f^{-1}(x) = \dfrac{x-2}{3}$

16. $y = \left(\dfrac{1}{2}\right)^x$

To graph the function, find and plot a few ordered pair solutions. Then connect the points with a smooth curve.

x	-2	-1	0	1	2
y	4	2	1	$\dfrac{1}{2}$	$\dfrac{1}{4}$

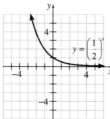

17. $y = 2^x + 1$

To graph the function, find and plot a few ordered pair solutions. Then connect the points with a smooth curve.

x	-2	-1	0	1	2
y	$\dfrac{5}{4}$	$\dfrac{3}{2}$	2	3	5

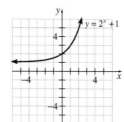

18. $y = \log_3 x$

To graph the logarithmic function, first write it in the exponential form $x = 3^y$. Then find and plot a few ordered pair solutions. Finally, connect the points with a smooth curve.

x	$\frac{1}{9}$	$\frac{1}{3}$	1	3
y	-2	-1	0	1

19. $y = \log_{1/3} x$

To graph the logarithmic function, first write it in the exponential form $x = \left(\dfrac{1}{3}\right)^y$. Then find and plot a few ordered pair solutions. Finally, connect the points with a smooth curve.

x	3	1	$\frac{1}{3}$	$\frac{1}{9}$
y	-1	0	1	2

20. $2^x = 8$
$2^x = 2^3$
$x = 3$
The solution is 3.

21. $9 = 3^{x-5}$
$3^2 = 3^{x-5}$
$2 = x - 5$
$7 = x$
The solution is 7.

22. $4^{x-1} = 8^{x+2}$
$\left(2^2\right)^{x-1} = \left(2^3\right)^{x+2}$
$2^{2x-2} = 2^{3x+6}$
$2x - 2 = 3x + 6$
$-8 = x$
The solution is -8.

23. $25^x = 125^{x-1}$
$\left(5^2\right)^x = \left(5^3\right)^{x-1}$
$5^{2x} = 5^{3x-3}$
$2x = 3x - 3$
$3 = x$
The solution is 3.

24. $\log_4 16 = x$
$4^x = 16$
$4^x = 4^2$
$x = 2$
The solution is 2.

25. $\log_{49} 7 = x$
$49^x = 7$
$\left(7^2\right)^x = 7$
$7^{2x} = 7$
$2x = 1$
$x = \dfrac{1}{2}$

The solution is $\dfrac{1}{2}$.

26. $\log_2 x = 5$
$2^5 = x$
$32 = x$
The solution is 32.

27. $\log_x 64 = 3$
$x^3 = 64$
$x = \sqrt[3]{64} = 4$
The solution is 4.

28. $\log_x \dfrac{1}{125} = -3$
$x^{-3} = \dfrac{1}{125}$
$\dfrac{1}{x^3} = \dfrac{1}{125}$
$x^3 = 125$
$x = \sqrt[3]{125} = 5$
The solution is 5.

SSM: *Intermediate Algebra: A Graphing Approach, 3e*

29. $\log_3 x = -2$

$3^{-2} = x$

$x = \dfrac{1}{3^2} = \dfrac{1}{9}$

The solution is $\dfrac{1}{9}$.

30. $5\log_2 x = \log_2 x^5$

31. $x\log_2 5 = \log_2 5^x$

32. $3\log_5 x - 5\log_5 y = \log_5 x^3 - \log_5 y^5$

$\qquad = \log_5 \dfrac{x^3}{y^5}$

33. $9\log_5 x + 3\log_5 y = \log_5 x^9 + \log_5 y^3$

$\qquad = \log_5 x^9 y^3$

34. $\log_2 x + \log_2(x-3) - \log_2\left(x^2+4\right)$

$= \log_2 x(x-3) - \log_2\left(x^2+4\right)$

$= \log_2 \dfrac{x(x-3)}{x^2+4}$

$= \log_2 \dfrac{x^2-3x}{x^2+4}$

35. $\log_3 y - \log_3(y+2) + \log_3\left(y^3+11\right)$

$= \log_3 y + \log_3\left(y^3+11\right) - \log_3(y+2)$

$= \log_3 y\left(y^3+11\right) - \log_3(y+2)$

$= \log_3 \dfrac{y\left(y^3+11\right)}{y+2}$

$= \log_3 \dfrac{y^4+11y}{y+2}$

36. $\log_7 \dfrac{9x^2}{y} = \log_7 9x^2 - \log_7 y$

$\qquad = \log_7 9 + \log_7 x^2 - \log_7 y$

$\qquad = \log_7 9 + 2\log_7 x - \log_7 y$

37. $\log_6 \dfrac{5y}{z^2} = \log_6 5y - \log_7 z^2$

$\qquad = \log_6 5 + \log_6 y - 2\log_6 z$

Exercise Set 9.6

1. $\log 8 \approx 0.9031$

3. $\log 2.31 \approx 0.3636$

5. $\ln 2 \approx 0.6931$

7. $\ln 0.0716 \approx -2.6367$

9. $\log 12.6 \approx 1.1004$

11. $\ln 5 \approx 1.6094$

13. $\log 41.5 \approx 1.6180$

15. Answers may vary. One possibility follows: When we try to approximate $\log 0$ on a calculator, we get an error message. This occurs because 0 is not in the domain of $y = \log x$. The domain is $\{x \mid x > 0\}$.

17. $\log 100 = \log 10^2 = 2$

19. $\log \dfrac{1}{1000} = \log 10^{-3} = -3$

21. $\ln e^2 = 2$

23. $\ln \sqrt[4]{e} = \ln e^{1/4} = \dfrac{1}{4}$

25. $\log 10^3 = 3$

27. $\ln e^2 = 2$

29. $\log 0.0001 = \log 10^{-4} = -4$

31. $\ln \sqrt{e} = \ln e^{1/2} = \dfrac{1}{2}$

33. $\ln 50$ is larger than $\log 50$. Explanations may vary. One possibility follows. The natural log function has a smaller base (e) than the common log function (10). The smaller base must be raised to a larger power than the larger base in order to obtain 50. That is, if $e^x = 50$ and $10^y = 50$, then $x > y$ because the base e is smaller than the base 10.

415

35. $\log x = 1.3$
$x = 10^{1.3} \approx 19.9526$

37. $\log 2x = 1.1$
$2x = 10^{1.1}$
$x = \dfrac{10^{1.1}}{2} \approx 6.2946$

39. $\ln x = 1.4$
$x = e^{1.4} \approx 4.0552$

41. $\ln(3x-4) = 2.3$
$3x - 4 = e^{2.3}$
$3x = 4 + e^{2.3}$
$x = \dfrac{4 + e^{2.3}}{3} \approx 4.6581$

43. $\log x = 2.3$
$x = 10^{2.3} \approx 199.5262$

45. $\ln x = -2.3$
$x = e^{-2.3} \approx 0.1003$

47. $\log(2x+1) = -0.5$
$2x + 1 = 10^{-0.5}$
$2x = 10^{-0.5} - 1$
$x = \dfrac{10^{-0.5} - 1}{2} \approx -0.3419$

49. $\ln 4x = 0.18$
$4x = e^{0.18}$
$x = \dfrac{e^{0.18}}{4} \approx 0.2993$

51. $\log_2 3 = \dfrac{\log 3}{\log 2} \approx 1.5850$

53. $\log_{1/2} 5 = \dfrac{\log 5}{\log\left(\frac{1}{2}\right)} \approx -2.3219$

55. $\log_4 9 = \dfrac{\log 9}{\log 4} \approx 1.5850$

57. $\log_3\left(\dfrac{1}{6}\right) = \log_3 6^{-1}$
$= (-1)\log_3 6$
$= -\dfrac{\log 6}{\log 3} \approx -1.6309$

59. $\log_8 6 = \dfrac{\log 6}{\log 8} \approx 0.8617$

61. Substitute in $a = 200$, $B = 2.1$ and $T = 1.6$.
$R = \log\left(\dfrac{a}{T}\right) + B = \log\left(\dfrac{200}{1.6}\right) + 2.1 \approx 4.2$
The earthquake measures 4.2 on the Richter scale.

63. Substitute in $a = 400$, $T = 2.6$, and $B = 3.1$.
$R = \log\left(\dfrac{a}{T}\right) + B = \log\left(\dfrac{400}{2.6}\right) + 3.1 \approx 5.3$
The earthquake measures 5.3 on the Richter scale.

65. Substitute in $t = 12$, $P = 1400$ and $r = 0.08$.
$A = Pe^{rt} = 1400e^{(0.08)12} = 1400e^{0.96} \approx 3656.38$
Dana has $3656.38 after 12 years.

67. Substitute in $t = 4$, $P = 2000$ and $r = 0.06$.
$A = Pe^{rt} = 2000e^{(0.06)4} = 2000e^{0.24} \approx 2542.50$
Barbara will owe $2542.50 at the end of 4 years.

69. $6x - 3(2-5x) = 6$
$6x - 6 + 15x = 6$
$21x - 6 = 6$
$21x = 12$
$x = \dfrac{12}{21} = \dfrac{4}{7}$

71. $2x + 3y = 6x$
$3y = 4x$
$\dfrac{3y}{4} = x$

73. $x^2 + 7x = -6$
$x^2 + 7x + 6 = 0$
$(x+6)(x+1) = 0$
$x + 6 = 0$ or $x + 1 = 0$
$x = -6$ or $x = -1$
The solutions are $\{-6, -1\}$.

75. $\begin{cases} x + 2y = -4 \\ 3x - y = 9 \end{cases}$
Multiply the second equation by 2 and add the result to the first equation:
$x + 2y = -4$
$\underline{6x - 2y = 18}$
$7x \quad\;\; = 14$
$x = 2$
Substitute $x = 2$ into the first equation and solve for y.
$2 + 2y = -4$
$2y = -6$
$y = -3$
The solution is $(2, -3)$.

77. ln 50 is larger than log 50. Explanations may vary. One possibility follows. The natural log function has a smaller base (e) than the common log function (10). The smaller base must be raised to a larger power than the larger base in order to obtain 50. That is, if $e^x = 50$ and $10^y = 50$, then $x > y$ because the base e is smaller than the base 10.

79. $f(x) = e^x$

To graph the function, find and plot a few ordered pair solutions. Then connect the points with a smooth curve.

x	−2	−1	0	1	2
y	0.14	0.37	1	2.72	7.39

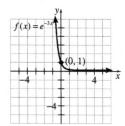

81. $f(x) = e^{-3x}$

To graph the function, find and plot a few ordered pair solutions. Then connect the points with a smooth curve.

x	−2	−1	0	1	2
y	403.43	20.09	1	0.05	0.002

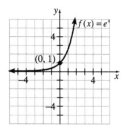

83. $f(x) = e^x + 2$

To graph the function, find and plot a few ordered pair solutions. Then connect the points with a smooth curve.

x	−2	−1	0	1	2
y	2.14	2.37	3	4.72	9.39

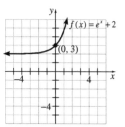

85. $f(x) = e^{x-1}$

To graph the function, find and plot a few ordered pair solutions. Then connect the points with a smooth curve.

x	−2	−1	0	1	2
y	0.05	0.14	0.37	1	2.72

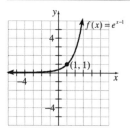

87. $f(x) = 3e^x$

To graph the function, find and plot a few ordered pair solutions. Then connect the points with a smooth curve.

x	−2	−1	0	1	2
y	0.41	1.10	3	8.15	22.17

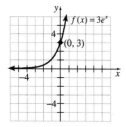

89. $f(x) = \ln x$

To graph the logarithmic function, first write it in the exponential form $x = e^y$. Then find and plot a few ordered pair solutions. Finally, connect the points with a smooth curve.

x	0.14	0.37	1	2.72	7.39
y	−2	−1	0	1	2

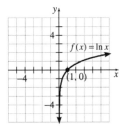

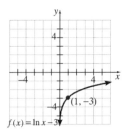

91. $f(x) = -2\log x$

To graph the logarithmic function, first write it in the exponential form $x = 10^{-y/2}$. Then find and plot a few ordered pair solutions. Finally, connect the points with a smooth curve.

x	10	3.16	1	0.32	0.1
y	−2	−1	0	1	2

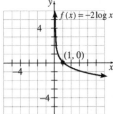

93. $f(x) = \log(x+2)$

To graph the logarithmic function, first write it in the exponential form $x = 10^y - 2$. Then find and plot a few ordered pair solutions. Finally, connect the points with a smooth curve.

x	−1.99	−1.9	−1	8	98
y	−2	−1	0	1	2

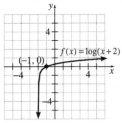

95. $f(x) = \ln x - 3$

To graph the logarithmic function, first write it in the exponential form $x = e^{y+3}$. Then find and plot a few ordered pair solutions. Finally, connect the points with a smooth curve.

x	0.37	1	2.72	7.39	20.09
y	−4	−3	−2	−1	0

97. Define $y_1 = e^x$, $y_2 = e^x + 2$, and $y_3 = e^x - 3$, and graph on a $[-6, 6, 1]$ by a $[-6, 6, 1]$ window.

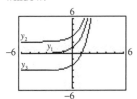

Discussions may vary. One possibility follows: The graphs of $y_2 = e^x + 2$ and $y_3 = e^x - 3$ have the same shape as the graph of $y_1 = e^x$, but they are shifted up 2 units and down 3 units, respectively.

Exercise Set 9.7

1. $3^x = 6$

$x = \log_3 6 = \dfrac{\log 6}{\log 3} \approx 1.6309$

3. $3^{2x} = 3.8$

$2x = \log_3 3.8$

$x = \dfrac{\log_3 3.8}{2} = \dfrac{\log 3.8}{2\log 3} \approx 0.6076$

5. $2^{x-3} = 5$

$x - 3 = \log_2 5$

$x = 3 + \log_2 5 = 3 + \dfrac{\log 5}{\log 2} \approx 5.3219$

7. $9^x = 5$

$x = \log_9 5 = \dfrac{\log 5}{\log 9} \approx 0.7325$

9. $4^{x+7} = 3$

$x + 7 = \log_4 3$

$x = -7 + \log_4 3 = -7 + \dfrac{\log 3}{\log 4} \approx -6.2075$

418

11. $7^{3x-4} = 11$
$3x - 4 = \log_7 11$
$3x = 4 + \log_7 11$
$x = \dfrac{1}{3}\left(4 + \dfrac{\log 11}{\log 7}\right) \approx 1.7441$

13. $e^{6x} = 5$
$6x = \ln 5$
$x = \dfrac{\ln 5}{6} \approx 0.2682$

15. $\log_2(x+5) = 4$
$x + 5 = 2^4$
$x + 5 = 16$
$x = 11$

17. $\log_3 x^2 = 4$
$x^2 = 3^4$
$x^2 = 81$
$x = \pm 9$

19. $\log_4 2 + \log_4 x = 0$
$\log_4(2x) = 0$
$2x = 4^0$
$2x = 1$
$x = \dfrac{1}{2}$

21. $\log_2 6 - \log_2 x = 3$
$\log_2\left(\dfrac{6}{x}\right) = 3$
$\dfrac{6}{x} = 2^3$
$\dfrac{6}{x} = 8$
$8x = 6$
$x = \dfrac{3}{4}$

23. $\log_4 x + \log_4(x+6) = 2$
$\log_4 x(x+6) = 2$
$x(x+6) = 4^2$
$x^2 + 6x = 16$
$x^2 + 6x - 16 = 0$
$(x+8)(x-2) = 0$
$x = -8 \text{ or } x = 2$
We discard -8 as extraneous. The solution is 2.

25. $\log_5(x+3) - \log_5 x = 2$
$\log_5\left(\dfrac{x+3}{x}\right) = 2$
$\dfrac{x+3}{x} = 5^2$
$x + 3 = 25x$
$3 = 24x$
$x = \dfrac{3}{24} = \dfrac{1}{8}$

27. $\log_3(x-2) = 2$
$x - 2 = 3^2$
$x - 2 = 9$
$x = 11$

29. $\log_4(x^2 - 3x) = 1$
$x^2 - 3x = 4$
$x^2 - 3x - 4 = 0$
$(x-4)(x+1) = 0$
$x = 4 \text{ or } x = -1$

31. $\ln 5 + \ln x = 0$
$\ln(5x) = 0$
$e^0 = 5x$
$1 = 5x$
$\dfrac{1}{5} = x$

33. $3\log x - \log x^2 = 2$
$3\log x - 2\log x = 2$
$\log x = 2$
$x = 10^2$
$x = 100$

35. $\log_2 x + \log_2(x+5) = 1$
$\log_2 x(x+5) = 1$
$x(x+5) = 2$
$x^2 + 5x - 2 = 0$
Use the quadratic formula to solve: $a = 1$, $b = 5$, and $c = -2$.
$x = \dfrac{-5 \pm \sqrt{5^2 - 4(1)(-2)}}{2(1)}$
$x = \dfrac{-5 \pm \sqrt{33}}{2}$
Discard $\dfrac{-5 - \sqrt{33}}{2}$ as extraneous. The solution is $\dfrac{-5 + \sqrt{33}}{2}$.

37. $\log_4 x - \log_4(2x-3) = 3$

$$\log_4\left(\frac{x}{2x-3}\right) = 3$$

$$\frac{x}{2x-3} = 64$$

$$x = 64(2x-3)$$

$$x = 128x - 192$$

$$192 = 127x$$

$$x = \frac{192}{127}$$

39. $\log_2 x + \log_2(3x+1) = 1$

$$\log_2 x(3x+1) = 1$$

$$x(3x+1) = 2$$

$$3x^2 + x - 2 = 0$$

$$(3x-2)(x+1) = 0$$

$$3x-2 = 0 \quad \text{or} \quad x+1 = 0$$

$$x = \frac{2}{3} \quad \text{or} \quad x = -1$$

We discard -1 as extraneous. The solution is $\frac{2}{3}$.

41. $y = y_0 e^{0.043t}$, $y_0 = 83$, $t = 5$

$y = 83e^{0.043(5)} = 83e^{0.215} \approx 103$

There should be 103 wolves in 5 years.

43. $y = y_0 e^{0.026t}$, $y_0 = 10,589,571$, $t = 6$

$y = 10,589,571e^{0.026(6)} \approx 12,380,000$

There will be approximately 12,380,000 inhabitants in 2008.

45. $y = y_0 e^{-0.005t}$; $y_0 = 144,979$; $y = 120,000$

$$120,000 = 144,979e^{-0.018t}$$

$$\frac{120,000}{144,979} = e^{-0.018t}$$

$$-0.018t = \ln\left(\frac{120,000}{144,979}\right)$$

$$t = \frac{\ln\left(\frac{120,000}{144,979}\right)}{-0.018} \approx 10.5$$

It will take approximately 10.5 years for the population of Russia to reach 120,000 thousand.

47. $P = 600$, $A = 2(600) = 1200$, $r = 0.07$, $n = 12$

$$A = P\left(1+\frac{r}{n}\right)^{nt}$$

$$1200 = 600\left(1+\frac{0.07}{12}\right)^{12t}$$

$$2 = \left(1+\frac{0.07}{12}\right)^{12t}$$

$$\log 2 = \log\left(1+\frac{0.07}{12}\right)^{12t}$$

$$\log 2 = 12t \log\left(1+\frac{0.07}{12}\right)$$

$$t = \frac{\log 2}{12\log\left(1+\frac{0.07}{12}\right)} \approx 9.9$$

It will take approximately 9.9 years for the $600 investment to double.

49. $P = 1200$, $A = P + I = 1200 + 200 = 1400$, $r = 0.009$, $n = 4$

$$A = P\left(1+\frac{r}{n}\right)^{nt}$$

$$1400 = 1200\left(1+\frac{0.09}{4}\right)^{4t}$$

$$\frac{7}{6} = (1.0225)^{4t}$$

$$\log\left(\frac{7}{6}\right) = \log(1.0225)^{4t}$$

$$\log\left(\frac{7}{6}\right) = 4t\log(1.0225)$$

$$t = \frac{\log\left(\frac{7}{6}\right)}{4\log(1.0225)} \approx 1.7$$

It would take the investment approximately 1.7 years to earn $200.

51. $P = 1000$, $A = 2(1000) = 2000$, $r = 0.08$, $n = 2$

$$A = P\left(1+\frac{r}{n}\right)^{nt}$$

$$2000 = 1000\left(1+\frac{0.08}{2}\right)^{2t}$$

$$2 = (1.04)^{2t}$$

$$\log 2 = \log(1.04)^{2t}$$

$$\log 2 = 2t\log(1.04)$$

$$t = \frac{\log 2}{2\log 1.04} \approx 8.8$$

It will take approximately 8.8 years for the $1000 investment to double.

53. Let $h = 35$.

$w = 0.00185h^{2.67} = 0.00185(35)^{2.67} \approx 24.5$

A boy 35 inches tall is expected to weight approximately 24.5 pounds.

55. Let $w = 85$.

$$w = 0.00185h^{2.67}$$
$$85 = 0.00185h^{2.67}$$
$$\frac{85}{0.00185} = h^{2.67}$$
$$h = \left(\frac{85}{0.00185}\right)^{1/2.67} \approx 55.7$$

A boy who weighs 85 pounds is expected to be approximately 55.7 inches tall.

57. Let $x = 1$.

$$P = 14.7e^{-0.21x} = 14.7e^{-0.21(1)} = 14.7e^{-0.21} \approx 11.9$$

The average atmospheric pressure of Denver is approximately 11.9 pounds per square inch.

59. Let $P = 7.5$.

$$P = 14.7e^{-0.21x}$$
$$7.5 = 14.7e^{-0.21x}$$
$$\frac{7.5}{14.7} = e^{-0.21x}$$
$$-0.21x = \ln\left(\frac{7.5}{14.7}\right)$$
$$x = -\frac{1}{0.21}\ln\left(\frac{7.5}{14.7}\right) \approx 3.2$$

The elevation of the jet is approximately 3.2 miles.

61. Let $N = 50$, $A = 75$, and $c = 0.09$.

$$t = \frac{1}{c}\ln\left(\frac{A}{A-N}\right)$$
$$t = \frac{1}{0.09}\ln\left(\frac{75}{75-50}\right) = \frac{1}{0.09}\ln(3) \approx 12.21$$

It will take approximately 12 weeks.

63. Let $N = 150$, $A = 210$, and $c = 0.07$.

$$t = \frac{1}{c}\ln\left(\frac{A}{A-N}\right)$$
$$t = \frac{1}{0.07}\ln\left(\frac{210}{210-150}\right) = \frac{1}{0.07}\ln(3.5) \approx 17.9$$

It will take approximately 18 weeks.

65. $\dfrac{x^2 - y + 2z}{3x} = \dfrac{(-2)^2 - 0 + 2(3)}{3(-2)} = \dfrac{10}{-6} = -\dfrac{5}{3}$

67. $\dfrac{3z - 4x + y}{x + 2z} = \dfrac{3(3) - 4(-2) + 0}{-2 + 2(3)} = \dfrac{17}{4}$

69.
$$f(x) = 5x + 2$$
$$y = 5x + 2$$
$$x = 5y + 2$$
$$x - 2 = 5y$$
$$\frac{x-2}{5} = y$$
$$f^{-1}(x) = \frac{x-2}{5}$$

71. $y = 5,130,632$, $y_0 = 3,665,228$

$$y = y_0 e^{kt}$$
$$5,130,632 = 3,665,228e^{10k}$$
$$\frac{5,130,632}{3,665,228} = e^{10k}$$
$$\ln\left(\frac{5,130,632}{3,665,228}\right) = 10k$$
$$k = \frac{1}{10}\ln\left(\frac{5,130,632}{3,665,228}\right) \approx 0.0336$$

The growth rate is 3.4% annually.

73. Answers may vary. One possibility follows. We must check our solutions because extraneous solutions may occur during the algebraic process of solving.

75. a. Enter the data into L1 and L2. Find an appropriate window and graph the data. We use $[-5, 25, 5]$ by $[0, 40000, 5000]$.

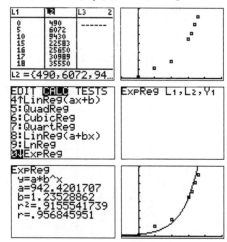

If a and b are rounded to three decimal places, the linear regression equation is $y = 942.420(1.235)^x$.

b. Note that 1987 will be 7 years after 1980. Since the equation is stored in Y1, we evaluate the equation for the year 1987 by finding Y1(8).

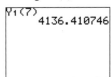

We predict that there was approximately 4136 thousand (or 4,136,000) shipments in 1987.

c. Note that 2005 will be 25 years after 1980. Since the equation is stored in Y1, we evaluate the equation for the year 2005 by finding Y1(25).

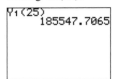

We predict that there will be approximately 188,548 thousand (or 188,548,000) shipments in 2005.

77. a. Enter the data into L1 and L2. Find an appropriate window and graph the data. We use [0, 25, 5] by [0, 80000, 10000].

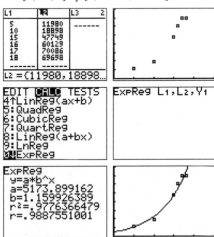

If *a* and *b* are rounded to three decimal places, the linear regression equation is
$y = 5172.899(1.160)^x$.

b. Note that 1992 will be 12 years after 1980. Since the equation is stored in Y1, we

evaluate the equation for the year 1992 by finding Y1(12).

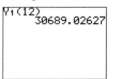

We predict that revenue in the U.S. was approximately \$30,689 million (or \$30,689,000,000) in 1992.

c. Note that 2005 will be 25 years after 1980. Since the equation is stored in Y1, we evaluate the equation for the year 2005 by finding Y1(25).

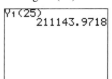

We predict that revenue in the U.S. will be approximately \$211,144 million (or \$211,144,000,000) in 2005.

79. a. Enter the data into L1 and L2. Find an appropriate window and graph the data. We use [0, 25, 5] by [0, 200000, 20000].

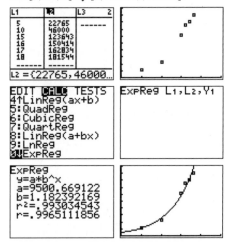

If *a* and *b* are rounded to three decimal places, the linear regression equation is
$y = 950.669(1.182)^x$.

b. Note that 1992 will be 12 years after 1980. Since the equation is stored in Y1, we evaluate the equation for the year 1992 by finding Y1(12).

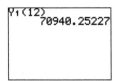

We predict that revenue worldwide was $70940 million (or $70,940,000,000) in 1992.

c. Note that 2005 will be 25 years after 1980. Since the equation is stored in Y1, we evaluate the equation for the year 2005 by finding Y1(25).

We predict that revenue worldwide will be $626,315 million (or $626,315,000,000) in 2005.

Chapter 9 Review

1. $(f+g)(x) = f(x)+g(x)$
$$= (x-5)+(2x+1)$$
$$= x-5+2x+1$$
$$= 3x-4$$

2. $(f-g)(x) = f(x)-g(x)$
$$= (x-5)+(2x+1)$$
$$= x-5-2x-1$$
$$= -x-6$$

3. $(f \cdot g)(x) = f(x) \cdot g(x)$
$$= (x-5)(2x+1)$$
$$= 2x^2 + x - 10x - 5$$
$$= 2x^2 - 9x - 5$$

4. $\left(\dfrac{g}{f}\right)(x) = \dfrac{g(x)}{f(x)} = \dfrac{2x+1}{x-5}, x \neq 5$

5. $(f \circ g)(x) = f(g(x))$
$$= f(x+1)$$
$$= (x+1)^2 - 2$$
$$= x^2 + 2x - 1$$

6. $(g \circ f)(x) = g(f(x))$
$$= g(x^2 - 2)$$
$$= x^2 - 2 + 1$$
$$= x^2 - 1$$

7. $(h \circ g)(2) = h(g(2))$
$$= h(3)$$
$$= 3^3 - 3^2$$
$$= 18$$

8. $(f \circ f)(x) = f(f(x))$
$$= f(x^2 - 2)$$
$$= (x^2 - 2)^2 - 2$$
$$= x^4 - 4x^2 + 4 - 2$$
$$= x^4 - 4x^2 + 2$$

9. $(f \circ g)(-1) = f(g(-1))$
$$= f(0)$$
$$= 0^2 - 2$$
$$= -2$$

10. $(h \circ h)(2) = h(h(2))$
$$= h(4)$$
$$= 4^3 - 4^2$$
$$= 48$$

11. The function is one-to-one since each *y*-value corresponds to only one *x*-value.
$$h^{-1} = \left\{ \begin{array}{l} (14,-9),(8,6),(12,-11) \\ ,(15,15) \end{array} \right\}$$

12. This function is not one-to-one because there are two inputs that correspond with the same output: $(-5, 5)$ and $(13, 5)$.

13. This function is one-to-one since each output corresponds to only one input. The inverse function is the following table.

Rank in Auto Theft (Input)	2	4	1	3
U.S. Region (Output)	West	Midwest	South	Northeast

14. This function is not one-to-one because there are three shapes with the same number of sides: (Square, 4), (Parallelogram, 4), and (Rectangle, 4).

15. $f(x) = \sqrt{x+2}$

    a. $f(7) = \sqrt{7+2} = \sqrt{9} = 3$

    b. $f^{-1}(3) = 7$

16. $f(x) = \sqrt{x+2}$

    a. $f(-1) = \sqrt{-1+2} = \sqrt{1} = 1$

    b. $f^{-1}(1) = -1$

17. The graph does not represent a one-to-one function because it fails the horizontal line function.

18. The graph does not represent a one-to-one function because it fails the horizontal line function.

19. The graph does not represent a one-to-one function because it fails the horizontal line function.

20. The graph represents a one-to-one function because it passes the horizontal line function.

21. $f(x) = x - 9$
$$y = x - 9$$
$$x = y - 9$$
$$y = x + 9$$
$$f^{-1}(x) = x + 9$$

22. $f(x) = x + 8$
$$y = x + 8$$
$$x = y + 8$$
$$y = x - 8$$
$$f^{-1}(x) = x - 8$$

23. $f(x) = 6x - 11$
$$y = 6x + 11$$
$$x = 6y + 11$$
$$6y = x - 11$$
$$y = \frac{x-11}{6}$$
$$f^{-1}(x) = \frac{x-11}{6}$$

24. $f(x) = 12x$
$$y = 12x$$
$$x = 12y$$
$$y = \frac{x}{12}$$
$$f^{-1}(x) = \frac{x}{12}$$

25. $f(x) = x^3 - 5$
$$y = x^3 - 5$$
$$x = y^3 - 5$$
$$y^3 = x + 5$$
$$y = \sqrt[3]{x+5}$$
$$f^{-1}(x) = \sqrt[3]{x+5}$$

26. $f(x) = \sqrt[3]{x+2}$
$$y = \sqrt[3]{x+2}$$
$$x = \sqrt[3]{y+2}$$
$$x^3 = y + 2$$
$$y = x^3 - 2$$
$$f^{-1}(x) = x^3 - 2$$

27. $g(x) = \dfrac{12x-7}{6}$
$$y = \frac{12x-7}{6}$$
$$x = \frac{12y-7}{6}$$
$$6x = 12y - 7$$
$$y = \frac{6x+7}{12}$$
$$g^{-1}(x) = \frac{6x+7}{12}$$

28. $r(x) = \dfrac{13}{2}x - 4$
$$y = \frac{13}{2}x - 4$$
$$x = \frac{13}{2}y - 4$$
$$x + 4 = \frac{13}{2}y$$
$$y = \frac{2(x+4)}{13}$$
$$r^{-1}(x) = \frac{2(x+4)}{13}$$

29. $g(x) = \sqrt{x}$
$$y = \sqrt{x}$$
$$x = \sqrt{y}$$
$$x^2 = y$$
$$g^{-1}(x) = x^2,\ x \geq 0$$

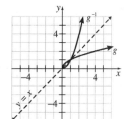

30. $h(x) = 5x - 5$
$y = 5x - 5$
$x = 5y - 5$
$5y = x + 5$
$y = \dfrac{x + 5}{5}$
$h^{-1}(x) = \dfrac{x + 5}{5}$

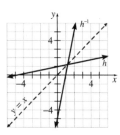

31. $f(x) = 2x - 3$
$x = 2y - 3$
$y = \dfrac{x + 3}{2}$
$f^{-1}(x) = \dfrac{x + 3}{2}$

Define $y_1 = 2x - 3$ and $y_2 = \dfrac{x + 3}{2}$, and graph in a $[-6, 6, 1]$ by $[-4, 4, 1]$ window.

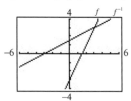

32. $4^x = 64$
$4^x = 4^3$
$x = 3$

33. $3^x = \dfrac{1}{9}$
$3^x = 3^{-2}$
$x = -2$

34. $2^{3x} = \dfrac{1}{16}$
$2^{3x} = 2^{-4}$
$3x = -4$
$x = -\dfrac{4}{3}$

35. $5^{2x} = 125$
$5^{2x} = 5^3$
$2x = 3$
$x = \dfrac{3}{2}$

36. $9^{x+1} = 243$
$(3^2)^{x+1} = 3^5$
$3^{2x+2} = 3^5$
$2x + 2 = 5$
$2x = 3$
$x = \dfrac{3}{2}$

37. $8^{3x-2} = 4$
$(2^3)^{3x-2} = 2^2$
$2^{9x-6} = 2^2$
$9x - 6 = 2$
$9x = 8$
$x = \dfrac{8}{9}$

38. $y = 3^x$

To graph the function, find and plot a few ordered pair solutions. Then connect the points with a smooth curve.

x	-2	-1	0	1	2
y	$\dfrac{1}{9}$	$\dfrac{1}{3}$	1	3	9

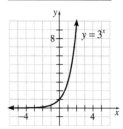

39. $y = \left(\dfrac{1}{3}\right)^x$

To graph the function, find and plot a few ordered pair solutions. Then connect the points with a smooth curve.

x	-2	-1	0	1	2
y	9	3	1	$\dfrac{1}{3}$	$\dfrac{1}{9}$

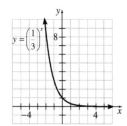

40. $y = 4 \cdot 2^x$

To graph the function, find and plot a few ordered pair solutions. Then connect the points with a smooth curve.

x	-4	-3	-2	-1	0	1
y	$\frac{1}{4}$	$\frac{1}{2}$	1	2	4	8

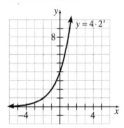

41. $y = 2^x + 4$

To graph the function, find and plot a few ordered pair solutions. Then connect the points with a smooth curve.

x	-3	-2	-1	0	1	2
y	4.125	4.25	4.5	5	6	8

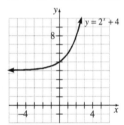

42. $A = P\left(1 + \dfrac{r}{n}\right)^{nt}$

$A = 1600\left(1 + \dfrac{0.09}{2}\right)^{(2)(7)}$

$A = \$2963.11$

The amount accrued is \$2963.11.

43. $A = P\left(1 + \dfrac{r}{n}\right)^{nt}$

$A = 800\left(1 + \dfrac{0.07}{4}\right)^{(4)(5)}$

$A \approx 1131.82$

The certificate will be worth \$1131.82 at the end of 5 years.

44. Define $y_1 = 4 \cdot 2^x$ and graph in a $[-6, 6, 1]$ by $[-2, 10, 1]$ window.

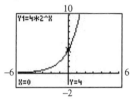

45. $7^2 = 49$ means $\log_7 49 = 2$.

46. $2^{-4} = \dfrac{1}{16}$ means $\log_2 \dfrac{1}{16} = -4$

47. $\log_{1/2} 16 = -4$ means $\left(\dfrac{1}{2}\right)^{-4} = 16$

48. $\log_{0.4} 0.064 = 3$ means $0.4^3 = 0.064$.

49. $\log_4 x = -3$

$4^{-3} = x$

$x = \dfrac{1}{64}$

50. $\log_3 x = 2$

$3^2 = x$

$x = 9$

51. $\log_3 1 = x$

$3^x = 1$

$3^x = 3^0$

$x = 0$

52. $\log_4 64 = x$

$4^x = 64$

$4^x = 4^3$

$x = 3$

53. $\log_x 64 = 2$

$x^2 = 64$

$x = \pm\sqrt{64} = \pm 8$

Discard -8 since the base must be positive. The solution is 8.

54. $\log_x 81 = 4$

$x^4 = 81$

$x = \pm 3$

Discard -3 since the base must be positive. The solution is 3.

55. $\log_4 4^5 = x$
$\quad\quad 5 = x$

56. $\log_7 7^{-2} = x$
$\quad\quad -2 = x$

57. $5^{\log_5 4} = x$
$\quad\quad 4 = x$

58. $2^{\log_2 9} = x$
$\quad\quad 9 = x$

59. $\log_2(3x-1) = 4$
$\quad\quad 3x-1 = 2^4$
$\quad\quad 3x-1 = 16$
$\quad\quad 3x = 17$
$\quad\quad x = \dfrac{17}{3}$

60. $\log_3(2x+5) = 2$
$\quad\quad 2x+5 = 3^2$
$\quad\quad 2x+5 = 9$
$\quad\quad 2x = 4$
$\quad\quad x = 2$

61. $\log_4(x^2-3x) = 1$
$\quad\quad x^2 - 3x = 4$
$\quad\quad x^2 - 3x - 4 = 0$
$\quad\quad (x+1)(x-4) = 0$
$\quad\quad x = -1 \text{ or } x = 4$

62. $\log_8(x^2+7x) = 1$
$\quad\quad x^2 + 7x = 8$
$\quad\quad x^2 + 7x - 8 = 0$
$\quad\quad (x+8)(x-1) = 0$
$\quad\quad x = -8 \text{ or } x = 1$

63. $y = 2^x$; $y = \log_2 x$

To graph the function $y = 2^x$, find and plot a few ordered pair solutions. Then connect the points with a smooth curve.

x	-2	-1	0	1	2
y	$\dfrac{1}{4}$	$\dfrac{1}{2}$	1	2	4

To graph the function $y = \log_2 x$, reverse the coordinates of the ordered pairs found above, plot the points, and connect them with smooth curve.

x	$\dfrac{1}{4}$	$\dfrac{1}{2}$	1	2	4
y	-2	-1	0	1	2

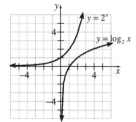

64. $y = \left(\dfrac{1}{2}\right)^x$; $y = \log_{1/2} x$

To graph the function $y = \left(\dfrac{1}{2}\right)^x$, find and plot a few ordered pair solutions. Then connect the points with a smooth curve.

x	-2	-1	0	1	2
y	4	2	1	$\dfrac{1}{2}$	$\dfrac{1}{4}$

To graph the function $y = \log_{1/2} x$, reverse the coordinates of the ordered pairs found above, plot the points, and connect them with smooth curve.

x	4	2	1	$\dfrac{1}{2}$	$\dfrac{1}{4}$
y	-2	-1	0	1	2

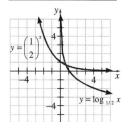

65. $\log_3 8 + \log_3 4 = \log_3(8\cdot 4) = \log_3 32$

66. $\log_2 6 + \log_2 3 = \log_2(6\cdot 3) = \log_2 18$

67. $\log_7 15 - \log_7 20 = \log_7 \dfrac{15}{20} = \log_7 \dfrac{3}{4}$

68. $\log 18 - \log 12 = \log \dfrac{18}{12} = \log \dfrac{3}{2}$

69. $\log_{11} 8 + \log_{11} 3 - \log_{11} 6 = \log_{11}\left(\dfrac{8 \cdot 3}{6}\right)$

$\qquad\qquad\qquad\qquad\qquad = \log_{11} 4$

70. $\log_5 14 + \log_5 3 - \log_5 21 = \log_5\left(\dfrac{14 \cdot 3}{21}\right)$

$\qquad\qquad\qquad\qquad\qquad = \log_5 2$

71. $2\log_5 x - 2\log_5(x+1) + \log_5 x$

$= \log_5 x^2 - \log_5(x+1)^2 + \log_5 x$

$= \log_5 \dfrac{x^2 \cdot x}{(x+1)^2}$

$= \log_5 \dfrac{x^3}{(x+1)^2}$

72. $4\log_3 x - \log_3 x + \log_3(x+2)$

$= 3\log_3 x + \log_3(x+2)$

$= \log_3 x^3 + \log_3(x+2)$

$= \log_3\left[x^3(x+2)\right]$

$= \log_3(x^4 + 2x^3)$

73. $\log_3 \dfrac{x^3}{x+2} = \log_3 x^3 - \log_3(x+2)$

$\qquad\qquad\quad = 3\log_3 x - \log_3(x+2)$

74. $\log_4 \dfrac{x+5}{x^2} = \log_4(x+5) - \log_4 x^2$

$\qquad\qquad\quad = \log_4(x+5) - 2\log_4 x$

75. $\log_2 \dfrac{3x^2 y}{z} = \log_2(3x^2 y) - \log_2 z$

$\qquad\qquad\quad = \log_2 3 + \log_2 x^2 + \log_2 y - \log_2 z$

$\qquad\qquad\quad = \log_2 3 + 2\log_2 x + \log_2 y - \log_2 z$

76. $\log_7 \dfrac{yz^3}{x} = \log_7(yz^3) - \log_7 x$

$\qquad\qquad\quad = \log_7 y + \log_7 z^3 - \log_7 x$

$\qquad\qquad\quad = \log_7 y + 3\log_7 z - \log_7 x$

77. $\log_6 50 = \log_6\left(2 \cdot 5^2\right)$

$\qquad\qquad = \log_6 2 + \log_6 5^2$

$\qquad\qquad = \log_6 2 + 2\log_6 5$

$\qquad\qquad = 0.36 + 2(0.83)$

$\qquad\qquad = 2.02$

78. $\log_b \dfrac{4}{5} = \log_b 4 - \log_b 5$

$\qquad\qquad = \log_b 2^2 - \log_b 5$

$\qquad\qquad = 2\log_b 2 - \log_b 5$

$\qquad\qquad = 2(0.36) - 0.83$

$\qquad\qquad = 0.72 - 0.83$

$\qquad\qquad = -0.11$

79. $\log 3.6 \approx 0.5563$

80. $\log 0.15 \approx -0.8239$

81. $\ln 1.25 \approx 0.2231$

82. $\ln 4.63 \approx 1.5326$

83. $\log 1000 = 3$

84. $\log \dfrac{1}{10} = \log 10^{-1} = -1$

85. $\ln \dfrac{1}{e} = \ln e^{-1} = -1$

86. $\ln(e^4) = 4$

87. $\ln(2x) = 2$

$\qquad 2x = e^2$

$\qquad x = \dfrac{e^2}{2}$

88. $\ln(3x) = 1.6$

$\qquad 3x = e^{1.6}$

$\qquad x = \dfrac{e^{1.6}}{3}$

89. $\ln(2x-3) = -1$

$\qquad 2x - 3 = e^{-1}$

$\qquad 2x = e^{-1} + 3$

$\qquad x = \dfrac{e^{-1} + 3}{2}$

90. $\ln(3x+1) = 2$

$\qquad 3x + 1 = e^2$

$\qquad 3x = e^2 - 1$

$\qquad x = \dfrac{e^2 - 1}{3}$

91.

$$\ln\frac{I}{I_0} = -kx$$

$$\ln\frac{0.03I_0}{I_0} = -2.1x$$

$$\ln 0.03 = -2.1x$$

$$\frac{\ln 0.03}{-2.1} = x$$

$$x \approx 1.67$$

The radiation will be reduced to 3% of its original intensity at a depth of approximately 1.67 mm.

92.

$$\ln\frac{I}{I_0} = -kx$$

$$\ln\frac{0.02I_0}{I_0} = -3.2x$$

$$\ln 0.02 = -3.2x$$

$$\frac{\ln 0.02}{-3.2} = x$$

$$x \approx 1.22$$

2% of the original radiation will penetrate at a depth of approximately 1.22 mm.

93. $\log_5 1.6 = \dfrac{\log 1.6}{\log 5} = 0.2920$

94. $\log_3 4 = \dfrac{\log 4}{\log 3} \approx 1.2619$

95. $A = Pe^{rt}$
$A = 1450e^{(0.06)(5)} = 1957.30$
The amount accrued is \$1957.30.

96. $A = Pe^{rt}$
$A = 940e^{0.11(3)} = 940e^{0.33} \approx 1307.51$
The amount accrued is \$1307.51.

97.

$$3^{2x} = 7$$

$$\log 3^{2x} = \log 7$$

$$2x\log 3 = \log 7$$

$$x = \frac{\log 7}{2\log 3} \approx 0.8856$$

98.

$$6^{3x} = 5$$

$$\log 6^{3x} = \log 5$$

$$3x\log 6 = \log 5$$

$$x = \frac{\log 5}{3\log 6} \approx 0.2994$$

99.

$$3^{2x+1} = 6$$

$$\log 3^{2x+1} = \log 6$$

$$(2x+1)\log 3 = \log 6$$

$$2x+1 = \frac{\log 6}{\log 3}$$

$$2x = \frac{\log 6}{\log 3} - 1$$

$$x = \frac{1}{2}\left(\frac{\log 6}{\log 3} - 1\right) \approx 0.3155$$

100.

$$4^{3x+2} = 9$$

$$\log 4^{3x+2} = \log 9$$

$$(3x+2)\log 4 = \log 9$$

$$3x+2 = \frac{\log 9}{\log 4}$$

$$3x = \frac{\log 9}{\log 4} - 2$$

$$x = \frac{1}{3}\left(\frac{\log 9}{\log 4} - 2\right) \approx -0.1383$$

101.

$$5^{3x-5} = 4$$

$$\log 5^{3x-5} = \log 4$$

$$(3x-5)\log 5 = \log 4$$

$$3x-5 = \frac{\log 4}{\log 5}$$

$$3x = \frac{\log 4}{\log 5} + 5$$

$$x = \frac{1}{3}\left(\frac{\log 4}{\log 5} + 5\right) \approx 1.9538$$

102.

$$8^{4x-2} = 3$$

$$\log 8^{4x-2} = \log 3$$

$$(4x-2)\log 8 = \log 3$$

$$4x-2 = \frac{\log 3}{\log 8}$$

$$4x = \frac{\log 3}{\log 8} + 2$$

$$x = \frac{1}{4}\left(\frac{\log 3}{\log 8} + 2\right) \approx 0.6321$$

103.

$$2 \cdot 5^{x-1} = 1$$

$$\log 2 + (x-1)\log 5 = \log 1$$

$$\log 2 + (x-1)\log 5 = 0$$

$$(x-1)\log 5 = -\log 2$$

$$x-1 = -\frac{\log 2}{\log 5}$$

$$x = -\frac{\log 2}{\log 5} + 1 \approx 0.5693$$

104.
$$3 \cdot 4^{x+5} = 2$$
$$4^{x+5} = \frac{2}{3}$$
$$\log 4^{x+5} = \log\left(\frac{2}{3}\right)$$
$$(x+5)\log 4 = \log\left(\frac{2}{3}\right)$$
$$x+5 = \frac{\log\left(\frac{2}{3}\right)}{\log 4}$$
$$x = \frac{\log\left(\frac{2}{3}\right)}{\log 4} - 5 \approx -5.2925$$

105.
$$\log_5 2 + \log_5 x = 2$$
$$\log_5 2x = 2$$
$$2x = 5^2$$
$$2x = 25$$
$$x = \frac{25}{2}$$

106.
$$\log_3 x + \log_3 10 = 2$$
$$\log_3(10x) = 2$$
$$10x = 3^2$$
$$10x = 9$$
$$x = \frac{9}{10}$$

107.
$$\log(5x) - \log(x+1) = 4$$
$$\log\frac{5x}{x+1} = 4$$
$$\frac{5x}{x+1} = 10^4$$
$$\frac{5x}{x+1} = 10,000$$
$$5x = 10000x + 10000$$
$$-9995x = 10000$$
$$x = \frac{10000}{-995} = -\frac{2000}{1999}$$

Discard $-\dfrac{2000}{1999}$ as extraneous. The equation has no solution. The solution set is $\varnothing$.

108.
$$\ln(3x) - \ln(x-3) = 2$$
$$\ln\left(\frac{3x}{x-3}\right) = 2$$
$$\frac{3x}{x-3} = e^2$$
$$3x = e^2 x - 3e^2$$

$$3x - e^2 x = -3e^2$$
$$(3 - e^2)x = -3e^2$$
$$x = \frac{3e^2}{e^2 - 3}$$

109.
$$\log_2 x + \log_2 2x - 3 = 1$$
$$\log_2(x \cdot 2x) - 3 = 1$$
$$\log_2(2x^2) = 4$$
$$2x^2 = 2^4$$
$$2x^2 = 16$$
$$x^2 = 8$$
$$x = \pm 2\sqrt{2}$$

Discard $-2\sqrt{2}$ as extraneous. The solution is $2\sqrt{2}$.

110.
$$-\log_6(4x+7) + \log_6 x = 1$$
$$\log_6 x - \log_6(4x+7) = 1$$
$$\log_6 \frac{x}{4x+7} = 1$$
$$\frac{x}{4x+7} = 6^1$$
$$x = 24x + 42$$
$$-23x = 42$$
$$x = -\frac{42}{23}$$

Discard $-\dfrac{42}{23}$ as extraneous. The equation has not solution. The solution set is $\varnothing$.

111.
$$y = y_0 e^{kt}$$
$$y = 155,000e^{0.06(4)} = 197,044$$
By the end of 4 weeks, expect 197,044 ducks.

112. Note: The year 2010 corresponds to $t = 8$.
$$y = y_0 e^{kt}$$
$$y = 232,073,071e^{0.015(8)} \approx 261,661,656$$
By the year 200 the population of Indonesia will be approximately 261,661,656.

113.
$$y = y_0 e^{kt}$$
$$130,000,000 = 126,975,000e^{0.001t}$$
$$e^{0.001t} = \frac{130,000,000}{126,975,000}$$
$$0.001t = \frac{130,000,000}{126,975,000}$$
$$t = \frac{\ln \dfrac{130,000,000}{126,975,000}}{0.001} \approx 24$$
It will take approximately 24 years for Japan's population to grow to 130,000,000.

114.
$$y = y_0 e^{kt}$$
$$2(31,902,268) = 31,902,268e^{0.008t}$$
$$2 = e^{0.008t}$$
$$\ln 2 = 0.008t$$
$$t = \frac{\ln 2}{0.008} \approx 87$$

It will take approximately 87 years for Canada's population to double in size.

115.
$$y = y_0 e^{kt}$$
$$2(70,712,345) = 70,712,345e^{0.016t}$$
$$2 = e^{0.016t}$$
$$\ln 2 = 0.016t$$
$$t = \frac{\ln 2}{0.016} \approx 43$$

It will take approximately 43 years for Egypt's population to double in size.

116.
$$A = P\left(1 + \frac{r}{n}\right)^{nt}$$
$$10,000 = 5,000\left(1 + \frac{0.08}{4}\right)^{4t}$$
$$2 = (1.02)^{4t}$$
$$\log 2 = \log(1.02)^{4t}$$
$$\log 2 = 4t \log 1.02$$
$$t = \frac{\log 2}{4 \log 1.02} \approx 8.8$$

It will take approximately 8.8 for the investment to grow to $10,000.

117.
$$A = P\left(1 + \frac{r}{n}\right)^{nt}$$
$$10,000 = 6,000\left(1 + \frac{0.06}{12}\right)^{12t}$$
$$\frac{5}{3} = (1.005)^{12t}$$
$$\log \frac{5}{3} = \log(1.005)^{12t}$$
$$\log \frac{5}{3} = 12t \log(1.005)$$
$$t = \frac{1}{12}\left(\frac{\log(5/3)}{\log(1.005)}\right) \approx 8.5$$

It was invested for approximately 8.5 years.

118. Define $y_1 = e^x$ and $y_2 = 2$, and graph in a standard viewing window. Find the intersection point.

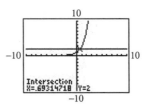

The solution is the x-coordinate of the intersection point, $x \approx 0.69$.

119. Define $y_1 = 10^{0.3x}$ and $y_2 = 7$, and graph in a standard viewing window. Find the intersection point.

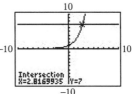

The solution is the x-coordinate of the intersection point, $x \approx 2.82$.

120. Enter the data into L1 and L2. Find an appropriate window and graph the data. We use [0, 25, 5] by [0, 80000, 10000].

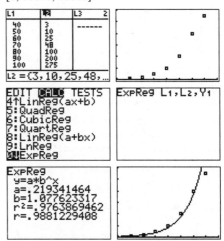

If a and b are rounded to three decimal places, the linear regression equation is
$$y = 0.219(1.078)^x.$$

Note that 2005 will correspond to $x = 105$. Since the equation is stored in Y1, we evaluate the equation for the year 2005 by finding Y1(105).

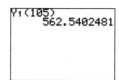

We predict that classroom cost will be $562.540 billion in 2005.

Chapter 9 Test

1. $(f \circ h)(0) = f(h(0)) = f(5) = 5$

2. $(g \circ f)(x) = g(f(x)) = g(x) = x - 7$

3. $(g \circ h)(x) = g(h(x))$
$$= g(x^2 - 6x + 5)$$
$$= (x^2 - 6x + 5) - 7$$
$$= x^2 - 6x - 2$$

4. $f(x) = 7x - 14$
$y = 7x - 14$
$x = 7y - 14$
$x + 14 = 7y$
$\dfrac{x+14}{7} = y$
$\dfrac{1}{7}x + 2 = y$
$f^{-1}(x) = \dfrac{1}{7}x + 2$

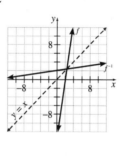

5. The graph represents a one-to-one function because it passes the horizontal line test.

6. The graph does not represent a one-to-one function because it fails the horizontal line test. [In fact, the graph does not represent a function because it fails the vertical line test.]

7. The function $y = 6 - 2x$ is one-to-one because its graph passes the horizontal line test.
$y = 6 - 2x$
$x = 6 - 2y$
$2y = -x + 6$
$y = \dfrac{-x+6}{2}$
$f^{-1}(x) = \dfrac{-x+6}{2}$ or $f^{-1}(x) = -\dfrac{1}{2}x + 3$

8. $f = \{(0,0),(2,3),(-1,5)\}$ is a one-to-one function since each y-value corresponds to only one x-value. $f^{-1} = \{(0,0),(3,2),(5,-1)\}$.

9. This function is not one-to-one because there are two words in the set whose first letters are d : (Dog, d) and (Desk, d).

10. $\log_3 6 + \log_3 4 = \log_3 (6 \cdot 4) = \log_3 24$

11. $\log_5 x + 3\log_5 x - \log_5 (x+1)$
$$= 4\log_5 x - \log_5 (x+1)$$
$$= \log_5 x^4 - \log_5 (x+1)$$
$$= \log_5 \frac{x^4}{x+1}$$

12. $\log_6 \dfrac{2x}{y^3} = \log_6 2x - \log_6 y^3$
$$= \log_6 2 + \log_6 x - 3\log_6 y$$

13. $\log_b \left(\dfrac{3}{25}\right) = \log_b 3 - \log_b 25$
$$= \log_b 3 - \log_b 5^2$$
$$= \log_b 3 - 2\log_b 5$$
$$= 0.79 - 2(1.16)$$
$$= -1.53$$

14. $\log_7 8 = \dfrac{\log 8}{\log 7} \approx 1.0686$

15. $8^{x-1} = \dfrac{1}{64}$
$8^{x-1} = 8^{-2}$
$x - 1 = -2$
$x = -1$

16. $3^{2x+5} = 4$
$\log 3^{2x+5} = \log 4$
$(2x+5)\log 3 = \log 4$
$2x + 5 = \dfrac{\log 4}{\log 3}$
$2x = \dfrac{\log 4}{\log 3} - 5$
$x = \dfrac{1}{2}\left(\dfrac{\log 4}{\log 3} - 5\right) \approx -1.8691$

17. $\log_3 x = -2$
$$x = 3^{-2} = \dfrac{1}{3^2} = \dfrac{1}{9}$$

18. $\ln \sqrt{e} = x$
$\ln e^{1/2} = x$
$\dfrac{1}{2} = x$

19. $\log_8(3x-2)=2$

$$3x-2=8^2$$
$$3x-2=64$$
$$3x=66$$
$$x=\frac{66}{3}=22$$

20. $\log_5 x + \log_5 3 = 2$

$$\log_5(3x)=2$$
$$3x=5^2$$
$$3x=25$$
$$x=\frac{25}{3}$$

21. $\log_4(x+1)-\log_4(x-2)=3$

$$\log_4 \frac{x+1}{x-2}=3$$
$$\frac{x+1}{x-2}=4^3$$
$$\frac{x+1}{x-2}=64$$
$$x+1=64x-128$$
$$129=63x$$
$$x=\frac{129}{63}=\frac{43}{21}$$

22. $\ln(3x+7)=1.31$

$$3x+7=e^{1.31}$$
$$3x=e^{1.31}-7$$
$$x=\frac{e^{1.31}-7}{3}\approx -1.0979$$

23. $y=\left(\frac{1}{2}\right)^x+1$

To graph the function, find and plot a few ordered pair solutions. Then connect the points with a smooth curve.

x	-2	-1	0	1	2
y	5	3	2	$\frac{3}{2}$	$\frac{5}{4}$

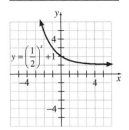

24. $y=3^x$ and $y=\log_3 x$

To graph the function $y=3^x$, find and plot a few ordered pair solutions. Then connect the points with a smooth curve.

x	-2	-1	0	1
y	$\frac{1}{9}$	$\frac{1}{3}$	1	3

To graph the function $y=\log_3 x$, reverse the coordinates of the ordered pairs found above, plot the points, and connect them with smooth curve.

x	$\frac{1}{9}$	$\frac{1}{3}$	1	3
y	-2	-1	0	1

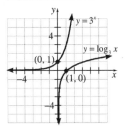

25. $P=4000$, $t=3$, $r=0.09$, and $n=12$.

$$A=\left(1+\frac{r}{n}\right)^{nt}$$
$$=4000\left(1+\frac{0.09}{12}\right)^{12(3)}$$
$$=4000(1.0075)^{36}$$
$$\approx 5234.58$$

There will be $5234.58 in the account.

26. $A=3000$, $P=2000$, $r=0.07$, and $n=2$.

$$A=P\left(1+\frac{r}{n}\right)^{nt}$$
$$3000=2000\left(1+\frac{0.07}{2}\right)^{2t}$$
$$1.5=(1.035)^{2t}$$
$$\log 1.5=\log(1.035)^{2t}$$
$$\log 1.5=2t\log(1.035)$$
$$t=\frac{\log 1.5}{2\log 1.035}\approx 6$$

It will take about 6 years for the investment to grow to $3000.

27. $y = y_0 e^{kt}$

$\qquad = 57,000 e^{0.026(5)}$

$\qquad = 57,000 e^{0.13}$

$\qquad \approx 64,913$

There should be approximately 64,913 prairie dogs 5 years from now.

28. $\qquad y = y_0 e^{kt}$

$1000 = 400 e^{0.062(t)}$

$\quad 2.5 = e^{0.062t}$

$0.062t = \ln 2.5$

$\qquad t = \dfrac{\ln 2.5}{0.062} \approx 15$

It should take the naturalist approximately 15 years to reach their goal.

29. $\log(1+k) = \dfrac{0.3}{D}$

$\log(1+k) = \dfrac{0.3}{56}$

$\quad 1+k = 10^{0.3/56}$

$\qquad k = -1 + 10^{0.3/56} \approx 0.012$

The population is increasing at a rate of approximately 1.2% per day.

30. Define $y_1 = e^{0.2x}$ and $y_2 = e^{-0.4x} + 2$, and graph in a standard viewing window. Find the intersection point.

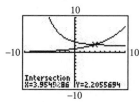

The solution is the x-coordinate of the intersection point, $x \approx 3.95$.

31. Enter the data into L1 and L2. Find an appropriate window and graph the data. We use $[-2, 14, 1]$ by $[0, 1200, 100]$.

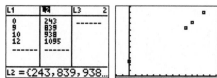

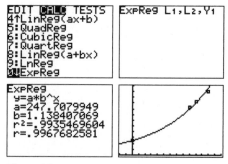

If a and b are rounded to three decimal places, the linear regression equation is

$y = 247.708(1.138)^x$.

Note that 2006 will be 16 years after 1990. Since the equation is stored in Y1, we evaluate the equation for the year 2006 by finding Y1(16).

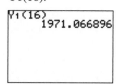

We predict that approximately $1971.1 billion (or $1,971,100,000,000) will be charged in 2006.

Chapter 9 Cumulative Review

1. a. $(-8)(-1) = 8$

b. $(-2)\left(\dfrac{1}{6}\right) = -\dfrac{2}{6} = -\dfrac{1}{3}$

c. $3(-3) = -9$

d. $0(11) = 0$

e. $\left(\dfrac{1}{5}\right)\left(-\dfrac{10}{11}\right) = -\dfrac{10}{55} = -\dfrac{2}{11}$

f. $(7)(1)(-2)(-3) = 7(-2)(-3) = -14(-3) = 42$

g. $8(-2)(0) = 0$

2. $\quad \dfrac{1}{3}(x-2) = \dfrac{1}{4}(x+1)$

$12 \cdot \dfrac{1}{3}(x-2) = 12 \cdot \dfrac{1}{4}(x+1)$

$\quad 4(x-2) = 3(x+1)$

$\qquad 4x - 8 = 3x + 3$

$\qquad x - 8 = 3$

$\qquad\qquad x = 11$

3. To graph the function $y = x^2$, find and plot a few ordered pair solutions. Then connect the points with a smooth curve.

x	-3	-2	-1	0	1	2	3
y	9	4	1	0	1	4	9

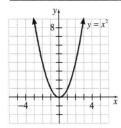

4. The slope of the function we seek is $m = \dfrac{1}{3}$, the negative reciprocal of the slope of the line $f(x) = -3x + 4$. The equation of the function is

$$y - y_1 = m(x - x_1)$$
$$y - 6 = \frac{1}{3}(x + 2)$$
$$y - 6 = \frac{1}{3}x + \frac{2}{3}$$
$$y = \frac{1}{3}x + \frac{20}{3}$$

Using function notation, we have

$$f(x) = \frac{1}{3}x + \frac{20}{3} \text{ or } f(x) = \frac{x + 20}{3}.$$

5. Equation 2 is twice the opposite of equation 1. Therefore, the system is dependent. Thus,
$$\{(x, y, z) \mid x - 5y - 2z = 6\}.$$

6. From the figure, we obtain the following system:
$$\begin{cases} x + y = 180 \\ y = x - 40 \end{cases}$$
Using substitution, we obtain
$$x + (x - 40) = 180$$
$$2x - 40 = 180$$
$$2x = 220$$
$$x = 110$$
Back substituting into the first equation, we obtain
$$110 + y = 180$$
$$y = 70$$
Thus, we have $x = 110$ and $y = 70$.

7. a. $\dfrac{x^7}{x^4} = x^{7-4} = x^3$

b. $\dfrac{5^8}{5^2} = 5^{8-2} = 5^6$

c. $\dfrac{20x^6}{4x^5} = \dfrac{20}{4} \cdot \dfrac{x^6}{x^5} = 5x^{6-5} = 5x$

d. $\dfrac{12y^{10}z^7}{14y^8 z^7} = \dfrac{12}{14} \cdot y^{10-8} \cdot z^{7-7}$
$$= \frac{6}{7} y^2 z^0$$
$$= \frac{6}{7} y^2 \text{ or } \frac{6y^2}{7}$$

8. a. $\left(4a^3\right)^2 = 4^2\left(a^3\right)^2 = 16a^6$

b. $\left(-\dfrac{2}{3}\right)^3 = \left(-\dfrac{2}{3}\right)\left(-\dfrac{2}{3}\right)\left(-\dfrac{2}{3}\right) = -\dfrac{8}{27}$

c. $\left(\dfrac{4a^5}{b^3}\right)^3 = \dfrac{4^3\left(a^5\right)^3}{\left(b^3\right)^3} = \dfrac{64a^{15}}{b^9}$

d. $\left(\dfrac{3^{-2}}{x}\right)^{-3} = \left(\dfrac{x}{3^{-2}}\right)^3 = \left(3^2 x\right)^3 = \left(9x\right)^3 = 729x^3$

e. $\left(a^{-2}b^3 c^{-4}\right)^{-2} = \left(a^{-2}\right)^{-2}\left(b^3\right)^{-2}\left(c^{-4}\right)^{-2}$
$$= a^4 b^{-6} c^8$$
$$= \frac{a^4 c^8}{b^6}$$

9. a. $C(100) = \dfrac{2.6(100) + 10,000}{100} = 102.60$
The cost per disc will be \$102.60.

b. $C(1000) = \dfrac{2.6(1000) + 10,000}{1000} = 12.60$
The cost per disc will be \$12.60.

10. a. $(3x - 1)^2 = (3x)^2 - 2(3x)(1) + 1^2$
$$= 9x^2 - 6x + 1$$

b. $\left(\dfrac{1}{2}x + 3\right)\left(\dfrac{1}{2}x - 3\right) = \dfrac{1}{4}x^2 + \dfrac{3}{2}x - \dfrac{3}{2}x - 9$
$$= \frac{1}{4}x^2 - 9$$

c. $(2x - 5)(6x + 7) = 12x^2 + 14x - 30x - 35$
$$= 12x^2 - 16x - 35$$

11. a. $\dfrac{x}{4}+\dfrac{5x}{4}=\dfrac{6x}{4}=\dfrac{3x}{2}$

b. $\dfrac{x^2}{x+7}-\dfrac{49}{x+7}=\dfrac{x^2-49}{x+7}$

$\qquad =\dfrac{(x-7)(x+7)}{x+7}$

$\qquad =x-7,\quad x\neq -7$

c. $\dfrac{x}{3y^2}-\dfrac{x+1}{3y^2}=\dfrac{x-x-1}{3y^2}=\dfrac{-1}{3y^2}$ or $-\dfrac{1}{3y^2}$

12. $\dfrac{5}{x-2}+\dfrac{3}{x^2+4x+4}-\dfrac{6}{x+2}$

$=\dfrac{5}{x-2}+\dfrac{3}{(x+2)^2}-\dfrac{6}{x+2}$

$=\dfrac{5(x+2)^2+3(x-2)-6(x-2)(x+2)}{(x-2)(x+2)^2}$

$=\dfrac{5(x^2+4x+4)+3(x-2)-6(x^2-4)}{(x-2)(x+2)^2}$

$=\dfrac{5x^2+20x+20+3x-6-6x^2+24}{(x-2)(x+2)^2}$

$=\dfrac{-x^2+23x+38}{(x-2)(x+2)^2}$

13.
$$x^2-1\overline{\smash{\big)}\,3x^4+2x^3+0x^2-8x+6}$$
with quotient $3x^2+2x+3$
$$\underline{3x^4\qquad -3x^2}$$
$$2x^3+3x^2-8x+6$$
$$\underline{2x^3\qquad -2x}$$
$$3x^2-6x+6$$
$$\underline{3x^3\qquad -3}$$
$$-6x+9$$

Answer: $3x^2+2x+3+\dfrac{-6x+9}{x^2-1}$

14. a. $\dfrac{\dfrac{a}{5}}{\dfrac{a-1}{10}}=\dfrac{a}{5}\cdot\dfrac{10}{a-1}=\dfrac{2a}{a-1}$

b. $\dfrac{\dfrac{3}{2+a}+\dfrac{6}{2-a}}{\dfrac{5}{a+2}-\dfrac{1}{a-2}}=\dfrac{\dfrac{3}{a+2}-\dfrac{6}{a-2}}{\dfrac{5}{a+2}-\dfrac{1}{a-2}}$

$=\dfrac{\left(\dfrac{3}{a+2}-\dfrac{6}{a-2}\right)(a+2)(a-2)}{\left(\dfrac{5}{a+2}-\dfrac{1}{a-2}\right)(a+2)(a-2)}$

$=\dfrac{3(a-2)-6(a+2)}{5(a-2)-1(a+2)}$

$=\dfrac{3a-6-6a-12}{5a-10-a-2}$

$=\dfrac{-3a-18}{4a-12}$

c. $\dfrac{x^{-1}+y^{-1}}{xy}=\dfrac{\dfrac{1}{x}+\dfrac{1}{y}}{xy}=\dfrac{\left(\dfrac{1}{x}+\dfrac{1}{y}\right)xy}{(xy)xy}=\dfrac{y+x}{x^2y^2}$

15. $\dfrac{2x}{2x-1}+\dfrac{1}{x}=\dfrac{1}{2x-1}$

$x(2x-1)\left(\dfrac{2x}{2x-1}+\dfrac{1}{x}\right)=x(2x-1)\left(\dfrac{1}{2x-1}\right)$

$2x^2+2x-1=x$

$2x^2+x-1=0$

$(2x-1)(x+1)=0$

$2x-1=0$ or $x+1=0$

$x=\dfrac{1}{2}$ or $\quad x=-1$

Discard $\dfrac{1}{2}$ as extraneous. The solution is -1.

16. $\dfrac{x^3-8}{x-2}=\dfrac{(x-2)(x^2+2x+4)}{(x-2)}=x^2+2x+4$

17. Let x = the speed of the current.

$$t_{up}=t_{down}$$
$$\dfrac{72}{30-x}=\dfrac{1.5(72)}{30+x}$$
$$1.5(72)(30-x)=72(30+x)$$
$$3240-108x=2160+72x$$
$$1080=180x$$
$$x=6$$

The speed of the current is 6 miles per hour.

18.
$$\begin{array}{r|rrr} 2 & 8 & -12 & -7 \\ & & 16 & 8 \\ \hline & 8 & 4 & 1 \end{array}$$

Answer: $8x+4+\dfrac{1}{x-2}$

19. a. $\sqrt[4]{81}=3$ because $3^4=81$.

b. $\sqrt[5]{-243}=-3$ because $(-3)^5=-243$.

c. $-\sqrt{25}=-5$ because $5^2=25$.

d. $\sqrt[4]{-81}$ is not a real number.

e. $\sqrt[3]{64x^3}=4x$ because $(4x)^3=64x^3$.

20. $\dfrac{1}{a+5} = \dfrac{1}{3a+6} - \dfrac{a+2}{a^2+7a+10}$

$\dfrac{1}{a+5} = \dfrac{1}{3(a+2)} - \dfrac{a+2}{(a+2)(a+5)}$

$3(a+2)(a+5)\left(\dfrac{1}{a+5}\right) =$

$\quad 3(a+2)(a+5)\left(\dfrac{1}{3(a+2)} - \dfrac{a+2}{(a+2)(a+5)}\right)$

$3(a+2) = a+5 - 3(a+2)$

$3a+6 = a+5 - 3a - 6$

$5a = -7$

$a = -\dfrac{7}{5}$

21. a. $\sqrt{x} \cdot \sqrt[4]{x} = x^{1/2} \cdot x^{1/4} = x^{1/2+1/4} = x^{3/4} = \sqrt[4]{x^3}$

b. $\dfrac{\sqrt{x}}{\sqrt[3]{x}} = \dfrac{x^{1/2}}{x^{1/3}} = x^{1/2-1/3} = x^{3/6-2/6} = x^{1/6} = \sqrt[6]{x}$

c. $\sqrt[3]{3} \cdot \sqrt{2} = \sqrt[6]{3^2} \cdot \sqrt[6]{2^3} = \sqrt[6]{9} \cdot \sqrt[6]{8} = \sqrt[6]{72}$

22. $y = kx$

$\dfrac{1}{2} = k \cdot 12$

$k = \dfrac{1}{24}, \; y = \dfrac{1}{24}x$

23. a. $\sqrt{3}\left(5 + \sqrt{30}\right) = 5\sqrt{3} + \sqrt{90}$

$\qquad = 5\sqrt{3} + \sqrt{9}\sqrt{10}$

$\qquad = 5\sqrt{3} + 3\sqrt{10}$

b. $\left(\sqrt{5} - \sqrt{6}\right)\left(\sqrt{7} + 1\right) = \sqrt{35} + \sqrt{5} - \sqrt{42} - \sqrt{6}$

c. $\left(7\sqrt{x} + 5\right)\left(3\sqrt{x} - \sqrt{5}\right)$

$\qquad = 21x - 7\sqrt{5x} + 15\sqrt{x} - 5\sqrt{5}$

d. $\left(4\sqrt{3} - 1\right)^2 = \left(4\sqrt{3}\right)^2 - 2\left(4\sqrt{3}\right)(1) + 1^2$

$\qquad = 48 - 8\sqrt{3} + 1$

$\qquad = 49 - 8\sqrt{3}$

e. $\left(\sqrt{2x} - 5\right)\left(\sqrt{2x} + 5\right) = \left(\sqrt{2x}\right)^2 - 5^2$

$\qquad = 2x - 25$

f. $\left(\sqrt{x-3} + 5\right)^2$

$\qquad = \left(\sqrt{x-3}\right)^2 + 2\left(\sqrt{x-3}\right)(5) + 5^2$

$\qquad = x - 3 + 10\sqrt{x-3} + 25$

$\qquad = x + 22 + 10\sqrt{x-3}$

24. a. $\sqrt[4]{81} = 3$ because $3^4 = 81$.

b. $\sqrt[3]{-27} = -3$ because $(-3)^3 = -27$.

c. $\sqrt{\dfrac{9}{64}} = \dfrac{3}{8}$ because $\left(\dfrac{3}{8}\right)^2 = \dfrac{9}{64}$.

d. $\sqrt[4]{x^{12}} = x^3$ because $\left(x^3\right)^4 = x^{12}$.

e. $\sqrt[3]{-125y^6} = -5y^2$ because $\left(-5y^2\right)^3 = -125y^6$.

25. $\dfrac{\sqrt[4]{x}}{\sqrt[4]{81y^5}} = \dfrac{\sqrt[4]{x}}{\sqrt[4]{81y^5}} \cdot \dfrac{\sqrt[4]{y^3}}{\sqrt[4]{y^3}} = \dfrac{\sqrt[4]{xy^3}}{\sqrt[4]{81y^8}} = \dfrac{\sqrt[4]{xy^3}}{3y^2}$

26. a. $a^{1/4}\left(a^{3/4} - a^8\right) = a^{1/4+3/4} - a^{1/4+8}$

$\qquad = a - a^{33/4}$

b. $x + 3x^{1/2} - 15$

27. $\sqrt{4-x} = x - 2$

$\left(\sqrt{4-x}\right)^2 = (x-2)^2$

$4 - x = x^2 - 4x + 4$

$0 = x^2 - 3x$

$x(x-3) = 0$

$x = 0$ or $x = 3$

Discard 0 as extraneous. The solution is 3.

28. a. $\dfrac{\sqrt{54}}{\sqrt{6}} = \sqrt{\dfrac{54}{6}} = \sqrt{9} = 3$

b. $\dfrac{\sqrt{108a^2}}{3\sqrt{3}} = \dfrac{1}{3}\sqrt{\dfrac{108a^2}{3}}$

$\qquad = \dfrac{1}{3}\sqrt{36a^2}$

$\qquad = \dfrac{1}{3} \cdot 6a$

$\qquad = 2a$

c. $\dfrac{3\sqrt[3]{81a^5b^{10}}}{\sqrt[3]{3b^4}} = 3\sqrt[3]{\dfrac{81a^5b^{10}}{3b^4}}$

$\qquad = 3\sqrt[3]{27a^5b^6}$

$\qquad = 9ab^2\sqrt[3]{a^2}$

29. $3x^2 - 9x + 8 = 0$

$$x^2 - 3x + \frac{8}{3} = 0$$

$$x^2 - 3x = -\frac{8}{3}$$

$$x^2 - 3x + \frac{9}{4} = -\frac{8}{3} + \frac{9}{4}$$

$$\left(x - \frac{3}{2}\right)^2 = -\frac{5}{12}$$

$$x - \frac{3}{2} = \pm\sqrt{-\frac{5}{12}}$$

$$x - \frac{3}{2} = \pm\frac{i\sqrt{15}}{6}$$

$$x = \frac{3}{2} \pm \frac{i\sqrt{15}}{6} = \frac{9 \pm i\sqrt{15}}{6}$$

30. a. $\dfrac{\sqrt{20}}{3} + \dfrac{\sqrt{5}}{4} = \dfrac{2\sqrt{5}}{3} + \dfrac{\sqrt{5}}{4}$

$$= \frac{8\sqrt{5}}{12} + \frac{3\sqrt{5}}{12}$$

$$= \frac{11\sqrt{15}}{12}$$

b. $\sqrt[3]{\dfrac{24x}{27}} - \dfrac{\sqrt[3]{3x}}{2} = \dfrac{2\sqrt[3]{3x}}{3} - \dfrac{\sqrt[3]{3x}}{2}$

$$= \frac{4\sqrt[3]{3x}}{6} - \frac{3\sqrt[3]{3x}}{6}$$

$$= \frac{\sqrt[3]{3x}}{6}$$

31.

$$\frac{3x}{x-2} - \frac{x+1}{x} = \frac{6}{x(x-2)}$$

$$x(x-2)\left(\frac{3x}{x-2} - \frac{x+1}{x}\right) = x(x-2)\frac{6}{x(x-2)}$$

$$3x(x) - (x+1)(x-2) = 6$$

$$3x^2 - x^2 + x + 2 = 6$$

$$2x^2 + x - 4 = 0$$

$$x = \frac{-1 \pm \sqrt{1^2 - 4(2)(-4)}}{2(2)}$$

$$x = \frac{-1 \pm \sqrt{33}}{4}$$

32. $\sqrt[3]{\dfrac{27}{m^4n^8}} = \sqrt[3]{\dfrac{27}{m^4n^8} \cdot \dfrac{m^2n}{m^2n}} = \sqrt[3]{\dfrac{27m^2n}{m^6n^9}} = \dfrac{3\sqrt[3]{m^2n}}{m^2n^3}$

33. $x^2 - 4x \le 0$

$$x(x-4) = 0$$

$$\begin{array}{c} \xleftarrow{\hspace{0.5em}} \;|\;|\;|\;|\;|\;[\;|\;|\;|\;|\;|\; \xrightarrow{\hspace{0.5em}} \\ {\scriptstyle -5\; -4\; -3\; -2\; -1\;\; 0\;\; 1\;\; 2\;\;\; 3\;\; 4\;\; 5} \end{array}$$

Check a test value in each region in the original inequality. Values in the region [0, 4] satisfy the inequality. Thus, the solution set is [0, 4].

34. Let $x =$ the length of the unknown side.

$$x^2 + 4^2 = 8^2$$

$$x^2 + 16 = 64$$

$$x^2 = 48$$

$$x = \pm\sqrt{48} = \pm 4\sqrt{3}$$

Discard $-4\sqrt{3}$ because the length cannot be negative. The unknown side measure $4\sqrt{3}$ in.

35. The graph of $F(x) = (x-3)^2 + 1$ is the graph of $y = x^2$ shifted right 3 units and up 1 unit. The vertex is (3, 1), and the axis of symmetry is $x = 3$.

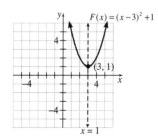

36. a. $i^8 = \left(i^4\right)^2 = 1^2 = 1$

b. $i^{21} = \left(i^4\right)^5 \cdot i = 1^5 \cdot i = i$

c. $i^{42} = \left(i^4\right)^{10} \cdot i^2 = 1^{10}(-1) = -1$

d. $i^{-13} = \left(i^4\right)^{-4} \cdot i^3 = 1^{-4}(-i) = -i$

37. a. $(f+g)(x) = (x-1) + (2x-3) = 3x - 4$

b. $(f-g)(x) = (x-1) - (2x-3)$
$$= x - 1 - 2x + 3$$
$$= -x + 2$$

c. $(f \cdot g)(x) = (x-1)(2x-3) = 2x^2 - 5x - 3$

d. $\left(\dfrac{f}{g}\right)(x) = \dfrac{x-1}{2x-3}$, where $x \ne \dfrac{3}{2}$

38. $4x^2 + 8x - 1 = 0$

$$x^2 + 2x - \frac{1}{4} = 0$$

$$x^2 + 2x = \frac{1}{4}$$

$$x^2 + 2x + 1 = \frac{1}{4} + 1$$

$$(x+1)^2 = \frac{5}{4}$$

$$x + 1 = \pm\sqrt{\frac{5}{4}}$$

$$x + 1 = \pm\frac{\sqrt{5}}{2}$$

$$x = -1 \pm \frac{\sqrt{5}}{2} \quad \text{or} \quad \frac{-2 \pm \sqrt{5}}{2}$$

39. $f(x) = x + 3$

$$y = x + 3$$
$$x = y + 3$$
$$x - 3 = y$$
$$f^{-1}(x) = x - 3$$

40. $\left(x - \dfrac{1}{2}\right)^2 = \dfrac{1}{2}x$

$$x^2 - x + \frac{1}{4} = \frac{1}{2}x$$

$$x^2 - \frac{3}{2}x + \frac{1}{4} = 0$$

$$4\left(x^2 - \frac{3}{2}x + \frac{1}{4}\right) = 4(0)$$

$$4x^2 - 6x + 1 = 0$$

$$a = 4, b = -6, c = 1$$

$$x = \frac{-(-6) \pm \sqrt{(-6)^2 - 4(4)(1)}}{2(4)}$$

$$= \frac{6 \pm \sqrt{20}}{8}$$

$$= \frac{6 \pm 2\sqrt{5}}{8}$$

$$= \frac{3 \pm \sqrt{5}}{4}$$

41. a. $\log_4 16 = \log_4 4^2 = 2$

b. $\log_{10} \dfrac{1}{10} = \log_{10} 10^{-1} = -1$

c. $\log_9 3 = \dfrac{1}{2}$ because $9^{1/2} = 3$.

42. The graph of $f(x) = -(x+1)^2 + 1$ is the graph of $y = x^2$ shifted left 1 unit, open down, and shift up 1 unit. The vertex is $(-1, 1)$, and the axis of symmetry is $x = -1$.

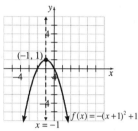

439

Chapter 10

Mental Math 10.1

1. The parabola $y = x^2 - 7x + 5$ opens upward because $a = 1$ is positive.

2. The parabola $y = -x^2 + 16$ opens downward because $a = -1$ is negative.

3. The parabola $x = -y^2 - y + 2$ opens to the left because $a = -1$ is negative.

4. The parabola $x = 3y^2 + 2y - 5$ opens to the right because $a = 3$ is positive.

5. The parabola $y = -x^2 + 2x + 1$ opens downward because $a = -1$ is negative.

6. The parabola $x = -y^2 + 2y - 6$ opens to the left because $a = -1$ is negative.

Exercise Set 10.1

1. $x = 3y^2 = 3(y - 0)^2 + 0$ is quadratic in y. The graph is similar to the graph of $x = y^2$, but narrower by a factor of $\frac{1}{3}$ because $a = 3$. The vertex is (0, 0), and the axis of symmetry is $y = 0$ (the x-axis).

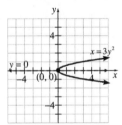

3. $x = (y - 2)^2 + 3$ is quadratic in y. The graph is similar to the graph of $x = y^2$, but is shifted up 2 units and to the right 3 units. The vertex is (3, 2), and the axis of symmetry is $y = 2$.

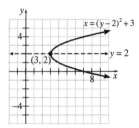

5. $y = 3(x - 1)^2 + 5$ is quadratic in x. The graph is similar to the graph of $y = x^2$, but narrower by a factor of $\frac{1}{3}$ because $a = 3$. The graph is shifted to the right 1 unit and up 5 units. The vertex is (1, 5), and the axis of symmetry is $x = 1$.

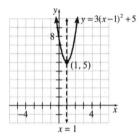

7.
$$x = y^2 + 6y + 8$$
$$x - 8 = y^2 + 6y$$
$$x - 8 + 9 = y^2 + 6y + 9$$
$$x + 1 = (y + 3)^2$$
$$x = (y + 3)^2 - 1$$

The equation is quadratic in y. The graph is similar to the graph of $x = y^2$, but is shifted down 3 units and to the left 1 unit. The vertex is $(-1, -3)$, and the axis of symmetry is $y = -3$.

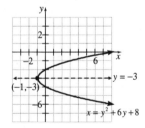

9.
$$y = x^2 + 10x + 20$$
$$y - 20 = x^2 + 10x$$
$$y - 20 + 25 = x^2 + 10x + 25$$
$$y + 5 = (x+5)^2$$
$$y = (x+5)^2 - 5$$

The equation is quadratic in x. The graph is similar to the graph of $y = x^2$, but shifted to the left 5 units and down 5 units. The vertex is $(-5, -5)$, and the axis of symmetry is $x = -5$.

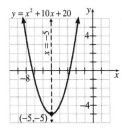

11.
$$x = -2y^2 + 4y + 6$$
$$x - 6 = -2(y^2 - 2y)$$
$$x - 6 + [-2(1)] = -2(y^2 - 2y + 1)$$
$$x - 8 = -2(y-1)^2$$
$$x = -2(y-1)^2 + 8$$

The equation is quadratic in y. The graph is similar to the graph of $x = y^2$, but opens to the left and is narrower because $a = -2$. The graph is shifted up 1 unit and to the right 8 units. The vertex is $(8, 1)$, and the axis of symmetry is $y = 1$.

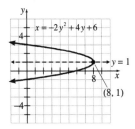

13. (5, 1), (8, 5)
$$d = \sqrt{(8-5)^2 + (5-1)^2}$$
$$= \sqrt{9+16}$$
$$= \sqrt{25}$$
$$= 5 \text{ units}$$

15. (–3, 2), (1, –3)
$$d = \sqrt{[1-(-3)]^2 + (-3-2)^2}$$
$$= \sqrt{4^2 + (-5)^2}$$
$$= \sqrt{16+25}$$
$$= \sqrt{41} \text{ units}$$

17. (–9, 4), (–8, 1)
$$d = \sqrt{[-8-(-9)]^2 + (1-4)^2}$$
$$= \sqrt{1^2 + (-3)^2}$$
$$= \sqrt{1+9}$$
$$= \sqrt{10} \text{ units}$$

19. $\left(0, -\sqrt{2}\right), \left(\sqrt{3}, 0\right)$
$$d = \sqrt{\left(\sqrt{3}-0\right)^2 + \left[0-\left(-\sqrt{2}\right)\right]^2}$$
$$= \sqrt{\left(\sqrt{3}\right)^2 + \left(\sqrt{2}\right)^2}$$
$$= \sqrt{3+5}$$
$$= \sqrt{5} \text{ units}$$

21. (1.7, –3.6), (–8.6, 5.7)
$$d = \sqrt{(-8.6-1.7)^2 + [5.7-(-3.6)]^2}$$
$$= \sqrt{(-10.3)^2 + (9.3)^2}$$
$$= \sqrt{192.58}$$
$$= 13.88 \text{ units}$$

23. $\left(2\sqrt{3}, \sqrt{6}\right), \left(-\sqrt{3}, 4\sqrt{6}\right)$
$$d = \sqrt{\left(-\sqrt{3}-2\sqrt{3}\right)^2 + \left(4\sqrt{6}-\sqrt{6}\right)^2}$$
$$= \sqrt{\left(-3\sqrt{3}\right)^2 + \left(3\sqrt{6}\right)^2}$$
$$= \sqrt{27+54}$$
$$= \sqrt{81}$$
$$= 9 \text{ units}$$

25. (6, –8), (2, 4)
$$\left(\frac{6+2}{2}, \frac{-8+4}{2}\right) = \left(\frac{8}{2}, \frac{-4}{2}\right) = (4, -2)$$
The midpoint of the segment is $(4, -2)$.

27. (–2, –1), (–8, 6)
$$\left(\frac{-2+(-8)}{2}, \frac{-1+6}{2}\right) = \left(\frac{-10}{2}, \frac{5}{2}\right) = \left(-5, \frac{5}{2}\right)$$
The midpoint of the segment is $\left(-5, \frac{5}{2}\right)$.

29. $(7, 3), (-1, -3)$

$$\left(\frac{7+(-1)}{2}, \frac{3+(-3)}{2}\right) = \left(\frac{6}{2}, \frac{0}{2}\right) = (3, 0)$$

The midpoint of the segment is $(3, 0)$.

31. $\left(\frac{1}{2}, \frac{3}{8}\right), \left(-\frac{3}{2}, \frac{5}{8}\right)$

$$\left(\frac{\frac{1}{2}+\left(-\frac{3}{2}\right)}{2}, \frac{\frac{3}{8}+\frac{5}{8}}{2}\right) = \left(\frac{-1}{2}, \frac{1}{2}\right)$$

The midpoint of the segment is $\left(-\frac{1}{2}, \frac{1}{2}\right)$.

33. $\left(\sqrt{2}, 3\sqrt{5}\right), \left(\sqrt{2}, -2\sqrt{5}\right)$

$$\left(\frac{\sqrt{2}+\sqrt{2}}{2}, \frac{3\sqrt{5}+\left(-2\sqrt{5}\right)}{2}\right) = \left(\frac{2\sqrt{2}}{2}, \frac{\sqrt{5}}{2}\right)$$

$$= \left(\sqrt{2}, \frac{\sqrt{5}}{2}\right)$$

The midpoint of the segment is $\left(\sqrt{2}, \frac{\sqrt{5}}{2}\right)$.

35. $(4.6, -3.5), (7.8, -9.8)$

$$\left(\frac{4.6+7.8}{2}, \frac{-3.5+(-9.8)}{2}\right) = \left(\frac{12.4}{2}, \frac{-13.2}{2}\right)$$

$$= (6.2, -6.65)$$

The midpoint of the segment is $(6.2, -6.65)$.

37. $x^2 + y^2 = 9$

$(x-0)^2 + (y-0)^2 = 3^2$

The center is $(0, 0)$, and the radius is 3.

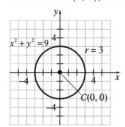

39. $x^2 + (y-2)^2 = 1$

$(x-0)^2 + (y-2)^2 = 1^2$

The center is $(0, 2)$, and the radius is 1.

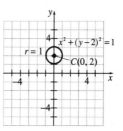

41. $(x-5)^2 + (y+2)^2 = 1$

$(x-5)^2 + (y+2)^2 = 1^2$

The center is $(5, -2)$, and the radius is 1.

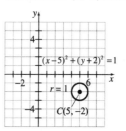

43. $x^2 + y^2 + 6y = 0$

$x^2 + (y^2 + 6y) = 0$

$x^2 + (y^2 + 6y + 9) = 9$

$(x-0)^2 + (y+3)^2 = 9$

The center is $(0, -3)$, and the radius is 3.

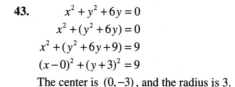

45. $$x^2 + y^2 + 2x - 4y = 4$$

$$(x^2 + 2x) + (y^2 - 4y) = 4$$

$$(x^2 + 2x + 1) + (y^2 - 4y + 4) = 4 + 1 + 4$$

$$(x+1)^2 + (y-2)^2 = 9$$

The center is $(-1, 2)$, and the radius is 3.

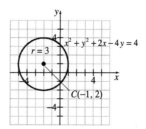

47.
$$x^2 + y^2 - 4x - 8y - 2 = 0$$
$$(x^2 - 4x) + (y^2 - 8y) = 2$$
$$(x^2 - 4x + 4) + (y^2 - 8y + 16) = 2 + 4 + 16$$
$$(x-2)^2 + (y-4)^2 = 22$$

The center is (2, 4), and the radius is $\sqrt{22}$.

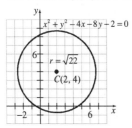

49. Center $(h, k) = (2, 3)$ and radius $r = 6$.
$$(x-h)^2 + (y-k)^2 = r^2$$
$$(x-2)^2 + (y-3)^2 = 6^2$$
$$(x-2)^2 + (y-3)^2 = 36$$

51. Center $(h, k) = (0, 0)$ and radius $r = \sqrt{3}$.
$$(x-h)^2 + (y-k)^2 = r^2$$
$$(x-0)^2 + (y-0)^2 = \left(\sqrt{3}\right)^2$$
$$x^2 + y^2 = 3$$

53. Center $(h, k) = (-5, 4)$ and radius $r = 3\sqrt{5}$.
$$(x-h)^2 + (y-k)^2 = r^2$$
$$[x-(-5)]^2 + (y-4)^2 = \left(3\sqrt{5}\right)^2$$
$$(x+2)^2 + (y-4)^2 = 45$$

55. Answers may vary. One possibility follows.
The equation of a circle will have both x^2 and y^2 terms. A parabola will contain either an x^2 term or a y^2 term, but not both. If the equation of the parabola contains an x^2 term, then it will be and upward or downward parabola. If the equation of the parabola contains a y^2 term, then it will be a left-opening or right-opening parabola.

57. $x = y^2 - 3$
$$x = (y-0)^2 - 3$$
The equation is quadratic in *y*. The graph is similar to the graph of $x = y^2$, but is shifted left 3 units. The vertex is $(-3, 0)$, and the axis of symmetry is $y = 0$ (the *x*-axis).

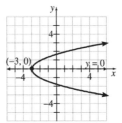

59. $y = (x-2)^2 - 2$
The equation is quadratic in *x*. The graph is similar to the graph of $y = x^2$, but is shifted right 2 units and down 3 units. The vertex is $(2, -2)$, and the axis of symmetry is $x = 2$.

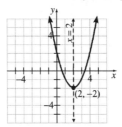

61. $x^2 + y^2 = 1$
The center is (0, 0), and the radius is $\sqrt{1} = 1$.

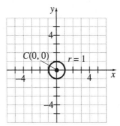

63. $x = (y+3)^2 - 1$
The equation is quadratic in *y*. The graph is similar to the graph of $x = y^2$, but is shifted down 3 units and left 1 unit. The vertex is $(-1, -3)$, and the axis of symmetry is $y = -3$.

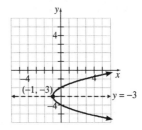

65. $(x-2)^2 + (y-2)^2 = 16$

The center is (2, 2), and the radius is $\sqrt{16} = 4$.

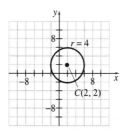

67. $x = -(y-1)^2$

The equation is quadratic in y. The graph is similar to the graph of $x = y^2$, but opens to the left because $a = -1$. The graph is shifted up 1 unit. The vertex is $(0,\ 1)$, and the axis of symmetry is $y = 1$.

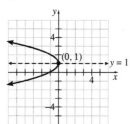

69. $(x-4)^2 + y^2 = 7$

The center is (4, 0), and the radius is $\sqrt{7}$.

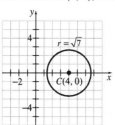

71. $y = 5(x+5)^2 + 3$

The equation is quadratic in x. The graph is similar to the graph of $y = x^2$, but narrower by a factor of $\dfrac{1}{5}$ because $a = 5$. The graph is shifted left 5 units and up 3 units. The vertex is $(-5,\ 3)$, and the axis of symmetry is $x = -5$.

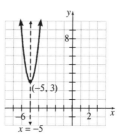

73.
$$\frac{x^2}{8} + \frac{y^2}{8} = 2$$
$$8\left(\frac{x^2}{8} + \frac{y^2}{8}\right) = 8(2)$$
$$x^2 + y^2 = 16$$

The center is (0, 0), and the radius is $\sqrt{16} = 4$.

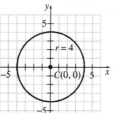

75.
$$y = x^2 + 7x + 6$$
$$y - 6 = x^2 + 7x$$
$$y - 6 + \frac{49}{4} = x^2 + 7x + \frac{49}{4}$$
$$y + \frac{25}{4} = \left(x + \frac{7}{2}\right)^2$$
$$y = \left(x + \frac{7}{2}\right)^2 - \frac{25}{4}$$

The equation is quadratic is x. The graph is similar to the graph of $y = x^2$, but is shifted left $\dfrac{7}{2}$ units and down $\dfrac{25}{4}$ units. The vertex is $\left(-\dfrac{7}{2}, -\dfrac{25}{4}\right)$, and the axis of symmetry is $x = -\dfrac{7}{2}$.

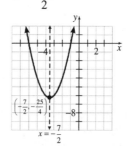

77.
$$x^2 + y^2 + 2x + 12y - 12 = 0$$
$$(x^2 + 2x) + (y^2 + 12y) = 12$$
$$(x^2 + 2x + 1) + (y^2 + 12y + 36) = 12 + 1 + 36$$
$$(x+1)^2 + (y+6)^2 = 49$$

The center is $(-1, -6)$, and the radius is $\sqrt{49} = 7$.

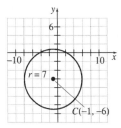

79.
$$x = y^2 + 8y - 4$$
$$x + 4 = y^2 + 8y$$
$$x + 4 + 16 = y^2 + 8y + 16$$
$$x + 20 = (y+4)^2$$
$$x = (y+4)^2 - 20$$

The equation is quadratic in y. The graph is similar to the graph of $x = y^2$, but is shifted down 4 units and left 20 units. The vertex is $(-20, -4)$, and the axis of symmetry is $y = -4$.

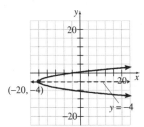

81.
$$x^2 - 10y + y^2 + 4 = 0$$
$$x^2 + (y^2 - 10y) = -4$$
$$x^2 + (y^2 - 10y + 25) = -4 + 25$$
$$x^2 + (y-5)^2 = 21$$

The center is $(-1, -6)$, and the radius is $\sqrt{21}$

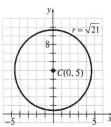

83.
$$x = -3y^2 + 30y$$
$$x = -3(y^2 - 10y)$$
$$x + [-3(25)] = -3(y^2 - 10y + 25)$$
$$x - 75 = -3(y-5)^2$$
$$x = -3(y-5)^2 + 75$$

The equation is quadratic in y. The graph is similar to the graph of $x = y^2$, but opens to the left and is narrower because $a = -2$. The graph is shifted up 5 units and right 75 units. The vertex is $(75, 5)$, and the axis of symmetry is $y = 5$.

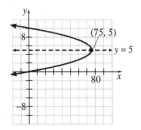

85.
$$5x^2 + 5y^2 = 25$$
$$x^2 + y^2 = 5$$

The center is $(0, 0)$, and the radius is $\sqrt{5}$

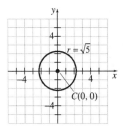

87.
$$y = 5x^2 - 20x + 16$$
$$y - 16 = 5(x^2 - 4x)$$
$$y - 16 + 5(4) = 5(x^2 - 4x + 4)$$
$$y + 4 = 4(x-2)^2$$
$$y = 4(x-2)^2 - 4$$

The equation is quadratic in x. The graph is similar to the graph of $y = x^2$, but narrower by a factor of $\frac{1}{4}$ because $a = 4$. The graph is shifted right 2 units and down 4 units. The vertex is $(2, -5)$, and the axis of symmetry is $x = 2$.

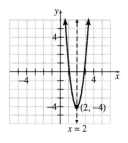

$x = 2$

89. $x^2 + y^2 = 20$

$$y^2 = 20 - x^2$$
$$y = \pm\sqrt{20 - x^2}$$

Graph $y_1 = \sqrt{20 - x^2}$ and $y_2 = -\sqrt{20 - x^2}$ in a $[-15, 15, 1]$ by $[-10, 10, 1]$ window.

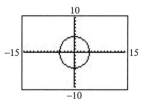

91. $x = -7 - 6y - y^2$

$$y^2 + 6y = -7 - x$$
$$y^2 + 6y + 9 = -7 - x + 9$$
$$(y + 3)^2 = 2 - x$$
$$y + 3 = \pm\sqrt{2 - x}$$
$$y = -3 \pm \sqrt{2 - x}$$

Graph $y_1 = -3 + \sqrt{2 - x}$ and $y_2 = -3 - \sqrt{2 - x}$ in a $[-15, 15, 1]$ by $[-10, 10, 1]$ window.

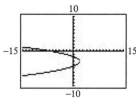

93. $(x + 3)^2 + (y - 1)^2 = 15$

$$(y - 1)^2 = 15 - (x + 3)^2$$
$$y - 1 = \pm\sqrt{15 - (x + 3)^2}$$
$$y = 1 \pm \sqrt{15 - (x + 3)^2}$$

Graph $y_1 = 1 + \sqrt{15 - (x + 3)^2}$ and $y_2 = 1 - \sqrt{15 - (x + 3)^2}$ in a $[-15, 15, 1]$ by $[-10, 10, 1]$ window.

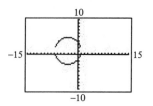

95. $x = 9y^2 - 6y + 4$

$$\frac{1}{9}x = y^2 - \frac{2}{3}y + \frac{4}{9}$$
$$y^2 - \frac{2}{3}y = \frac{1}{9}x - \frac{4}{9}$$
$$y^2 - \frac{2}{3}y + \frac{1}{9} = \frac{1}{9}x - \frac{4}{9} + \frac{1}{9}$$
$$\left(y - \frac{1}{3}\right)^2 = \frac{x - 3}{9}$$
$$y - \frac{1}{3} = \pm\sqrt{\frac{x - 3}{9}}$$
$$y - \frac{1}{3} = \pm\frac{\sqrt{x - 3}}{3}$$
$$y = \frac{1 \pm \sqrt{x - 3}}{3}$$

Graph $y_1 = \dfrac{1 + \sqrt{x - 3}}{3}$ and $y_2 = \dfrac{1 - \sqrt{x - 3}}{3}$ in a $[-15, 15, 1]$ by $[-10, 10, 1]$ window.

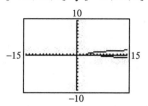

97. $y = -3x + 3$

The slope of the line is $m = -3$, and the y-intercept is $b = 3$. Begin at the point $(0, 3)$. Using the slope, move down 3 units and to the right 1 unit to the point $(1, 0)$. Connect the point to obtain the graph.

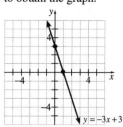

$y = -3x + 3$

99. The equation $x = -2$ represents a vertical line through x-intercept $(-2, 0)$.

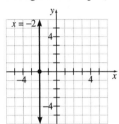

101. $\dfrac{\sqrt{5}}{\sqrt{8}} = \dfrac{\sqrt{5}}{2\sqrt{2}} = \dfrac{\sqrt{5} \cdot \sqrt{2}}{2\sqrt{2} \cdot \sqrt{2}} = \dfrac{\sqrt{10}}{2 \cdot 2} = \dfrac{\sqrt{10}}{4}$

103. $\dfrac{10}{\sqrt{5}} = \dfrac{10 \cdot \sqrt{5}}{\sqrt{5} \cdot \sqrt{5}} = \dfrac{10\sqrt{5}}{5} = 2\sqrt{5}$

105. Height = 264 ft and diameter $d = 250$ ft

    a. radius $= \dfrac{1}{2}d = \dfrac{1}{2}(250) = 125$ ft

    b. $264 - 250 = 14$ ft from the ground

    c. $125 + 14 = 139$ ft from the ground

    d. Center: $(0, 139)$

    e. $(x-h)^2 + (y-k)^2 = r^2$
$$(x-0)^2 + (y-139)^2 = 125^2$$
$$x^2 + (y-139)^2 = 15{,}625$$

107. $B(3, 1)$ and $C(19, 13)$
$$d = \sqrt{(13-1)^2 + (19-3)^2}$$
$$= \sqrt{12^2 + 16^2}$$
$$= \sqrt{144 + 256}$$
$$= \sqrt{400}$$
$$= 20 \text{ meters}$$

109. $y = a(x-h)^2 + k$

Vertex: $(0, 40)$

$y = a(x-0)^2 + 40$

$y = ax^2 + 40$

The parabola passes through $(50, 0)$.

$0 = a(50)^2 + 40$

$-40 = 2500a$

$a = \dfrac{-40}{2500} = -\dfrac{2}{125}$

Thus, the equation is $y = -\dfrac{2}{125}x^2 + 40$.

111. $5x^2 + 5y^2 = 25$
$$5y^2 = 25 - 5x^2$$
$$y^2 = 5 - x^2$$
$$y = \pm\sqrt{5 - x^2}$$

Graph $y_1 = \sqrt{5 - x^2}$ and $y_2 = -\sqrt{5 - x^2}$ in a $[-6, 6, 1]$ by $[-4, 4, 1]$ window.

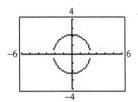

113. $y = 5x^2 - 20x + 16$

Graph $y_1 = 5x^2 - 20x + 16$ in a $[-12, 12, 1]$ by $[-4, 12, 1]$ window.

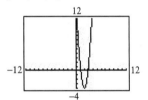

Mental Math 10.2

1. $\dfrac{x^2}{16} + \dfrac{y^2}{4} = 1$; Ellipse

2. $\dfrac{x^2}{16} - \dfrac{y^2}{4} = 1$; Hyperbola

3. $x^2 - 5y^2 = 3$; Hyperbola

4. $-x^2 + 5y^2 = 3$
$$5y^2 - x^2 = 3; \text{ Hyperbola}$$

5. $-\dfrac{y^2}{25} + \dfrac{x^2}{36} = 1$
$$\dfrac{x^2}{36} - \dfrac{y^2}{25} = 1; \text{ Hyperbola}$$

6. $\dfrac{y^2}{25} + \dfrac{x^2}{36} = 1$; Ellipse

Exercise Set 10.2

1. $\dfrac{x^2}{4} + \dfrac{y^2}{25} = 1$

$\dfrac{x^2}{2^2} + \dfrac{y^2}{5^2} = 1$

Center: $(0, 0)$
x-intercepts: $(-2, 0), (2, 0)$
y-intercepts: $(0, -5), (0, 5)$

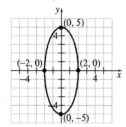

3. $\dfrac{x^2}{16} + \dfrac{y^2}{9} = 1$

$\dfrac{x^2}{4^2} + \dfrac{y^2}{3^2} = 1$

Center: $(0, 0)$
x-intercepts: $(-4, 0), (4, 0)$
y-intercepts: $(0, -3), (0, 3)$

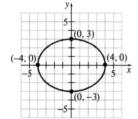

5. $9x^2 + 4y^2 = 36$

$\dfrac{x^2}{4} + \dfrac{y^2}{9} = 1$

$\dfrac{x^2}{2^2} + \dfrac{y^2}{3^2} = 1$

Center: $(0, 0)$
x-intercepts: $(-2, 0), (2, 0)$
y-intercepts: $(0, -3), (0, 3)$

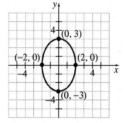

7. $4x^2 + 25y^2 = 100$

$\dfrac{x^2}{25} + \dfrac{y^2}{4} = 1$

$\dfrac{x^2}{5^2} + \dfrac{y^2}{2^2} = 1$

Center: $(0, 0)$
x-intercepts: $(-5, 0), (5, 0)$
y-intercepts: $(0, -2), (0, 2)$

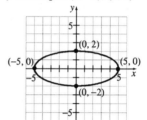

9. $\dfrac{(x+1)^2}{36} + \dfrac{(y-2)^2}{49} = 1$

$\dfrac{(x+1)^2}{6^2} + \dfrac{(y-2)^2}{7^2} = 1$

Center: $(-1, 2)$
Other points:
$(-1-6, 2) = (-7, 2);\ (-1+6, 2) = (5, 2);$
$(-1, 2-7) = (-1, -5);\ (-1, 2+7) = (-1, 9)$

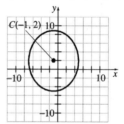

11. $\dfrac{(x-1)^2}{4} + \dfrac{(y-1)^2}{25} = 1$

$\dfrac{(x-1)^2}{2^2} + \dfrac{(y-1)^2}{5^2} = 1$

Center: $(1, 1)$
Other points:
$(1-2, 2) = (-1, 2);\ (1+2, 2) = (3, 2);$
$(1, 1-5) = (1, -4);\ (1, 1+5) = (1, 6)$

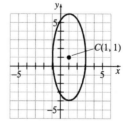

13.

$$\frac{x^2}{4} - \frac{y^2}{9} = 1$$

$$\frac{x^2}{2^2} - \frac{y^2}{3^2} = 1$$

$$a = 2, b = 3$$

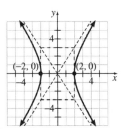

15.

$$\frac{y^2}{25} - \frac{x^2}{16} = 1$$

$$\frac{x^2}{5^2} - \frac{y^2}{4^2} = 1$$

$$a = 5, b = 4$$

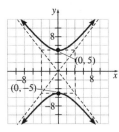

17.

$$x^2 - 4y^2 = 16$$

$$\frac{x^2}{16} - \frac{y^2}{4} = 1$$

$$\frac{x^2}{4^2} - \frac{y^2}{2^2} = 1$$

$$a = 4, b = 2$$

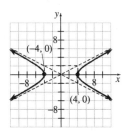

19.

$$16y^2 - x^2 = 16$$

$$\frac{y^2}{1} - \frac{x^2}{16} = 1$$

$$\frac{y^2}{1^2} - \frac{x^2}{4^2} = 1$$

$$a = 4, b = 1$$

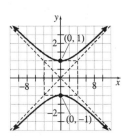

21. Answers may vary. One possibility follows: We can distinguish the different conic sections by the form of the equation. The general forms are:

Circle: $(x-h)^2 + (y-k)^2 = r^2$

Parabola: $y = a(x-h)^2 + k$ or $x = a(y-k)^2 + h$

Ellipse: $\dfrac{(x-h)^2}{a^2} + \dfrac{(y-k)^2}{b^2} = 1$

Hyperbola: $\dfrac{(x-h)^2}{a^2} - \dfrac{(y-k)^2}{b^2} = 1$ or

$\dfrac{(y-k)^2}{b^2} - \dfrac{(x-h)^2}{a^2} = 1$

23. Parabola

$$y = x^2 + 4$$

Vertex: $(0, 4)$

Axis of symmetry:

$x = 0$

Opens upward

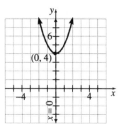

25. Ellipse

$$\frac{x^2}{4} + \frac{y^2}{9} = 1$$

$$\frac{x^2}{2^2} + \frac{y^2}{3^2} = 1$$

Center: $(0, 0)$

$a = 2$, $b = 3$

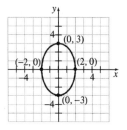

27. Hyperbola

$$\frac{x^2}{16} - \frac{y^2}{4} = 1$$

$$\frac{x^2}{4^2} - \frac{y^2}{2^2} = 1$$

Center: $(0, 0)$

$a = 4, b = 2$

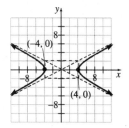

29. Circle

$$x^2 + y^2 = 16$$

Center: $(0, 0)$

Radius: $\sqrt{16} = 4$

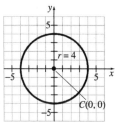

31. Parabola:

$$x = -y^2 + 6y$$

$$y = -\frac{b}{2a} = \frac{-6}{2(-1)} = 3$$

$$x = -(3)^2 + 6(3)$$

$$= -9 + 18$$

$$= 9$$

Vertex: $(9, 3)$

Axis of symmetry:

$y = 3$

Opens to the left

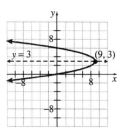

33. Ellipse

$$9x^2 + 4y^2 = 36$$

$$\frac{x^2}{4} + \frac{y^2}{9} = 1$$

$$\frac{x^2}{2^2} - \frac{y^2}{3^2} = 1$$

Center: (0, 0)
$a = 2, b = 3$

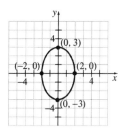

35. Hyperbola

$$y^2 = x^2 + 16$$

$$y^2 - x^2 = 16$$

$$\frac{y^2}{16} - \frac{x^2}{16} = 1$$

$$\frac{y^2}{4^2} - \frac{x^2}{4^2} = 1$$

Center: (0, 0)
$a = 4, b = 4$

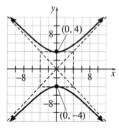

37. Parabola

$$y = -2x^2 + 4x - 3$$

$$x = -\frac{b}{2a} = \frac{-4}{2(-2)} = 1$$

$$y = -2(1)^2 + 4(1) - 3$$
$$= -1$$

Vertex: $(1, -1)$

Axis of symmetry:
$x = 1$

Opens downward

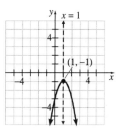

39. $20x^2 + 5y^2 = 100$

$$4x^2 + y^2 = 20$$

$$y^2 = 20 - 4x^2$$

$$y = \pm\sqrt{20 - 4x^2}$$

Graph $y_1 = \sqrt{20 - 4x^2}$ and $y_2 = -\sqrt{20 - 4x^2}$ in a $[-15, 15, 1]$ by $[-10, 10, 1]$ window.

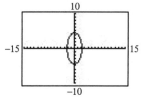

41. $7y^2 - 3x^2 = 21$

$$7y^2 = 3x^2 + 21$$

$$y^2 = \frac{3x^2 + 21}{7}$$

$$y = \pm\sqrt{\frac{3x^2 + 21}{7}}$$

Graph $y_1 = \sqrt{\frac{3x^2 + 21}{7}}$ and $y_2 = -\sqrt{\frac{3x^2 + 21}{7}}$ in a $[-15, 15, 1]$ by $[-10, 10, 1]$ window.

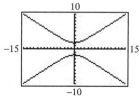

43. $18.8x^2 + 36.1y^2 = 205.8$

$$36.1y^2 = 205.8 - 18.8x^2$$

$$y^2 = \frac{205.8 - 18.8x^2}{36.1}$$

$$y = \pm\sqrt{\frac{205.8 - 18.8x^2}{36.1}}$$

Graph $y_1 = \sqrt{\frac{205.8 - 18.8x^2}{36.1}}$ and

$y_2 = -\sqrt{\frac{205.8 - 18.8x^2}{36.1}}$ in a $[-15, 15, 1]$ by $[-10, 10, 1]$ window.

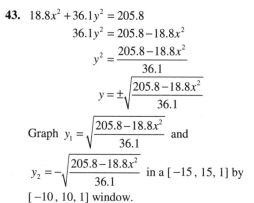

45. $4.5x^2 - 6.7y^2 = 50.7$

$$4.5x^2 - 50.7 = 6.7y^2$$

$$y^2 = \frac{4.5x^2 - 50.7}{6.7}$$

$$y = \pm\sqrt{\frac{4.5x^2 - 50.7}{6.7}}$$

Graph $y_1 = \sqrt{\frac{4.5x^2 - 50.7}{6.7}}$ and

$y_2 = -\sqrt{\frac{4.5x^2 - 50.7}{6.7}}$ in a $[-15, 15, 1]$ by $[-10, 10, 1]$ window.

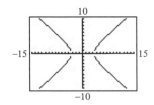

47. $x < 5$ or $x < 1$

$x < 5$

The solution set is $(-\infty, 5)$.

49. $2x - 1 \geq 7$ and $-3x \leq -6$

$2x \geq 8$ and $x \geq 2$

$x \geq 4$

$x \geq 4$

The solution set is $[4, \infty)$.

51. $2x^3 - 4x^3 = -2x^3$

53. $(-5x^2)(x^2) = -5x^{2+2} = -5x^4$

55. Circles: B, F

Ellipses: C, E, H

Hyperbolas: A, D, G

57. A: $c^2 = 36 + 13 = 49$; $c = \sqrt{49} = 7$

B: $c^2 = 4 - 4 = 0$; $c = \sqrt{0} = 0$

C: $c^2 = |25 - 16| = 9$; $c = \sqrt{9} = 3$

D: $c^2 = 39 + 25 = 64$; $c = \sqrt{64} = 8$

E: $c^2 = |81 - 17| = 64$; $c = \sqrt{64} = 8$

F: $c^2 = |36 - 36| = 0$; $c = \sqrt{0} = 0$

G: $c^2 = 65 + 16 = 81$; $c = \sqrt{81} = 9$

H: $c^2 = |144 - 140| = 4$; $c = \sqrt{4} = 2$

59. A: $e = \dfrac{7}{6}$ B: $e = \dfrac{0}{2} = 0$

C: $e = \dfrac{3}{5}$ D: $e = \dfrac{8}{5}$

E: $e = \dfrac{8}{9}$ F: $e = \dfrac{0}{6} = 0$

G: $e = \dfrac{9}{4}$ H: $e = \dfrac{2}{12} = \dfrac{1}{6}$

61. They are equal to 0.

63. Answers may vary. One possibility follows: If the eccentricity value is between 0 and 1, then the conic section will be an ellipse. If the eccentricity value is equal to 0, then the conic section will be a circle. If the eccentricity value is greater than 1, then the conic section will be a hyperbola. If the eccentricity value is equal to 1, then the conic section will be a parabola.

65. $a = 130,000,000$ and $b = 125,000,000$, so

$a^2 = (130,000,000)^2 = 1.69 \times 10^{16}$

$b^2 = (125,000,000)^2 = 1.5625 \times 10^{16}$

Thus, the equation is

$\dfrac{x^2}{1.69 \times 10^{16}} + \dfrac{y^2}{1.5625 \times 10^{16}} = 1$.

67. $9x^2 + 4y^2 = 36$

$4y^2 = 36 - 9x^2$

$y^2 = \dfrac{36 - 9x^2}{4}$

$y = \pm\sqrt{\dfrac{36 - 9x^2}{4}} = \pm\dfrac{\sqrt{36 - 9x^2}}{2}$

Graph $y_1 = \dfrac{\sqrt{36 - 9x^2}}{2}$ and $y_2 = -\dfrac{\sqrt{36 - 9x^2}}{2}$ in a $[-6, 6, 1]$ by $[-4, 4, 1]$ window.

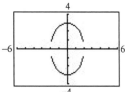

65. Hyperbola

$\dfrac{(x-1)^2}{4} - \dfrac{(y+1)^2}{25} = 1$

$\dfrac{(x-1)^2}{2^2} - \dfrac{(y+1)^2}{5^2} = 1$

Center: $(1, -1)$

$a = 2, b = 5$

71. Hyperbola

$\dfrac{y^2}{16} - \dfrac{(x+3)^2}{9} = 1$

$\dfrac{y^2}{4^2} - \dfrac{(x+3)^2}{3^2} = 1$

Center: $(-3, 0)$

$a = 3, b = 4$

73. Hyperbola

$$\frac{(x+5)^2}{16}-\frac{(y+2)^2}{25}=1$$

$$\frac{(x+5)^2}{4^2}-\frac{(y+2)^2}{5^2}=1$$

Center: (−5, −2)

$a=4, b=5$

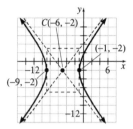

Integrated Review

1. Circle

$(x-7)^2+(y-2)^2=4$

Center: (7, 2)

radius: $\sqrt{4}=2$

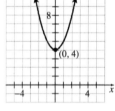

2. Parabola

$y=x^2+4$

Vertex: (0, 4)

Axis of symmetry:

$x=0$

Opens upward

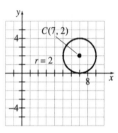

3. Parabola

$y=x^2+12x+36$

$x=-\dfrac{b}{2a}=-\dfrac{12}{2(1)}=-6$

$y=(-6)^2+12(-6)+36$

$\quad=0$

Vertex: (−6, 0)

Axis of symmetry:

$x=-6$

Opens upward

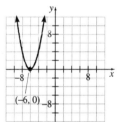

4. Ellipse

$$\frac{x^2}{4}+\frac{y^2}{9}=1$$

$$\frac{x^2}{2^2}+\frac{y^2}{3^2}=1$$

Center: (0, 0)

$a=2, b=3$

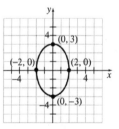

5. Hyperbola

$$\frac{y^2}{9}-\frac{x^2}{9}=1$$

$$\frac{y^2}{3^2}-\frac{x^2}{3^2}=1$$

Center: (0, 0)

$a=3, b=3$

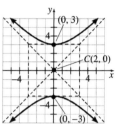

6. Hyperbola

$$\frac{x^2}{16}-\frac{y^2}{4}=1$$

$$\frac{x^2}{4^2}-\frac{y^2}{2^2}=1$$

Center: (0, 0)

$a=4, b=2$

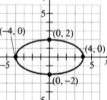

7. Ellipse

$$\frac{x^2}{16}+\frac{y^2}{4}=1$$

$$\frac{x^2}{4^2}+\frac{y^2}{2^2}=1$$

Center: (0, 0)

$a=4, b=2$

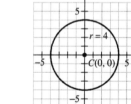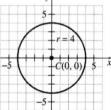

8. Circle

$x^2+y^2=16$

center: (0, 0)

radius: $\sqrt{16}=4$

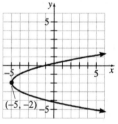

9. Parabola

$x=y^2+4y-1$

$y=-\dfrac{b}{2a}=\dfrac{-4}{2(1)}=-2$

$x=(-2)^2+4(-2)-1$

$\quad=-5$

Vertex: (−5, −2)

Axis of symmetry:

$y=-2$

Opens to the right

10. Parabola

$x = -y^2 + 6y$

$y = -\dfrac{b}{2a} = \dfrac{-6}{2(-1)} = 3$

$x = -(3)^2 + 6(3) = 9$

Vertex: (9, 3)

Axis of Symmetry:

$y = 3$

Opens to the left

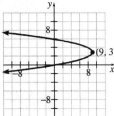

11. Hyperbola

$9x^2 - 4y^2 = 36$

$\dfrac{x^2}{4} - \dfrac{y^2}{9} = 1$

$\dfrac{x^2}{2^2} - \dfrac{y^2}{3^2} = 1$

Center: (0, 0)

$a = 2, b = 3$

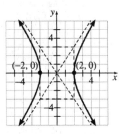

12. Ellipse

$9x^2 + 4y^2 = 36$

$\dfrac{x^2}{4} + \dfrac{y^2}{9} = 1$

$\dfrac{x^2}{2^2} + \dfrac{y^2}{3^2} = 1$

Center: (0, 0)

$a = 2, b = 3$

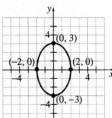

13. Ellipse

$\dfrac{(x-1)^2}{49} + \dfrac{(y+2)^2}{25} = 1$

$\dfrac{(x-1)^2}{7^2} + \dfrac{(y+2)^2}{5^2} = 1$

Center: (1, –2)

$a = 7, b = 5$

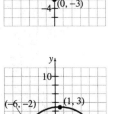

14. Hyperbola

$y^2 = x^2 + 16$

$y^2 - x^2 = 16$

$\dfrac{y^2}{16} - \dfrac{x^2}{16} = 1$

$\dfrac{y^2}{4^2} - \dfrac{x^2}{4^2} = 1$

Center: (0, 0)

$a = 4, b = 4$

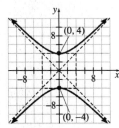

15. Circle

$\left(x + \dfrac{1}{2}\right)^2 + \left(y - \dfrac{1}{2}\right)^2 = 1$

Center: $\left(-\dfrac{1}{2}, \dfrac{1}{2}\right)$

Radius: $\sqrt{1} = 1$

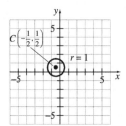

Exercise Set 10.3

1. $\begin{cases} x^2 + y^2 = 25 & (1) \\ 4x + 3y = 0 & (2) \end{cases}$

Solve the second equation for y.

$3y = -4x$

$y = -\dfrac{4x}{3}$

Substitute the result into the second equation.

$x^2 + \left(-\dfrac{4x}{3}\right)^2 = 25$

$x^2 + \dfrac{16x^2}{9} = 25$

$9\left(x^2 + \dfrac{16x^2}{9}\right) = 9(25)$

$9x^2 + 16x^2 = 225$

$25x^2 = 225$

$x^2 = 9$

$x = \pm\sqrt{9} = \pm 3$

Substitute these x values into the first equation to find the corresponding y values.

$x = 3 : y = -\dfrac{4(3)}{3} = -4$

$x = -3 : y = -\dfrac{4(-3)}{3} = 4$

The solutions are (3, –4) and (–3, 4).

3. $\begin{cases} x^2 + 4y^2 = 10 & (1) \\ y = x & (2) \end{cases}$

Substitute x for y in the first equation.

$x^2 + 4x^2 = 10$

$5x^2 = 10$

$x^2 = 2$

$x = \pm\sqrt{2}$

Substitute these x values into the second equation to find the corresponding y values.

$x = \sqrt{2}: \quad y = x = \sqrt{2}$

$x = -\sqrt{2}: \quad y = x = -\sqrt{2}$

The solutions are $\left(\sqrt{2}, \sqrt{2}\right)$ and $\left(-\sqrt{2}, -\sqrt{2}\right)$.

5. $\begin{cases} y^2 = 4 - x & (1) \\ x - 2y = 4 & (2) \end{cases}$

Solve the second equation for x.

$x = 2y + 4$

Substitute the result into the first equation.

$y^2 = 4 - (2y + 4)$

$y^2 = -2y$

$y^2 + 2y = 0$

$y(y + 2) = 0$

$y = 0 \ \text{ or } \ y + 2 = 0$

$\qquad\qquad\qquad y = -2$

Substitute these y values into the second equation to find the corresponding y values.

$y = 0: \quad x = 2(0) + 4 = 4$

$y = -2: x = 2(-2) + 4 = 0$

The solutions are (4, 0) and (0, –2).

7. $\begin{cases} x^2 + y^2 = 9 & (1) \\ 16x^2 - 4y^2 = 64 & (2) \end{cases}$

Multiply the first equation by 4, and add the result to the second equation.

$4x^2 + 4y^2 = 36$

$\underline{16x^2 + 4y^2 = 64}$

$20x^2 \qquad\ = 100$

$\qquad x^2 = 5$

$\qquad x = \pm\sqrt{5}$

Substitute 5 for x^2 into the first equation.

$5 + y^2 = 9$

$\quad y^2 = 4$

$\quad y = \pm 2$

The solutions are $\left(-\sqrt{5}, -2\right)$, $\left(-\sqrt{5}, 2\right)$,

$\left(\sqrt{5}, -2\right)$, and $\left(\sqrt{5}, 2\right)$.

9. $\begin{cases} x^2 + 2y^2 = 2 & (1) \\ x - y = 2 & (2) \end{cases}$

Solve the second equation for x: $x = y + 2$

Substitute the result into the first equation.

$(y + 2)^2 + 2y^2 = 2$

$y^2 + 4y + 4 + 2y^2 = 2$

$3y^2 + 4y + 2 = 0$

$y = \dfrac{-4 \pm \sqrt{(4)^2 - 4(3)(2)}}{2(3)} = \dfrac{-4 \pm \sqrt{-8}}{6}$

which yields no real solutions. The solution set is $\varnothing$.

11. $\begin{cases} y = x^2 - 3 & (1) \\ 4x - y = 6 & (2) \end{cases}$

Substitute $x^2 - 3$ for y in the second equation.

$4x - (x^2 - 3) = 6$

$4x - x^2 + 3 = 6$

$0 = x^2 - 4x + 3$

$0 = (x - 3)(x - 1)$

$x - 3 = 0 \ \text{ or } \ x - 1 = 0$

$\quad x = 3 \ \text{ or } \quad x = 1$

Substitute these x values into the first equation to find the y values.

$x = 3: y = (3)^2 - 3 = 6$

$x = 1: y = (1)^2 - 3 = -2$

The solutions are (3, 6) and (1, –2).

13. $\begin{cases} y = x^2 & (1) \\ 3x + y = 10 & (2) \end{cases}$

Substitute x^2 for y in the second equation.

$3x + x^2 = 10$

$x^2 + 3x - 10 = 0$

$(x + 5)(x - 2) = 0$

$x + 5 = 0 \ \text{ or } \ x - 2 = 0$

$\quad x = -5 \ \text{ or } \quad x = 2$

Substitute these x values into the first equation to find the y values.

$x = -5: y = (-5)^2 = 25$

$x = 2: \ \ y = (2)^2 = 4$

The solutions are (–5, 25) and (2, 4).

15. $\begin{cases} y = 2x^2 + 1 & (1) \\ x + y = -1 & (2) \end{cases}$

Substitute $2x^2 + 1$ for y in the second equation.

$x + 2x^2 + 1 = -1$

$2x^2 + x + 2 = 0$

$x = \dfrac{-1 \pm \sqrt{(1)^2 - 4(2)(2)}}{2(2)} = \dfrac{-1 \pm \sqrt{-15}}{4}$

which yields no real solutions. The solution set is $\varnothing$.

17. $\begin{cases} y = x^2 - 4 & (1) \\ y = x^2 - 4x & (2) \end{cases}$

Substitute $x^2 - 4$ for y in the second equation.

$x^2 - 4 = x^2 - 4x$
$\quad -4 = -4x$
$\quad\quad 1 = x$

Substitute this value into the first equation to find the y values.

$y = (1)^2 - 4 = -3$

The solution is $(1, -3)$.

19. $\begin{cases} 2x^2 + 3y^2 = 14 & (1) \\ -x^2 + y^2 = 3 & (2) \end{cases}$

Multiply the second equation by 2 and add the result to the first equation.

$\begin{array}{r} -2x^2 + 2y^2 = 6 \\ \underline{2x^2 + 3y^2 = 14} \\ 5y^2 = 20 \\ y^2 = 4 \\ y = \pm 2 \end{array}$

Substitute 4 for y^2 into the second equation to find the x values.

$-x^2 + 4 = 3$
$\quad -x^2 = -1$
$\quad\quad x^2 = 1$
$\quad\quad x = \pm 1$

The solutions are $(-1, -2)$, $(-1, 2)$, $(1, -2)$, and $(1, 2)$.

21. $\begin{cases} x^2 + y^2 = 1 & (1) \\ x^2 + (y+3)^2 = 4 & (2) \end{cases}$

Multiply the first equation by -1 and add the result to the second equation.

$\begin{array}{r} -x^2 - y^2 = -1 \\ \underline{x^2 + (y+3)^2 = 4} \\ (y+3)^3 - y^2 = 3 \end{array}$

$y^2 + 6y + 9 - y^2 = 3$
$\quad\quad\quad 6y = -6$
$\quad\quad\quad\quad y = -1$

Substitute -1 for y into the first equation to find the x values.

$x^2 + (1)^2 = 1$
$\quad\quad x^2 = 0$
$\quad\quad x = 0$

The solution is $(0, -1)$.

23. $\begin{cases} y = x^2 + 2 & (1) \\ y = -x^2 + 4 & (2) \end{cases}$

Add the two equation:

$2y = 6$
$\quad y = 3$

Substitute this y value into the first equation to find the x values.

$3 = x^2 + 2$
$1 = x^2$
$\pm 1 = x$

The solutions are $(-1, 3)$ and $(1, 3)$.

25. $\begin{cases} 3x^2 + y^2 = 9 & (1) \\ 3x^2 - y^2 = 9 & (2) \end{cases}$

Add the two equations.

$6x^2 = 18$
$\quad x^2 = 3$
$\quad x = \pm\sqrt{3}$

Substitute 3 for x^2 into the first equation to find the y values.

$3(3) + y^2 = 9$
$\quad\quad y^2 = 0$
$\quad\quad y = 0$

The solutions are $\left(-\sqrt{3}, 0\right)$ and $\left(\sqrt{3}, 0\right)$.

27. $\begin{cases} x^2 + 3y^2 = 6 & (1) \\ x^2 - 3y^2 = 10 & (2) \end{cases}$

Solve the second equation for x^2:

$x^2 = 3y^2 + 10$.

Substitute the result into the first equation.

$(3y^2 + 10) + 3y^2 = 6$
$\quad\quad\quad 6y^2 = -4$
$\quad\quad\quad\quad y^2 = -\dfrac{2}{3}$

which yields no real solutions. The solution set is $\varnothing$.

29. $\begin{cases} x^2 + y^2 = 36 & (1) \\ \quad y = \dfrac{1}{6}x^2 - 6 & (2) \end{cases}$

Solve the first equation for x^2: $x^2 = 36 - y^2$.

Substitute the result into the second equation.

$y = \dfrac{1}{6}(36 - y^2) - 6$

$y = 6 - \dfrac{1}{6}y^2 - 6$

$$6y = -y^2$$
$$y^2 + 6y = 0$$
$$y(y+6) = 0$$
$$y = 0 \text{ or } y = -6$$

Substitute these y values into the first equation to find the x values.

$$y = 0: \quad x^2 + y^2 = 36$$
$$x^2 + 0^2 = 36$$
$$x^2 = 36$$
$$x = \pm 6$$
$$y = -6: \quad x^2 + y^2 = 36$$
$$x^2 + 6^2 = 36$$
$$x^2 + 36 = 36$$
$$x^2 = 0$$
$$x = 0$$

The solutions are (–6, 0), (6, 0) and (0, –6).

31. $x > -3$

Graph the boundary line $x = -3$ as a dashed line because the inequality symbol is >.

Test: (0, 0)

$0 > -3$ True

Shade the half-plane that contains (0, 0).

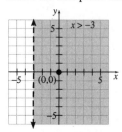

33. $y < 2x - 1$

Graph the boundary line $y = 2x - 1$ as a dashed line because the inequality symbol is <.

Test: (0, 0)

$0 \leq 2(0) - 1$
$0 \leq -1$ False

Shade the half-plane that does not contain (0, 0).

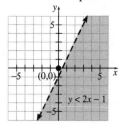

35. $P = x + (2x - 5) + (5x - 20)$
$= (8x - 25)$ inches

37. $P = 2(x^2 + 3x + 1) + 2(x^2)$
$= 2x^2 + 6x + 2 + 2x^2$
$= (4x^2 + 6x + 2)$ meters

39. There are 0, 1, 2, 3, or 4 possible real solutions. Answers may vary. Possible sketches follow:

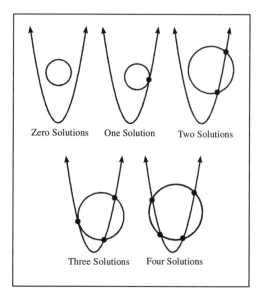

41. Let x and y represent the numbers.
$$\begin{cases} x^2 + y^2 = 130 \\ x^2 - y^2 = 32 \end{cases}$$

Add the two equations.
$$2x^2 = 162$$
$$x^2 = 81$$
$$x = \pm 9$$

Substitute 81 for x^2 in the first equation to find the y values.
$$81 + y^2 = 130$$
$$y^2 = 49$$
$$y = \pm 7$$

The numbers are –9 and –7; –9 and 7; 9 and –7; and 9 and 7.

43. Let x and y be the length and width, respectively.
$$\begin{cases} xy = 285 \\ 2x + 2y = 68 \end{cases}$$

Solve the first equation for y: $y = \dfrac{285}{x}$.

Substitute the result into the second equation.

$$2x + 2\left(\frac{285}{x}\right) = 68$$
$$x + \frac{285}{x} = 34$$
$$x^2 + 285 = 34x$$
$$x^2 - 34x + 285 = 0$$
$$(x - 19)(x - 15) = 0$$
$$x = 19 \ \text{ or } \ x = 15$$

Substitute the x values into the first equation to find the value of y.

$x = 19$: $19y = 285$.
$$y = 15$$

The dimensions are 19 cm by 15 cm.

[Note: If we substitute $x = 15$ into the first equation, we obtain $y = 19$, leaving the overall dimensions the same.]

45. $\begin{cases} p = -0.01x^2 - 0.2x + 9 \\ p = 0.01x^2 - 0.1x + 3 \end{cases}$

Substitute:
$$-0.01x^2 - 0.2x + 9 = 0.01x^2 - 0.1x + 3$$
$$0 = 0.02x^2 + 0.1x - 6$$
$$0 = x^2 + 5x - 300$$
$$0 = (x + 20)(x - 15)$$
$$x + 20 = 0 \quad \text{or } x - 15 = 0$$
$$x = -20 \text{ or } \qquad x = 15$$

Disregard the negative. Substitute 15 for x into the first equation.
$$p = -0.01(15)^2 - 0.2(15) + 9$$
$$p = 3.75$$

The equilibrium quantity is 15,000 compact discs, and the corresponding price is \$3.75.

47. $x^2 + 4y^2 = 10$
$$4y^2 = 10 - x^2$$
$$y^2 = \frac{10 - x^2}{4}$$
$$y = \pm\sqrt{\frac{10 - x^2}{4}} = \pm\frac{\sqrt{10 - x^2}}{2}$$

Graph $y_1 = \dfrac{\sqrt{10 - x^2}}{2}$, $y_2 = -\dfrac{\sqrt{10 - x^2}}{2}$, and $y_3 = x$ in a $[-15, 15, 1]$ by $[-10, 10, 1]$ window.

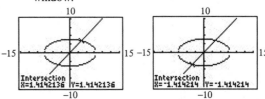

From the intersection points, we verify the solutions of Exercise 3.

49. Graph $y_1 = x^2 + 2$ and $y_2 = -x^2 + 4$ in a $[-15, 15, 1]$ by $[-10, 10, 1]$ window.

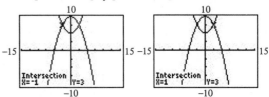

From the intersection points, we verify the solutions of Exercise 23.

Exercise Set 10.4

1. $y < x^2$

First graph the parabola with dashes.

Test Point	$y < x^2$; Result
$(0, 1)$	$1 < 0^2$; False

Shade the portion of the graph which does not contain $(0, 1)$.

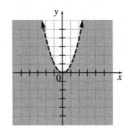

3. $x^2 + y^2 \geq 16$

First graph the circle with a solid curve.

Test Point	$x^2 + y^2 \geq 16$; Result
(0, 0)	$0^2 + 0^2 \geq 16$; False

Shade the portion of the graph which does not contain (0, 0).

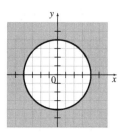

5. $\dfrac{x^2}{4} - y^2 < 1$

First graph the hyperbola with a dashed curve.

Test Points	$\dfrac{x^2}{4} - y^2 < 1$; Result
(−4, 0)	$\dfrac{(-4)^2}{4} - 0^2 < 1$; False
(0, 0)	$\dfrac{(0)^2}{4} - 0^2 < 1$; True
(4, 0)	$\dfrac{(4)^2}{4} - 0^2 < 1$; False

Shade the portion of the graph that contains (0, 0).

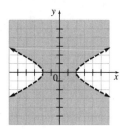

7. $y > (x-1)^2 - 3$

First graph the parabola with a dashed curve.

Test Point	$y > (x-1)^2 - 3$; Result
(0, 0)	$0 > (0-1)^2 - 3$; True

Shade the portion of the graph which contains (0, 0).

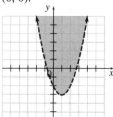

9. $x^2 + y^2 \leq 9$

First graph the circle with a solid curve.

Test Point	$x^2 + y^2 \leq 9$; Result
(0, 0)	$0^2 + 0^2 \leq 9$; True

Shade the portion of the graph which contains (0, 0).

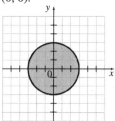

11. $y > -x^2 + 5$

First graph the parabola with a dashed curve.

Test Point	$y > -x^2 + 5$; Result
(0, 0)	$0 > -(0)^2 + 5$; False

Shade the portion of the graph which does not contain (0, 0).

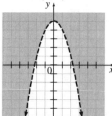

458

13. $\dfrac{x^2}{4} + \dfrac{y^2}{9} \le 1$

First graph the ellipse with a solid curve.

Test Point	$\dfrac{x^2}{4} + \dfrac{y^2}{9} \le 1$; Result
$(0, 0)$	$\dfrac{(0)^2}{4} + \dfrac{(0)^2}{9} \le 1$; True

Shade the portion of the graph that contains $(0, 0)$.

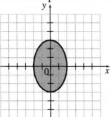

15. $\dfrac{y^2}{4} - x^2 \le 1$

First graph the hyperbola with solid curves.

Test Points	$\dfrac{y^2}{4} - x^2 \le 1$; Result
$(0, 4)$	$\dfrac{(-4)^2}{4} - 0^2 \le 1$; False
$(0, 0)$	$\dfrac{(0)^2}{4} - 0^2 \le 1$; True
$(0, 4)$	$\dfrac{(4)^2}{4} - 0^2 \le 1$; False

Shade the portion of the graph that contains $(0, 0)$.

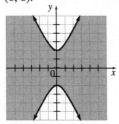

17. $y < (x-2)^2 + 1$

First graph the parabola with a dashed curve.

Test Point	$y < (x-2)^2 + 1$; Result
$(0, 0)$	$0 < (0-2)^2 + 1$; True

Shade the portion of the graph which contains $(0, 0)$.

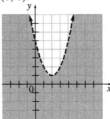

19. $y \le x^2 + x - 2$

First graph the parabola with a solid curve.

Test Point	$y \le x^2 + x - 2$; Result
$(0, 0)$	$0 \le (0)^2 + (0) - 2$; False

Shade the portion of the graph which contains $(0, 0)$.

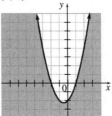

21. $\begin{cases} 2x - y < 2 \\ \quad\ y \le -x^2 \end{cases}$

First graph $2x - y = 2$ with a dashed line.

Test Point	$2x - y < 2$; Result
$(0, 0)$	$2(0) - 0 < 2$; True

Shade the portion of the graph which contains $(0, 0)$. Next, graph the parabola $y = -x^2$ with a solid curve.

Test Point	$y \le -x^2$; Result
$(0, 1)$	$1 \le -(0)^2$; False

Shade the portion of the graph which does not contain (0, 1).

The solution to the system is the overlapping region.

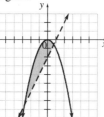

23. $\begin{cases} 4x+3y \geq 12 \\ x^2+y^2 < 16 \end{cases}$

First graph $4x+3y=12$ with a solid line.

Test Point	$4x+3y \geq 12$; Result
(0, 0)	$4(0)+3(0) \geq 12$; False

Shade the portion of the graph which does not contain (0, 0).

Next, graph the circle $x^2+y^2=16$ with a dashed curve.

Test Point	$x^2+y^2 < 16$; Result
(0, 0)	$0^2+0^2 < 16$; True

Shade the portion of the graph which contains (0, 0).

The solution to the system is the overlapping region.

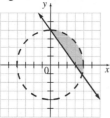

25. $\begin{cases} x^2+y^2 \leq 9 \\ x^2+y^2 \geq 1 \end{cases}$

First graph the circle with radius 3 with a solid curve.

Test Point	$x^2+y^2 \leq 9$; Result
(0, 0)	$0^2+0^2 \leq 9$; True

Shade the portion of the graph which contains (0, 0).

Next, graph the circle with 1 with a dashed curve.

Test Point	$x^2+y^2 \geq 1$; Result
(0, 0)	$0^2+0^2 \geq 1$; False

Shade the portion of the graph which does not contain (0, 0).

The solution to the system is the overlapping region.

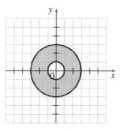

27. $\begin{cases} y > x^2 \\ y \geq 2x+1 \end{cases}$

First graph the parabola with a dashed curve.

Test Point	$y > x^2$; Result
(0, 1)	$1 > 0^2$; True

Shade the portion of the graph which contains (0, 1).

Next, graph $y=2x+1$ with a solid line.

Test Point	$y \geq 2x+1$; Result
(0, 0)	$0 \geq 2(0)+1$; False

Shade the portion of the graph which does not contain (0, 0).

The solution to the system is the overlapping region.

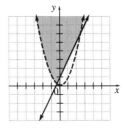

29. $\begin{cases} x > y^2 \\ y > 0 \end{cases}$

First graph the parabola with a dashed curve.

Test Point	$x > y^2$; Result
(1, 0)	$1 > 0^2$; True

Shade the portion of the graph which contains (1, 0).

Next, graph $y = 0$ with a dashed line.

Test Point	$y > x^2$; Result
(0, 1)	$1 \geq 0^2$; True

Shade the portion of the graph which contains (0, 1).

The solution to the system is the overlapping region.

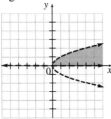

31. $\begin{cases} x^2 + y^2 > 9 \\ y > x^2 \end{cases}$

First graph the circle with a dashed curve.

Test Point	$x^2 + y^2 > 9$; Result
(0, 0)	$0^2 + 0^2 > 9$; False

Shade the portion of the graph which does not contain (0, 0).

Next, graph the parabola with a dashed curve.

Test Point	$y > x^2$; Result
(0, 1)	$1 > 0^2$; True

Shade the portion of the graph which contains (0, 1).

The solution to the system is the overlapping region.

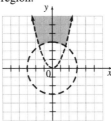

33. $\begin{cases} \dfrac{x^2}{4} + \dfrac{y^2}{9} \geq 1 \\ x^2 + y^2 \geq 4 \end{cases}$

First graph the ellipse with a solid curve.

Test Point	$\dfrac{x^2}{4} + \dfrac{y^2}{9} \geq 1$; Result
(0, 0)	$\dfrac{0^2}{4} + \dfrac{0^2}{9} \geq 1$; False

Shade the portion of the graph which does not contain (0, 0).

Next, graph the circle with a solid curve.

Test Point	$x^2 + y^2 \geq 4$; Result
(0, 0)	$0^2 + 0^2 \geq 4$; False

Shade the portion of the graph which does not contain (0, 0).

The solution to the system is the overlapping region.

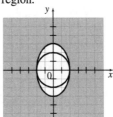

35. $\begin{cases} x^2 - y^2 \geq 1 \\ y \geq 0 \end{cases}$

First graph the hyperbola with solid curves.

Test Point	$x^2 - y^2 \geq 1$; Result
$(0, 0)$	$0^2 - 0^2 \geq 1$; False

Shade the portion of the graph which does not contain $(0, 0)$.

Next, graph $y = 0$ with a solid line.

Test Point	$y > 0$; Result
$(0, 1)$	$1 \geq 0$; True

Shade the portion of the graph which contains $(0, 1)$.

The solution to the system is the overlapping region.

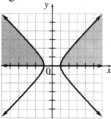

37. $\begin{cases} x + y \geq 1 \\ 2x + 3y < 1 \\ x > -3 \end{cases}$

First graph $x + y = 1$ with a solid line.

Test Point	$x + y \geq 1$; Result
$(0, 0)$	$0 + 0 \geq 1$; False

Shade the portion of the graph which does not contain $(0, 0)$.

Next, graph $2x + 3y = 1$ with a dashed line.

Test Point	$2x + 3y < 1$; Result
$(0, 0)$	$2(0) + 3(0) < 1$; True

Shade the portion of the graph which contains $(0, 0)$.

Now graph the line $x = -3$ with a dashed line.

Test Point	$x > -3$; Result
$(0, 0)$	$0 > -3$; True

Shade the portion of the graph which contains $(0, 0)$.

The solution to the system is the overlapping region.

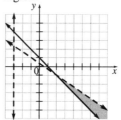

39. $\begin{cases} x^2 - y^2 < 1 \\ \dfrac{x^2}{16} + y^2 \leq 1 \\ x \geq -2 \end{cases}$

First graph the hyperbola with dashed curves.

Test Point	$x^2 - y^2 < 1$; Result
$(0, 0)$	$0^2 - 0^2 < 1$; True

Shade the portion of the graph which contains $(0, 0)$.

Next, graph the ellipse with a solid curve.

Test Point	$\dfrac{x^2}{16} + y^2 \leq 1$; Result
$(0, 0)$	$\dfrac{0^2}{16} + 0^2 \leq 1$; True

Shade the portion of the graph which contains $(0, 0)$.

Now graph the line $x = -2$ with a solid line.

Test Point	$x \geq -2$; Result
$(0, 0)$	$0 \geq -2$; True

Shade the portion of the graph which contains $(0, 0)$.

The solution to the system is the overlapping region.

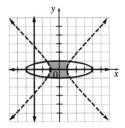

41. This is not a function because a vertical line can cross the graph in more than one place.

43. This is a function because a vertical line can cross the graph no more than one place.

45. $f(x) = 3x^2 - 2$
$f(-1) = 3(-1)^2 - 2 = 3 - 2 = 1$

47. $f(x) = 3x^2 - 2$
$f(a) = 3(a)^2 - 2 = 3a^2 - 2$

49. Answers may vary.

51. $\begin{cases} y \le x^2 \\ y \ge x + 2 \\ x \ge 0 \\ y \ge 0 \end{cases}$

First graph $y = x^2$ with a solid curve.

Test Point	$y \le x^2$; Result
(0, 1)	$1 \le 0^2$; False

Shade the portion of the graph which does not contain (0, 1).

Next, graph $y = x + 2$ with a solid line.

Test Point	$y \ge x + 2$; Result
(0, 0)	$0 \ge 0 + 2$; False

Shade the portion of the graph which does not contain (0, 0).

Next graph the line $x = 0$ with a solid line, and shade to the right.

Now graph the line $y = 0$ with a solid line, and shade above the line.

The solution to the system is the overlapping region.

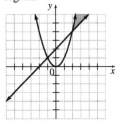

Chapter 10 Review

1. (–6, 3), (8, 4)
$d = \sqrt{(4-3)^2 + [8-(-6)]^2}$
$= \sqrt{1^2 + 14^2}$
$= \sqrt{1 + 196}$
$= \sqrt{197}$ units

2. (3, 5), (8, 9)
$d = \sqrt{(8-3)^2 + (9-5)^2}$
$= \sqrt{5^2 + 4^2}$
$= \sqrt{25 + 16}$
$= \sqrt{41}$ units

3. (–4, –6), (–1, 5)
$d = \sqrt{[-1-(-4)]^2 + [5-(-6)]^2}$
$= \sqrt{3^2 + 11^2}$
$= \sqrt{9 + 121}$
$= \sqrt{130}$ units

4. (–1, 5), (2, –3)
$d = \sqrt{[2-(-1)]^2 + (-3-5)^2}$
$= \sqrt{3^2 + (-8)^2}$
$= \sqrt{9 + 64}$
$= \sqrt{73}$ units

5. $\left(-\sqrt{2}, 0\right), \left(0, -4\sqrt{6}\right)$
$d = \sqrt{\left[0-\left(-\sqrt{2}\right)\right]^2 + \left(-4\sqrt{6}-0\right)^2}$
$= \sqrt{\left(\sqrt{2}\right)^2 + \left(-4\sqrt{6}\right)^2}$
$= \sqrt{2 + 16 \cdot 6}$
$= \sqrt{98}$
$= 7\sqrt{2}$ units

6. $\left(-\sqrt{5}, -\sqrt{11}\right), \left(-\sqrt{5}, -3\sqrt{11}\right)$

$$d = \sqrt{\left[-\sqrt{5} - \left(-\sqrt{5}\right)\right]^2 + \left[-3\sqrt{11} - \left(-\sqrt{11}\right)\right]^2}$$
$$= \sqrt{0^2 + \left(-2\sqrt{11}\right)^2}$$
$$= \sqrt{4 \cdot 11}$$
$$= 2\sqrt{11} \text{ units}$$

7. $(7.4, -8.6), (-1.2, 5.6)$

$$d = \sqrt{(-1.2 - 7.4)^2 + [5.6 - (-8.6)]^2}$$
$$= \sqrt{(-8.6)^2 + (14.2)^2}$$
$$= \sqrt{275.6}$$
$$\approx 16.60 \text{ units}$$

8. $(2.3, 1.8), (10.7, -9.2)$

$$d = \sqrt{(10.7 - 2.3)^2 + (-9.2 - 1.8)^2}$$
$$= \sqrt{(8.4)^2 + (-11)^2}$$
$$= \sqrt{191.56}$$
$$\approx 13.84 \text{ units}$$

9. $(2, 6), (-12, 4)$

$$\left(\frac{2 + (-12)}{2}, \frac{6 + 4}{2}\right) = \left(\frac{-10}{2}, \frac{10}{2}\right) = (-5, 5)$$

The midpoint of the line segment is $(-5, 5)$.

10. $(-3, 8), (11, 24)$

$$\left(\frac{-3 + 11}{2}, \frac{8 + 24}{2}\right) = \left(\frac{8}{2}, \frac{32}{2}\right) = (4, 16)$$

The midpoint of the line segment is $(4, 16)$.

11. $(-6, -5), (-9, 7)$

$$\left(\frac{-6 + (-9)}{2}, \frac{-5 + 7}{2}\right) = \left(\frac{-15}{2}, \frac{2}{2}\right) = -\left(\frac{15}{2}, 1\right)$$

The midpoint of the line segment is $\left(-\frac{15}{2}, 1\right)$.

12. $(4, -6), (-15, 2)$

$$\left(\frac{4 + (-15)}{2}, \frac{-6 + 2}{2}\right) = \left(-\frac{11}{2}, -2\right)$$

The midpoint of the line segment is $\left(-\frac{11}{2}, -2\right)$.

13. $\left(0, -\frac{3}{8}\right), \left(\frac{1}{10}, 0\right)$

$$\left(\frac{0 + \left(\frac{1}{10}\right)}{2}, \frac{-\frac{3}{8} + 0}{2}\right) = \left(\frac{1}{20}, -\frac{3}{16}\right)$$

The midpoint of the line segment is $\left(\frac{1}{20}, -\frac{3}{16}\right)$.

14. $\left(\frac{3}{4}, -\frac{1}{7}\right), \left(-\frac{1}{4}, -\frac{3}{7}\right)$

$$\left(\frac{\frac{3}{4} + \left(-\frac{1}{4}\right)}{2}, \frac{-\frac{1}{7} + \left(-\frac{3}{7}\right)}{2}\right) = \left(\frac{\frac{1}{2}}{2}, -\frac{\frac{4}{7}}{2}\right)$$
$$= \left(\frac{1}{4}, -\frac{2}{7}\right)$$

The midpoint of the line segment is $\left(\frac{1}{4}, -\frac{2}{7}\right)$.

15. $\left(\sqrt{3}, -2\sqrt{6}\right), \left(\sqrt{3}, -4\sqrt{6}\right)$

$$\left(\frac{\sqrt{3} + \sqrt{3}}{2}, \frac{-2\sqrt{6} + \left(-4\sqrt{6}\right)}{2}\right) = \left(\frac{2\sqrt{3}}{2}, -\frac{6\sqrt{6}}{2}\right)$$
$$= \left(\sqrt{3}, -3\sqrt{6}\right)$$

The midpoint of the segment is $\left(\sqrt{3}, -3\sqrt{6}\right)$.

16. $\left(-5\sqrt{3}, 2\sqrt{7}\right), \left(-3\sqrt{3}, 10\sqrt{7}\right)$

$$\left(\frac{-5\sqrt{3} + \left(-3\sqrt{3}\right)}{2}, \frac{2\sqrt{7} + 10\sqrt{7}}{2}\right)$$
$$= \left(\frac{-8\sqrt{3}}{2}, \frac{12\sqrt{7}}{2}\right)$$
$$= \left(-4\sqrt{3}, 6\sqrt{7}\right)$$

The midpoint of the segment is $\left(-4\sqrt{3}, 6\sqrt{7}\right)$.

17. Center $(-4, 4)$, radius 3

$$[x - (-4)]^2 + (y - 4)^2 = 3^2$$
$$(x + 4)^2 + (y - 4)^2 = 9$$

18. Center (5, 0), radius 5
$$(x-5)^2 + (y-0)^2 = 5^2$$
$$(x-5)^2 + y^2 = 25$$

19. Center (–7, –9), radius $\sqrt{11}$
$$[x-(-7)]^2 + [y-(-9)]^2 = \left(\sqrt{11}\right)^2$$
$$(x+7)^2 + (y+9)^2 = 11$$

20. Center (0, 0), radius $\dfrac{7}{2}$
$$(x-0)^2 + (y-0)^2 = \left(\dfrac{7}{2}\right)^2$$
$$x^2 + y^2 = \dfrac{49}{4}$$

21. Circle: $x^2 + y^2 = 7$

Center (0, 0), radius $r = \sqrt{7}$

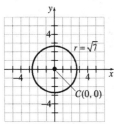

22. Parabola: $x = 2(y-5)^2 + 4$

The equation is quadratic in y. The graph is similar to the graph of $x = y^2$, but is narrower because $a = 2$. The graph is shifted up 5 units and right 4 units. The vertex is $(4, 5)$, and the axis of symmetry is $y = 5$.

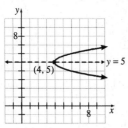

23. Parabola: $x = -(y+2)^2 + 3$

The equation is quadratic in y. The graph is similar to the graph of $x = y^2$, but opens to the left because $a = -1$. The graph is shifted down 2 units and right 3 units. The vertex is $(3, -2)$, and the axis of symmetry is $y = -2$.

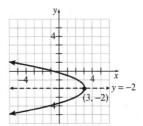

24. Circle; $(x-1)^2 + (y-2)^2 = 4$

Center (1, 2), radius $r = \sqrt{4} = 2$

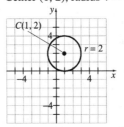

25. Parabola: $y = -x^2 + 4x + 10$
$$x = -\dfrac{b}{2a} = \dfrac{-4}{2(-1)} = 2$$
$$y = -(2)^2 + 4(2) + 10 = 14$$
Vertex: (2, 14);   Axis of symmetry: $x = 2$
Opens downward

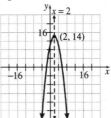

26. Parabola: $x = -y^2 - 4y + 6$
$$y = -\dfrac{b}{2a} = \dfrac{-(-4)}{2(-1)} = -2 ;$$
$$x = -(-2)^2 - 4(-2) + 6 = 10$$
Vertex: (10, –2);   Axis of symmetry: $y = -2$
Opens downward

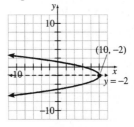

27. Parabola ; $x = \frac{1}{2}y^2 + 2y + 1$

$$y = -\frac{b}{2a} = \frac{-2}{2(1/2)} = -2 \; ;$$

$$x = \frac{1}{2}(-2)^2 + 2(-2) + 1 = -1$$

Vertex: $(-1, -2)$;   Axis of symmetry: $y = -2$

Opens to the right and is wider by a factor of 2

because $a = \frac{1}{2}$.

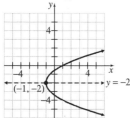

28. Parabola: $y = -3x^2 + \frac{1}{2}x + 4$

$$x = -\frac{b}{2a} = \frac{-1/2}{2(-3)} = \frac{1}{12} \; ;$$

$$y = -3\left(\frac{1}{12}\right)^2 + \frac{1}{2}\left(\frac{1}{12}\right) + 4 = \frac{193}{48}$$

Vertex: $\left(\frac{1}{12}, \frac{193}{48}\right)$;   Axis of symmetry: $x = \frac{1}{12}$

Opens downward and is narrower by a factor of

$\frac{1}{3}$ because $a = -3$.

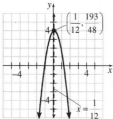

29. Circle: $x^2 + y^2 + 2x + y = \frac{3}{4}$

$$(x^2 + 2x) + (y^2 + y) = \frac{3}{4}$$

$$(x^2 + 2x + 1) + \left(y^2 + y + \frac{1}{4}\right) = \frac{3}{4} + 1 + \frac{1}{4}$$

$$(x+1)^2 + \left(y + \frac{1}{2}\right)^2 = 2$$

Center $\left(-1, -\frac{1}{2}\right)$; radius $r = \sqrt{2}$

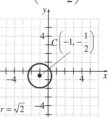

30. Circle: $x^2 + y^2 + 3y = \frac{7}{4}$

$$x^2 + \left(y^2 + 3y + \frac{9}{4}\right) = \frac{7}{4} + \frac{9}{4}$$

$$x^2 + \left(y + \frac{3}{2}\right)^2 = 4$$

center $\left(0, -\frac{3}{2}\right)$; radius $r = \sqrt{4} = 2$

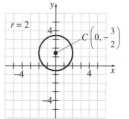

31. Circle: $4x^2 + 4y^2 + 16x + 8y = 1$

$$(x^2 + 4x) + (y^2 + 2y) = \frac{1}{4}$$

$$(x^2 + 4x + 4) + (y^2 + 2y + 1) = \frac{1}{4} + 4 + 1$$

$$(x+2)^2 + (y+1)^2 = \frac{21}{4}$$

Center $(-2, -1)$; radius $r = \sqrt{\frac{21}{4}} = \frac{\sqrt{21}}{2}$

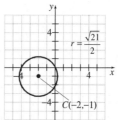

32. Circle: $3x^2 + 6x + 3y^2 = 9$

$x^2 + 2x + y^2 = 3$

$(x^2 + 2x + 1) + y^2 = 3 + 1$

$(x + 1)^2 + y^2 = 4$

Center $(-1, 0)$; radius $r = \sqrt{4} = 2$

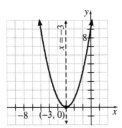

33. Parabola: $y = x^2 + 6x + 9$

$y = (x + 3)^2$

Vertex: $(-3, 0)$; Axis of symmetry: $x = -3$

Opens upward

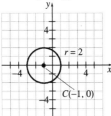

34. Parabola: $x = y^2 + 6y + 9$

$x = (y + 3)^2$

Vertex: $(0, -3)$; Axis of symmetry: $y = -3$

Opens to the right

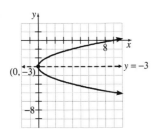

35. Center: $(5.6, -2.4)$, radius $\dfrac{6.2}{2} = 3.1$

$(x - 5.6)^2 + [y - (-2.4)]^2 = (3.1)^2$

$(x - 5.6)^2 + (y + 2.4)^2 = 9.61$

36. Ellipse: $x^2 + \dfrac{y^2}{4} = 1$

$\dfrac{x^2}{1^2} + \dfrac{y^2}{2^2} = 1$

Center: $(0, 0)$; $a = 1$, $b = 2$

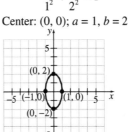

37. Hyperbola: $x^2 - \dfrac{y^2}{4} = 1$

$\dfrac{x^2}{1^2} - \dfrac{y^2}{2^2} = 1$

Center: $(0, 0)$; $a = 1$, $b = 2$

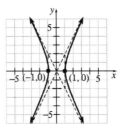

38. Hyperbola: $\dfrac{y^2}{4} - \dfrac{x^2}{16} = 1$

$\dfrac{y^2}{2^2} - \dfrac{x^2}{4^2} = 1$

Center: $(0, 0)$; $a = 4$, $b = 2$

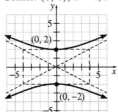

39. $\dfrac{y^2}{4} + \dfrac{x^2}{16} = 1$

$\dfrac{y^2}{2^2} + \dfrac{x^2}{4^2} = 1$

Center: $(0, 0)$; $a = 4$, $b = 2$

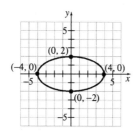

40. Circle: $\dfrac{x^2}{5} + \dfrac{y^2}{5} = 1$

$x^2 + y^2 = 5$

Center: (0, 0); radius $r = \sqrt{5}$

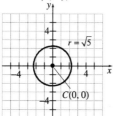

41. Hyperbola: $\dfrac{x^2}{5} - \dfrac{y^2}{5} = 1$ $\left(\sqrt{5},\, 0\right)$

Center: (0, 0); $a = \sqrt{5}$, $b = \sqrt{5}$

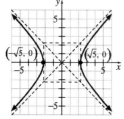

42. Hyperbola: $-5x^2 + 25y^2 = 125$

$\dfrac{y^2}{5} - \dfrac{x^2}{25} = 1$

Center: (0, 0); $a = 5$, $b = \sqrt{5}$

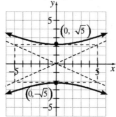

43. Ellipse: $4y^2 + 9x^2 = 36$

$\dfrac{y^2}{9} + \dfrac{x^2}{4} = 1$

$\dfrac{y^2}{3^2} + \dfrac{x^2}{2^2} = 1$

Center: (0, 0); $a = 2$, $b = 3$

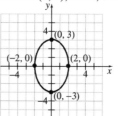

44. Ellipse: $\dfrac{(x-2)^2}{4} + (y-1)^2 = 1$

Center: (2, 1); $a = 2$, $b = 1$

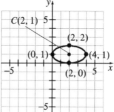

45. Ellipse: $\dfrac{(x+3)^2}{9} + \dfrac{(y-4)^2}{25} = 1$

$\dfrac{(x+3)^2}{3^2} + \dfrac{(y-4)^2}{5^2} = 1$

Center: (−3, 4); $a = 3$, $b = 5$

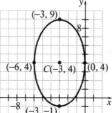

46. Hyperbola: $x^2 - y^2 = 1$

Center: (0, 0); $a = 1$, $b = 1$

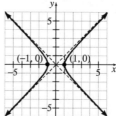

47. Hyperbola: $36y^2 - 49x^2 = 1764$

$$\frac{y^2}{49} - \frac{x^2}{36} = 1$$

$$\frac{y^2}{7^2} - \frac{x^2}{6^2} = 1$$

Center: $(0, 0)$; $a = 6$, $b = 7$

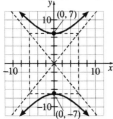

48. Hyperbola: $\quad y^2 = x^2 + 9$

$$y^2 - x^2 = 9$$

$$\frac{y^2}{9} - \frac{x^2}{9} = 1$$

$$\frac{y^2}{3^2} - \frac{x^2}{3^3} = 1$$

Center: $(0, 0)$; $a = 3$, $b = 3$

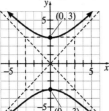

49. Hyperbola: $\quad x^2 = 4y^2 - 16$

$$4y^2 - x^2 = 16$$

$$\frac{y^2}{4} - \frac{x^2}{16} = 1$$

$$\frac{y^2}{2^2} - \frac{x^2}{4^2} = 1$$

Center: $(0, 0)$; $a = 4$, $b = 2$

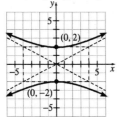

50. Ellipse: $\quad 100 - 25x^2 = 4y^2$

$$25x^2 + 4y^2 = 100$$

$$\frac{x^2}{4} + \frac{y^2}{25} = 1$$

$$\frac{x^2}{2^2} + \frac{y^2}{5^2} = 1$$

Center: $(0, 0)$; $a = 2$, $b = 5$

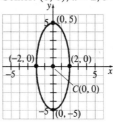

51. Parabola: $y = x^2 + 4x + 6$

$$x = -\frac{b}{2a} = \frac{-4}{2(1)} = -2; \quad y = (-2)^2 + 4(-2) + 6 = 2$$

Vertex: $(-2, 2)$; Axis of symmetry: $x = -2$
Opens upward

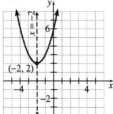

52. Hyperbola: $\quad y^2 = x^2 + 6$

$$y^2 - x^2 = 6$$

$$\frac{y^2}{6} - \frac{x^2}{6} = 1$$

Center: $(0, 0)$; $a = \sqrt{6}$, $b = \sqrt{6}$

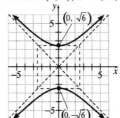

53. Circle:
$$y^2 + x^2 = 4x + 6$$
$$(x^2 - 4x) + y^2 = 6$$
$$(x^2 - 4x + 4) + y^2 = 6 + 4$$
$$(x - 2)^2 + y^2 = 10$$
Center: (2, 0); radius $r = \sqrt{10}$

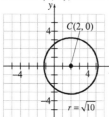

54. Ellipse:
$$y^2 + 2x^2 = 4x + 6$$
$$(2x^2 - 4x) + y^2 = 6$$
$$2(x^2 - 2x + 1) + y^2 = 6 + 2$$
$$2(x - 1)^2 + y^2 = 8$$
$$\frac{(x - 1)^2}{4} + \frac{y^2}{8} = 1$$
Center: (1, 0); $a = \sqrt{4} = 2$, $b = \sqrt{8} = 2\sqrt{2}$

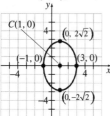

55. Circle:
$$x^2 + y^2 - 8y = 0$$
$$x^2 + (y^2 - 8y + 16) = 0 + 16$$
$$x^2 + (y - 4)^2 = 16$$
Center: (0, 4); radius $r = \sqrt{16} = 4$

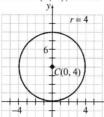

56. Parabola:
$$x - 4y = y^2$$
$$x = y^2 + 4y$$
$$x + 4 = y^2 + 4y + 4$$
$$x = (y + 2)^2 - 4$$

Vertex: (–4, –2); Axis of symmetry: $y = -2$
Opens to the right.

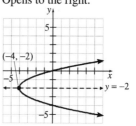

57. Hyperbola:
$$x^2 - 4 = y^2$$
$$x^2 - y^2 = 4$$
$$\frac{x^2}{4} - \frac{y^2}{4} = 1$$
Center: (0, 0); $a = 2$, $b = 2$

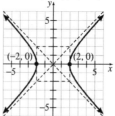

58. Circle:
$$x^2 = 4 - y^2$$
$$x^2 + y^2 = 4$$
Center: (0, 0); radius $r = \sqrt{4} = 2$

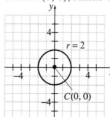

59. Ellipse: $6(x - 2)^2 + 9(y + 5)^2 = 36$
$$\frac{(x - 2)^2}{6} + \frac{(y + 5)^2}{4} = 1$$
Center: (2, –5); $a = \sqrt{6}$, $b = 2$

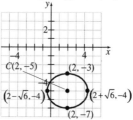

60. Hyperbola: $36y^2 = 576 + 16x^2$

$$36y^2 - 16x^2 = 576$$

$$\frac{y^2}{16} - \frac{x^2}{36} = 1$$

$$\frac{y^2}{4^2} - \frac{x^2}{6^2} = 1$$

Center: (0, 0); $a = 6$, $b = 4$

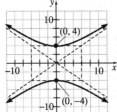

61. Hyperbola: $\dfrac{x^2}{16} - \dfrac{y^2}{25} = 1$

$$\frac{x^2}{4^2} - \frac{y^2}{5^2} = 1$$

Center: (0, 0), $a = 4$, $b = 5$

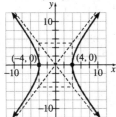

62. Circle: $3(x-7)^2 + 3(y+4)^2 = 1$

$$(x-7)^2 + (y+4)^2 = \frac{1}{3}$$

Center: (7, –4); radius $r = \sqrt{\dfrac{1}{3}} = \dfrac{1}{\sqrt{3}} = \dfrac{\sqrt{3}}{3}$

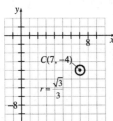

63. $\dfrac{y^2}{4} + \dfrac{x^2}{16} = 1$

$$16\left(\frac{y^2}{4} + \frac{x^2}{16}\right) = 16(1)$$

$$4y^2 + x^2 = 16$$

$$4y^2 = 16 - x^2$$

$$y^2 = \frac{16 - x^2}{4}$$

$$y = \pm\sqrt{\frac{16 - x^2}{4}} = \pm\frac{\sqrt{16 - x^2}}{2}$$

Graph $y_1 = \dfrac{\sqrt{16 - x^2}}{2}$ and $y_2 = -\dfrac{\sqrt{16 - x^2}}{2}$ in a $[-6, 6, 1]$ by $[-4, 4, 1]$ window.

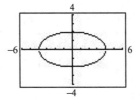

64. $\dfrac{x^2}{5} + \dfrac{y^2}{5} = 1$

$$x^2 + y^2 = 5$$

$$y^2 = 5 - x^2$$

$$y = \pm\sqrt{5 - x^2}$$

Graph $y_1 = \sqrt{5 - x^2}$ and $y_2 = -\sqrt{5 - x^2}$ in a $[-6, 6, 1]$ by $[-4, 4, 1]$ window.

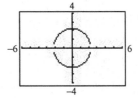

65. Define $y_1 = x^2 + 4x + 6$, and graph is a $[-15, 15, 1]$ by $[-10, 10, 1]$ window.

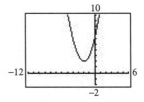

66. $x^2 = 4 - y^2$

$$y^2 = 4 - x^2$$

$$y = \pm\sqrt{4 - x^2}$$

Graph $y_1 = \sqrt{4 - x^2}$ and $y_2 = -\sqrt{4 - x^2}$ in a $[-6, 6, 1]$ by $[-4, 4, 1]$ window.

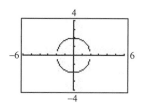

67. $\begin{cases} y = 2x - 4 & (1) \\ y^2 = 4x & (2) \end{cases}$

Substitute $2x - 4$ for y into the second equation.

$$(2x - 4)^2 = 4x$$
$$4x^2 - 16x + 16 = 4x$$
$$4x^2 - 20x + 16 = 0$$
$$x^2 - 5x + 4 = 0$$
$$(x - 4)(x - 1) = 0$$
$$x = 4 \text{ or } x = 1$$

Substitute these results into the first equation to find the corresponding y values.

$x = 4 : y = 2(4) - 4 = 4$
$x = 1 : y = 2(1) - 4 = -2$

The solutions are $(4, 4)$ and $(1, -2)$.

68. $\begin{cases} x^2 + y^2 = 2 & (1) \\ x - y = 4 & (2) \end{cases}$

Solve the second equation for x: $x = y + 4$.
Substitute the result into the first equation.

$$(y + 4)^2 + y^2 = 4$$
$$(y^2 + 8y + 16) + y^2 = 4$$
$$2y^2 + 8y + 12 = 0$$
$$y^2 + 4y + 6 = 0$$

$$y = \frac{-4 \pm \sqrt{(4)^2 - 4(1)(6)}}{2(1)} = \frac{-4 \pm \sqrt{-8}}{2}$$

which yields no real solutions. The solution set is $\varnothing$.

69. $\begin{cases} y = x + 2 & (1) \\ y = x^2 & (2) \end{cases}$

Substitute $x + 2$ for y into the second equation.

$$x + 2 = x^2$$
$$0 = x^2 - x - 2$$
$$0 = (x - 2)(x + 1)$$
$$x = 2 \text{ or } x = -1$$

Substitute these results into the first equation to find the corresponding y values.

$x = 2 : y = 2 + 2 = 4$
$x = -1 : y = -1 + 2 = 1$

The solutions are $(2, 4)$ and $(-1, 1)$.

70. $\begin{cases} y = x^2 - 5x + 1 & (1) \\ y = -x + 6 & (2) \end{cases}$

Substitute $-x + 6$ for y into the second equation.

$$-x + 6 = x^2 - 5x + 1$$
$$0 = x^2 - 4x - 5$$
$$0 = (x - 5)(x + 1)$$
$$x = 5 \text{ or } x = -1$$

Substitute these values in the second equation.

$x = 5 : y = -(5) + 6 = 1$
$x = -1 : y = -(-1) + 6 = 7$

The solutions are $(5, 1)$ and $(-1, 7)$.

71. $\begin{cases} 4x - y^2 = 0 & (1) \\ 2x^2 + y^2 = 16 & (2) \end{cases}$

Solve the first equation for y^2: $y^2 = 4x$.
Substitute the result into the second equation.

$$2x^2 + 4x = 16$$
$$2x^2 + 4x - 16 = 0$$
$$x^2 + 2x - 8 = 0$$
$$(x + 4)(x - 2) = 0$$
$$x = -4 \text{ or } x = 2$$

Use these values in the equation $y^2 = 4x$.

$$x = -4 : y^2 = 4(-4)$$
$$y^2 = -16$$
$$y = \pm\sqrt{-16} \quad \text{(which is not real)}$$

$$x = 2 : y^2 = 4(2)$$
$$y^2 = 8$$
$$y = \pm\sqrt{8} = \pm 2\sqrt{2}$$

The solutions are $\left(2, -2\sqrt{2}\right)$ and $\left(2, 2\sqrt{2}\right)$.

72. $\begin{cases} x^2 + 4y^2 = 16 & (1) \\ x^2 + y^2 = 4 & (2) \end{cases}$

Multiply the second equation by -1 and add the result to the second equation.

$$-x^2 - y^2 = -4$$
$$\underline{x^2 + 4y^2 = 16}$$
$$3y^2 = 12$$
$$y^2 = 4$$
$$y = \pm 2$$

Substitute 4 for y^2 into the second equation.

$$x^2 + 4 = 4$$
$$x^2 = 0$$
$$x = 0$$

The solutions are $(0, 2)$ and $(0, -2)$.

73. $\begin{cases} x^2 + y^2 = 10 & (1) \\ 9x^2 + y^2 = 18 & (2) \end{cases}$

Multiply the first equation by -1 and add the result to the second equation.

$-x^2 - y^2 = -10$
$\underline{9x^2 + y^2 = 18}$
$8x^2 \qquad = 8$
$\qquad x^2 = 1$
$\qquad x = \pm 1$

Substitute 1 for x^2 into the first equation.

$1 + y^2 = 10$
$\quad y^2 = 9$
$\quad y = \pm 3$

The solutions are $(-1, -3)$, $(-1, 3)$, $(1, -3)$ and $(1, 3)$.

74. $\begin{cases} x^2 + 2y = 9 & (1) \\ 5x - 2y = 5 & (2) \end{cases}$

Add the two equations:

$x^2 \quad + 2y = 9$
$\underline{\quad 5x - 2y = 5}$
$x^2 \quad + 5x = 14$
$x^2 + 5x - 14 = 0$
$(x + 7)(x - 2) = 0$
$x = -7 \text{ or } x = 2$

Substitute these results into the first equation to find the corresponding y values.

$x = -7: \quad (-7)^2 + 2y = 9$
$\qquad\qquad 49 + 2y = 9$
$\qquad\qquad\quad 2y = -40$
$\qquad\qquad\quad\ y = -20$

$x = 2: \quad (2)^2 + 2y = 9$
$\qquad\qquad 4 + 2y = 9$
$\qquad\qquad\ 2y = 5$
$\qquad\qquad\ y = \dfrac{5}{2}$

The solutions are $(-7, -20)$ and $\left(2, \dfrac{5}{2}\right)$.

75. $\begin{cases} y = 3x^2 + 5x - 4 & (1) \\ y = 3x^2 - x + 2 & (2) \end{cases}$

Multiply the first equation by -1 and add to the result to the second equation.

$-y = -3x^2 - 5x + 4$
$\underline{\ y = \ 3x^2 \ - x + 2}$
$\ 0 = -6x + 6$
$6x = 6$
$\ x = 1$

Substitute this result into the first equation to find the corresponding y value.

$y = 3(1)^2 + 5(1) - 4 = 4$

The solution is $(1, 4)$.

76. $\begin{cases} x^2 - 3y^2 = 1 & (1) \\ 4x^2 + 5y^2 = 21 & (2) \end{cases}$

Multiply the first equation by -4 and add the result to the second equation.

$-4x^2 + 12y^2 = -4$
$\underline{\ 4x^2 + \ 5y^2 = 21}$
$\qquad\quad 17y^2 = 17$
$\qquad\qquad y^2 = 1$
$\qquad\qquad\ y = \pm 1$

Substitute 1 for y^2 into the first equation.

$x^2 - 3(1) = 1$
$\qquad x^2 = 4$
$\qquad\ x = \pm 2$

The solutions are $(-2, -1)$, $(-2, 1)$, $(2, -1)$ and $(2, 1)$.

77. Let x and y be the length and width.

$\begin{cases} \quad xy = 150 \\ 2x + 2y = 50 \end{cases}$

Solve the first equation for y: $\ y = \dfrac{150}{x}$.

Substitute the result into the second equation.

$2x + 2\left(\dfrac{150}{x}\right) = 50$
$\qquad x + \dfrac{150}{x} = 25$
$\qquad x^2 + 150 = 25x$
$\quad x^2 - 25x + 150 = 0$
$\quad (x - 15)(x - 10) = 0$
$\qquad x = 15 \text{ or } x = 10$

Substitute these values into the first equation to find the corresponding y values.

$15y = 150 \qquad\qquad 10y = 150$
$\ y = 10 \qquad\qquad\quad\ y = 15$

The room is 15 feet by 10 feet.

78. Four real solutions are the most possible, as is demonstrated by the figure below.

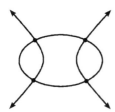

79. $y \leq -x^2 + 3$

Graph $y = -x^2 + 3$ with a solid curve.

Test Point	$y \leq -x^2 + 3$; Result
(0, 0)	$0 \leq -(0)^2 + 3$; True

Shade the portion of the graph which contains (0, 0).

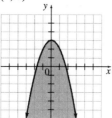

80. $x^2 + y^2 < 9$

First graph the circle with a dashed curve.

Test Point	$x^2 + y^2 < 9$; Result
(0, 0)	$0^2 + 0^2 < 9$; True

Shade the portion of the graph which contains (0, 0).

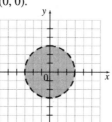

81. $x^2 - y^2 < 1$

First graph the hyperbola with a dashed curve.

Test Points	$x^2 - y^2 < 1$; Result
(–2, 0)	$(-2)^2 - 0^2 < 1$; False
(0, 0)	$0^2 - 0^2 < 1$; True
(2, 0)	$2^2 - 0^2 < 1$; False

Shade the portion of the graph that contains (0, 0).

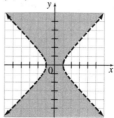

82. $\dfrac{x^2}{4} + \dfrac{y^2}{9} \geq 1$

First graph the ellipse with a solid curve.

Test Point	$\dfrac{x^2}{4} + \dfrac{y^2}{9} \geq 1$; Result
(0, 0)	$\dfrac{(0)^2}{4} + \dfrac{(0)^2}{9} \geq 1$; False

Shade the portion of the graph that does not contain (0, 0).

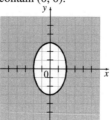

83. $\begin{cases} 2x \leq 4 \\ x + y \geq 1 \end{cases}$

First graph $2x = 4$, or $x = 2$, with a solid line, and shade to the left of the line.

Next, graph $x + y = 1$ with a solid line.

Test Point	$x + y \geq 1$; Result
(0, 0)	$0 + 0 \geq 1$; False

Shade the portion of the graph which does not contain (0, 0).

The solution to the system is the overlapping region.

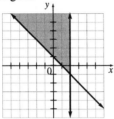

84. $\begin{cases} 3x + 4y \le 12 \\ x - 2y > 6 \end{cases}$

First graph $3x + 4y = 12$ with a solid line.

Test Point	$3x + 4y \le 12$; Result
(0, 0)	$3(0) + 4(0) \le 12$; True

Shade the portion of the graph which contains (0, 0).

Next, graph $x - 2y = 6$ with a dashed line.

Test Point	$x - 2y > 6$; Result
(0, 0)	$0 - 2(0) > 6$; False

Shade the portion of the graph which does not contain (0, 0).

The solution to the system is the overlapping region.

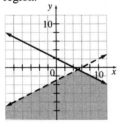

85. $\begin{cases} y > x^2 \\ x + y \ge 3 \end{cases}$

First graph the parabola with a dashed curve.

Test Point	$y > x^2$; Result
(0, 1)	$1 > 0^2$; True

Shade the portion of the graph which contains (0, 1).

Next, graph $x + y = 3$ with a solid line.

Test Point	$x + y \ge 3$; Result
(0, 0)	$0 + 0 \ge 3$; False

Shade the portion of the graph which does not contain (0, 0).

The solution to the system is the overlapping region.

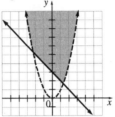

86. $\begin{cases} x^2 + y^2 \le 16 \\ x^2 + y^2 \ge 4 \end{cases}$

First graph the first circle with a solid curve.

Test Point	$x^2 + y^2 \le 16$; Result
(0, 0)	$0^2 + 0^2 \le 16$; True

Shade the portion of the graph which contains (0, 0).

Next, graph the second circle with a solid curve.

Test Point	$x^2 + y^2 \ge 4$; Result
(0, 0)	$0^2 + 0^2 \ge 4$; False

Shade the portion of the graph which does not contain (0, 0).

The solution to the system is the overlapping region.

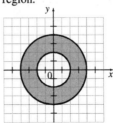

87. $\begin{cases} x^2 + y^2 < 4 \\ x^2 - y^2 \leq 1 \end{cases}$

First graph the first circle with a dashed curve.

Test Point	$x^2 + y^2 < 4$; Result
(0, 0)	$0^2 + 0^2 < 4$; True

Shade the portion of the graph which contains (0, 0).

Next, graph the hyperbola with a solid curve.

Test Point	$x^2 - y^2 \leq 1$; Result
(0, 0)	$0^2 - 0^2 \leq 1$; True

Shade the portion of the graph which contains (0, 0).

The solution to the system is the overlapping region.

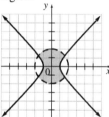

88. $\begin{cases} x^2 + y^2 < 4 \\ y \geq x^2 - 1 \\ x \geq 0 \end{cases}$

First graph the first circle with a dashed curve.

Test Point	$x^2 + y^2 < 4$; Result
(0, 0)	$0^2 + 0^2 < 4$; True

Shade the portion of the graph which contains (0, 0).

Next, graph the parabola with a solid curve.

Test Point	$y^2 \geq x^2 - 1$; Result
(0, 0)	$0 \geq 0^2 - 1$; True

Shade the portion of the graph which contains (0, 0).

Now graph the line $x = 0$ with a solid line, and shade to the right.

The solution to the system is the overlapping region.

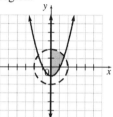

Chapter 10 Test

1. (–6, 3), (–8, –7)

$d = \sqrt{[-8 - (-6)]^2 + (-7 - 3)^2}$

$ = \sqrt{(-2)^2 + (-10)^2}$

$ = \sqrt{4 + 100}$

$ = \sqrt{104}$

$ = 2\sqrt{26}$ units

2. $\left(-2\sqrt{5}, \sqrt{10}\right), \left(-\sqrt{5}, 4\sqrt{10}\right)$

$d = \sqrt{\left[-\sqrt{5} - \left(-2\sqrt{5}\right)\right]^2 + \left(4\sqrt{10} - \sqrt{10}\right)^2}$

$ = \sqrt{\left(\sqrt{5}\right)^2 + \left(3\sqrt{10}\right)^2}$

$ = \sqrt{5 + 9 \cdot 10}$

$ = \sqrt{95}$ units

3. (–2, –5), (–6, 12)

$\left(\dfrac{-2 + (-6)}{2}, \dfrac{-5 + 12}{2}\right) = \left(\dfrac{-8}{2}, \dfrac{7}{2}\right) = \left(-4, \dfrac{7}{2}\right)$

The midpoint is $\left(-4, \dfrac{7}{2}\right)$.

4. Circle: $x^2 + y^2 = 36$

Center: (0, 0); radius $r = \sqrt{36} = 6$

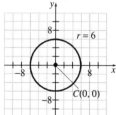

5. Hyperbola : $x^2 - y^2 = 36$

$$\frac{x^2}{36} - \frac{y^2}{36} = 1$$

$$\frac{x^2}{6^2} - \frac{y^2}{6^2} = 1$$

Center: $(0, 0)$; $a = 6$, $b = 6$

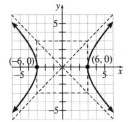

6. Ellipse: $16x^2 + 9y^2 = 144$

$$\frac{x^2}{9} + \frac{y^2}{16} = 1$$

$$\frac{x^2}{3^2} + \frac{y^2}{4^2} = 1$$

Center: $(0, 0)$; $a = 3$, $b = 4$

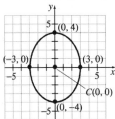

7. Parabola: $y = x^2 - 8x + 16$

$$y = (x - 4)^2$$

Vertex: $(4, 0)$; Axis of symmetry: $x = 4$
Opens upward.

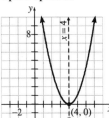

8. Circle: $x^2 + y^2 + 6x = 16$

$$(x^2 + 6x) + y^2 = 16$$

$$(x^2 + 6x + 9) + y^2 = 16 + 9$$

$$(x + 3)^2 + y^2 = 25$$

Center: $(-3, 0)$; radius $r = \sqrt{25} = 5$

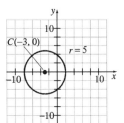

9. Parabola: $x = y^2 + 8y - 3$

$$x + 16 = (y^2 + 8y + 16) - 3$$

$$x = (y + 4)^2 - 19$$

Vertex: $(-19, -4)$; Axis of symmetry: $y = -4$
Opens to the right.

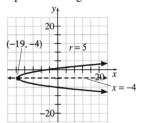

10. Ellipse: $\dfrac{(x - 4)^2}{16} + \dfrac{(y - 3)^2}{9} = 1$

$$\frac{(x - 4)^2}{4^2} + \frac{(y - 3)^2}{3^2} = 1$$

Center: $(4, 3)$; $a = 4$, $b = 3$

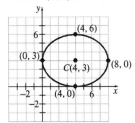

11. Hyperbola: $y^2 - x^2 = 1$
Center: $(0, 0)$; $a = 1$, $b = 1$

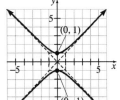

12. $\begin{cases} x^2 + y^2 = 26 & (1) \\ x^2 - 2y^2 = 23 & (2) \end{cases}$

Solve the first equation for x^2: $x^2 = 26 - y^2$.

Substitute the result into the second equation.

$(26 - y^2) - 2y^2 = 23$
$$-3y^2 = -3$$
$$y^2 = 1$$
$$y = \pm 1$$

Substitute 1 for y^2 into the first equation.

$x^2 + 1 = 26$
$$x^2 = 25$$
$$x = \pm 5$$

The solutions are $(-5, -1)$, $(-5, 1)$, $(5, -1)$, and $(5, 1)$.

13. $\begin{cases} y = x^2 - 5x + 6 & (1) \\ y = 2x & (2) \end{cases}$

Substitute $2x$ for y in the first equation.

$2x = x^2 - 5x + 6$
$$0 = x^2 - 7x + 6$$
$$0 = (x - 6)(x - 1)$$
$$x = 6 \text{ or } x = 1$$

Substitute these x values into the second equation to find the corresponding y values.

$x = 6: y = 2(6) = 12$
$x = 1: y = 2(1) = 2$

The solutions are $(1, 2)$ and $(6, 12)$.

14. $\begin{cases} 2x + 5y \geq 10 \\ y \geq x^2 + 1 \end{cases}$

First graph $2x + 5y = 10$ with a solid line.

Test Point	$2x + 5y \geq 10$; Result
$(0, 0)$	$2(0) + 5(0) \geq 10$; False

Shade the portion of the graph which does not contain $(0, 0)$.

Next, graph $y = x^2 + 1$ with a solid curve.

Test Point	$y \geq x^2 + 1$; Result
$(0, 0)$	$0 \geq 0^2 + 1$; False

Shade the portion of the graph which does not contain $(0, 0)$.

The solution to the system is the overlapping region.

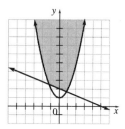

15. $\begin{cases} \dfrac{x^2}{4} + y^2 \leq 1 \\ x + y > 1 \end{cases}$

First graph the ellipse with a solid curve.

Test Point	$\dfrac{x^2}{4} + y^2 \leq 1$; Result
$(0, 0)$	$\dfrac{0^2}{4} + 0^2 \leq 1$; True

Shade the portion of the graph which contains $(0, 0)$.

Next, graph $x + y = 1$ with a solid line.

Test Point	$x + y > 1$; Result
$(0, 0)$	$0 + 0 > 1$; False

Shade the portion of the graph which does not contain $(0, 0)$.

The solution to the system is the overlapping region.

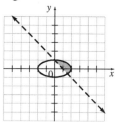

16. $\begin{cases} x^2 + y^2 \geq 4 \\ x^2 + y^2 < 16 \\ y \geq 0 \end{cases}$

First graph the circle $x^2 + y^2 = 4$ with a solid curve.

Test Point	$x^2 + y^2 \geq 4$; Result
$(0, 0)$	$0^2 + 0^2 \geq 4$; False

Shade the portion of the graph which does not contain (0, 0).

Next graph the circle $x^2 + y^2 = 16$ with a dashed curve.

Test Point	$x^2 + y^2 < 16$; Result
(0, 0)	$0^2 + 0^2 < 16$; True

Shade the portion of the graph which contains (0, 0).

Now graph the inequality $y = 0$ by shading the region above the *x*-axis.

The solution to the system is the overlapping region.

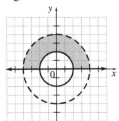

17. $100x^2 + 225y^2 = 22,500$

$$\frac{x^2}{225} + \frac{y^2}{100} = 1$$

$$\frac{x^2}{15^2} + \frac{y^2}{10^2} = 1$$

$$a = 15; \quad b = 10$$

Width = 15 + 15 = 30 feet

Height = 10 feet

Chapter 10 Cumulative Review

1. $4 \cdot (9y) = (4 \cdot 9)y = 36y$

2. $3x + 4 > 1$ and $2x - 5 \le 9$
$3x > -3$ and $2x \le 14$
$x > -1$ and $x \le 7$
$-1 < x \le 7$
The solution set is (−1, 7].

3. $x - 3y = 6$

x	y
0	−2
6	0
3	−1

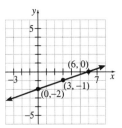

4. (3, 2), (1, −4)

$$m = \frac{-4 - 2}{1 - 3} = \frac{-6}{-2} = 3$$

5. $\begin{cases} 3x + \dfrac{y}{2} = 2 \quad (1) \\ 6x + y = 5 \quad (2) \end{cases}$

Multiply the first equation by −2 and add the result to the second equation.

$-6x - y = -4$
$\underline{6x + y = 5}$
$0 = 1$, which is impossible.

Thus, the solution set is $\varnothing$.

6. Let x = speed of one plane. Then
$x + 25$ = speed of the other plane.
$d_{\text{plane 1}} + d_{\text{plane 2}} = 650$ miles
$2x + 2(x + 25) = 650$
$2x + 2x + 50 = 650$
$4x = 600$
$x = 150$
$x + 25 = 150 + 25 = 175$
The planes are traveling at 150 mph and 175 mph.

7. a. $\left(5x^2\right)^3 = 5^3\left(x^2\right)^3 = 125x^6$

b. $\left(\dfrac{2}{3}\right)^3 = \dfrac{2^3}{3^3} = \dfrac{8}{27}$

c. $\left(\dfrac{3p^4}{q^5}\right)^2 = \dfrac{3^2\left(p^4\right)^2}{\left(q^5\right)^2} = \dfrac{9p^8}{q^{10}}$

d. $\left(\dfrac{2^{-3}}{y}\right)^{-2} = \left(\dfrac{1}{2^3 y}\right)^{-2} = \dfrac{1^{-2}}{2^{-6} y^{-2}} = \dfrac{2^6 y^2}{1} = 64y^2$

e. $\left(x^{-5}y^2z^{-1}\right)^7 = x^{-35}y^{14}z^{-7} = \dfrac{y^{14}}{x^{35}z^7}$

8. a. $\dfrac{4^8}{4^3} = 4^{8-3} = 4^5$

b. $\dfrac{y^{11}}{y^5} = y^{11-5} = y^6$

c. $\dfrac{32x^7}{4x^6} = 8x^{7-6} = 8x$

d. $\dfrac{18a^{12}b^6}{12a^8b^6} = \dfrac{3a^{12-8}b^{6-6}}{2} = \dfrac{3a^4b^0}{2} = \dfrac{3a^4}{2}$

9.
$$2x^2 = \frac{17}{3}x + 1$$
$$3(2x^2) = 3\left(\frac{17}{3}x + 1\right)$$
$$6x^2 = 17x + 3$$
$$6x^2 - 17x - 3 = 0$$
$$(6x+1)(x-3) = 0$$
$$6x+1 = 0 \quad \text{or} \quad x - 3 = 0$$
$$6x = -1 \quad \text{or} \qquad x = 3$$
$$x = -\frac{1}{6}$$

The solutions are $-\dfrac{1}{6}$ and 3.

10. a. $3y^2 + 14y + 15 = (3y+5)(y+3)$

b. $20a^5 + 54a^4 + 10a^3$
$$= 2a^3(10a^2 + 27a + 5)$$
$$= 2a^3(2a+5)(5a+1)$$

c. $(y-3)^2 - 2(y-3) - 8$
Let $u = y - 3$. Then $u^2 = (y-3)^2$ and
$$u^2 - 2u - 8 = (u-4)(u+2)$$
$$= [(y-3)-4][(y-3)+2]$$
$$= (y-7)(y-1)$$

11. $\dfrac{7}{x-1} + \dfrac{10x}{x^2-1} - \dfrac{5}{x+1} = \dfrac{7}{x-1} + \dfrac{10x}{(x+1)(x-1)} - \dfrac{5}{x+1}$
$$= \frac{7(x+1)+10x-5(x-1)}{(x+1)(x-1)}$$
$$= \frac{7x+7+10x-5x+5}{(x+1)(x-1)}$$
$$= \frac{12x+12}{(x+1)(x-1)}$$
$$= \frac{12(x+1)}{(x+1)(x-1)}$$
$$= \frac{12}{x-1}$$

12. $\dfrac{2}{3a-15} - \dfrac{a}{25-a^2} = \dfrac{2}{3(a-5)} + \dfrac{a}{a^2-25}$
$$= \frac{2}{3(a-5)} + \frac{a}{(a+5)(a-5)}$$
$$= \frac{2(a+5)+3a}{3(a+5)(a-5)}$$
$$= \frac{2a+10+3a}{3(a+5)(a-5)}$$
$$= \frac{5a+10}{3(a+5)(a-5)}$$

13. a. $\dfrac{\dfrac{2x}{27y^2}}{\dfrac{6x^2}{9}} = \dfrac{2x}{27y^2} \cdot \dfrac{9}{6x^2} = \dfrac{1}{3y^2} \cdot \dfrac{1}{3x} = \dfrac{1}{9xy^2}$

b. $\dfrac{\dfrac{5x}{x+2}}{\dfrac{10}{x-2}} = \dfrac{5x}{x+2} \cdot \dfrac{x-2}{10} = \dfrac{x(x-2)}{2(x+2)}$

c. $\dfrac{\dfrac{x}{y^2}+\dfrac{1}{y}}{\dfrac{y}{x^2}+\dfrac{1}{x}} = \dfrac{\left(\dfrac{x}{y^2}+\dfrac{1}{y}\right)x^2y^2}{\left(\dfrac{y}{x^2}+\dfrac{1}{x}\right)x^2y^2}$
$$= \frac{x^3 + x^2y}{y^3 + xy^2}$$
$$= \frac{x^2(x+y)}{y^2(y+x)}$$
$$= \frac{x^2}{y^2}$$

14. a. $(a^{-1}-b^{-1})^{-1} = \left(\dfrac{1}{a}-\dfrac{1}{b}\right)^{-1} = \left(\dfrac{b-a}{ab}\right)^{-1} = \dfrac{ab}{b-a}$

b. $\dfrac{2-\dfrac{1}{x}}{4x-\dfrac{1}{x}} = \dfrac{\left(2-\dfrac{1}{x}\right)x}{\left(4x-\dfrac{1}{x}\right)x}$
$$= \frac{2x-1}{4x^2-1}$$
$$= \frac{2x-1}{(2x+1)(2x-1)}$$
$$= \frac{1}{2x+1}$$

15.

$$x+2 \overline{\smash{\big)}\, 2x^2 - x - 10}$$

quotient $2x - 5$

$$2x^2 + 4x$$
$$-5x - 10$$
$$-5x - 10$$
$$0$$

Answer: $2x - 5$

16.
$$\frac{2}{x+3} = \frac{1}{x^2-9} - \frac{1}{x-3}$$
$$\frac{2}{x+3} = \frac{1}{(x+3)(x-3)} - \frac{1}{x-3}$$
$$2(x-3) = 1 - 1(x+3)$$
$$2x - 6 = 1 - x - 3$$
$$2x - 6 = -x - 2$$
$$3x = 4$$
$$x = \frac{4}{3}$$

17.
$$\begin{array}{r|rrrrrrr} 4 & 4 & -25 & 35 & 0 & 17 & 0 & 0 \\ & & 16 & -36 & -4 & -16 & 4 & 16 \\ \hline & 4 & -9 & -1 & -4 & 1 & 4 & 16 \end{array}$$

Thus, $P(4) = 16$.

18. $y = \dfrac{k}{x}$

$$3 = \frac{k}{\frac{2}{3}}$$
$$k = 3\left(\frac{2}{3}\right) = 2$$

Thus, the equation is $y = \dfrac{2}{x}$.

19.
$$\frac{2x}{x-3} + \frac{6-2x}{x^2-9} = \frac{x}{x+3}$$
$$\frac{2x}{x-3} + \frac{-2(x-3)}{(x+3)(x-3)} = \frac{x}{x+3}$$
$$\frac{2x}{x-3} - \frac{2}{x+3} = \frac{x}{x+3}$$
$$\frac{2x}{x-3} = \frac{x}{x+3} + \frac{2}{x+3}$$
$$\frac{2x}{x-3} = \frac{x+2}{x+3}$$
$$2x(x+3) = (x+2)(x-3)$$
$$2x^2 + 6x = x^2 - x - 6$$
$$x^2 + 7x + 6 = 0$$
$$(x+6)(x+1) = 0$$

$x + 6 = 0$ or $x + 1 = 0$
$x = -6$ or $x = -1$
The solutions are -6 and -1.

20. a. $\sqrt[5]{-32} = -2$ because $(-2)^5 = -32$.

b. $\sqrt[4]{625} = 5$ because $5^4 = 625$.

c. $-\sqrt{36} = -6$ because $6^2 = 36$.

d. $-\sqrt[3]{-27x^3} = -(-3x) = 3x$

e. $\sqrt{144y^2} = 12y$

21. Let t = time it will take together.

$$\frac{1}{4} + \frac{1}{5} = \frac{1}{t}$$
$$20t\left(\frac{1}{4} + \frac{1}{5}\right) = 20t\left(\frac{1}{t}\right)$$
$$5t + 4t = 20$$
$$9t = 20$$
$$t = \frac{20}{9} = 2\frac{2}{9}$$

It will take them $2\frac{2}{9}$ hours. No, they cannot finish before the movie starts.

22. a. $\dfrac{\sqrt{32}}{\sqrt{4}} = \sqrt{\dfrac{32}{4}} = \sqrt{8} = \sqrt{4 \cdot 2} = 2\sqrt{2}$

b.
$$\frac{\sqrt[3]{240y^2}}{5\sqrt[3]{3y^{-4}}} = \frac{1}{5}\sqrt[3]{\frac{240y^2}{3y^{-4}}}$$
$$= \frac{1}{5}\sqrt[3]{80y^6}$$
$$= \frac{1}{5}\sqrt[3]{8y^6 \cdot 10}$$
$$= \frac{2y^2\sqrt[3]{10}}{5}$$

c.
$$\frac{\sqrt[5]{64x^9y^2}}{\sqrt[5]{2x^2y^{-8}}} = \sqrt[5]{\frac{64x^9y^2}{2x^2y^{-8}}}$$
$$= \sqrt[5]{32x^7y^{10}}$$
$$= \sqrt[5]{32x^5y^{10} \cdot x^2}$$
$$= 2xy^2\sqrt[5]{x^2}$$

23. a. $\sqrt[3]{1} = 1$

b. $\sqrt[3]{-64} = -4$

c. $\sqrt[3]{\dfrac{8}{125}} = \dfrac{\sqrt[3]{8}}{\sqrt[3]{125}} = \dfrac{2}{5}$

d. $\sqrt[3]{x^6} = x^2$

e. $\sqrt[3]{-27x^9} = -3x^3$

24. a. $\sqrt{5}\left(2 + \sqrt{15}\right) = 2\sqrt{5} + \sqrt{5} \cdot \sqrt{15}$
$$= 2\sqrt{5} + \sqrt{75}$$
$$= 2\sqrt{5} + 5\sqrt{3}$$

b. $\left(\sqrt{3} - \sqrt{5}\right)\left(\sqrt{7} - 1\right)$
$$= \sqrt{3} \cdot \sqrt{7} - \sqrt{3} \cdot 1 - \sqrt{5} \cdot \sqrt{7} + \sqrt{5} \cdot 1$$
$$= \sqrt{21} - \sqrt{3} - \sqrt{35} + \sqrt{5}$$

c. $\left(2\sqrt{5} - 1\right)^2 = \left(2\sqrt{5}\right)^2 - 2 \cdot 2\sqrt{5} \cdot 1 + 1^2$
$$= 4(5) - 4\sqrt{5} + 1$$
$$= 21 - 4\sqrt{5}$$

d. $\left(3\sqrt{2} + 5\right)\left(3\sqrt{2} - 5\right) = \left(3\sqrt{2}\right)^2 - 5^2$
$$= 9(2) - 25$$
$$= 18 - 25$$
$$= -7$$

25. a. $z^{2/3}\left(z^{1/3} - z^5\right) = z^{2/3 + 1/3} - z^{2/3 + 5}$
$$= z^{3/3} - z^{2/3 + 15/3}$$
$$= z - z^{17/3}$$

b. $(x^{1/3} - 5)(x^{1/3} + 2)$
$$= x^{1/3} \cdot x^{1/3} + 2x^{1/3} - 5x^{1/3} - 5(2)$$
$$= x^{2/3} - 3x^{1/3} - 10$$

26. $\dfrac{-2}{\sqrt{3} + 3} = \dfrac{-2\left(\sqrt{3} - 3\right)}{\left(\sqrt{3} + 3\right)\left(\sqrt{3} - 3\right)}$

$$= \dfrac{-2\left(\sqrt{3} - 3\right)}{\left(\sqrt{3}\right)^2 - 3^2}$$

$$= \dfrac{-2\left(\sqrt{3} - 3\right)}{3 - 9}$$

$$= \dfrac{-2\left(\sqrt{3} - 3\right)}{-6}$$

$$= \dfrac{\sqrt{3} - 3}{3}$$

27. a. $\dfrac{\sqrt{20}}{\sqrt{5}} = \sqrt{\dfrac{20}{5}} = \sqrt{4} = 2$

b. $\dfrac{\sqrt{50x}}{2\sqrt{2}} = \dfrac{1}{2}\sqrt{\dfrac{50x}{2}} = \dfrac{1}{2}\sqrt{25x} = \dfrac{5\sqrt{x}}{2}$

c. $\dfrac{7\sqrt[3]{48x^4 y^8}}{\sqrt[3]{6y^2}} = 7\sqrt[3]{\dfrac{48x^4 y^8}{6y^2}}$
$$= 7\sqrt[3]{8x^4 y^6}$$
$$= 7\sqrt[3]{8x^3 y^6 \cdot x}$$
$$= 7 \cdot 2xy^2 \sqrt[3]{x}$$
$$= 14xy^2 \sqrt[3]{x}$$

d. $\dfrac{2\sqrt[4]{32a^8 b^6}}{\sqrt[4]{a^{-1} b^2}} = 2\sqrt[4]{\dfrac{32a^8 b^6}{a^{-1} b^2}}$
$$= 2\sqrt[4]{32a^9 b^4}$$
$$= 2\sqrt[4]{16a^8 b^4 \cdot 2a}$$
$$= 2 \cdot 2a^2 b\sqrt[4]{2a}$$
$$= 4a^2 b\sqrt[4]{2a}$$

28. $\sqrt{2x - 3} = x - 3$
$$2x - 3 = (x - 3)^2$$
$$2x - 3 = x^2 - 6x + 9$$
$$0 = x^2 - 8x + 12$$
$$0 = (x - 6)(x - 2)$$
$$x - 6 = 0 \text{ or } x - 2 = 0$$
$$x = 6 \text{ or } \quad x = 2$$
Discard 2 as an extraneous solution. The solution is 6.

29. a. $\dfrac{\sqrt{45}}{4} - \dfrac{\sqrt{5}}{3} = \dfrac{3\sqrt{5}}{4} - \dfrac{\sqrt{5}}{3} = \dfrac{9\sqrt{5} - 4\sqrt{5}}{12} = \dfrac{5\sqrt{5}}{12}$

b. $\sqrt[3]{\dfrac{7x}{8}} + 2\sqrt[3]{7x} = \dfrac{\sqrt[3]{7x}}{2} + 2\sqrt[3]{7x}$
$$= \dfrac{\sqrt[3]{7x}}{2} + \dfrac{4\sqrt[3]{7x}}{2}$$
$$= \dfrac{5\sqrt[3]{7x}}{2}$$

30. $9x^2 - 6x = -4$
$$9x^2 - 6x + 4 = 0$$
$$a = 9, b = -6, c = 4$$
$$b^2 - 4ac = (-6)^2 - 4(9)(4) = 36 - 144 = -108$$
Two complex but not real solutions

31. $\sqrt{\dfrac{7x}{3y}} = \dfrac{\sqrt{7x}}{\sqrt{3y}} = \dfrac{\sqrt{7x}\cdot\sqrt{3y}}{\sqrt{3y}\cdot\sqrt{3y}} = \dfrac{\sqrt{21xy}}{3y}$

32.

$\dfrac{4}{x-2} - \dfrac{x}{x+2} = \dfrac{16}{x^2-4}$

$\dfrac{4}{x-2} - \dfrac{x}{x+2} = \dfrac{16}{(x+2)(x-2)}$

$4(x+2) - x(x-2) = 16$

$4x+8-x^2+2x = 16$

$0 = x^2-6x+8$

$0 = (x-4)(x-2)$

$x-4=0 \ \text{ or } \ x-2=0$

$x=4 \ \text{ or } \quad x=2$

Discard the solutions 2 as extraneous. The solution is 4.

33. $\sqrt{2x-3} = 9$

$2x-3 = 9^2$

$2x-3 = 81$

$2x = 84$

$x = 42$

The solution is 42.

34. $x^3 + 2x^2 - 4x \ge 8$

$x^3 + 2x^2 - 4x - 8 \ge 0$

$x^2(x+2) - 4(x+2) \ge 0$

$(x+2)(x^2-4) \ge 0$

$(x+2)(x+2)(x-2) \ge 0$

$(x+2)^2(x-2) \ge 0$

$(x+2)^2 = 0 \quad \text{ or } x-2=0$

$x+2=0 \quad \text{ or } \quad x=2$

$x=-2$

Region	Test Point	$(x+2)^2(x-2) \ge 0$ Result
$A: (-\infty, -2)$	-3	$(-3+2)^2(-3-2) \ge 0$ False
$B: (-2, 2)$	0	$(0+2)^2(0-2) \ge 0$ False
$C: (2, \infty)$	3	$(3+2)^2(3-2) \ge 0$ True

The solution set is $[2, \infty)$.

35. a. $i^7 = i^4 \cdot i^3 = 1\cdot(-i) = -i$

   b. $i^{20} = (i^4)^5 = 1^5 = 1$

   c. $i^{46} = i^{44} \cdot i^2 = (i^4)^{11} \cdot (-1) = 1^{11}(-1) = -1$

   d. $i^{-12} = \dfrac{1}{i^{12}} = \dfrac{1}{(i^4)^3} = \dfrac{1}{1^3} = 1$

36. $f(x) = (x+2)^2 - 1$

The graph is similar to the graph of $y = x^2$, but is shifted to the left 2 units and down 1 unit. The vertex is $(-2, -1)$, and the axis of symmetry is $x = -2$.

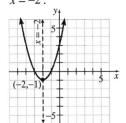

37.

$p^2 + 2p = 4$

$p^2 + 2p + 1 = 4 + 1$

$(p+1)^2 = 5$

$p+1 = \pm\sqrt{5}$

$p = -1 \pm \sqrt{5}$

The solutions are $-1+\sqrt{5}$ and $-1-\sqrt{5}$.

38. $f(x) = -x^2 - 6x + 4$

The maximum will occur at the vertex.

$x = -\dfrac{b}{2a} = \dfrac{-(-6)}{2(-1)} = -3;$

$y = f(-3) = -(-3)^2 - 6(-3) + 4 = 13$

The maximum value is 13.

39.

$\dfrac{1}{4}m^2 - m + \dfrac{1}{2} = 0$

$4\left(\dfrac{1}{4}m^2 - m + \dfrac{1}{2}\right) = 4(0)$

$m^2 - 4m + 2 = 0$

$a = 1, b = -4, c = 2$

$x = \dfrac{4 \pm \sqrt{(-4)^2 - 4(1)(2)}}{2(1)}$

$= \dfrac{4 \pm \sqrt{16-8}}{2}$

$= \dfrac{4 \pm \sqrt{8}}{2}$

$= \dfrac{4 \pm 2\sqrt{2}}{2} = 2 \pm \sqrt{2}$

The solutions are $2+\sqrt{2}$ and $2-\sqrt{2}$.

40. $f(x) = \dfrac{x+1}{2}$

$y = \dfrac{x+1}{2}$

$x = \dfrac{y+1}{2}$

$2x = y+1$

$2x-1 = y$

$f^{-1}(x) = 2x-1$

41.
$$p^4 - 3p^2 - 4 = 0$$
$$(p^2 - 4)(p^2 + 1) = 0$$
$$(p+2)(p-2)(p^2 + 1) = 0$$
$$p+2 = 0 \quad \text{or} \quad p-2 = 0 \quad \text{or} \quad p^2 + 1 = 0$$
$$p = -2 \quad \text{or} \quad p = 2 \quad \text{or} \quad p^2 = -1$$
$$p = \pm i$$

The solutions are -2, 2, $-i$, i.

42. $f(x) = x^2 - 3x + 2; \quad g(x) = -3x + 5$

a. $(f \circ g)(x) = f[g(x)]$
$$= f(-3x+5)$$
$$= (-3x+5)^2 - 3(-3x+5) + 2$$
$$= 9x^2 - 30x + 25 + 9x - 15 + 2$$
$$= 9x^2 - 21x + 12$$

b. $(f \circ g)(-2) = f[g(-2)]$
$$= f[-3(-2)+5]$$
$$= f(11)$$
$$= (11)^2 - 3(11) + 2$$
$$= 121 - 33 + 2$$
$$= 90$$

c. $(g \circ f)(x) = g[f(x)]$
$$= g(x^2 - 3x + 2)$$
$$= -3(x^2 - 3x + 2) + 5$$
$$= -3x^2 + 9x - 6 + 5$$
$$= -3x^2 + 9x - 1$$

d. $(g \circ f)(5) = g[f(5)]$
$$= g[(5)^2 - 3(5) + 2)]$$
$$= g(12)$$
$$= -3(12) + 5$$
$$= -36 + 5$$
$$= -31$$

43. $\dfrac{x+2}{x-3} \le 0$

$x + 2 = 0 \quad \text{or} \quad x - 3 = 0$

$x = -2 \quad \text{or} \quad \quad x = 3$

Region	Test Point	$\dfrac{x+2}{x-3} \le 0$ Result
$A: (-\infty, -2)$	-3	$\dfrac{-3+2}{-3-3} \le 0; \text{False}$
$B: (-2, 3)$	0	$\dfrac{0+2}{0-3} \le 0; \text{True}$
$C: (3, \infty)$	4	$\dfrac{4+2}{4-3} \le 0; \text{False}$

The solution set is $[-2, 3)$.

44. Ellipse: $4x^2 + 9y^2 = 36$

$$\dfrac{x^2}{9} + \dfrac{y^2}{4} = 1$$

$$\dfrac{x^2}{3^2} + \dfrac{y^2}{2^2} = 1$$

Center: $(0, 0)$; $a = 3$, $b = 2$

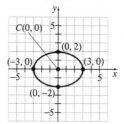

45. $g(x) = \dfrac{1}{2}(x+2)^2 + 5$

The graph is similar to the graph of $y = x^2$, but wider by a factor of 3 because $a = \dfrac{1}{2}$. The graph is shifted to the left 2 units and up 5 units. The vertex is $(-2, 5)$, and the axis of symmetry is $x = -2$.

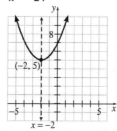

46. a. $64^x = 4$

$(4^3)^x = 4^1$

$4^{3x} = 4^1$

$3x = 1$

$x = \dfrac{1}{3}$

b. $125^{x-3} = 25$

$(5^3)^{x-3} = 5^2$

$5^{3x-9} = 5^2$

$3x - 9 = 2$

$3x = 11$

$x = \dfrac{11}{3}$

c. $\dfrac{1}{81} = 3^{2x}$

$\dfrac{1}{3^4} = 3^{2x}$

$3^{-4} = 3^{2x}$

$-4 = 2x$

$-2 = x$

47. $f(x) = x^2 - 4x - 12$

$x = -\dfrac{b}{2a} = \dfrac{-(-4)}{2(1)} = 2$

$f(2) = (2)^2 - 4(2) - 12 = -16$

The vertex is $(2, -16)$.

48. $\begin{cases} x + 2y < 8 \\ y \geq x^2 \end{cases}$

First, graph $x + 2y = 8$ with a dashed line.

Test Point	$x + 2y > 8$; Result
$(0, 0)$	$0 + 2(0) > 8$; False

Shade the portion of the graph which does not contain $(0, 0)$.

Next, graph the parabola $y = x^2$ with a solid curve.

Test Point	$y \geq x^2$; Result
$(0, 1)$	$1 \geq 0^2$; True

Shade the portion of the graph which contains $(0, 1)$.

The solution to the system is the overlapping region.

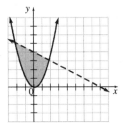

49. $(2, -5), (1, -4)$

$d = \sqrt{\left[-4 - (-5)\right]^2 + (1 - 2)^2}$

$ = \sqrt{1^2 + (-1)^2}$

$ = \sqrt{2} \approx 1.414$

50. $\begin{cases} x^2 + y^2 = 36 & (1) \\ y = x + 6 & (2) \end{cases}$

Substitute $x + 6$ for y into the first equation.

$x^2 + (x + 6)^2 = 36$

$x^2 + (x^2 + 12x + 36) = 36$

$2x^2 + 12x = 0$

$2x(x + 6) = 0$

$2x = 0$ or $x + 6 = 0$

$x = 0$ or $\quad x = -6$

Substitute these x values into the first equation to find the corresponding y values.

$x = 0 \;:\; y = 0 + 6 = 6$

$x = -6: y = -6 + 6 = 0$

The solutions are $(0, 6)$ and $(-6, 0)$.

Chapter 11

Exercise Set 11.1

1. $a_n = n + 4$
$a_1 = 1 + 4 = 5$
$a_2 = 2 + 4 = 6$
$a_3 = 3 + 4 = 7$
$a_4 = 4 + 4 = 8$
$a_5 = 5 + 4 = 9$
The first five terms of the sequence $a_n = n + 4$ are
5, 6, 7, 8, 9 .

3. $a_n = (-1)^n$
$a_1 = (-1)^1 = -1$
$a_2 = (-1)^2 = 1$
$a_3 = (-1)^3 = -1$
$a_4 = (-1)^4 = 1$
$a_5 = (-1)^5 = -1$
The first five terms of the sequence $a_n = (-1)^n$
are -1, 1, -1, 1, and -1 .

5. $a_n = \dfrac{1}{n + 3}$
$a_1 = \dfrac{1}{1 + 3} = \dfrac{1}{4}$
$a_2 = \dfrac{1}{2 + 3} = \dfrac{1}{5}$
$a_3 = \dfrac{1}{3 + 3} = \dfrac{1}{6}$
$a_4 = \dfrac{1}{4 + 3} = \dfrac{1}{7}$
$a_5 = \dfrac{1}{5 + 3} = \dfrac{1}{8}$

The first five terms of the sequence $a_n = \dfrac{1}{n + 3}$ are

$\dfrac{1}{4}$, $\dfrac{1}{5}$, $\dfrac{1}{6}$, $\dfrac{1}{7}$, and $\dfrac{1}{8}$.

7. $a_n = 2n$
$a_1 = 2(1) = 2$
$a_2 = 2(2) = 4$
$a_3 = 2(3) = 6$
$a_4 = 2(4) = 8$
$a_5 = 2(5) = 10$
The first five terms of the sequence $a_n = 2n$ are 2,
4, 6, 8, and 10.

9. $a_n = -n^2$
$a_1 = -1^2 = -1$
$a_2 = -2^2 = -4$
$a_3 = -3^2 = -9$
$a_4 = -4^2 = -16$
$a_5 = -5^2 = -25$
The first five terms of the sequence $a_n = -n^2$ are
-1, -4, -9, -16, and -25 .

11. $a_n = 2^n$
$a_1 = 2^1 = 2$
$a_2 = 2^2 = 4$
$a_3 = 2^3 = 8$
$a_4 = 2^4 = 16$
$a_5 = 2^5 = 32$
The first five terms of the sequence $a_n = 2^n$ are 2,
4, 8, 16, and 32.

13. $a_n = 2n + 5$
$a_1 = 2(1) + 5 = 2 + 5 = 7$
$a_2 = 2(2) + 5 = 4 + 5 = 9$
$a_3 = 2(3) + 5 = 6 + 5 = 11$
$a_4 = 2(4) + 5 = 8 + 5 = 13$
$a_5 = 2(5) + 5 = 10 + 5 = 15$
The first five terms of the sequence $a_n = 2n + 5$
are 7, 9, 11, 13, and 15.

15. $a_n = (-1)^n n^2$
$a_1 = (-1)^1 (1)^1 = -1(1) = -1$
$a_2 = (-1)^2 (2)^2 = 1(4) = 4$
$a_3 = (-1)^3 (3)^2 = -1(9) = -9$
$a_4 = (-1)^4 (4)^2 = 1(16) = 16$
$a_5 = (-1)^5 (5)^2 = -1(25) = -25$
The first five terms of the sequence $a_n = (-1)^n n^2$
are -1, 4, -9, 16, and -25 .

17. $a_n = 3n^2$
$a_5 = 3(5)^2 = 3(25) = 75$

19. $a_n = 6n - 2$
$a_{20} = 6(20) - 2 = 120 - 2 = 118$

SSM: Intermediate Algebra A Graphing Approach, 3e

21. $a_n = \dfrac{n+3}{n}$

$a_{15} = \dfrac{15+3}{15} = \dfrac{18}{15} = \dfrac{6}{5}$

23. $a_n = (-3)^n$

$a_6 = (-3)^6 = 729$

25. $\dfrac{n-2}{n+1}$

$a_6 = \dfrac{6-2}{6+1} = \dfrac{4}{7}$

27. $a_n = \dfrac{(-1)^n}{n}$

$a_8 = \dfrac{(-1)^8}{8} = \dfrac{1}{8}$

29. $a_n = -n^2 + 5$

$a_{10} = -10^2 + 5 = -100 + 5 = -95$

31. $a_n = \dfrac{(-1)^n}{n+6}$

$a_{19} = \dfrac{(-1)^{19}}{19+6} = \dfrac{-1}{25} = -\dfrac{1}{25}$

33. These numbers are 1 less than the product of 4 and the first four natural numbers.

$3 = 4(1)-1, 7 = 4(2)-1, 11 = 4(3)-1,$
$15 = 4(4)-1.$

In general, $a_n = 4n - 1$.

35. $-2 = -(2)^1$
$-4 = -(2)^2$
$-8 = -(2)^3$
$-16 = -(2)^4$

In general, $a_n = -2^n$.

37. $\dfrac{1}{3} = \dfrac{1}{3^1}$

$\dfrac{1}{9} = \dfrac{1}{3^2}$

$\dfrac{1}{27} = \dfrac{1}{3^3}$

$\dfrac{1}{81} = \dfrac{1}{3^4}$

In general, $a_n = \dfrac{1}{3^n}$.

39. $a_n = 32n - 16$

$a_2 = 32(2)-16 = 64-16 = 48$ ft
$a_3 = 32(3)-16 = 96-16 = 80$ ft
$a_4 = 32(4)-16 = 128-16 = 112$ ft

41. The sequence would begin as $0.10, 0.20, 0.40, \ldots$.
The terms can be rewritten as follows:

$0.10 = 0.10(1) = 0.10(2)^0$

$0.20 = 0.10(2) = 0.10(2)^1$

$0.40 = 0.10(4) = 0.10(2)^2$

$\vdots$

In general, $a_n = 0.10(2)^{n-1}$.

$a_{14} = 0.10(2)^{14-1} = 0.10(2)^{13} = 819.20$

Mark would receive $819.20 on the last day of his vacation.

43. $a_n = 75(2)^{n-1}$

$a_6 = 75(2)^5 = 75(32) = 2400$ cases
$a_1 = 75(2)^0 = 75(1) = 75$ cases

There were 2400 cases at the beginning of the sixth year and 75 cases at the beginning of the first year.

45. $a_1 = 800$

$a_2 = \dfrac{1}{2} \cdot 800 = 400$

$a_3 = \dfrac{1}{2} \cdot 400 = \dfrac{1}{2} \cdot \left(\dfrac{1}{2} \cdot 800\right) = \left(\dfrac{1}{2}\right)^2 \cdot 800 = 200$

$a_4 = \dfrac{1}{2} \cdot 200 = \dfrac{1}{2} \cdot \left(\dfrac{1}{2}\right)^2 \cdot 800 = \left(\dfrac{1}{2}\right)^3 \cdot 800 = 100$

Since the sparrow population decreases by $\frac{1}{2}$ each year after the first year, we can model the population each year with the sequence

$$a_n = 800\left(\frac{1}{2}\right)^{n-1}$$

where $n = 1$ represents the year 2000.
In 2004, we have $n = 5$ (5 years after 2000) Thus,

$$a_5 = 800\left(\frac{1}{2}\right)^{5-1} = 800\left(\frac{1}{2}\right)^4 = 50$$

There will be an estimated 50 such sparrows in 2004.

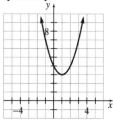

From the calculator, the species will be extinct in 2010 (an estimated 11 years after 2000). This is when the estimated number of sparrows first goes below 1.

47. $f(x) = (x-1)^2 + 3$

The graph of $f(x) = (x-1)^2 + 3$ is the same as the graph of $y = x^2$ shifted right 1 unit and shifted up 3 units. The vertex is $(1,3)$ and the axis of symmetry is $x = 1$.

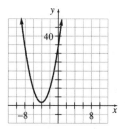

49. $f(x) = 2(x+4)^2 + 2$

The graph of $f(x) = 2(x+4)^2 + 2$ is the same as the graph of $y = x^2$ shifted left 4 units, made narrower by a factor of 2, and shifted up 2 units. The vertex is $(-4,3)$ and the axis of symmetry is $x = -4$.

51. $(-4,-1)$ and $(-7,-3)$

$$d = \sqrt{[-7-(-4)]^2 + [-3-(-1)]^2}$$
$$d = \sqrt{(-7+4)^2 + (-3+1)^2}$$
$$d = \sqrt{(-3)^2 + (-2)^2}$$
$$d = \sqrt{9+4} = \sqrt{13} \text{ units}$$

53. $(2,-7)$ and $(-3,-3)$

$$d = \sqrt{(-3-2)^2 + [-3-(-7)]^2}$$
$$d = \sqrt{(-5)^2 + (-3+7)^2}$$
$$d = \sqrt{(-5)^2 + (4)^2}$$
$$d = \sqrt{25+16} = \sqrt{41} \text{ units}$$

55. $a_n = \dfrac{1}{\sqrt{n}}$

n	$u(n)$
1	1
2	.70711
3	.57735
4	.5
5	.44721
6	.40825
7	.37796

$u(n) = 1/\sqrt{(n)}$

The first five terms of the sequence (to four decimal places) are 1, 0.7071, 0.5774, 0.5, and 0.4472.

57. $a_n = \left(1+\dfrac{1}{n}\right)^n$

n	$u(n)$
1	2
2	2.25
3	2.3704
4	2.4414
5	2.4883
6	2.5216
7	2.5465

$u(n) = (1+1/n)^n$

The first five terms of the sequence (to four decimal places) are 2, 2.25, 2.3704, 2.4414, and 2.4883.

Exercise Set 11.2

1. $a_n = a_1 + (n-1)d$
$a_1 = 4;\ d = 2$
$a_1 = 4$
$a_2 = 4 + (2-1)2 = 6$
$a_3 = 4 + (3-1)2 = 8$
$a_4 = 4 + (4-1)2 = 10$
$a_5 = 4 + (5-1)2 = 12$

The first five terms are 4, 6, 8, 10, and 12.

3. $a_n = a_1 + (n-1)d$

$a_1 = 6,\ d = -2$

$a_1 = 6$

$a_2 = 6 + (2-1)(-2) = 4$

$a_3 = 6 + (3-1)(-2) = 2$

$a_4 = 6 + (4-1)(-2) = 0$

$a_5 = 6 + (5-1)(-2) = -2$

The first five terms are 6, 4, 2, 0, and -2.

5. $a_n = a_1 r^{n-1}$

$a_1 = 1,\ r = 3$

$a_1 = 1$

$a_2 = 1(3)^{2-1} = 3$

$a_3 = 1(3)^{3-1} = 9$

$a_4 = 1(3)^{4-1} = 27$

$a_5 = 1(3)^{5-1} = 81$

The first five terms are 1, 3, 9, 27, and 81.

7. $a_n = a_1 r^{n-1}$

$a_1 = 48,\ r = \dfrac{1}{2}$

$a_1 = 48$

$a_2 = 48\left(\dfrac{1}{2}\right)^{2-1} = 24$

$a_3 = 48\left(\dfrac{1}{2}\right)^{3-1} = 12$

$a_4 = 48\left(\dfrac{1}{2}\right)^{4-1} = 6$

$a_5 = 48\left(\dfrac{1}{2}\right)^{5-1} = 3$

The first five terms are 48, 24, 12, 6, and 3.

9. $a_n = a_1 + (n-1)d$

$a_1 = 12,\ d = 3$

$a_n = 12 + (n-1)3$

$= 12 + 3n - 3$

$= 3n + 9$

$a_8 = 3(8) + 9 = 24 + 9 = 33$

11. $a_n = a_1 r^{n-1}$

$a_1 = 7,\ r = -5$

$a_n = a_1 r^{n-1}$

$= 7(-5)^{n-1}$

$a_4 = 7(-5)^{4-1} = 7(-5)^3 = 7(-125) = -875$

13. $a_n = a_1 + (n-1)d$

$a_1 = -4,\ d = -4$

$a_n = -4 + (n-1)(-4)$

$= -4 - 4n + 4$

$= -4n$

$a_{15} = -4(15) = -60$

15. 0, 12, 24,...

$d = a_2 - a_1 = 12 - 0 = 12$

$a_1 = 0$ and $d = 12$

$a_n = 0 + (n-1)12$

$= 12n - 12$

$a_9 = 12(9) - 12 = 108 - 12 = 96$

17. 20, 18, 16,...

$d = a_2 - a_1 = 18 - 20 = -2$

$a_1 = 20$ and $d = -2$

$a_n = 20 + (n-1)(-2)$

$= 20 - 2n + 2$

$= 22 - 2n$

$a_{25} = 22 - 2(25) = 22 - 50 = -28$

19. 2, -10, 50,...

$r = \dfrac{a_2}{a_1} = \dfrac{-10}{2} = -5$

$a_1 = 2$ and $r = -5$

$a_n = 2(-5)^{n-1}$

$a_5 = 2(-5)^{5-1} = 2(-5)^4 = 2(625) = 1250$

21. $a_4 = 19,\ a_{15} = 52$

$\begin{cases} a_4 = a_1 + (4-1)d \\ a_{15} = a_1 + (15-1)d \end{cases}$ or $\begin{cases} 19 = a_1 + 3d \\ 52 = a_1 + 14d \end{cases}$

Subtract the two equations to get

$-33 = -11d$

$3 = d$

Substitute this result into the first equation of the system to find a_1.

$19 = a_1 + 3(3)$

$19 = a_1 + 9$

$10 = a_1$

$a_n = 10 + (n-1)3$

$= 10 + 3n - 3$

$= 3n + 7$

$a_8 = 3(8) + 7 = 24 + 7 = 31$

23. $a_2 = -1$, $a_4 = 5$

$$\begin{cases} a_2 = a_1 + (2-1)d \\ a_4 = a_1 + (4-1)d \end{cases}$$

or

$$\begin{cases} -1 = a_1 + d \\ 5 = a_1 + 3d \end{cases}$$

Subtract the two equations to get

$-6 = -2d$

$3 = d$

Substitute this result into the first equation of the system to find a_1.

$-1 = a_1 + 3$

$-4 = a_1$

$a_n = -4 + (n-1)3$

$\quad = -4 + 3n - 3$

$\quad = 3n - 7$

$a_9 = 3(9) - 7 = 27 - 7 = 20$

25. $a_2 = -\dfrac{4}{3}$ and $a_3 = \dfrac{8}{3}$

Note that $\dfrac{8}{3} \div \dfrac{-4}{3} = \dfrac{8}{3} \cdot -\dfrac{3}{4} = -2$, so $r = -2$.

Then ,

$a_2 = a_1(-2)^{2-1}$

$-\dfrac{4}{3} = a_1(-2)$

$\dfrac{2}{3} = a_1$

The first term is $a_1 = \dfrac{2}{3}$ and the common ratio is

$r = -2$.

27. Answers may vary. When considering signed numbers, we can think of subtraction as 'adding a negative'.

29. Notice that the difference between successive terms is 2. Therefore, $2, 4, 6$ is an arithmetic sequence.

$a_1 = 2$ and $d = 2$

31. Notice that the ratio between successive terms is 2. Therefore, $5, 10, 20$ is a geometric sequence.

$a_1 = 5$ and $r = 2$

33. Notice that the ratio between successive terms is

$\dfrac{1}{5}$. Therefore, $\dfrac{1}{2}, \dfrac{1}{10}, \dfrac{1}{50}$ is a geometric sequence.

$a_1 = \dfrac{1}{2}; r = \dfrac{1}{5}$

35. Notice that the ratio between successive terms is 5. Therefore, $x, 5x, 25x$ is a geometric sequence.

$a_1 = x$ and $r = 5$

37. Notice that the difference between successive terms is 4. Therefore, $p, p+4, p+8$ is an arithmetic sequence.

$a_1 = p$ and $d = 4$

39. $a_1 = 14$ and $d = \dfrac{1}{4}$

$a_n = 14 + (n-1)\dfrac{1}{4}$

$\quad = 14 + \dfrac{1}{4}n - \dfrac{1}{4}$

$\quad = \dfrac{1}{4}n + \dfrac{55}{4}$

$a_{21} = \dfrac{1}{4}(21) + \dfrac{55}{4} = \dfrac{21}{4} + \dfrac{55}{4} = \dfrac{76}{4} = 19$

41. $a_1 = 3$ and $r = -\dfrac{2}{3}$

$a_n = 3\left(-\dfrac{2}{3}\right)^{n-1}$

$a_4 = 3\left(-\dfrac{2}{3}\right)^{4-1} = 3\left(-\dfrac{2}{3}\right)^3 = 3\left(-\dfrac{8}{27}\right) = -\dfrac{8}{9}$

43. $\dfrac{3}{2}, 2, \dfrac{5}{2}, \ldots$

$d = a_2 - a_1 = 2 - \dfrac{3}{2} = \dfrac{1}{2}$

$a_1 = \dfrac{3}{2}$ and $d = \dfrac{1}{2}$

$a_n = \dfrac{3}{2} + (n-1)\dfrac{1}{2}$

$\quad = \dfrac{3}{2} + \dfrac{1}{2}n - \dfrac{1}{2}$

$\quad = \dfrac{1}{2}n + 1$

$a_{15} = \dfrac{1}{2}(15) + 1 = \dfrac{15}{2} + 1 = \dfrac{17}{2}$

45. $24, 8, \dfrac{8}{3}, \ldots$

$$r = \frac{a_2}{a_1} = \frac{8}{24} = \frac{1}{3}$$

$a_1 = 24$ and $r = \dfrac{1}{3}$

$$a_n = 24\left(\frac{1}{3}\right)^{n-1}$$

$$a_6 = 24\left(\frac{1}{3}\right)^{6-1} = 24\left(\frac{1}{3}\right)^5 = 24\left(\frac{1}{243}\right) = \frac{8}{81}$$

47. $a_3 = 2,\ a_{17} = -40$

$$\begin{cases} a_3 = a_1 + (3-1)d \\ a_{17} = a_1 + (17-1)d \end{cases} \text{ or}$$

$$\begin{cases} 2 = a_1 + 2d \\ -40 = a_1 + 16d \end{cases}$$

Solving the system gives $d = -3$
and $a_1 = 8$.

$$\begin{aligned} a_n &= 8 + (n-1)(-3) \\ &= 8 - 3n + 3 \\ &= 11 - 3n \end{aligned}$$

$$a_{10} = 11 - 3(10) = 11 - 30 = -19$$

49. $54, 58, 62, \ldots$

$$d = a_2 - a_1 = 58 - 54 = 4$$

$a_1 = 54$ and $d = 4$

$$\begin{aligned} a_n &= 54 + (n-1)4 \\ &= 54 + 4n - 4 \\ &= 4n + 50 \end{aligned}$$

$$a_{20} = 4(20) + 50 = 80 + 50 = 130$$

There are 130 seats in the twentieth row.

51. Since the size triples every day, we have a
common ratio of 3.

$a_1 = 6$ and $r = 3$

$$a_n = 6(3)^{n-1} = 2 \cdot 3 \cdot (3)^{n-1} = 2 \ (3)^n$$

The general term of the sequence is
$a_n = 6(3)^{n-1}$.

53. $a_1 = 486$

$$a_2 = \frac{1}{3}(486) = 162$$

$$a_3 = \frac{1}{3}(162) = 54$$

$$a_4 = \frac{1}{3}(54) = 18$$

$$a_5 = \frac{1}{3}(18) = 6$$

Since the ball loses one-third of its height with
each bounce, we have a common ratio of $\frac{1}{3}$. Thus,

$a_1 = 486$ and $r = \dfrac{1}{3}$.

$$a_n = a_1\left(r\right)^{n-1} = 486\left(\frac{1}{3}\right)^{n-1}$$

To find when the ball will first rebound to less
than 1 foot, we switch to sequence mode and enter
the general term in $u(n)$. Then we look at a table
of values.

n	$u(n)$
1	486
2	162
3	54
4	18
5	6
6	2
7	.66667

$u(n)\text{目}486(1/3)^{\wedge}(\ldots$

From the table, the ball will rebound to less than
one foot after 6 bounces.

55. $a_1 = 4000$ and $d = 125$

$$\begin{aligned} a_n &= 4000 + (n-1)125 \\ &= 4000 + 125n - 125 \\ &= 3875 + 125n \end{aligned}$$

$$a_{12} = 3875 + 125(12) = 5375$$

Jose will have a monthly salary of \$5375 at the
end of his training.

57. $a_1 = 400$ and $r = \dfrac{1}{2}$

12 hrs = 4(3 hrs), so we seek the
fourth term after a_1, namely a_5.

$$a_n = a_1 r^{n-1}$$

$$a_5 = 400\left(\frac{1}{2}\right)^4 = \frac{400}{16} = 25$$

25 grams of the radioactive
material remains after 12 hours.

59. $\dfrac{1}{3(1)} + \dfrac{1}{3(2)} + \dfrac{1}{3(3)} = \dfrac{1}{3} + \dfrac{1}{6} + \dfrac{1}{9}$

$$= \dfrac{6}{18} + \dfrac{3}{18} + \dfrac{2}{18}$$

$$= \dfrac{11}{18}$$

61. $3^0 + 3^1 + 3^2 + 3^3 = 1 + 3 + 9 + 27 = 40$

63. $\dfrac{8-1}{8+1} + \dfrac{8-2}{8+2} + \dfrac{8-3}{8+3} = \dfrac{7}{9} + \dfrac{6}{10} + \dfrac{5}{11}$

$$= \dfrac{770}{990} + \dfrac{594}{990} + \dfrac{450}{990}$$

$$= \dfrac{1814}{990}$$

$$= \dfrac{907}{495}$$

65. $a_1 = \$11{,}782.40$, $r = 0.5$

$$a_n = 11{,}782.40(0.5)^{n-1}$$

Plot1 Plot2 Plot3		n	$u(n)$
nMin=1		1	11782
$\cdot u(n)$⯄11782.4(.5		2	5891.2
)^(n–1)		3	2945.6
$u(n$Min)⯄		4	1472.8
$\cdot v(n)=$		5	736.4
$v(n$Min)$=$		6	368.2
$\cdot w(n)=$		7	184.1
		$u(n)$⯄11782.4(.5...	

The first four terms of the sequence are
$\$11{,}782.40$, $\$5891.20$, $\$2945.60$, $\$1472.80$.

67. $a_1 = 19.652$ and $d = -0.034$

$$a_n = 19.652 + (n-1)(-0.034)$$

$$= 19.652 - 0.034n + 0.034$$

$$= 19.686 - 0.034n$$

Plot1 Plot2 Plot3		n	$u(n)$
nMin=1		1	19.652
$\cdot u(n)$⯄19.686–.03		2	19.618
4n		3	19.584
$u(n$Min)⯄		4	19.55
$\cdot v(n)=$		5	19.516
$v(n$Min)$=$		6	19.482
$\cdot w(n)=$		7	19.448
		$u(n)$⯄19.686–.03...	

The first four terms of the sequence are
19.652, 19.618, 19.584, and 19.55.

69. Answers may vary.

Exercise Set 11.3

1. $\displaystyle\sum_{i=1}^{4}(i-3) = (1-3) + (2-3) + (3-3) + (4-3)$

$$= -2 + (-1) + 0 + 1$$

$$= -2$$

3. $\displaystyle\sum_{i=4}^{7}(2i+4)$

$$= [2(4)+4] + [2(5)+4] + [2(6)+4] + [2(7)+4]$$

$$= 12 + 14 + 16 + 18$$

$$= 60$$

5. $\displaystyle\sum_{i=2}^{4}(i^2-3) = (2^2-3) + (3^2-3) + (4^2-3)$

$$= (4-3) + (9-3) + (16-3)$$

$$= 1 + 6 + 13$$

$$= 20$$

7. $\displaystyle\sum_{i=1}^{3}\dfrac{1}{i+5} = \dfrac{1}{1+5} + \dfrac{1}{2+5} + \dfrac{1}{3+5}$

$$= \dfrac{1}{6} + \dfrac{1}{7} + \dfrac{1}{8}$$

$$= \dfrac{28}{168} + \dfrac{24}{168} + \dfrac{21}{168}$$

$$= \dfrac{73}{168}$$

9. $\displaystyle\sum_{i=1}^{3}\dfrac{1}{6i} = \dfrac{1}{6(1)} + \dfrac{1}{6(2)} + \dfrac{1}{6(3)}$

$$= \dfrac{1}{6} + \dfrac{1}{12} + \dfrac{1}{18}$$

$$= \dfrac{6}{36} + \dfrac{3}{36} + \dfrac{2}{36}$$

$$= \dfrac{11}{36}$$

11. $\displaystyle\sum_{i=2}^{6}3i = 3(2) + 3(3) + 3(4) + 3(5) + 3(6)$

$$= 6 + 9 + 12 + 15 + 18$$

$$= 60$$

13. $\displaystyle\sum_{i=3}^{5}i(i+2)$

$$= 3(3+2) + 4(4+2) + 5(5+2)$$

$$= 3(5) + 4(6) + 5(7)$$

$$= 15 + 24 + 35$$

$$= 74$$

15. $\displaystyle\sum_{i=1}^{5} 2^i = 2^1 + 2^2 + 2^3 + 2^4 + 2^5$

$\qquad = 2 + 4 + 8 + 16 + 32$

$\qquad = 62$

17. $\displaystyle\sum_{i=1}^{4} \frac{4i}{i+3} = \frac{4(1)}{1+3} + \frac{4(2)}{2+3} + \frac{4(3)}{3+3} + \frac{4(4)}{4+3}$

$\qquad = 1 + \frac{8}{5} + 2 + \frac{16}{7}$

$\qquad = \frac{105}{35} + \frac{56}{35} + \frac{80}{35}$

$\qquad = \frac{241}{35}$

19. $1 + 3 + 5 + 7 + 9$

$\qquad = [2(1)-1] + [2(2)-1] + [2(3)-1]$

$\qquad\qquad + [2(4)-1] + [2(5)-1]$

$\qquad = \displaystyle\sum_{i=1}^{5} (2i-1)$

21. $4 + 12 + 36 + 108$

$\qquad = 4(3)^0 + 4(3)^1 + 4(3)^2 + 4(3)^3$

$\qquad = \displaystyle\sum_{i=1}^{4} 4(3)^{i-1}$

23. $12 + 9 + 6 + 3 + 0 + (-3)$

$\qquad = [-3(1)+15] + [-3(2)+15] + [-3(3)+15]$

$\qquad\quad + [-3(4)+15] + [-3(5)+15] + [-3(6)+15]$

$\qquad = \displaystyle\sum_{i=1}^{6} (-3i+15)$

25. $12 + 4 + \frac{4}{3} + \frac{4}{9} = \frac{4}{3^{-1}} + \frac{4}{3^0} + \frac{4}{3^1} + \frac{4}{3^2}$

$\qquad\qquad\qquad = \displaystyle\sum_{i=1}^{4} \frac{4}{3^{i-2}}$

27. $1 + 4 + 9 + 16 + 25 + 36 + 49$

$\qquad = 1^2 + 2^2 + 3^2 + 4^2 + 5^2 + 6^2 + 7^2$

$\qquad = \displaystyle\sum_{i=1}^{7} i^2$

29. $a_n = (n+2)(n-5)$

$S_2 = \displaystyle\sum_{i=1}^{2} (i+2)(i-5)$

$\qquad = (1+2)(1-5) + (2+2)(2-5)$

$\qquad = (3)(-4) + (4)(-3)$

$\qquad = -12 - 12$

$\qquad = -24$

31. $a_n = n(n-6)$

$S_2 = \displaystyle\sum_{i=1}^{2} i(i-6)$

$\qquad = 1(1-6) + 2(2-6)$

$\qquad = 1(-5) + 2(-4)$

$\qquad = -5 - 8$

$\qquad = -13$

33. $a_n = (n+3)(n+1)$

$S_4 = \displaystyle\sum_{i=1}^{4} (i+3)(i+1)$

$\qquad = (1+3)(1+1) + (2+3)(2+1)$

$\qquad\quad + (3+3)(3+1) + (4+3)(4+1)$

$\qquad = (4)(2) + (5)(3) + (6)(4) + (7)(5)$

$\qquad = 8 + 15 + 24 + 35$

$\qquad = 82$

35. $a_n = -2n$

$\displaystyle\sum_{i=1}^{4} (-2i) = -2(1) + (-2)(2) + (-2)(3) + (-2)(4)$

$\qquad\qquad = -2 - 4 - 6 - 8$

$\qquad\qquad = -20$

37. $a_n = -\dfrac{n}{3}$

$S_3 = \displaystyle\sum_{i=1}^{3} \left(-\frac{i}{3}\right)$

$\qquad = -\frac{1}{3} + \left(-\frac{2}{3}\right) + \left(-\frac{3}{3}\right)$

$\qquad = -\frac{1}{3} - \frac{2}{3} - \frac{3}{3}$

$\qquad = -\frac{6}{3}$

$\qquad = -2$

39. $1, 2, 3, \ldots, 10$

$a_n = n$

$\displaystyle\sum_{i=1}^{10} i = 1 + 2 + 3 + \ldots + 10$

$\qquad = \frac{10(11)}{2} = 55$

A total of 55 trees were planted.

41. $a_1 = 6$ and $r = 2$

$a_n = 6 \cdot 2^{n-1}$

$a_5 = 6 \cdot 2^4 = 6 \cdot 16 = 96$

There will be 96 fungus units at the beginning of the 5th day.

43. $a_0 = 50$ and $r = 2$

The general term of the sequence is

$a_n = 50(2)^n$

where n represents the number of 12-hr periods. Since $48 = 4(12)$, we have $n = 4$.

$a_4 = 50(2)^4 = 50(16) = 800$

There are 800 bacteria after 48 hours.

45. $a_n = (n+1)(n+2)$

$a_4 = (4+1)(4+2)$
$= 5(6) = 30$ opossums

$a_1 = (1+1)(1+2) = 2(3) = 6$
$a_2 = (2+1)(2+2) = 3(4) = 12$
$a_3 = (3+1)(3+2) = 4(5) = 20$

$\sum_{i=1}^{4} a_i = 6 + 12 + 20 + 30 = 68$ opossums

There were 30 opossums killed in the fourth month, and 68 opossums killed in the first four months.

47. $a_n = 100(0.5)^n$

$a_4 = 100(0.5)^4 = 6.25$ lbs of decay.

$a_1 = 100(0.5)^1 = 50$
$a_2 = 100(0.5)^2 = 25$
$a_3 = 100(0.5)^3 = 12.5$

$\sum_{i=1}^{4} a_i = 50 + 25 + 12.5 + 6.25$
$= 93.75$ lbs of decay

There was 6.25 pounds of decay in the fourth year, and a total of 93.75 pounds of decay in the first four years.

49. $a_1 = 40$ and $r = \frac{4}{5}$

$a_5 = 40\left(\frac{4}{5}\right)^4 = 16.384$ or 16.4 in.

$a_2 = 40\left(\frac{4}{5}\right)^1 = 32$

$a_3 = 40\left(\frac{4}{5}\right)^2 = 25.6$

$a_4 = 40\left(\frac{4}{5}\right)^3 = 20.48$

$\sum_{i=1}^{5} a_i = 40 + 32 + 25.6 + 20.48 + 16.384$
$= 134.464$ or 134.5 in.

The length of the fifth swing was 16.4 inches. The pendulum swung a total of 134.5 inches in its first five swings.

51. $\dfrac{5}{1-\frac{1}{2}} = \dfrac{5}{\frac{1}{2}} = 5 \cdot \dfrac{2}{1} = 10$

53. $\dfrac{\frac{1}{3}}{1-\frac{1}{10}} = \dfrac{\frac{1}{3}}{\frac{9}{10}} = \dfrac{1}{3} \cdot \dfrac{10}{9} = \dfrac{10}{27}$

55. $\dfrac{3(1-2^4)}{1-2} = \dfrac{3(1-16)}{-1} = \dfrac{3(-15)}{-1} = \dfrac{-45}{-1} = 45$

57. $\dfrac{10}{2}(3+15) = \dfrac{10}{2}(18) = \dfrac{180}{2} = 90$

59. a. $\sum_{i=1}^{7}(i+i^2) = (1+1^2) + (2+2^2) + (3+3^2)$
$+ (4+4^2) + (5+5^2) + (6+6^2)$
$+ (7+7^2)$
$= 2 + 6 + 12 + 20 + 30 + 42 + 56$

b. $\sum_{i=1}^{7} i + \sum_{i=1}^{7} i^2$
$= (1+2+3+4+5+6+7) + (1+4$
$+9+16+25+36+49)$

c. Answers may vary. The two sums both equal 168.

d. True. Answers may vary.

Integrated Review

1. $a_n = n - 3$
$a_1 = 1 - 3 = -2$
$a_2 = 2 - 3 = -1$
$a_3 = 3 - 3 = 0$
$a_4 = 4 - 3 = 1$
$a_5 = 5 - 3 = 2$
Therefore, the first five terms are
$-2, -1, 0, 1, 2.$

2. $a_n = \dfrac{7}{1+n}$

$a_1 = \dfrac{7}{1+1} = \dfrac{7}{2}$

$a_2 = \dfrac{7}{1+2} = \dfrac{7}{3}$

$a_3 = \dfrac{7}{1+3} = \dfrac{7}{4}$

$a_4 = \dfrac{7}{1+4} = \dfrac{7}{5}$

$a_5 = \dfrac{7}{1+5} = \dfrac{7}{6}$

The first five terms are
$\dfrac{7}{2}, \dfrac{7}{3}, \dfrac{7}{4}, \dfrac{7}{5}, \text{ and } \dfrac{7}{6}.$

3. $a_n = 3^{n-1}$
$a_1 = 3^{1-1} = 3^0 = 1$
$a_2 = 3^{2-1} = 3^1 = 3$
$a_3 = 3^{3-1} = 3^2 = 9$
$a_4 = 3^{4-1} = 3^3 = 27$
$a_5 = 3^{5-1} = 3^4 = 81$
The first five terms are
$1, 3, 9, 27, \text{ and } 81.$

4. $a_n = n^2 - 5$
$a_1 = 1^2 - 5 = 1 - 5 = -4$
$a_2 = 2^2 - 5 = 4 - 5 = -1$
$a_3 = 3^2 - 5 = 9 - 5 = 4$
$a_4 = 4^2 - 5 = 16 - 5 = 11$
$a_5 = 5^2 - 5 = 25 - 5 = 20$
The first five terms are
$-4, -1, 4, 11, \text{ and } 20.$

5. $a_n = (-2)^n; a_6$
$a_6 = (-2)^6 = 64$

6. $a_n = -n^2 + 2; a_4$
$a_4 = -(4)^2 + 2$
$ = -16 + 2$
$ = -14$

7. $a_n = \dfrac{(-1)^n}{n}; a_{40}$

$a_{40} = \dfrac{(-1)^{40}}{40} = \dfrac{1}{40}$

8. $a_n = \dfrac{(-1)^n}{2n}; a_{41}$

$a_{41} = \dfrac{(-1)^{41}}{2(41)}$

$\phantom{a_{41}} = \dfrac{-1}{82}$

$\phantom{a_{41}} = -\dfrac{1}{82}$

9. $a_1 = 7; d = -3$
$a_1 = 7$
$a_2 = 7 + (-3) = 4$
$a_3 = 4 + (-3) = 1$
$a_4 = 1 + (-3) = -2$
$a_5 = -2 + (-3) = -5$
The first five terms are
$7, 4, 1, -2, -5.$

10. $a_1 = -3; r = 5$
$a_1 = -3$
$a_2 = -3(5) = -15$
$a_3 = -15(5) = -75$
$a_4 = -75(5) = -375$
$a_5 = -375(5) = -1875$
The first five terms are
$-3, -15, -75, -375, -1875.$

11. $a_1 = 45; r = \dfrac{1}{3}$

$a_1 = 45$

$a_2 = 45\left(\dfrac{1}{3}\right) = 15$

$a_3 = 15\left(\dfrac{1}{3}\right) = 5$

$a_4 = 5\left(\dfrac{1}{3}\right) = \dfrac{5}{3}$

$a_5 = \dfrac{5}{3}\left(\dfrac{1}{3}\right) = \dfrac{5}{9}$

The first five terms are

$45, 15, 5, \dfrac{5}{3}, \dfrac{5}{9}$.

12. $a_1 = -12; d = 10$

$a_1 = -12$

$a_2 = -12 + 10 = -2$

$a_3 = -2 + 10 = 8$

$a_4 = 8 + 10 = 18$

$a_5 = 18 + 10 = 28$

The first five terms are

$-12, -2, 8, 18, 28$.

13. $a_1 = 20; d = 9$

$a_n = a_1 + (n-1)d$

$\quad = 20 + (n-1)(9)$

$\quad = 20 + 9n - 9$

$\quad = 9n + 11$

$a_{10} = 9(10) + 11 = 90 + 11 = 101$

14. $a_1 = 64; r = \dfrac{3}{4}$

$a_n = a_1 r^{n-1}$

$a_6 = 64\left(\dfrac{3}{4}\right)^{6-1}$

$\quad = 64\left(\dfrac{3}{4}\right)^{5}$

$\quad = 64\left(\dfrac{243}{1024}\right)$

$\quad = \dfrac{243}{16}$

15. $a_1 = 6; r = \dfrac{-12}{6} = -2$

$a_n = a_1 r^{n-1}$

$a_7 = 6(-2)^{7-1}$

$\quad = 6(-2)^{6}$

$\quad = 6(64)$

$\quad = 384$

16. $a_1 = -100; d = -85 - (-100) = 15$

$a_n = a_1 + (n-1)d$

$\quad = -100 + (n-1)(15)$

$\quad = -100 + 15n - 15$

$\quad = 15n - 115$

$a_{20} = 15(20) - 115 = 300 - 115 = 185$

17. $a_4 = -5, a_{10} = -35$

$a_n = a_1 + (n-1)d$

$\begin{cases} a_4 = a_1 + (4-1)d \\ a_{10} = a_1 + (10-1)d \end{cases}$

$\begin{cases} -5 = a_1 + 3d \\ -35 = a_1 + 9d \end{cases}$

Subtract the two equations to get

$30 = -6d$

$-5 = d$

Substitute this result into either equation to solve for a_1.

$-5 = a_1 + 3(-5)$

$-5 = a_1 - 15$

$10 = a_1$

$a_n = a_1 + (n-1)d$

$\quad = 10 + (n-1)(-5)$

$\quad = 10 - 5n + 5$

$\quad = 15 - 5n$

$a_5 = 15 - 5(5) = 15 - 25 = -10$

18. $a_4 = 1; a_7 = \dfrac{1}{125}$

$a_n = a_1 r^{n-1}$

Also note that we can rewrite the general term as follows:

$a_n = a_1 \cdot r^{n-1+3-3}$

$\quad = a_1 \cdot r^{(n-4)+3}$

$\quad = a_1 \cdot r^3 \cdot r^{n-4}$

$\quad = \left(a_1 \cdot r^3\right) \cdot r^{n-4}$

$\quad = a_4 \cdot r^{n-4}$

Therefore, we can write

$$a_7 = a_4 r^{7-4}$$
$$\frac{1}{125} = 1r^3$$
$$\frac{1}{5} = r$$
$$a_4(r) = a_5$$
$$1\left(\frac{1}{5}\right) = a_5$$
$$\frac{1}{5} = a_5$$

19. $\sum_{i=1}^{4} 5i = 5(1)+5(2)+5(3)+5(4)$
$$= 5+10+15+20$$
$$= 50$$

20. $\sum_{i=1}^{7}(3i+2)$
$$= (3(1)+2)+(3(2)+2)+(3(3)+2)+(3(4)+2)$$
$$+(3(5)+2)+(3(6)+2)+(3(7)+2)$$
$$= 5+8+11+14+17+20+23$$
$$= 98$$

21. $\sum_{i=3}^{7} 2^{i-4} = 2^{3-4}+2^{4-4}+2^{5-4}+2^{6-4}+2^{7-4}$
$$= 2^{-1}+2^0+2^1+2^2+2^3$$
$$= \frac{1}{2}+1+2+4+8$$
$$= 15\frac{1}{2} = \frac{31}{2}$$

22. $\sum_{i=2}^{5} \frac{i}{i+1} = \frac{2}{2+1}+\frac{3}{3+1}+\frac{4}{4+1}+\frac{5}{5+1}$
$$= \frac{2}{3}+\frac{3}{4}+\frac{4}{5}+\frac{5}{6}$$
$$= \frac{61}{20}$$

23. $a_n = n(n-4)$
$$S_3 = \sum_{i=1}^{3} i(i-4)$$
$$= 1(1-4)+2(2-4)+3(3-4)$$
$$= -3-4-3$$
$$= -10$$

24. $a_n = (-1)^n(n+1)$
$$S_{10} = \sum_{i=1}^{10}(-1)^i(i+1)$$
$$= (-1)^1(1+1)+(-1)^2(2+1)+(-1)^3(3+1)+$$
$$(-1)^4(4+1)+(-1)^5(5+1)+(-1)^6(6+1)+$$
$$(-1)^7(7+1)+(-1)^8(8+1)+(-1)^9(9+1)+$$
$$(-1)^{10}(10+1)$$
$$= -2+3-4+5-6+7-8+9-10+11$$
$$= 5$$

Exercise Set 11.4

1. $1,3,5,7,...$
$d = 3-1 = 2$
$a_6 = 1+(6-1)2 = 11$
The first term is 1 and the sixth term is 11.
$$S_6 = \frac{6}{2}(1+11) = 3(12) = 36$$

3. $4, 12, 36, ...$
$a_1 = 4, r = 3, n = 5$
$$S_5 = \frac{4(1-3^5)}{1-3} = 484$$

5. $3,6,9,...$
$d = 6-3 = 3$
$a_6 = 3+(6-1)3 = 18$
The first term is 3 and the sixth term is 18.
$$S_6 = \frac{6}{2}(3+18)$$
$$= 3(21)$$
$$= 63$$

7. $2, \frac{2}{5}, \frac{2}{25}, ...$
$a_1 = 2, r = \frac{1}{5}, n = 4$
$$S_4 = \frac{2\left[1-\left(\frac{1}{5}\right)^4\right]}{1-\frac{1}{5}} = 2.496$$

9. $1, 2, 3, \ldots, 10$

These terms form an arithmetic sequence.
The first term is 1 and the tenth term is 10.

$$S_{10} = \frac{10}{2}(1+10)$$
$$= 5(11)$$
$$= 55$$

11. $1, 3, 5, 7$

These terms form an arithmetic sequence.
The first term is 1 and the fourth term is 7.

$$S_4 = \frac{4}{2}(1+7)$$
$$= 2(8)$$
$$= 16$$

13. $12, 6, 3, \ldots$

$$a_1 = 12, \quad r = \frac{1}{2}$$
$$S_\infty = \frac{12}{1-\frac{1}{2}} = \frac{12}{\frac{1}{2}} = 24$$

15. $\frac{1}{10}, \frac{1}{100}, \frac{1}{1000}, \ldots$

$$a_1 = \frac{1}{10}, \quad r = \frac{1}{10}$$
$$S_\infty = \frac{\frac{1}{10}}{1-\frac{1}{10}} = \frac{1}{9}$$

17. $-10, -5, -\frac{5}{2}, \ldots$

$$a_1 = -10, \quad r = \frac{1}{2}$$
$$S_\infty = \frac{-10}{1-\frac{1}{2}} = -20$$

19. $2, -\frac{1}{4}, \frac{1}{32}, \ldots$

$$a_1 = 2, \quad r = -\frac{1}{8}$$
$$S_\infty = \frac{2}{1-\left(-\frac{1}{8}\right)} = \frac{16}{9}$$

21. $\frac{2}{3}, -\frac{1}{3}, \frac{1}{6}, \ldots$

$$a_1 = \frac{2}{3}, \quad r = -\frac{1}{2}$$
$$S_\infty = \frac{\frac{2}{3}}{1-\left(-\frac{1}{2}\right)} = \frac{4}{9}$$

23. $-4, 1, 6, \ldots, 41$

Notice that this is an arithmetic sequence because there is a common difference of $d = 5$ between each term.
The first term is -4 and the tenth term is 41.

$$S_{10} = \frac{10}{2}(-4+41)$$
$$= 5(37)$$
$$= 185$$

25. $3, \frac{3}{2}, \frac{3}{4}, \ldots$

Notice that the sequence is geometric because there is a common ratio of $r = \frac{1}{2}$.

$$a_1 = 3, \, r = \frac{1}{2}, \, n = 7$$
$$S_7 = \frac{3\left[1-\left(\frac{1}{2}\right)^7\right]}{1-\frac{1}{2}} = \frac{381}{64}$$

27. $-12, 6, -3, \ldots$

Notice that the sequence is geometric because there is a common ratio of $r = -\frac{1}{2}$.

$$a_1 = -12, \, r = -\frac{1}{2}, \, n = 5$$
$$S_5 = \frac{-12\left[1-\left(-\frac{1}{2}\right)^5\right]}{1-\left(-\frac{1}{2}\right)} = -\frac{33}{4}$$

29. $\frac{1}{2}, \frac{1}{4}, 0, \ldots, -\frac{17}{4}$

Notice that this is an arithmetic sequence because there is a common difference of $d = -\frac{1}{4}$ between each term.

The first term is $\dfrac{1}{2}$ and the 20th term is $-\dfrac{17}{4}$.

$$S_{20} = \dfrac{20}{2}\left(\dfrac{1}{2}+\left(-\dfrac{17}{4}\right)\right)$$
$$= 10\left(\dfrac{-15}{4}\right)$$
$$= -\dfrac{75}{2}$$

31. $a_1 = 8, \ r = -\dfrac{2}{3}, \ n = 3$

$$S_3 = \dfrac{8\left[1-\left(-\dfrac{2}{3}\right)^3\right]}{1-\left(-\dfrac{2}{3}\right)} = \dfrac{56}{9}$$

33. The first five terms are 4000, 3950, 3900, 3850, 3800

$a_1 = 4000, \ d = -50, \ n = 12$
$a_{12} = 4000 + 11(-50)$
$\quad = 3450$ cars sold in month 12.

$S_{12} = \dfrac{12}{2}(4000+3450)$
$\quad = 44{,}700$ cars sold in the first 12 months.

35. Firm A:
The first term is 22,000 and the tenth term is 31,000.

$S_{10} = \dfrac{10}{2}(22000+31000)$
$\quad = \$265{,}000$

Firm B:
The first term is 20,000 and the tenth term is 30,800.

$S_{10} = \dfrac{10}{2}(20000+30800)$
$\quad = \$254{,}000$
Thus, Firm A is making the better offer.

37. $a_1 = 30{,}000, \ r = 1.10, \ n = 4$

$a_4 = 30000(1.10)^{4-1}$
$a_4 = 39{,}930$

$S_4 = \dfrac{30000(1-1.10^4)}{1-1.10}$
$\quad = 139{,}230$

The woman made \$39,930 in her fourth year, and a total of \$139,230 in her first four years.

39. $a_1 = 30, \ r = 0.9, \ n = 5$

$a_5 = 30(0.9)^{5-1} = 19.63$

$S_5 = \dfrac{30(1-0.9^5)}{1-0.9} = 122.853$

It takes the trainee about 20 minutes to assemble the fifth computer, and a total of about 123 minutes to assemble the first five computers.

41. $a_1 = 20, \ r = \dfrac{4}{5}$

$S_\infty = \dfrac{20}{1-\dfrac{4}{5}} = 100$

We double the sum (to account for the flight up as well as down) and subtract 20 (since the first bounce was preceded by only a downward flight).
$2(100) - 20 = 200 - 20 = 180$

Thus, the ball covers a distance of 180 feet before coming to rest.

43. Player A:
The first term is 1 and the ninth term is 9.

$S_9 = \dfrac{9}{2}(1+9)$
$\quad = 45$ points

Player B:
The first term is 10 and the sixth term is 15.

$S_6 = \dfrac{6}{2}(10+15)$
$\quad = 75$ points

45. This is an arithmetic sequence with first term $a_1 = 200$ and common difference $d = -5$.

$a_{20} = 200 + (20-1)(-5) = 200 + 19(-5) = 105$
The first term is 200 and the twentieth is 105.

$S_{20} = \dfrac{20}{2}(200+105)$
$\quad = 3050$

Thus, \$3050 in rent is paid for 20 days during in the holiday rush.

47. This is a geometric sequence with $a_1 = 0.01, \ r = 2, \ n = 30$.

$S_{30} = \dfrac{0.01\left[1-2^{30}\right]}{1-2} = 10{,}737{,}418.23$

The student would pay \$10,737,418.23 in room and board for the 30 days.

49. $6 \cdot 5 \cdot 4 \cdot 3 \cdot 2 \cdot 1 = 720$

51. $\dfrac{3 \cdot 2 \cdot 1}{2 \cdot 1} = 3$

53. $(x+5)^2 = x^2 + 2(x)(5) + 5^2 = x^2 + 10x + 25$

55. $(2x-1)^3 = (2x-1)(2x-1)(2x-1)$
$$= \left(4x^2 - 4x + 1\right)(2x-1)$$
$$= 8x^3 - 8x^2 + 2x - 4x^2 + 4x - 1$$
$$= 8x^3 - 12x^2 + 6x - 1$$

57. $0.\overline{888} = 0.8 + 0.08 + 0.008 + \cdots$
$$= \dfrac{8}{10} + \dfrac{8}{100} + \dfrac{8}{1000} + \cdots$$
This is a geometric series with
$$a_1 = \dfrac{8}{10}, \ r = \dfrac{1}{10}$$
$$S_\infty = \dfrac{\dfrac{8}{10}}{1 - \dfrac{1}{10}} = \dfrac{\dfrac{8}{10}}{\dfrac{9}{10}} = \dfrac{8}{10} \cdot \dfrac{10}{9} = \dfrac{8}{9}$$

59. The sequence 5, 5, 5, … is both arithmetic and geometric. As an arithmetic sequence, we would have a common difference of $d = 0$. As a geometric sequence, we would have a common ratio of $r = 1$.

Exercise Set 11.5

1. $(m+n)^3 = m^3 + 3m^2n + 3mn^2 + n^3$

3. $(c+d)^5$
$$= c^5 + 5c^4d + 10c^3d^2 + 10c^2d^3 + 5cd^4 + d^5$$

5. $(y-x)^5$
$$= [y + (-x)]^5$$
$$= y^5 - 5y^4x + 10y^3x^2 - 10y^2x^3 + 5yx^4 - x^5$$

7. Answers may vary.

9. $\dfrac{8!}{7!} = \dfrac{8 \cdot 7!}{7!} = 8$

11. $\dfrac{7!}{5!} = \dfrac{7 \cdot 6 \cdot 5!}{5!} = 7 \cdot 6 = 42$

13. $\dfrac{10!}{7!2!} = \dfrac{10 \cdot 9 \cdot 8 \cdot 7!}{7!2!} = \dfrac{10 \cdot 9 \cdot 8}{2 \cdot 1} = 360$

15. $\dfrac{8!}{6!0!} = \dfrac{8 \cdot 7 \cdot 6!}{6!1} = 8 \cdot 7 = 56$

17. $(a+b)^7 = a^7 + 7a^6b + \dfrac{7 \cdot 6}{2!}a^5b^2 + \dfrac{7 \cdot 6 \cdot 5}{3!}a^4b^3 + \dfrac{7 \cdot 6 \cdot 5 \cdot 4}{4!}a^3b^4 + \dfrac{7 \cdot 6 \cdot 5 \cdot 4 \cdot 3}{5!}a^2b^5 + \dfrac{7 \cdot 6 \cdot 5 \cdot 4 \cdot 3 \cdot 2}{6!}ab^6 + b^7$
$$= a^7 + 7a^6b + 21a^5b^2 + 35a^4b^3 + 35a^3b^4 + 21a^2b^5 + 7ab^6 + b^7$$

19. $(a+2b)^5 = a^5 + 5a^4(2b) + \dfrac{5 \cdot 4}{2!}a^3(2b)^2 + \dfrac{5 \cdot 4 \cdot 3}{3!}a^2(2b)^3 + \dfrac{5 \cdot 4 \cdot 3 \cdot 2}{4!}a(2b)^4 + (2b)^5$
$$= a^5 + 10a^4b + 40a^3b^2 + 80a^2b^3 + 80ab^4 + 32b^5$$

21. $(q+r)^9 = q^9 + \dfrac{9}{1!}q^8r + \dfrac{9 \cdot 8}{2!}q^7r^2 + \dfrac{9 \cdot 8 \cdot 7}{3!}q^6r^3 + \dfrac{9 \cdot 8 \cdot 7 \cdot 6}{4!}q^5r^4 + \dfrac{9 \cdot 8 \cdot 7 \cdot 6 \cdot 5}{5!}q^4r^5$
$$+ \dfrac{9 \cdot 8 \cdot 7 \cdot 6 \cdot 5 \cdot 4}{6!}q^3r^6 + \dfrac{9 \cdot 8 \cdot 7 \cdot 6 \cdot 5 \cdot 4 \cdot 3}{7!}q^2r^7 + \dfrac{9 \cdot 8 \cdot 7 \cdot 6 \cdot 5 \cdot 4 \cdot 3 \cdot 2}{8!}qr^8 + r^9$$
$$= q^9 + 9q^8r + 36q^7r^2 + 84q^6r^3 + 126q^5r^4 + 126q^4r^5 + 84q^3r^6 + 36q^2r^7 + 9qr^8 + r^9$$

23. $(4a+b)^5 = (4a)^5 + \dfrac{5}{1!}(4a)^4b + \dfrac{5 \cdot 4}{2!}(4a)^3b^2 + \dfrac{5 \cdot 4 \cdot 3}{3!}(4a)^2b^3 + \dfrac{5 \cdot 4 \cdot 3 \cdot 2}{4!}(4a)b^4 + b^5$
$$= 1024a^5 + 1280a^4b + 640a^3b^2 + 160a^2b^3 + 20ab^4 + b^5$$

25. $(5a-2b)^4 = (5a)^4 + \dfrac{4}{1!}(5a)^3(-2b) + \dfrac{4 \cdot 3}{2!}(5a)^2(-2b)^2 + \dfrac{4 \cdot 3 \cdot 2}{3!}(5a)(-2b)^3 + (-2b)^4$
$$= 625a^4 - 1000a^3b + 600a^2b^2 - 160ab^3 + 16b^4$$

27. $(2a+3b)^3 = (2a)^3 + \dfrac{3}{1!}(2a)^2(3b) + \dfrac{3\cdot 2}{2!}(2a)(3b)^2 + (3b)^3$

$= 8a^3 + 36a^2b + 54ab^2 + 27b^3$

29. $(x+2)^5 = x^5 + \dfrac{5}{1!}x^4(2) + \dfrac{5\cdot 4}{2!}x^3(2)^2 + \dfrac{5\cdot 4\cdot 3}{3!}x^2(2)^3 + \dfrac{5\cdot 4\cdot 3\cdot 2}{4!}x(2)^4 + (2)^5$

$= x^5 + 10x^4 + 40x^3 + 80x^2 + 80x + 32$

31. 5th term of $(c-d)^5$ corresponds to

$r = 4$:

$\dfrac{5!}{4!(5-4)!}c^{5-4}(-d)^4 = 5cd^4$

33. 8th term of $(2c+d)^7$ corresponds to

$r = 7$:

$\dfrac{7!}{7!(7-7)!}(2c)^{7-7}(d)^7 = d^7$

35. 4th term of $(2r-s)^5$ corresponds to

$r = 3$:

$\dfrac{5!}{3!(5-3)!}(2r)^{5-3}(-s)^3 = -40r^2s^3$

37. 3rd term of $(x+y)^4$ corresponds to

$r = 2$:

$\dfrac{4!}{2!(4-2)!}(x)^{4-2}(y)^2 = 6x^2y^2$

39. 2nd term of $(a+3b)^{10}$ corresponds to

$r = 1$:

$\dfrac{10!}{1!(10-1)!}(a)^{10-1}(3b)^1 = 30a^9b$

41. $f(x) = |x|$

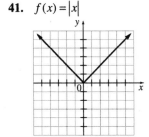

The function is not one-to-one since it fails the horizontal line test.

43. $H(x) = 2x+3$

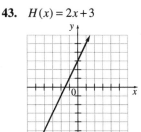

The function is one-to-one. It passes the horizontal line test.

45. $f(x) = x^2 + 3$

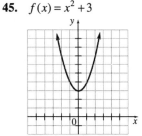

The function is not one-to-one since it fails the horizontal line test.

47. $\left(\sqrt{x}+\sqrt{3}\right)^5$

$= \left(\sqrt{x}\right)^5 + \dfrac{5}{1!}\left(\sqrt{x}\right)^4\left(\sqrt{3}\right) + \dfrac{5\cdot 4}{2!}\left(\sqrt{x}\right)^3\left(\sqrt{3}\right)^2$

$+ \dfrac{5\cdot 4\cdot 3}{3!}\left(\sqrt{x}\right)^2\left(\sqrt{3}\right)^3 + \dfrac{5\cdot 4\cdot 3\cdot 2}{4!}\left(\sqrt{x}\right)\left(\sqrt{3}\right)^4$

$+ \left(\sqrt{3}\right)^5$

$= x^2\sqrt{x} + 5\sqrt{3}x^2 + 30x\sqrt{x} + 30\sqrt{3}x + 45\sqrt{x} + 9\sqrt{3}$

49. $\dbinom{9}{5} = \dfrac{9!}{5!(9-5)!}$

$= \dfrac{9!}{5!4!}$

$= \dfrac{9\cdot 8\cdot 7\cdot 6\cdot 5!}{5!(4\cdot 3\cdot 2\cdot 1)}$

$= \dfrac{9\cdot 8\cdot 7\cdot 6}{4\cdot 3\cdot 2\cdot 1}$

$= 126$

51. $\dbinom{8}{2} = \dfrac{8!}{2!(8-2)!}$

$= \dfrac{8!}{2!6!}$

$= \dfrac{8 \cdot 7 \cdot 6!}{(2 \cdot 1)6!}$

$= \dfrac{8 \cdot 7}{2 \cdot 1}$

$= 28$

53. $\dbinom{n}{n} = \dfrac{n!}{n!(n-n)!} = \dfrac{1}{0!} = \dfrac{1}{1} = 1$

Chapter 11 Review

1. $a_n = -3n^2$

$a_1 = -3(1)^2 = -3$
$a_2 = -3(2)^2 = -12$
$a_3 = -3(3)^2 = -27$
$a_4 = -3(4)^2 = -48$
$a_5 = -3(5)^2 = -75$

2. $a_n = n^2 + 2n$

$a_1 = 1^2 + 2(1) = 3$
$a_2 = 2^2 + 2(2) = 8$
$a_3 = 3^2 + 2(3) = 15$
$a_4 = 4^2 + 2(4) = 24$
$a_5 = 5^2 + 2(5) = 35$

3. $a_n = \dfrac{(-1)^n}{100}$

$a_{100} = \dfrac{(-1)^{100}}{100} = \dfrac{1}{100}$

4. $a_n = \dfrac{2n}{(-1)^2}$

$a_{50} = \dfrac{2(50)}{(-1)^2} = 100$

5. $\dfrac{1}{6 \cdot 1}, \dfrac{1}{6 \cdot 2}, \dfrac{1}{6 \cdot 3}, \cdots$

In general, $a_n = \dfrac{1}{6n}$

6. $-1, 4, -9, 16, \ldots$

$(-1)^1 \cdot 1^2, (-1)^2 \cdot 2^2, (-1)^3 \cdot 3^2, (-1)^4 \cdot 4^2, \ldots$

$a_n = (-1)^n n^2$

7. $a_n = 32n - 16$

$a_5 = 32(5) - 16 = 144$ ft
$a_6 = 32(6) - 16 = 176$ ft
$a_7 = 32(7) - 16 = 208$ ft

8. $a_n = 100(2)^{n-1}$

$10,000 = 100(2)^{n-1}$
$100 = 2^{n-1}$
$\log 100 = (n-1)\log 2$
$n = \dfrac{\log 100}{\log 2} + 1 \approx 7.6$

Eighth day culture will be at least 10,000.

Originally we have not completed any days, so we need $n = 0$.

$a_0 = 100(2)^{0-1} = 100\left(\dfrac{1}{2}\right) = 50$.

The yeast culture originally measured 50.

9. $a_1 = 450$

$a_2 = 3(450) = 1350$
$a_3 = 3(1350) = 4050$
$a_4 = 3(4050) = 12,150$
$a_5 = 3(12,150) = 36,450$

In 2007, the number of infected people should be about 36,450.

10. $a_n = 50 + (n-1)8$

$a_1 = 50$
$a_2 = 50 + 8 = 58$
$a_3 = 50 + 2(8) = 66$
$a_4 = 50 + 3(8) = 74$
$a_5 = 50 + 4(8) = 82$
$a_6 = 50 + 5(8) = 90$
$a_7 = 50 + 6(8) = 98$
$a_8 = 50 + 7(8) = 106$
$a_9 = 50 + 8(8) = 114$
$a_{10} = 50 + 9(8) = 122$

There are 122 seats in the tenth row.

11. $a_1 = -2, \ r = \dfrac{2}{3}$

$a_1 = -2$

$a_2 = -2\left(\dfrac{2}{3}\right) = -\dfrac{4}{3}$

$a_3 = \left(-\dfrac{4}{3}\right)\left(\dfrac{2}{3}\right) = -\dfrac{8}{9}$

$a_4 = \left(-\dfrac{8}{9}\right)\left(\dfrac{2}{3}\right) = -\dfrac{16}{27}$

$a_5 = \left(-\dfrac{16}{27}\right)\left(\dfrac{2}{3}\right) = -\dfrac{32}{81}$

The first 5 terms of the sequence are

$-2, \ -\dfrac{4}{3}, \ -\dfrac{8}{9}, \ -\dfrac{16}{27}, \ -\dfrac{32}{81}.$

12. $a_n = 12 + (n-1)(-1.5)$

$a_1 = 12$

$a_2 = 12 + (1)(-1.5) = 10.5$

$a_3 = 12 + 2(-1.5) = 9$

$a_4 = 12 + 3(-1.5) = 7.5$

$a_5 = 12 + 4(-1.5) = 6$

13. $a_1 = -5, \ d = 4, \ n = 30$

$a_{30} = -5 + (30-1)4 = 111$

14. $a_n = 2 + (n-1)\dfrac{3}{4}$

$a_{11} = 2 + 10\left(\dfrac{3}{4}\right) = \dfrac{19}{2}$

15. $12, 7, 2, \dots$

$a_1 = 12, \ d = -5, \ n = 20$

$a_{20} = 12 + (20-1)(-5) = -83$

16. $a_n = a_1 r^{n-1}$

$a_6 = 4\left(\dfrac{3}{2}\right)^{6-1} = \dfrac{243}{8}$

17. $a_4 = 18, \ a_{20} = 98$

There are 16 differences between the fourth term and the twentieth term. Therefore, we have:

$a_4 + 16d = a_{20}$

$18 + 16d = 98$

$d = 5$

Now,

$a_4 = a_1 + 3d$

$18 = a_1 + 3(5)$

$a_1 = 3$

18. $r = \dfrac{a_4}{a_3} = \dfrac{192}{-48} = -4$

$-48 = a_1 r^2$

$-48 = a_1(-4)^2$

$-3 = a_1$

$r = -4, \ a_1 = -3.$

19. $\dfrac{3}{10}, \dfrac{3}{100}, \dfrac{3}{1000}, \dots$ can be rewritten as:

$\dfrac{3}{10^1}, \dfrac{3}{10^2}, \dfrac{3}{10^3}, \dots$

In general, $a_n = \dfrac{3}{10^n}$

20. $50, 58, 66, \dots$

This is an arithmetic sequence with first term $a_1 = 50$ and common difference $r = 8$.

$a_n = 50 + (n-1)8$

$ = 50 + 8n - 8$

$ = 8n + 42$

21. $\dfrac{8}{3}, 4, 6, \dots$

Geometric, $a_1 = \dfrac{8}{3}$,

$r = \dfrac{4}{\frac{8}{3}} = 4 \cdot \dfrac{3}{8} = \dfrac{12}{8} = \dfrac{3}{2}$

22. Arithmetic; $a_1 = -10.5$,

$d = -6.1 - (-10.5) = 4.4$

23. $7x, \ -14x, \ 28x$

$r = \dfrac{-14x}{7x} = -2$

Geometric: $a_1 = 7x, \ r = -2$

24. Neither. There is no common ratio, nor a common difference.

25. $a_1 = 8, \ r = 0.75$

$a_2 = a_1(0.75) = 6, \ a_3 = a_2(0.75) = 4.5,$

$a_4 = a_3(0.75) \approx 3.4, \ a_5 = a_4(0.75) \approx 2.5,$

$a_6 = a_5(0.75) \approx 1.9$

The height after the fifth bounce is the sixth term of the sequence.

Yes, a ball that rebounds to a height of 2.5 feet after the fifth bounce is good since 2.5 > 1.9.

26. $a_1 = 25 \quad d = -4$

$a_n = a_1 + (n-1)d$

$a_n = 25 + (n-1)(-4)$

$\quad = 25 - 4n + 4$

$\quad = 29 - 4n$

n	$u(n)$
2	21
3	17
4	13
5	9
6	5
7	1
8	-3

$u(n) = 29 - 4n$

There will be 1 can in the top row (the 7th row).

27. $a_1 = 1, r = 2$

$a_n = 2^{n-1}$

$a_{10} = 2^9 = \$512$

$a_{30} = 2^{29} = \$536,870,912$

You will save \$512 on the tenth day and \$536,870,912 on the thirtieth day.

28. $a_n = a_1 r^{n-1}$

$a_5 = 30(0.7)^4 = 7.203$ in.

The length of the arc on the fifth swing will be 7.203 inches.

29. $a_1 = 900, d = 150$

$a_n = 900 + (n-1)150$

$\quad = 900 + 150n - 150$

$\quad = 750 + 150n$

$a_6 = 750 + 150(6) = 750 + 900 = 1650$

Rosa will be making \$1650 per month at the end of her training.

30. $\dfrac{1}{512}, \dfrac{1}{256}, \dfrac{1}{128}, \ldots$

first fold: $a_1 = \dfrac{1}{256}, r = 2$

$a_{15} = \dfrac{1}{256}(2)^{15-1} = 64$ inches

After 15 folds, the paper will be 64 inches thick.

31. $\displaystyle\sum_{i=1}^{5}(2i-1)$

$= [2(1)-1] + [2(2)-1] + [2(3)-1]$

$\quad + [2(4)-1] + [2(5)-1]$

$= 1 + 3 + 5 + 7 + 9$

$= 25$

32. $\displaystyle\sum_{i=1}^{5} i(i+2)$

$= 1(1+2) + 2(2+2) + 3(3+2) + 4(4+2) + 5(5+2)$

$= 3 + 8 + 15 + 24 + 35$

$= 85$

33. $\displaystyle\sum_{i=2}^{4}\dfrac{(-1)^i}{2i} = \dfrac{(-1)^2}{2(2)} + \dfrac{(-1)^3}{2(3)} + \dfrac{(-1)^4}{2(4)}$

$= \dfrac{1}{4} - \dfrac{1}{6} + \dfrac{1}{8}$

$= \dfrac{5}{24}$

34. $\displaystyle\sum_{i=3}^{5} 5(-1)^{i-1} = 5(-1)^{3-1} + 5(-1)^{4-1} + 5(-1)^{5-1}$

$= 5(1) + 5(-1) + 5(1)$

$= 5 - 5 + 5$

$= 5$

35. $a_n = (n-3)(n+2)$

$S_4 = (1-3)(1+2) + (2-3)(2+2) +$

$\quad (3-3)(3+2) + (4-3)(4+2)$

$= -6 - 4 + 0 + 6$

$= -4$

36. $a_n = n^2$

$S_6 = (1)^2 + (2)^2 + (3)^2 + (4)^2 + (5)^2 + (6)^2$

$= 1 + 4 + 9 + 16 + 25 + 36$

$= 91$

37. $a_n = -8 + (n-1)3$

$a_1 = -8 + (1-1)3 = -8$

$a_2 = -8 + (2-1)3 = -5$

$a_3 = -8 + (3-1)3 = -2$

$a_4 = -8 + (4-1)3 = 1$

$a_5 = -8 + (5-1)3 = 4$

So $S_5 = -10$

38. $a_n = 5(4)^{n-1}$

$S_3 = 5(4)^0 + 5(4)^1 + 5(4)^2$

$= 5 \cdot 1 + 5 \cdot 4 + 5 \cdot 16$

$= 5 + 20 + 80$

$= 105$

39. $1 + 3 + 9 + 27 + 81 + 243$

$= 3^0 + 3^1 + 3^2 + 3^3 + 3^4 + 3^5$

$= \displaystyle\sum_{i=1}^{6} 3^{i-1}$

40. $6 + 2 + (-2) + (-6) + (-10) + (-14) + (-18)$

$a_1 = 6 \quad d = -4$

$a_n = 6 + (n-1)(-4) \quad \text{or} \quad a_n = 10 - 4n$

$\sum_{i=1}^{7} (6 + (i-1)(-4)) \quad \text{or} \quad \sum_{i=1}^{7} (10 - 4i)$

41. $\dfrac{1}{4} + \dfrac{1}{16} + \dfrac{1}{64} + \dfrac{1}{256}$

$= \dfrac{1}{4^1} + \dfrac{1}{4^2} + \dfrac{1}{4^3} + \dfrac{1}{4^4}$

$= \sum_{i=1}^{4} \dfrac{1}{4^i}$

42. $1 + \left(-\dfrac{3}{2}\right) + \dfrac{9}{4}$

$= \left(-\dfrac{3}{2}\right)^0 + \left(-\dfrac{3}{2}\right)^1 + \left(-\dfrac{3}{2}\right)^2$

$= \sum_{i=1}^{3} \left(-\dfrac{3}{2}\right)^{i-1}$

43. $a_1 = 20, \ r = 2$

$a_n = 20(2)^n$ represents the number of yeast, where n represents the number of 8-hr periods. Since $48 = 6(8)$, here $n = 6$.

$a_6 = 20(2)^6 = 1280$ yeast

44. $a_n = n^2 + 2n - 1$

$a_4 = (4)^2 + 2(4) - 1 = 23$ cranes

$\sum_{i=1}^{4} i^2 + 2i - 1$

$= (1 + 2 - 1) + (4 + 4 - 1) +$

$\quad + (9 + 6 - 1) + (16 + 8 - 1)$

$= 46$ cranes

23 cranes were born in the fourth year and a total of 46 cranes in the first four years.

45. For Job A: $a_1 = 39,500, \ d = 2200$;

$a_5 = 39,500 + (5-1)2200 = \$48,300$

For Job B: $a_1 = 41,000, \ d = 1400$

$a_5 = 41,000 + (5-1)1400 = \$46,600$

For the fifth year, Job A has a higher salary.

46. $a_n = 200(0.5)^n$

$a_3 = 200(0.5)^3 = 25$ kg

$\sum_{i=1}^{3} 200(0.5)^i = 200(0.5) + 200(0.5)^2 + 200(0.5)^3$

$\qquad\qquad = 175$ kg

25 kg decay in the third year, and a total of 175 kg decay in the first three years.

47. 15, 19, 23, ...

$a_1 = 15, \ d = 4$

$a_6 = 15 + (6-1)(4) = 35$

$S_6 = \dfrac{6}{2}[15 + 35] = 3 \cdot 50 = 150$

48. 5, −10, 20,...

$a_1 = 5, \ r = -2$

$S_n = \dfrac{a_1(1 - r^n)}{1 - r}$

$S_9 = \dfrac{5(1 - (-2)^9)}{1 - (-2)} = 855$

49. $a_1 = 1, \ d = 2, \ n = 30$

$S_{30} = \dfrac{30}{2}[2(1) + (30-1)2] = 900$

50. 7, 14, 21, 28, ...

$a_1 = 7, d = 7$

$a_n = 7 + (n-1)7$

$a_{20} = 7 + (20-1)7 = 140$

$S_{20} = \dfrac{20}{2}(7 + 140) = 1470$

51. 8, 5, 2, ...

$a_1 = 8, \ d = -3, \ n = 20$

$a_{20} = 8 + (20-1)(-3) = -49$

$S_{20} = \dfrac{20}{2}[8 + (-49)] = -410$

52. $\dfrac{3}{4}, \dfrac{9}{4}, \dfrac{27}{4}, ...$

$a_1 = \dfrac{3}{4}, \ r = 3$

$S_8 = \dfrac{\dfrac{3}{4}(1 - 3^8)}{1 - 3} = 2460$

53. $a_1 = 6$, $r = 5$

$$S_4 = \frac{6(1-5^4)}{1-5} = 936$$

54. $a_1 = -3$, $d = -6$

$a_n = -3 + (n-1)(-6)$

$a_{100} = -3 + (100-1)(-6) = -597$

$$S_{100} = \frac{100}{2}(-3 + (-597)) = -30,000$$

55. $5, \dfrac{5}{2}, \dfrac{5}{4}, \ldots$

$a_1 = 5$, $r = \dfrac{1}{2}$

$$S_\infty = \frac{5}{1-\dfrac{1}{2}} = 10$$

56. $18, -2, \dfrac{2}{9}, \ldots$

$a_1 = 18$, $r = -\dfrac{1}{9}$

$$S_\infty = \frac{18}{1+\dfrac{1}{9}} = \frac{81}{5}$$

57. $-20, -4, -\dfrac{4}{5}, \ldots$

$a_1 = -20$, $r = \dfrac{1}{5}$

$$S_\infty = \frac{-20}{1-\dfrac{1}{5}} = -25$$

58. $0.2, 0.02, 0.002, \ldots$

$a_1 = 0.2$, $r = \dfrac{1}{10}$

$$S_\infty = \frac{0.2}{1-\dfrac{1}{10}} = \frac{2}{9}$$

59. $a_1 = 20,000$, $r = 1.15$, $n = 4$

$a_4 = 20,000(1.15)^{4-1} \approx \$30,418$

Earned in his fourth year.

$$S_4 = \frac{20,000(1-1.15^4)}{1-1.15} \approx \$99,868$$

earned in his first four years.

60. $a_n = 40(0.8)^{n-1}$

$a_4 = 40(0.8)^{4-1} = 20.48$ min

$$S_4 = \frac{40(1-0.8^4)}{1-0.8} = 118 \text{ min}$$

It takes him about 20 minutes to assemble the fourth television, and a total of about 118 minutes to assemble the first four.

61. $a_1 = 100$, $d = -7$, $n = 7$

$a_7 = 100 + (7-1)(-7)$

= \$58 rent paid for the seventh day.

$S_7 = \dfrac{7}{2}[100+58]$

= \$553 rent paid for the first seven days.

62. $a_1 = 15$, $r = 0.8$

$S_\infty = \dfrac{15}{1-0.8} = 75$ feet downward

$a_1 = 12$, $r = 0.8$

$S_\infty = \dfrac{12}{1-0.8} = 60$ feet upward

The total is 135 feet.

63. $1800, 600, 200, \ldots$

$a_1 = 1800$, $r = \dfrac{1}{3}$, $n = 6$

$$S_6 = 1800 \frac{\left(1-\left(\dfrac{1}{3}\right)^6\right)}{1-\dfrac{1}{3}}$$

≈ 2696 mosquitoes killed during the first six days after the spraying.

64. $1800, 600, 200, \ldots$

For which n is $a_n > 1$?

$a_n = 1800\left(\dfrac{1}{3}\right)^{n-1} > 1$

$(n-1)\log\left(\dfrac{1}{3}\right) > \log\dfrac{1}{1800}$

$n < 7.8$

$$S_8 = 1800 \frac{\left(1-\left(\dfrac{1}{3}\right)^8\right)}{1-\dfrac{1}{3}} \approx 2700$$

No longer effective on the 8th day. About 2700 mosquitoes were killed.

65. $0.5\overline{55} = 0.5 + 0.05 + 0.005 + \cdots$

$a_1 = 0.5,\ r = 0.1$

$S_\infty = \dfrac{0.5}{1-0.1} = \dfrac{5}{9}$

66. 27, 30, 33, ...

$a_1 = 27, d = 3$

$a_n = 27 + (n-1)(3)$

$a_{20} = 27 + (20-1)(3) = 84$

$S_{20} = \dfrac{20}{2}(27 + 84) = 1110$

The theater has 1110 seats.

67. $(x+z)^5 = x^5 + 5x^4 z + 10x^3 z^2 + 10x^2 z^3 + 5xz^4 + z^5$

68. $(y-r)^6 = y^6 - 6y^5 r + 15y^4 r^2 - 20y^3 r^3 + 15y^2 r^4 - 6yr^5 + r^6$

69. $(2x+y)^4 = 16x^4 + 32x^3 y + 24x^2 y^2 + 8xy^3 + y^4$

70. $(3y-z)^4 = 81y^4 - 108y^3 z + 54y^2 z^2 - 12yz^3 + z^4$

71. $(b+c)^8 = b^8 + \dfrac{8}{1!}b^7 c + \dfrac{8\cdot 7}{2!}b^6 c^2 + \dfrac{8\cdot 7\cdot 6}{3!}b^5 c^3 + \dfrac{8\cdot 7\cdot 6\cdot 5}{4!}b^4 c^4 + \dfrac{8\cdot 7\cdot 6\cdot 5\cdot 4}{5!}b^3 c^5$

$\qquad + \dfrac{8\cdot 7\cdot 6\cdot 5\cdot 4\cdot 3}{6!}b^2 c^6 + \dfrac{8\cdot 7\cdot 6\cdot 5\cdot 4\cdot 3\cdot 2}{7!}bc^7 + c^8$

$\qquad = b^8 + 8b^7 c + 28b^6 c^2 + 56b^5 c^3 + 70b^4 c^4 + 56b^3 c^5 + 28b^2 c^6 + 8bc^7 + c^8$

72. $(x-w)^7 = x^7 + \dfrac{7}{1!}x^6(-w) + \dfrac{7\cdot 6}{2!}x^5(-w)^2 + \dfrac{7\cdot 6\cdot 5}{3!}x^4(-w)^3 + \dfrac{7\cdot 6\cdot 5\cdot 4}{4!}x^3(-w)^4$

$\qquad + \dfrac{7\cdot 6\cdot 5\cdot 4\cdot 3}{5!}x^2(-w)^5 + \dfrac{7\cdot 6\cdot 5\cdot 4\cdot 3\cdot 2}{6!}x(-w)^6 + (-w)^7$

$\qquad = x^7 - 7x^6 w + 21x^5 w^2 - 35x^4 w^3 + 35x^3 w^4 - 21x^2 w^5 + 7xw^6 - w^7$

73. $(4m-n)^4 = (4m)^4 + \dfrac{4}{1!}(4m)^3(-n) + \dfrac{4\cdot 3}{2!}(4m)^2(-n)^2 + \dfrac{4\cdot 3\cdot 2}{3!}(4m)(-n)^3 + (-n)^4$

$\qquad = 256m^4 - 256m^3 n + 96m^2 n^2 - 16mn^3 + n^4$

74. $(p-2r)^5 = p^5 + \dfrac{5}{1!}p^4(-2r) + \dfrac{5\cdot 4}{2!}p^3(-2r)^2 + \dfrac{5\cdot 4\cdot 3}{3!}p^2(-2r)^3 + \dfrac{5\cdot 4\cdot 3\cdot 2}{4!}p(-2r)^4 + (-2r)^5$

$\qquad = p^5 - 10p^4 r + 40p^3 r^2 - 80p^2 r^3 + 80pr^4 - 32r^5$

75. The 4th term corresponds to $r = 3$.

$\dfrac{7!}{3!(7-3)!}a^{7-3}b^3 = 35a^4 b^3$

76. The 11th term is $\dfrac{10!}{10!0!}y^{10-10}(2z)^{10} = 1024z^{10}$

Chapter 11 Test

1. $a_n = \dfrac{(-1)^n}{n+4}$

$a_1 = \dfrac{(-1)^1}{1+4} = -\dfrac{1}{5}$

$a_2 = \dfrac{(-1)^2}{2+4} = \dfrac{1}{6}$

$a_3 = \dfrac{(-1)^3}{3+4} = -\dfrac{1}{7}$

$a_4 = \dfrac{(-1)^4}{4+4} = \dfrac{1}{8}$

$a_5 = \dfrac{(-1)^5}{5+4} = -\dfrac{1}{9}$

2. $a_n = 10 + 3(n-1)$

$a_{80} = 10 + 3(80-1) = 247$

3. $\dfrac{2}{5}, \dfrac{2}{25}, \dfrac{2}{125}, \ldots = \dfrac{2}{5^1}, \dfrac{2}{5^2}, \dfrac{2}{5^3}, \ldots$

In general, $a_n = \dfrac{2}{5^n}$ or $a_n = \dfrac{2}{5}\left(\dfrac{1}{5}\right)^{n-1}$

4. $(-1)^1 9 \cdot 1, (-1)^2 9 \cdot 2, (-1)^3 9 \cdot 3, \ldots, a_n = (-1)^n 9n$

5. $a_n = 5(2)^{n-1}, S_5 = \dfrac{5(1-2^5)}{1-2} = 155$

6. $a_n = 18 + (n-1)(-2)$

$a_1 = 18, \ d = -2$

$a_{30} = 18 + (30-1)(-2) = -40$

$S_{30} = \dfrac{30}{2}\left[18 + (-40)\right] = -330$

7. $a_1 = 24, \ r = \dfrac{1}{6}$

$S_\infty = \dfrac{24}{1-\dfrac{1}{6}} = \dfrac{144}{5}$

8. $\dfrac{3}{2}, -\dfrac{3}{4}, \dfrac{3}{8}, \ldots$

$a_1 = \dfrac{3}{2}, \ r = -\dfrac{1}{2}$

$S_\infty = \dfrac{\dfrac{3}{2}}{1-\left(-\dfrac{1}{2}\right)} = 1$

9. $\displaystyle\sum_{i=1}^{4} i(i-2)$

$= 1(1-2) + 2(2-2) + 3(3-2) + 4(4-2)$

$= 1(-1) + 2(0) + 3(1) + 4(2)$

$= -1 + 0 + 3 + 8$

$= 10$

10. $\displaystyle\sum_{i=2}^{4} 5(2)^i(-1)^{i-1}$

$= 5(2)^2(-1)^{2-1} + 5(2)^3(-1)^{3-1} + 5(2)^4(-1)^{4-1}$

$= 5(4)(-1) + 5(8)(1) + 5(16)(-1)$

$= -20 + 40 - 80$

$= -60$

11. $(a-b)^6 = a^6 - 6a^5b + 15a^4b^2 - 20a^3b^3 + 15a^2b^4 - 6ab^5 + b^6$

12. $(2x+y)^5 = (2x)^5 + \dfrac{5}{1!}(2x)^4 y + \dfrac{5\cdot4}{2!}(2x)^3 y^2 + \dfrac{5\cdot4\cdot3}{3!}(2x)^2 y^3 + \dfrac{5\cdot4\cdot3\cdot2}{4!}(2x)y^4 + y^5$

$= 32x^5 + 80x^4 y + 80x^3 y^2 + 40x^2 y^3 + 10xy^4 + y^5$

13. $a_n = 250 + 75(n-1)$

$a_{10} = 250 + 75(10-1) = 925$

$a_1 = 250 + 75(1-1) = 250$

There were 925 people in the town at the beginning of the tenth year.
There were 250 people in the town at the beginning of the first year.

14. $1, 3, 5, \cdots$

$a_1 = 1, d = 2, n = 8$

$a_8 = 1 + (8-1)2 = 15$

We want $1+3+5+7+9+11+13+15$

$S_8 = \dfrac{8}{2}[1+15] = 64$

There were a total of 64 shrubs planted.

15. $a_1 = 80$, $r = \dfrac{3}{4}$, $n = 4$

$a_4 = 80\left(\dfrac{3}{4}\right)^{4-1} = 33.75$

The arc length is 33.75 cm on the 4th swing.

$S_4 = \dfrac{80\left(1-\left(\dfrac{3}{4}\right)^4\right)}{1-\dfrac{3}{4}} = 218.75$

The total of the arc lengths is 218.75 cm for the first 4 swings.

16. $a_1 = 80$, $r = \dfrac{3}{4}$

$S_\infty = \dfrac{80}{1-\dfrac{3}{4}} = 320$

The total of the arc lengths is 320 cm before the pendulum comes to rest.

17. 16, 48, 80,...

$a_{10} = 16 + (10-1)32 = 304$

$S_{10} = \dfrac{10}{2}[16 + 304] = 1600$

He falls 304 feet during the 10th second.
He falls 1600 feet during the first 10 seconds.

18. $0.42\overline{42} = 0.42 + 0.0042 + 0.000042 + ...$

$S_\infty = \dfrac{0.42}{1-0.01} = \dfrac{14}{33}$

Thus, $0.42\overline{42} = \dfrac{14}{33}$

Chapter 11 Cumulative Review

1. a. $\dfrac{20}{-4} = -5$

b. $\dfrac{-9}{-3} = 3$

c. $-\dfrac{3}{8} \div 3 = -\dfrac{3}{8} \cdot \dfrac{1}{3} = -\dfrac{1}{8}$

d. $\dfrac{-40}{10} = -4$

e. $\dfrac{-1}{10} \div \dfrac{-2}{5} = \dfrac{-1}{10} \cdot \dfrac{5}{-2} = \dfrac{1}{4}$

f. $\dfrac{8}{0}$ is undefined.

2. a. $3a - (4a + 3) = 3a - 4a - 3$
$= -a - 3$

b. $(5x - 3) + (2x + 6) = 7x + 3$

c. $4(2x - 5) - 3(5x + 1) = 8x - 20 - 15x - 3$
$= -7x - 23$

3. Let $x =$ the original price.
$x - 0.08x = 2162$
$0.92x = 2162$
$x = \$2350$
The original price is \$2350.

4. Let $x =$ the price before taxes.
$x + 0.06x = 344.50$
$1.06x = 344.50$
$x = 325$
The price before taxes was \$325.

5. a. $\begin{cases} 3x + 4y = -7 \\ x - 2y = -9 \end{cases}$

$D = \begin{vmatrix} 3 & 4 \\ 1 & -2 \end{vmatrix} = 3(-2) - 4(1) = -10$

$D_x = \begin{vmatrix} -7 & 4 \\ -9 & -2 \end{vmatrix} = (-7)(-2) - (-9)(4) = 50$

$D_y = \begin{vmatrix} 3 & -7 \\ 1 & -9 \end{vmatrix} = 3(-9) - 1(-7) = -20$

$x = \dfrac{D_x}{D} = \dfrac{50}{-10} = -5$; $y = \dfrac{D_y}{D} = \dfrac{-20}{-10} = 2$

The solution is $(-5,\ 2)$.

b. $\begin{cases} 5x + y = 5 \\ -7x - 2y = -7 \end{cases}$

$D = \begin{vmatrix} 5 & 1 \\ -7 & -2 \end{vmatrix} = 5(-2) - (-7)(1) = -3$

$D_x = \begin{vmatrix} 5 & 1 \\ -7 & -2 \end{vmatrix} = 5(-2) - (-7)(1) = -3$

$D_y = \begin{vmatrix} 5 & 5 \\ -7 & -7 \end{vmatrix} = 5(-7) - (-7)(5) = 0$

$x = \dfrac{D_x}{D} = \dfrac{50}{-10} = 1$; $y = \dfrac{D_y}{D} = \dfrac{-20}{-10} = 0$

The solution is $(1,\ 0)$.

6. The slope of the line we seek is $m = \dfrac{3}{2}$, the same

as the slope of $3x - 2y = 6\ \left(y = \dfrac{3}{2}x - 3\right)$. Thus,

the equation of the line we seek is:

$$y - y_1 = m(x - x_1)$$

$$y - (-2) = \frac{3}{2}(x - 3)$$

$$y + 2 = \frac{3}{2}(x - 3)$$

$$y + 2 = \frac{3}{2}x - \frac{9}{2}$$

$$y = \frac{3}{2}x - \frac{13}{2}$$

$$f(x) = \frac{3}{2}x - \frac{13}{2}$$

7. a. $(3x^6)(5x) = 15x^{6+1} = 15x^7$

   b. $(-2x^3 p^2)(4xp^{10}) = -8x^{3+1}p^{2+10} = -8x^4 p^{12}$

8.

$$y^3 + 5y^2 - y - 5 = 0$$
$$(y^3 + 5y^2) + (-y - 5) = 0$$
$$y^2(y + 5) - 1(y + 5) = 0$$
$$(y^2 - 1)(y + 5) = 0$$
$$(y + 1)(y - 1)(y + 5) = 0$$
$$y = -1 \text{ or } y = 1 \text{ or } y = -5$$

The solution set is $\{-5,\ -1,\ 1\}$.

9.

$$\begin{array}{r|rrrrr} -2 & 1 & -2 & -11 & 5 & 34 \\ & & -2 & 8 & 6 & -22 \\ \hline & 1 & -4 & -3 & 11 & 12 \end{array}$$

Answer: $x^3 - 4x^2 - 3x + 11 + \dfrac{12}{x + 2}$

10. $\dfrac{5}{3a - 6} - \dfrac{a}{a - 2} + \dfrac{3 + 2a}{5a - 10}$

$$= \frac{5}{3(a - 2)} - \frac{a}{a - 2} + \frac{3 + 2a}{5(a - 2)}$$

$$= \frac{5 \cdot 5}{15(a - 2)} - \frac{15a}{15(a - 2)} + \frac{3(3 + 2a)}{15(a - 2)}$$

$$= \frac{25 - 15a + 9 + 6a}{15(a - 2)}$$

$$= \frac{34 - 9a}{15(a - 2)}$$

11. a. $\sqrt{50} = \sqrt{2}\sqrt{25} = 5\sqrt{2}$

   b. $\sqrt[3]{24} = \sqrt[3]{8}\sqrt[3]{3} = 2\sqrt[3]{3}$

   c. $\sqrt{26}$ (simplified as it is)

   d. $\sqrt[4]{32} = \sqrt[4]{16}\sqrt[4]{2} = 2\sqrt[4]{2}$

12. $\sqrt{3x + 6} - \sqrt{7x - 6} = 0$

$$\left(\sqrt{3x + 6}\right)^2 = \left(\sqrt{7x - 6}\right)^2$$
$$3x + 6 = 7x - 6$$
$$-4x = -12$$
$$x = 3$$

13. $A = P(1 + r)^t$

$$2420 = 2000(1 + r)^2$$
$$1.21 = (1 + r)^2$$
$$1 + r = \pm\sqrt{1.21}$$
$$1 + r = 1.1$$
$$r = 0.1 = 10\%$$

The interest rate is 10%.

14. a. $\sqrt[3]{\dfrac{4}{3x}} = \dfrac{\sqrt[3]{4}}{\sqrt[3]{3x}} \cdot \dfrac{\sqrt[3]{9x^2}}{\sqrt[3]{9x^2}} = \dfrac{\sqrt[3]{36x^2}}{\sqrt[3]{27x^3}} = \dfrac{\sqrt[3]{36x^2}}{3x}$

   b. $\dfrac{\sqrt{2} + 1}{\sqrt{2} - 1} = \dfrac{\sqrt{2} + 1}{\sqrt{2} - 1} \cdot \dfrac{\sqrt{2} + 1}{\sqrt{2} + 1}$

$$= \frac{2 + \sqrt{2} + \sqrt{2} + 1}{2 + \sqrt{2} - \sqrt{2} - 1}$$

$$= \frac{3 + 2\sqrt{2}}{1}$$

$$= 3 + 2\sqrt{2}$$

15. $(x - 3)^2 - 3(x - 3) - 4 = 0$

Let $y = x - 3$

$$y^2 - 3y - 4 = 0$$
$$(y + 1)(y - 4) = 0$$
$$y = -1 \text{ or } y = 4$$
$$x - 3 = -1 \quad \text{or} \quad x - 3 = 4$$
$$x = 2 \quad \text{or} \quad x = 7$$

The solution set is $\{2,\ 7\}$.

16.

$$\frac{10}{(2x+4)^2} - \frac{1}{2x+4} = 3$$

$$(2x+4)^2\left(\frac{10}{(2x+4)^2} - \frac{1}{2x+4}\right) = (2x+4)^2(3)$$

$$10 - (2x+4) = 3(2x+4)^2$$

$$10 - 2x - 4 = 3(4x^2 + 16x + 16)$$

$$-2x + 6 = 12x^2 + 48x + 48$$

$$12x^2 + 50x + 42 = 0$$

$$6x^2 + 25x + 21 = 0$$

$$(6x+7)(x+3) = 0$$

$$6x + 7 = 0 \quad \text{or} \quad x + 3 = 0$$

$$x = -\frac{7}{6} \quad \text{or} \quad x = -3$$

The solution set is $\left\{-3, \ -\frac{7}{6}\right\}$.

17. $\dfrac{5}{x+1} < -2$

Determine the values of x that cause the denominator to be 0.

$$x + 1 = 0$$

$$x = -1$$

Next solve: $\dfrac{5}{x+1} = -2$

$$5 = -2(x+1)$$

$$5 = -2x - 2$$

$$-2x = 7$$

$$x = -\frac{7}{2}$$

Region	Test Point	$\dfrac{5}{x+1} < -2$ Result
$A:\left(-\infty, -\dfrac{7}{2}\right)$	-6	$\dfrac{5}{-6+1} < -2;$ False
$B:\left(-\dfrac{7}{2}, -1\right)$	-2	$\dfrac{5}{-2+1} < -2;$ True
$C:(-1, \infty)$	0	$\dfrac{5}{0+1} < -2;$ False

The solution set is $\left(\dfrac{-7}{2}, -1\right)$.

18. $f(x) = (x+2)^2 - 6$

The graph is similar to the graph of $y = x^2$, but is shifted to the left 2 units and down 6 unit. The vertex is $(-2, -6)$, and the axis of symmetry is $x = -2$.

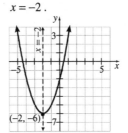

19.

$$-16t^2 + 20t = 0$$

$$-16(t - \frac{5}{8})^2 + \frac{25}{4} = 0$$

$$t = \frac{25}{4} \text{ feet}, \ \frac{5}{2} \text{sec}$$

20. $x = -\dfrac{b}{2a} = -\dfrac{3}{2(1)} = -\dfrac{3}{2}$

$$y = f\left(-\frac{3}{2}\right) = \left(-\frac{3}{2}\right)^2 + 3\left(-\frac{3}{2}\right) - 18$$

$$= \frac{9}{4} - \frac{9}{2} - 18$$

$$= -\frac{81}{4}$$

The vertex is $\left(-\dfrac{3}{2}, -\dfrac{81}{4}\right)$.

21. a. $(f \circ g)(2) = f(g(2))$

$$= f(2+3)$$

$$= f(5)$$

$$= 5^2$$

$$= 25$$

$$(g \circ f)(2) = g(f(2))$$

$$= g(2^2)$$

$$= g(4)$$

$$= 4 + 3$$

$$= 7$$

b.
$$(f \circ g)(x) = f(g(x))$$
$$= f(x+3)$$
$$= (x+3)^2$$
$$= x^2 + 6x + 9$$
$$(g \circ f)(x) = g(f(x))$$
$$= g(x^2)$$
$$= x^2 + 3$$

22.
$$f(x) = -2x + 3$$
$$y = -2x + 3$$
$$x = -2y + 3$$
$$x - 3 = -2y$$
$$y = \frac{x-3}{-2} = \frac{3-x}{2}$$
$$f^{-1}(x) = \frac{3-x}{2}$$

23. $f^{-1} = \{(1,0),\ (7,-2),\ (-6,3),\ (4,4)\}$

24. a.
$$(f \circ g)(2) = f(g(2))$$
$$= f(2+1)$$
$$= f(3)$$
$$= 3^2 - 2$$
$$= 7$$
$$(g \circ f)(2) = g(f(2))$$
$$= g(2^2 - 2)$$
$$= g(2)$$
$$= 2 + 1$$
$$= 3$$

b.
$$(f \circ g)(x) = f(g(x))$$
$$= f(x+1)$$
$$= (x+1)^2 - 2$$
$$= x^2 + 2x - 1$$
$$(g \circ f)(x) = g(f(x))$$
$$= g(x^2 - 2)$$
$$= (x^2 - 2) + 1$$
$$= x^2 - 1$$

25. a.
$$2^x = 16$$
$$2^x = 2^4$$
$$x = 4$$

b.
$$9^x = 27$$
$$(3^2)^x = 3^3$$
$$3^{2x} = 3^3$$
$$2x = 3$$
$$x = \frac{3}{2}$$

c.
$$4^{x+3} = 8^x$$
$$(2^2)^{x+3} = (2^3)^x$$
$$2^{2x+6} = 2^{3x}$$
$$2x + 6 = 3x$$
$$6 = x$$

26. a.
$$\log_2 32 = x$$
$$2^x = 32$$
$$2^x = 2^5$$
$$x = 5$$

b.
$$\log_4 \frac{1}{64} = x$$
$$4^x = \frac{1}{64}$$
$$4^x = 4^{-3}$$
$$x = -3$$

c.
$$\log_{1/2} x = 5$$
$$\left(\frac{1}{2}\right)^5 = x$$
$$\frac{1}{32} = x$$

27. a. $\log_3 3^2 = 2$

b. $\log_7 7^{-1} = -1$

c. $5^{\log_5 3} = 3$

d. $2^{\log_2 6} = 6$

28. a.
$$4^x = 64$$
$$4^x = 4^3$$
$$x = 3$$

b. $8^x = 32$

$(2^3)^x = 2^5$

$3x = 5$

$x = \dfrac{5}{3}$

c. $9^{x+4} = 243^x$

$(3^2)^{x+4} = (3^5)^x$

$3^{2x+8} = 3^{5x}$

$2x + 8 = 5x$

$8 = 3x$

$\dfrac{8}{3} = x$

29. a. $\log_{11} 10 + \log_{11} 3 = \log_{11}(10 \cdot 3) = \log_{11} 30$

b. $\log_3 \dfrac{1}{2} + \log_3 12 = \log_3\left(\dfrac{1}{2} \cdot 12\right) = \log_3 6$

c. $\log_2(x+2) + \log_2 x = \log_2 x(x+2)$
$= \log_2(x^2 + 2x)$

30. a. $\log 100,000 = \log 10^5 = 5$

b. $\log 10^{-3} = -3$

c. $\ln = \sqrt[5]{e} = \ln e^{1/5} = \dfrac{1}{5}$

d. $\ln e^4 = 4$

31. $A = Pe^{rt}$
$A = 1600 e^{0.09(5)}$
$A \approx 2509.30$
The total amount owed is \$2509.30.

32. a. $\log_6 5 + \log_6 4 = \log_6(5 \cdot 4) = \log_6 20$

b. $\log_8 12 - \log_8 4 = \log_8 \dfrac{12}{4} = \log_8 3$

c. $2\log_2 x + 3\log_2 x - 2\log_2(x-1)$
$= 5\log_2 x - 2\log_2(x-1)$
$= \log_2 x^5 - \log_2(x-1)^2$
$= \log_2 \dfrac{x^5}{(x-1)^2}$

33. $3^x = 7$

$\log 3^x = \log 7$

$x \log 3 = \log 7$

$x = \dfrac{\log 7}{\log 3} \approx 1.7712$

34. $A = P\left(1 + \dfrac{r}{n}\right)^{nt}$

$10,000 = 5000\left(1 + \dfrac{0.02}{4}\right)^{4t}$

$10,000 = 5000(1.005)^{4t}$

$2 = (1.005)^{4t}$

$\log 2 = \log(1.005)^{4t}$

$\log 2 = 4t \log(1.005)$

$t = \dfrac{\log 2}{4 \log 1.005} \approx 34.7 \text{ years}$

35. $\log_4(x-2) = 2$

$4^2 = x - 2$

$x - 2 = 16$

$x = 18$

36. $\log_4 10 - \log_4 x = 2$

$\log_4 \dfrac{10}{x} = 2$

$4^2 = \dfrac{10}{x}$

$16 = \dfrac{10}{x}$

$16x = 10$

$x = \dfrac{10}{16} = \dfrac{5}{8}$

37. Hyperbola: $\dfrac{x^2}{16} - \dfrac{y^2}{25} = 1$

$\dfrac{x^2}{4^2} - \dfrac{y^2}{5^2} = 1$

Center: $(0, 0)$; $a = 4$, $b = 5$

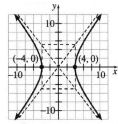

38.
$$d = \sqrt{(-2-8)^2 + (4-5)^2}$$
$$= \sqrt{(-10)^2 + (-1)^2}$$
$$= \sqrt{100+1}$$
$$= \sqrt{101} \text{ units}$$

39. $\begin{cases} y = \sqrt{x} \\ x^2 + y^2 = 6 \end{cases}$

Substitute $\sqrt{x}$ for y into the second equation.
$$(x)^2 + \left(\sqrt{x}\right)^2 = 6$$
$$x^2 + x - 6 = 0$$
$$(x+3)(x-2) = 0$$
$$x+3 = 0 \quad \text{or} \quad x-2 = 0$$
$$x = -3 \quad \text{or} \quad x = 2$$

Substitute these x values into the first equation to find the corresponding y values.
$$x = -3 : y = \sqrt{-3} \text{ not a real number}$$
$$x = 2 \ : y = \sqrt{2}$$

Since we are interested only in real number solutions, the solution is $\left(2, \sqrt{2}\right)$.

40. $\begin{cases} x^2 + y^2 = 36 \\ x - y = 6 \end{cases}$

Solve the second equation for x: $x = y + 6$.
Substitute $y + 6$ for x into the first equation.
$$(y+6)^2 + y^2 = 36$$
$$y^2 + (y^2 + 12y + 36) = 36$$
$$2y^2 + 12y = 0$$
$$2y(y+6) = 0$$
$$2y = 0 \quad \text{or} \quad y + 6 = 0$$
$$y = 0 \quad \text{or} \qquad y = -6$$

Substitute these y values into the equation $x = y + 6$ to find the corresponding x values.
$$y = 0 \ : x = 0 + 6 = 6$$
$$y = -6 : x = -6 + 6 = 0$$

The solutions are $(6, \ 0)$ and $(0, -6)$.

41. $\dfrac{x^2}{9} + \dfrac{y^2}{16} \le 1$

First graph the ellipse with a solid curve.

Test Point	$\dfrac{x^2}{9} + \dfrac{y^2}{16} \le 1$; Result
$(0, 0)$	$\dfrac{(0)^2}{9} + \dfrac{(0)^2}{16} \le 1$; True

Shade the portion of the graph that contains $(0, 0)$.

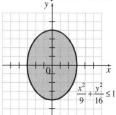

42. $\begin{cases} y \ge x^2 \\ y \le 4 \end{cases}$

First graph the parabola with a solid curve.

Test Point	$y \ge x^2$; Result
$(0, 1)$	$1 \ge 0^2$; True

Shade the portion of the graph which contains $(0, 1)$.

Next, graph $y = 4$ with a solid line.

Test Point	$y \le 4$; Result
$(0, 0)$	$0 \le 4$; True

Shade the portion of the graph which contains $(0, 0)$.

The solution to the system is the overlapping region.

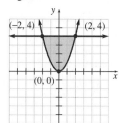

43. $a_n = n^2 - 1$

$a_1 = 1^2 - 1 = 0$

$a_2 = 2^2 - 1 = 3$

$a_3 = 3^2 - 1 = 8$

$a_4 = 4^2 - 1 = 15$

$a_5 = 5^2 - 1 = 24$

The first five terms of $a_n = n^2 - 1$ are 0, 3, 8, 15, and 24.

44. $a_n = \dfrac{n}{n+4}$

$a_8 = \dfrac{8}{8+4} = \dfrac{8}{12} = \dfrac{2}{3}$

45. $a_n = a_1 + (n-1)d$, $a_1 = 2$, and $d = 9 - 2 = 7$

$a_{11} = 2 + (11-1)(7) = 72$

46. $a_n = a_1 r^{n-1}$, $a_1 = 2$, and $r = \dfrac{10}{2} = 5$

$a_6 = 2 \cdot 5^{6-1} = 6250$

47. a. $\displaystyle\sum_{i=0}^{6} \dfrac{i-2}{2} = -1 - \dfrac{1}{2} + 0 + \dfrac{1}{2} + 1 + \dfrac{3}{2} + 2 = \dfrac{7}{2}$

b. $\displaystyle\sum_{i=3}^{5} 2^i = 8 + 16 + 32 = 56$

48. a. $\displaystyle\sum_{i=0}^{4} i(i+1) = 0 + 2 + 6 + 12 + 20 = 40$

b. $\displaystyle\sum_{i=0}^{3} 2^i = 1 + 2 + 4 + 8 = 15$

49. The sequence 1, 2, 3, . . . , 30 is arithmetic with $n = 30$, $a_1 = 1$, and $a_n = 30$.

$S_n = \dfrac{n}{2}(a_1 + a_n) = \dfrac{30}{2}(1 + 30) = 15(31) = 465$

50. To find the third term of $(x - y)^6$, use the formula

$\dfrac{n!}{r!(n-r)!} a^{n-r} b^r$ where $a = x$, $b = -y$, $n = 6$,

and $r = 3 - 1 = 2$.

$\dfrac{6!}{2!(6-2)!} x^{6-2} y^2 = 15x^4 y^2$

The third term of $(x - y)^6$ is $15x^4 y^2$.

Appendices

Appendix A Exercise Set

Section 1.5

1. $3x - 4 = 3(2x - 1) + 7$
$3x - 4 = 6x - 3 + 7$
$3x - 4 = 6x + 4$
$-3x = 8$
$x = -\dfrac{8}{3}$

   The solution is $-\dfrac{8}{3}$.

3. $5 + 2x = 5(x + 1)$
$5 + 2x = 5x + 5$
$-3x = 0$
$x = 0$
   The solution is 0.

Section 3.2

1. $\dfrac{x + 3}{2} > 1$
$x + 3 > 2$
$x > -1$
   The solution is $(-1, \infty)$.

3. $\dfrac{x - 2}{2} - \dfrac{x - 4}{3} = \dfrac{5}{6}$
$6\left(\dfrac{x - 2}{2} - \dfrac{x - 4}{3}\right) = 6\left(\dfrac{5}{6}\right)$
$3(x - 2) - 2(x - 4) = 5$
$3x - 6 - 2x + 8 = 5$
$x + 2 = 5$
$x = 3$
   The solution is 3.

Section 3.3

1. $x - 2 \le 1$ and $3x - 1 \ge -4$
$x \le 3$ and $3x \ge -3$
$x \ge -1$
$-1 \le x \le 3$
   The solution is $[-1, 3]$.

3. $-2x + 2.5 = -7.7$
$-2x = -10.2$
$x = \dfrac{-10.2}{-2} = 5.1$
   The solution is 5.1.

5. $x \le -3$ or $x \le -5$
$x \le -3$
   The solution is $(-\infty, -3]$.

Section 3.4

1. $|2 + 3x| = 7$
$2 + 3x = 7$ or $2 + 3x = -7$
$3x = 5$ or $3x = -9$
$x = \dfrac{5}{3}$ or $x = -3$

   The solutions are -3 and $\dfrac{5}{3}$.

3. $\dfrac{5t}{2} - \dfrac{3t}{4} = 7$
$4\left(\dfrac{5t}{2} - \dfrac{3t}{4}\right) = 4(7)$
$2(5t) - 3t = 28$
$10t - 3t = 28$
$7t = 28$
$t = 4$
   The solution is 4.

5. $5(x - 3) + x + 2 \ge 3(x + 2) + 2x$
$5x - 15 + x + 2 \ge 3x + 6 + 2x$
$6x - 13 \ge 5x + 6$
$x \ge 19$
   The solution is $[19, \infty)$.

Section 3.5

1. $|x - 11| \ge 7$
$x - 11 \le -7$ or $x - 11 \ge 7$
$x \le 4$ or $x \ge 18$
   The solution is $(-\infty, 4] \cup [18, \infty)$.

3. $-5 < x - (2x + 3) < 0$
$-5 < x - 2x - 3 < 0$
$-5 < -x - 3 < 0$
$-2 < -x < 3$
$2 > x > -3$
$-3 < x < 2$

   The solution is $(-3, 2)$.

516

5. $\dfrac{4x}{5} - 1 = \dfrac{x}{2} + 2$

$10\left(\dfrac{4x}{5} - 1\right) = 10\left(\dfrac{x}{2} + 2\right)$

$2(4x) - 10 = 5x + 20$

$8x - 10 = 5x + 20$

$3x = 30$

$x = 10$

The solution is 10.

Section 5.8

1. $2x^2 - 17x = 9$

$2x^2 - 17x - 9 = 0$

$(2x + 1)(x - 9) = 0$

$2x + 1 = 0 \quad$ or $\quad x - 9 = 0$

$2x = -1 \quad$ or $\quad x = 9$

$x = -\dfrac{1}{2}$

The solutions are $-\dfrac{1}{2}$ and 9.

3. $|4x + 7| = |-35|$

$|4x + 7| = 35$

$4x + 7 = 35$ or $4x + 7 = -35$

$4x = 28$ or $\quad 4x = -42$

$x = 7 \quad$ or $\quad x = \dfrac{-42}{4} = -\dfrac{21}{2}$

The solutions are $-\dfrac{21}{2}$ and 7.

5. $3(2x - 1) < 9$ and $-4x > -12$

$6x - 3 < 9$ and $\quad x < 3$

$6x < 12$

$x < 2$

$x < 2$

The solution is $(-\infty, 2)$.

Section 6.6

1. $\dfrac{x}{10} - \dfrac{1}{2} = \dfrac{7}{5x}$

$10x\left(\dfrac{x}{10} - \dfrac{1}{2}\right) = 10x\left(\dfrac{7}{5x}\right)$

$x^2 - 5x = 2(7)$

$x^2 - 5x - 14 = 0$

$(x + 2)(x - 7) = 0$

$x + 2 = 0 \quad$ or $\quad x - 7 = 0$

$x = -2 \quad$ or $\qquad x = 7$

The solutions are –2 and 7.

3. $x + 2 \le 0 \quad$ or $\quad 5x \le 0$

$x \le -2 \quad$ or $\quad x \le 0$

$x \le 0$

The solution is $(-\infty, 0]$.

5. $-8 + |2x - 4| \le -2$

$|2x - 4| \le 6$

$-6 \le 2x - 4 \le 6$

$-2 \le 2x \le 10$

$-1 \le x \le 5$

The solution is $[-1, 5]$.

Section 7.6

1. $x(3x + 14) = 5$

$3x^2 + 14x = 5$

$3x^2 + 14x - 5 = 0$

$(3x - 1)(x + 5) = 0$

$3x - 1 = 0 \quad$ or $\quad x + 5 = 0$

$3x = 1 \quad$ or $\qquad x = -5$

$x = \dfrac{1}{3}$

The solutions are –5 and $\dfrac{1}{3}$.

3. $|5x - 4| = |4x + 1|$

$5x - 4 = 4x + 1$ or $5x - 4 = -(4x + 1)$

$x = 5 \qquad$ or $5x - 4 = -4x - 1$

$9x = 3$

$x = \dfrac{1}{3}$

The solutions are $\dfrac{1}{3}$ and 5.

5. $-2(x-4)+3x \le -3(x+2)-2$
$-2x+8+3x \le -3x-6-2$
$x+8 \le -3x-8$
$4x \le -16$
$x \le -4$
The solution is $(-\infty, -4]$.

Section 8.2

1. $(x-2)^2 = 17$
$x-2 = \pm\sqrt{17}$
$x = 2 \pm \sqrt{17}$
The solutions are $2+\sqrt{17}$ and $2-\sqrt{17}$.

3. $x^2 - 5x + 6 = 0$
$(x-2)(x-3) = 0$
$x-2 = 0$ or $x-3 = 0$
$x = 2$ or $x = 3$
The solutions are 2 and 3.

5. $\sqrt{2x+30} = x+3$
$2x+30 = (x+3)^2$
$2x+30 = x^2 + 6x + 9$
$0 = x^2 + 4x - 21$
$0 = (x+7)(x-3)$
$x+7 = 0$ or $x-3 = 0$
$x = -7$ or $x = 3$
Exclude -7 as an extraneous solution.
The solution is 3.

7. $\dfrac{3x^2-7}{3x^2-8x-3} = \dfrac{1}{x-3} + \dfrac{2}{3x+1}$
$\dfrac{3x^2-7}{(3x+1)(x-3)} = \dfrac{1}{x-3} + \dfrac{2}{3x+1}$
$3x^2 - 7 = 1(3x+1) + 2(x-3)$
$3x^2 - 7 = 3x + 1 + 2x - 6$
$3x^2 - 7 = 5x - 5$
$3x^2 - 5x - 2 = 0$
$(3x+1)(x-2) = 0$
$3x+1 = 0$ or $x-2 = 0$
$3x = -1$ or $x = 2$
$x = -\dfrac{1}{3}$
Exclude $x = -\dfrac{1}{3}$ since it is a restricted value.
The solution is 2.

Section 8.4

1. $x^2 - 3x - 10 = 0$
$(x-5)(x+2) = 0$
$x-5 = 0$ or $x+2 = 0$
$x = 5$ or $x = -2$
The solutions are -2 and 5.

3. $\dfrac{x+4}{x-10} = 0$
$x+4 = 0$
$x = -4$
The solution is -4.

5. $\sqrt{x-7} - 12 = -8$
$\sqrt{x-7} = 4$
$x-7 = 4^2$
$x-7 = 16$
$x = 23$
The solution is 23.

7. $\left|\dfrac{3x+5}{2}\right| = -9$ is impossible.
There is no solution, or $\varnothing$.

9. $-4(x-3)+2x < 6x+4$
$-4x+12+2x < 6x+4$
$-2x+12 < 6x+4$
$-8x < -8$
$x > 1$
The solution is $(1, \infty)$.

Section 9.7

1. $4^x = 8^{x-1}$
$(2^2)^x = (2^3)^{x-1}$
$2^{2x} = 2^{3x-3}$
$2x = 3x - 3$
$-x = -3$
$x = 3$
The solution is 3.

3. $x(x-9) > 0$

$x = 0$ or $x - 9 = 0$

$\quad\quad\quad\quad\quad x = 9$

Region	Test Point	$x(x-9) > 0$; Result
A: $(-\infty, 0)$	-1	$-1(-10) > 0$; True
B: $(0, 9)$	1	$1(-8) > 0$; False
C: $(9, \infty)$	10	$10(1) > 0$; True

The solution is $(-\infty, 0) \cup (9, \infty)$.

5. $\log_4(x^2 - 3x) = 1$

$\quad x^2 - 3x = 4^1$

$\quad x^2 - 3x - 4 = 0$

$\quad (x-4)(x+1) = 0$

$\quad x - 4 = 0$ or $x + 1 = 0$

$\quad\quad x = 4$ or $\quad x = -1$

The solutions are -1 and 4.

7. $\dfrac{6}{x-2} \geq 3$

The denominator is 0 when $x - 2 = 0$, or $x = 2$.

$\dfrac{6}{x-2} = 3$

$\quad 6 = 3(x-2)$

$\quad 6 = 3x - 6$

$\quad 12 = 3x$

$\quad 4 = x$

Region	Test Point	$\dfrac{6}{x-2} \geq 3$; Result
A: $(-\infty, 2)$	0	$\dfrac{6}{-2} \geq 3$; False
B: $(2, 4)$	3	$\dfrac{6}{1} \geq 3$; True
C: $(4, \infty)$	5	$\dfrac{6}{3} \geq 3$; False

The solution is $(2, 4]$.

9. $\log_3(2x+1) - \log_3 x = 1$

$\quad \log_3 \dfrac{2x+1}{x} = 1$

$\quad\quad \dfrac{2x+1}{x} = 3^1$

$\quad\quad 2x + 1 = 3x$

$\quad\quad\quad\quad 1 = x$

The solution is 1.

Appendix C Exercise Set

1. $V = lwh$

$\quad = (6 \text{ in.})(4 \text{ in.})(3 \text{ in.}) = 72$ cubic inches

$SA = 2lh + 2wh + 2lw$

$\quad = 2(6 \text{ in.})(3 \text{ in.}) + 2(4 \text{ in.})(3 \text{ in.})$

$\quad\quad + 2(6 \text{ in.})(4 \text{ in.})$

$\quad = 36 \text{ sq. in.} + 24 \text{ sq. in.} + 48 \text{ sq. in.}$

$\quad = 108$ square inches

3. $V = s^3$

$\quad = (8 \text{ cm})^3 = 512$ cu. cm

$SA = 6s^2 = 6(8 \text{ cm})^2 = 384$ sq. cm

5. $V = \dfrac{1}{3}\pi r^2 h$

$\quad = \dfrac{1}{3}\pi(2 \text{ yd})^2(3 \text{ yd}) = 4\pi$ cu. yd

$\quad \approx 4\left(\dfrac{22}{7}\right)$ cu. yd

$\quad = 12.56$ cu. yd

$SA = \pi r \sqrt{r^2 + h^2} + \pi r^2$

$\quad = \pi(2 \text{ yd})\sqrt{(2 \text{ yd})^2 + (3 \text{ yd})^2} + \pi(2 \text{ yd})^2$

$\quad = \pi(2 \text{ yd})\left(\sqrt{13} \text{ yd}\right) + \pi(4 \text{ sq. yd})$

$\quad = \left(2\sqrt{13} + 4\right)\pi$ sq. yd

$\quad \approx 3.14\left(2\sqrt{13} + 4\right)$ sq. yd

$\quad \approx 35.20$ sq. yd

7. $V = \dfrac{4}{3}\pi r^3$

$\quad = \dfrac{4}{3}\pi(5 \text{ in.})^3$

$\quad = \dfrac{500}{3}\pi$ cu. in.

$\quad \approx \dfrac{500}{3}\left(\dfrac{22}{7}\right)$ cu. in.

$\quad = 523\dfrac{17}{21}$ cu. in.

$SA = 4\pi r^2$

$\quad = 4\pi(5 \text{ in.})^2$

$\quad = 100\pi$ sq. in.

$\quad \approx 100\left(\dfrac{22}{7}\right)$ sq. in.

$\quad = 314\dfrac{2}{7}$ sq. in.

9. $V = \dfrac{1}{3}s^2 h$

$\quad = \dfrac{1}{3}(6\text{ cm})^2(4\text{ cm})$

$\quad = 48$ cu. cm

$SA = B + \dfrac{1}{2}pl$

$\quad = (6\text{ cm})^2 + \dfrac{1}{2}(24\text{ cm})(5\text{ cm})$

$\quad = 36$ sq. cm $+ 60$ sq. cm

$\quad = 96$ sq. cm

11. $V = s^3$

$\quad = \left(1\dfrac{1}{3}\text{ in.}\right)^3$

$\quad = \left(\dfrac{4}{3}\text{ in.}\right)^3$

$\quad = \dfrac{64}{27}$ cu. in.

$\quad = 2\dfrac{10}{27}$ cu. in.

13. $SA = 2lh + 2wh + 2lw$

$\quad = 2(2\text{ ft})(1.4\text{ ft}) + 2(2\text{ ft})(3\text{ ft})$

$\quad\quad + 2(1.4\text{ ft})(3\text{ ft})$

$\quad = 5.6$ sq. ft $+ 12$ sq. ft $+ 8.4$ sq. ft

$\quad = 26$ sq. ft

15. $V = \dfrac{1}{3}s^2 h$

$\quad = \dfrac{1}{3}(5\text{ in.})^2(1.3\text{ in.})$

$\quad = \dfrac{65}{6}$ cu. in.

$\quad = 10\dfrac{5}{6}$ cu. in.

17. $V = \dfrac{1}{3}s^2 h$

$\quad = \dfrac{1}{3}(12\text{ cm})^2(20\text{ cm})$

$\quad = 960$ cu. cm

19. $SA = 4\pi r^2 = 4\pi(7\text{ in.})^2 = 196\pi$ sq. in.

21. $V = (2\text{ ft})\left(2\dfrac{1}{2}\text{ ft}\right)\left(1\dfrac{1}{2}\text{ ft}\right)$

$\quad = 2\left(\dfrac{5}{2}\right)\left(\dfrac{3}{2}\right)$ cu. ft

$\quad = \dfrac{15}{2}$ cu. ft

$\quad = 7\dfrac{1}{2}$ cu. ft

23. $V = \dfrac{1}{3}\pi r^2 h$

$\quad \approx \dfrac{1}{3}\left(\dfrac{22}{7}\right)(2\text{ cm})^2(3\text{ cm})$

$\quad = \dfrac{88}{7}$ cu. cm

$\quad = 12\dfrac{4}{7}$ cu. cm

Appendix D

Viewing Window and Interpreting Window Exercise Set

1. Yes, since every coordinate is between -10 and 10.

3. No, since -11 is less than -10.

5. Answers may vary. Any values such that Xmin < -90, Ymin < -80, Xmax > 55, and Ymax > 80.

7. Answers may vary. Any values such that Xmin < -11, Ymin < -5, Xmax > 7, and Ymax > 2.

9. Answers may vary. Any values such that Xmin < 50, Ymin < -50, Xmax > 200, and Ymax > 200.

11. Xmax $= -12$ Ymax $= -12$
    Xmin $= 12$ Ymin $= 12$
    Xscl $= 3$ Yscl $= 3$

13. Xmax $= -9$ Ymax $= -12$
    Xmin $= 9$ Ymin $= 12$
    Xscl $= 1$ Yscl $= 2$

15. Xmax $= -10$ Ymax $= -25$
    Xmin $= 10$ Ymin $= 25$
    Xscl $= 2$ Yscl $= 5$

17. $\text{Xmax} = -10 \quad \text{Ymax} = -30$
$\ \text{Xmin} = 10 \quad\ \text{Ymin} = 30$
$\ \text{Xscl} = 1 \quad\quad\ \text{Yscl} = 3$

19. $\text{Xmax} = -20 \quad \text{Ymax} = -30$
$\ \text{Xmin} = 30 \quad\ \text{Ymin} = 50$
$\ \text{Xscl} = 5 \quad\quad\ \text{Yscl} = 10$

Graphing Equations and Square Viewing Window
Exercise Set

1.

Setting A

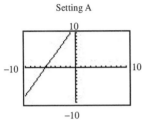

Setting B

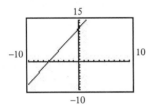

Setting B shows both intercepts.

3.

Setting A

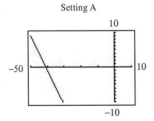

Setting B

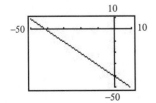

Setting B shows both intercepts.

5.

Setting A

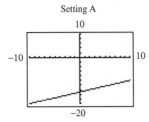

Setting B

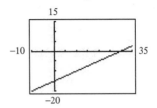

Setting B shows both intercepts.

7. $3x = 5y$
$\ y = \dfrac{3}{5}x$

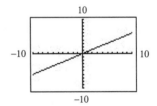

9. $9x - 5y = 30$
$\ {-5y} = -9x + 30$
$\quad y = \dfrac{9}{5}x - 6$

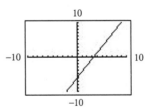

11. $y = -7$

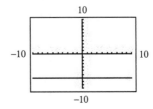

13. $x + 10y = -5$

$\quad\quad 10y = -x - 5$

$\quad\quad\quad y = -\dfrac{1}{10}x - \dfrac{1}{2}$

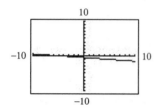

15. $y = \sqrt{x}$

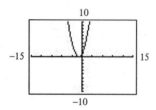

17. $y = x^2 + 2x + 1$

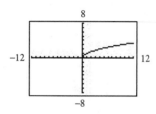

19. $y = |x|$

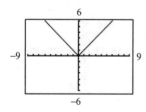

21. $x + 2y = 30$

$\quad\quad 2y = -x + 30$

$\quad\quad\quad y = -\dfrac{1}{2}x + 15$

Standard Window

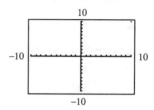

The standard window does not allow us to see the intercepts. Therefore, we need to adjust our window settings.

Revised Window

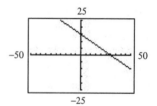